Student's t (comparing two means)	$t = \dfrac{(\bar{x}_1 - \bar{x}_2) - D_0}{s\sqrt{\dfrac{1}{n_1} + \dfrac{1}{n_2}}}$

Pooled Estimate of σ^2

$$s^2 = \frac{\sum\limits_{i=1}^{n_1}(x_i - \bar{x}_1)^2 + \sum\limits_{i=1}^{n_2}(x_i - \bar{x}_2)^2}{n_1 + n_2 - 2}$$

Correlation Coefficient

$$r = \frac{SS_{xy}}{\sqrt{SS_x SS_y}}$$

where

$$SS_y = \sum_{i=1}^{n}(y_i - \bar{y})^2 = \sum_{i=1}^{n} y_i^2 - \frac{\left(\sum\limits_{i=1}^{n} y_i\right)^2}{n}$$

$$SS_x = \sum_{i=1}^{n}(x_i - \bar{x})^2 = \sum_{i=1}^{n} x_i^2 - \frac{\left(\sum\limits_{i=1}^{n} x_i\right)^2}{n}$$

$$SS_{xy} = \sum_{i=1}^{n}(x_i - \bar{x})(y_i - \bar{y})$$

$$= \sum_{i=1}^{n} x_i y_i - \frac{\left(\sum\limits_{i=1}^{n} x_i\right)\left(\sum\limits_{i=1}^{n} y_i\right)}{n}$$

Least Squares Estimators of β_0 and β_1

$$\hat{\beta}_1 = \frac{SS_{xy}}{SS_x} \quad \text{and} \quad \hat{\beta}_0 = \bar{y} - \hat{\beta}_1 \bar{x}$$

Least Squares Line (single independent variable)

$$\hat{y} = \hat{\beta}_0 + \hat{\beta}_1 x$$

Mann–Whitney U

$$U_A = n_1 n_2 + \frac{n_1(n_1 + 1)}{2} - T_A$$

and

$$U_B = n_1 n_2 + \frac{n_2(n_2 + 1)}{2} - T_B$$

Chi-Square Statistic for Contingency Tables

$$X^2 = \sum_{i=1}^{k} \frac{[n_i - E(n_i)]^2}{E(n_i)}$$

Spearman's Rank Correlation Coefficient

$$r_s = 1 - \frac{6\sum\limits_{i=1}^{n} d_i^2}{n(n^2 - 1)}$$

A COURSE IN
BUSINESS STATISTICS

THE DUXBURY SERIES IN STATISTICS AND DECISION SCIENCES

Applications, Basics, and Computing of Exploratory Data Analysis, Velleman and Hoaglin

Applied Regression Analysis and Other Multivariable Methods, Second Edition, Kleinbaum and Kupper

Classical and Modern Regression with Applications, Myers

A Course in Business Statistics, Second Edition, Mendenhall

Elementary Statistics for Business, Second Edition, Johnson and Siskin

Elementary Statistics, Fifth Edition, Johnson

Elementary Survey Sampling, Third Edition, Scheaffer, Mendenhall, and Ott

Essential Business Statistics: A Minitab Framework, Bond and Scott

A First Course in Linear Regression, Second Edition, Younger

Fundamental Statistics for Human Services and Social Work, Krishef

Fundamental Statistics for the Behavioral Sciences, Howell

Fundamentals of Biostatistics, Second Edition, Rosner

Fundamentals of Statistics in the Biological, Medical, and Health Sciences, Runyon

Introduction to Contemporary Statistical Methods, Second Edition, Koopmans

Introduction to Probability and Mathematical Statistics, Bain and Engelhardt

Introduction to Probability and Statistics, Seventh Edition, Mendenhall

An Introduction to Statistical Methods and Data Analysis, Third Edition, Ott

Introductory Statistics for Management and Economics, Second Edition, Kenkel

Linear Statistical Models: An Applied Approach, Bowerman, O'Connell, and Dickey

Management Science: An Introduction, Davis, McKeown, and Rakes

Mathematical Statistics with Applications, Third Edition, Mendenhall, Scheaffer, and Wackerly

Minitab Handbook, Second Edition, Ryan, Joiner, and Ryan

Minitab Handbook for Business and Economics, Miller

Operations Research: Applications and Algorithms, Winston

Probability Modeling and Computer Simulation, Matloff

Probability and Statistics for Engineers, Second Edition, Scheaffer and McClave

Probability and Statistics for Modern Engineering, Lapin

Quantitative Management: An Introduction, Second Edition, Anderson and Lievano

Quantitative Models for Management, Second Edition, Davis and McKeown

Statistical Experiments Using BASIC, Dowdy

Statistical Methods for Psychology, Second Edition, Howell

Statistical Thinking for Behavioral Scientists, Hildebrand

Statistical Thinking for Managers, Second Edition, Hildebrand and Ott

Statistics for Management and Economics, Fifth Edition, Mendenhall, Reinmuth, Beaver, and Duhan

Statistics: A Tool for the Social Sciences, Fourth Edition, Ott, Larson, and Mendenhall

Time Series Analysis, Cryer

Time Series Forecasting: Unified Concepts and Computer Implementation, Second Edition, Bowerman and O'Connell

Understanding Statistics, Fourth Edition, Ott and Mendenhall

A COURSE IN BUSINESS STATISTICS

SECOND EDITION

William Mendenhall

PWS-KENT Publishing Company
Boston

PWS-KENT
Publishing Company

20 Park Plaza
Boston, Massachusetts 02116

Library of Congress Cataloging-in-Publication Data
Mendenhall, William.
  A course in business statistics/William Mendenhall.—2nd ed.
    p. cm.
  Bibliography: p.
  Includes index.
  ISBN 0-534-91488-8
  1. Commercial statistics.   I. Title.
HF1017.M458   1988
519.5—dc19   87-20731
                                                                  CIP

Printed in the United States of America
  89 90 91 92—10 9 8 7 6 5 4 3 2

Sponsoring editor: *Michael Payne*
Editorial assistants: *Sandi Sonnenfeld and Julie Shea*
Production: *Technical Texts, Inc./Sylvia Dovner*
Interior design: *S. London with Sylvia Dovner*
Cover design: *S. London*
Cover photograph: *Greg Bowl Studio*
Cover blueprints: *Graham & Schlageter, Inc.*
Technical art: *J & R Art Services, Inc.*
Typesetting: *Polyglot Pte., Ltd.*
Cover printing: *New England Book Components, Inc.*
Printing and binding: *R. R. Donnelley & Sons*

PREFACE

A Course in Business Statistics is designed for a one- or two-semester course in business statistics. The mathematics prerequisite for the course is a knowledge of high school algebra. Reference to elementary concepts of calculus appear in a few optional sections, but coverage of these sections is not essential to an understanding of the nonoptional text material.

This second edition of *A Course in Business Statistics* contains substantial changes. These changes shift topical emphasis to coincide with the conclusions of a conference on business statistics held at the Graduate School of the University of Chicago in June 1986 (George Easton, Harry V. Roberts, and George C. Tiao, "Preliminary Report on Making Statistics More Effective in Schools of Business: Overview and Summary," University of Chicago, December 1986). The conferees' report noted a consensus on the following points:

(1) Students are most effectively motivated by real applications.

(2) It is desirable to reduce the emphasis on probability and the formal theory of statistics and to increase emphasis on applications.

(3) Certain topics, now omitted or treated lightly, should receive greater emphasis. These topics include sampling, experimental design, quality control, time series analysis, and report writing.

I tend to agree with these conference conclusions. As a consequence, coverage of the theory of probability has been greatly reduced in this second edition by combining old Chapters 3, 4, and 5 into a single new Chapter 3 on probability and discrete probability distributions. The basic concepts of probability, presented in the first three sections of this new chapter, cover the concepts of unconditional and conditional probability, mutually exclusive and independent events, and the rules for calculating the probabilities of unions and intersections of events. Although brief, this material covers all of the basic concepts that a student needs to know in order to understand the inferential and applied topics that follow. It also is most likely the most that an instructor might expect a student to retain upon completing a one- or two-semester sequence of courses in business statistics.

The reduction in emphasis on probability is replaced by greater emphasis on the role that the sampling distribution of a statistic plays in statistical inference and greater emphasis on applications of statistics in business problems. The sampling distribution for a statistic is introduced in a new Chapter 5 by showing how a distribution can be generated using the Monte Carlo sampling procedure. This method of presentation enables the student to see why statistical inference involves error and how that error can be measured and evaluated.

Greater emphasis on applications and realism in this new edition is achieved by adding the following material:

(1) A coverage of one-sided confidence intervals—where they are used, how they are interpreted, and how to find them—has been added in Chapter 6. The Case Study for Chapter 6 shows how (in Section 6.10) the Internal Revenue Service uses a one-sided confidence interval to arrive at a disallowance. In doing so, it shows that one-sided confidence intervals have very useful applications.

(2) Chapter 9, the analysis of variance, has been expanded to include the following:
   (a) A discussion of how and why randomized block designs and factorial experiments can increase the information in experiments.
   (b) The analysis of variance for randomized block designs and factorial experiments. Each analysis of variance is explained by examining the computer output for an example for each design. Practical interpretations are given for each relevant item in the output. An optional section gives the computational formulas for each analysis of variance and illustrates how they can be applied to obtain the quantities shown in the computer printouts.
   (c) Tukey's method for paired comparisons for ranking population means.
   (d) Methods to stabilize the variance of a response when the assumptions required for an analysis of variance have not been satisfied.

(3) Chapter 12, multiple regression analysis, has been expanded to include the following:
   (a) More examples. Particularly, a second-order model is fit to productivity data using multiple regression analysis. The computer output is shown for each multiple regression analysis, and each relevant item in the output is explained and interpreted.
   (b) An expanded discussion of the different types of models that can be used to characterize the relationship between a response variable and a set of predictor variables.
   (c) A new section explaining why one might wish to test sets of model parameters and explaining how the test is performed.
   (d) A new section explaining how to perform and interpret a residual analysis.
   (e) A brief section describing a stepwise regression analysis and its uses.
   (f) A new section showing how multiple regression analysis can be used to perform an analysis of variance when data are missing.
   (g) A new section that summarizes the steps to follow when building a linear model.

(4) The coverage of nonparametric statistics, in Chapter 15, has been expanded to include sections on the Kruskal-Wallis H test and the Friedman F_r test for analyzing data collected according to simple random sampling and randomized block designs.

(5) A new Chapter 16, introducing the basic concepts, methods, and applications of statistical quality control, has been added.

(6) New realistic case studies have been added to supplement the best case studies retained from the first edition (see the IRS Case Study in Chapter 6). As in the first

edition, a separate section in each chapter shows how one or more of the chapter topics can be used to reach practical conclusions concerning the Case Study.

(7) Many new exercises, drawn from the literature, add realism and confirm that statistics can be useful in solving business problems.

(8) Although some computation, such as computing a sample variance and fitting a simple linear regression line, assist a student in understanding concepts, we have tried to minimize computation and to emphasize concepts and the practical interpretation of results. Consequently, the computation in the analysis of variance and multiple regression chapters is done by a computer and presented in printouts. The computing formulas are available in optional sections.

(9) Exercises at the ends of chapters have been divided into two groups to aid the instructor in exercise assignments. The first, under the heading "Basic Techniques," are devoid of practical settings. This format eliminates the confusing aspects contributed by "word problems" and permits the student to concentrate solely on the methodology. The second group of exercises represents practical "Applications" of the methodology.

The preparation of a text and of a subsequent new edition is always a team effort, and I am fortunate to have had the assistance of many talented people. My appreciation to the many reviewers who aided me in this revision: Dinesh Bhoj, Rutgers University; Thomas Box, University of Tulsa; Michael Broida, Miami University–Oxford; A. Halati, California Polytechnic State; Thomas Johnson, North Carolina University; Martin Kotler, Pace University; John Laughlin, Southern Oregon State; Charles Lienert, Metropolitan State College; Janet R. Muzos, Portland Community College; Leonard Presby, William Patterson State College; Jackie Redder, Virginia Polytechnic Institute and State University; R. Singmsetti, University of Hartford; Perri Stinson, California State University–Long Beach; Justin Stolen, University of Nebraska; William Terrell, Wichita State University; and Frederick Weston, Colorado State University.

The author also extends his thanks to the editorial staff of PWS–KENT Publishing Company — especially those involved with the Duxbury Series in Statistics and Decision Sciences, including my editor, Michael Payne, and editorial assistant, Sandi Sonnenfeld—and to the staff at Technical Texts, Inc., including Sylvia Dovner and Carol Beal. A special note of gratitude is extended to Barbara Beaver, for once more assisting me in her preparation of a solutions manual, and to my typist Carol A. Springer. Finally, as always, I acknowledge the assistance of my family and their partnership in this writing endeavor.

William Mendenhall

CONTENTS

4 The Normal Probability Distribution   128

5 Sampling Distributions   154

6 Large-Sample Estimation   193

THE CHI-SQUARE GOODNESS-OF-FIT TEST   404

10

LINEAR REGRESSION AND CORRELATION   435

11

MULTIPLE REGRESSION ANALYSIS   487

12

13   TIME SERIES AND INDEX NUMBERS   553

14   SAMPLING METHODS   609

15   NONPARAMETRIC STATISTICS   645

16 QUALITY CONTROL   691

17 DECISION ANALYSIS   730

APPENDIX TABLES   753

ANSWERS TO SELECTED EXERCISES   796

INDEX   807

The purpose of this chapter is to identify the nature of statistics, its objective, and how it plays an important role in the sciences, in industry, and, ultimately, in our daily lives.

1

WHAT IS STATISTICS?

CASE STUDY

Reaping the Rewards of Refunds

Will court-enforced retail refunds make us rich? Not likely, according to the *Wall Street Journal* article (June 9, 1981), which reported on a court case stemming from a price-fixing indictment. According to the article, approximately 54,000 persons—customers of Saks Fifth Avenue, Bonwit Teller, and Bergdorf Goodman—during the period of 1968 to 1974, may be due refunds if they can resurrect the ancient records of their purchases and file the necessary applications. This case raises a serious question about this and other court-directed refund programs that are often the result of price-fixing indictments. Who profits (other than the attorneys involved in the lawsuit)? Specifically, how many of the 54,000 customers eligible for refunds will actually find their receipts and be willing to submit the necessary applications? And how much of the settlement money will actually be distributed to those customers? To answer these questions, we would need to either interview all 54,000 customers who are potentially eligible—an impossible task—or select a sample from among the 54,000 and use statistical methods to estimate the number eligible for refunds and the amount of money that will eventually be refunded.

Our intention is not to answer the question "Who profits from refunding?" but to present a difficult problem that can be solved by the use of a very powerful tool, statistics. In this chapter we will describe the objective of statistics. Specifically, we will identify the types of problems that statistical methodology can solve and then explain how this valuable tool can be used to answer some practical questions. We will revisit the refunding case study in Section 1.5.

1.1 ILLUSTRATIVE STATISTICAL PROBLEMS

What is statistics? How does it function? How does it help to solve certain practical problems? Rather than attempt a definition at this point, let us examine several problems that might come to the attention of the statistician. From these examples we can then select the essential elements of a statistical problem.

In predicting the outcome of a national election, pollsters interview a predetermined number of people throughout the country and record their preferences. On the basis of this information a prediction is made. Similar problems are encountered in market research (What fraction of potential buyers prefer automobile brand A?); in sociology (What fraction of rural homes have electricity?); in industry (What fraction of items purchased, or produced, are defective?).

An auditor wants to determine the inventory of a large hospital. To count the number and value of each expendable and nonexpendable item in stock would not only be very costly but would also, because of the size of the task, be subject to error. To reduce the cost and obtain a reliable estimate of value, the auditor selects a sample of items from the list of the hospital's supplies and equipment, carefully counts the number of each item on hand, and records its value. The ratio of the total value of this sample of items to the total value shown in the hospital's records provides an estimate of the shrinkage due to theft, failure to record use of items, and so on. This shrinkage rate can then be applied to the total value of inventory shown in the hospital's records, thereby obtaining an estimate of the actual value of current inventory. How accurate is this estimate? How far might we expect the estimate to deviate from the actual value of the hospital's inventory?

The yield (production) of a chemical plant is dependent upon many factors. By observing these factors and the yield over a period of time, we can construct a prediction equation relating yield to the observed factors. As another example, the economist wants to develop prediction equations, which will be useful in predicting economic growth or some other measure of economic health, as a function of various other economic and sociological variables. Similarly, a manager may want to predict the sales of a product as a function of advertising expenditure, number of salespersons employed, or various other variables that may be related to the company's sales.

How do we find a good prediction equation? If the equation is used to predict yield, the prediction will rarely equal the true yield; that is, the prediction will almost always be in error. Can we place a limit on the prediction error? Which factors are the most important in predicting yield?

In addition to being involved in prediction, statistics is concerned with decision making based on observed data. Consider the problem of determining the effectiveness of a new cold vaccine. For simplification, let us assume that ten people have received the new cold vaccine and are observed over a winter season. Of these ten, eight survive the winter without acquiring a cold. Is the vaccine effective?

Two physically different teaching techniques are used to present a subject to two groups of students of comparable ability. At the end of the instructional period a measure of achievement is obtained for each group. On the basis of this information we ask: Do the data present sufficient evidence to indicate that one method produces, on the average, higher student achievement?

Consider the inspection of items purchased for a manufacturing plant. On the basis of such an inspection each lot of incoming goods must be either accepted or rejected and returned to the supplier. The inspection might involve drawing a sample of ten items from each lot and recording the number of defectives. The decision to accept or reject the lot could then be based on the number of defective items observed.

A company manufacturing complex electronic equipment produces some systems that function properly but also some that, for unknown reasons, do not. What makes good systems good and bad systems bad? In attempting to answer this question, we might make certain internal measurements on a system in order to find important factors that differentiate between an acceptable and an unacceptable product. From a sample of good and bad systems data could then be collected that might shed light on the fundamental design or on production variables affecting system quality.

1.2 THE POPULATION AND THE SAMPLE

The examples we have cited are varied in nature and complexity, but each involves prediction or decision making. In addition, each of these examples involves sampling. A specified number of items (objects or bits of information)—a **sample**—is drawn from a much larger body of data, which we call the **population**. The pollster draws a sample of opinions (those interviewed) from the statistical population, which is the set of opinions corresponding to all the eligible voters in the country. In predicting the fraction of potential buyers who prefer automobile brand A, we assume that those interviewed yield a representative sample of the population of all potential automobile buyers. The sample for the cold vaccine experiment consists of observations made on the ten individuals receiving the vaccine. The sample is presumably representative of data pertinent to a much larger body of people—the population—who could have received the vaccine.

Which is of primary interest, the sample or the population? In all of the examples given above, we are primarily interested in the population. We cannot interview all the people in the United States; therefore, we must predict their behavior on the basis of information we obtain from a representative sample. Similarly, it is practically impossible to give all possible users a cold vaccine. The manufacturer of the drug is interested in its effectiveness to prevent colds in the purchasing public (the population). It must predict this effectiveness from information extracted from the sample. Therefore, the sample may be of immediate interest, but we are primarily interested in describing the population from which the sample is drawn.

DEFINITION   The *population* is the set representing all measurements of interest to the sample collector.   ■

DEFINITION   A *sample* is a subset of measurements selected from the population of interest.   ■

Most people give the word *sample* two meanings. They refer to it as the set of objects on which measurements are to be taken, or they use it to refer to the objects themselves. A similar double use could be made of the word *population*.

For example, we read in the newspapers that a Gallup Poll was based on a sample of 1823 people. In this use of the word *sample* the objects selected for the sample are obviously people. Presumably, each person is interviewed on a particular question and that person's response represents a single item of data. The collection of data corresponding to the people represents a sample of data.

In a study of sample survey methods we must distinguish between the objects measured and the measurements themselves. To experimenters, the objects measured are called "experimental units." The sample survey statistician calls them "elements of the sample."

To avoid a proliferation of terms, we will use the word *sample* in its everyday meaning. Most of the time, we will be referring to the set of measurements made on the experimental units (elements of the sample). If occasionally we use the term to refer to a collection of experimental units, the context of the discussion will clarify the meaning.

EXAMPLE 1.1   A fast-food company wishes to know how much money Americans, say age 16 and over, will spend on fast foods during the forthcoming first week of June. Describe the population of data of interest to the company. Explain how the company might acquire the information it desires.

SOLUTION   The information that the fast-food company wishes to acquire is associated with a population of measurements—one measurement for a week's expenditure on fast foods for each of the many millions of Americans in the age group 16 and over. These measurements will vary.

Some persons will purchase no fast foods during the week; others will purchase varying amounts. To acquire information on this vast population of measurements, the fast-food company likely will hire a marketing research organization to sample the population. From the sample measurements the marketing organization will estimate the average amount spent by all Americans age 16 and over, will estimate the proportion of all Americans who buy fast foods, and will answer other similar questions posed by the fast-food company. Thus the marketing organization will use information contained in the sample to infer the nature of the population of fast-food expenditures during the first week of June.   ■

1.3   THE ESSENTIAL ELEMENTS OF A STATISTICAL PROBLEM

You can see from the preceding discussion that statistics is concerned with describing a data set called a population. In some rare instances, such as the United States census, the population will be stored in a computer, and the statistical problem is one of describing and extracting information from a large mass of data. The branch of statistics concerned with this type of problem is called **descriptive statistics**. Usually, the population is unavailable. Either observing and recording every single member of the population is too costly (as in the case of the hospital audit), or the population is conceptual—that is, the set of measurements (such as the daily yields of a chemical plant over the next two years) exists in our minds but is not actually available. Using a sample from a population, we attempt to deduce its nature by using the branch of statistics known as **inferential statistics**. Each of the examples described in Section 1.1 represents a problem in inferential statistics. All have the same objective.

THE OBJECTIVE OF INFERENTIAL STATISTICS

> The objective of inferential statistics is to make inferences (predictions, decisions) about a population based on information contained in a sample.

How will we achieve this objective? We will find that every statistical problem contains five elements. The first and foremost of these is a clear specification of the question to be answered and identification of the population of data related to it.

The second element of a statistical problem is the decision about how the sample will be selected. This element, called the **design of the experiment** or the **sampling**

procedure, is important because data cost money and time. In fact, it is not unusual for an experiment or a statistical survey to cost $50,000 to $500,000, and the costs of many biological or technological experiments can run into the millions. What do these experiments and surveys produce? Numbers on a sheet of paper or, in brief, information. Therefore, planning the experiment is important. Including too many observations in the sample is often costly and wasteful; including too few is also unsatisfactory. Most importantly, you will learn that the method used to collect the sample will often affect the amount of information per observation. A good sampling design can sometimes reduce the costs of data collection to one-tenth or as little as one-hundredth of the cost of another sampling design.

The third element of a statistical problem involves the analysis of the sample data. No matter how much information the data contain about the practical question, you must use an appropriate method of data analysis to extract the desired information from the data.

The fourth element of a statistical problem is the use of the sample data to make an **inference** about the population. As you will subsequently learn, many different procedures can be used to make an estimate or decision about some characteristic of a population or to predict the value of some member of the population. For example, two different methods may be available to estimate consumer response to an advertising campaign, but one procedure may be much more accurate than another. Therefore, you will want to use the best inference-making procedure when you use sample data to make an estimate or decision about a population or a prediction about some member of a population.

The final element of a statistical problem identifies what is perhaps the most important contribution of statistics to inference making. It answers the question "How good is the inference?" To illustrate, suppose you manage a small manufacturing concern. You arrange for an agency to conduct a statistical survey for you, and it estimates that your company's product will gain 34% of the market this year. How much faith can you place in this estimate? You will quickly discern that you are lacking some important information. Of what value is the estimate without a measure of its reliability? Is the estimate accurate to within 1%, 5%, or 20%? Is it reliable enough to be used in setting production goals? As you will subsequently learn, statistical estimation, decision making, and prediction procedures enable you to calculate a measure of goodness for every inference. Consequently, in a practical inference-making situation, every inference should be accompanied by a measure that tells you how much faith you can place in the inference.

To summarize, a statistical problem involves the following:

(1) A clear definition of the objective of the experiment and the pertinent population.

(2) The design of the experiment or sampling procedure.

(3) The collection and analysis of data.

(4) The procedure for making inferences about the population on the basis of sample information.

(5) The provision of a measure of goodness (reliability) for the inference.

Note that the steps in the solution of a statistical problem are sequential; that is, you must identify the population of interest and plan how you will collect the data before you can collect and analyze it. And all these operations must precede the ultimate goal, making inferences about the population based on information contained in the sample. These steps—carefully identifying the pertinent population and designing the experiment or sampling procedure—often are omitted. The experimenter may select the sample from the wrong population or may plan the data collection in a manner that intuitively seems reasonable or logical but that may be an extremely poor plan from a statistical point of view. The resulting data may be difficult or impossible to analyze or may contain little or no pertinent information, or inadvertently, the sample may not be representative of the population of interest. Thus every experimenter should be knowledgeable in the statistical design of experiments and/or sample surveys, or the experimenter should consult an applied statistician for the appropriate design *before* the data are collected.

1.4 THE ROLE OF STATISTICS IN INFERENCE MAKING

What is the role of the statistician, given our description of statistical problems? People have been making observations and collecting data for centuries. Furthermore, they have been using the data as a basis for prediction and decision making completely unaided by statistics. What, then, do statisticians and statistics have to offer?

Statistics is an area of science concerned with the extraction of information from numerical data and its use in making inferences about a population from which the data are obtained. In some respects the statistician quantifies information and studies various designs and sampling procedures, searching for the procedure that yields a specified amount of information in a given situation at a minimum cost. Therefore, one major contribution of statistics is in designing experiments and surveys, thereby reducing their cost and size. The second major contribution is in the inference making itself. The statistician studies various inferential procedures, looking for the best predictor or decision-making process for a given situation. More importantly, the statistician provides information concerning the goodness of an inferential procedure. When we predict, we would like to know something about the error in our prediction. If we make a decision, we want to know the chance that our decision is correct. Our built-in individual prediction and decision-making systems do not provide immediate answers to these important questions. They can be evaluated only by observation over a long period of time. In contrast, statistical procedures do provide answers to these questions. Thus statistics enables us to make inferences from sample data and to evaluate the reliability of those inferences; this information will be useful in making business decisions.

1.5 MORE ON THE CONSUMER REFUND CASE STUDY

Let us examine the consumer refund problem in greater detail and identify the populations associated with the two questions posed in the Case Study.

How many of the 54,000 customers eligible for refunds will actually find their receipts and be willing to submit the required applications? Presumably, each of the

54,000 customers will or will not file for a refund. If we assign a 0 to each customer who will not file for a refund and a 1 to those who will, then the population pertinent to the question consists of a large (54,000) set of 0s and 1s. The sum of the number of 1s in the population is equal to the number of customers who will file for a refund.

Although this sum is unknown to us, we can gain insight into its value by selecting a sample from the population; that is, we select a subset of the 54,000 customers and, for each, record whether the customer planned to apply for a refund. For example, if we were to sample 540 customers from among the 54,000 and 54 (i.e., 10% of the number of customers in the sample) planned to apply for a refund, we might estimate that 5400 (10%) of the total number of 54,000 customers would take similar actions. Thus statistical methods can be used to estimate the unknown number of customers who will file for a refund. More importantly, it will enable us to evaluate the accuracy of the estimate—that is, to give some information about how far the estimate might depart from the actual number of persons in the population who will apply for a refund.

How much of the refund money will actually be distributed to the eligible customers? To answer this question, we envision a large (54,000) set of dollar values, each value corresponding to the dollar refund that a specific customer will receive. Naturally, the refund associated with a customer who does not file for a refund will be 0. Those who do file will receive a refund (in dollars), which will vary from one customer to another. Then (the answer to our question) the total amount of money to be refunded will be the sum of the 54,000 refund measurements in the population.

Although this sum is unknown to us, we can estimate its value by sampling. For example, suppose that each of a sample of 540 customers (i.e., 1% of the total number of potentially eligible customers) is questioned concerning the amount (if any) of refund money received from the merchandisers, and the researcher determines that the total amount of refund money for the sample is $4000. Then because the sample represents only 1% (1/100) of the total number of measurements in the population, we might estimate that the total amount of money to be refunded to the 54,000 potentially eligible customers will be (100)($4000), or $400,000.

How reliable is this number as an estimate of the unknown, actual amount of money that will be refunded to the 54,000 customers? In performing extrapolation from sample to population, we made an inference that is subject to error. How large might this error be? The ability to answer this question (the topic of Chapter 6) is one of the major contributions of statistics.

SUMMARY

1.6

Statistics is an area of science concerned with the design of experiments or sampling procedures, the analysis of data, and the making of inferences about a population of measurements from information contained in a sample. Statistics is concerned with developing and using procedures for design, analysis, and inference making that will provide the best inference at a minimum cost. In addition, statistics is concerned with providing a quantitative measure of the goodness of the inference-making procedure.

A careful identification of the target population and the design of the sampling procedure are often omitted, but they are essential steps in drawing inferences from experimental data. Poorly designed sampling procedures will often produce data that are of little or no value (although this may not be obvious to the experimenter). After you make an inference, cast a critical eye upon it; be sure you acquire a measure of its reliability.

1.7   A NOTE TO THE READER

We have stated the objective of statistics and have attempted to give you some idea of the types of business problems for which statistics can be of assistance. The remainder of this text is devoted to the development of the basic concepts involved in statistical methodology. In other words, we want to explain how statistical techniques actually work and why.

Statistics is a very heavy user of applied mathematics. Most of the fundamental rules (called theorems in mathematics) are developed and based on a knowledge of the calculus or higher mathematics. Inasmuch as this text is meant to be an introductory one, we omit proofs except where they can be easily derived. Where concepts or theorems can be shown to be intuitively reasonable, we will attempt to give a logical explanation. Hence, we will attempt to convince you with the aid of examples and intuitive arguments rather than with rigorous mathematical derivations.

You should refer occasionally to Chapter 1 and review the objective of statistics and the elements of a statistical problem. Each of the following chapters should, in some way, be directed toward answering the questions posed here. Each is essential to completing the overall picture of statistics.

REFERENCES

American Statistical Association and the Institute of Mathematical Statistics. *Careers in Statistics,* 1974.

Tanur, J. M., et al., eds. *Statistics: A Guide to the Unknown.* 2nd ed. San Francisco: Holden-Day, 1978.

KEY TERMS

Population (page 4)	**Inferential statistics** (page 5)
Sample (page 4)	**Design of an experiment** (page 5)
Descriptive statistics (page 5)	**Inference** (page 6)

EXERCISES

UNDERSTANDING THE CONCEPTS

  1.1   In order to control the cost of inventory, the manager of a hardware store wants to limit the number of each item in stock and, at the same time, avoid turning customers away due to insufficient inventory. To accomplish this goal, the manager wants to know the customer demand characteristics per month for each item.

(a) Describe the population of interest to the manager for a single item.

(b) Can the manager actually acquire this population so that it can be studied? Explain.

(c) Explain how you might learn something about the characteristics of the population without actually having the population in hand.

 1.2 Suppose that you are a potential buyer of 100 acres of raw land. How much is it worth? If you were to ask 100 different land appraisers, you might receive 100 different answers. Thus the "value of the land" might be characterized by a population of measurements.

(a) Describe the population.

(b) Does this population actually exist or is it conceptual? Explain.

(c) Does the population associated with experienced appraisers differ from the population associated with buyers, sellers, or the public at large? Explain.

(d) If you plan to base your offering price on the advice of experienced appraisers, would you employ one appraiser or would you seek the advice of several? Explain.

 1.3 A substantial amount of emission control tampering in cars and light trucks is cited in a recent federal study (*New York Times,* November 4, 1985). Emission tampering is defined to have occurred if an emission control system is either removed from a vehicle or is inoperable. In a 14-city survey of cars and light trucks manufactured between 1974 and 1984, deliberate tampering was found in 22% of the vehicles. Another 29% of the vehicles showed evidence of tampering, but there was no evidence to confirm that the tampering was deliberate.

(a) Describe the population from which this sample was selected.

(b) Describe the sample.

(c) Does the sample selected from the population appear to be representative of all cars and light trucks operating in the United States that were manufactured between 1974 and 1984?

 1.4 Economic forecasts are sometimes based on a survey of nationally known economists and business executives. One of these, conducted by the Conference Board, sampled the opinions of 38 senior business executives. As part of the survey, each respondent was asked to guess the average United States inflation rate over the next five years. The average of this sample of 38 "best guesses" was an inflation rate of 5.9% per year (*Wall Street Journal,* April 16, 1984).

(a) Describe the population from which the sample was selected.

(b) If you actually knew all of the measurements in the sampled population, would you be able to determine the average annual inflation rate over the next five years?

(c) What was the objective of the Conference Board's survey?

 1.5 The *Orlando Sentinel Star* (April 16, 1981) describes a survey conducted by the Merit Systems Protection Board, a government agency charged with the protection of whistle blowers, federal workers who report observed fraud, waste, or mismanagement. Only 8500 of the 13,000 questioned (probably by mailed questionnaires) responded. In response to one question, 70% of the respondents stated that they told no one and did nothing about observed improper activity for fear of reprisal or because they thought that nothing would be done about it.

(a) Describe the population of interest to the Merit Systems Protection Board.

(b) Describe the sample.

(c) Explain why the sample data might give a distorted view of the nature of the population.

 1.6 Unless you are a close follower of corporate common stock, you may choose to invest some of your future savings in shares of one or more mutual stock funds. The growth in the value of a fund's shares over a period of time will depend upon the skill of the fund manager in choosing the fund's investments and upon general economic conditions.

(a) How would you characterize the percentage return of mutual stock funds over the past year?

(b) Does the population you described in part (a) exist, or is it conceptual?

(c) Suppose that you wished to characterize the percentage return of mutual stock funds over the next 12 months. Does this population exist, or is it conceptual?

1.7 Ronald E. Milliman conducted a study to investigate the effect of background music on several variables that measure the performance of supermarkets ("Using Background Music to Affect the Behavior of Supermarket Shoppers," *Journal of Marketing,* Vol. 46, 1982). In one part of the study 200 patrons of a New York area supermarket were surveyed to determine whether they preferred music playing in the background while they shopped.

(a) Describe the population and the sample associated with this survey.

(b) Would it be possible to sample the entire population if you wanted to? Explain.

(c) Will the percentage of patrons in the sample equal the percentage of patrons in the population who prefer background music while they shop? Explain.

Sometimes, the data that we have collected represent a sample selected from a population. Other times (such as a national census), the data may represent the entire population. In either case, we need to be able to describe the data set. The objective of this chapter is to present two methods for describing data sets: (1) a graphical descriptive method and (2) numerical descriptive methods. Graphical descriptive methods describe the data by using charts and graphs. Numerical descriptive methods utilize numbers to help us construct a mental picture of the data.

2

DESCRIBING SETS OF DATA

CASE STUDY

So You Want to Be a Millionaire?

Shortly after the passage of the Tax Act of 1981, many newspaper ads portrayed the local banker as counselor, revealing the simple process by which we can all become millionaires. According to the ads, all we had to do was to invest $2000 per year in an Individual Retirement Account. After 40 years of participation your nest egg would have grown to over a million dollars. Of course, the tax laws have been changed several times since 1981, and with the latest tax revision IRAs will no longer be available for most of us. But the principle espoused in the advertisements is still valid. The best way to accumulate a large sum of money is to participate in a systematic savings and investment program, one that compounds the invested funds over the years.

If you are saving for retirement or for some other objective, the amount that you accumulate will depend on the amount you invest each year, where you invest it (a bank savings account, a money fund, or one of the various common stock funds), and who manages your account. Basically, the growth of your account and its ultimate value will depend upon the annual rate of return that your account manager is able to obtain for you.

Although the rate of return on your money will vary from day to day, Table 2.1 gives you an indication of the amount of money that you might expect to accumulate in 40 years. The amounts shown are based on the assumption that you invest $2000 at the beginning of each year for a period of 40 years and that the money is compounded monthly at a fixed annual rate of interest I.

Monthly rates of return vary not only between investment vehicles (banks, stock funds, money funds, etc.) but also within an investment vehicle itself. For example, consider a money fund, one that invests in short-term commercial rates. Since the notes will be negotiated at different times and will vary in length of time to maturity, the rate of return for the total fund at any one point in time will depend upon the fund manager's skill in placing the loans. If the interest rate rises in the future, it pays to hold notes with a small average time to maturity. If it drops, it pays to hold notes with a large average time to maturity.

The characteristics of money funds as a vehicle for investment are imbedded in the data of Table 2.2. Table 2.2 presents the asset size (in millions of dollars); the average maturity (in days) for notes; and the average 7-day as well as the average 30-day yields (%) (for the period ending April 23, 1986) for 227 large money funds available to investors. An examination of Table 2.2 clearly indicates a statistical problem. While it is possible to obtain a general feeling about the asset size, the average maturity time, and the average rate of return by examining the data, it is difficult to obtain a clear picture of the characteristics of these data sets by simply scanning the table. This problem motivates the topic of Chapter 2. In this chapter we will examine methods for describing data sets. Then in Section 2.12 we will apply these techniques to describe the money fund data and see how this descriptive information is relevant to our prospects of becoming millionaires.

TABLE 2.1 Withdrawal Amount for an Account After an Annual Investment of $2000 at a Fixed Annual Rate of Return I (%) for 40 Years

Interest Rate I (%)	Amount in Account After 40 Years ($)
4	197,652
6	328,095
8	559,562
10	973,704
12	1,718,285

Fund	Assets ($Million)	Average Maturity	7-Day Yield	30-Day Yield	Fund	Assets ($Million)	Average Maturity	7-Day Yield	30-Day Yield
AARP	85	86	6.18	6.37	DelawareTr	50	64	6.22	6.42
AMEV Fd	69	28	6.71	6.94	Dreyfinstit	629	41	6.70	6.92
ActiveAssetGovt	197	66	6.40	6.61	DreyfLiqAssets	7749	47	6.81	7.04
ActiveAssetMoney	2273	68	6.89	7.12	DreyGovtSeries	987	95	6.47	6.68
AlexBrownCash	695	38	6.62	6.84	DryInstGovt	981	85	6.68	6.90
AlexBrownGovt	164	43	6.51	6.72	DreyfMMktSer	669	44	6.78	7.01
AmerCapResrv a	199	26	8.10	8.44	EGT MoneyMkt f	64	47	6.19	6.39
AmNatl	16	16	6.54	6.76	EatonVanceCshMg	170	29	6.64	6.80
AutCsh	795	44	6.79	7.02	EquitableMoney	195	48	6.59	6.85
AutGvt	1420	46	6.48	6.69	FBL MoneyMkt	25	24	5.95	6.13
BLC Cash	39	17	6.26	6.46	FahnstckDaily	143	1	6.10	6.54
BabsonMoneyMkt	56	23	6.35	6.55	FidelityCashRes	4045	34	6.82	7.06
BirrWilson	66	30	5.60	5.76	FidelityDlyIncm b	2420	37	6.73	6.96
BostonCoCash	236	40	6.69	6.91	FidelGovtPortf	764	35	6.83	7.07
BostonCoGovt	31	27	6.01	6.19	FidelDomesticPort	1324	33	6.90	7.14
BullBearDollr	66	67	7.00	7.25	FidelMM US Treas	260	40	6.59	6.81
CAM Fund	46	22	6.08	6.27	FidelityUS Gvt	451	47	6.53	6.75
CBA MoneyFd	102	78	7.01	7.26	FinancialDlyIncSh	174	15	6.22	6.42
CIMCO	17	54	6.76	6.99	FinancialPlanFed	2	32	1.20	1.72
CalvertSociai af	53	50	6.44	6.65	FstAmerMoneyFd	51	38	7.11	7.36
CapitalCashMgt	90	15	6.57	6.79	FstInvestCshMgt f	275949	22	6.24	6.42
CapitalPreservFd	1820	51	7.30	6.93	FstVariGvtIncm f	520	61	6.52	6.73
CapitPreserv II	426	2	6.04	6.43	FlexFund	36	16	6.74	6.97
CapT MM	193	49	6.47	6.68	FoundersMMkt	18	13	6.39	6.79
CardinalGvtSec	434	4	6.41	6.62	FranklinMoneyFd a	972	29	6.17	6.36
CarnegieGvtSecur	150	44	6.40	6.60	FranklnFedMon b	135	1	6.00	6.18
CashAssets	79	24	6.64	6.86	FundGvtInvest	723	50	6.31	6.51
CashEquivM	5557	29	6.77	7.00	GenGvtSecur	122	88	6.17	6.36
CashEquivIntGvt	621	17	6.62	6.84	GenlMMkt	562	46	6.48	6.69
CashMgmtTrAm a	612	17	6.69	6.82	GovtInvestorsTr a	230	30	6.26	6.45
CashPlusFedl	93	41	6.72	6.95	GovtSecurityCash	9	5	5.34	5.44
CashPlusMMkt	350	42	7.07	7.32	GradisonCashRes	422	62	6.47	6.65
CashResrvMgmt a	4536	32	6.74	6.96	GradisonUSGvt	25	33	5.86	6.12
CentennialGvtTr	78	41	6.24	6.43	GuardianCshFd	63	23	6.59	6.81
CentennialMMTr	179	39	6.39	6.60	GuardianCshMgt	21	19	6.20	6.39
ChurchillCashRsv	76	16	6.49	6.70	HeritageCash	135	39	6.58	6.80
CignaCash	39	42	6.64	6.86	HilliardLyons	102	4	5.83	8.26
CignaMMkt b	183	50	6.72	6.95	HummerWayne	79	21	6.30	6.50
ColonialMMkt	10	20	6.09	6.27	HuttonAMA	2150	33	6.72	6.94
ColumbDlyIncm af	420	31	6.51	6.68	HuttonGvt	1124	33	6.29	6.47
CommandGovt	112	56	7.01	7.26	IDS CashMgmt	830	33	6.82	7.05
CommandMny a	1233	48	6.86	7.10	IDS Strategy	7	33	5.45	5.60
CompositeCshMg a	129	25	6.38	6.59	IntegMMSec	193	50	6.49	6.74
CortlandGeneral	164	40	6.37	6.58	InvCashResv	43	50	6.38	6.60
CortlandUSGvt	35	59	6.00	5.90	JohnHancockCshM	323	48	6.35	6.55
CountryCapital	22	21	6.00	6.18	KemperGovtMMkt	87	14	6.23	6.42
CurrentInterest	928	39	6.38	6.59	KemperMMkt	4643	31	7.07	7.32
CurrentIntUSGvt	86	40	6.03	6.21	KeyCap T	49	35	5.99	6.17
DBL MM Portfolio	1474	52	6.82	7.10	KeystoneLiqd	193	45	6.34	6.54
DBL GvtSec	243	70	6.90	7.14	KidderPeabGvt	184	44	6.42	6.63
DailyCashAccum	2488	40	6.59	6.81	KidderPeabPrem	578	44	6.71	6.98
DailyDollar	206	37	6.90	6.94	LandmarkCshRsv	147	44	6.58	6.80
DailyIncomeFd	489	54	6.71	6.86	LazardCash	733	25	6.80	7.03
DailyPassportCsh f	656	47	6.34	6.54	LazardGovt	512	8	6.60	6.82
DWitterSearLqd	6766	68	6.89	7.13	LeggMasonCsRs f	266	41	6.40	6.61
DWitrSearUS	439	65	6.28	6.48	LehmanMgtCash	268	34	6.85	7.09
DelawareCashRes f	1260	60	6.81	7.05	LehmanMgtGvt	43	32	6.43	6.64

Fund	Assets ($Million)	Average Maturity	7-Day Yield	30-Day Yield	Fund	Assets ($Million)	Average Maturity	7-Day Yield	30-Day Yield
LexingtonGvtSec a	16	72	5.88	6.05	RothschldEarn	452	18	6.44	6.65
LexingtonMonMt a	215	23	6.57	6.79	RowePricePrmR f	2785	35	6.65	6.87
LibertyCash	38	30	6.04	6.23	RowePriceUSTr f	178	35	5.70	5.86
LibertyUSGovt	2024	49	6.00	6.18	SafecoMMkt f	39	32	6.66	6.87
LiquidCapitalIncm	1237	21	6.37	6.57	StClair	59	28	6.51	6.73
LiquidGreenTr	186	34	6.46	6.67	ScudderCshInv	1033	43	6.55	6.76
LordAbbettCshRes	182	28	6.33	6.54	ScudderGovt	147	59	5.87	6.04
LutheranBroth	381	46	6.27	6.47	SelectedMoneyMkt	17	52	6.17	6.37
Map Gvt	19	48	6.86	7.09	SeligmanCsh Gvt	20	1	5.88	6.05
MarinerCash	636	19	6.82	7.05	SeligmanCsh prime	309	35	6.48	6.69
MarinerGvt	368	12	6.59	6.81	SentinlCash b	42	46	6.43	6.64
MarinerUS	123	17	6.44	6.65	ShearsonDailyDiv f	3863	34	6.53	6.74
MassCashMgmt a	587	44	6.55	6.77	Shearson FMA Csh	1420	34	6.65	6.87
MassCashMgmtGvt	36	43	5.98	6.26	Shearson FMA Gvt	363	88	6.54	6.75
MassMutlLiquid	40	32	6.57	6.74	ShearsonGovAgen	1554	90	6.57	6.79
McDonald	149	33	5.98	6.16	ShortTermMM	458	53	6.70	6.71
MerLyCMA Gvt a	2056	77	6.43	6.64	ShortTrmUSGvt	208	57	6.28	6.43
MerLyCMA Mon a	18428	74	6.69	6.92	ShortTermAsset	150	41	6.70	6.92
MerrLynchGovt a	1649	46	6.92	7.16	ShortTermYldSec a	9	15	5.46	5.74
MerrLynchInst af	1739	49	7.22	7.49	SigmaMMkt	6	11	5.89	6.06
MerrLynchReadyA	12182	73	6.66	6.89	SthnFarmBur	22	33	6.39	6.59
MerrLynchRetir a	2772	71	6.57	6.79	StandbyResve	327	37	6.76	6.99
MerrLynchUSA	264	78	6.32	6.52	SteinRoeCashRes	751	32	6.55	6.72
MidwIncTrGvt	130	44	5.90	6.08	SteinRoeGovtRes	33	27	5.66	5.86
MidwIncTrCsh	41	17	6.18	6.37	StrongMMkt	4	110	6.36	6.56
MonManPrime	23	33	6.32	6.53	SummitCash	627	64	6.96	7.21
MonManGovt	6	35	6.32	6.52	TemporaryInvstFd	7829	28	6.99	7.24
MoneyMktMgmt f	230	50	6.57	6.78	ThomMcNtlMMkt	1899	33	6.57	6.79
MoneyMarketFund	20	10	6.26	6.46	ThomMcNtlGvt	46	22	6.29	6.49
MorganKegDly f	81	44	6.23	6.43	TransamCashRes	212	34	6.75	6.97
MunicipalCshRsv c	1886	64	4.81	4.93	TrinityLiqd	366	33	6.82	7.05
MunicipalTempInv c	1842	39	4.66	4.77	TrustCashRes f	178	44	6.39	6.59
MutualOmahMM	242	40	6.50	6.71	TrstfdTreasry	1918	44	6.68	6.91
MutualOmahaCash	57	31	6.37	6.58	TrstfdUS Agen	258	49	6.77	7.00
NEL CashMgmt	737	58	6.69	6.91	TrstfdPrmeOblig	1525	40	6.95	7.20
NEL CshMgtUSGvt	42	118	6.22	6.41	TrstfdCommcl	106	40	6.91	7.16
NatlCashReserve	26	31	5.81	5.99	TrustShortTerm	1980	29	6.74	6.97
NatnwdeMMkt	439	44	6.53	6.74	TrstShtFdT	1544	30	6.77	7.00
NeubergerGovt	96	46	6.17	6.36	TuckerAnthony	537	33	6.48	6.70
NewtonMoney	30	49	6.78	7.01	TuckerAnthGvt	175	55	5.95	6.13
OppenMoneyMkt	698	41	6.57	6.79	TwentCentCsh	50	39	6.42	6.70
OxfordCash	152	16	6.57	6.79	UMB FedPort	100	27	6.37	6.57
PacHrzGvtMM	914	74	6.69	6.91	UMB Prime	61	23	6.62	6.84
PacHrzMMktPort	564	24	6.77	7.00	USAA FedlSec	19	88	5.90	6.07
PW Cash	4159	40	6.61	6.83	USAA MutualFd	268	54	6.70	6.92
ParkCsh	130	37	6.46	6.67	US Treasury	79	39	5.98	6.11
Phoenix	46	70	6.70	6.93	UST MasterGvt	61	26	6.56	6.78
PrimeCash	154	37	6.66	6.88	UST MasterMoney	179	57	6.82	7.05
PruBacGvt	287	55	6.99	6.65	UnitedCashMgmt a	2	67	6.78	7.00
PruBacMMart	3885	46	6.82	7.02	ValueLineCashFd	443	69	6.78	6.94
PutnamDailyDiv	250	50	6.66	6.88	VangrdMMFed f	496	37	6.60	6.87
PW RMA Mony	1747	42	6.40	6.61	VangrdMMPR f	1807	36	6.89	7.14
PW RMA USGvt	201	68	6.19	6.39	VangrdInsured f	52	16	6.25	6.49
RenaissanceGvt	79	1	6.47	6.76	VikingMnyMkt	30	19	6.35	6.55
RenaissanceMMkt	194	22	6.77	7.01	WebsterCashRes	1438	39	6.68	6.90
ReserveFund	1673	24	6.36	6.57	WorkingAssets	82	44	6.46	6.68
ReserveFd Gvt	326	2	6.01	6.36	Average yield 5.96				

Source: Data from NASD Inc., "Money Market Summary as of April 23, 1986." Reprinted with permission.

2.1 TYPES OF DATA

Data can be classified according to whether they are **quantitative** or **qualitative**. Quantitative data represent the amount or quantity of something. Dividend yields, the daily production of oil, the length of time required to complete a government form, or the value of an inventory are examples of quantitative data. Data that are not quantitative—that is, they can only be categorized or described—are qualitative. For example, the recorded occupations of a group of people is a qualitative data set.

Qualitative data are described by counting the number of observations in each category. For example, if the data represent the recorded occupations for a group of people, we count and record the number of plumbers, the number of computer specialists, and so on, and then calculate the percentage of the total number of observations falling in each category. These percentages are displayed graphically in the pie charts and bar graphs that we encounter so frequently in newspapers and journals. The methods for describing quantitative data sets are not as familiar or easy to understand. Consequently, we will devote the remainder of this chapter to a study of some graphical and numerical methods for describing quantitative data.

DEFINITION   *Quantitative data* represent the amount or quantity of something.   ∎

DEFINITION   *Qualitative data* can be categorized but cannot be quantified.   ∎

2.2 A GRAPHICAL METHOD FOR DESCRIBING A SET OF DATA: RELATIVE FREQUENCY DISTRIBUTIONS

We will introduce some graphical and numerical descriptive methods for describing quantitative data sets as we examine the 1986 year-end dividend yields for a sample of 25 bank common stocks. The dividend yield for a stock is the percentage of the stock's price represented by its dividend. The 25 dividend yields are shown in Table 2.3.

TABLE 2.3   The Dividend Yields (%) for 25 Bank Common Stocks

3.1	4.2	2.3	3.3	2.8
5.3	3.5	3.1	2.6	3.3
4.7	3.7	3.0	2.6	4.0
3.8	4.4	3.2	3.2	3.8
5.1	3.7	2.3	4.3	3.9

A cursory examination of the data indicates that the lowest dividend yield in the sample is 2.3, the largest, 5.3. How are the other 23 measurements distributed? Do most lie near 2.3, near 5.3, or are they evenly distributed over the interval from 2.3 to 5.3? To answer this question, we divide the interval into an arbitrary number of subintervals of equal length, the number depending upon the amount of data available. (As a rule of thumb, the number of subintervals chosen can range from 5 to 20; the larger the amount of data available, the more subintervals used.) For instance, we might use the subintervals 2.25 to 2.75, 2.75 to 3.25, 3.25 to 3.75, and so on. Note that the points dividing the subintervals have been chosen so that it is impossible for a measurement to fall on the point of division, thus eliminating any ambiguity regarding the disposition of a particular measurement. The subintervals, called **classes** in statistical language, form cells or pockets similar to the pockets of a billiard table. We want to determine the manner in which the measurements are distributed among the pockets, or classes. A tally of the data from Table 2.3 is presented in Table 2.4.

TABLE 2.4   Tabulation of Relative Frequencies for a Histogram

Class, i	Class Boundaries	Tally	Class Frequency, f_i	Class Relative Frequency
1	2.25–2.75	||||	4	4/25 = .16
2	2.75–3.25	₩|	6	6/25 = .24
3	3.25–3.75	₩	5	5/25 = .20
4	3.75–4.25	₩	5	5/25 = .20
5	4.25–4.75	|||	3	3/25 = .12
6	4.75–5.25	|	1	1/25 = .04
7	5.25–5.75	|	1	1/25 = .04
Total n = 25				1.00

Each of the 25 measurements falls in one of seven classes which, for purposes of identification, we will number. The identification number appears in the first column of Table 2.4 and the corresponding **class boundaries** are given in the second column. The third column of the table is used for the tally, a mark entered opposite the appropriate class for each measurement falling in the class. For example, 4 of the 25 measurements fall in class 1, 6 in class 2, 5 in class 3, 5 in class 4, and so forth. The number of measurements falling in a particular class, say class i, is called the **class frequency** and is designated by the symbol f_i. The class frequency is given in the fourth column of Table 2.4. The last column of this table presents the fraction of the total number of measurements falling in each class, called the **class relative frequency**. If we let n represent the total number of measurements (for instance, in our example $n = 25$), then the relative frequency for the ith class equals f_i divided by n:

$$\text{relative frequency} = \frac{f_i}{n}$$

The resulting tabulation can be presented graphically in the form of a **relative frequency histogram** (see Figure 2.1). Rectangles are constructed over each class interval, their height proportional to the fraction (or proportion) of the total number of measurements (the class relative frequency) falling in each class interval. Viewing the

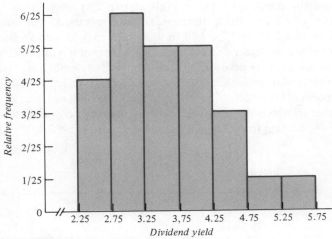

FIGURE 2.1   Relative Frequency Histogram

relative frequency histogram, we see at a glance the manner in which the stock dividend yields are distributed over the interval.

Relative frequency histograms for data sets can be constructed quickly and easily by using an electronic computer and one of several good statistical computer program packages. Figure 2.2 shows the computer printout of the relative frequency histogram for the 25 bank stock dividend yield averages using the Statistical Analysis System (SAS) statistical computer program package. Note that it presents a graphical description of the data that is, for all practical purposes, identical to our relative frequency histogram shown in Figure 2.1.

We can use the relative frequency histogram in Figure 2.1 to answer some interesting questions. What fraction of the stocks had dividend yields greater than 4.25%? Checking the relative frequency histogram, we see that the fraction involves all classes to the right of 4.25. Using Table 2.4, we see that five stocks possessed dividend yields greater than 4.25. Hence, the fraction is 5/25, or 20%. We note that this value is also the percentage of the total area of the histogram in Figure 2.2 located to the right of 4.25. Suppose that we were to write each dividend yield on a piece of paper, place the 25 slips of paper in a hat, mix them, and then draw one piece of paper from the hat. What is the chance that this paper will contain a dividend yield greater than 4.25? Because 5 of the 25 slips are marked with numbers greater than 4.25, we say that we have 5 chances out of 25. Or we might say that the probability is .2. (You have undoubtedly encountered the word *probability* in ordinary conversation, and we defer definition and discussion of its significance until Chapter 3.)

What fraction of the dividend yields for all bank stocks were greater than 4.25? If we possessed the relative frequency histogram for the population, we could give the exact answer to this question by calculating the fraction of total area lying to the right of 4.25. Unfortunately, since we do not have such a histogram, we are forced to make an

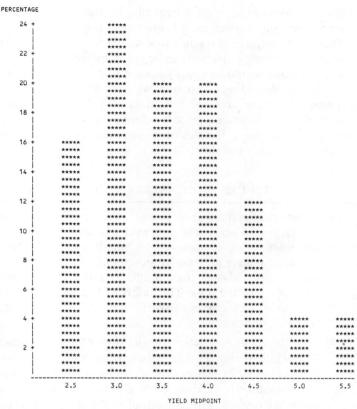

FIGURE 2.2   The Relative Frequency Histogram for the 25 Bank Stock Dividend Yields Produced by the SAS Statistical Computer Package

inference. We must estimate the true population fraction, basing our estimate upon information contained in the sample. Our estimate would likely be .2 or 20%. Suppose that we want to state the chance or probability that a bank stock from the population will have a dividend yield greater than 4.25. Without knowledge of the population relative frequency histogram, we infer that the population histogram is similar to the sample histogram and that approximately .2 of the measurements in the population will be greater than 4.25. Naturally, this estimate is subject to error. We will examine the magnitude of this estimation error in Chapter 6.

The relative frequency histogram is often called a **relative frequency distribution** (or simply a **frequency distribution**) because it shows the manner in which the data are distributed along the horizontal axis of the graph. **The rectangles constructed above each class are subject to two interpretations. They represent the fraction of observations falling in a given class. Also, if a measurement is drawn from the data, a particular class relative frequency is also the chance or probability that the measurement will fall in that class.** The most significant feature of the sample frequency histogram is that it provides information on the population frequency histogram that describes the population. We would expect the two frequency histograms, sample and population, to be similar. Such is the case. The degree of resemblance will increase as more and more data are added to the sample. If the sample were enlarged to include the entire population, the sample and population would be synonymous, and the histograms would be identical.

In the preceding discussion we showed you how to construct a frequency distribution for the dividend yield data of Table 2.3, and we explained how such a distribution could be interpreted. Before concluding this topic, we summarize in the following box the principles that you should use in constructing a frequency distribution for a set of data.

PRINCIPLES TO USE IN CONSTRUCTING A FREQUENCY DISTRIBUTION

(1) Determine the number of classes. It is usually best to have from 5 to 20 classes. The larger the amount of data available, the more classes that should be used. If the number of classes is too small, we might be concealing important characteristics of the data by grouping. If the number of classes is very large, too many empty classes may result, and the distribution will provide a poor description of the data. The number of classes should be determined from the amount of data present and the uniformity of the data. A small sample will require fewer classes.

(2) Find the range and determine the **class width**. As a general rule for finding the class width, divide the difference between the largest and smallest measurement by the number of classes desired, and add enough to the quotient to arrive at a convenient figure for class width. All classes should be of equal width so that we can make uniform comparisons of the class frequencies.

(3) Locate the class boundaries. To locate the class boundaries, start with the lowest class so that you include the smallest measurement. Then, add the remaining classes. Class boundaries should be chosen so that it is impossible for a measurement to fall on a boundary.

EXERCISES

BASIC TECHNIQUES

2.1 Consider the following set of data.

3	4	4	3	6	5
7	5	3	5	4	2
5	4	6	4	3	5
2	7	5	6	2	6
3	4	5	1	8	4

(a) Construct a relative frequency histogram for the data. Use classes starting at .5 with a class width of 1—that is, .5 to 1.5, 1.5 to 2.5, and so forth.
(b) What fraction of the measurements are less than 4.5?
(c) What fraction of the measurements fall between 3.5 and 5.5?

2.2 Consider the following set of data.

3.1	4.9	2.8	3.6	2.5
4.5	3.5	3.7	4.1	4.9
2.9	2.1	3.5	4.0	3.7
2.7	4.0	4.4	3.7	4.2
3.8	6.2	2.5	2.9	2.8
5.1	1.8	5.6	2.2	3.4
2.5	3.6	5.1	4.8	1.6
3.6	6.1	4.7	3.9	3.9
4.3	5.7	3.7	4.6	4.0
5.6	4.9	4.2	3.1	3.9

(a) Suppose that you wish to construct a relative frequency histogram for the data. Approximately how many class intervals should you use?

(b) Suppose that you decide to use classes starting at 1.55 with a class width of .5—that is, 1.55 to 2.05, 2.05 to 2.55, and so on. Construct the relative frequency histogram for the data.

(c) What fraction of the measurements are less than 5.05?

(d) What fraction of the measurements are larger than 3.55?

APPLICATIONS

 2.3 Table 2.5 gives the per capita spending (on Social Security, Medicare, grants to local and state governments, and so forth) per state by the federal government in 1984. Construct a relative frequency histogram to describe the data on federal per capita spending per state.

TABLE 2.5 Per Capita Spending Data for Exercise 2.3

State (Rank)	Per Capita Spending	State (Rank)	Per Capita Spending
Ala. (27)	$2,868	N.J. (30)	$2,719
Alaska (1)	$4,642	N.Mex. (3)	$4,306
Ariz. (18)	$3,005	N.Y. (17)	$3,005
Ark. (34)	$2,592	N.C. (49)	$2,210
Calif. (9)	$3,579	N.Dak. (12)	$3,317
Colo. (25)	$2,884	Ohio (44)	$2,388
Conn. (7)	$4,055	Okla. (36)	$2,549
Del. (32)	$2,668	Oreg. (42)	$2,448
D.C.	*	Pa. (29)	$2,724
Fla. (16)	$3,027	R.I. (14)	$3,099
Ga. (28)	$2,727	S.C. (31)	$2,711
Hawaii (5)	$4,073	S.Dak. (21)	$2,912
Idaho (39)	$2,494	Tenn. (23)	$2,885
Ill. (48)	$2,216	Ky. (38)	$2,517
Ind. (45)	$2,371	La. (43)	$2,396
Iowa (50)	$2,176	Maine (22)	$2,891
Kans. (11)	$3,346	Md. (2)	$4,319
Mont. (24)	$2,884	Mass. (8)	$3,695
Nebr. (35)	$2,565	Mich. (47)	$2,237
Nev. (15)	$3,081	Minn. (37)	$2,545
N.H. (19)	$2,971	Miss. (13)	$3,187

(continues)

TABLE 2.5   *(Continued)*

State (Rank)	Per Capita Spending	State (Rank)	Per Capita Spending
Mo. (6)	$4,060	Wash. (10)	$3,406
Tex. (41)	$2,456	W. Va. (40)	$2,472
Utah (20)	$2,930	Wis. (46)	$2,277
Vt. (33)	$2,631	Wyo. (26)	$2,879
Va. (4)	$4,303	Average	$3,022*

*Because of its great number of federal employees, per capita spending for Washington, D.C., was $20,652 and not included in rankings.

Source: U.S. Census Bureau data from *USA Today,* March 29, 1985. Copyright 1985, USA TODAY. Reprinted with permission.

2.4 In order to decide on the number of service counters needed for stores built in the future, a supermarket chain wanted to obtain information on the length of time (in minutes) required to service customers. To obtain information on the distribution of customer service times, a sample of 1000 customers' service times was recorded. Sixty of these are shown in the accompanying tabulation.

3.6	1.9	2.1	.3	.8	.2
1.0	1.4	1.8	1.6	1.1	1.8
.3	1.1	.5	1.2	.6	1.1
.8	1.7	1.4	.2	1.3	3.1
.4	2.3	1.8	4.5	.9	.7
.6	2.8	2.5	1.1	.4	1.2
.4	1.3	.8	1.3	1.1	1.2
.8	1.0	.9	.7	3.1	1.7
1.1	2.2	1.6	1.9	5.2	.5
1.8	.3	1.1	.6	.7	.6

(a) Construct a relative frequency histogram for the data.

(b) What fraction of the service times are less than or equal to one minute?

2.5 The number of home loan applications granted during a particular month was recorded for a sample of $n = 50$ commercial banks and/or lending institutions. These data are as follows:

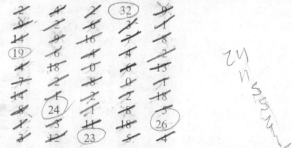

(a) Construct a relative frequency histogram for the data.

(b) Determine the fraction of the 50 commercial banks and/or lending institutions that granted 10 or less home loans during this particular month.

2.6 If you filed an income tax return this year, what are the chances that your return will be audited?

Although the odds will vary from year to year, depending upon the auditing manpower available to the IRS and its policies, Table 2.6 may provide some clues. It shows the number of tax returns filed per state in 1984, the associated number of returns audited, and the percentage of returns audited. Describe the 50 state percentages of returns audited, using a relative frequency histogram.

TABLE 2.6   Audited Returns Data for Exercise 2.6

State	Tax Returns Filed in 1984	Returns Audited	Percent Audited
Alabama	1,415,228	15,648	1.11
Alaska	233,681	5,801	2.48
Arizona	1,203,483	17,403	1.45
Arkansas	818,335	10,579	1.29
California	10,744,350	160,054	1.49
Colorado	1,365,174	18,722	1.37
Connecticut	1,488,512	18,160	1.22
Delaware	263,243	3,495	1.33
Florida	4,635,091	63,334	1.37
Georgia	2,247,309	27,293	1.21
Hawaii	448,974	6,217	1.38
Idaho	361,732	5,737	1.59
Illinois	4,735,759	46,986	.99
Indiana	2,175,952	14,988	.69
Iowa	1,159,039	10,287	.89
Kansas	991,703	11,533	1.16
Kentucky	1,306,226	10,879	.83
Louisiana	1,608,806	21,066	1.31
Maine	474,054	4,009	.85
Maryland*	2,227,632	22,259	1.00
Massachusetts	2,635,761	21,515	.82
Michigan	3,568,506	32,188	.90
Minnesota	1,723,152	20,170	1.17
Mississippi	866,031	11,112	1.28
Missouri	1,995,262	19,184	.96
Montana	335,248	4,625	1.38
Nebraska	664,821	7,844	1.18
Nevada	414,127	10,395	2.51
New Hampshire	438,330	3,485	.80
New Jersey	3,562,840	47,755	1.34
New Mexico	549,869	7,892	1.44
New York	7,270,949	102,253	1.41
North Carolina	2,439,658	24,897	1.02
North Dakota	279,156	4,723	1.69
Ohio	4,342,810	47,543	1.09
Oklahoma	1,247,364	15,048	1.21
Oregon	1,085,829	14,792	1.36
Pennsylvania	4,874,417	42,198	.87
Rhode Island	416,463	4,821	1.16
South Carolina	1,218,832	11,875	.97

(continues)

TABLE 2.6   (*Continued*)

State	Tax Returns Filed in 1984	Returns Audited	Percent Audited
South Dakota	278,962	3,961	1.42
Tennessee	1,796,439	20,589	1.15
Texas	11,171,215	82,426	.74
Utah	557,826	10,966	1.97
Vermont	217,588	2,482	1.14
Virginia	2,324,937	21,340	.92
Washington	1,800,810	25,525	1.42
West Virginia	655,551	6,217	.95
Wisconsin	1,949,953	16,098	.83
Wyoming	206,902	4,060	1.93

*District of Columbia figures included in Maryland totals.

Source: USA Today, April 15, 1985. Copyright 1985, USA TODAY. Reprinted with permission.

 2.7 Table 2.7 gives the amounts of internally generated funds (in millions of dollars) spent by the 50 largest corporate spenders for research and development in 1985. Construct a relative frequency histogram to describe the amounts spent for research and development.

TABLE 2.7   Corporate Spending Data for Exercise 2.7

1985 Rank	Company	1985 Spending (Millions)	Change from 1984 (in Percent)	R&D as Percent of Sales	1985 Rank	Company	1985 Spending (Millions)	Change from 1984 (in Percent)	R&D as Percent of Sales
1	General Motors	$3,625.2	17.9	3.8	26	Texas Instruments	$402.0	9.5	8.2
2	IBM	3,457.0	9.8	6.9	27	Procter & Gamble	400.0	8.4	3.0
3	AT&T	2,209.7	1.0	3.9	28	Eli Lilly	369.8	8.4	11.3
4	Ford	2,018.0	5.4	3.8	29	Rockwell	367.2	21.5	3.2
5	Du Pont	1,144.0	4.3	3.9	30	Allied-Signal	343.0	32.9	3.8
6	ITT	1,085.0	13.7	9.1	31	Control Data	316.1	6.4	8.6
7	General Electric	1,069.0	3.0	3.8	32	GTE	313.0	18.1	2.0
8	Eastman Kodak	976.0	16.5	9.2	33	SmithKline	309.6	10.9	9.5
9	United Technologies	916.2	−1.6	6.1	34	NCR	299.1	3.5	6.9
10	Digital Equipment	717.3	13.7	10.7	35	Goodyear	298.6	6.9	3.1
11	Hewlett-Packard	685.0	15.7	10.5	36	Chevron	296.0	−4.2	0.7
12	Exxon	681.0	−7.5	0.8	37	Northrop	287.5	20.5	5.7
13	Chrysler	609.0	34.7	2.9	38	Pfizer	286.7	12.5	7.1
14	Xerox	603.1	7.4	6.9	39	Burroughs	285.2	3.9	5.7
15	Dow Chemical	547.0	7.9	4.7	40	Upjohn	284.1	15.2	14.1
16	3M	507.0	10.9	6.5	41	Union Carbide	275.0	3.8	3.1
17	Sperry	503.5	9.2	8.8	42	Bristol-Myers	261.7	23.2	5.9
18	Johnson & Johnson	471.1	11.8	7.3	43	Raytheon	260.3	10.3	4.1
19	Monsanto	470.0	27.0	7.0	44	Shell Oil	254.0	17.1	1.2
20	Motorola	464.0	9.2	8.5	45	RCA	251.3	3.5	2.8
21	Honeywell	451.4	7.0	6.8	46	American Cyanamid	250.6	7.9	7.1
22	Lockheed	429.0	13.5	4.5	47	Westinghouse	246.0	3.8	2.3
23	Merck	426.3	8.4	12.0	48	Abbott Labs	240.6	10.0	7.2
24	McDonnell Douglas	423.1	14.2	3.7	49	General Dynamics	228.0	15.7	2.8
25	Boeing	409.0	−19.2	3.0	50	Mobil	224.0	4.2	0.7

Source: Inside R&D, Technical Insights Inc., 1986. Reprinted with permission.

2.8 Refer to Exercise 2.7. Use a relative frequency histogram to describe research and development expenditures expressed as a percentage of annual sales.

2.9 The data in Table 2.8 show the dividend yields (in percentages) on the common stock for 25 electric utilities at year-end 1985 and on November 13, 1986.

(a) Construct a relative frequency histogram for the 1985 year-end dividend yields for the 25 electric utility common stocks.

(b) What proportion of the dividend yields exceed 7.0%?

(c) Notice that the dividend yields for 1985 vary from a low of 6.2% to a high of 12.7%. Can you give a reason for this large variation?

TABLE 2.8   Dividend Yield Data for Exercise 2.9

| | Yield (%) | |
Electric Utility	Year-End 1985	November 13, 1986
Allegheny Power	8.2	6.1
Atlantic City Electric	9.1	6.4
Carolina Power	8.9	6.7
Duke Power	7.3	5.6
Duquesne Light	12.7	9.3
Florida Progress	7.4	5.2
FPL Group	6.9	5.9
Houston Industries	9.4	8.1
Idaho Power	7.5	6.3
Illinois Power	11.1	8.7
Iowa-Illinois Gas & Electric	7.6	6.6
Kansas Power & Light	7.4	5.3
Minnesota Power & Light	7.0	4.7
Montana Power	7.4	6.4
Ohio Edison	11.5	9.5
Pacific Gas & Electric	9.2	7.8
Pennsylvania Power & Light	8.9	6.6
Philadelphia Electric	12.7	9.6
San Diego Gas & Electric	8.3	6.5
Southern California Edison	8.1	6.6
Southern Company	9.2	8.4
TECO Energy, Inc.	6.8	5.2
Texas Utilities	8.4	8.1
Union Electric	8.6	6.3
Wisconsin Electric Power	6.2	5.6

Source: Data from various issues, *Wall Street Journal* and *Standard & Poor's Stock Guide.*

2.10 Refer to Exercise 2.9. Construct a relative frequency histogram for the November 13, 1986, dividend yields for the 25 electric utility common stocks. Use the same class widths as used in Exercise 2.9. Compare this relative frequency histogram with the histogram for the corresponding year-end 1985 yields. Notice the large downward shift in yields from year-end 1985 to November 13, 1986. What does this shift say about the change in the prices of these utility stocks from year-end 1985 to November 13, 1986?

2.11 In a study of reporting delays for failed firms, Edward C. Lawrence found "that a significant number of failing firms incur delays in releasing annual reports for the final year before bankruptcy." The delay times (or time lags, as they are sometimes called) for 58 failing firms are described by the frequency histogram shown in Figure 2.3. Examine the frequency histogram and answer the following questions.

(a) What proportion of the failing firms waited five or more months after the firm's year-end before releasing their annual reports?

(b) What proportion of the firms had time lags exceeding two months?

(c) What proportion of the firms released their annual reports within three months of year-end?

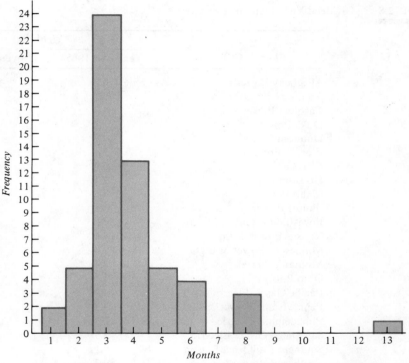

FIGURE 2.3   Frequency Histogram for Delay Times for Exercise 2.11 (*Source:* E. C. Lawrence, "Reporting Delays for Failed Firms," *Journal of Accounting Research,* Vol. 21, No. 2, 1983.)

MKTG 2.12 Is a company's success related to its use of modern marketing methods? To shed some light on this question, Tom Griffin surveyed 49 Puerto Rican food companies. Each company responded to each of two questionnaires, one designed to measure the extent to which a company used modern marketing methods and the other designed to measure the company's success. Prior to discussing the relationship between a company's scores on the marketing and the company success questionnaires, Griffin gives a tabulation of the 49 scores for each of the two questionnaires. Since some companies received the same score on a questionnaire, the data are presented in Tables 2.9(a) and 2.9(b). Examine the 49 marketing methods scores and note that they vary from a low (use) of 2.09 to a high score of 3.69. Construct a relative frequency distribution to describe this data set.

TABLE 2.9   Marketing Methods and Success Data for Exercise 2.12

(a) Marketing Methods Scores and Frequencies				(b) Company Success Scores and Frequencies			
Score	Frequency	Score	Frequency	Score	Frequency	Score	Frequency
2.09	1	2.80	1	1.27	1	2.14	3
2.20	1	2.84	2	1.50	1	2.18	1
2.29	1	2.89	2	1.68	1	2.23	1
2.42	1	2.91	1	1.73	1	2.27	7
2.47	1	2.93	3	1.77	3	2.32	4
2.49	1	2.98	1	1.91	1	2.36	2
2.53	3	3.02	1	1.95	1	2.41	5
2.60	2	3.07	4	2.00	1	2.45	3
2.62	3	3.09	1	2.05	3	2.50	4
2.64	1	3.16	2	2.09	1	2.55	4
2.67	1	3.18	3			2.64	1
2.71	1	3.24	2	$n = 49$			
2.73	2	3.27	1	Mean score: 2.22			
2.76	1	3.38	1				
2.78	2	3.47	1				
		3.69	1				

$n = 49$
Mean score: 2.85

Source: Tom Griffin, "Linking the Use of Modern Marketing Methods to Company Success," *Columbia Journal of World Business,* Fall 1982. Reprinted with permission.

2.13 Describe the 49 company success scores of Exercise 2.12 by using a relative frequency histogram.

2.3   STEM AND LEAF DISPLAYS☆

A second method for describing data sets that has become popular in recent years is the stem and leaf display. As an example, we will use the data listed in Table 2.10, which gives the mathematical ratings for 20 college Division I basketball teams selected from among the ratings of 282 Division I team ratings.

To construct a stem and leaf display for this data, we first partition each observation into two parts, one called the *stem* of the observation and the other called the *leaf*. For example, we could decide to divide each rating between the tens and the hundreds digits. The portion to the left of the point of division is the stem; the portion to the right is the leaf. For example, the stem and the leaf for the rating 82.45 are

stem	leaf
8	2.45

☆This section is optional.

TABLE 2.10   Mathematical Ratings for 20 College Division I Basketball Teams Through March 10, 1985

College	Rating	College	Rating
Clemson	82.45	Duke	89.26
Portland	72.81	Towson State	65.70
Texas Tech	84.84	Akron	70.62
Citadel	75.19	Nebraska	81.02
Drake	75.10	Marshall	78.08
Idaho	70.03	Navy	82.12
Ohio University	81.09	Wyoming	73.64
George Washington	76.98	Boston University	75.61
Arizona	83.74	Cornell	73.41
Delaware	68.90	Illinois	90.38

Source: Mathematical rating system devised by Jeff Sagarin, a Massachusetts Institute of Technology mathematics graduate; from *USA Today*, March 12, 1985. Copyright 1985, USA TODAY. Reprinted with permission.

Similarly, the stem and the leaf for the rating 72.81 are

stem	leaf
7	2.81

The **stem and leaf display** for the 20 ratings is shown in Figure 2.4. Note that the left-hand column lists the stems from the smallest (at the top of the column) to the largest. The leaves for each stem appear in their appropriate stem row in order of magnitude from left to right. For example, two leaves (5.70 and 8.90) appear in stem row 6, with the smaller leaf listed first. Similarly, stem row 7 contains ten leaves from left to right in order of magnitude, from the smallest (0.03) to the largest (8.08).

6	5.70, 8.90
7	0.03, 0.62, 2.81, 3.41, 3.64, 5.10, 5.19, 5.61, 6.98, 8.08
8	1.02, 1.09, 2.12, 2.45, 3.74, 4.84, 9.26
9	0.38

FIGURE 2.4   Stem and Leaf Display for the Basketball Team Ratings in Table 2.10

How does the stem and leaf display of Figure 2.4 describe the 20 ratings? If you turn the display sideways (stem at the bottom), you can see that the listings have produced a frequency histogram for the data. The histogram contains four classes, 59.995 to 69.995, 69,995 to 79.995, 79.995 to 89.995, and 89.995 to 99.995. You can tell from the display that the data set contains two ratings in the 60s, ten in the 70s, seven in the 80s, and one in the 90s.

From Figure 2.4 you can see that the stem and leaf display shows how the data are distributed in classes and presents a picture of the distribution that is similar to a frequency histogram. The stem and leaf display has an advantage over the frequency histogram in that it allows you to reconstruct the actual data set, and it lists the observations in order of magnitude. For example, not only does the display tell you that the data set contains two observations in the 60s class, it also tells you that the observations are 65.70 and 68.90. In addition, if you want to find the tenth and the eleventh largest measurements, the ratings in the middle of the data set, you can count up from the smallest observation and identify them to be 75.61 and 76.98.

We can change the class width for a stem and leaf display by redefining the stem and leaf for the observations. For example, we can define the stem for the data set in Table 2.5 to be all digits to the left of the decimal point. Then the stem and leaf for 82.45 are

stem	leaf
82	.45

Similarly, the stem and leaf for 72.81 are

stem	leaf
72	.81

You can see why we did not choose this definition for the stem and leaf. Since the smallest rating is 65.70 and the largest is 90.38, this stem and leaf display will contain too many stems (classes)—stem numbers from 65 to 90—for such a small data set.

This example pinpoints one of the disadvantages of a stem and leaf display. For any particular set of data the number of ways that you can define a stem and leaf is small, and the number of stems produced by a particular definition may be too large or too small to produce a nicely grouped description of the data set.* The preceding example illustrates a stem and leaf definition that produces too many stems. In contrast, a definition for the bank stock dividend yield data of Table 2.3 will produce too few.

The dividend yield data of Table 2.3 vary from 2.3 (the smallest) to 5.3 (the largest). If we partition the stem and leaf at the decimal points (i.e., the stem and leaf for 3.1 will be 3 and .1, respectively), all of the observations will fall in four stem rows, corresponding to 2, 3, 4, and 5. It is possible to define the stem and leaf for an observation so that the number of stems will be larger, but doing so makes construction of the display more complex.

To summarize, a stem and leaf display is easy to construct, and the display creates the same sort of figure produced by a relative frequency distribution. In addition, it permits the viewer to reconstruct the data set and also to identify ordered observations (such as the fifth largest).

There are three disadvantages to the stem and leaf display. It is only suitable for describing small sets of data. (If the number of observations is too large, the number of leaves in a stem row may run off the paper!) The second disadvantage is that there is little flexibility in the choice of the stems (and therefore in the choice of the number of stems, or classes, in the display). Finally, the display does not convey a rapid reading of class relative frequency.

*The number of ways to define the stem and leaf combinations can be increased by splitting the leaf digits within a stem. This technique increases the options for defining stems and leaves, but it complicates the procedure and thereby minimizes one of the major advantages of a stem and leaf display—its simplicity.

EXERCISES

BASIC TECHNIQUES

2.14 Construct a stem and leaf display for the data given in Exercise 2.1. Compare it with the relative frequency histogram that you constructed in Exercise 2.1.

2.15 Construct a stem and leaf display for the data in Exercise 2.2. Compare it with the relative frequency histogram that you constructed in Exercise 2.2.

2.16 Construct a stem and leaf display for the following data.

3.1	1.8	4.9	3.1
4.4	3.7	3.6	4.3
5.9	4.8	4.0	3.8
5.2	2.5	4.7	3.0
4.3	3.2	3.6	2.9

(a) Examine the stem and leaf display and describe the data set verbally.

(b) Find the sixth measurement when the measurements are ranked from the smallest to largest.

APPLICATIONS

2.17 Construct a stem and leaf display for the state per capita spending data of Exercise 2.3. Compare the stem and leaf display with the relative frequency histogram of Exercise 2.3. Do the two graphical descriptions of the data seem to convey the same information?

2.18 Construct a stem and leaf display for the supermarket service times of Exercise 2.4. Compare the stem and leaf display with the relative frequency histogram of Exercise 2.4. Do the two graphical descriptions of the data seem to convey the same information?

2.19 Refer to Exercise 2.5. Construct a stem and leaf display for the number of home loan applications data. Compare the stem and leaf display with the relative frequency histogram of Exercise 2.5. Do the two graphical descriptions of the data seem to convey the same information?

2.20 Refer to Exercise 2.6. Construct a stem and leaf display for the data on percent of income tax returns audited per state. Compare the stem and leaf display with the relative frequency histogram of Exercise 2.6. Do the two graphical descriptions of the data seem to convey the same information?

2.21 Refer to Exercise 2.9. Construct stem and leaf displays for the utility common stock dividend yields for year-end 1985 and for November 13, 1986. Compare the two displays and note the substantial change in the displays over the 10 1/2 months period of time.

NUMERICAL METHODS FOR DESCRIBING A SET OF DATA

2.4

Graphical methods are extremely useful in conveying a rapid, general description of collected data and in presenting data. This supports, in many respects, the saying that a picture is worth a thousand words. There are, however, limitations to the use of graphical techniques for describing and analyzing data. For instance, suppose that we want to discuss our data before a group of people and have no method of describing the data other than verbally. Unable to present the histogram visually, we would be forced to use other descriptive measures that would convey to the listeners a mental picture of the histogram. A second and not so obvious limitation of the histogram and other graphical techniques is that they are difficult to use for purposes of statistical inference. Presumably, we use the sample histogram to make inferences about the shape and position of the population histogram, which describes the population and is unknown to us. Our inference is based upon the correct assumption that some degree of similarity will exist between the two histograms, but we are then faced with the problem of measuring the degree of similarity. We know when two figures are identical, but this situation will not likely occur in practice. Therefore, if the sample and population histograms differ, how can we measure the degree of difference or, to express it positively, the degree of similarity? To be more specific, we might wonder about the degree of similarity between the histogram in Figure 2.1 and the frequency histogram for the population of bank dividend yields from which the sample was drawn. Although these difficulties are not insurmountable, we will examine other descriptive measures that readily lend themselves for use as predictors of the shape of the population frequency distribution.

The limitations of the graphical method of describing data can be overcome by the use of **numerical descriptive measures**. Numerical descriptive measures for a population are called **parameters**. The corresponding numerical descriptive measures calculated from a sample are called **statistics**. Thus we would like to use the sample data to calculate a set of numbers, statistics, that will convey a good mental picture of the sample relative frequency distribution and that will be useful in making inferences concerning the population relative frequency distribution.

DEFINITION   Numerical descriptive measures computed from population measurements are called *parameters;* those computed from sample measurements are called *statistics.*   ∎

MEASURES OF CENTRAL TENDENCY

2.5

In constructing a mental picture of the frequency distribution for a set of measurements, we would likely envision a histogram similar to that shown in Figure 2.1 for the data on bank stock dividend yields. One of the first descriptive measures of interest is a **measure of central tendency**—that is, a measure that locates the center of the distribution. We note that the dividend yields ranged from a low of 2.3 to a high of 5.3, with the center of the histogram located in the vicinity of 3.6. Let us now consider some definite rules for locating the center of a distribution of data.

One of the most common and useful measures of central tendency is the arithmetic average of a set of measurements. This value is also often referred to as the **arithmetic mean**, or simply the **mean**, of a set of measurements. Since we will want to distinguish between the means for the sample and for the population, we will use the symbol $\bar{x}$ (x bar) to represent the sample mean and μ (lowercase Greek letter mu) to represent the mean of the population.

DEFINITION

The *arithmetic mean* of a set of n measurements, $x_1, x_2, x_3, \ldots, x_n$, is equal to the sum of the measurements divided by n. ∎

The procedures for calculating a sample mean and many other statistics are conveniently expressed as formulas. Consequently, we will need a symbol to represent the process of summation. If we denote the n quantities that are to be summed as $x_1, x_2, \ldots, x_n$, then their sum is denoted by the symbol

$$\sum_{i=1}^{n} x_i$$

The symbol $\sum_{i=1}^{n}$ ($\sum$ is the Greek capital letter sigma) tells us to sum the elements that are to the right of the $\sum$ sign, starting with x_1 (i.e., $i = 1$) and proceeding in order to x_n. Thus

$$\sum_{i=1}^{3} x_i = x_1 + x_2 + x_3$$

Using this notation, we can express the formula for the sample mean as

$$\bar{x} = \frac{\sum_{i=1}^{n} x_i}{n}$$

where

$$\sum_{i=1}^{n} x_i = x_1 + x_2 + \cdots + x_n$$

is used to denote the sum of the n sample measurements.

EXAMPLE 2.1

Find the mean of the set of measurements 2, 9, 11, 5, 6.

SOLUTION

$$\bar{x} = \frac{\sum_{i=1}^{n} x_i}{n} = \frac{2 + 9 + 11 + 5 + 6}{5} = 6.6$$ ∎

Even more important than locating the center of a set of sample measurements, $\bar{x}$ will be used as an estimator (predictor) of the value of the unknown population mean μ. For example, the mean of the data listed in Table 2.3 is equal to

$$\bar{x} = \frac{\sum_{i=1}^{n} x_i}{n} = \frac{89.2}{25} = 3.568$$

Note that this value falls approximately in the center of the set of measurements. The mean of the entire population of dividend yields, μ, is unknown to us; but if we were to estimate its value, our estimate of μ would be 3.568.

SYMBOLS

Sample Mean: $$\bar{x} = \frac{\sum\limits_{i=1}^{n} x_i}{n}$$

Population Mean: μ

A second measure of central tendency is the **median**.

DEFINITION   The *median m* of a set of *n* measurements, $x_1, x_2, x_3, \ldots, x_n$, is the value of *x* that falls in the middle when the measurements are ranked in order from the smallest to the largest. ■

If the measurements in a data set are ranked from the smallest to the largest, the median will be the value of *x* that falls in the middle. If the number *n* of measurements is odd, this number will be the measurement with rank equal to $(n + 1)/2$. If the number of measurements is even, the median is chosen as the value of *x* halfway between the two middle measurements—that is, halfway between the measurement ranked $n/2$ and the one ranked $(n/2) + 1$. The rule for calculating the median is given in the following box.

RULE FOR CALCULATING A MEDIAN

Rank the *n* measurements from the smallest to the largest.

(1) If *n* is odd, the median *m* is the measurement with rank $(n + 1)/2$.

(2) If *n* is even, the median *m* is the value of *x* that is halfway between the measurement with rank $n/2$ and the one with rank $(n/2) + 1$.

EXAMPLE 2.2   Find the median for the following set of five measurements.

9, 2, 7, 11, 14

SOLUTION   We first rank the $n = 5$ measurements from the smallest to the largest, 2, 7, 9, 11, 14. Then since $n = 5$ is odd, we choose 9 as the median. This value is the measurement with rank $(n + 1)/2 = (5 + 1)/2 = 3$. ■

EXAMPLE 2.3   Find the median for the following set of measurements.

9, 2, 7, 11, 14, 6

SOLUTION   Since $n = 6$ is even, we rank the measurements as 2, 6, 7, 9, 11, 14 and choose the median halfway between the two middle measurements, 7 and 9. Therefore, the median is equal to 8. ■

Although both the mean and the median are good locations of the center of a distribution of measurements, the median is less sensitive to extreme values. For

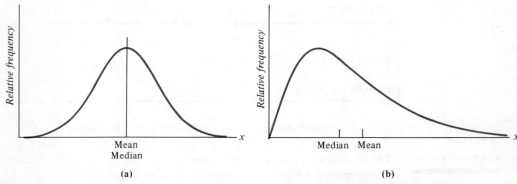

FIGURE 2.5   Relative Frequency Distributions Showing the Effect of Extreme Values on the Mean and Median

example, if the distribution is symmetric about its mean [see Figure 2.5(a)], the mean and the median are equal. In contrast, if a distribution is skewed to the left or to the right, the mean shifts toward the direction of skewness. For example, Figure 2.5(b) shows a distribution skewed to the right. Since the large extreme values in the upper tail of the distribution increase the sum of the measurements, the mean shifts toward the direction of skewness. The median is not affected by these extreme values because the numerical values of the measurements are not used in its computation.

Measures of Variability

2.6

Having located the center of a distribution of data, we next must provide a **measure of the variability** or dispersion of the data. Consider the two distributions shown in Figure 2.6. Both distributions are located with a center of $x = 4$, but there is a vast difference in the variability of the measurements about the mean for the two distributions. Most of the measurements in Figure 2.6(a) vary from 3 to 5, but in Figure 2.6(b) they vary from 0 to 8. Variation is a very important characteristic of data. For example, if we are manufacturing bolts, excessive variation in the bolt diameter would imply a high

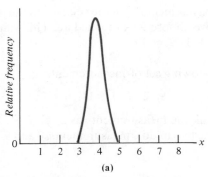

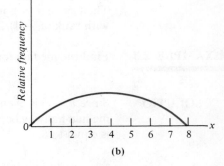

FIGURE 2.6   Variability or Dispersion of Data

percentage of defective product. On the other hand, if we are using an examination to discriminate between good and poor accountants, we would be very unhappy if the examination always produced test grades with little variation, which would make discrimination very difficult indeed. In addition to the practical importance of variation in data, a measure of this characteristic is necessary to the construction of the mental image of the frequency distribution. Numerous measures of variability exist, and we will discuss a few of the most important.

The simplest measure of variation is the **range**.

DEFINITION The *range* of a set of n measurements, $x_1, x_2, x_3, \ldots, x_n$, is defined as the difference between the largest and smallest measurements. ∎

The dividend yield data in Table 2.3 varied from 2.3 to 5.3. Therefore, the range is equal to $(5.3 - 2.3) = 3.0$. The range is easy to calculate and easy to interpret, and it is quite adequate as a measure of variation for small sets of data. But for large sets of data it can be insensitive to substantial differences in data variation. This insensitivity is illustrated by the two relative frequency distributions shown in Figure 2.7. Both distributions have the same range, but the data of Figure 2.7(b) are more variable than the data of Figure 2.7(a).

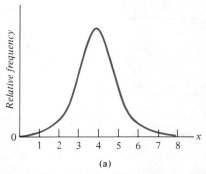
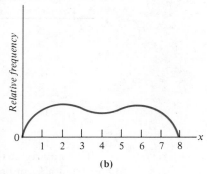

FIGURE 2.7 Distributions with Equal Ranges and Unequal Variability

To find a more sensitive measure of data variation, we will examine a set of data—say the set of measurements 5, 7, 1, 2, 4. These data can be displayed graphically as in Figure 2.8 by showing the measurements as dots falling along the x axis. Figure 2.8 is called a **dot diagram**.

Calculating the mean as the measure of central tendency, we obtain

$$\bar{x} = \frac{\sum_{i=1}^{n} x_i}{n} = \frac{19}{5} = 3.8$$

and locate it on the dot diagram. We can now view variability in terms of distance

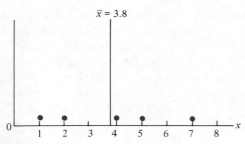

FIGURE 2.8   Dot Diagram

between each dot (measurement) and the mean $\bar{x}$. If the distances are large, we can say that the data are more variable than if the distances are small. More explicitly, we will define the **deviation** of a measurement from its mean to be the quantity $(x_i - \bar{x})$. Note that measurements to the right of the mean represent positive deviations, and those to the left, negative deviations. The values of x and the deviations for our example are shown in columns 1 and 2 of Table 2.11.

TABLE 2.11   Computation of $\sum_{i=1}^{n} (x_i - \bar{x})^2$

x_i	$x_i - \bar{x}$	$(x_i - \bar{x})^2$
5	1.2	1.44
7	3.2	10.24
1	-2.8	7.84
2	-1.8	3.24
4	.2	.04
$\sum_{i=1}^{5} x_i = 19$	0	22.80

If we now agree that deviations contain information on variation, our next step is to construct a formula based on the deviations that will provide a good measure of variation. As a first possibility, we might choose the average of the deviations. Unfortunately, this average will not work because some of the deviations are positive and some are negative; so the sum of the deviations is always equal to zero (unless round-off errors have been introduced into the calculations). Note, for example, that the deviations in the second column of Table 2.11 sum to zero.

There are ways to avoid this problem. Why not calculate the average of the absolute values of the deviations? This method has, in fact, been used as a measure of variability; but it is difficult to interpret, and it tends to be unsatisfactory for purposes of statistical inference. We prefer overcoming the difficulty caused by the sign of the deviations by working with the sum of their squares,

$$\sum_{i=1}^{n} (x_i - \bar{x})^2$$

For a fixed number of measurements, when this quantity is large, the data will be more variable than when it is small.

DEFINITION   The *variance of a population* of N measurements, $x_1, x_2, \ldots, x_N$, is defined to be the average of the square of the deviations of the measurements about their mean μ. The population variance is denoted by σ^2 (σ is the lowercase Greek letter sigma) and is given by the formula

$$\sigma^2 = \frac{\sum_{i=1}^{N}(x_i - \mu)^2}{N}$$ ∎

Note that we use N to denote the number of measurements in the population and n to denote the number of measurements in the sample.

In defining the variance of the sample measurements, we will modify our averaging procedure, dividing the sum of squared deviations by $(n - 1)$ rather than n.

DEFINITION   The *variance of a sample* of n measurements, $x_1, x_2, \ldots, x_n$, is defined to be the sum of the squared deviations of the measurements about their mean $\bar{x}$ divided by $(n - 1)$. The sample variance is denoted by s^2 and is given by the formula

$$s^2 = \frac{\sum_{i=1}^{n}(x_i - \bar{x})^2}{n - 1}$$ ∎

We divide by $(n - 1)$ because, ultimately, we will want to use the sample variance s^2 to estimate the population variance σ^2. Dividing the sum of squares of deviations by n yields estimates that tend to underestimate σ^2. Division by $(n - 1)$ eliminates this difficulty.

As an example, we can calculate the variance for the set of $n = 5$ measurements presented in Table 2.11. The square of the deviation of each measurement is recorded in the third column of Table 2.11. Adding, we obtain

$$\sum_{i=1}^{5}(x_i - \bar{x})^2 = 22.80$$

The sample variance is

$$s^2 = \frac{\sum_{i=1}^{5}(x_i - \bar{x})^2}{n - 1} = \frac{22.80}{5 - 1} = 5.70$$

What practical significance can be attached to the variance as a measure of variability? Large variances imply a large amount of variation, but this statement only permits comparison of several sets of data. When we attempt to say something specific concerning a single set of data, we are at a loss. For example, what can be said about the variability of a set of data with a variance equal to 100? The answer to these questions is given by a theorem and a rule of thumb that we will state and explain in the following section. These rules interpret the variability of a set of data in terms of its standard deviation.

DEFINITION   The *standard deviation* of a set of n measurements, $x_1, x_2, x_3, \ldots, x_n$, is equal to the positive square root of the variance. ∎

The variance is measured in terms of the square of the original units of measurement. Thus if the original measurements were in inches, the variance would be expressed in square inches. Taking the positive square root of the variance, we obtain the **standard deviation**, which returns our measure of variability to the original units of measurement. The sample standard deviation is denoted by the symbol s and the population standard deviation by the symbol σ.

SAMPLE STANDARD DEVIATION

$$s = \sqrt{s^2} = \sqrt{\frac{\sum\limits_{i=1}^{n} (x_i - \bar{x})^2}{n-1}}$$

SYMBOLS

Sample Standard Deviation: $s = \sqrt{\dfrac{\sum\limits_{i=1}^{n} (x_i - \bar{x})^2}{n-1}}$

Population Standard Deviation: σ

ON THE PRACTICAL SIGNIFICANCE OF THE STANDARD DEVIATION

2.7   We now introduce an interesting and useful theorem developed by the Russian mathematician Tchebysheff. Proof of the theorem is not difficult, but we omit it from our discussion.

THEOREM 2.1: *TCHEBYSHEFF'S THEOREM*

Given a number k greater than or equal to 1 and a set of n measurements, $x_1, x_2, \ldots, x_n$, at least $(1 - 1/k^2)$ of the measurements will lie within k standard deviations of their mean.

Tchebysheff's Theorem applies to any set of measurements, and for purposes of illustration we could refer to either the sample or the population. We will use the notation appropriate for populations, but we could just as easily use $\bar{x}$ and s, the mean and standard deviation for the sample.*

The idea involved in Tchebysheff's Theorem is illustrated in Figure 2.9. An interval is constructed by measuring a distance of $k\sigma$ on either side of the mean μ. Note that the theorem is true for any value we wish to choose for k as long as it is at least 1. Then computing the fraction $1 - 1/k^2$, we see that Tchebysheff's Theorem states that *at least* that fraction of the total number n of measurements will lie in the constructed interval.

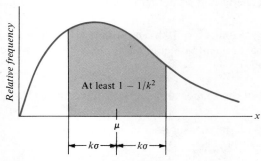

FIGURE 2.9   Illustrating Tchebysheff's Theorem

Let us choose a few numerical values for k and compute $1 - 1/k^2$ (see Table 2.12). When $k = 1$, the theorem states that at least $1 - 1/(1)^2 = 0$ of the

TABLE 2.12   Illustrative Values of $1 - 1/k^2$

k	$1 - 1/k^2$
1	0
2	3/4
3	8/9

*The proof of Tchebysheff's Theorem for a finite number of measurements is based on a variance defined as

$$s'^2 = \frac{\sum_{i=1}^{n}(x_i - \bar{x})^2}{n}$$

that is, with a divisor of n rather than the $(n - 1)$ used in s^2. Since s^2 will always be larger than s'^2, because $n > (n - 1)$, Tchebysheff's Theorem will always hold when s is used to form the intervals about $\bar{x}$. In any case, there will be very little numerical difference in the values of s and s' for moderate to large values of n.

measurements lie in the interval $\mu - \sigma$ to $\mu + \sigma$, an unhelpful and uninformative result. However, when $k = 2$, we see that at least $1 - 1/(2)^2 = 3/4$ of the measurements will lie in the interval $(\mu - 2\sigma)$ to $(\mu + 2\sigma)$. At least 8/9 of the measurements will lie within three standard deviations of the mean—that is, in the interval $(\mu - 3\sigma)$ to $(\mu + 3\sigma)$.

Now let us consider an example where we will use the mean and standard deviation (or variance) to construct a mental image of the distribution of measurements from which the mean and standard deviation were obtained.

EXAMPLE 2.4   The mean and variance of a sample of $n = 25$ measurements are 75 and 100, respectively. Use Tchebysheff's Theorem to describe the distribution of measurements.

SOLUTION   We are given $\bar{x} = 75$ and $s^2 = 100$. The standard deviation is $s = \sqrt{100} = 10$. The distribution of measurements is centered about $\bar{x} = 75$, and Tchebysheff's Theorem states the following:

(a) *At least* 3/4 of the 25 measurements lie in the interval $(\bar{x} \pm 2s) = [75 \pm 2(10)]$, that is, 55 to 95.

(b) *At least* 8/9 of the measurements lie in the interval $(\bar{x} \pm 3s) = [75 \pm 3(10)]$, that is, 45 to 105.   ▪

Tchebysheff's Theorem is very conservative. It applies to *any* distribution of measurements and provides a lower bound on the fraction of measurements falling in a specified interval. In most cases, the true fraction will be much larger than $(1 - 1/k^2)$.

Examination of many data sets suggests a rule of thumb that is of value in interpreting a standard deviation. It describes accurately the variability of a particular bell-shaped distribution (see Figure 2.10) (known as a normal distribution and discussed in detail in Chapter 4). But it also provides an excellent description of variation for many other types of data that possess mound-shaped relative frequency distributions. For this reason we call it the **Empirical Rule**.

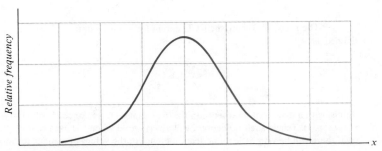

FIGURE 2.10   The Normal Distribution

THE EMPIRICAL RULE

Given a distribution of measurements that is approximately bell-shaped (see Figure 2.10).

(1) The interval $(\mu \pm \sigma)$ will contain approximately 68% of the measurements.
(2) The interval $(\mu \pm 2\sigma)$ will contain approximately 95% of the measurements.
(3) The interval $(\mu \pm 3\sigma)$ will contain all or almost all of the measurements.

EXAMPLE 2.5

A time study was conducted to determine the length of time necessary to perform a specified operation in a manufacturing plant. The length of time (in minutes) necessary to complete the operation was measured for each of $n = 40$ workers. The mean and standard deviation were found to equal 12.8 and 1.7 minutes, respectively. Describe the data.

SOLUTION

To describe the data, we calculate the following intervals:

$$\bar{x} \pm s = 12.8 \pm 1.7 \qquad \text{or} \qquad 11.1 \text{ to } 14.5$$
$$\bar{x} \pm 2s = 12.8 \pm 2(1.7) \qquad \text{or} \qquad 9.4 \text{ to } 16.2$$
$$\bar{x} \pm 3s = 12.8 \pm 3(1.7) \qquad \text{or} \qquad 7.7 \text{ to } 17.9$$

Although we have no prior information on the distribution of the data, there is a very good chance that it will be mound-shaped and that the Empirical Rule will provide a good description of the data. According to the Empirical Rule, we expect approximately 68% of the measurements to fall in the interval 11.1 to 14.5, approximately 95% in the interval 9.4 to 16.2, and all or almost all in the interval 7.7 to 17.9.

If we doubt that the distribution of measurements is mound-shaped or, for some reason, want to be conservative, we can apply Tchebysheff's Theorem and be absolutely certain of our statements. Tchebysheff's Theorem will tell us that at least 3/4 of the measurements will fall in the interval 9.4 to 16.2 and at least 8/9 in the interval 7.7 to 17.9. ∎

How well does the Empirical Rule apply to the dividend yield data of Table 2.3? We will show in Section 2.8 that the mean and standard deviation for the $n = 25$ measurements are $\bar{x} = 3.57$ and $s = .81$. The appropriate intervals were calculated, and the number of measurements falling in each interval were recorded. The results are shown in Table 2.13, with k in the first column and the interval $(\bar{x} \pm ks)$ in the second

TABLE 2.13

Frequency of Measurements Lying Within k Standard Deviations of the Mean for the Data in Table 2.3

k	Interval $\bar{x} \pm ks$	Frequency in Interval	Relative Frequency
1	2.76–4.38	17	.68
2	1.95–5.19	24	.96
3	1.14–6.00	25	1.00

column, using $\bar{x} = 3.57$ and $s = .81$. The frequency or number of measurements falling in each interval is given in the third column, and the relative frequency is given in the fourth column. Note that the observed relative frequencies agree with Tchebysheff's Theorem and are reasonably close to the relative frequencies specified in the Empirical Rule.

Another way to see how well the Empirical Rule and Tchebysheff's Theorem apply to the dividend yield data is to mark off the intervals $(\bar{x} \pm s)$, $(\bar{x} \pm 2s)$, and $(\bar{x} \pm 3s)$ on the relative frequency histogram for the data, as shown in Figure 2.11. Now recall that the area under the histogram over an interval is proportional to the number of measurements falling in the interval; visually observe the proportion of the area above the interval $(\bar{x} \pm s)$. You will see that this proportion is near the .68 specified by the Empirical Rule. Similarly, you will note that almost all of the area lies above the interval $\bar{x} \pm 2s$. Clearly, both the Empirical Rule and Tchebysheff's Theorem, using $\bar{x}$ and s, provide a good description for the dividend yield data.

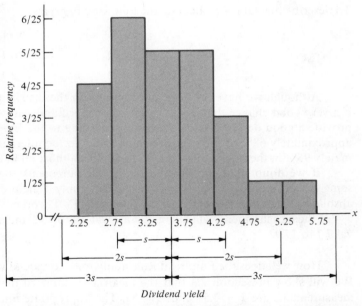

FIGURE 2.11   Histogram for the Dividend Yield Data (Figure 2.1) with Intervals $\bar{x} \pm s$, $\bar{x} \pm 2s$, and $\bar{x} \pm 3s$ Superimposed

To conclude, note that Tchebysheff's Theorem is a fact that can be proved mathematically, and it applies to any set of data. It gives a *lower* bound to the fraction of measurements to be found in an interval $(\bar{x} \pm ks)$, where k is some number greater than or equal to 1. In contrast, the Empirical Rule is an arbitrary statement about the behavior of data—a rule of thumb. Although, the percentages contained in the rule come from the area under the normal curve (Figure 2.10), the same percentages hold approximately for distributions with varying shapes as long as they tend to be roughly mound-shaped (the data tend to pile up near the center of the distribution). We have shown this rule to be true for the dividend yield data. If you need further convincing, calculate $\bar{x}$ and s for a set of data of your choosing and check the fraction of measurements falling in the intervals $(\bar{x} \pm s)$, $(\bar{x} \pm 2s)$, and $(\bar{x} \pm 3s)$. We think you will find that the observed relative frequencies are reasonably close to the values specified in the Empirical Rule.

EXERCISES

BASIC TECHNIQUES

2.22 Given $n = 5$ measurements, 0, 5, 1, 1, 3. Find the following.

    (a) $\bar{x}$ **(b)** m **(c)** s

2.23 Given $n = 8$ measurements, 3, 1, 5, 6, 4, 4, 3, 5. Find the following.

    (a) $\bar{x}$ **(b)** m **(c)** s

2.24 Given $n = 10$ measurements, 3, 5, 4, 6, 10, 5, 6, 9, 2, 8. Find the following.

    (a) $\bar{x}$ **(b)** m **(c)** s

2.25 Given $n = 6$ measurements, 3, 0, 2, 2, 1, 4. Find the following.

    (a) $\bar{x}$ **(b)** m **(c)** s

2.26 Given $n = 5$ measurements, 2, 4, 0, 3, 1. Find the following.

    (a) $\bar{x}$ **(b)** m **(c)** s

2.27 Suppose that you want to create a mental picture of the relative frequency histogram for a large data set consisting of 1000 observations and that you know that the mean and standard deviation of the data set were equal to 36 and 3, respectively.

(a) If you are fairly certain that the relative frequency distribution of the data was mound-shaped, how might you describe the relative frequency distribution? (*Hint:* Use the Empirical Rule.)

(b) If you had no prior information concerning the shape of the relative frequency distribution, what could you say about the relative frequency histogram?

APPLICATIONS

2.28 The average length of patient stay in U.S. hospitals has declined from approximately 7.1 days in 1983, the year that Congress and the Reagan administration began to modify the Medicare repayment systems, to 6.7 days in 1984 ("Hospital Suppliers Strike Back," *New York Times*, March 31, 1985). Suppose that you were managing a hospital and were therefore concerned with the distribution of lengths of patient stays. If the standard deviation of the distribution is 7 days, within what limits would most patient stays fall?

2.29 In Exercise 2.28 we noted that the average length of time that patients stayed in a hospital in 1984 was 6.7 days. Visualize the distribution of lengths of patient hospital stays in 1984, and answer the following questions.

(a) Do you think that the distribution of lengths of stays is symmetric about the mean, or is it skewed? Explain.

(b) If you were choosing a measure of central tendency to locate the center of the distribution, would you choose the mean or the median? Explain.

2.30 Is the cost of a new American-built automobile beyond the reach of low- and middle-income shoppers? *Time* magazine (November 9, 1981) reports that since 1979, the average price of a new car manufactured in this country has escalated from $6475 to $10,200. Suppose that this year the costs of new American-built automobiles possess a relative frequency distribution that is mound-shaped with a mean equal to $11,500 and a standard deviation of $3200. What fraction of all new American cars are priced in the following intervals?

(a) $8300 to $14,700.

(b) $5100 to $17,900.

(c) More than $21,100 or less than $1900.

2.31 An inspector from the Food and Drug Administration (FDA) wished to determine the actual average weight of the contents of all boxes of a particular cereal labeled "16 ounces." A sample of $n = 30$ boxes of this cereal was selected, and the contents of each was weighed. The average content weight for the $n = 30$ boxes was found to be 15.92 ounces; the standard deviation was .04 ounce. Describe the distribution of the weight measurements for the $n = 30$ boxes.

(a) Use Tchebysheff's Theorem.

(b) Use the Empirical Rule. (Would you expect the Empirical Rule to be suitable for describing these data?)

(c) Suppose the inspector had weighed the contents of only $n = 4$ boxes of cereal and obtained the weights 15.84, 16.00, 15.92, and 15.84. Would the Empirical Rule be suitable for describing the $n = 4$ measurements? Why or why not?

2.32 "More Work, Less Play," says the *New York Times* (September 22, 1985). According to a national survey by Louis Harris and Associates, Inc., the median workweek increased to 47.3 hours in 1984, up from 43.1 hours in 1975. Correspondingly, the median time for leisure dropped to 18.1 hours per week in 1984, down from 24.3 hours in 1975.

(a) From these statistics and your general knowledge about work schedules, describe the distribution of the length of the workweek for American workers in 1984.

(b) Would you expect the mean length of the workweek to be greater than, less than, or equal to the median? Explain.

(c) How would your answer to part (b) provide information about the shape of the distribution?

2.33 The cost of driving an automobile has gone up again. Marshall Schuon, reporting on the results of several surveys, notes that the national average cost of owning and operating a typical compact has increased more than 3 cents a mile, to 49.6 cents per mile ("About Cars," *New York Times*, March 31, 1985). The most costly metropolitan area in which to own and operate a car was Los Angeles, at 60.69 cents per mile. Cincinnati was the least expensive, at 44.65 cents per mile. Visualize the national distribution of costs for operating a compact car, and suppose that the standard deviation of the distribution is 6.1 cents per mile.

(a) Within what limits would you expect 95% of the costs of operating individual cars to fall?

(b) Within what limits would you expect almost all costs per mile to fall?

2.34 In Exercise 2.33 we stated that the national average cost per mile for owning and operating a compact car was 44.65 cents per mile.

(a) Do you think that the distribution of costs per mile of operating compacts in the United States is symmetric about the mean of 44.65, or do you think the distribution is skewed? Explain.

(b) If you were choosing a measure of central tendency to locate the center of the distribution, would you choose the mean or the median? Explain.

2.35 In an article titled "You Aren't Paranoid If You Think Someone Eyes Your Every Move," the *Wall Street Journal* (March 19, 1985) notes that big business collects detailed statistics on your behavior. It states that Jockey International knows how many undershorts you own; Frito-Lay, Inc., knows which you eat first, the broken pretzels in a pack or the whole ones; and, to get to specifics, Coca-Cola knows that we put 3.2 ice cubes in a glass. Have you ever put 3.2 ice cubes in a glass? What did the *Wall Street Journal* article mean by that statement?

2.36 Reporting on a Columbia University survey of 2239 American authors, the *New York Times* (June 15, 1981) notes that the "average" American author's writings net less than $5000 per year. Each of the authors in the survey had published at least one book, and the books covered a wide range of topics—everything from fact to fiction. The median hourly writing income for the 2239 authors in 1979 was only $4.90 per hour, and only a rare few of the authors had annual incomes equal to $100,000 per year or more.

(a) What proportion of the authors in the sample had hourly incomes from writing in 1979 that were less than or equal to $4.90?

(b) From the survey results the population of the incomes of all American authors (who had published at least one book) could conceivably possess a relative frequency distribution with a mean equal to $5000 and a standard deviation equal to $20,000. If this were true, approximately what proportion of American authors would have annual salaries less than or equal to $45,000 per year?

2.37 Table 2.5 for Exercise 2.3 gives the per capita spending per state by the federal government in 1984. Find the median per capita expenditure per state, and compare it with the mean ($\bar{x} = 3022$) given in Exercise 2.3. Noting the relative values of the mean and median for the data set, would you conclude that the distribution of per capita expenditures is skewed? Explain.

2.38 In Exercise 2.11, Figure 2.3, we gave the distribution of time lags in the filing of annual reports for 58 failing companies (E. C. Lawrence, "Reporting Delays for Failed Firms," *Journal of Accounting Research*, Vol. 21, No. 2, 1983). Lawrence states that the mean delay in filing annual reports for the 58 companies was 3.9 months and the standard deviation was 2.0 months. Examine the frequency histogram for the data, given in Exercise 2.11.

(a) Does the mean, 3.9 months, appear to locate the center of the distribution?

(b) Calculate the interval ($\bar{x} \pm 2s$) and the proportion of time lags that fall in this interval. Is this proportion near the 95% specified by the Empirical Rule?

A Shorter Method for Calculating the Variance

2.8

The calculation of the variance and standard deviation of a set of measurements is no small task regardless of the method used, but it is particularly tedious if one proceeds according to the definition—by calculating each deviation individually, as shown in Table 2.11. We will use the data of Table 2.11 to illustrate a shorter method of calculation. The tabulations are presented in Table 2.14, in two columns, the first

TABLE 2.14

Table for Simplified Calculations of $\sum_{i=1}^{n} (x_i - \bar{x})^2$

x_i	x_i^2
5	25
7	49
1	1
2	4
4	16
$\sum_{i=1}^{n} x_i = 19$	$\sum_{i=1}^{n} x_i^2 = 95$

containing the individual measurements and the second containing the squares of the measurements.

We now calculate

$$\sum_{i=1}^{n} x_i^2 - \frac{\left(\sum_{i=1}^{n} x_i\right)^2}{n} = 95 - \frac{(19)^2}{5}$$

$$= 95 - \frac{361}{5}$$

$$= 95 - 72.2$$

$$= 22.8$$

and notice that it is exactly equal to the sum of squares of the deviations,

$$\sum_{i=1}^{n} (x_i - \bar{x})^2$$

given in the third column of Table 2.11. This result demonstrates the following rule (proof omitted) for calculating the sum of squares of deviations of the x values about their mean:

$$\sum_{i=1}^{n} (x_i - \bar{x})^2 = \sum_{i=1}^{n} x_i^2 - \frac{\left(\sum_{i=1}^{n} x_i\right)^2}{n}$$

We call this formula the shortcut method of calculating the sum of squares of deviations needed in the formula for the variance and standard deviation. Comparatively speaking, it is shorter because it eliminates all the subtractions required for calculating the individual deviations. A second and not so obvious advantage is that it tends to give better computational accuracy than the method using the deviations. The beginning statistics student frequently finds the variance that he has calculated at odds with the answer in the text. This difference is usually caused by rounding off decimal numbers in the computations. We suggest that rounding off be held at a minimum since it may seriously affect the results of computation of the variance. A third advantage is that the shortcut method is especially suitable for use with many electronic calculators, some of which accumulate $\sum_{i=1}^{n} x_i$ and $\sum_{i=1}^{n} x_i^2$ simultaneously.

SHORTCUT FORMULA FOR CALCULATING $\sum_{i=1}^{n} (x_i - \bar{x})^2$

$$\sum_{i=1}^{n} (x_i - \bar{x})^2 = \sum_{i=1}^{n} x_i^2 - \frac{\left(\sum_{i=1}^{n} x_i\right)^2}{n}$$

EXAMPLE 2.6   Calculate $\bar{x}$ and s for the measurements 85, 70, 60, 90, 81.

SOLUTION

x_i	x_i^2
85	7,225
70	4,900
60	3,600
90	8,100
81	6,561
386	30,386

$\bar{x} = \dfrac{386}{5} = 77.2$

$$\sum_{i=1}^{n}(x_i - \bar{x})^2 = \sum_{i=1}^{n} x_i^2 - \frac{\left(\sum_{i=1}^{n} x_i\right)^2}{n}$$

$$= 30,386 - \frac{(386)^2}{5}$$

$$= 30,386 - 29,799.2$$

$$= 586.8$$

$$s = \sqrt{\frac{\sum_{i=1}^{n}(x_i - \bar{x})^2}{n-1}} = \sqrt{\frac{586.8}{4}} = \sqrt{146.7}$$

$$= 12.1$$

EXAMPLE 2.7   Calculate the standard deviation for the $n = 25$ dividend yields listed in Table 2.3.

SOLUTION   You can verify the following:

$$\sum_{i=1}^{n} x_i = 89.2 \qquad \sum_{i=1}^{n} x_i^2 = 333.82$$

Using the shortcut formula, we obtain

$$\sum_{i=1}^{n}(x_i - \bar{x})^2 = \sum_{i=1}^{n} x_i^2 - \frac{\left(\sum_{i=1}^{n} x_i\right)^2}{n}$$

$$= 333.82 - \frac{(89.2)^2}{25} = 333.82 - 318.2656$$

$$= 15.5544$$

It follows that the standard deviation is

$$s = \sqrt{\frac{\sum_{i=1}^{n}(x_i - \bar{x})^2}{n-1}} = \sqrt{\frac{15.5544}{24}} = .81$$

As we have noted, the shortcut formula for calculating the sum of squares of deviations of the x values about their mean reduces rounding error and saves time, but it is still (like many other statistical calculations) tedious. Many calculations of this type, particularly for large sets of data, are performed on a computer by using one of a number of statistical computer program packages. Three of these packages, Minitab, SAS, and SPSS, are referenced at the end of this chapter.

2.9 A Check on the Calculation of s

Tchebysheff's Theorem and the Empirical Rule can be used to detect gross errors in the calculation of s. Thus we know that at least 3/4 or, in the case of a mound-shaped distribution, approximately 95% of a set of measurements will lie within two standard deviations of their mean. Consequently, most of the sample measurements will lie in the interval ($\bar{x} \pm 2s$), and the range will approximately equal $4s$. This is, of course, a very rough approximation, but from it we can acquire a useful check that will detect large errors in the calculation of s.

Letting R equal the range,

$$R \approx 4s$$

Then s is approximately equal to $R/4$; that is,

$$s \approx \frac{R}{4}$$

The computed value of s using the shortcut formula should be of roughly the same order as the approximation.

EXAMPLE 2.8   Use the range approximation to check the calculation of s for Example 2.6.

SOLUTION   The range of the five measurements is

$$R = 90 - 60 = 30$$

Then

$$s \approx \frac{R}{4} = \frac{30}{4} = 7.5$$

This result is of the same order as the calculated value, $s = 12.1$.   ■

You should note that the range approximation is not intended to provide an accurate value for s.* Rather, its purpose is to detect gross errors in calculating—such as the failure to divide the sum of squares of deviations by $(n - 1)$ or the failure to take the square root of s^2. Both of these errors yield solutions that are many times larger than the range approximation to s.

---

*The range for a sample of n measurements will depend on the sample size n. The larger the value of n, the more likely you will observe extremely large or small values of x. The range for large samples, say $n = 50$ or more observations, may be as large as $6s$; the range for small samples, say $n = 5$ or less, may be as small as or smaller than $2s$.

EXAMPLE 2.9   Use the range approximation to determine an approximate value for the standard deviation for the data of Table 2.3.

SOLUTION   The range is $R = 5.3 - 2.3 = 3.0$. Then

$$s \approx \frac{R}{4} = \frac{3.0}{4} = .75$$

We have shown that $s = .81$ for the data of Table 2.3. The approximation is close to this value of s.   ∎

Some tips for problem solving are given in the following box.

TIPS ON PROBLEM SOLVING

(1) Always use the shortcut formula when calculating $\sum_{i=1}^{n} (x_i - \bar{x})^2$. This formula will help reduce rounding errors. The formula is

$$\sum_{i=1}^{n} (x_i - \bar{x})^2 = \sum_{i=1}^{n} x_i^2 - \frac{\left(\sum_{i=1}^{n} x_i\right)^2}{n}$$

(2) Be careful about rounding numbers. Carry your calculations of $\sum_{i=1}^{n} (x_i - \bar{x})^2$ to six significant figures.

(3) After you have calculated the standard deviation s for a set of data, compare its value with the range of the data. The Empirical Rule tells you that most of the data should fall in the interval $(\bar{x} \pm 2s)$; that is, a very approximate value for the range will be $4s$. Consequently, a very rough rule of thumb is that

$$s \approx \frac{\text{range}}{4}$$

This crude check will help you to detect large errors, such as failure to divide the sum of squares of deviations by $(n - 1)$ or failure to take the square root of s^2.

EXERCISES

BASIC TECHNIQUES

2.39   Given $n = 8$ measurements, 4, 1, 3, 1, 3, 1, 2, 2.
   (a) Calculate $\bar{x}$.
   (b) Use the shortcut formula given in Section 2.8 to calculate s^2 and s.
   (c) Calculate a range estimate of s (Section 2.9) as a rough check on your calculations in part (b).

2.40   Given $n = 5$ measurements, 2, 1, 1, 3, 5.
   (a) Calculate $\bar{x}$.
   (b) Use the shortcut formula of Section 2.8 to calculate s^2 and s.
   (c) Calculate a range estimate of s (Section 2.9) as a rough check on your calculations in part (b).

2.41 Calculate $\bar{x}$, m, and s for the data in Exercise 2.1. Then examine the relative frequency histogram that you constructed for the data in Exercise 2.1. Do these numerical descriptive measures provide a good description of the histogram?

2.42 Given $n = 8$ measurements, 0, -1, -3, 1, 1, 2, 4, 1.

(a) Calculate $\bar{x}$.

(b) Use the shortcut formula of Section 2.8 to calculate s^2 and s.

APPLICATIONS

2.43 The length of time required for a cashier to check out food items at a supermarket that employs automated checkers was recorded for $n = 10$ customers. The times, in seconds, were 15, 62, 53, 11, 38, 75, 112, 40, 22, 57.

(a) Scan the data and use the procedure of Section 2.9 to find an approximate value for s. Use this value to check your calculations in part (b).

(b) Calculate the sample mean $\bar{x}$ and the standard deviation s. Compare your answers with the answer obtained in part (a).

2.44 The number of television viewing hours per household and the prime viewing times are two factors that affect television advertising income. A random sample of 25 households in a particular viewing area produced the following estimates of viewing hours per household:

3.0	6.0	7.5	15.0	12.0
6.5	8.0	4.0	5.5	6.0
5.0	12.0	1.0	3.5	3.0
7.5	5.0	10.0	8.0	3.5
9.0	2.0	6.5	1.0	5.0

(a) Scan the data and use the procedure of Section 2.9 to find an approximate value for s. Use this value to check your calculations in part (b).

(b) Calculate the sample mean $\bar{x}$ and the sample standard deviation s. Compare s with the approximate value obtained in part (a).

(c) Find the percentage of the viewing hours per household that fall in the interval $\bar{x} \pm 2s$. Compare your answer with the corresponding percentage given by the Empirical Rule.

2.45 "Cruising" is a procedure used by timber owners when determining the amount of saleable lumber in a tract of land. To estimate the amount of lumber in a particular tract of timber, an owner "cruises" randomly selected 50 × 50-foot squares and counts the number of trees with diameters exceeding 12 inches. Suppose seventy 50 × 50 squares were "cruised" and the number of trees (with diameters in excess of 12 inches) were counted for each. The data follow:

(a) Construct a relative frequency histogram to describe the data.

(b) Calculate the sample mean $\bar{x}$ as an estimate of μ, the mean number of timber trees with diameters exceeding 12 inches for all 50 × 50-foot squares in the tract.

(c) Calculate s for the data. Construct the intervals $(\bar{x} \pm s)$, $(\bar{x} \pm 2s)$, and $(\bar{x} \pm 3s)$. Find the percentage of squares falling in each of the three intervals, and compare your answers with the corresponding percentages given by the Empirical Rule and Tchebysheff's Theorem.

2.46 Refer to the home loan applications data of Exercise 2.5.

(a) Find the range.

(b) Use the procedure of Section 2.9 to find an approximate value for s.

(c) Compute s for the data and compare with your answer for part (b).

2.47 Refer to the home loan applications data of Exercise 2.5. Examine the data and count the number of observations falling in the intervals $(\bar{x} \pm s)$, $(\bar{x} \pm 2s)$, and $(\bar{x} \pm 3s)$. (Use the value of s computed in Exercise 2.46.)

(a) Do the fractions falling in these intervals agree with Tchebysheff's Theorem? The Empirical Rule?

(b) Why might the Empirical Rule be unsuitable for describing these data?

2.48 Refer to the 60 supermarket service times given in Exercise 2.4.

(a) Look at the data and use the range to calculate a rough approximation to the value of s.

(b) Calculate $\bar{x}$ and s.

(c) Calculate the intervals $(\bar{x} \pm s)$, $(\bar{x} \pm 2s)$, and $(\bar{x} \pm 3s)$.

(d) Count the number of service times falling in each interval. Do the fractions falling in these intervals agree with Tchebysheff's Theorem? The Empirical Rule?

2.49 Examine the data on the percentage of income tax returns audited per state by the Internal Revenue Service given in Exercise 2.6.

(a) Use the range to calculate an approximate value for s.

(b) Calculate $\bar{x}$ and s.

(c) Find the proportions of the percentages of income taxes audited per state that fall in the intervals $(\bar{x} \pm s)$, $(\bar{x} \pm 2s)$, and $(\bar{x} \pm 3s)$. Do these proportions agree with Tchebysheff's Theorem? The Empirical Rule?

2.50 Suppose that some measurements occur more than once and that the data $x_1, x_2, \ldots, x_k$ are arranged in a frequency table as shown here.

Observations	Frequency f_i
x_1	f_1
x_2	f_2
$\vdots$	$\vdots$
x_k	f_k
	n

Then

$$\bar{x} = \frac{\sum_{i=1}^{k} x_i f_i}{n} \quad \text{where } n = \sum_{i=1}^{k} f_i$$

and

$$\sum_{i=1}^{n} (x_i - \bar{x})^2 = \sum_{i=1}^{k} x_i^2 f_i - \frac{\left(\sum_{i=1}^{k} x_i f_i\right)^2}{n}$$

Although these formulas for grouped data are primarily of value when you have a large number of measurements, demonstrate their use for the sample 1, 0, 0, 1, 3, 1, 3, 2, 3, 0, 0, 1, 1, 3, 2.

(a) Calculate $\bar{x}$ and $\sum_{i=1}^{n} (x_i - \bar{x})^2$ directly using the formulas for ungrouped data.

(b) The frequency table for the $n = 15$ measurements follows.

x	f_i
0	4
1	5
2	2
3	4
	$n = 15$

Calculate $\bar{x}$ and $\sum_{i=1}^{n} (x_i - \bar{x})^2$, using the formulas for grouped data. Compare the results with your answers to part (a).

2.51 To illustrate the Empirical Rule, consider a distribution that is heavily skewed to the right, as shown in Figure 2.12.

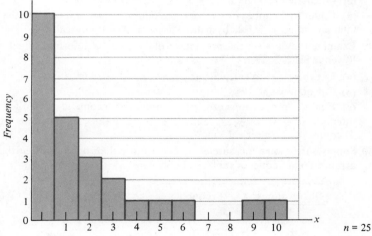

FIGURE 2.12   Skewed Distribution for Exercise 2.51

(a) Calculate $\bar{x}$ and s for the data shown. (*Note*: There are ten 0s, five 1s, etc.)

(b) Construct the intervals $(\bar{x} \pm s)$, $(\bar{x} \pm 2s)$, and $(\bar{x} \pm 3s)$, and locate them on the frequency distribution.

(c) Calculate the proportion of the $n = 25$ measurements falling in each of the three intervals. Compare the results with Tchebysheff's Theorem and the Empirical Rule. Note that although the proportion falling in the interval $(\bar{x} \pm s)$ does not agree closely with the Empirical Rule, the proportions falling in the intervals $(\bar{x} \pm 2s)$ and $(\bar{x} \pm 3s)$ agree very well. Many times this result occurs, even for non-mound-shaped distributions of data.

2.52 Calculate the mean and standard deviation of the 49 marketing scores given in Exercise 2.12. The data are reproduced in Table 2.15. (*Note*: Some of the scores occur more than once. Be sure to include all 49 scores in your sums when calculating $\bar{x}$ and s.) What percentage of the scores fall in the intervals $(\bar{x} \pm s)$, $(\bar{x} \pm 2s)$, and $(\bar{x} \pm 3s)$? Does the Empirical Rule provide a rough but useful description of the data set?

TABLE 2.15   Marketing Methods Scores and Frequencies for Exercise 2.52

Score	Frequency	Score	Frequency
2.09	1	2.80	1
2.20	1	2.84	2
2.29	1	2.89	2
2.42	1	2.91	1
2.47	1	2.93	3
2.49	1	2.98	1
2.53	3	3.02	1
2.60	2	3.07	4
2.62	3	3.09	1
2.64	1	3.16	2
2.67	1	3.18	3
2.71	1	3.24	2
2.73	2	3.27	1
2.76	1	3.38	1
2.78	2	3.47	1
		3.69	1

$n = 49$
Mean Score: 2.85

Source: Tom Griffin, "Linking the Use of Modern Marketing Methods to Company Success," *Columbia Journal of World Business*, Fall 1982.

2.53 Calculate the mean and standard deviation of the 49 company success scores given in Exercise 2.12. The data are reproduced in Table 2.16. (*Note:* Some of the scores occur more than once. Be

TABLE 2.16   Company Success Scores and Frequencies for Exercise 2.53

Score	Frequency	Score	Frequency
1.27	1	2.14	3
1.50	1	2.18	1
1.68	1	2.23	1
1.73	1	2.27	7
1.77	3	2.32	4
1.91	1	2.36	2
1.95	1	2.41	5
2.00	1	2.45	3
2.05	3	2.50	4
2.09	1	2.55	4
		2.64	1

$n = 49$
Mean Score: 2.22

Source: Tom Griffin, "Linking the Use of Modern Marketing Methods to Company Success," *Columbia Journal of World Business*, Fall 1982.

sure to include all 49 scores in your sums when calculating $\bar{x}$ and s.) What percentage of the scores fall in the intervals $(\bar{x} \pm s)$, $(\bar{x} \pm 2s)$, and $(\bar{x} \pm 3s)$? Does the Empirical Rule provide a rough but useful description of the data set?

MEASURES OF RELATIVE STANDING☆

2.10

Sometimes, we want to know the position of an observation relative to others in a set of data. For example, if you took a placement examination and scored 640, you might like to know the percentage of participants who scored lower than 640. Such a **measure of relative standing** of an observation within a data set is called a **percentile**.

DEFINITION

Let $x_1, x_2, \ldots, x_n$ be a set of n measurements arranged in increasing order. The pth *percentile* is the value of x such that p percent of the measurements are less than that value of x and $(100 - p)$ percent are greater. ∎

EXAMPLE 2.10

Before being accepted in the master of business administration (MBA) program at a university, you have been notified that your score of 610 on the Verbal Graduate Record Examination placed you at the 60th percentile in the distribution of scores. Where does your score of 610 stand in relation to the scores of others who took the examination?

SOLUTION

Scoring at the 60th percentile means that 60% of the other examination scores were lower than your score of 610 and 40% were higher. ∎

  Viewed graphically, a particular percentile, say the 60th percentile, is a point on the x axis located so that 60% of the area under the relative frequency histogram for the data lies to the left of the 60th percentile (see Figure 2.13) and 40% of the area lies to the right. Thus by our definition, the median of a set of data is the 50th percentile, because half of the measurements in a data set are smaller than the median and half are larger.

  The 25th and 75th percentiles, called the **lower and upper quartiles**, along with the median (the 50th percentile) locate points that divide the data into four sets of equal

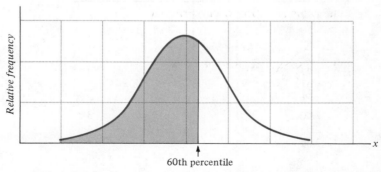

FIGURE 2.13 The 60th Percentile Shown on the Relative Frequency Histogram for a Data Set

☆This section is optional.

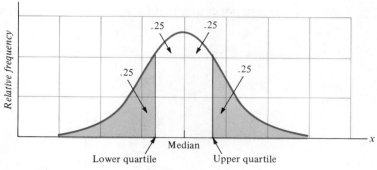

FIGURE 2.14   Location of Quartiles

size. Twenty-five percent of the measurements will be less than the lower (first) quartile, 50% will be less than the median (the second quartile), and 75% of the measurements will be less than the upper (third) quartile. Thus the median and the lower and upper quartiles are located at points on the x axis so that the area under the relative frequency histogram for the data is partitioned into four equal areas, as shown in Figure 2.14. You can see (Figure 2.14) that 1/4 of the area lies to the left of the lower quartile and 3/4 to the right. The upper quartile is the value of x such that 3/4 of the area lies to the left and 1/4 to the right.

DEFINITION   Let $x_1, x_2, \ldots, x_n$ be a set of n measurements arranged in increasing order. The *lower quartile* (first quartile) is the value of x that exceeds 1/4 of the measurements and is less than the remaining 3/4. The *second quartile* is the median. The *upper quartile* (third quartile) is the value of x that exceeds 3/4 of the measurements and is less than 1/4 of the measurements.   ■

There are occasions (see optional Section 2.11) where we may wish to use the sample quartiles to estimate the corresponding population quartiles. Since samples usually involve small sets of data, a quartile may fall between a pair of observations. When this situation occurs, we will use the rules in the following box to locate the sample quartiles.

RULES FOR LOCATING SAMPLE QUARTILES

Rank the n measurements in the data set from the smallest (rank 1) to the largest (rank n).

(1) Calculate $(n + 1)/4$ and round to the nearest integer. The measurement with this rank is the *lower quartile*, Q_L. (*Note:* If $(n + 1)/4$ falls halfway between two integers, *round upward.*)

(2) Calculate $(n + 1)(3/4)$ and round to the nearest integer. The measurement with this rank is the *upper quartile*, Q_U. (*Note:* If $(n + 1)(3/4)$ falls halfway between two integers, *round downward.*)

EXAMPLE 2.11   Find the lower and upper quartiles for the following set of measurements.

$$16, \ 25, \ 4, \ 18, \ 11, \ 13, \ 20, \ 8, \ 11, \ 9$$

SOLUTION   We first rank the $n = 10$ observations:

$$4, \ 8, \ 9, \ 11, \ 11, \ 13, \ 16, \ 18, \ 20, \ 25$$

Then

$$\frac{n+1}{4} = \frac{10+1}{4}$$

$$= 2.75$$

Rounding this number to the nearest integer 3, we choose the lower quartile Q_L as the measurement with rank 3, or

$$Q_L = 9$$

To find the upper quartile Q_U, we calculate

$$(n+1)\left(\frac{3}{4}\right) = (10+1)\left(\frac{3}{4}\right)$$

$$= 8.25$$

Rounding to the nearest integer 8, we choose the upper quartile Q_U as the measurement with rank 8, or

$$Q_U = 18$$ ∎

EXERCISES

BASIC TECHNIQUES

2.54 Find the median and the lower and upper quartiles for the following data.

$$3, \ 9, \ 6, \ 5, \ 5, \ 4, \ 7, \ 6, \ 8, \ 2, \ 6, \ 7, \ 3$$

2.55 Find the median and the lower and upper quartiles for the following data.

$$19, \ 12, \ 16, \ 6, \ 14, \ 9, \ 6, \ 1, \ 12, \ 13, \ 10, \ 19, \ 7, \ 5, \ 8$$

2.56 Find the median and the lower and upper quartiles for the following data.

$$8, \ 7, \ 1, \ 4, \ 6, \ 6, \ 4, \ 5, \ 7, \ 6, \ 3, \ 0$$

APPLICATIONS

2.57 Refer to the state per capita spending data in Exercise 2.3.

(a) Find the median and the lower and upper quartiles for the data set.

(b) Consult Table 2.5 for Exercise 2.3 to find the per capita spending by the federal government in your state in 1984. Use the median and the quartiles calculated in part (a) to describe how the per capita spending by the federal government in your state compared with corresponding expenditures in other states.

2.58 Refer to Exercise 2.6 and the data giving the percentage of income tax returns audited per state.

(a) Find the median and the lower and upper quartiles for the data set.

(b) See Table 2.6 for Exercise 2.6, and find the percentage of income tax returns audited in your state. Use the median and quartiles calculated in part (a) to describe how this percentage compares with the percentage of returns audited in other states.

2.59 Refer to Exercise 2.4 and the supermarket service time data.

(a) Find the median and the lower and upper quartiles for the data set.

(b) Use the median and the quartiles calculated in part (a) to describe the distribution of supermarket service times.

 2.60 A computer analysis of the money market mutual fund case study data in Table 2.2 gives the percentile information on asset size (in millions) listed in Table 2.17.

TABLE 2.17 Percentile and Money Market Asset Size Data for Exercise 2.60

Percentile	Asset Size	Percentile	Asset Size
100%	275949	25%	63
99%	16679	10%	24.6
95%	3981	5%	16.4
90%	1930	1%	2.56
75%	723	0%	2
50%	197		

(a) Give the values of the median and the lower and upper quartiles.

(b) Find the fifth percentile for the data and interpret its value.

(c) The asset size for the Capital Cash Management Fund is given in Table 2.2 as $90 million. Describe its relative standing in relation to the asset sizes of the other funds in Table 2.2.

 2.61 Percentiles for the average number of days to maturity for notes held by the 227 money market mutual funds listed in Table 2.2 are given in Table 2.18.

TABLE 2.18 Percentile and Days to Maturity Data for Exercise 2.61

Percentile	Average Days to Maturity	Percentile	Average Days to Maturity
100%	118	25%	28
99%	105.8	10%	16
95%	77.6	5%	10.4
90%	68	1%	1
75%	49	0%	1
50%	39		

(a) Give the values of the median and the lower and upper quartiles.

(b) Find the tenth percentile for the data and interpret its value.

(c) The average number of days to maturity for notes held by the Merrill Lynch USA Fund is given in Table 2.2 as 78. Describe its relative standing in relation to the averages of the numbers of days to maturity for the other funds in Table 2.2.

 2.62 Percentiles for the seven-day average yields for the 227 money market funds listed in Table 2.2 are given in Table 2.19.

TABLE 2.19   Percentile and Seven-Day Average Yield Data for Exercise 2.62

Percentile	Seven-Day Average Yield	Percentile	Seven-Day Average Yield
100%	8.1	25%	6.27
99%	7.28	10%	5.98
95%	6.98	5%	5.84
90%	6.86	1%	4.7
75%	6.71	0%	1.2
50%	6.51		

(a) Give the values of the median and the lower and upper quartiles.

(b) Find the tenth percentile for the data and interpret its value.

(c) The seven-day yield for the Nationwide Money Market Mutual Fund is given in Table 2.2 as 6.53%. Describe its relative standing in relation to the seven-day yields for the other funds in Table 2.2.

OUTLIERS: z SCORES AND BOX PLOTS☆

2.11

On occasion we may select a sample and note that one of the measurements appears to be improbably large (or small) in relation to other measurements in the sample. Such a measurement is called an **outlier**, and it poses a problem for us. Should we retain the outlier in the sample, or should we toss it out?

An outlier can arise in one of two ways. The particular arrangement of the sample measurements, with one very much larger or smaller than the others, can be just a highly improbable event but one that will occur on occasion. Or the outlier may be a faulty measurement, one that really does not belong to the population that you are sampling. Faulty observations can occur in many ways. Sometimes, a measuring instrument may go awry for a particular observation, the experimental unit itself may be flawed, or perhaps the experimenter recorded the measurement incorrectly.

When an extreme measurement (one that is very large or very small) in a sample is identified as a highly improbable outcome, we need to decide whether this observation is an important member of the sample and should be retained or whether we should toss it out. To see the consequences of our decision, suppose that we drew a sample of $n = 4$ measurements from a population and they appeared as shown in the dot diagram in Figure 2.15(a). Notice that three of the measurements are grouped closely together and the fourth is extremely large. If the distribution of the sampled population, indicated by the curve in Figure 2.15(b), is located over the three measurements, then the outlier lies more than 3σ away from the population mean μ and is not representative of the sampled population. Its inclusion when we calculate the sample mean $\bar{x}$ and standard deviation s will produce overly large estimates of μ and σ. In contrast, suppose that the distribution of the sampled population, indicated by the

☆This section is optional.

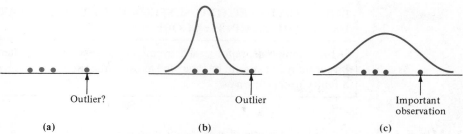

| | (a) | (b) | (c) |

FIGURE 2.15   Dot Diagrams Demonstrating the Implications of an Outlier

curve in Figure 2.15(c), straddles all four measurements. For this particular case the outlier is not a nuisance observation. In fact, it is badly needed to balance the three sample measurements lying below the mean.

The preceding illustration shows that an outlier can sometimes lead to overly large (or small) values of $\bar{x}$ and large values of s, statistics that we will subsequently use to estimate the population mean μ and standard deviation σ. Other times, it may be the needed balance to counter the relatively small (or large) values of the other measurements in a sample. Since we never know the nature of the sampled population, we cannot be sure whether an outlier is a faulty measurement or whether it is a useful member of the sample. Therefore, the safe method for treating an outlier is to recheck the method used to acquire that observation. Examination may clearly indicate that the outlier is a faulty measurement and that it should be deleted from the sample. If you cannot find a reason to indicate that the outlier is faulty, retain it in the sample. It may be the most important observation in the data set.

There are a number of statistical methods for detecting outliers. One very rough procedure is suggested by the Empirical Rule. Since we know that almost all of the measurements in a set of data should fall within three standard deviations of their mean, we can calculate a z score for the suspect outlier. A **z score** is the distance between an observation and its mean, measured in units of standard deviation. We define the sample z score next.

SAMPLE z SCORE

$$z = \frac{x - \bar{x}}{s}$$

If an extreme value is used to calculate both the sample mean and the standard deviation s, the standard deviation s will be inflated; and the sample z score will likely be smaller in absolute value than a population z score calculated using the population parameters μ and σ. This means that it is highly improbable that a sample z score will exceed 3 or be less than -3. Observations with z scores exceeding 2 or less than -2 will be improbable and will be identified as suspect faulty observations. These guidelines are summarized in the following box.

RULE FOR DETECTING SUSPECT FAULTY OBSERVATIONS, USING THE SAMPLE z SCORE

> If the sample z score for a measurement x is as small or smaller than -2 or as large or larger than 2, it should be regarded as an outlier and checked to see whether it might be a faulty observation.

EXAMPLE 2.12

Consider a sample of $n = 10$ measurements.

$$3,\ 2,\ 0,\ 15,\ 2,\ 3,\ 4,\ 0,\ 1,\ 3$$

You can see at a glance that the measurement $x = 15$ appears to be an outlier. Calculate the z score for this observation, and state your conclusions.

SOLUTION

For the sample we have the following calculations:

$$\sum_{i=1}^{10} x_i = 33 \quad \text{and} \quad \sum_{i=1}^{10} x_i^2 = 277$$

Then

$$\bar{x} = \frac{\sum_{i=1}^{10} x_i}{n} = \frac{33}{10} = 3.3$$

$$\sum_{i=1}^{n}(x_i - \bar{x})^2 = \sum_{i=1}^{n} x_i^2 - \frac{\left(\sum_{i=1}^{n} x_i\right)^2}{n}$$

$$= 277 - \frac{(33)^2}{10} = 168.1$$

$$s^2 = \frac{\sum_{i=1}^{n}(x_i - \bar{x})^2}{n-1} = \frac{168.1}{9} = 18.6778$$

$$s = 4.32$$

Using these quantities to calculate the z score for the suspect outlier $x = 15$, we find

$$z = \frac{x - \bar{x}}{s} = \frac{15 - 3.3}{4.32} = 2.71$$

Thus the measurement $x = 15$ lies 2.71 sample standard deviations away from the sample mean $\bar{x} = 3.3$. Since this z score exceeds 2, we identify $x = 15$ as an outlier. We should examine our sampling procedure to see whether evidence exists to indicate that $x = 15$ is a faulty observation. ∎

A second method for identifying outliers is provided by a **box plot**. Rather than measure the distance between a suspect outlier and the sample mean, we measure the distance between the outlier and the upper (or lower) quartile using the **interquartile range**, the distance between two quartiles, as the unit of measurement. The advantage of this method is that the sample quartiles, unlike the sample mean and standard deviation, do not depend upon the values of extreme observations.

DEFINITION   The *interquartile range* (IQR) is equal to the difference between the upper quartile Q_U and the lower quartile Q_L:

$$\text{IQR} = Q_U - Q_L$$ ∎

EXAMPLE 2.13   Construct a box plot for the data of Example 2.12.

SOLUTION   The $n = 10$ measurements in the sample, ranked from the smallest to the largest, are

$$0, \ 0, \ 1, \ 2, \ 2, \ 3, \ 3, \ 3, \ 4, \ 15$$

From the rules for locating the median and the lower and upper quartiles given in Sections 2.5 and 2.10,

$$m = 2.5 \qquad Q_L = 1 \qquad Q_U = 3$$

The interquartile range is

$$\text{IQR} = Q_U - Q_L = 3 - 1 = 2$$

To construct a box plot for the data, we locate a box with width equal to the interquartile range, $\text{IQR} = 2$, over a horizontal line representing the scale of measurement (see Figure 2.16). The lower edge of the box is located at Q_L and the upper edge at Q_U. We expect approximately half of the measurements to fall within the box — that is, between Q_L and Q_U.

The next step in constructing the box plot is to decide how far away from the median a measurement must lie before it is classified as an outlier. The decision is made by constructing two sets of *fences*. The *inner fences* are located a distance equal to 1.5 (IQR) below Q_L and above Q_U (see Figure 2.16). Since the interquartile range is

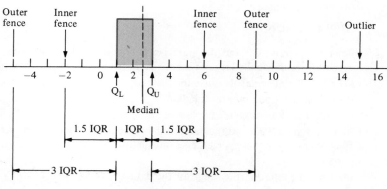

FIGURE 2.16   A Box Plot for the Data of Example 2.12

equal to 2, 1.5 (IQR) = 1.5(2) = 3. Therefore, the lower inner fence is located at -2 (3 units below Q_L), and the upper is located at 6 (3 units above Q_U). The second set of fences, called *outer fences*, are located a distance equal to 3 (IQR) = 3(2) = 6 below Q_L and above Q_U.

To determine whether a measurement is an outlier, plot the values of all measurements that fall outside the inner fences. Those lying between the inner and outer fences are regarded as suspect outliers; those outside the outer fences are unquestionably outliers and should be checked to see whether they might be faulty observations. Checking our data, we see that only one observation, $x = 15$, lies outside the inner fences and, in fact, lies a considerable distance above the upper outer fence. Therefore, $x = 15$ is judged an outlier, and its origin should be checked to see whether it can be identified as a faulty observation.   ■

Although both the z score (Example 2.12) and the box plot (Example 2.13) identified $x = 15$ as an outlier for the same set of data, the box plot is the more sensitive of the two procedures. The critical distance from the center of the data set that locates the inner and outer fences (and hence an outlier) in a box plot is based on the interquartile range IQR and is not affected by the value of one or more outliers. In contrast, the z score is sensitive to the values of outliers because they are used to calculate the standard deviation s.

EXERCISES

BASIC TECHNIQUES

2.63 Check the following data set for outliers.

$$25, \ 22, \ 26, \ 23, \ 27, \ 26, \ 28, \ 18, \ 25, \ 24, \ 12$$

(a) Use the sample z score.   (b) Use a box plot.

2.64 Check the following data set for outliers.

$$3, \ 9, \ 10, \ 2, \ 6, \ 7, \ 5, \ 8, \ 6, \ 6, \ 4, \ 9, \ 22$$

(a) Use the sample z score.   (b) Use a box plot.

APPLICATIONS

2.65 Refer to Exercise 2.3 and the state per capita spending data. Were any of these per capita expenditures unusually large or small? To answer this question, complete parts (a)–(c).

(a) Find the interquartile range for the data set.

(b) Construct a box plot for the data.

(c) Are there any outliers? Explain.

2.66 Refer to Exercise 2.6 and the data on the percentage of income tax returns audited per state in 1984. Were any of these percentages unusually large or small? To answer this question, complete parts (a)–(c).

(a) Find the interquartile range for the data set.

(b) Construct a box plot for the data.

(c) Are there any outliers? Explain.

2.67 Table 2.20 gives the length in months of the 11 business slumps since 1929.

TABLE 2.20   Business Slump Data for Exercise 2.67

Business Slump	Length (Months)
August 1929–March 1933	43
May 1937–June 1938	13
February 1945–October 1945	8
November 1948–October 1949	11
July 1953–May 1954	10
August 1957–April 1958	8
April 1960–February 1961	10
December 1969–November 1970	11
November 1973–March 1975	16
January 1980–July 1980	6
July 1981–November 1982	16

Source: Wall Street Journal, October 12, 1984. Reprinted by permission of the Wall Street Journal, © Dow Jones & Company, Inc., 1984. All rights reserved.

(a) Construct a box plot for the lengths of the 11 business slumps.

(b) Does the box plot indicate that the length of the 1929–1933 business slump is an outlier — that is, a length of slump inconsistent with the lengths of the other 10 slumps?

2.12 DESCRIBING THE MONEY MARKET FUND DATA

A graphical description of the money fund data given in Table 2.1 of the Case Study is provided by the relative frequency histograms in Figures 2.17, 2.18, 2.19, and 2.20. These graphs are based on histograms* that were plotted by computer using the SAS[†] statistical computer program package. The SAS package also was used to compute the means, medians, and standard deviations for the data sets.

Figure 2.17 shows the relative frequency histogram for the asset sizes of the 98 funds. Notice that this distribution is strongly skewed to the right, a situation where the median is a better measure of central tendency than the mean. We can see from the histogram that most of the funds had assets near the median, $197 million. In contrast, the mean $\bar{x} = \$2018.35$ million is quite large because its value is inflated by asset values for a few large funds (one fund, First Investment Cash Management, contained assets of $275,949 million!). More than 75% of the funds' asset values were less than the mean. The fact that the mean is much larger than the median indicates that the distribution is highly skewed to the right (which is shown in Figure 2.17). Consequently, the median gives a better measure of the asset value of a typical money market fund.

---

*The histograms provided by the SAS package show the percentage (rather than the proportion) of the total number of observations in each class.

[†]The SAS computer program packages were developed by SAS Institute. (See the References at the end of this chapter.)

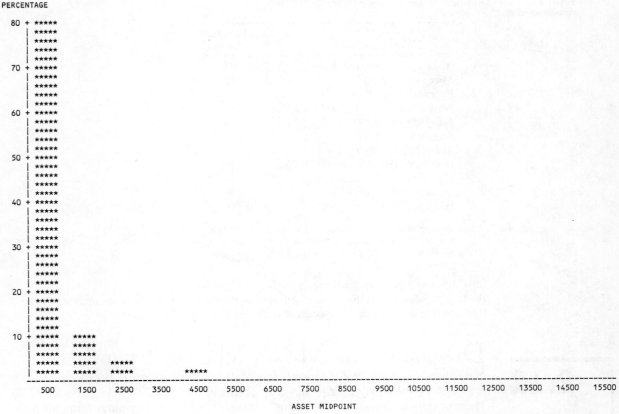

FIGURE 2.17   Assets (Millions of Dollars) for 227 Money Funds (Period Ending April 23, 1986); Mean, $\bar{x} = \$2018.35$ million; Median, $m = \$197$ million; Standard Deviation, $s = \$18,355$ million

Figure 2.18 gives the distribution of the average number of days to maturity for the notes held by the funds. This distribution is slightly skewed to the right, although the mean ($\bar{x} = 40.07$ days) and the median ($m = 39$ days) are nearly equal. Surprisingly, the average number of days for notes held to maturity by some of the funds was very small (the smallest was 1 day). The largest average number of days notes were held to maturity was 118 days. Most of the observations fell within the interval ($\bar{x} \pm 2s$), or 0 to 80 days. The 95% percentile computed in the SAS computer analysis was 77.6 days.

The relative frequency distributions of the 7- and the 30-day average yields are shown in Figures 2.19 and 2.20, respectively. You can see that the means and the medians of both distributions of yields are near 6.6%. The variation in the fund yields is not very large ($2s \approx 1.05\%$), although a few funds performed very poorly, deviating more than 1.5 percentage points below the mean yield.

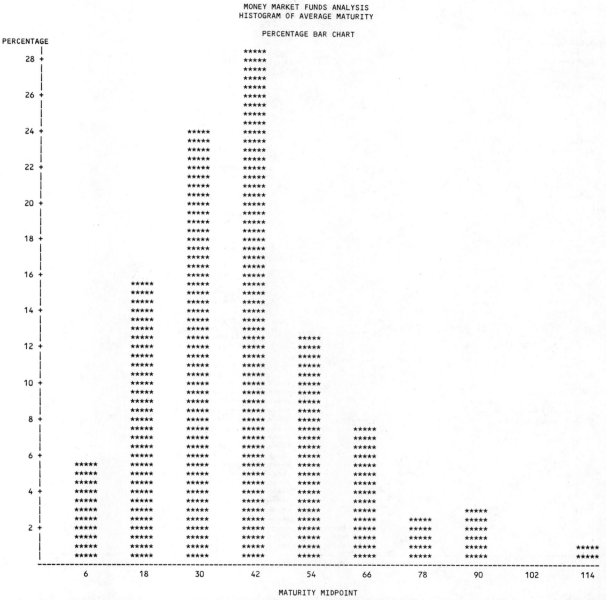

FIGURE 2.18   Average Maturity (Days) for Notes Held by 227 Money Funds (Period Ending April 23, 1986);
Mean $\bar{x}$ = 40.07 Days; Median, m = 39 Days; Standard Deviation, s = 19.96 Days

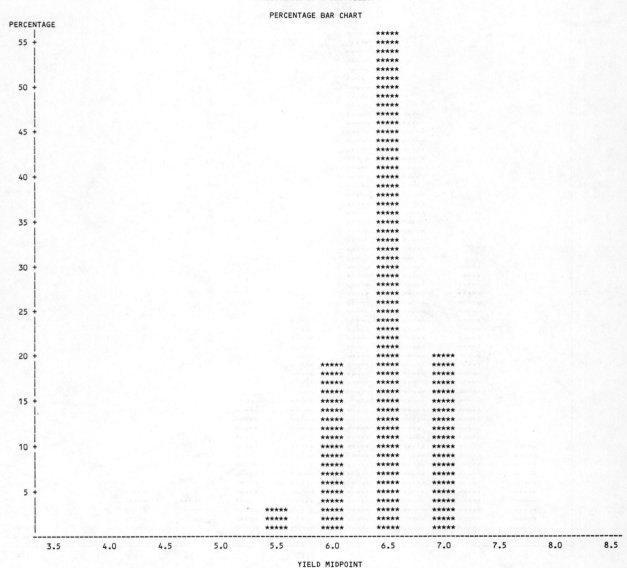

FIGURE 2.19   Seven-Day Average Yields for 227 Money Funds (Period Ending April 23, 1986); Mean, $\bar{x} = 6.44\%$; Median, $m = 6.51\%$; Standard Deviation, $s = .52\%$

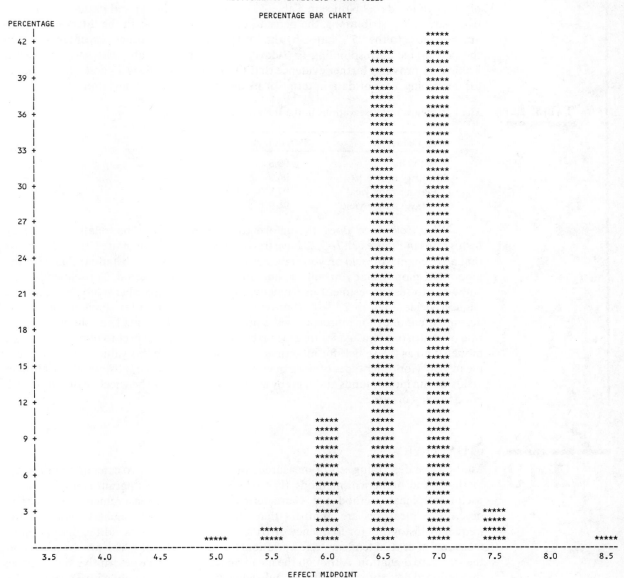

FIGURE 2.20   30-Day Average Yields for 227 Money Funds (Period Ending April 23, 1986); Mean, $\bar{x} = 6.66\%$; Median, $m = 6.73\%$; Standard Deviation, $s = .53\%$

How well do the means and standard deviations describe the four distributions of money fund data? Notice in Table 2.21 that despite the skewed nature of the relative frequency distributions, the percentages of observations in the interval ($\bar{x} \pm 2s$) are very close to the 95% stated by the Empirical Rule. The other percentages—even the percentage corresponding to 7-day yields—are reasonably close to 95%. Thus Table 2.21 provides further evidence that the Empirical Rule is a good rule of thumb for describing a set of data in terms of its mean and standard deviation.

TABLE 2.21 The Percentage of Observations in the Interval $\bar{x} \pm 2s$

Data Type	Percentage
Asset value	99.6
Maturity time	96.0
7-Day average yield	97.8
30-Day average yield	96.9

What relevance does the information provided by the relative frequency histograms in Figures 2.17–2.20 have to your becoming a millionaire? Table 2.1 shows that a 2% change in yield on your invested money can make a substantial change in the amount of money that you will accumulate over a 40-year period. Consequently, you will want to seek investment instruments that, given comparable safety, produce the highest yields. Figures 2.17–2.20 provide useful information for someone seeking to accumulate money for retirement via a money market account. They show the mean rate of return (unadjusted for income taxes) that you might expect to obtain by using a money fund as the vehicle for investment; you can compare this value with the current mean yields for other types of investments. They also show the substantial variation in yields within money funds and thereby emphasize the need to be selective in acquiring a good money manager.

SUMMARY

2.13

Methods for describing sets of measurements fall into one of two categories, graphical methods and numerical methods. The relative frequency histogram is an extremely useful graphical method for characterizing a set of measurements. Numerical descriptive measures are numbers that attempt to create a mental image of the frequency histogram (or frequency distribution). We have restricted the discussion to measures of central tendency and variation, the most useful of which are the mean and the standard deviation. Although the mean possesses intuitive descriptive significance, the standard deviation is significant only when used in conjunction with Tchebysheff's Theorem and the Empirical Rule. The objective of sampling is the description of (making inferences about) the population from which the sample was obtained. This objective is accomplished by using the sample mean $\bar{x}$ and the quantity s^2 as estimators of the population mean μ and variance σ^2.

Many descriptive methods and numerical measures have been presented in this chapter, but they constitute only a small percentage of those that might have been discussed. In addition, many special computational techniques usually found in elementary texts have been omitted. This omission was necessitated by the limited time available in an elementary course and because the advent and common use of electronic calculators and computers have minimized the importance of special computational formulas. But more importantly, the inclusion of such techniques would tend to detract from and obscure the main objective of modern satistics and this text—statistical inference.

REFERENCES

Billingsley, P., Huntsberger, D. V., Croft, D. J., and Watson, C. J. *Statistical Inference for Management and Economics.* 3rd ed. Boston: Allyn and Bacon, 1986. Chapter 3.

Hamburg, M. *Statistical Analysis for Decision Making.* 3rd ed. New York: Harcourt Brace Jovanovich, 1983. Chapter 1.

McClave, J. T., and Benson, P. G. *Statistics for Business and Economics.* 3rd ed. San Francisco: Dellen, 1985.

Mendenhall, W., Reinmuth, J., Beaver, R., and Duhan, D. *Statistics for Management and Economics.* 5th ed. Boston: PWS-KENT, 1986.

Mendenhall, W., Scheaffer, R. L., and Wackerly, D. *Mathematical Statistics with Applications.* 3rd ed. Boston: PWS-KENT, 1986.

Norusis, M. J. *SPSS/PC +: SPSS for the IBM PC/XT/AT.* Chicago: SPSS, 1986.

Norusis, M. J. *The SPSS Guide to Data Analysis.* Chicago: SPSS, 1986.

Ryan, T. A., Joiner, B. L., and Ryan, B. F. *Minitab Reference Manual.* University Park, Pa.: Minitab Project, 1985.

Ryan, T. A., Joiner, B. L., and Ryan, B. F. *Minitab Handbook.* 2nd ed. Boston: PWS-KENT, 1985.

SAS Procedures Guide for Personal Computers. Version 6 ed. Cary, N. C.: SAS Institute, 1986.

SAS User's Guide: Basics. Version 5 ed. Cary, N. C.: SAS Institute, 1985.

SAS User's Guide: Statistics. Version 5 ed. Cary, N. C.: SAS Institute, 1985.

SPSS^x User's Guide. Chicago: SPSS, 1983.

KEY TERMS

Qualitative data (page 16)

Quantitative data (page 16)

Class (page 17)

Class frequency (page 17)

Class relative frequency (page 17)

Class boundaries (page 17)

Relative frequency histogram (or distribution) (page 17)

Frequency histogram (or distribution) (page 19)

Class width (page 20)

Stem and leaf display (page 28)

Numerical descriptive measures (page 31)

Parameter (page 31)

Statistic (page 31)

Measures of central tendency (page 31)

Mean (page 31)

Median (page 33)

Measures of variability (page 34)

Range (page 35)

Dot diagram (page 35)

Variance (page 37)

Standard deviation (page 38)

Tchebysheff's Theorem (page 38)

The Empirical Rule (page 40)

Measures of relative standing (page 54)

Percentiles (page 54)

Quartiles (page 54)

Outlier (page 58)

z score (page 59)

Box plots (page 60)

Interquartile range (page 61)

SUPPLEMENTARY EXERCISES

2.68 Conduct the following experiment: toss 10 coins and record x, the number of heads observed. Repeat this process $n = 50$ times, thus providing 50 values of x. Construct a relative frequency for these measurements.

2.69 Refer to Exercise 2.68.

(a) Calculate $\bar{x}$ and s.

(b) Calculate the intervals $(\bar{x} \pm s)$, $(\bar{x} \pm 2s)$, and $(\bar{x} \pm 3s)$.

(c) Find the fractions of observations in the intervals. Do these fractions agree with Tchebysheff's Theorem? The Empirical Rule?

2.70 The following measurements represent the grade-point average of 25 college freshmen marketing majors.

2.6	1.8	2.6	3.7	1.9
2.1	2.7	3.0	2.4	2.3
3.1	2.6	2.6	2.5	2.7
2.7	2.9	3.4	1.9	2.3
3.3	2.2	3.5	3.0	2.5

Construct a relative frequency histogram for these data.

2.71 Refer to Exercise 2.70.

(a) Calculate $\bar{x}$ and s.

(b) Calculate the intervals $(\bar{x} \pm s)$, $(\bar{x} \pm 2s)$, and $(\bar{x} \pm 3s)$.

(c) Find the fractions of observations in the intervals. Do these fractions agree with Tchebysheff's Theorem? The Empirical Rule?

2.72 Given the set of $n = 6$ measurements 5, 7, 2, 1, 3, 0, calculate $\bar{x}$, s^2, and s.

2.73 Given the set of $n = 7$ measurements 3, 0, 1, 5, 3, 0, 4, calculate $\bar{x}$, s^2, and s.

 2.74 Each week the net amount of electric energy distributed by electric utilities across the country is compiled by the Edison Electric Institute. In one particular week the electric output (in thousands of kilowatt-hours) for ten midsized cities reads as follows: 49, 70, 54, 67, 59, 40, 61, 69, 71, 52.

(a) Observe the data and guess the value of s by use of the range approximation.

(b) Calculate $\bar{x}$ and s, and compare s with the range approximation of part (a).

2.75 An important consideration in planning urban mass transit systems in metropolitan areas is the cost of construction per mile. Studies at the University of Pennsylvania's Department of City and Regional Planning estimate the mean construction cost per mile of subways in 1980 at $45 million (*Journal of Advanced Transportation*, Spring 1981). If the distribution of subway construction costs is bell-shaped with a standard deviation of $10 million per mile, what percentage of subway systems constructed in 1980 had a cost per mile between $35 million and $65 million?

2.76 Refer to Exercise 2.9 and the data on the dividend yields for the 25 utility common stocks.

(a) Calculate $\bar{x}$ and s for the year-end 1985 dividend yield data.

(b) Calculate the intervals $(\bar{x} \pm s)$, $(\bar{x} \pm 2s)$, and $(\bar{x} \pm 3s)$.

(c) Find the fractions of observations in the intervals. Do these fractions agree with Tchebysheff's Theorem? The Empirical Rule?

2.77 Follow the instructions of Exercise 2.76, except use the dividend yields for November 13, 1986.

2.78 The range approximation for s can be improved if it is known that the sample is drawn from a bell-shaped distribution of data. Thus the calculated s should not differ substantially from the range divided by the appropriate ratio given in the following table.

Number of Measurements	5	10	25
Expected Ratio of Range to s	2.5	3	4

Consider the $n = 5$ measurements, 0, 2, 2, 4, 1.

(a) Approximate s by using the accompanying table.

(b) Calculate s, and compare it with your approximation.

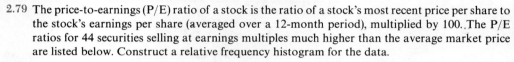

2.79 The price-to-earnings (P/E) ratio of a stock is the ratio of a stock's most recent price per share to the stock's earnings per share (averaged over a 12-month period), multiplied by 100. The P/E ratios for 44 securities selling at earnings multiples much higher than the average market price are listed below. Construct a relative frequency histogram for the data.

25.8	14.8	76.0	17.2	19.8	17.1
14.3	30.5	20.0	19.5	19.2	23.4
16.9	39.7	18.3	15.8	50.6	17.8
18.1	20.0	45.5	44.3	15.1	16.8
40.2	16.2	14.9	18.5	23.6	
21.3	15.2	17.7	14.7	17.4	
19.7	14.5	15.5	20.0	15.7	
15.6	20.8	19.4	18.7	16.4	

Source: Forbes, September 28, 1981.

2.80 Refer to Exercise 2.79.

(a) Calculate $\bar{x}$ and s.

(b) Use the range approximation for s to check your calculations.

(c) Find the number of P/E ratios in the intervals $(\bar{x} \pm s)$, $(\bar{x} \pm 2s)$, and $(\bar{x} \pm 3s)$. Compare the proportions of measurements in these intervals with the proportions specified by Tchebysheff's Theorem and the Empirical Rule.

2.81 First introduced in the United States in 1960, industrial robots (e.g., mechanical arms, automated assemblers, computerized welders) have come into much wider use over the past decade. Initially, a typical assembly line robot cost (on the average) $4.20 per hour, just slightly higher than the average factory worker's hourly wage. Today factory workers are paid between $15 and $20 per hour, but robots can still be operated for less than $5 per hour. Suppose the operating costs per hour were recorded for 100 firms that employ industrial robots. The mean and variance of the sample were found to be $4.86 and $2.50(\$)^2$. Calculate $(\bar{x} \pm s)$, $(\bar{x} \pm 2s)$, $(\bar{x} \pm 3s)$, and state the approximate fraction of measurements we would expect to fall in these intervals according to the Empirical Rule:

$$\bar{x} + s \text{ ——— fraction ———}$$

$$\bar{x} \pm 2s \text{ ——— fraction ———}$$

$$\bar{x} \pm 3s \text{ ——— fraction ———}$$

2.82 The mean duration of television commercials on a given network is 75 seconds, and the standard deviation is 20 seconds. Assume that duration times are approximately normally distributed.

(a) Approximately what fraction of commercials will last less than 35 seconds?

(b) Approximately what fraction of commercials will last longer than 55 seconds?

2.83 A random sample of 100 large law firms was surveyed to determine the prevalence of computerized office equipment in the industry. The number of pieces of computerized equipment (word processors, data terminals, microprocessors, minicomputers, etc.) in use at each firm was recorded. Sixty-nine law firms were found to utilize no computerized equipment, 17 employed one piece, and so on. The following table is a frequency tabulation of the data.

Number of Computerized Pieces, x	0	1	2	3	4	5	6	7	8
Number of Law Firms, f	69	17	6	3	1	2	1	0	1

(a) Construct a relative frequency histogram for x, the number of pieces of computerized office equipment per firm.

(b) Calculate $\bar{x}$ and s for the sample.

(c) What fraction of the equipment counts fall within two standard deviations of the mean? Three? Do the results agree with Tchebysheff's Theorem? The Empirical Rule?

2.84 Consider a population consisting of the numbers of professors employed in the business departments at large four-year universities. Suppose that the number of business professors per college has an average of $\mu = 25$ and a standard deviation of $\sigma = 5$.

(a) Use Tchebysheff's Theorem to make a statement about the percentage of colleges that employ between 15 and 35 business professors.

(b) Assume that the population is normally distributed. What fraction of the colleges have more than 30 business professors?

2.85 One method of generating additional revenue for a periodical is to allow more full-page advertisements in each issue. The following data represent the number of full-page advertisements in randomly selected issues of a weekly magazine.

12	10	16	7	18
13	14	20	9	23
8	13	14	6	19
6	11	15	10	16

Computing s for these data, the magazine's production manager obtained a value of 8.90. Use the range approximation for s as a check on this computation. Do these estimated and computed values for s appear to differ excessively?

2.86 A recent study by the Highway Loss Data Institute reported that the average loss payment per insurance claim by automobile owners during the first half of 1974 was $495 with a standard deviation of $75 (*Money*, September 1974). Assume that the distribution of loss-payment per claim is mound-shaped.

(a) Describe the distribution of loss payments during this period.

(b) Approximately what fraction of the loss payments exceeded $570 during this period?

2.87 In an article titled "If Fido Takes a Piece of the Postman, Feds May Take a Chunk Out of You," the *Wall Street Journal* (July 10, 1981) notes that the U.S. Postal Service is assisting letter carriers in assembling the necessary evidence to seek damages from dog owners for the harmful antipostman behavior of their pets. The article notes that the mean cost in medical bills and lost time per dog bite is $300; of course, the actual cost can run much higher. Suppose that the distribution of cost per bite possesses a mean equal to $300 and a standard deviation equal to $200.

(a) Why might the relative frequency distribution of costs per bite be skewed to the right as shown in Figure 2.21?

(b) Approximately what percentage of the costs per bite are less than $700?

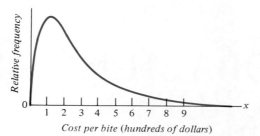

Cost per bite (hundreds of dollars)

FIGURE 2.21 Frequency Histogram of Cost-per-Bite Data for Exercise 2.87

2.88 In these days of escalating home prices and soaring interest rates, it is rare to find a home that sells for under $20,000. However, of the 430 homes sold through the Orlando–Winter Park (Fla.) Board of Realtors' Multiple Listing Service in September 1981, 4 went for less than $20,000 (*Orlando Sentinel Star*, October 10, 1981). In addition, 16 homes were sold for less than $30,000, and 263 of the 430 homes were sold under $70,000. However, the board did report an increase in the sales of houses in the upper price range: 50 of the houses sold in September cost more than $120,000, with 13 of those sold at more than $200,000. Identify any percentiles for the distribution of September home sale prices that can be determined from the information given.

2.89 Each year, the U.S. Brewers Association ranks the 50 states according to their total malt beverage consumption (the number of six-packs consumed). In 1980 Hawaii (49,101,228 six-packs), South Carolina (116,729,215), and Virginia (207,412,019) represented the lower quartile, median, and upper quartile, respectively, of the distribution of malt beverage consumptions for the 50 states (*Beer and Supermarkets*, 1980 Annual Report). What are the relative standings of Hawaii, South Carolina, and Virginia among the 50 states, with respect to 1980 malt beverage consumption?

The objective of this chapter is to lay the foundation for statistical inference. We will introduce some basic concepts of probability, and then we will present some models for calculating the probabilities of sample outcomes.

3

PROBABILITY AND DISCRETE PROBABILITY DISTRIBUTIONS

CASE STUDY

The Fear of Flying

Are you afraid to fly? A study by the Boeing Aircraft Company, reported in the *Orlando Sentinel Star* (June 28, 1981), reveals some surprising statistics on consumer attitudes toward flying. The study estimated that nearly 25 million Americans are afraid to fly and that one in ten who fly do so in a state of fear. Fear of flying is more prevalent among blacks than whites and among lower socioeconomic groups. Fifteen percent of those who have flown consider flying to be dangerous, in comparison to 29% of those who have not flown.

Thousands of businesspeople and vacationers consciously or unconsciously fly only when it is absolutely necessary. These people, along with those who refuse to fly, represent an enormous loss of income to the airlines, particularly considering that in the first six months of 1981 the airlines were operating at 56.5% of capacity. Consequently, the need to learn more about the fear of flying, its causes, and the effects of measures to cope with it motivates sample surveys of the type conducted by the Boeing Aircraft Company.

Sample surveys, conducted by mail, telephone, or by personal interview, are usually used to sample consumer attitudes or opinions. Although sometimes quantitative, the answers solicited by the survey questions (questions like "Are you afraid of flying?") are often the dichotomous, yes-or-no variety. Typical surveys by the Gallup, Harris, or various other consumer polling organizations usually involve sampling and questioning 1000 to 2000 consumers. A summary of these dichotomous responses to a question yields the number of yeses (or the number of noes) in the sample.

Ultimately, the polling organization will use the number of yeses in the sample to estimate the proportion of yeses in the entire population and will state how far the sample estimate is likely to depart from the population proportion. Note that x, the number of yeses in, say, a sample of 1000 people, will vary from one sample to another and will cause the sample proportions to vary in a similar manner. Consequently, the key to evaluating the reliability of an estimate of a population proportion is the probability distribution of the discrete random variable x.

In this chapter you will learn that many sampling situations generate data sets whose population relative frequency distributions can be modeled by a single probability distribution. We will present this important probability distribution and will see how it can be applied to an analysis of the responses in a consumer survey in Section 3.5. The probability distributions for several other discrete random variables will be presented as optional topics in Sections 3.6, 3.7, and 3.8.

3.1 THE ROLE OF PROBABILITY IN STATISTICS

The role that probability plays in statistics can be demonstrated with a simple example. Consider a die (singular for dice) with its familiar six faces. If the die is tossed, we will observe either 1, 2, 3, 4, 5, or 6 dots. If the die is tossed millions and millions of times and the number x of dots is recorded for each toss, we will generate a population of data that characterizes the die toss. If the die is balanced, we would expect approximately 1/6 of the numbers in the population to be 1s, 1/6 to be 2s, . . . , and 1/6 to be 6s.

A probabilist reasons from a known population to an unknown sample. Thus a probabilist would assume the population is known (e.g., the die is balanced) and calculate the probability of observing some sample outcome, say observing a pair of 1s in two tosses of the die. In contrast, the statistician reverses the reasoning process, assumes the sample known, the population unknown, and reasons from the sample to the population.

To illustrate how probability is used in statistical inference, consider the following example: Suppose that a die is tossed $n = 10$ times and the number x of dots appearing is recorded after each toss. This experiment represents a sample of $n = 10$ measurements drawn from a much larger body of tosses (the population), which could be generated if we wished. Suppose that all 10 measurements resulted in $x = 1$. We want to use this information to make an inference concerning the population of tosses; specifically, we want to infer that the die is or is not balanced. Having observed 10 tosses, each resulting in $x = 1$, we would be somewhat suspicious of the die and would likely reject the theory that the die was balanced. We reason as follows: If the die were balanced as we hypothesize, then observing 10 identical measurements is most improbable. Therefore, either we observed a rare event or else our hypothesis is false. We would likely be inclined to the latter conclusion. Notice that the decision was based on the probability of observing the sample under the assumption that our theory was true.

This illustration emphasizes the importance of probability in making statistical inferences. In the following discussion of the theory of probability, we will assume the population is known and calculate the probability of drawing various samples. In doing so, we are really choosing a model for a physical situation, because the actual composition of a population is rarely known in practice. Thus the probabilist models a physical situation (the population) with probability much as the sculptor models with clay.

In the sections that follow we will present some basic concepts of probability, concepts that will help you understand future references to probability as they enter our discussions of statistical inference. To make it easier for you to grasp these concepts, we will illustrate them by using easily understood coin- and die-tossing experiments. Practical applications will follow the simple examples.

THE ADDITIVE PROPERTIES OF PROBABILITIES

3.2

Data are obtained either by observation of uncontrolled events in nature or by controlled experimentation in the laboratory. To simplify our terminology, we seek a word that will apply to either method of data collection and hence define the term **experiment**.

DEFINITION   An *experiment* is the process by which an observation (or measurement) is obtained. ■

Note that the observation need not be numerical. Typical examples of experiments are given in the following list:

(1) Recording the daily production of a manufacturing plant.
(2) Recording the exchange rate between the dollar and the British pound.

(3) Interviewing a consumer to determine product preference among a group of ten types of automobiles.

(4) Inspecting a light bulb to determine whether it is a defective or an acceptable product.

(5) Tossing a coin and observing the face that appears.

Experiments can result in one or more outcomes, which are called **events** and are designated by capital letters. For example, if an experiment consists of recording the number of new orders per month received by a manufacturer, some possible events are the following:

A: no new orders are received

B: the number of new orders exceeds 50

C: the number of new orders is 25

D: the number of new orders is less than 15

We could list many other events associated with this experiment, some more likely to occur than others.

The **probability of an event** A is a measure of our belief that an experiment will result in event A. In order to attach meaning to this concept, we note that populations of observations are generated by repeating an experiment over and over again a very large number of times. If in this large number N of repetitions of the experiment, event A is observed n times, then we view the probability of event A as

$$P(A) = \frac{n}{N}$$

This practical interpretation of the meaning of probability—an interpretation held by most laypersons—is called the *relative frequency concept of probability*.

Viewing the probability of an event in terms of relative frequency is intuitively appealing but it does not provide us with a way of determining the probability of an event. In the real world we cannot repeat experiments millions of times. We can, however, agree that the probability of an event must satisfy properties consistent with the relative frequency concept of probability. If an event A cannot occur, then $P(A) = 0$. If it is certain to occur, $P(A) = 1$. In general, $P(A)$ is a fraction. The closer its value is to 1, the more likely A is to occur. In practice, we assign probability to an event on the basis of experience, observation of prior experimental outcomes, and knowledge of the many variables that may affect the outcomes of an experiment.

We are frequently interested in **intersections** and **unions** of two events A and B.

DEFINITION   The *intersection* of two events A and B, denoted by the symbol AB, is the event that *both* A and B occur.   ∎

DEFINITION   The *union* of two events A and B, denoted by the symbol $A \cup B$, is the event that *either* A or B or both occur.   ∎

Some events A and B possess the unique property that $P(AB) = 0$—that is, if one event occurs, the other cannot occur (and vice versa). Events that possess this property are said to be **mutually exclusive**. For example, suppose that an experiment consists of observing next month's action by the Federal Reserve Board on the prime interest rate, and define the following events:

A: the prime rate is raised

B: the prime rate is lowered

C: the prime rate is unchanged

Then events A and B are mutually exclusive events because a single experiment cannot result in both A and B. If the next declaration of prime rate policy results in A, then B cannot also occur. If the prime rate is raised, it could not have been lowered at the same time. Events A, B, and C are also said to be mutually exclusive events. If any one of the group is observed, neither of the remaining two events could have occurred.

DEFINITION

Two events A and B are said to be *mutually exclusive* if $P(AB) = 0$—that is, when A occurs, B cannot occur (and vice versa).   ■

If two events A and B are mutually exclusive, then $P(AB) = 0$ and the probability that either A or B will occur is

$$P(A \cup B) = P(A) + P(B)$$

This additive rule for the probability of the union of two mutually exclusive events agrees with our relative frequency concept of probability. Suppose that an experiment is repeated a very large number of times. If 20% of the experiments result in event A and 30% in B, then when A and B are mutually exclusive, it follows that 50% of the experiments will result in either event A or event B. That is,

$$P(A \cup B) = P(A) + P(B) = .2 + .3 = .5$$

ADDITIVE PROPERTY OF PROBABILITIES FOR MUTUALLY EXCLUSIVE EVENTS

If A and B are mutually exclusive events, then the probability that either A or B occurs is

$$P(A \cup B) = P(A) + P(B)$$

The **sample space** for an experiment is a very special set of mutually exclusive events.

DEFINITION

If an experiment can result in one and only one of a set of r mutually exclusive events, $E_1, E_2, \ldots, E_r$, the set of events is called the *sample space S* for the experiment. The individual events are called *simple events*.   ■

Since an experiment will result in one and only one **simple event**, the relative frequencies of the occurrences of all simple events in a sample space S must sum to 1.

PROPERTIES OF THE PROBABILITIES OF SIMPLE EVENTS

If the set of simple events $E_1, E_2, \ldots, E_r$ represents the sample space S for an experiment, then

$$0 \leq P(E_i) \leq 1$$

and

$$\sum_{i=1}^{r} P(E_i) = 1$$

The simple events for an experiment can be used to calculate the probability of any event A.

ADDITIVE PROBABILITY RULE FOR FINDING $P(A)$

If event A will occur if and only if one of a set of k simple events $E_1, E_2, \ldots, E_k$ occurs, then

$$P(A) = P(E_1) + P(E_2) + \cdots + P(E_k)$$

EXAMPLE 3.1   Calculate the probability of observing exactly one head in a toss of two coins.

SOLUTION   Construct the sample space, letting H represent a head, T a tail. See Table 3.1.

TABLE 3.1   Sample Space for Example 3.1

Event	First Coin	Second Coin	$P(E_i)$
E_1	H	H	1/4
E_2	H	T	1/4
E_3	T	H	1/4
E_4	T	T	1/4

The sample space S for the experiment contains the four simple events listed in Table 3.1. Since a reasonable assumption is that any one of the simple events is as likely to occur as any other, we will assign a probability of 1/4 to each. We are interested in

event A: observe exactly one head

Event A will occur if and only if E_2 or E_3 occur. Therefore,

$$P(A) = P(E_2) + P(E_3)$$
$$= \frac{1}{4} + \frac{1}{4}$$
$$= \frac{1}{2}$$

EXAMPLE 3.2

Refer to our observation of the Federal Reserve Board's action on the prime rate, and define the events A, B, and C as follows:

A: the prime rate is raised

B: the prime rate is lowered

C: the prime rate is unchanged

Suppose that we know that $P(A) = .2$ and $P(B) = .3$. Find $P(C)$.

SOLUTION

Examining A, B, and C, we can see that the experiment can result in one and only one of these three mutually exclusive events. Therefore, A, B, and C are simple events that represent the sample space S for the experiment, and

$$P(A) + P(B) + P(C) = 1$$

Substituting $P(A)$ and $P(B)$ into this equation yields

$$.2 + .3 + P(C) = 1$$

Solving for $P(C)$, we obtain

$$P(C) = 1 - .3 - .2 = .5$$

EXAMPLE 3.3

The most common complaints of airline passengers to the Department of Transportation for the period January through September 1986 and the proportions of each type of complaint are shown in Table 3.2. Suppose that all complaints received by the Department of Transportation fall into one and only one of the categories and that the proportions of complaints in the categories hold true today. Consider the following experiment: A complaint is received by the Department of Transportation and its type is observed. Find the probability that the complaint is not due to flight cancellations, delays, or overbooked flights.

TABLE 3.2

Airline Passenger Complaint Data for Example 3.3

Complaint	Proportion of Total
Flight cancellations, delays	.33
Lost or damaged baggage	.22
Problems in obtaining refunds	.17
Overbooked flights	.09
Customer service	.07
Problems with reservations (ticketing or boarding)	.07
Confusing fares	.05

Source: Data from *Wall Street Journal*, November 10, 1986. Reprinted by permission of *Wall Street Journal*, © Dow Jones & Company, Inc. 1986. All rights reserved.

SOLUTION

Since the observation will result in one and only one of the seven complaints listed in Table 3.2, the simple events in S, along with their probabilities, are as shown in Table 3.3.

TABLE 3.3   Simple Events and Probabilities for the Data of Table 3.2

Simple Event	Complaint	$P(E_i)$
E_1	Flight cancellations, delays	.33
E_2	Lost or damaged baggage	.22
E_3	Problems in obtaining refunds	.17
E_4	Overbooked flights	.09
E_5	Customer service	.07
E_6	Problems with reservations (ticketing or boarding)	.07
E_7	Confusing fares	.05

The event

A: the complaint is not due to flight cancellations, delays, or overbooked flights

contains the simple events E_2, E_3, E_5, E_6, E_7. Therefore, the probability that the complaint is not due to flight cancellations, delays, or overbooked flight is

$$P(A) = P(E_2) + P(E_3) + P(E_5) + P(E_6) + P(E_7)$$
$$= .22 + .17 + .07 + .07 + .05 = .58$$ ■

EXAMPLE 3.4   An investor plans to invest $10,000 in each of two investments.

(a) If the investor has decided to select the two from among a group of six, how many different simple events can result from this experiment?

(b) Although the future outcome of the investments is unknown, it is likely that the return over a fixed period of time will vary from one investment to another. If all of the investments appear to be equally good and the investor selects the two investments at random, what is the probability that the investor will select two of the three investments that will ultimately yield the best return?

SOLUTION   (a) If we identify the six investments as $I_1, I_2, \ldots, I_6$, then the investor can select one and only one of the 15 pairs of investments that follow. Each pair represents a simple event, and the 15 pairs comprise the sample space S for the experiment.

E_1: I_1, I_2	E_6: I_2, I_3	E_{10}: I_3, I_4	E_{13}: I_4, I_5	E_{15}: I_5, I_6
E_2: I_1, I_3	E_7: I_2, I_4	E_{11}: I_3, I_5	E_{14}: I_4, I_6	
E_3: I_1, I_4	E_8: I_2, I_5	E_{12}: I_3, I_6		
E_4: I_1, I_5	E_9: I_2, I_6			
E_5: I_1, I_6				

(b) The event

A: the investor selects two of the three investments with the best return

is the event that two of a specific set of three investments appear in the selection. In order to list the simple events that comprise the event A, we assume that the best, second-best, and third-best investments are I_1, I_2, and I_3. Then the event A will occur if and only if simple events involving pairs of the three investments I_1, I_2, and I_3 occur. Therefore, A will occur if

$$I_1, I_2, \qquad I_1, I_3, \qquad \text{and} \qquad I_2, I_3$$

occur. Since there are 15 simple events in S, all equiprobable, it follows that the probability of a simple event is 1/15. Therefore, the probability of selecting two of the best three investments is

$$P(A) = P(I_1, I_2) + P(I_1, I_3) + P(I_2, I_3)$$
$$= P(E_1) + P(E_2) + P(E_6)$$
$$= \frac{1}{15} + \frac{1}{15} + \frac{1}{15} = \frac{3}{15} = .2 \qquad \blacksquare$$

EXERCISES   14

BASIC TECHNIQUES

3.1 An experiment involves tossing a single die. Specify the simple events in the following events:

> A: observe a 2
>
> B: observe an odd number
>
> C: observe a number less than 4
>
> D: observe both A and B
>
> E: observe either A or B or both
>
> F: observe both A and C

Calculate the probabilities of the events D, E, and F by summing the probabilities of the appropriate simple events.

3.2 An experiment can result in one of four simple events, with

$$P(E_1) = .1 \qquad P(E_2) = .15 \qquad P(E_3) = .6 \qquad P(E_4) = .15$$

Explain why this assignment of probabilities to the simple events is or is not valid.

3.3 An experiment can result in one of five simple events, $E_1, E_2, \ldots, E_5$. For $P(E_1) = P(E_2) = P(E_3) = P(E_4) = .15$, find $P(E_5)$.

3.4 A sample space contains five simple events, E_1, E_2, E_3, E_4, and E_5. For $P(E_3) = .4$, $P(E_4) = 2P(E_5)$, and $P(E_1) = P(E_2) = .15$, find the probabilities of E_4 and E_5.

3.5 A sample space contains ten simple events, $E_1, E_2, \ldots, E_{10}$. For $P(E_1) = 3P(E_2) = .45$, with the remaining simple events being equiprobable, find the probabilities of these remaining simple events.

3.6 The game of roulette uses a wheel containing 38 pockets. Thirty-six pockets are numbered 1, 2, ..., 36, and the remaining two are marked 0 and 00. A wheel is spun and one of these pockets is identified as the "winner." Assume that the observance of any one pocket is just as likely as any other.

(a) Identify the simple events in a single spin of the roulette wheel.

(b) Assign probabilities to the simple events.

(c) Let A be the event that you observe either a 0 or a 00. List the simple events in the event A, and find $P(A)$.

(d) Suppose that you were to place bets on the numbers 1 through 18. What is the probability that one of your numbers will be the winner?

3.7 An experiment can result in one of five equally likely simple events. Events A, B, and C include the following simple events:

$$A: E_1, E_3 \qquad B: E_1, E_2, E_4, E_5 \qquad C: E_3, E_4$$

List the simple events in the following events, and find their respective probabilities.*

(a) S	(b) A	(c) B
(d) C	(e) $\bar{A}$	(f) $\bar{B}$
(g) AB	(h) AC	(i) BC
(j) $A \cup B$	(k) $A \cup C$	(l) $B \cup C$

3.8 Refer to Exercise 3.7. Are events A and B mutually exclusive? Explain.

3.9 An experiment consists of tossing a single die and observing the number of dots shown on the upper face. The events A, B, and C are defined as follows:

A: observe a number less than 4

B: observe a number less than or equal to 2

C: observe a number greater than 3

List the simple events in the following events, and find their respective probabilities.

(a) S	(b) A	(c) B	(d) C	(e) AB
(f) AC	(g) BC	(h) $A \cup B$	(i) $A \cup C$	(j) $B \cup C$

3.10 Refer to Exercise 3.9. Are events A and B mutually exclusive? A and C? B and C?

3.11 An experiment generates a sample space containing eight simple events $E_1, E_2, \ldots, E_8$, with $P(E_1) = .1$, $P(E_2) = P(E_3) = P(E_4) = .05$, $P(E_5) = .3$, $P(E_6) = .2$, $P(E_7) = .1$, and $P(E_8) = .15$. The events A and B are

$$A: E_1, E_4, E_6 \qquad B: E_3, E_4, E_5, E_6, E_7$$

(a) Find $P(A)$.

(b) Find $P(B)$.

(c) Find $P(AB)$.

(d) Find $P(A \cup B)$.

(e) Are events A and B mutually exclusive? Why?

APPLICATIONS

 3.12 An oil-prospecting firm hits oil or gas on 10% of its drillings. If the firm drills 2 wells, the four possible simple events and three of their associated probabilities are as shown in Table 3.4.

---

*An overbar over an event symbol, say $\bar{A}$, represents the event that A will not occur.

TABLE 3.4   Events and Probabilities for Exercise 3.12

Simple Event	Outcome of 1st Drilling	Outcome of 2nd Drilling	Probability
1	Hit (oil or gas)	Hit (oil or gas)	.01
2	Hit	Miss	?
3	Miss	Hit	.09
4	Miss	Miss	.81

(a) Find the probability that the company will hit oil or gas on the first drilling and miss on the second.

(b) Find the probability that the company will hit oil or gas on at least one of the two drillings.

 3.13 A marketing survey for a large department store classified the store's customers according to whether they were male or female and according to their residence, suburban or city. The proportions of customers falling in the four categories are shown in Table 3.5.

TABLE 3.5   Sex and Residence Data for Exercise 3.13

Residence	Male	Female
	Sex	
Suburban	.17	.67
City	.04	.12

Suppose a single adult is selected from among this group of customers. Find the following probabilities.

(a) That the customer resides in the suburbs.

(b) That the customer is a female who lives in the city.

(c) That the customer is a male.

 3.14 Two stock market analysts are each asked to forecast whether the Dow-Jones stock average will gain 100 points or more, lose 100 points or more, or change less than 100 points by the end of the next 12 months. Thus the experiment consists of observing the pair of forecasts produced by the two market analysts. Suppose that each of the analysts is as likely to select any one of the three choices as he or she is likely to select any other.

(a) List the simple events in the sample space S.

(b) Let A be the event that at least one of the analysts forecasts a rise in the Dow-Jones average of 100 points or more. Find the simple events in A.

(c) Let B be the event that both analysts agree in their forecasts. Find the simple events in B.

(d) Assign probabilities to the simple events in S, and find $P(A)$.

(e) Find $P(B)$.

 3.15 A food company plans to conduct an experiment to compare its brand of tea with that of two competitors. In actual practice a number of tea tasters would be employed. For this example we will assume that only one tea taster tastes each of the three brands of tea, which are unmarked except for identifying symbols, A, B, and C.

(a) Define the experiment.

(b) List the simple events in S.

(c) If the taster had no ability to distinguish a difference in taste between teas, what is the probability that the taster will rank tea type A as best? As the least desirable?

3.16 Four union men, two from a minority group, are assigned to four distinctly different one-man jobs.

(a) Define the experiment.

(b) List the simple events in S.

(c) If the assignment to the jobs is unbiased—that is, if any one ordering of assignments is as probable as any other—what is the probability that the two men from the minority group are assigned to the two least desirable jobs?

CONDITIONAL PROBABILITY AND INDEPENDENT EVENTS

3.3

Two events are often related in such a way that the probability of the occurrence of one event depends upon whether the other event has or has not occurred. For example, suppose that you are a money trader who trades dollars against the British pound, and the experiment consists in observing whether the dollar is up (has increased in value) against the pound. Let A be the event that the dollar is up against the pound on the English currency market before our market opens at 9:00 A.M., and let B be the event that the dollar is up on the American market after it opens. Events A and B are certainly related because the two markets will likely move in the same direction most (but not necessarily all) days. Therefore, the probability $P(B)$ that the dollar will be up against the pound on the U.S. market is not the same as the probability that B will occur, given that you know that the dollar is already up (event A) on the British market.

For example, suppose that the dollar is up against the pound 60% of all days on the British market, and 50% of all days it is up on both the U.S. and British markets [i.e., $P(A) = .6$ and $P(AB) = .5$]. Then if you already know that the dollar is up against the pound on the British market, the probability that it will be up on the U.S. market is 5/6. This fraction, $P(AB)/P(A)$, is called the **conditional probability** of B, given that event A has occurred, and is denoted by the symbol

$$P(B \mid A)$$

The vertical bar in the expression $P(B \mid A)$ is read "given," and the events appearing to the right of the bar are the events that have occurred.

DEFINITION

The *conditional probability* of B given that event A has occurred is

$$P(B \mid A) = \frac{P(AB)}{P(A)}$$

and the conditional probability of A given that event B has occurred is

$$P(A \mid B) = \frac{P(AB)}{P(B)}$$

If the probability that an outcome A occurs does not depend upon whether a second event B has occurred (or vice versa), we say that A and B are **independent events**. In terms of probabilities we say that A and B are independent events if

$$P(A|B) = P(A) \qquad \text{or} \qquad P(B|A) = P(B)$$

DEFINITION

Two events A and B are said to be *independent* if and only if either

$$P(A|B) = P(A)$$

or

$$P(B|A) = P(B)$$

Otherwise, the events are said to be *dependent*.   ∎

The concept of independent events is important when we want to calculate the probability $P(AB)$ that both events A and B occur. From our definition of conditional probability,

$$P(A|B) = \frac{P(AB)}{P(B)} \qquad \text{and} \qquad P(B|A) = \frac{P(AB)}{P(A)}$$

or equivalently,

$$P(AB) = P(A)P(B|A) = P(B)P(A|B)$$

But if A and B are independent events,

$$P(A|B) = P(A) \qquad \text{and} \qquad P(B|A) = P(B)$$

and the formula for $P(AB)$ reduces to the product of the unconditional probabilities of A and B. That is,

$$P(AB) = P(A)P(B)$$

See the following box.

THE MULTIPLICATIVE RULE FOR THE INTERSECTION OF TWO EVENTS

The probability that both of two events, A and B, occur is

$$P(AB) = P(A)P(B|A) = P(B)P(A|B)$$

If A and B are independent events,

$$P(AB) = P(A)P(B)$$

Similarly, if A, B, and C are mutually independent events, then the probability that A, B, and C will occur is

$$P(ABC) = P(A)P(B)P(C)$$

EXAMPLE 3.5   Suppose that you randomly select three common stocks, A, B, C, from among the 500 stocks used to calculate Standard & Poor's (S&P) 500 stock average. What is the probability that the yearly gain for all three stocks will exceed the gain of the S&P average? Let, A, B, and C represent the events that stocks A, B, and C individually outperform the S&P average, and assume that $P(A) = P(B) = P(C) = 1/2$.

SOLUTION   The event that all three stock choices will beat the S&P average is the intersection of the outcomes A, B, and C. We do not know the conditional probabilities of A, B, and C, so we cannot use the definition of conditional probability to test for independence. Rather, we must rely on our intuition. Since we selected the three stocks in an unrelated manner, it seems unlikely that the selection of one stock from among the 500 would greatly affect the selection of another. For this reason we will declare the events to be independent and calculate

$$P(ABC) = P(A)P(B)P(C)$$

$$= \left(\frac{1}{2}\right)\left(\frac{1}{2}\right)\left(\frac{1}{2}\right) = \frac{1}{8}$$

Thus we calculate the probability of selecting three stocks that will beat the S&P average to be $1/8$.   ■

EXAMPLE 3.6   A mail-order merchandiser of clothing sells two product lines, one relatively expensive, the other inexpensive. A survey of 1000 orders produced the frequencies of orders by product line and sex of the customer shown in Table 3.6. Suppose that a single order is selected from among the 1000.

TABLE 3.6   Data for Frequencies of Orders for Example 3.6

Sex	Product Line		Total
	1	2	
Male	132	147	279
Female	516	205	721
Total	648	352	1000

(a) Find the probability of event A: the customer is female.

(b) Find the probability of event B: the order is for product line 1.

(c) Find the probability that the order is from product line 1 and the customer is female.

(d) Find the probability that the order is from product line 1, given that the customer is female.

(e) Show that A and B are or are not independent events.

(f) Use the probabilities calculated in parts (a) through (e) to show that $P(AB) = P(A)P(B|A)$.

SOLUTION

(a) Since 721 of the 1000 orders were from female customers, the probability $P(A)$ of selecting an order from a female customer is

$$P(A) = \frac{721}{1000}$$

(b) By similar reasoning,

$$P(B) = \frac{648}{1000}$$

(c) Of the 1000 orders, 516 were from female customers who ordered product line 1. Therefore,

$$P(AB) = \frac{516}{1000}$$

(d) The probability that an order is from product line 1 (event B), given that the order was from a female customer (event A), is

$$P(B|A) = \frac{P(AB)}{P(A)}$$

$$= \frac{516/1000}{721/1000} = \frac{516}{721}$$

(e) To determine whether A and B are independent, we need to compare $P(B)$ with $P(B|A)$. Since $P(B) = 648/1000$ is not equal to $P(B|A) = 516/721$, A and B are dependent events.

(f) In parts (a), (c), and (d) we found

$$P(A) = \frac{721}{1000} \qquad P(AB) = \frac{516}{1000} \qquad P(B|A) = \frac{516}{721}$$

Therefore,

$$P(AB) = P(A)P(B|A) = \left(\frac{721}{1000}\right)\left(\frac{516}{721}\right) = \frac{516}{1000} \qquad \blacksquare$$

EXAMPLE 3.7

A company found that 85% of the persons selected for its sales trainee program completed the course. Of these, only 60% became productive salespersons. If a new trainee enters the course, what is the probability that the trainee will become a productive salesperson?

SOLUTION

Define the following events:

A: a sales trainee completes the course

B: the sales trainee becomes a productive salesperson

From the information given

$$P(A) = .85 \qquad \text{and} \qquad P(B|A) = .60$$

Therefore, the probability that a trainee will both complete the course and become a productive salesperson is

$$P(AB) = P(A)P(B|A) = (.85)(.60) = .51 \quad \blacksquare$$

EXERCISES

BASIC TECHNIQUES

3.17 An experiment can result in one of five equally likely simple events. Events A, B, and C include the following simple events:

$$A:\ E_1, E_3$$
$$B:\ E_1, E_2, E_4, E_5$$
$$C:\ E_3, E_4$$

$$\frac{P(AB)}{P(B)}$$

(a) Find $P(A|B)$.
(b) Find $P(B|A)$.
(c) Find $P(A|C)$.
(d) Find $P(B|C)$.
(e) Are A and B independent events? Verify your answer.

3.18 An experiment consists of tossing a single die and observing the number of dots shown on the upper face. The events A, B, and C are defined as follows:

A: observe a number less than 4

B: observe a number less than or equal to 2

C: observe a number greater than 3

(a) Find $P(A|B)$.
(b) Find $P(B|A)$.
(c) Find $P(A|C)$.
(d) Find $P(B|C)$.
(e) Are A and B independent events? Verify your answer.

3.19 An experiment generates a sample space containing eight simple events $E_1, E_2, \ldots, E_8$, with $P(E_1) = .1$, $P(E_2) = P(E_3) = P(E_4) = .05$, $P(E_5) = .3$, $P(E_6) = .2$, $P(E_7) = .1$, and $P(E_8) = .15$. The events A and B are

$$A:\ E_1, E_4, E_6$$
$$B:\ E_3, E_4, E_5, E_6, E_7$$

(a) Find $P(A|B)$.
(b) Find $P(B|A)$.
(c) Are A and B independent events? Why?

APPLICATIONS

3.20 New orders for a company's products vary in dollar size according to the following probability distribution.

Size of Sale ($)	0–1000	1001–2000	2001–3000	3001–4000	4001–5000
Probability	.10	.35	.25	.20	.10

(a) Find the probability that a new order will exceed $2000.

(b) Find the probability that a new order will be $2000 or less, given that the order exceeds $1000.

(c) Find the probability that a new order will be larger than $3000, given that the sale exceeds $2000.

MKTG 3.21 The data in Table 3.7 represent a small portion of a telephone survey conducted by Jerry R. Lynn to determine the characteristics of newspaper readership for the small towns, rural areas, and farms in Tennessee and to determine the impact of advertising on that market. A sample of 1486 persons was selected from among the small towns, rural areas, and farms of Tennessee. One survey question asked whether the respondent did or did not read a newspaper. The proportions of respondents in the six community-readership categories are shown in Table 3.7. Suppose a single telephone subscriber is randomly selected from among those listed in the survey.

TABLE 3.7   Community-Readership Data for Exercise 3.21

Community	Readers	Nonreaders
Urban	.36	.08
Rural	.25	.09
Farm	.16	.06

Source: Data from Jerry R. Lynn, "Newspaper Ad Impact in Nonmetropolitan Markets," *Journal of Advertising Research,* Vol. 21, No. 4, 1981.

(a) What is the probability that the subscriber will live on a farm?

(b) What is the probability that the subscriber will be an urban reader?

(c) What is the probability that the subscriber will be a nonreader, given that the telephone subscriber lives in an urban area?

(d) What is the probability that the subscriber will be a reader, given that the telephone subscriber does not live on a farm?

3.22 In an article titled "Drug Tests for Jobs Spreads, Raises Questions," the *St. Augustine Record* (November 5, 1985) quotes a Miami drug-testing consultant as saying, "Testing of prospective employees for drug use has become so prevalent that detectable users may soon find it impossible to get work." Proponents of the procedure point to the improvement in worker efficiency and the reduction of absenteeism, accidents, and theft that can be achieved by eliminating drug users from the work force. Opponents claim that the procedure is creating a class of unhirables and that some may be placed in this class because the tests themselves are not 100% reliable. The article notes that EMIT, the test most used by companies, is 97% to 98% accurate. Suppose that a company uses a test procedure that is 98% accurate—that is, it correctly identifies a person as a drug user or as a non–drug user with probability .98—and suppose that in an effort to reduce the chance of error, each job applicant is required to take two tests. Assume the outcomes of the two tests on the same person are independent events.

(a) What is the probability that a non-drug user will fail both tests?

(b) What is the probability that a drug user will be detected—that is, will fail at least one of the two tests?

(c) What is the probability that a drug user will pass both tests?

 3.23 Television commercials are designed to appeal to the most likely viewing audience of the sponsored program. However, one study notes that children often have a very low understanding of commercials, even for those designed to appeal especially to children. Ward's studies show that the percentages of children understanding TV commercials for different age groups are as given in Table 3.8. Suppose an advertising agent has shown a television commercial to a six-year-old child and another to a nine-year-old child in a laboratory experiment to test their understanding of the commercials.

TABLE 3.8   TV Commercials Data for Exercise 3.23

| | | Age | |
Response	5–7	8–10	11–12
Don't understand	55%	40%	15%
Understand	45%	60%	85%

Source: Data from S. Ward, "Children's Reactions to Commercials," *Journal of Advertising Research,* Vol. 12, No. 2, April 1972.

(a) What is the probability that the message of the commercial is understood by the six-year-old child?

(b) What is the probability that both children demonstrate an understanding of the TV commercial?

(c) What is the probability that one or the other, or both, children demonstrate an understanding of the TV commercial?

 3.24 A survey by the U.S. government's Merit Systems Protection Board found that 69% of workers who knew firsthand of some example of government waste failed to report it. Approximately 23% of those who had reported a case of fraud said that they had suffered some type of reprisal, such as demotion or poor performance rating (*Orlando Sentinel,* January 20, 1985). Assume that the probability that a worker will fail to report a case of fraud is the same as the probability of failing to report waste; that is, it is .69. Find the probability that a worker who observes a case of fraud will report it and will subsequently suffer some form of reprisal.

 3.25 The results of a Robert Half International, Inc., survey, published in the *Wall Street Journal* (April 29, 1986), suggest that "executive smokers are the exception and not the rule." The survey of a large number of big corporations found that only 22% of top executives are smokers, but of the nonsmokers, 61% used to smoke. If you were to randomly select a top executive from a large corporation, what would the probability be that the executive has never smoked?

 3.26 Are men subject to sexual harassment on the job? According to a study conducted by the U.S. Merit Systems Protection Board, you had better believe it (*Fortune,* June 1, 1981). The report suggests that the probability that a male may be harassed on the job is approximately .15; and if harassed, the probability is approximately .72 that he was harassed by a woman. If you were to randomly select an employee who was surveyed by the U.S. Merit Systems Protection Board, what would the probability be that the employee is being harassed on the job by a woman?

DISCRETE RANDOM VARIABLES AND THEIR PROBABILITY DISTRIBUTIONS

3.4

Observations generated by an experiment are often numerical. For example, the daily production in a manufacturing plant is an experimental outcome that is a number. Similarly, the number of sales closed per day by a salesperson is a **numerical event**.

The numerical outcomes of experiments vary from one experiment to another and therefore represent observations on a variable, which we will denote by the symbol x. Each value of x represents an event and, therefore, a specific collection of simple events in the sample space. For this reason it is called a **random variable**.

DEFINITION   A variable x is a *random variable* if the values that x assumes, corresponding to the various outcomes of an experiment, are chance or random events.   ■

A random variable can be one of two types, discrete or continuous. If the number of values that the random variable can assume is countable, it is said to be a **discrete random variable**. If these values were plotted as points on a line, pairs of points would be separated. A **continuous random variable** is one that can assume any of the infinitely large number of points in a line interval.

DEFINITION   A *discrete random variable* is one that can assume a countable number of values.   ■

DEFINITION   A *continuous random variable* is one that can assume the infinitely large number of values corresponding to the points on a line interval.   ■

A discrete random variable is easily identified by examining the number of values it can assume. If the number of values that the random variable can assume can be counted, it must be discrete. Typical discrete random variables are the number of delinquent accounts at a department store, the number of bank deposits per day that exceed $10,000, and the number of new orders received by a manufacturing plant. In contrast, the waiting time for service at a supermarket, the amount of gasoline produced per day at a refinery, and the length of time until the next major power blackout are examples of continuous random variables.

The **probability distribution** $p(x)$ for a discrete random variable is a formula, table, or graph that provides the probability associated with each value of the random variable. These probabilities can be calculated by using the methods of Section 3.2. Since one and only one value of x is assigned to each simple event, the values of x represent mutually exclusive numerical events. Summing $p(x)$ over all values of x will equal the sum of the probabilities of all simple events and, thus, equal 1. We can therefore state two requirements for a probability distribution:

(1) $0 \leq p(x) \leq 1.$

(2) $\sum_{\text{all } x} p(x) = 1.$

DEFINITION

The *probability distribution* for a discrete random variable is a formula, table, or graph that provides the probability associated with each value of the random variable. ∎

EXAMPLE 3.8

Consider an experiment that consists of tossing two coins, and let x equal the number of heads observed. Find the probability distribution for x.

SOLUTION

The simple events for this experiment with the respective probabilities are as given in Table 3.9. Because simple event E_1 is "observe a head on coin 1 and a head on coin 2," we assign it the value $x = 2$. Similarly, we assign $x = 1$ to point E_2, and so on. The probability of each value of x can be calculated by adding the probabilities of the simple events in that numerical event. The numerical event $x = 0$ contains one simple event, E_4; $x = 1$ contains two simple events, E_2 and E_3; and $x = 2$ contains one simple event, E_1. The values of x with respective probabilities are given in Table 3.10. Observe that $\sum_{x=0}^{2} p(x) = 1$.

TABLE 3.9

Simple Events and Probabilities for Example 3.8

Simple Event	Coin 1	Coin 2	$P(E_i)$	x
E_1	H	H	1/4	2
E_2	H	T	1/4	1
E_3	T	H	1/4	1
E_4	T	T	1/4	0

TABLE 3.10

Probability Distribution for x (Number of Heads)

x	Simple Events in x	$p(x)$
0	E_4	1/4
1	E_2, E_3	1/2
2	E_1	1/4

$$\sum_{x=0}^{2} p(x) = 1$$

∎

The probability distribution in Table 3.10 can be presented graphically in the form of the relative frequency histogram that was discussed in Section 2.2.* The histogram for the random variable x contains three classes, corresponding to $x = 0$, $x = 1$, and $x = 2$. Since $p(0) = 1/4$, the theoretical relative frequency for $x = 0$ is 1/4; $p(1) = 1/2$ and hence the theoretical frequency for $x = 1$ is 1/2; and so on. The histogram is given in Figure 3.1.

---

*The probability distribution of Table 3.10 can also be presented by using a formula. This formula is given in Section 3.5.

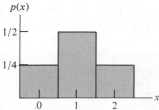

$p(x)$

FIGURE 3.1   Probability Histogram Showing $p(x)$ for Example 3.8

If you were to draw a sample from this population—that is, if you were to throw two balanced coins, say $n = 100$ times, and each time record the number of heads observed, x, and then construct a histogram by using the 100 measurements on x—you would find that the histogram for your sample would appear very similar to that for $p(x)$ in Figure 3.1. If you were to repeat the experiment $n = 1000$ times, the similarity would be much more pronounced.

The probability distribution provides a model for the theoretical frequency distribution of a random variable and therefore must possess a mean, variance, standard deviation, and other descriptive measures associated with the theoretical population that it represents. The method for calculating the population mean or expected value of a random variable can be more easily understood if you recall that both the mean and the variance are averages (Sections 2.5 and 2.6). For example, let x equal the number of heads observed in the toss of two coins. The probability distribution for x was given in Table 3.10 and is reproduced here:

x	$p(x)$
0	1/4
1	1/2
2	1/4

Suppose that this experiment is repeated a large number of times, say $n = 4$ million times. Intuitively, we will expect to observe approximately 1 million zeros, 2 million ones, and 1 million twos. Then the average value of x equals

$$\frac{\text{sum of measurements}}{n} = \frac{1{,}000{,}000(0) + 2{,}000{,}000(1) + 1{,}000{,}000(2)}{4{,}000{,}000}$$

$$= \frac{1{,}000{,}000(0)}{4{,}000{,}000} + \frac{2{,}000{,}000(1)}{4{,}000{,}000} + \frac{1{,}000{,}000(2)}{4{,}000{,}000}$$

$$= \left(\frac{1}{4}\right)(0) + \left(\frac{1}{2}\right)(1) + \left(\frac{1}{4}\right)(2)$$

Note that the first term in this sum is equal to $(0)p(0)$, the second is equal to $(1)p(1)$, and the third is equal to $(2)p(2)$. The average value of x is then equal to

$$\sum_{x=0}^{2} xp(x) = 1$$

You can see that this result is not an accident and that it will be intuitively reasonable to define the **expected value of** x for a discrete **random variable** as the sum of $xp(x)$.

DEFINITION

Let x be a discrete random variable with probability distribution $p(x)$, and let $E(x)$ represent the *expected value of* x. Then

$$E(x) = \sum_x xp(x)$$

where the elements are summed over all values of the random variable x. ∎

Note that if $p(x)$ is an accurate description of the relative frequencies for a real population of data, then $E(x) = \mu$, the mean of the population. We shall assume this to be true and let $E(x)$ be synonymous with μ. That is, we shall assume that

$$\mu = E(x)$$

EXAMPLE 3.9

Let x represent the number observed on the toss of a single die. Find the expected value of x.

SOLUTION

Since x can assume any one of the values $x = 1, 2, \ldots, 6$ with equal probability, we have

$$p(1) = p(2) = \cdots = p(6) = \frac{1}{6}$$

Then the expected value of x is

$$E(x) = \sum_{x=1}^{6} xp(x) = (1)p(1) + (2)p(2) + \cdots + (6)p(6)$$

$$= (1)\left(\frac{1}{6}\right) + (2)\left(\frac{1}{6}\right) + \cdots + (6)\left(\frac{1}{6}\right)$$

$$= \frac{1}{6} \sum_{x=1}^{6} x$$

$$= \frac{21}{6} = 3.5$$

Note that this value, $\mu = E(x) = 3.5$, exactly locates the center of the probability distribution, which is shown in Figure 3.2.

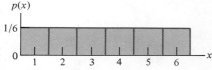

FIGURE 3.2   Probability Histogram for $p(x) = 1/6$ in Example 3.9 ∎

EXAMPLE 3.10   Eight thousand tickets are to be sold at $5.00 each in a lottery conducted to benefit the local fire company. The prize is a $12,000.00 automobile. If you purchase two tickets, what is your expected gain?

SOLUTION   Your gain, x, can take one of two values. Either you will lose $10.00 (i.e., your gain will be $-$10.00) or will win $11,990.00, with probabilities 7998/8000 and 2/8000, respectively. The probability distribution for the gain, x, is as follows:

x	$p(x)$
$-$10.00	$\dfrac{7998}{8000}$
$11,990.00	$\dfrac{2}{8000}$

The expected gain is

$$E(x) = \sum_x xp(x)$$

$$= (-\$10.00)\left(\frac{7998}{8000}\right) + (\$11,990.00)\left(\frac{2}{8000}\right)$$

$$= -\$7.00$$

Recall that the expected value of x is the average of the theoretical population that would result if the lottery were repeated an infinitely large number of times. If it were, your average or expected gain per lottery would be a loss of $7.00. ■

EXAMPLE 3.11   Determine the yearly premium for a $1000.00 insurance policy covering an event that, over a long period of time, has occurred at the rate of 2 times in 100. Let x equal the yearly financial gain to the insurance company resulting from the sale of the policy, and let C equal the unknown yearly premium. We will calculate the value of C such that the expected gain, $E(x)$, will equal zero. Then C is the premium required to break even. To this figure the company will add administrative costs and profit.

SOLUTION   The first step in the solution is to determine the values that the gain x can take and then to determine $p(x)$. If the event does not occur during the year, the insurance company will gain the premium of $x = C$ dollars. If the event does occur, the gain will be negative. That is, the company will lose $1000 less the premium of C dollars already collected. Then $x = -(1000 - C)$ dollars. The probabilities associated with these two values of x are 98/100 and 2/100, respectively. The probability distribution for the gain is as follows:

x = gain	$p(x)$
C	$\dfrac{98}{100}$
$-(1,000 - C)$	$\dfrac{2}{100}$

Since we want the insurance premium C such that, in the long run (for many similar policies), the mean gain will equal 0, we will set the expected value of x equal to zero and solve for C. Then

$$E(x) = \sum_x xp(x)$$

$$= C\left(\frac{98}{100}\right) + [-(1000 - C)]\left(\frac{2}{100}\right) = 0$$

or

$$\frac{98}{100}C + \left(\frac{2}{100}\right)C - 20 = 0$$

Solving this equation for C, we obtain

$$C = \$20$$

Thus if the insurance company were to charge a yearly premium of $20, the average gain calculated for a large number of similar policies would equal zero. The actual premium would equal $20 plus administrative costs and profit. ▪

Recall that in Section 2.6 the variance σ^2 of a population was defined to be the average of the square of the deviations of the x values about their mean μ. Therefore, we define the variance of a random variable to be the expected value of $(x - \mu)^2$.

DEFINITION

The *variance* σ^2 of a random variable x is the expected value of $(x - \mu)^2$; that is,*

$$\sigma^2 = E[(x - \mu)^2] = \sum_x (x - \mu)^2 p(x)$$ ▪

We conclude this section with two examples.

EXAMPLE 3.12

The expected value of x, μ was shown to equal 1. Find the variance σ^2 for the number x of heads in two tosses of a coin.

SOLUTION

The variance is equal to the expected value of $(x - \mu)^2$, or

$$\sigma^2 = E[(x - \mu)^2] = \sum_x (x - \mu)^2 p(x)$$

$$= (0 - 1)^2 p(0) + (1 - 1)^2 p(1) + (2 - 1)^2 p(2)$$

$$= 1\left(\frac{1}{4}\right) + 0\left(\frac{1}{2}\right) + 1\left(\frac{1}{4}\right)$$

$$= \frac{1}{2}$$

---

*We can show (proof omitted) that

$$\sigma^2 = \sum_x (x - \mu)^2 p(x) = \sum_x x^2 p(x) - \mu^2 = E(x^2) - \mu^2$$

This result is analogous to the shortcut formula for the sum of squares of deviations given in Chapter 2.

TABLE 3.11   Computations for Calculating σ^2

x	$(x - \mu)^2$	$p(x)$	$(x - \mu)^2 p(x)$
0	1	1/4	1/4
1	0	1/2	0
2	1	1/4	1/4
			1/2

Calculating σ^2 can be facilitated by using Table 3.11. Recall that $\mu = 1$. Then $(x - \mu)^2$ is as shown in the second column of Table 3.11, and σ^2 is the total of column 4.   ∎

EXAMPLE 3.13   Let x be a random variable with probability distribution given by the following table:

x	$p(x)$
-1	.05
0	.10
1	.40
2	.20
3	.10
4	.10
5	.05

Find μ, σ^2, and σ. Graph $p(x)$, and locate the interval $(\mu \pm 2\sigma)$ on the graph. What is the probability that x will fall in the interval $(\mu \pm 2\sigma)$?

SOLUTION

$$\mu = E(x) = \sum_{x=-1}^{5} xp(x)$$

$$= (-1)(.05) + (0)(.10) + (1)(.40) + \cdots + (4)(.10) + (5)(.05)$$

$$= 1.70$$

$$\sigma^2 = E[(x - \mu)^2] = \sum_{x=-1}^{5} (x - \mu)^2 p(x)$$

$$= (-1 - 1.7)^2(.05) + (0 - 1.7)^2(.10) + \cdots + (5 - 1.7)^2(.05)$$

$$= 2.11$$

and

$$\sigma = \sqrt{\sigma^2}$$

$$= \sqrt{2.11}$$

$$= 1.45$$

The interval $(\mu \pm 2\sigma)$ is $[1.70 \pm (2)(1.45)]$, or -1.20 to 4.60.

c hello

I

The graph of $p(x)$ and the interval $\mu \pm 2\sigma$ are shown in Figure 3.3. You can see that $x = -1, 0, 1, 2, 3, 4$ fall in the interval. Therefore,

$$P[\mu - 2\sigma < x < \mu + 2\sigma] = p(-1) + p(0) + p(1) + \cdots + p(4)$$
$$= (.05) + (.10) + (.40) + (.20) + (.10) + (.10)$$

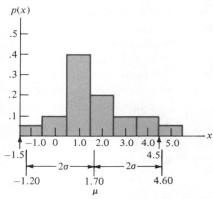

FIGURE 3.3   The Probability Histogram for $p(x)$ for Example 3.13

TIPS ON PROBLEM SOLVING

To find the expected value of a discrete random variable x, construct a table containing three columns, the first for x and the second for $p(x)$. Then multiply each x value by its corresponding probability and enter the results in the third column. The sum of this third column, the sum of $xp(x)$, will give you the expected value of x.

To find σ^2 for a discrete random variable x, start with a table containing four columns, the first for x, the second for $(x - \mu)^2$, the third for $p(x)$, and the fourth for the cross products, $(x - \mu)^2 p(x)$. First, calculate the value of $(x - \mu)^2$ for each value of x, and enter the results in column 2. Then obtain the cross product $(x - \mu)^2 p(x)$ for each value of x, and enter the results in column 4. The sum of column 4 will give you the value of σ^2.

EXERCISES

BASIC TECHNIQUES

3.27   Identify the following as discrete or continuous random variables.
   (a) The appraised value of a house, in dollars.
   (b) The length of time until the fan belt of a car needs replacement.
   (c) The number of miles traveled by a salesperson in a given month.
   (d) The number of accounts held by a bank at a point in time.
   (e) The length of time a customer must wait at a bank's cashier counter.

3.28 Identify the following as discrete or continuous random variables.

(a) The number of new clients acquired by a law firm in a month.

(b) The shelf life of a particular drug.

(c) The weight of a railway carload of wheat.

(d) The velocity of a pitched baseball.

(e) The number of fatal accidents at a manufacturing facility in a year.

3.29 Identify the following as discrete or continuous random variables.

(a) The number of bank failures in a given year.

(b) The floor space area in a new office building.

(c) The number of people waiting for treatment at a hospital emergency room.

(d) The total points scored in a football game.

(e) The number of claims received by an insurance company during a day.

3.30 A random variable x possesses the following probability distribution:

x	0	1	2	3	4	5
$p(x)$	.1	.3	.4	.1	?	.05

(a) Find $p(4)$.

(b) Construct a probability histogram to describe $p(x)$.

3.31 A random variable x can assume five values, 0, 1, 2, 3, and 4. A portion of the probability distribution follows.

x	0	1	2	3	4
$p(x)$	.1	.3	.3	?	.1

(a) Find $p(3)$.

(b) Construct a probability histogram for $p(x)$.

(c) Simulate the experiment by marking ten poker chips (or coins), one with a 0, three with a 1, three with a 2, and so on. Mix the chips thoroughly, draw one, and record the observed value of x. Repeat the process 100 times. Construct a relative frequency histogram for the 100 values of x, and compare your result with the probability histogram in part (b).

3.32 A jar contains two black and two white balls. Suppose the balls are thoroughly mixed, and then two are selected from the jar.

(a) List all simple events for this experiment, and assign appropriate probabilities to each.

(b) Let x equal the number of white balls in the selection. Then assign the appropriate value of x to each simple event.

(c) Calculate the values of $p(x)$ and display them in tabular form. Show that $\sum_{x=0}^{2} p(x) = 1$.

(d) Construct a probability histogram for $p(x)$.

(e) Simulate the experiment by actually drawing two balls (coins, etc.) from a jar that contains two "black" and two "white" balls. Repeat the drawing process 100 times, each time recording the value of x that was observed. Construct a relative frequency histogram for the 100 observed values of x, and compare your result with the probability histogram in part (d).

3.33 Let x be a discrete random variable with the probability distribution given in the following table:

x	0	1	2	3	4	5
$p(x)$	.05	.1	.2	4	.2	.05

(a) Find μ, σ^2, and σ.
(b) Construct a probability histogram for $p(x)$.
(c) Locate the interval $(\mu \pm 2\sigma)$ on the x axis of the histogram. What is the probability that x will fall in this interval?
(d) If you were to select a very large number of values of x from the population, would most fall in the interval $\mu \pm 2\sigma$? Explain.

3.34 Let x be a discrete random variable with the probability distribution given in the following table:

x	1	2	3	4	5	6	7
$p(x)$	.05	.2	.35	.2	.1	.05	.05

(a) Find μ, σ^2, and σ.
(b) Construct a probability histogram for $p(x)$.
(c) Locate the interval $(\mu \pm 2\sigma)$ on the x axis of the histogram. What is the probability that x will fall in this interval?
(d) If you were to select a very large number of values of x from the population, would most fall in the interval, $\mu \pm 2\sigma$? Explain.

3.35 Let x be the number observed when a single die is tossed. In Example 3.9 we found that the mean value of x is $\mu = 3.5$.
(a) Find the variance of x.
(b) Find σ.
(c) What is the probability that the number observed in a single toss of a die falls in the interval $(\mu \pm 2\sigma)$?
(d) The probability distribution for the number x observed in the toss of a single die is not mound-shaped—that is, $p(x) = 1/6$. Despite this fact, how does your answer to part (c) agree with the Empirical Rule?

3.36 The probability distribution for a discrete random variable x is as shown in the following table:

x	0	1	2	3	4	5
$p(x)$	.05	.3	.3	.2	.1	.05

(a) Find $E(x)$.
(b) Find σ^2.
(c) Sketch $p(x)$ and locate the interval $(\mu \pm 2\sigma)$ on the graph.
(d) Find the probability that x falls in the interval $(\mu \pm 2\sigma)$.

APPLICATIONS

 3.37 A \$50,000 diamond is insured to its total value by paying a premium of D dollars. If the probability of theft in a given year is estimated to be .01, what premium should the insurance company charge if it wishes the expected gain to equal \$1000?

 3.38 The maximum patent life for a new drug is 17 years. Subtracting the length of time required for testing and approval of the drug by the Food and Drug Administration, you obtain the actual patent life of the drug—that is, the length of time that a company has to recover research and development costs and make a profit. Suppose that the distribution of the length of patent life for new drugs is as shown in the following table:

Years, x	3	4	5	6	7	8	9	10	11	12	13
$p(x)$	.03	.05	.07	.10	.14	.20	.18	.12	.07	.03	.01

(a) Find the expected number of years of patent life for a new drug.
(b) Find the standard deviation of x.
(c) Find the probability that x falls in the interval ($\mu \pm 2\sigma$).

 3.39 A manufacturing representative is considering the option of taking out an insurance policy to cover possible losses incurred by marketing a new product. If the product is a complete failure, the representative feels that a loss of \$80,000 would be incurred; if it is only moderately successful, a loss of \$25,000 would be incurred. Insurance actuaries have determined from market surveys and other available information that the probabilities that the product will be a failure or only moderately successful are .01 and .05, respectively. Assuming that the manufacturing representative would be willing to ignore all other possible losses, what premium should the insurance company charge for the policy in order to break even?

 3.40 A manufacturing company ships its product in two different sizes of truck trailers, an 8 × 10 × 30 and an 8 × 10 × 40. If 30% of its shipments are made by using the 30-foot trailer and 70% by using the 40-foot trailer, find the mean volume shipped per trailerload (assume that the trailers are always full).

 3.41 The number N of residential homes that a fire company can serve depends on the distance r (in city blocks) that a fire engine can cover in a specified (fixed) period of time. If we assume that N is proportional to the area of a circle r blocks from the firehouse, then

$$N = C\pi r^2$$

where C is a constant, $\pi = 3.1416\ldots$, and r, a random variable, is the number of blocks that a fire engine can move in the specified time interval. For a particular fire company, $C = 8$, the probability distribution for r is as shown in the accompanying table, and $p(r) = 0$ for $r \le 20$ and $r \ge 27$. Find the expected value of N, the number of homes that the fire department can serve.

r	21	22	23	24	25	26
$p(r)$	.05	.20	.30	.25	.15	.05

THE BINOMIAL PROBABILITY DISTRIBUTION

3.5 In a sense, the coin-tossing experiment described in Example 3.8 occurs very often in business. The only difference is that the probability of observing a head is not 1/2.

Consider a market survey conducted to predict product preferences. Interviewing a single consumer bears a similarity, in many respects, to tossing a single coin, because the consumer may be in favor of a particular product—a head—or the consumer may not be in favor of the product (or may indicate indecision)—a tail. In most cases the fraction of consumers favoring a particular product will not equal 1/2.

Similar polls are conducted in the social sciences, in industry, and in education. The sociologist is interested in the fraction of rural homes that have electricity; the cigarette manufacturer wants to know the fraction of smokers who prefer its brand; the teacher is interested in the fraction of students who pass his course. Each person sampled is analogous to the toss of an unbalanced (since the probability of a head is usually not 1/2) coin. Although dissimilar in some respects, the experiments described here will often exhibit, to a reasonable degree of approximation, the characteristics of a **binomial experiment**.

DEFINITION A *binomial experiment* is one that possesses the following properties:

(1) The experiment consists of n identical trials.

(2) Each trial results in one of two outcomes. For lack of a better nomenclature, we will call the one outcome a success, S, and the other a failure, F.*

(3) The probability of success on a single trial is equal to p and remains the same from trial to trial. The probability of a failure is equal to $(1 - p) = q$.

(4) The trials are independent.

(5) We are interested in x, the number of successes observed during the n trials. ■

EXAMPLE 3.14 Suppose that there are approximately 1 million adults in a certain sales region who are potential buyers for a new product and that an unknown proportion p would purchase the product if offered for sale and $(1 - p)$ would not. A random sample of 1000 adults will be selected from among the 1 million in the sales region, and each adult in the sample will be asked whether he or she would purchase the product if offered for sale. (The ultimate objective of this survey is to estimate the unknown proportion p, a problem that we will learn how to solve in Chapter 6.) Is this a binomial experiment?

SOLUTION To decide whether this is a binomial experiment, we must see if the sampling satisfies the five characteristics described in the definition.

(1) The sampling consists of $n = 1000$ identical trials. One trial represents the selection of a single adult from the 1 million adults in the sales region.

---

*Although it is traditional to call the two possible outcomes of a trial "success" and "failure," they could have been called "head" and "tail," "red" and "white," or any other pair of words. Consequently, the outcome called a success need not be viewed as a success in the ordinary usage of the word.

(2) Each trial will result in one of two outcomes. A person will either state that she would buy the new product or that she would not. These two outcomes could be associated with the "success" and "failure" of a binomial experiment.

(3) The probability of a success will equal the proportion of the 1 million adults who would buy the new product. For example, if 500,000 of the 1 million adults in the region would buy the product, then the probability that the first adult selected would buy the product is $p = .5$. The probability that the second adult selected would buy the product is either 499,999/999,999 or 500,000/999,999, depending on whether the first person would or would not buy the product. In either case the probability is so close to .5 that the slight difference can be ignored. Thus, for all practical purposes, the probability will remain the same from trial to trial even though adults selected in the earlier trials are not replaced as the sampling continues.

(4) For all practical purposes, the probability of a success on any one trial will be unaffected by the outcome on any of the others (it will remain very close to p).

(5) We are interested in the number x of adults in the sample of 1000 who would buy the product.

Because the survey satisfies the five characteristics reasonably well, for all practical purposes, it (like many other opinion polls) can be viewed as a binomial experiment.

■

EXAMPLE 3.15   A purchaser, who has received a boxcar containing 20 large electronic computers, wishes to sample 3 of the computers to see whether they are in working order before he unloads the shipment. The 3 nearest the door of the boxcar are removed for testing and, afterward, are declared either defective or nondefective. Unknown to the purchaser, 2 of the computers are defective. Is this a binomial experiment?

SOLUTION   As for Example 3.14, we check the sampling procedure against the characteristics of a binomial experiment.

(1) The experiment consists of $n = 3$ identical trials. Each trial represents the selection and testing of one computer from the total of 20.

(2) Each trial results in one of two outcomes. Either a computer is defective (call this a "success") or it is not (a "failure").

(3) Suppose that the computers were randomly loaded into the boxcar so that any one of the 20 computers could been placed near the boxcar door. Then the unconditional probability of drawing a defective computer on a given trial will be 2/20.

(4) The condition of independence between trials is *not* satisfied because the probability of drawing a defective computer on the second and third trials will be dependent on the outcome of the first trial. For example, if the first trial results in a defective computer, then there is only one defective left of the remaining 19 in the boxcar. Therefore, the conditional probability of success on trial 2, given a

success on trial 1, is 1/19. This result differs from the unconditional probability of a success on the second trial (which is 2/20). Therefore, the trials are dependent and the sampling does not represent a binomial experiment.

This example illustrates a point. If the sample size n is large relative to the number N of observations in the population, then the sampling will violate the assumption that the probability p of success remains the same from trial to trial. The outcomes of trials will be dependent events and will violate the assumptions of a binomial experiment. ■

The probability distribution for a simple binomial random variable, the number of heads in the tosses of two coins, was derived in Section 3.4. The probability distribution for a binomial experiment consisting of n tosses is derived in exactly the same way, but the procedure is much more complex when the number n of trials is large. We will omit this tedious derivation and will simply present the **binomial probability distribution** and its mean, variance, and standard deviation. The formulas are shown in the following box.

THE BINOMIAL PROBABILITY DISTRIBUTION

$$p(x) = \frac{n!}{x!(n - x)!} p^x q^{n-x}, \qquad x = 0, 1, 2, 3, \ldots, n$$

$$= C_x^n p^x q^{n-x}$$

where

n = number of trials

p = probability of success on a single trial

$q = 1 - p$

and C_x^n is a symbol used to represent

$$\frac{n!}{x!(n - x)!}$$

Mean: $\qquad \mu = np$

Variance: $\qquad \sigma^2 = npq$

Standard Deviation: $\qquad \sigma = \sqrt{npq}$

The factorial notation $n!$ is used to represent the product $n(n - 1)(n - 2) \cdots (3)(2)(1)$. For example, $5! = (5)(4)(3)(2)(1) = 120$, and $0!$ is defined to be equal to 1. The notation C_x^n is shorthand for $n!/x!(n - x)!$, an expression that appears in the formula for the binomial probability distribution.

Graphs of three binomial probability distributions are shown in Figure 3.4: the first for $n = 10, p = .1$; the second for $n = 10, p = .5$; and the third for $n = 20, p = .5$.

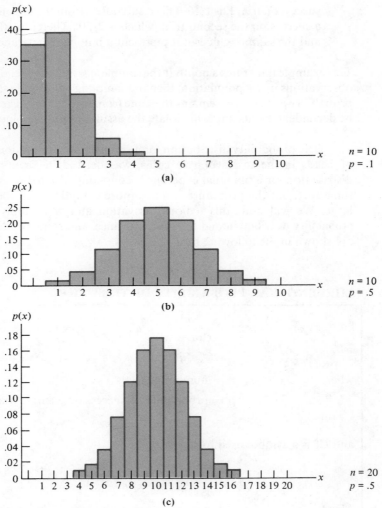

FIGURE 3.4   Binomial Probability Distributions

EXAMPLE 3.16   Observations over a long period of time have shown that a particular salesperson can make a sale on a single contact with probability equal to .2. Suppose the salesperson contacts four prospects.

(a) What is the probability that exactly two prospects purchase the product?

(b) What is the probability that at least two prospects purchase the product?

(c) What is the probability that all of the prospects purchase the product?

SOLUTION   (a) Define the random variable x to be the number of the four prospects contacted who will purchase the product. Assuming that the outcome of any one sales contact is independent of the outcome of any other and that p remains constant from sales contact to sales contact, then x is a binomial random variable with $n = 4$, $p = .2$, and

$$p(x) = C_x^4(.2)^x(.8)^{4-x}$$

$$p(2) = C_2^4(.2)^2(.8)^{4-2}$$

$$= \frac{4!}{2!2!}(.04)(.64) = \frac{4(3)(2)(1)}{2(1)(2)(1)}(.04)(.64)$$

$$= .1536$$

(b)
$$P(\text{at least two}) = p(2) + p(3) + p(4)$$

$$= 1 - p(0) - p(1)$$

$$= 1 - C_0^4(.2)^0(.8)^4 - C_1^4(.2)(.8)^3$$

$$= 1 - .4096 - .4096$$

$$= .1808$$

(c)
$$p(4) = C_4^4(.2)^4(.8)^0$$

$$= \frac{4!}{4!0!}(.2)^4(1) = .0016$$ ∎

EXAMPLE 3.17

Large lots of incoming products at a manufacturing plant are inspected for defectives by means of a *sampling plan*. A random sample of n items is selected from each lot and inspected, and the number x of defectives in the sample is recorded. If x is less than or equal to some specified *acceptance number a*, the lot is accepted. If x is larger than a, the lot is rejected. Suppose that a manufacturer employs a sampling plan with $n = 10$ and $a = 1$. If a lot contains exactly 5% defectives, what is the probability that the lot will be accepted? Rejected?

SOLUTION

Since the lot contains 5% defectives, the probability that an item drawn from the lot is defective is $p = .05$. Then the probability of observing x defectives in a sample of $n = 10$ items is

$$p(x) = C_x^{10}(.05)^x(.95)^{10-x}$$

The probability of accepting the lot is the probability that x is less than or equal to the acceptance number $a = 1$. Therefore,

$$P(\text{accept}) = p(0) + p(1) = C_0^{10}(.05)^0(.95)^{10} + C_1^{10}(.05)^1(.95)^9$$

$$= .914$$

$$P(\text{reject}) = 1 - P(\text{accept})$$

$$= 1 - .914$$

$$= .086$$

Although in a practical situation we would not know the exact value of p, we would want to know the probability of accepting bad lots (lots for which p is large) and good lots (lots for which p is small). This example shows how we can calculate this probability of acceptance for various values of p.   ∎

EXAMPLE 3.18   A graph of the probability of lot acceptance versus the lot fraction defective p is called the **operating characteristic curve** for a lot acceptance sampling plan. Calculate the probability of lot acceptance for a sampling plan with sample size $n = 5$ and acceptance number $a = 0$ for lot fraction defective $p = .1, .3,$ and $.5$. Sketch the operating characteristic curve for the plan.

SOLUTION

$$P(\text{accept}) = p(0) = C_0^5 p^0 q^5 = q^5$$
$$P(\text{accept} \mid p = .1) = (.9)^5 = .590$$
$$P(\text{accept} \mid p = .3) = (.7)^5 = .168$$
$$P(\text{accept} \mid p = .5) = (.5)^5 = .031$$

A sketch of the operating characteristic curve can be obtained by plotting the three points obtained from the calculations. In addition, we know that the probability of acceptance must equal 1 when $p = 0$ and must equal 0 when $p = 1$. The operating characteristic curve is given in Figure 3.5.

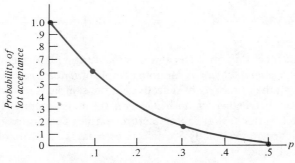

FIGURE 3.5   Operating Characteristic Curve for $n = 5, a = 0$

Note that acceptance sampling is an example of statistical inference because the procedure implies a decision concerning the lot fraction defective p. If you accept a lot, you infer that the true lot fraction defective p is some relatively small, acceptable value. If you reject a lot, it is clear that you think p is too large. Consequently, lot acceptance sampling is a procedure that implies inference making concerning the lot fraction defective. The operating characteristic curve for the sampling plan provides a measure of the goodness of this inferential procedure.

Calculating the binomial probabilities is a tedious task when n is large. To simplify the calculations, we present the sum of the binomial probabilities from $x = 0$ to $x = a$ in Table 1 of the Appendix, for sample sizes $n = 5, 10, 15, 20,$ and 25. To see how you use Table 1, suppose that you wish to find the sum of the binomial probabilities from $x = 0$ to $x = 3$ for $n = 5$ trials and $p = .6$. That is, you wish to find

$$\sum_{x=0}^{3} p(x) = p(0) + p(1) + p(2) + p(3)$$

where

$$p(x) = C_x^5(.6)^x(.4)^{5-x}$$

Turn to Table 1(a) in the Appendix for $n = 5$. Since the tabulated values in the table give

$$\sum_{x=0}^{a} p(x)$$

you seek the tabulated value in the row corresponding to $a = 3$ and the column for $p = .6$. The tabulated value, .663, is shown in Table 3.12 as it appears in Table 1(a). Thus $\sum_{x=0}^{3} p(x)$, the sum of the binomial probabilities from $x = 0$ to $a = 3$ (for $n = 5$, $p = .6$), is .663.

TABLE 3.12   Format of Table 1(a) in the Appendix

| | | | | | | | p | | | | | | | |
a	0.01	0.05	0.10	0.20	0.30	0.40	0.50	0.60	0.70	0.80	0.90	0.95	0.99	a
0	—	—	—	—	—	—	—	—	—	—	—	—	—	0
1	—	—	—	—	—	—	—	—	—	—	—	—	—	1
2	—	—	—	—	—	—	—	.317	—	—	—	—	—	2
3	—	—	—	—	—	—	—	.663	—	—	—	—	—	3
4	—	—	—	—	—	—	—	—	—	—	—	—	—	4

Table 1 in the Appendix can also be used to find an individual binomial probability, say $p(3)$ for $n = 5$, $p = .6$. We calculate

$$p(3) = [p(0) + p(1) + p(2) + p(3)] - [p(0) + p(1) + p(2)]$$

$$= \sum_{x=0}^{3} p(x) - \sum_{x=0}^{2} p(x)$$

$$= .663 - .317$$

$$= .346$$

Thus an individual value of $p(x)$ is equal to the difference between two sums which are adjacent entries given in a column of the table.

EXAMPLE 3.19   Find the mean and standard deviation for the binomial probability distribution in Figure 3.4(a). Find the probability that x falls in the interval $(\mu \pm 2\sigma)$.

SOLUTION   The probability distribution in Figure 3.4(a) corresponds to a binomial experiment with $n = 10$ and $p = .1$. Therefore, the mean and standard deviation for the probability distribution are

$$\mu = np = (10)(.1) = 1$$
$$\sigma = \sqrt{npq} = \sqrt{(10)(.1)(.9)} = .95$$

You can see that $\mu = 1$ falls near the center of the probability histogram and that the interval

$$\mu \pm 2\sigma = 1 \pm 2(.95) = 1 \pm 1.90$$

or

$$-.9 \text{ to } 2.90$$

includes $x = 0, 1,$ and 2. Therefore, the probability that x falls in the interval $(\mu \pm 2\sigma)$ is

$$p(0) + p(1) + p(2) = \sum_{x=0}^{2} p(x)$$

This probability is given in Table 1(b) for $n = 10, p = .1, a = 2$ as .930.

If we view the probability distribution of Figure 3.4(a) as the relative frequency distribution for a theoretical population of x values, then 93% of all observations in the population would fall in the interval $(\mu \pm 2\sigma)$. This result agrees with Tchebysheff's Theorem and agrees reasonably well with the Empirical Rule. ■

EXAMPLE 3.20

Suppose that you are the personnel director of a company and that you wish to evaluate scores on a multiple-choice aptitude test. A score of 0 on an objective test (questions requiring complete recall of the material) indicates that the person was unable to recall the test material at the time the test was given. In contrast, a person with little or no recall knowledge of the test material can score higher on a multiple-choice test because the person only needs to recognize (in contrast to recall) the correct answer and because some questions will be answered correctly, just by chance, even if the person does not know the correct answers. Consequently, the no-knowledge score for a multiple-choice test may be well above 0. If a multiple-choice test contains 100 questions, each with six possible answers, what is the expected score for a person who possesses no knowledge of the test material? Within what limits would you expect a no-knowledge score to be?

SOLUTION

Let p equal the probability of a correct choice on a single question and let x equal the number of correct responses out of the $n = 100$ questions. We will assume that no knowledge means that a person will randomly select one of the six possible answers for each question, so that $p = 1/6$. Then for $n = 100$ questions, a no-knowledge student's expected score is $E(x)$, where

$$E(x) = np = 100\left(\frac{1}{6}\right) = 16.7 \text{ correct questions}$$

To evaluate the variation of no-knowledge scores, we need to know σ, where

$$\sigma = \sqrt{npq} = \sqrt{(100)\left(\frac{1}{6}\right)\left(\frac{5}{6}\right)} = 3.7$$

Then from our knowledge of Tchebysheff's Theorem and the Empirical Rule,* we would expect most no-knowledge scores to lie in the interval $(\mu \pm 2\sigma)$, or $[16.7 \pm (2)(3.7)]$, or from 9.3 to 24.1. This result compares with a score of 0 for a no-knowledge person taking an objective recall test. ■

*A histogram of $p(x)$ for $n = 100, p = 1/6$ will be mound-shaped. Hence, we would expect the Empirical Rule to work very well. The reason that it does will be explained in Chapter 5.

EXERCISES

BASIC TECHNIQUES

3.42 A jar contains 5 balls—3 red and 2 white. Two balls are randomly selected without replacement from the jar and the number x of red balls is recorded. Explain why x is or is not a binomial random variable. (*Hint:* Compare the characteristics of this experiment with the characteristics of a binomial experiment given in Section 3.5.) If the experiment is binomial, give the values of n and p.

3.43 Answer Exercise 3.42 by assuming that the sampling was conducted with replacement. That is, the first ball was selected from the jar and observed. It was then replaced and the balls were mixed before the second ball was selected.

3.44 Find the following.

(a) $3!$ (b) $5!$ (c) C_4^6

(d) C_3^8 (e) C_2^{10} (f) C_6^6

(g) C_0^6 (h) C_1^9 (i) C_0^9

3.45 Calculate the value of $p(x)$ and construct a probability histogram for the following.

(a) $n = 5, p = .2$ (b) $n = 5, p = .5$ (c) $n = 5, p = .8$

3.46 Calculate $p(x)$ for $x = 0, 1, 2, \ldots, 5, 6$ for $n = 6$ and $p = .1$. Graph $p(x)$. Repeat these instructions for binomial probability distributions for $p = .5$ and $p = .9$. Compare the graphs. How does the value of p affect the shape of $p(x)$? (*Note:* This exercise does not require extensive calculations. For example, you need calculate the coefficients C_x^n only once because they will be the same for all three probability distributions.)

3.47 Use Table 1 in the Appendix to find the sum of the binomial probabilities from $x = 0$ to $x = a$ for the following.

(a) $n = 10, p = .1, a = 3$

(b) $n = 15, p = .6, a = 7$

(c) $n = 25, p = .5, a = 14$

3.48 Use the formula for the binomial probability distribution to calculate the values of $p(x)$ for $n = 5, p = .5$ (this calculation was done in Exercise 3.45). Next find $\sum_{y=0}^{a} p(x)$ for $a = 0, 1, 2, 3, 4,$ using the values of $p(x)$ that you computed. Then compare these sums with the values given in Table 1 in the Appendix.

3.49 Use the information given in Table 1 in the Appendix to find $p(3)$ for $n = 5, p = .5$. Then compare this answer with the value of $p(3)$ calculated in Exercise 3.48.

3.50 Use the information given in Table 1 in the Appendix to find $p(3) + p(4)$ for $n = 5, p = .5$. Verify this answer by using the values of $p(x)$ that you calculated in Exercises 3.48.

3.51 Use Table 1 in the Appendix to calculate the values of $p(x)$ for the following.

(a) $n = 5, p = .2$ (b) $n = 5, p = .8$

Compare these values of $p(x)$ with the values of $p(x)$ that you calculated by formula in Exercise 3.45.

3.52 Find $\sum_{x=0}^{a} p(x)$ for the following.

(a) $n = 20, p = .05, a = 2$

(b) $n = 15, p = .7, a = 8$

(c) $n = 10, p = .9, a = 9$

3.53 Use Table 1 in the Appendix to find the following.

(a) $P(x < 12)$ for $n = 20, p = .5$ (b) $P(x \le 6)$ for $n = 15, p = .4$

(c) $P(x > 4)$ for $n = 10, p = .4$ (d) $P(x \ge 6)$ for $n = 15, p = .6$

(e) $P(3 < x < 7)$ for $n = 10, p = .5$

3.54 Find the mean and standard deviation for the following binomial distributions.

(a) $n = 1000, p = .3$ (b) $n = 400, p = .01$

(c) $n = 500, p = .5$ (d) $n = 1600, p = .8$

3.55 Find the mean and standard deviation for a binomial distribution with $n = 100$ and the following values of p.

(a) $p = .01$ (b) $p = .9$ (c) $p = .3$ (d) $p = .7$ (e) $p = .5$

3.56 Use the values of μ and σ calculated in Exercise 3.55 to make rough sketches of the five distributions. In each case, locate the distribution over an x axis marked from 0 to 100. How does the distribution in part (a) differ from those in parts (b), (c), and (d)?

3.57 In Exercise 3.55 we calculated the mean and standard deviation for a binomial random variable for a fixed sample size, $n = 100$, and for different values of p. Graph the values of the standard deviation for the five values of p given in Exercise 3.55. For what value of p does the standard deviation seem to be a maximum?

3.58 Use Table 1 in the Appendix to find the following.

(a) $P(x \le 5)$ for $n = 10, p = .4$ (b) $P(x < 3)$ for $n = 5, p = .6$

(c) $P(x \le 17)$ for $n = 20, p = .7$ (d) $P(x > 17)$ for $n = 20, p = .7$

(e) $P(x < 6)$ for $n = 15, p = .4$

3.59 Use Table 1 in the Appendix to find the following.

(a) $P(x \le 1)$ for $n = 5, p = .2$ (b) $P(x > 1)$ for $n = 5, p = .2$

(c) $P(x < 1)$ for $n = 5, p = .2$ (d) $P(x = 1)$ for $n = 5, p = .2$

(e) $P(x = 1)$ for $n = 10, p = .2$

3.60 Use Table 1 in the Appendix to find the following.

(a) $P(x \le 4)$ for $n = 10, p = .5$ (b) $P(x < 4)$ for $n = 10, p = .5$

(c) $P(x > 4)$ for $n = 10, p = .5$ (d) $P(x = 4)$ for $n = 10, p = .5$

APPLICATIONS

3.61 The *Wall Street Journal* (August 20, 1985) reports that many firms are tightening résumé checks of job applicants. The need for this action is supported by a survey of 501 business executives by Ward Howell International, Inc., an executive search firm. According to the *Journal,* the survey showed that 17% of the executives said their new hires misrepresented their job qualifications. Explain why this sampling is or is not a binomial experiment.

3.62 In Exercise 1.4 we described a survey of 38 senior business executives by the Conference Board. Each of the business executives gave an estimate of the average annual U.S. inflation rate over the next five years. The average of the 38 estimates was 5.9%. Explain why this sampling does or does not represent a binomial experiment.

3.63 Ralph Nader's Health Research Group has petitioned the Occupational Safety and Health Administration to reduce the maximum allowable exposure to ethylene oxide from 50 parts per million parts of air to 1 part per million per 8 hours of exposure (*Washington Post,* August 14, 1981). Ethylene oxide is a gas used as a pesticide and fumigant, and it is used in the manufacture of some cosmetics and chemicals. Let x represent the number of parts of ethylene oxide in 1 million parts of air. Explain why x is or is not a binomial random variable.

3.64 Writing on investor psychology, Srully Blotnick notes that most individual investors in the stock market hold their losing stocks, hoping eventually to make a profit ("What to Do with Losses," *Forbes*, August 11, 1986). Specifically, he states that for every investor who has recovered a "paper loss" and then sells, 6 others continue to hold the stock, hoping for an eventual profit. (A stockholder suffers a "paper loss" if the price of the stock drops below its purchase price. The stockholder does not sustain a real loss unless he or she actually sells the stock.) Suppose you were to randomly sample 4 individual investors in the stock market, and let x be the number of investors who sell losing stocks once they have recovered their paper losses.

(a) What is the probability that x is exactly equal to 4?
(b) What is the probability that x is 1 or larger?
(c) What is the probability that x is exactly equal to 1?

3.65 In Exercise 1.3 we noted that a recent 14-city federal study found that in approximately 50% of a large sample of cars and light trucks manufactured between 1974 and 1984, the emission control systems had been removed or were inoperable. Suppose you were to randomly sample six vehicles from among all cars and light trucks in the 14 cities that were manufactured between 1974 and 1984. Find the probability that the number containing inoperable or nonexistent emission control systems is as follows:

(a) Exactly 3   (b) At least 3   (c) More than 5

3.66 Many employers are finding that some of the people they hire are not who and what they claim to be. Detecting job applicants who falsify their application information has spawned some new businesses: credential-checking services. *U.S. News & World Report* (July 13, 1981) reported on this problem and noted that one service in a two-month period found that 35% of all credentials examined were falsified. Suppose that you hired five new employees last week and that the probability that a single employee would falsify the information on his or her application form is .35. What is the probability that at least one of the five application forms has been falsified? Two or more?

3.67 Records show that 30% of all patients admitted to a medical clinic fail to pay their bills and eventually the bills are forgiven. Suppose that $n = 4$ new patients represent a random selection from the large set of prospective patients served by the clinic. Find the following probabilities.

(a) That all the patients' bills will eventually have to be forgiven.
(b) That one will have to be forgiven.
(c) That none will have to be forgiven.

3.68 Refer to Exercise 3.67, and let x equal the number of patients in the sample of $n = 4$ whose bills will have to be forgiven. Construct a probability histogram for $p(x)$.

3.69 Many utility companies have begun to promote energy conservation by offering discount rates to consumers who keep their energy use below certain established subsidy standards. A recent EPA report notes that 70% of the island residents of Puerto Rico have reduced their electricity use sufficiently to qualify for discounted rates. Suppose five residential subscribers are randomly selected from San Juan, Puerto Rico. Find the following probabilities.

(a) That all five qualify for the favorable rates.
(b) That at least four qualify for the favorable rates.

3.70 Can corporations expand into new fields and improve their profitability by acquiring other firms? A study by McKinsey and Company of 58 corporate acquisitions between 1975 and 1985 found that only 6 were successful (*Wall Street Journal*, July 1, 1986). Assume that the probability that a corporate acquisition will be successful is .1. Suppose you randomly select 10 corporations involved in acquiring another company.

(a) What is the probability that all 10 of the acquisitions will be unsuccessful?

(b) What is the probability that at least 2 of the acquisitions will be successful?

(c) What is the probability that exactly 2 of the acquisitions will be successful?

3.71 A U.S. government study of telephone calls made by its employees suggests that 1 in every 3 calls is for nonbusiness purposes (*New York Times,* June 23, 1986). Suppose that you are a government employee and that 3 out of every 10 of your telephone calls are for personal reasons. The government randomly sampled 10 numbers that you dialed.

(a) What is the probability that no more than one of the calls was for personal reasons?

(b) What is the probability that more than 5 of the calls were for personal reasons?

(c) What is the probability that exactly 3 of the calls were for personal reasons?

3.72 In Exercise 3.71 we noted that a government study suggests that 1 in every 3 telephone calls made by government employees is for nonbusiness purposes. Suppose that a government facility makes 10 million calls per year and that each call costs the taxpayer $1.50 for the use of the communications equipment and for the employees' time.

(a) What is the expected number of nonbusiness calls?

(b) What is the standard deviation?

(c) Could the number x of nonbusiness calls be less than 3.3 million? Explain.

3.73 Let us consider the medical payment problem in Exercise 3.67 in a more realistic setting. We were given the fact that 30% of all patients admitted to a medical clinic fail to pay their bills and that the bills are eventually forgiven. If over a year period of time the clinic treats 2000 different patients, what is the mean (expected) number of bills that would have to be forgiven? If x is the number of forgiven bills in the group of 2000 patients, find the variance and standard deviation of x. What can you say about the probability that x will exceed 700? (*Hint:* Use the values of μ and σ, along with Tchebysheff's Theorem, to answer this question.)

3.74 The Energy Policy Center of the EPA reports that 75% of the homes in New England are heated by oil-burning furnaces. If a certain New England community is known to have 2500 homes, find the expected number of homes in the community that are heated by oil furnaces. If x is the number of homes in the community that are heated by oil, find the variance and standard deviation of x. Use Tchebysheff's Theorem to describe limits within which one could expect x to fall.

3.75 It is known that 10% of a brand of television tubes will burn out before their guarantee has expired. If 1000 tubes are sold, find the expected value and variance of x, the number of original tubes that must be replaced. Within what limits would x be expected to fall? (*Hint:* Use Tchebysheff's Theorem.)

3.76 Bank failures are eroding the public's confidence in our banking system. A survey by the American Bankers Association suggests that more than one-third of Americans have less confidence in the U.S. banking system than they had in prior years (*Orlando Sentinel,* October 22, 1984). Suppose that the proportion of adults in the United States who have less confidence in the U.S. banking system is 1/3. Also, suppose that customers of your local bank are representative of those throughout the United States, and you randomly sample 600.

(a) What is the expected number and standard deviation of x, the number in the sample who have less confidence in the banking system?

(b) Suppose that the number x of persons with decreased confidence at your bank was equal to 270. Would you believe your initial assumption, that your bank's customers were representative of those throughout the United States? Explain.

3.6

THE HYPERGEOMETRIC PROBABILITY DISTRIBUTION*

Recall that if you select a random sample of n consumers from a population containing N consumers, the number x of consumers favoring a specific product will possess a binomial probability distribution when the sample size n is small, relative to the number N of consumers in the population (see Example 3.14). When n is large relative to N (as in Example 3.15), the number x favoring the product possesses a **hypergeometric probability distribution**. Its formulas are given in the following box.

HYPERGEOMETRIC PROBABILITY DISTRIBUTION

$$p(x) = \frac{C_x^r C_{n-x}^{N-r}}{C_n^N}$$

where N = number of elements in the population

r = number of elements possessing some specific characteristic, say, the number of persons favoring a particular product

n = number of elements in the sample

Mean: $\mu = \dfrac{nr}{N}$

Variance: $\sigma^2 = \dfrac{r(N-r)n(N-n)}{N^2(N-1)}$

Standard Deviation: $\sigma = \sqrt{\dfrac{r(N-r)n(N-n)}{N^2(N-1)}}$

EXAMPLE 3.21

In Example 3.15 a boxcar contained 20 large electronic computers, 2 of which were defective. If 3 computers are randomly selected from the boxcar, what is the probability that two of them will be defective?

SOLUTION   For this example

$$N = 20 \qquad n = 3$$
$$r = 2 \text{ (defective computers)}$$
$$x = \text{number of defective computers in the sample}$$

Then

$$p(x) = \frac{C_x^r C_{n-x}^{N-r}}{C_n^N}$$

and

$$p(2) = \frac{C_2^2 C_{3-2}^{20-2}}{C_3^{20}}$$

*This section is optional.

where

$$C_2^2 = \frac{2!}{2!0!} = 1, \qquad C_{3-2}^{20-2} = C_1^{18} = \frac{18!}{1!17!} = 18$$

and

$$C_3^{20} = \frac{20!}{3!17!} = \frac{(20)(19)(18)}{6} = 1140$$

Then the probability of drawing $x = 2$ defective computers in a sample of $n = 3$ is

$$p(2) = \frac{(1)(18)}{1140} = .016 \qquad \blacksquare$$

EXERCISES

BASIC TECHNIQUES

3.77 (a) Calculate $p(x)$, where x has a hypergeometric probability distribution with $N = 10, n = 2,$ $r = 3$, and $x = 0,\ 1,\ 2$.
(b) Graph $p(x)$.

3.78 (a) Calculate $p(x)$, where x has a hypergeometric probability distribution with $N = 20, n = 3,$ $r = 3$, and $x = 0,\ 1,\ 2,\ 3$.
(b) Graph $p(x)$.

3.79 Find the mean and standard deviation for the random variable x described in Exercise 3.78. What is the probability that x lies in the interval $(\mu \pm 2\sigma)$?

APPLICATIONS

 3.80 A problem encountered by personnel directors and others faced with the selection of the best in a finite set of elements is indicated by the following situation: From a group of 20 Ph.D. engineers, 10 are selected for employment. What is the probability that the 10 selected include the 5 best engineers in the group of 20?

 3.81 A particular industrial product is shipped in lots of 20. Testing to determine whether an item is defective is costly; thus the manufacturer samples the production rather than uses a 100% inspection plan. A sampling plan designed to minimize the number of defectives shipped to customers calls for sampling 5 items from each lot and rejecting the lot if more than one defective is observed. (If rejected, each item in the lot is tested.) If a lot contains 4 defectives, what is the probability that it will be rejected?

 3.82 A warehouse contains ten printing machines, four of which are defective. A company selects five of the machines at random, thinking all are in working condition. What is the probability that all five of the machines are nondefective?

 3.83 A union claims that 45 of the 80 employees of a company favor unionization. Suppose the union is correct, and the plant manager informally samples the opinion of 20 employees.

(a) What is the expected value of the number x of employees in the sample that will favor unionization?

(b) Find the standard deviation of x.

(c) If the union is correct, is it likely that less than 9 employees in the sample will favor unionization? Explain.

THE GEOMETRIC PROBABILITY DISTRIBUTION*

3.7

You will recall (Section 3.5) that a binomial experiment involves a series of identical and independent trials, each resulting in "success" S or "failure" F, with $P(S) = p$ and $P(F) = 1 - p = q$. If we are interested in the number x of trials before we observe the first success, then x possesses a **geometric probability distribution**. Note that the number of trials could continue forever and that x is an example of a discrete random variable that can assume an infinite (but countable) number of values. The formulas for the geometric distribution are given in the following box.

GEOMETRIC PROBABILITY DISTRIBUTION

$$p(x) = pq^{x-1} \qquad x = 1, 2, \ldots, \infty$$

where x = number of independent trials until the first success occurs

p = probability of success on a single trial

$q = 1 - p$

Mean: $\mu = \dfrac{1}{p}$

Variance: $\sigma^2 = \dfrac{1 - p}{p^2}$

Standard Deviation: $\sigma = \sqrt{\dfrac{1 - p}{p^2}}$

The geometric probability distribution is a model for the length of time that a gambler (investor?) must wait before he or she wins. For example, the mean gain in a series of identical bets at roulette (or some other series of identical trials) is not a good gauge of your prospect of winning. You might have a series of bad luck and run out of money before you have a chance to recoup your losses.

The geometric probability distribution also provides a discrete model for the length of time, say the number x of minutes, before a customer in a waiting line (department store, repair facility, hospital clinic, etc.) receives service. [Note that length of time is a continuous random variable. The geometric probability distribution is a discrete analogue (an approximation to) a particular continuous probability distribution known as an *exponential distribution*.] This discrete model for the probability distribution of waiting time x is based on the assumption that the probability of receiving service any one minute is identical to and independent of the outcome during any other minute and that x is measured in whole minutes—that is, $x = 1, 2, 3, \ldots$.

*This section is optional.

EXAMPLE 3.22   Records indicate that a particular salesperson is successful in making a sale on 30% of her contacts. Suppose that a sale on one contact is independent of a sale on any other.

(a) What is the probability that the salesperson will have to contact 10 people before making the first sale?

(b) What is the probability that the first sale will be made on or before the tenth contact?

SOLUTION   (a) The probability of making a sale on a single contact is $p = .3$. Then the probability that it will require exactly $x = 10$ contacts before the salesperson makes the first sale is

$$p(x) = pq^{x-1}$$

or

$$p(10) = (.3)(.7)^9 = .012$$

(b) The probability that the first sale will be made on or before the tenth contact is

$$P(x \leq 10) = p(0) + p(1) + p(2) + \cdots + p(10)$$

The easiest way to find this probability is to express it as the complement of an infinite series. That is,

$$P(x \leq 10) = 1 - P(x > 10)$$

where

$$P(x > 10) = p(11) + p(12) + \cdots$$
$$= pq^{10} + pq^{11} + \cdots$$

The sum of an infinite geometric series is equal to $a/(1 - r)$, where a is the first term of the series, r is the common ratio, and $r^2 < 1$. Using this result, we get

$$P(x \leq 10) = 1 - P(x > 10) = 1 - \frac{pq^{10}}{1 - q} = 1 - q^{10} = 1 - (.7)^{10}$$

$$= 1 - .028$$

$$= .972$$

Thus there is a high probability (.972) that the salesperson will make her first sale on or before the tenth sales contact.   ■

EXERCISES

BASIC TECHNIQUES

3.84 The probability of success p in a series of independent binomial trials is .8, and x is a geometric random variable.

(a) Find $p(x)$ for $x = 1, 2, 3, 4, 5, 6$.

(b) Graph $p(x)$.

3.85 The probability of success p in a series of independent binomial trials is .6, and x is a geometric random variable.

   (a) Find $p(x)$ for $x = 1, 2, 3, 4, 5, 6$.

   (b) Graph $p(x)$.

APPLICATIONS

3.86 Past experience has shown that on the average only one in ten wells drilled hits oil. Let x be the number of drillings until the first success (oil is struck). Assume that the drillings represent independent events.

   (a) Find $p(1)$, $p(2)$, and $p(3)$.

   (b) Give a formula for $p(x)$.

   (c) Graph $p(x)$.

3.87 Suppose that the company in Exercise 3.86 commenced drilling for oil. Is it unlikely that as many as 20 drillings would be made before the company encountered its first success? Explain.

3.88 In earlier exercises we noted that a government study suggests that one in every three phone calls made by government employees is for personal reasons (*New York Times,* June 23, 1986). Suppose that you are a government employee and that three of every ten calls that you make are for personal reasons. Also suppose that the government randomly samples the numbers you dialed and checks the source of each call.

   (a) Give the probability distribution for x, the number of calls checked until the government encounters the first nonbusiness call.

   (b) Give the mean and standard deviation for x.

   (c) Is it likely that x will be as large as ten? Explain.

3.89 An insurance company has found that 1 in 100 property insurance claims exceeds $1 million. Let x equal the number of claims filed until the first claim exceeding $1 million is observed.

   (a) Find the mean and standard deviation of x.

   (b) Is it improbable that x could be as large as 200? Explain.

3.8   THE POISSON PROBABILITY DISTRIBUTION*

The **Poisson probability distribution** is a good model for the relative frequency distribution of the number of rare events that occur in a unit of time, distance, space, and so on. For this reason it is often employed by business management to model the relative frequency distribution of the number of industrial accidents per unit of time (such as the nuclear accident at Three Mile Island) or by personnel managers to model the relative frequency distribution for the number of employee accidents or the number of insurance claims per unit of time. The Poisson probability distribution can also, in some situations, provide a good model for the relative frequency distribution of the number of arrivals per unit of time at a servicing unit (say, the number of orders received at a manufacturing plant or the number of customers at a servicing facility, a supermarket counter, etc.). The formulas for the Poisson distribution are given in the following box.

*This section is optional.

THE POISSON PROBABILITY DISTRIBUTION

$$p(x) = \frac{\mu^x e^{-\mu}}{x!} \qquad x = 0, 1, 2, \ldots, \infty$$

where x = number of rare events per unit of time, distance, space, and so forth.

Mean: symbol μ that appears in $p(x)$

Variance: $\sigma^2 = \mu$

Standard Deviation: $\sigma = \sqrt{\mu}$

Note that, in practice, x is usually small; theoretically, it could be large beyond all bound. Thus the Poisson random variable is an example of a discrete random variable that can assume an infinitely large (but countable) number of values.

The Poisson probability distribution can also be used to approximate a binomial probability distribution when n is large, p is small,* and when the mean $\mu = np$ of the binomial probability distribution is less than, roughly, 7. This approximation eliminates the tedious calculation necessary in determining the binomial probabilities when n is large.

We will illustrate these two types of applications in the following examples. Others will be suggested by the exercises.

EXAMPLE 3.23   Serious worker injuries at a steel-fabricating company average 2.7 per year. Given that safety conditions at the plant remain the same next year, what is the probability that the number of serious injuries will be less than two?

SOLUTION   The event that fewer than two serious injuries will occur is the event that $x = 0$ or 1. Therefore,

$$P(x < 2) = p(0) + p(1) \qquad \text{where} \qquad p(x) = \frac{(2.7)^x e^{-2.7}}{x!}$$

Substituting into the formula for $p(x)$ and from Table 2 in the Appendix, using $e^{-2.7} = .067206$, we obtain

$$P(x < 2) = p(0) + p(1) = \frac{(2.7)^0(.067206)}{0!} + \frac{(2.7)^1(.067206)}{1!}$$

$$= (.067206) + (2.7)(.067206)$$

$$= .249$$

(Recall that $0! = 1$.) Therefore, the probability that fewer than two serious worker injuries will occur next year in the steel-fabricating plant is .249.   ■

For your convenience, we provide in Table 3 of the Appendix the partial sums, $\sum_{x=0}^{a} p(x)$, for the Poisson probability distribution for values of μ from .25 to 5.0 in steps

*If p is near 1, interchange your definition of success and failure so that p will be near 0.

of .25. This table is constructed in the same manner as the table of partial sums for the binomial probability distribution, Table 1 of the Appendix. The following example will illustrate the use of Table 3 and will also demonstrate the use of the Poisson probability distribution to approximate the binomial probability distribution.

EXAMPLE 3.24

Suppose that you have a binomial experiment with $n = 25$ and $p = .1$. Find the exact value of $P(x \leq 3)$, using the table of partial sums for the binomial probability distribution, Table 1 of the Appendix. Then find the corresponding partial sum by using the Poisson approximation in Table 3 of the Appendix. Compare the exact and approximate values for $P(x \leq 3)$.

SOLUTION

From Table 1 in the Appendix the exact value of $P(x \leq 3)$ is $\sum_{x=0}^{3} p(x) = .764$. The corresponding Poisson partial sum, for $\mu = np = (25)(.1) = 2.5$, given in Table 3 of the Appendix is $P(x \leq 3) = \sum_{x=0}^{3} p(x) = .758$. Comparing the exact and approximate values of $P(x \leq 3)$, we see that the approximation is quite good. It differs from the exact value by only .006.

EXERCISES

BASIC TECHNIQUES

3.90 Suppose x is a Poisson random variable with $\mu = 1.2$. Find the following. (*Note:* Values of $e^{-\mu}$ are given in Table 2 of the Appendix.)

(a) $p(0)$ (b) $p(1)$ (c) $P(x \leq 2)$ (d) $P(x > 1)$

3.91 Suppose x is a Poisson random variable with $\mu = 2$. Find the following. (*Note:* Values of $e^{-\mu}$ are given in Table 2 of the Appendix.)

(a) $p(0)$ (b) $P(x > 1)$ (c) $P(x < 2)$

3.92 Use Table 3 in the Appendix to find $p(x)$ for a Poisson probability distribution with $\mu = 1$ and $x = 0, 1, 2, 3, 4, \ldots$. Then graph $p(x)$.

3.93 Repeat the instructions of Exercise 3.92 for $\mu = 3$. Notice how the distribution tends to become more mound-shaped as μ increases.

3.94 Use Table 3 in the Appendix to find the following.

(a) $P(x \leq 2)$ when $\mu = 3$.

(b) $P(x \geq 1)$ when $\mu = 1$.

(c) $P(x = 2)$ when $\mu = 2$. $\left[\textit{Hint: } p(2) = \sum_{x=0}^{2} p(x) - \sum_{x=0}^{1} p(x).\right]$

3.95 A binomial experiment has $n = 20$ and $p = .2$.

(a) Use Table 1 to find the exact value of $p(2)$.

(b) Use Table 3 to find the Poisson approximation to $p(2)$.

APPLICATIONS

3.96 Suppose that a random system of police patrol is devised so that a patrolman may visit a given location on his beat $x = 0, 1, 2, 3, \ldots$ times per half-hour period and that the system is arranged so that he visits each location on an average of once per time period. Assume that x

possesses, approximately, a Poisson probability distribution. Calculate the probability that the patrolman will miss a given location during a half-hour period. What is the probability that he will visit it once? Twice? At least once?

3.97 The accidents in a particular industrial plant average 3.5 per week.

(a) What is the probability that no accidents will occur in a given week?

(b) Is it likely that the number of accidents per week would exceed 7? Explain.

(c) If the number of accidents in a particular week was equal to 9, would you still believe that $\mu = 3.5$? Explain.

3.98 The number x, per week, of sales of a piece of large earth-moving equipment for a construction equipment company possesses a Poisson probability distribution with mean equal to 4.

(a) What is the probability that the number of earth movers sold per week is equal to 1? Less than or equal to 1?

(b) Is it likely that x will exceed 9? Explain.

3.99 The average number of passenger complaints to the Department of Transportation about United Airlines, per 100,000 passengers flown, January through September 1986, was 2.77 (*Wall Street Journal*, November 10, 1986). Suppose we were to randomly select 100,000 passengers flown during this period.

(a) What is the probability that two or more would register complaints with the Department of Transportation?

(b) Could the number complaining to the Department of Transportation be as large as 10? Explain.

3.100 The number x of people entering the intensive care unit at a particular hospital on any one day possesses a Poisson probability distribution with mean equal to 5 persons per day.

(a) What is the probability that the number of people entering the intensive care unit on a particular day is equal to 2? Less than or equal to 2?

(b) Is it likely that x will exceed 10? Explain.

MORE ON THE FEAR-OF-FLYING SURVEY

3.9

As we noted in the Case Study, estimation of the proportion of potential airline customers who possess some common characteristic is dependent upon the probability distribution of x [the number of yes (or no) responses to a survey question]. Since the number of persons contacted in a survey will constitute a random sample from among a very large number of persons, x will possess, for all practical purposes, a binomial probability distribution.

To illustrate, suppose that 2000 potential airline travelers have been randomly selected from among a specific group (say, all potential travelers who are 18 to 22 years old) and that 5% of those in this group are afraid to fly. Then the probability distribution for x, the number of persons who would indicate a fear of flying (yes responses), would be binomial with mean and standard deviation equal to

$$\mu = np = (2000)(.05) = 100$$
$$\sigma = \sqrt{npq} = \sqrt{(2000)(.05)(.95)} = 9.75$$

Thus if our suggestion is true—that 5% of all people in the 18- to 22-year-old age group have a fear of flying—we would expect the number x of yes responses to assume a

3,5

value in the interval

$$\mu \pm 2\sigma = 100 \pm 2(9.75)$$

or from 80.5 to 119.5.

Suppose that the response to a survey was $x = 69$ persons who indicated a fear of flying. What would you conclude? Either you observed a highly improbable event (a very small number of yes responses, $x = 69$, considering that $p = .05$), or you could conclude that p is less than .05.

If you reach the latter conclusion, be careful how you interpret the result. The fraction p of persons in the 18- to 22-year-old bracket who fear flying may be less than .05. Or perhaps you are sampling a population of yeses and noes that is of no use to you. For example, suppose that some people would be embarrassed to admit that they were afraid to fly and therefore would respond "no" to the survey question. Then the population would contain a higher fraction of noes than if the respondents had given truthful answers and would yield a population that would not truly characterize the phenomenon of interest to you. Methods for coping with questions that might prove embarrassing and yield false responses are called randomized response techniques (see Scheaffer, Mendenhall, and Ott, 1986).

You can inadvertently sample from the wrong population of yeses and noes when you sample by mail or telephone. For example, businesspeople, many of whom fly and have no fear of flying, may not be willing to take the time to respond to the survey question. The exclusion of many of these respondents from the sample changes the nature of the population and is likely to reduce the proportion of noes. In general, sampling procedures that elicit responses from only a portion of the persons originally selected for the sample may alter the nature of the sampled population and lead to invalid inferences.

The point to note is that the causes of improbable sample results must be examined carefully. They may arise because you made incorrect assumptions about one or more population parameters (in this case, p), but it is also possible that they were caused by an inappropriate sampling procedure.

SUMMARY

3.10

Random variables, representing numerical events defined over a sample space, may be classified as discrete or continuous, depending upon whether the number of values that the random variable can assume is or is not countable. The theoretical population frequency distribution for the discrete random variable is called a probability distribution and often can be derived by using the techniques of Chapter 2.

A mathematical expectation is the average of a random variable calculated for the theoretical population defined by its probability distribution.

Four useful discrete probability distributions are discussed in Chapter 3. The binomial probability distribution, which plays an important role in consumer preference surveys, is discussed in detail in Section 3.5. The hypergeometric, geometric, and Poisson probability distributions are presented in optional Sections 3.6, 3.7, and 3.8. Although they have practical application, they are not required for an understanding of the material presented in later chapters and can, for the sake of brevity, be omitted.

REFERENCES

Feller, W. *An Introduction to Probability Theory and Its Applications.* Vol. 1, 3rd ed. New York: Wiley, 1968.

Freund, J. E., and Walpole, R. E. *Mathematical Statistics.* 4th ed. Englewood Cliffs, N.J.: Prentice-Hall, 1987.

Handbook of Tables for Probability and Statistics. 2nd. ed. Cleveland, Ohio: The Chemical Rubber Co., 1968.

Mendenhall, W., Scheaffer, R. L., and Wackerly, D. D. *Mathematical Statistics with Applications.* 3rd ed. Boston: PWS-KENT, 1986.

Mood, A. M., et al. *Introduction to the Theory of Statistics.* 3rd ed. New York: McGraw-Hill, 1973.

Mosteller, F., Rourke, R. E. K., and Thomas, G. B., Jr. *Probability with Statistical Applications.* 2nd ed. Reading, Mass.: Addison-Wesley, 1970.

National Bureau of Standards. *Tables of the Binomial Probability Distribution.* Washington, D. C.: Government Printing Office, 1949.

Scheaffer, R. L., Mendenhall, W., and Ott, R. L. *Elementary Survey Sampling.* 3rd ed. Boston: PWS-KENT, 1986.

Sincich, T. *Statistics by Example.* 3rd ed. New York: Macmillan, 1987.

KEY TERMS

Experiment (page 76)
Event (page 77)
Probability of an event (page 77)
Union of events (page 77)
Intersection of events (page 77)
Mutually exclusive events (page 78)
Sample space (page 78)
Simple event (page 78)
Conditional probability (page 85)
Independent events (page 86)
Numerical event (page 92)

Random variable (page 92)
Discrete random variable (page 92)
Continuous random variable (page 92)
Probability distribution (page 92)
Expected value of a random variable (page 95)
Binomial experiment (page 103)
Binomial probability distribution (page 105)
Hypergeometric probability distribution (page 115)
Geometric probability distribution (page 117)
Poisson probability distribution (page 119)

SUPPLEMENTARY EXERCISES

Starred (*) exercises are optional.

3.101 List the five identifying characteristics of the binomial experiment.

3.102 A balanced coin is tossed three times. Let x equal the number of heads observed.

(a) Use the formula for the binomial probability distribution to calculate the probabilities associated with $x = 0$, 1, 2, and 3.

(b) Construct a probability distribution similar to the one shown in Figure 3.1.

(c) Find the expected value and standard deviation of x, using the formulas

$$E(x) = np \qquad \sigma = \sqrt{npq}$$

(d) Using the probability distribution you derived in (b), find the fraction of the population measurements lying within one standard deviation of the mean. Repeat for two standard deviations. How do your results agree with Tchebysheff's Theorem and the Empirical Rule?

3.103 Let x equal the number of dots observed when a die is tossed, and let $p(x)$ equal $1/6$, $x = 1, 2, 3, \ldots, 6$. We found in Example 3.9 that $\mu = E(x) = 3.5$. Find σ^2 and show that $\sigma = 1.71$. Then find the probability that x will fall in the interval $(\mu \pm 2\sigma)$.

3.104 A recent study of commuter trains shows that they run more than 35 minutes late with probability equal to .5. If we are using a commuter train that exhibits these characteristics and we randomly select 5 days within the past year, what is the probability that the train is always late? What is the probability the train is late more than 3 times out of 5?

3.105 Use Table 1 in the Appendix to find the partial sum

$$\sum_{x=0}^{a} p(x)$$

for a binomial random variable x with the following characteristics.

(a) $n = 10, p = .7, a = 8$ (b) $n = 15, p = .05, a = 1$
(c) $n = 20, p = .9, a = 14$

3.106 Use Table 1 in the Appendix to find $p(x)$ for a binomial random variable x with the following.

(a) $n = 10, p = .6, x = 6$ (b) $n = 15, p = .5, x = 5$
(c) $n = 20, p = .2, x = 3$

3.107 Use Table 1 in the Appendix to find

$$\sum_{x=a}^{b} p(x)$$

for a binomial random variable x with the following characteristics.

(a) $n = 10, p = .1, a = 1, b = 10$ (b) $n = 10, p = .8, a = 7, b = 9$
(c) $n = 15, p = .4, a = 4, b = 15$

3.108 You know that 90% of those who purchase a color television will have no claims covered by the guarantee during the duration of the guarantee. Suppose that 20 customers each buy a color television set from a certain appliance dealer. What is the probability that at least 2 of these 20 customers will have claims against the guarantee?

3.109 Suppose that you know that 1 out of 10 undergraduate college textbooks is an outstanding financial success. A publisher has selected 10 new textbooks for publication.

(a) What is the probability that exactly one will be an outstanding financial success?
(b) What is the probability that at least one will be an outstanding financial success?
(c) What is the probability that at least 2 will be outstanding financial successes?

3.110 The proportion of residential households in Burlington, Vermont, that are heated by natural gas is approximately .2. A randomly selected city block within the Burlington city limits has 20 residential households. Assume that the properties of a binomial experiment are satisfied.

(a) Find the probability that none of the households are heated by natural gas.
(b) Find the probability that no more than 4 of the 20 are heated by natural gas.
(c) Why might the binomial experiment not provide a good model for this sampling situation?

3.111 In his feature article on psychology and investing (*Forbes*, June 2, 1985), Dr. Srully Blotnick notes that job security for company managers is decreasing. During the 1950s and 1960s the probability of dismissal for managers in their fifties was $1/24$. Now it is $2/5$. Suppose that you were to randomly sample 20 company managers from among the population of all company managers in the United States. Suppose that the probability that a manager selected at random will be fired in the coming year is 2/5.

(a) What is the probability that more than 10 will be fired?

(b) What is the probability that exactly 10 will be fired?

(c) What is the probability that less than 6 will be fired?

 3.112 Suppose, as noted in Exercise 3.66, that approximately 35% of all applicants for jobs falsify the information on their application forms. Suppose a company has 2300 employees.

(a) What is the expected value of the number x of application forms that have been falsified?

(b) Find the standard deviation of x.

(c) Calculate the interval $(\mu \pm 2\sigma)$.

(d) Suppose that the company had a credentials-checking firm verify the information on the 2300 application forms and that 249 application forms contained falsified information. Do you think that the company's application falsification rate is consistent with the contention that 35% of all job applicants falsify information on their applications? Explain.

 3.113 A quality control engineer wishes to study the alternative sampling plans $n = 5$, $a = 1$ and $n = 25$, $a = 5$. On the same sheet of graph paper, construct the operating characteristic curves for both plans, making use of acceptance probabilities at $p = .05$, $p = .10$, $p = .20$, $p = .30$, and $p = .40$ in each case.

(a) If you were a seller producing lots with fraction defective ranging from $p = 0$ to $p = .10$, which of the two sampling plans would you prefer?

(b) If you were a buyer wishing to be protected against accepting lots with fraction defective exceeding $p = .30$, which of the two sampling plans would you prefer?

 3.114 Consider a lot acceptance plan with $n = 20$, $a = 1$. Calculate the probability of accepting lots having the following fraction defective values. Sketch the operating characteristic curve for the plan.

(a) $p = .01$ **(b)** $p = .05$ **(c)** $p = .10$ **(d)** $p = .20$

 3.115 The administrator of the North Florida Regional Hospital (a private hospital) applied to the health planning council in 1975 for permission to make a 100-bed addition to the hospital, an application that was subsequently denied because of the uncertain impact that the addition would have on the existing public county hospital (*Gainesville Sun,* February 12, 1977). To support their application and, presumably, those applications to be resubmitted in the future, the hospital administrators conducted a telephone survey of 180 people in Gainesville area. In response to the question "Should North Florida be allowed to expand . . . even if [there are] empty beds at AGH [the county hospital]," 62% answered yes. If the public is really split 50–50 on this question, is it likely that the telephone poll would result in as many as 62% in favor of the North Florida expansion? In order for the preceding probability calculation to be correct, what must you know about the sampling procedure? Do you think the poll supports North Florida's request? Explain. (*Hint:* Recall Tchebysheff's Theorem and the Empirical Rule.)

 3.116 In a random sample of 20 executive secretaries, 15 favor copy machine A over copy machine B. If the machines are equally desirable, the probability that a person will select machine A over B is .5. What is the probability that the number x, favoring machine A, in the sample of 20 is equal to 15 or larger if $p = .5$?

3.117 Refer to Exercise 3.116. Manufacturer A hired a marketing company to sample 500 executive secretaries to determine which of the two copy machines was preferred, A or B.

(a) If $p = .5$, find the mean and standard deviation of the number x in the sample that prefer copy machine A.

(b) Suppose that 280 executive secretaries in the sample of 500 prefer copy machine A. Is this sample result likely if, in fact, the two copy machines are equally desirable? Explain.

3.118 According to estimates, a fourth of all workers in the United States are dissatisfied with their jobs (*U.S. News & World Report,* April 6, 1981). Suppose a random sample of 25 workers is selected from this population.

(a) What is the expected number of workers who are dissatisfied with their jobs?

(b) What is the standard deviation of the number who are dissatisfied with their jobs?

(c) Is it likely that the number of workers who are dissatisfied with their jobs will be greater than ten? Explain.

 *3.119 A shipment of 200 portable television sets is received by a retailer. To protect himself against a "bad" shipment, he will inspect 5 sets and accept the entire lot if he observes zero or one defective. Suppose there are actually 20 defective sets in the shipment.

(a) What is the probability that he accepts the entire shipment?

(b) Given that the retailer accepts the entire lot, what is the probability that he observed exactly one defective set?

 *3.120 A study conducted by a bank found that the average number of transaction errors per cashier per day was 1.5. Is it likely that any one cashier will make more than 4 transaction errors per day? Explain.

*3.121 The binomial probability distribution receives its name from the fact that the values of $p(x)$ for n trials and probability of success p correspond to the terms of the expansion of $(q + p)^n$. For example, for $n = 2$ trials,

$$(q + p)^2 = q^2 + 2pq + p^2$$

where $p(0) = q^2$, $p(1) = 2pq$, and $p(2) = p^2$. Expand $(q + p)^3$. Then use the formula for $p(x)$ to show that $p(0) = q^3$, $p(1) = 3q^2p$, and so on.

*3.122 This exercise will give you an opportunity to see how the formula for a binomial probability distribution is derived.

(a) List the simple events for a binomial experiment with $n = 3$ and probability of success on a single trial equal to p.

(b) Calculate the probabilities associated with the simple events.

(c) Assign the appropriate simple events to the events $x = 0, 1, 2,$ and 3.

(d) Calculate $p(x)$ for $x = 0, 1, 2,$ and 3 by summing the probabilities of the appropriate simple events.

(e) Use the formula for $p(x)$, $n = 3$, to find $p(x)$ for $x = 0, 1, 2,$ and 3. Compare the result with your answer to part (d).

 *3.123 The number of near midair collisions appears to be on the rise. In the Atlanta region alone there were 10 near midair collisions in 1985, compared with only 4 in 1984 (*Gainesville Sun,* February 26, 1986). Assume that the number of near midair collisions per year in the Atlanta area is a Poisson random variable with a mean equal to 4.

(a) What is the probability that there will be no near midair collisions in the Atlanta area in a given year?

(b) Is it likely that the number of near midair collisions per year could be as large as 10? Explain.

 *3.124 A certified public accountant (CPA) has found that nine of ten company audits contain substantial errors. The CPA audits a series of company accounts.

(a) What is the probability that the first account containing substantial errors is the third one to be audited?

(b) What is the probability that the first account containing substantial errors will occur on or after the third audited account?

Several discrete random variables and their probability distributions were presented in Chapter 3. The objective of this chapter is to introduce you to the normal random variable, one of the most important and most commonly encountered continuous random variables. We give its probability distribution, and we show how the probability distribution can be used.

4

THE NORMAL PROBABILITY DISTRIBUTION

The Long and the Short of It

If you were the boss, would height play a role in your selection of a successor for your job? In his *Fortune* magazine (July 27, 1981) column "Keeping Up," Daniel Seligman discussed his ideas concerning height as a factor in Deng Xiaoping's choice of Hu Yaobang for his replacement as chairman of the Chinese Communist Party. As Seligman notes, the facts surrounding the case are enough to arouse suspicion when examined in terms of statistics.

Deng, it seems, is only 5 feet tall, a height that is short even in China. Therefore, the choice of Hu Yaobang, who is also 5 feet tall, raised (or lowered) some eyebrows because, as *Fortune* notes, "the odds against a 'height blind' decision producing a chairman as short as Deng are about 40 to 1." In other words, if we possessed the relative frequency distribution of the heights of all Chinese males, only 1 in 41, that is, 2.4% of them, would possess heights less than or equal to 5 feet. To calculate these odds, *Fortune*'s author made some interesting assumptions concerning the relative frequency distribution of the heights of Chinese males, most notably that the distribution follows the "normal bell-shaped Gaussian curve (as it does in the United States)."

The normal curve, used as the model for the relative frequency distributions for many continuous random variables, is the topic of Chapter 4. We will examine its properties, learn how it can be used to calculate probabilities, and will see how *Fortune*'s author used it to arrive at the 40-to-1 odds.

4.1 CONTINUOUS RANDOM VARIABLES

A continuous random variable, as noted in Section 3.4, is one that can assume the infinitely large number of values corresponding to the points on a line interval. The heights and weights of humans, the length of time between successive sales, or the length of life of a piece of business equipment are typical examples of continuous random variables.

The probabilistic model for the frequency distribution of a continuous random variable involves the selection of a curve, usually smooth, called the **probability distribution or probability density function** of the random variable. If the equation of this continuous probability distribution is denoted as $f(x)$, then the probability that x falls in the interval $a < x < b$ is the area under the distribution curve for $f(x)$ between the two points a and b (see Figure 4.1). This agrees with the interpretation of a relative frequency histogram (Chapter 2), where areas over an interval under the histogram corresponded to the proportion of observations falling in that interval. Since the number of values that x may assume is infinitely large and uncountable, the probability that x equals some specific value, say a, is 0. Thus probability statements about continuous random variables always correspond to areas under the probability

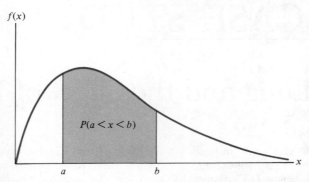

FIGURE 4.1   The Probability Distribution for a Continuous Random Variable

distribution over an interval, say a to b, and are expressed as $P(a < x < b)$. Note that the probability at $a < x < b$ is equal to the probability that $a < x \leq b$ because $P(x = a) = P(x = b) = 0$.

There are many different continuous probability distributions, each of which is described by a mathematical equation $f(x)$ that is chosen so that the total area under the probability distribution curve is equal to 1.

Once we know the equation $f(x)$ of a particular probability distribution, we can find specific probabilities, say the probability that x will fall in the interval $a < x < b$, in two ways. We can graph the equation (see Figure 4.1) and use numerical methods to approximate the area over the interval $a < x < b$. This calculation can be done by using very approximate methods or by using a computer to obtain any desired degree of accuracy. Or if $f(x)$ is of a particular form, we can use the integral calculus to find $P(a < x < b)$.* Fortunately, in practice, we do not have to use either process because the areas under most of the useful continuous probability distributions have been calculated and tabulated.

In the sections that follow we will discuss one of the most useful continuous probability distributions, the bell-shaped normal probability distribution. Several other continuous probability distributions and their applications are described in Section 4.5.

THE NORMAL PROBABILITY DISTRIBUTION

4.2

The **normal probability distribution**, given by the equation

$$f(x) = \frac{e^{-(x-\mu)^2/2\sigma^2}}{\sigma\sqrt{2\pi}} \qquad (-\infty < x < \infty)$$

graphs as the bell-shaped curve shown in Figure 4.2. The symbols e and π represent irrational numbers whose values are approximately 2.7183 and 3.1416, respectively; μ

$$*P(a < x < b) = \int_a^b f(x)\,dx.$$

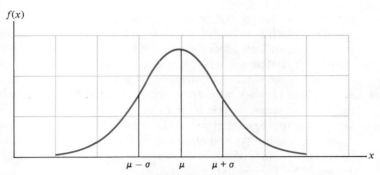

FIGURE 4.2   Normal Probability Density Function

and σ are the population mean and standard deviation. The equation for the density function is constructed such that the area under the curve will represent probability. Therefore, the total area under the curve is equal to 1.

The normal probability distribution shown in Figure 4.2 is symmetric about the mean μ. The light gray squares in Figure 4.2 are equal in width to one standard deviation σ.

In practice, we seldom encounter variables that range in value from "minus infinity" to "plus infinity," whatever meaning we may wish to attach to these phrases. Certainly, the height of humans or length of life of a piece of business equipment do not satisfy this requirement. Nevertheless, a relative frequency histogram plotted for many types of measurements will generate a bell-shaped figure that can be approximated by the function shown in Figure 4.2.

TABULATED AREAS OF THE NORMAL PROBABILITY DISTRIBUTION

4.3

Recall (Section 4.1) that the probability that a continuous random variable assumes a value in the interval a to b is the area under the probability density function between the points a and b (see Figure 4.3). To find areas under the normal curve, we note that the

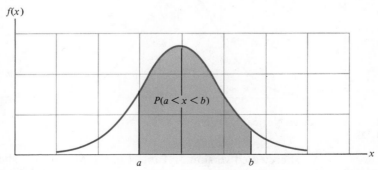

FIGURE 4.3   The Probability $P(a < x < b)$ for a Normally Distributed Random Variable

equation for the normal probability distribution, given in Section 4.2, is dependent on the numerical values of μ and σ and that by supplying various values for these parameters, we can generate an infinitely large number of bell-shaped normal distributions. A separate table of areas for each of these curves is obviously impractical; rather, we would like one table of areas applicable to all. The easiest way to use one table is to work with areas lying within a specified number of standard deviations of the mean, as was done in the case of the Empirical Rule. For instance, we know that approximately .68 of the area will lie within one standard deviation of the mean, .95 within two, and almost all within three. What fraction of the total area will lie within .7 standard deviation, for instance? This question, as well as others, will be answered by Table 4 in the Appendix.

Inasmuch as the normal curve is symmetrical about the mean, half of the area under the curve will lie to the left of the mean and half to the right (see Figure 4.3). Also, because of the symmetry, we can simplify our table of areas by listing the areas between the mean and a specified number z of standard deviations to the right of μ. Areas to the left of the mean can be calculated by using the corresponding and equal area to the right of the mean. The distance from the mean to a given value of x is $(x - \mu)$. Expressing this distance in units of standard deviation σ, we obtain

$$z = \frac{x - \mu}{\sigma}$$

Note that there is a one-to-one correspondence between z and x and, particularly, that $z = 0$ when $x = \mu$. The value of z will be positive when x lies above the mean and negative when x lies below the mean. The probability distribution for z is often called the **standardized normal distribution**, because its mean is equal to zero and its standard deviation is equal to 1. It is shown in Figure 4.4. The area under the normal curve between the mean $z = 0$ and a specified value of $z > 0$, say z_0, is the probability $P(0 \leq z \leq z_0)$. This area is recorded in Table 4 in the Appendix and is shown as the shaded area in Figure 4.4.

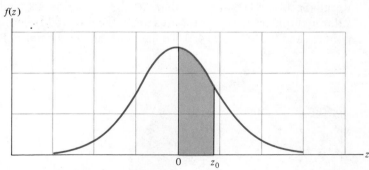

FIGURE 4.4   Standardized Normal Distribution

An abbreviated version of Table 4 in the Appendix is shown in Table 4.1. Note that z, correct to the nearest tenth, is recorded in the left-hand column. The second decimal place for z, corresponding to hundredths, is given across the top row. Thus the

TABLE 4.1   Abbreviated Version of Table 4 in the Appendix

z	.00	.01	.02	.03	.04	.05	.06	.07	.08	.09
0.0	.0000	.0040	.0080	.0120	.0160	.0199	.0239	.0279	.0319	.0359
0.1	.0398	.0438	.0478	.0517	.0557	.0596	.0636	.0675	.0714	.0753
0.2	.0793	.0832	.0871	.0910	.0948	.0987	.1026	.1064	.1103	.1141
0.3	.1179	.1217	.1255	.1293	.1331	.1368	.1406	.1443	.1480	.1517
0.4	.1554	.1591	.1628	.1664	.1700	.1736	.1772	.1808	.1844	.1879
0.5	.1915	.1950	.1985	.2019	.2054	.2088	.2123	.2157	.2190	.2224
0.6	.2257	:	:	:	:	:	:	:	:	:
0.7	.2580									
:	:									
1.0	.3413									
:	:									
2.0	.4772									

area between the mean and a point $z = .7$ standard deviation to the right, located in the second column of the table opposite $z = .7$, is found to equal .2580. Similarly, the area between the mean and $z = 1.0$ is .3413. The area lying within one standard deviation on either side of the mean is two times the quantity .3413, or .6826. The area lying within two standard deviations of the mean, correct to four decimal places, is $2(.4772) = .9544$. These numbers provide the approximate values, 68% and 95%, used in the Empirical Rule of Chapter 2. To find the area $z = .57$ standard deviation to the right of the mean, proceed down the left-hand column to the .5 row. Then move across the top row of the table to the .07 column. The intersection of this row-column combination gives the approximate area, .2157. We conclude this section with some examples.

EXAMPLE 4.1   Find $P(0 \leq z \leq 1.63)$. This probability corresponds to the area between the mean ($z = 0$) and a point $z = 1.63$ standard deviations to the right of the mean (see Figure 4.5).

SOLUTION   The area is shaded and indicated by the symbol A in Figure 4.5. Since Table 4 in the Appendix gives areas under the normal curve to the right of the mean, we need only find

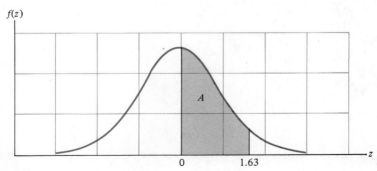

FIGURE 4.5   Area Required for Example 4.1

the tabulated value corresponding to $z = 1.63$. Go down the left-hand column of the table to the row corresponding to $z = 1.6$ and across the top of the table to the column marked .03. The intersection of this row and column combination gives the area, $A = .4484$. Therefore, $P(0 < z < 1.63) = .4484$. ∎

EXAMPLE 4.2 Find $P(-.5 \leq z \leq 1.0)$. This probability corresponds to the area between $z = -.5$ and $z = 1.0$, as shown in Figure 4.6.

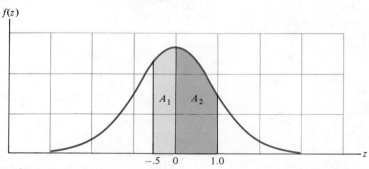

FIGURE 4.6 Area Required for Example 4.2

SOLUTION The area required is equal to the sum of A_1 and A_2 shown in Figure 4.6. From Table 4 in the Appendix we read $A_2 = .3413$. The area A_1 is equal to the corresponding area between $z = 0$ and $z = .5$, or $A_1 = .1915$. Thus the total area is

$$A = A_1 + A_2$$
$$= .1915 + .3413$$
$$= .5328$$ ∎

EXAMPLE 4.3 Find the values of z, say z_0, such that exactly (to four decimal places) .95 of the area is within $\pm z_0$ standard deviations of the mean.

SOLUTION Half of the .95 area will lie to the left of the mean and half to the right, because the normal distribution is symmetrical. Therefore, we want to find the value z_0 cor-

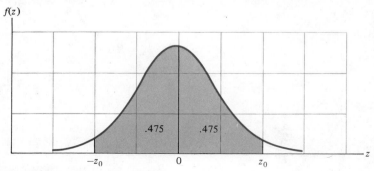

FIGURE 4.7 Area Required for Example 4.3

responding to an area equal to .475. This area is shaded in Figure 4.7. Referring to Table 4 in the Appendix, we see that the area .475 falls in the row corresponding to $z = 1.9$ and the .06 column. Therefore, $z_0 = 1.96$. Note that this result is very close to the approximate value, $z = 2$, used in the Empirical Rule. ■

EXAMPLE 4.4

Let x be a normally distributed random variable with mean equal to 10 and standard deviation equal to 2. Find the probability that x will lie between 11 and 13.6.

SOLUTION

As a first step, we must calculate the values of z corresponding to $x = 11$ and $x = 13.6$. Thus

$$z_1 = \frac{x_1 - \mu}{\sigma} = \frac{11 - 10}{2} = .5$$

$$z_2 = \frac{x_2 - \mu}{\sigma} = \frac{13.6 - 10}{2} = 1.80$$

These z values are located below the standard normal z curve; see Figure 4.8. The probability desired, P, is therefore the area lying between these z values, $z_1 = .5$ and $z_2 = 1.80$, as shown in Figure 4.8. The areas between $z = 0$ and z_1, $A_1 = .1915$, and between $z = 0$ and z_2, $A_2 = .4641$, are obtained from Table 4 in the Appendix. The probability P is equal to the difference between the two areas A_1 and A_2; that is,

$$P = A_2 - A_1$$
$$= .4641 - .1915 = .2726$$

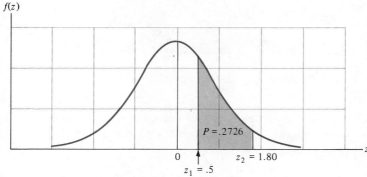

FIGURE 4.8   Probability Required for Example 4.4 ■

EXAMPLE 4.5

Studies show that gasoline use for compact cars sold in the United States is normally distributed with a mean use of 30.5 miles per gallon (mpg) and a standard deviation of 4.5 mpg. What percentage of compacts obtain 35 or more miles per gallon?

SOLUTION

Let x be a normally distributed random variable with mean equal to 30.5 and standard deviation equal to 4.5. We want to find the value x_0 such that

$$P(x < x_0) = .95$$

(See Figure 4.9.) As a first step, we find the value of z_0 corresponding to x_0—that is, a

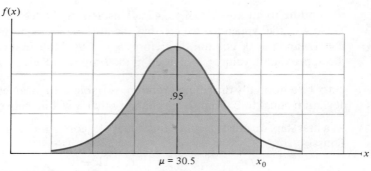

FIGURE 4.9   The Location of x_0 Such That $P(x < x_0) = .95$

value z_0 such that the area to its left is equal to .95. Since the area to the left of $z = 0$ is .5, z_0 will be the z value in Table 4 of the Appendix corresponding to an area equal to .45 (see Figure 4.10). This value is $z_0 = 1.645$.

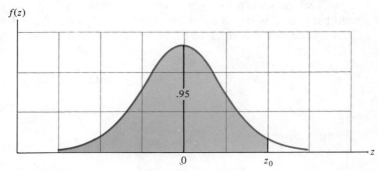

FIGURE 4.10   The Location of z_0 Such That $P(z < z_0) = .95$

The final step is to find the value x_0 corresponding to $z_0 = 1.645$. We find this value by using the equation relating x and z, namely,

$$z = \frac{x - \mu}{\sigma}$$

where $\mu = 30.5$ and $\sigma = 4.5$. Substituting the values of μ, σ, and z_0 into this equation and solving for x_0, we obtain

$$1.645 = \frac{x_0 - 30.5}{4.5}$$

$$x_0 = (4.5)(1.645) + 30.5$$

or

$$x_0 = 37.9$$

Thus the manufacturer's new compact car must obtain a fuel economy of 37.9 mpg to outperform 95% of the compact cars currently available on the U.S. market. ∎

EXERCISES

BASIC TECHNIQUES

4.1 Using Table 3 in the Appendix, calculate the area under the normal curve between these z values.

(a) $z = 0$ and $z = 1.6$ (b) $z = 0$ and $z = 1.83$

4.2 Repeat Exercise 4.1 for these z values.

(a) $z = 0$ and $z = .90$ (b) $z = 0$ and $z = -.90$

4.3 Repeat Exercise 4.1 for these z values.

(a) $z = -1.3$ and $z = 1.8$ (b) $z = .6$ and $z = 1.2$

4.4 Repeat Exercise 4.1 for these z values.

(a) $z = -1.4$ and $z = 1.4$ (b) $z = -2.0$ and $z = 2.0$

(c) $z = -3.0$ and $z = 3.0$

4.5 Repeat Exercise 4.1 for these z values.

(a) $z = -1.43$ and $z = .68$ (b) $z = .58$ and $z = 1.74$

(c) $z = -1.55$ and $z = -.44$

4.6 Repeat Exercise 4.1 for these z values.

(a) $z = -1.80$ and $z = .52$ (b) $z = -.25$ and $z = 1.50$

(c) $z = .50$ and $z = 1.50$

4.7 Find a z_0 such that $P(z > z_0) = .025$.

4.8 Find a z_0 such that $P(z < z_0) = .9251$.

4.9 Find a z_0 such that $P(z < z_0) = .2981$.

4.10 Find a z_0 such that $P(z > z_0) = .6985$.

4.11 Find a z_0 such that $P(z > z_0) = .9750$.

4.12 Find a z_0 such that $P(z > z_0) = .3594$.

4.13 Find a z_0 such that $P(-z_0 < z < z_0) = .8262$.

4.14 Find a z_0 such that $P(-z_0 < z < z_0) = .4714$.

4.15 Find a z_0 such that $P(-z_0 < z < z_0) = .7458$.

4.16 Find a z_0 such that $P(z < z_0) = .0968$.

4.17 Find a z_0 such that $P(z < z_0) = .9505$.

4.18 Find a z_0 such that $P(z < z_0) = .05$.

4.19 Find a z_0 such that $P(-z_0 < z < z_0) = .90$.

4.20 Find a z_0 such that $P(-z_0 < z < z_0) = .99$.

4.21 A variable x is normally distributed with mean $\mu = 10$ and standard deviation $\sigma = 2$. Find these probabilities.

(a) $P(x > 13.5)$ (b) $P(x < 8.2)$ (c) $P(9.4 < x < 10.6)$

4.22 A variable x is normally distributed with mean $\mu = 1.20$ and standard deviation $\sigma = .15$. Find the probability that x falls in the interval given.

(a) $1.00 < x < 1.10$ (b) $x > 1.38$ (c) $1.35 < x < 1.50$

4.23 A variable is normally distributed with unknown mean μ and standard deviation $\sigma = 2$. If the probability that x exceeds 7.5 is .8, find μ.

4.24 A variable is normally distributed with unknown mean μ and standard deviation $\sigma = 1.8$. If the probability that x exceeds 14.4 is .3, find μ.

4.25 A variable is normally distributed with unknown mean and standard deviation. The probability that x exceeds 4 is .9772, and the probability that x exceeds 5 is .9332. Find μ and σ.

APPLICATIONS

 4.26 One method of arriving at economic forecasts is to use a consensus approach. A forecast is obtained from each of a large number of analysts; the average of these individual forecasts is the consensus forecast. Suppose that the individual 1985 January prime interest rate forecasts of all economic analysts is approximately normally distributed with mean equal to 14% and a standard deviation of 2.6%. A single analyst is randomly selected from among this group.

(a) What is the probability that the analyst's forecast of the prime interest rate will exceed 18%?
(b) What is the probability that the analyst's forecast of the prime interest rate will be less than 16%?

 4.27 Suppose that you must establish regulations concerning the maximum number of people who can occupy an elevator. A study of elevator occupancies indicates that if 8 people occupy the elevator, the probability distribution of the total weight of the 8 people possesses a mean equal to 1200 pounds and a variance equal to 9800 (pounds)^2. What is the probability that the total weight of eight people exceeds 1300 pounds? 1500 pounds? (Assume that the probability distribution is approximately normal.)

 4.28 The discharge of suspended solids from a phosphate mine is normally distributed, with a mean daily discharge of 27 milligrams per liter (mg/l) and a standard deviation of 14 mg/l. What proportion of days will the daily discharge exceed 50 mg/l?

 4.29 Philatelists (stamp collectors) often buy stamps at or near retail prices, but when they sell, the price is considerably lower. For example, it may be reasonable to assume that (depending on the collection, its condition, the demand, economic conditions, etc.), a collection may be expected to sell at x percent of retail price, where x is normally distributed with a mean equal to 45% and a standard deviation of 4.5%. A philatelist has a collection to sell that has a retail value of $30,000.

(a) What is the probability that the philatelist receives more than $15,000 for the collection?
(b) What is the probability that the philatelist receives less than $15,000 for the collection?
(c) What is the probability that the philatelist receives less than $12,000 for the collection?

 4.30 How does the Internal Revenue Service (IRS) decide on the percentage of income tax returns to audit for each state? Suppose that it did so by randomly selecting 50 values from a normal distribution with a mean equal to 1.55% and a standard deviation equal to .45%. (Computer programs are available for this type of sampling.)

(a) What is the probability that a particular state will have more than 2.5% of its income tax returns audited?
(b) What is the probability that a state will have less than 1% of its income tax returns audited?

 4.31 Problems with the Internal Revenue Service's new computer created an enormous backlog in the processing of 1984 income tax returns and in responding to inquiries. According to *USA Today* (April 29, 1985), "As of March 29, 1985, 53 percent of inquiries had not been answered 45 days after being received." Suppose that the distribution of length of time required by the IRS to answer an inquiry is normally distributed with a standard deviation equal to 10 days.

(a) Find the mean length of time to answer an inquiry.
(b) Find the probability that the length of time required to answer an inquiry is 60 days or more.

 4.32 A survey of chief executives of some of the largest U.S. corporations found them to be health-conscious. Of the 85 executives responding to a questionnaire, 49% exercise at least 3 times per week, and 66% claim to be within 10 pounds of their ideal weight (*USA Today*, March 21, 1985). Suppose that the deviation from ideal weight for all large-corporation chief executives is normally distributed with a mean equal to zero and that 66% of the weights are within 10 pounds of the ideal.

(a) What is the standard deviation of the distribution?

(b) What is the probability that a chief executive chosen at random will be more than 5 pounds overweight?

 4.33 The daily sales (except Saturday) at a small restaurant have a probability distribution that is approximately normal, with mean μ equal to $530 per day and standard deviation σ equal to $120.

(a) What is the probability that the sales will exceed $700 on a given day?

(b) The restaurant must have at least $300 sales per day in order to break even. What is the probability that on a given day the restaurant will not break even?

 4.34 The length of life of a type of automatic washer is approximately normally distributed with mean and standard deviation equal to 3.1 and 1.2 years, respectively. If this type of washer is guaranteed for one year, what fraction of original sales will require replacement?

 4.35 A grain loader can be set to discharge grain in amounts that are normally distributed with mean μ bushels and a standard deviation equal to 25.7 bushels. If a company wishes to use the loader to fill containers that hold 2000 bushels of grain and wants to overfill only one container in 100, at what value of μ should the company set the loader?

 4.36 A publisher has discovered that the number of words contained in a new manuscript is normally distributed with a mean equal to 20,000 words in excess of that specified in the author's contract and a standard deviation of 10,000 words. If the publisher wants to be almost certain (say with a probability of .95) that the manuscript will be less than 100,000 words, what number of words should the publisher specify in the contract?

THE NORMAL APPROXIMATION TO THE BINOMIAL PROBABILITY DISTRIBUTION

4.4

Many probability distributions possess a useful characteristic. When certain conditions are satisfied, these distributions become approximately normal in shape. The binomial probability distribution is one of these. In particular, when the number n of trials in a binomial experiment is large and p is not too close to 0 or 1, the binomial probability distribution assumes a shape that is closely approximated by a normal curve with mean $\mu = np$ and standard deviation $\sigma = \sqrt{npq}$. This particular property of the binomial probability distribution becomes of value when we have to calculate binomial probabilities $p(x)$ for large values of n. The great labor and tedium encountered in these calculations can be avoided by using the normal approximating curve.

Since the best way to show how and why the normal approximation works is to use graphs and a small value of n, we will illustrate the procedure for a binomial probability distribution with $n = 10$ and $p = 1/2$. The probability histogram for a binomial probability distribution, $n = 10$, $p = 1/2$, is shown in Figure 4.11 along with

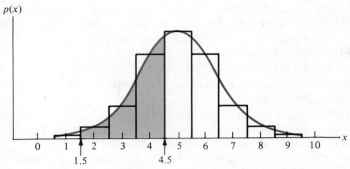

FIGURE 4.11   Comparison of a Binomial Probability Distribution and the Approximating Normal Distribution, $n = 10$, $p = 1/2$ ($\mu = np = 5$; $\sigma = \sqrt{npq} = 1.58$)

an approximating normal curve with

$$\mu = np = 10\left(\frac{1}{2}\right) = 5$$

$$\sigma = \sqrt{npq} = \sqrt{(10)\left(\frac{1}{2}\right)\left(\frac{1}{2}\right)} = \sqrt{2.5} = 1.58$$

A visual comparison of the figure suggests that the approximation is reasonably good, even though a small sample, $n = 10$, was necessary for this graphical illustration.

Suppose that we wish to approximate the probability that x equals 2, 3, or 4. You can see in Figure 4.11 that this probability is exactly equal to the area of the three rectangles lying over $x = 2$, 3, and 4. We can approximate this probability with the area under the normal curve from $x = 1.5$ to $x = 4.5$, which is shaded in Figure 4.11. Note that the area under the normal curve between $x = 2$ and $x = 4$ *would not* be a good approximation to the probability that $x = 2$, 3, or 4 because it would exclude one-half of the probability rectangles corresponding to $x = 2$ and $x = 4$. To get a good approximation, you must remember to approximate the entire areas of the probability rectangles corresponding to $x = 2$ and $x = 4$ by including the area under the normal curve from $x = 1.5$ to $x = 4.5$.

Although the normal probability distribution provides a reasonably good approximation to the binomial probability distribution in Figure 4.11, this will not always be the case. When the mean np of a binomial probability distribution is near 0 or n, the binomial probability distribution will be nonsymmetrical.* For example, when p is near zero, most values of x will be small, producing a distribution that is con-centrated near $x = 0$ and that tails gradually toward n (see Figure 4.12). Certainly, when this is true, the normal distribution, symmetrical and bell-shaped, will provide a poor approximation to the binomial probability distribution. How, then, can we tell whether n and p are such that the binomial distribution will be symmetrical?

Recall the Empirical Rule from Chapter 2; approximately 95% of the measure-ments associated with a normal distribution will lie within two standard deviations of

*A skewed binomial probability distribution can be approximated by a Poisson probability distribution. This approximation, which is discussed in optional Section 3.8, is satisfactory when n is large and np is small, say $np < 7$.

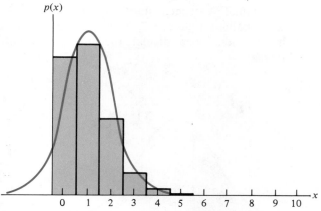

FIGURE 4.12   Comparison of a Binomial Probability Distribution (Shaded) and the Approximating Normal Distribution, $n = 10$, $p = .1$ ($\mu = np = 1$; $\sigma = \sqrt{npq} = .95$)

the mean and almost all will lie within three. We suspect that the binomial probability distribution would be nearly symmetrical if the distribution were able to spread out a distance equal to two standard deviations on either side of the mean and this is, in fact, the case. **Hence, to determine when the normal approximation will be adequate, calculate $\mu = np$ and $\sigma = \sqrt{npq}$. If the interval ($\mu \pm 2\sigma$) lies within the binomial bounds, 0 and n, the approximation will be adequate. The approximation will be good if the interval ($\mu \pm 3\sigma$) lies in the interval 0 to n.** Note that this criterion is satisfied for the binomial probability distribution of Figure 4.11, but it is not satisfied for the distribution shown in Figure 4.12.

The formulas for the **normal approximation to the binomial distribution** are given in the following box.

THE NORMAL APPROXIMATION TO THE BINOMIAL PROBABILITY DISTRIBUTION

Approximate the binomial probability distribution by using a normal curve with

$$\mu = np$$
$$\sigma = \sqrt{npq}$$

where
     n = number of trials

     p = probability of success on a single trial

     $q = 1 - p$

The approximation will be adequate when n is large and when the interval

$$\mu \pm 2\sigma$$

falls between 0 and n.

EXAMPLE 4.6   Refer to the binomial experiment illustrated in Figure 4.13, where $n = 10$, $p = .5$. Calculate the probability that $x = 2$, 3, or 4, correct to three decimal places, using Table 1 in the Appendix. Then calculate the corresponding normal approximation to this probability.

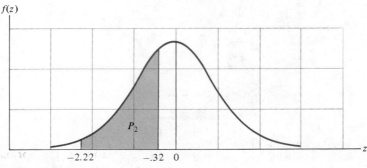

FIGURE 4.13   Area Required for Example 4.6

SOLUTION   The exact probability P_1 can be calculated by using Table 1(b) in the Appendix. Thus

$$P_1 = \sum_{x=2}^{4} p(x) = \sum_{x=0}^{4} p(x) - \sum_{x=0}^{1} p(x)$$
$$= .377 - .011$$
$$= .366$$

The normal approximation requires the area lying between $x_1 = 1.5$ and $x_2 = 4.5$ (see Figure 4.13), where $\mu = 5$ and $\sigma = 1.58$. The corresponding values of z are

$$z_1 = \frac{x_1 - \mu}{\sigma} = \frac{1.5 - 5}{1.58} = -2.22$$

$$z_2 = \frac{x_2 - \mu}{\sigma} = \frac{4.5 - 5}{1.58} = -.32$$

The probability P_2 is shown in Figure 4.13. The area between $z = 0$ and $z = 2.22$ is $A_1 = .4868$. Likewise, the area between $z = 0$ and $z = .32$ is $A_2 = .1255$. We can see from Figure 4.13 that

$$P_2 = A_1 - A_2$$
$$= .4868 - .1255 = .3613$$

Note that the normal approximation is quite close to the exact binomial probability obtained from Table 1.

You must be careful not to exclude half of the two extreme probability rectangles when using the normal approximation to the binomial probability distribution. Thus the x values used to calculate z values will always have a 5 in the tenths decimal place. To be certain that you include all the probability rectangles in your approximation, always draw a sketch similar to Figure 4.13.   ∎

EXAMPLE 4.7   The reliability of an electrical fuse is the probability that a fuse, chosen at random from production, will function under the conditions for which it has been designed. A random sample of 1000 fuses was tested and $x = 27$ defectives were observed. Calculate the probability of observing 27 or more defectives, assuming that the fuse reliability is .98.

SOLUTION   The probability of observing a defective when a single fuse is tested is $p = .02$, given that the fuse reliability is .98. Then

$$\mu = np = 1000(.02) = 20$$
$$\sigma = \sqrt{npq} = \sqrt{1000(.02)(.98)} = 4.43$$

The probability of 27 or more defective fuses, given $n = 1000$, is

$$P = P(x \geq 27)$$
$$P = p(27) + p(28) + p(29) + \cdots + p(999) + p(1000)$$

The normal approximation to P is the area under the normal curve to the right of $x = 26.5$. (Note that we must use $x = 26.5$ rather than $x = 27$ so as to include the entire probability rectangle associated with $x = 27$.) The z value corresponding to $x = 26.5$ is

$$z = \frac{x - \mu}{\sigma} = \frac{26.5 - 20}{4.43} = \frac{6.5}{4.43} = 1.47$$

and the area between $z = 0$ and $z = 1.47$ is equal to .4292, as shown in Figure 4.14. Since the total area to the right of the mean is equal to .5,

$$P = .5 - .4292 = .0708$$

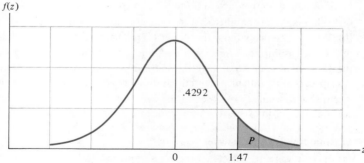

FIGURE 4.14   Normal Approximation to the Binomial for Example 4.7

EXERCISES

BASIC TECHNIQUES

4.37   Let x be a binomial random variable with $n = 25$, $p = .3$.

(a) Use Table 1 in the Appendix to find $P(8 \leq x \leq 10)$.

(b) Find μ and σ for the binomial distribution, and use the normal approximation to find $P(8 \leq x \leq 10)$. Compare the approximation with the exact value calculated in part (a).

4.38 Find the normal approximation to $P(x \geq 6)$ for a binomial probability distribution with $n = 10$, $p = .5$.

4.39 Find the normal approximation to $P(x > 6)$ for a binomial probability distribution with $n = 10$, $p = .5$.

4.40 Find the normal approximation to $P(x > 22)$ for a binomial probability distribution with $n = 100$, $p = .2$.

4.41 Find the normal approximation to $P(x \geq 22)$ for a binomial probability distribution with $n = 100$, $p = .2$.

4.42 Let x be a binomial random variable for $n = 25$, $p = .2$.

(a) Use Table 1 in the Appendix to calculate $P(4 \leq x \leq 6)$.

(b) Find μ and σ for the binomial probability distribution, and use the normal distribution to approximate the probability $P(4 \leq x \leq 6)$. Note that this value is a good approximation to the exact value of $P(4 \leq x \leq 6)$.

4.43 Consider a binomial experiment with $n = 20$, $p = .4$. Calculate $P(x \geq 10)$ by use of the following.

(a) Table 1 in the Appendix.

(b) The normal approximation to the binomial probability distribution.

4.44 Find the normal approximation to $P(355 \leq x \leq 360)$ for a binomial probability distribution with $n = 400$, $p = .9$.

APPLICATIONS

4.45 Estimates show that U.S. banks lost as much as $70 to $100 million in 1983 owing to the fraudulent use of its automatic teller machines. Furthermore, 45% of the "troubled" automatic teller transactions were potentially fraudulent—that is, they involved the use of stolen bank cards, overdrafts, bad deposits, and so on (*New York Times,* March 12, 1985). Suppose that a bank observed 56 troubled automatic teller transactions in a given day.

(a) What is the probability that half or more are potentially fraudulent?

(b) What is the probability that fewer than 20 are potentially fraudulent?

(c) What assumptions must you make in order to find the probabilities in parts (a) and (b)?

(d) If the bank found that 39 of the 56 troubled transactions were potentially fraudulent, should it suspect that its rate of potentially fraudulent transactions exceeds the national rate? Explain.

4.46 According to a survey reported at the 1981 convention of the American Bar Association, there was one lawyer in every 700 Americans in 1960, one in every 600 in 1970, and one in every 410 Americans in 1981 (*Philadelphia Inquirer,* August 18, 1981). One in every 64 residents in Washington, D.C. is a lawyer.

(a) If you were to select a random sample of 1500 Americans, what is the approximate probability that the sample would contain at least one lawyer?

(b) If the sample is selected from among the residents of Washington, D.C., what is the approximate probability that the sample would contain more than 30 lawyers?

(c) If you stood on a Washington, D.C., street corner and interviewed the first 1500 persons who walked by and 30 were lawyers, would this result suggest that the density of lawyers passing the corner exceeds the density within the city? Explain.

4.47 Airlines and hotels often grant reservations in excess of capacity to minimize losses due to no-shows. Suppose that the records of a motel show that, on the average, 10% of their prospective guests will not claim their reservation. If the motel accepts 215 reservations and there are only 200 rooms in the motel, what is the probability that all guests who arrive to claim a room will receive one?

4.48 In Exercise 3.115 we described a telephone survey conducted by the administration of the North Florida Regional Hospital, Gainesville, Florida. The purpose of the survey was to determine public attitude toward the hospital's desire to expand, even though the expansion might have a negative effect on the occupancy of the beds in the local county hospital. Of the 180 persons polled, 112 stated that they favored the expansion. What is the probability that x, the number of people favoring the expansion, is as large or larger than 112, given that the proportion of adults in the community who favor the expansion is only .5?

 4.49 A survey by Merrill Lynch Relocation Management, Inc., reported in the *Wall Street Journal* (November 20, 1979) indicates that approximately 30% of all companies actively assist working spouses in continuing their careers when company employees are transferred to new locations. To determine whether this percentage is growing over time, suppose that we conducted a survey in 1988 and found that $x = 38$ of 110 companies aided working spouses in finding new jobs when the companies' employees were transferred to new locations.

(a) What is the probability that $x \geq 38$ when, in fact, the percentage of all companies who assist working spouses continue their careers is unchanged at 30%?

(b) From your answer to part (a), explain why you believe that the population percentage has or has not changed from 1979 to 1988.

 4.50 Worker firings in Britain can be contested at no cost by appealing to a unique British institution, an industrial tribunal. A tribunal is empowered to award damages to a worker in an amount up to $17,000. In fact, of the approximately 400,000 people who get fired each year, one in 10 appeal their firings to a tribunal (*Wall Street Journal*, February 24, 1986). Suppose 500 unrelated firings occur in a particular locale in Britain.

(a) What is the probability that less than 40 of the firings will be brought before an industrial tribunal?

(b) What is the probability that 55 or more will be brought before an industrial tribunal?

 4.51 The day after Thanksgiving is traditionally an up day for the Dow-Jones Industrial Average. Although it dropped on Friday, November 28, 1986, it has gone up on the Friday following Thanksgiving in 16 of the past 20 years (*New York Times*, November 29, 1986). Suppose that there is no rhyme or reason for the odds to favor a rise in the Dow-Jones average on the Friday following Thanksgiving and that the probability of a rise is really .5.

(a) Find the exact probability that the Dow-Jones average will rise on 16 or more post-Thanksgiving Fridays in a sample of 20. (*Hint:* Use Table 1 in the Appendix.)

(b) Find the probability described in part (a) by using the normal approximation to the binomial probability distribution.

OTHER USEFUL CONTINUOUS PROBABILITY DISTRIBUTIONS✩

4.5

Not all relative frequency distributions are approximately normally distributed or even mound-shaped. In particular, random variables that can assume only nonnegative values, such as the length of time until the occurrence of some event, can possess relative frequency distributions that are skewed, as shown in Figure 4.15. Examples are the length of time to complete a maintenance program for an aircraft engine, the length

✩This section is optional.

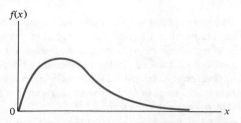

FIGURE **4.15**   A Skewed Relative Frequency Distribution

of time between changes in the Federal Reserve Board's discount rate, or the length of time to complete the sale of a new issue of stock or bonds at a brokerage company.

One useful model for skewed relative frequency distributions is the **gamma-type probability distribution**. The equation for this probability distribution contains two parameters, α and β, and therefore graphs as a family of curves. Each different combination of values of α and β produces a different shape for the distribution. Three of these, for $\alpha = 1, 2,$ and $4, \beta = 1$, are shown in Figure 4.16.

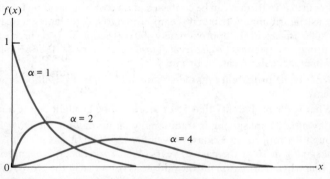

FIGURE **4.16**   Gamma-Type Probability Distributions, $\beta = 1$

Although not necessary for our discussion, the equation of the gamma-type probability distribution is shown in the following box.

PROBABILITY DISTRIBUTION FOR A GAMMA-TYPE RANDOM VARIABLE

$$f(y) = \begin{cases} \dfrac{x^{\alpha-1}e^{-x/\beta}}{\beta^{\alpha}\Gamma(\alpha)}, & \alpha, \beta > 0; 0 \leq x \leq \infty \\ 0 & \text{elsewhere} \end{cases}$$

where

$$\Gamma(\alpha) = \int_{0}^{\infty} x^{\alpha-1}e^{-x}\, dx$$

An **exponential probability distribution** is a gamma-type probability for the special case where $\alpha = 1$. A graph of this distribution appears in Figure 4.16 (the curve corresponding to $\alpha = 1$). Its formula is given in the next box.

PROBABILITY DENSITY FUNCTION FOR AN EXPONENTIAL RANDOM VARIABLE

$$f(x) = \begin{cases} \dfrac{e^{-x/\beta}}{\beta}, & \beta > 0; 0 \leq x \leq \infty \\ 0, & \text{elsewhere} \end{cases}$$

This distribution is used to model the length of time until the occurrence of some event, but it differs from other gamma-type distributions because it is said to possess the **memoryless property**. This property states that the probability distribution of the length of time to the next event is independent of what has occurred beforehand. If used to model the length of life of a particular piece of industrial equipment, this property implies that the equipment operates without fatigue. Thus if we were to use it to model the length of time to malfunction for a paper machine, we are saying that the length of time from this moment to the next malfunction is independent of the length of time the machine has been operating up to this point. Oddly enough, this probability distribution does provide a good model for the length of time to malfunction for many pieces of industrial equipment, particularly those that receive periodic maintenance and parts replacements. It also may provide a good model for the probability distribution of the length of time between arrivals at some service facility if the arrivals appear to occur in a random manner. Business simulations of the operation of service facilities often assume an exponential distribution for the length of time between customer arrivals.

Another useful model for the relative frequency distribution of continuous random variables is the **beta probability distribution**. This distribution is especially useful for modeling the relative frequency distribution of a random variable that can only assume values between two constants, say a and b. For this reason it provides a good model for the probability distributions of percentages or proportions. It could be used, for example, to model the probability distribution of the proportion of a tank of fuel or some other liquid commodity sold per week by a wholesaler. For this application the proportion x falls in the interval $a = 0$ to $b = 1$.

Like the gamma-type distribution, the beta probability distribution contains two parameters, α and β, and provides a family of curves of varying shapes, some mound-shaped, some skewed to the right, others to the left. Three of these curves are shown in Figure 4.17 for the special case $a = 0$, $b = 1$. The corresponding equation of the beta probability distribution for $a = 0$, $b = 1$ is given in the following box.

BETA PROBABILITY DENSITY FUNCTION

$$f(x) = \begin{cases} \dfrac{x^{\alpha-1}(1-x)^{\beta-1}}{B(\alpha, \beta)}, & \alpha, \beta > 0; 0 \leq x \leq 1 \\ 0, & \text{elsewhere} \end{cases}$$

where

$$B(\alpha, \beta) = \int_0^1 x^{\alpha-1}(1-x)^{\beta-1}dx = \frac{\Gamma(\alpha)\Gamma(\beta)}{\Gamma(\alpha+\beta)}$$

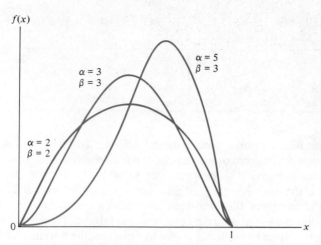

FIGURE 4.17   Beta Probability Distributions

FORTUNE'S FORTY-TO-ONE ODDS

4.6

To support the contention that the "height-blind" selection of a 5-foot-tall Chinese male is a highly improbable event, the author of the *Fortune* article notes that the Chinese equivalent of the U.S. Health Service does not exist, and therefore, the health statistics on the current population of China are difficult to acquire. However, the author notes that "it is generally held that a boy's length at birth represents 28.6% of his final height" and that in prerevolutionary China the average length of a Chinese boy at birth was 18.9 inches. From this data the author deduces that the mean height of a mature male Chinese is

$$\frac{18.9}{.286} = 66.08 \text{ inches or 5 feet, 6.08 inches}$$

The author then assumes that the distribution of the heights of males in China follows a normal distribution "(as it does in the United States)" with a mean of 66 inches and a standard deviation equal to 2.7 inches, "a figure that looks about right for that mean."

If we are willing to accept the assumption that the heights of adult Chinese males are normally distributed with

$$\mu = 66 \text{ inches} \qquad \text{and} \qquad \sigma = 2.7 \text{ inches}$$

we are ready to calculate the probability that a single adult Chinese male, chosen at random, will have a height that is less than or equal to 5 feet or, equivalently, 60 inches. This probability will be the area under a normal curve lying to the left of 60 inches (see Figure 4.18).

The z value corresponding to 60 inches is

$$z = \frac{x - \mu}{\sigma} = \frac{60 - 66}{2.7} = -2.22$$

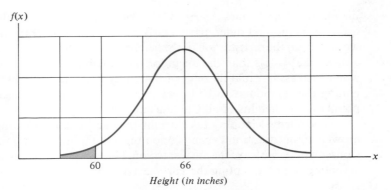

$f(x)$

60   66

Height (in inches)

FIGURE 4.18   The Assumed Distribution of Heights for Adult Male Chinese

and the area between $z = 0$ and $z = 2.22$ (see Table 4 in the Appendix) is .4868. Then the tail area to the left of $x = 60$ is

$$P = .5 - .4868$$
$$= .0132$$

This probability, the probability of randomly selecting a Chinese male less than 5 feet in height, is approximately 1 in 76, which corresponds to odds of 75 to 1.*

Odds of 75 to 1 certainly agree with our intuition because it is difficult to believe that the proportion of adult male Chinese who are less than 5 feet tall is very large. Nevertheless, the validity of our calculated odds depends upon the validity of our assumptions. The author of the article makes a good case for assuming that the distribution of the heights of Chinese males is approximately normal, and we would be willing to accept the claim that the mean height is equal to 66 inches or larger. (If in fact the mean height of adult Chinese males is larger than 66 inches, the probability of randomly selecting a male with a height less than or equal to 5 feet is even less than .0132.) Choosing σ equal to 2.7 inches, solely because it is "a figure that looks about right for that mean" is more difficult to accept because the choice of σ greatly affects the calculated odds. For example, if σ equals 3 inches, then 60 inches lies $z = 2$ standard deviations below $\mu = 66$ inches. If $\sigma = 6$ inches, then 60 inches lies only $z = 1.0$ standard deviation below $\mu = 66$ inches. In spite of this point, we agree with *Fortune*'s author. It is difficult to believe that σ could be very large, say larger than 4 or 5 inches, but that is probably because we find it difficult to believe that the proportion of adult male Chinese who are 5 feet tall is very large! Thus we have returned to our original point. Choosing a *reasonable* value for σ is equivalent to choosing *reasonable* odds.

Finally, there is another possible basic flaw in our assumptions. It is not clear that the distribution of the heights of all adult male Chinese is a good model for the distribution of the heights of potential candidates for Deng Xiaoping's replacement. Presumably, the candidates would be a very select group of senior, and elderly,

*The probability that a randomly selected Chinese male will be less than 60 inches or more than 72 inches in height (i.e., will deviate from the mean $\mu = 66$ inches by more than 6 inches) is 2(.0132) = .0264. This probability corresponds to odds of slightly less than 40 to 1.

members of the Chinese party. It is a well-known fact that the heights of humans decrease as they get older, particularly as they reach 60 years or older. Therefore, we would expect the distribution of the heights of the candidates for Deng's post to possess a mean that is less than the mean for the distribution of all adult male Chinese. We would also assume that the odds of randomly selecting a person 5 feet tall (or less) from among the candidates to be larger than a corresponding selection from among the population of heights of all Chinese adult males.

Did Deng Xiaoping take height into account in selecting his successor? The answer to this question depends upon the assumptions that you are willing to make. Consequently, we leave the answer to you. Perhaps you will have additional reasons for accepting or not accepting the *Fortune* assumptions.

4.7 SUMMARY

Many continuous random variables observed in nature possess probability distributions that are bell-shaped and that can be approximated by the normal probability distribution of Section 4.2. As a case in point, the number x of successes associated with a binomial experiment can be approximated by a normal probability distribution when the number n of trials is large.

One explanation for this phenomenon is a mathematical result known as the Central Limit Theorem. In Chapter 5 we will learn why so many statistics possess probability distributions that are approximately normal and why the Central Limit Theorem (and the normal distribution) plays such a prominent role in statistical inference.

TIPS ON PROBLEM SOLVING

(1) Always sketch a normal curve and locate the probability areas pertinent to the exercise. If you are approximating a binomial probability distribution, sketch in the probability rectangles as well as the normal curve.

(2) Read each exercise carefully to see whether the data come from a binomial experiment or whether they possess a distribution that, by its very nature, is approximately normal. If you are approximating a binomial probability distribution, do not forget to make a half-unit correction so that you will include the half rectangles at the ends of the interval. If the distribution is not binomial, *do not* make the half-unit corrections. If you make a sketch (as suggested in step 1), you will see why the half-unit correction is or is not needed.

REFERENCES

Freund, J. E., and Williams, F. J.; revised by B. Perles and C. Sullivan. *Modern Business Statistics.* Englewood Cliffs, N. J.: Prentice-Hall, 1969.

Hamburg, M. *Statistical Analysis for Decision Making.* 3rd ed. New York: Harcourt Brace Jovanovich, 1983.

Hoel, P. G. *Elementary Statistics.* 4th ed. New York: Wiley, 1976.

Huntsberger, D. V., and Billingsley, P. *Elements of Statistical Inference*. 4th ed. Boston: Allyn and Bacon, 1977.

McClave, J. T., and Benson, P. G. *Statistics for Business and Economics*. 3rd ed. San Francisco: Dellen, 1985.

Mendenhall, W., Scheaffer, R. L., and Wackerly, D. D. *Mathematical Statistics with Applications*. 3rd ed. Boston: PWS-KENT, 1986.

Neter, J., Wasserman, W., and Whitmore, G. A. *Fundamental Statistics for Business and Economics*. 4th ed. Boston: Allyn and Bacon, 1973.

Sincich, T. *Statistics by Example*. 3rd ed. New York: Macmillan, 1987.

KEY TERMS

Random variable (page 92)
Normal probability distribution (page 130)
Standardized normal distribution (page 132)
Normal approximation to the binomial probability distribution (page 141)

Gamma-type frequency probability distribution (page 146)
Beta probability distribution (page 147)

SUPPLEMENTARY EXERCISES

4.52 Using Table 4 in the Appendix, calculate the area under the normal curve between these values.
(a) $z = 0$ and $z = 1.2$ (b) $z = 0$ and $z = -.9$

4.53 Repeat Exercise 4.52 for these values.
(a) $z = 0$ and $z = 1.6$ (b) $z = 0$ and $z = .75$

4.54 Repeat Exercise 4.52 for these values.
(a) $z = 0$ and $z = 1.46$ (b) $z = 0$ and $z = -.42$

4.55 Repeat Exercise 4.52 for these values.
(a) $z = 0$ and $z = -1.44$ (b) $z = 0$ and $z = 2.01$

4.56 Repeat Exercise 4.52 for these values.
(a) $z = .3$ and $z = 1.56$ (b) $z = .2$ and $z = -.2$

4.57 Repeat Exercise 4.52 for these values.
(a) $z = .88$ and $z = 1.85$ (b) $z = -.31$ and $z = 1.63$

4.58 Repeat Exercise 4.52 for these values.
(a) $z = 1.21$ and $z = 1.75$ (b) $z = -1.3$ and $z = 1.74$

4.59 Find the probability that z is greater than $-.75$.

4.60 Find the probability that z is less than 1.35.

4.61 Find a z_0 such that $P(z > z_0) = .5$.

4.62 Find a z_0 such that $P(z < z_0) = .8643$.

4.63 Find the probability that z lies between $z = .7$ and $z = 1.63$.

4.64 Let x be a normally distributed random variable with mean equal to 7 and standard deviation equal to 1.5. If a value of x is chosen at random from the population, find the probability that x falls between $x = 8$ and $x = 9$.

4.65 Find the probability that z lies between $z = -.2$ and $z = 1.83$.

4.66 Find the probability that z lies between $z = -1.48$ and $z = 1.48$.

4.67 Find a z_0 such that $P(-z_0 < z < z_0) = .5$.

4.68 The length of life of oil-drilling bits depends upon the types of rock and soil that the drill encounters, but it is estimated that the mean length of life is 75 hours. An oil exploration company purchases drill bits that have a length of life that is approximately normally distributed with mean equal to 75 hours and standard deviation equal to 12 hours.

   (a) What proportion of the company's drill bits will fail before 60 hours of use?

   (b) What proportion will last at least 60 hours?

   (c) What proportion will have to be replaced after more than 90 hours of use?

4.69 The influx of new ideas into a college or university, introduced primarily by hiring new young faculty, is becoming a matter of concern because of the increasing ages of faculty members. That is, the distribution of faculty ages is shifting upward, due most likely to a shortage of vacant positions and an oversupply of Ph.D.'s. Thus faculty members are more reluctant to move and give up a secure position. If the retirement age at most universities is 65, would you expect the distribution of faculty ages to be normal?

4.70 A machine operation produces bearings whose diameters are normally distributed with mean and standard deviation equal to .498 and .002, respectively. If specifications require that the bearing diameter equal .500 inch plus or minus .004 inch, what fraction of the production will be unacceptable?

4.71 A used-car dealership has found that, for the cars it sells, the length of time before a major repair is required is normally distributed with a mean equal to ten months and a standard deviation of three months. If the dealer wants only 5% of the cars to fail before guarantee time, for how long (in months) should the cars be guaranteed?

4.72 Most users of automatic garage door openers activate their openers at distances that are normally distributed with a mean of 30 feet and a standard deviation of 11 feet. In order to minimize interference with other radio-controlled devices, the manufacturer is required to limit the operating distance to 50 feet. What percentage of the time will users attempt to operate the opener outside of its operating limit?

4.73 Consider a binomial experiment with $n = 25$, $p = .4$. Calculate $P(8 \le x \le 11)$ by use of the following.

   (a) The binomial probabilities, Table 1 in the Appendix.

   (b) The normal approximation to the binomial.

4.74 Consider a binomial experiment with $n = 25$, $p = .2$. Calculate $P(x \le 4)$ by use of the following.

   (a) Table 1 in the Appendix.

   (b) The normal approximation to the binomial.

4.75 You are told that 30% of all calls coming into a telephone exchange are long-distance calls. If 200 calls come in to the exchange, what is the probability that at least 50 will be long-distance calls?

4.76 An airline finds that 5% of the persons making reservations on a certain flight will not show up for the flight. If the airline sells 160 tickets for a flight with only 155 seats, what is the probability that a seat will be available for every person holding a reservation and planning to fly?

4.77 The admissions office of a small college is asked to accept deposits from a number of qualified prospective freshmen so that with probability about .95 the size of the freshman class will be less than or equal to 120. Consider that the applicants comprise a random sample from a population of applicants, 80% of whom would actually enter the freshman class if accepted.

   (a) How many deposits should the admissions counselor accept?

   (b) If applicants in the number determined in part (a) are accepted, what is the probability that the freshman class size will be less than 105?

4.78 A newly designed portable radio was styled on the assumption that 50% of all purchasers are female. If a random sample of 400 purchasers is selected, what is the probability that the number of female purchasers in the sample will be greater than 175?

 4.79 A salesman has found that, on the average, the probability of a sale on a single contact is equal to .3. If the salesman contacts 50 customers, what is the probability that at least 10 will buy? (Assume that x, the number of sales, follows a binomial probability distribution.)

 4.80 David Dreiman, writing in *Forbes* magazine (August 3, 1981), notes that senior corporation executives are not very accurate forecasters of their own annual earnings. He states that his studies of a large number of company executive forecasts "showed that the average estimate missed the mark by 15%."

(a) Suppose that the distribution of these forecast errors has a mean of 15% and a standard deviation of 10%. Is it likely that the distribution of forecast errors is approximately normal?

(b) Suppose that the probability is .5 that a corporate executive's forecast error exceeds 15%. If you were to sample the forecasts of 100 corporate executives, what is the approximate probability that more than 60 would be in error by more than 15%?

 4.81 A soft-drink machine can be regulated so that it discharges an average of μ ounces per cup. If the ounces of fill are normally distributed with standard deviation equal to .3 ounce, give the setting for μ so that 8-ounce cups will overflow only 1% of the time.

 4.82 A manufacturing plant utilizes 3000 electric light bulbs that have a length of life that is normally distributed with mean and standard deviation equal to 500 and 50 hours, respectively. In an effort to minimize the number of bulbs that burn out during operating hours, all the bulbs are replaced after a given period of operation. How often should the bulbs be replaced if we wish no more than 1% of the bulbs to burn out between replacement periods?

In the preceding chapters we discussed some useful random variables and their probability distributions. In practical sampling situations we do not usually sample a single value of *x*. Rather, we select a sample of *n* values and then use those values to calculate statistics such as the sample mean and standard deviation. Then we use these statistics to make inferences about the sampled population. The objective of this chapter is to study some useful statistics and their probability distributions. Then we will explain why, under rather general conditions, all of these statistics possess probability distributions that can be approximated by the normal curve. In subsequent chapters we will show how sample statistics and their probability distributions are used to make inferences about sampled populations.

5

SAMPLING DISTRIBUTIONS

CASE STUDY

Sampling the Roulette
at Monte Carlo

How would you like to try your hand at gambling without the risk of losing? You could do it by simulating the gambling process, making imaginary bets, and observing the results. If you were to repeat the simulation over and over again for a large number of times, you would be able to see how your winnings might vary if you were to gamble "for real."

The technique of simulating a process that contains random elements and repeating the process over and over to see how it behaves is called a **Monte Carlo procedure**. It is widely used in business and other fields to investigate the properties of an operation that is subject to a number of random effects such as weather or human behavior. For example, you can model the behavior of a manufacturing company's inventory by creating, on paper, daily arrivals and departures of manufactured product from the company's warehouse. Each day, a random number of items produced by the company will be received into inventory. Similarly, each day a random number of orders of varying random sizes will be shipped. Based on the input and output of items, you can calculate the inventory, the number of items on hand at the end of each day. The values of the random variables, the number of items produced, the number of orders, and the number of items per order needed for each day's simulation can be obtained from theoretical distributions of observations that closely model the corresponding distributions of the variables that have been observed over time in the manufacturing operation. By repeating the simulation of the supply and shipping and the calculation of daily inventory for a large number of days (a sampling of what might really happen), you can observe the behavior of the plant's daily inventory. The Monte Carlo procedure is particularly valuable because it enables the manufacturer to see how the daily inventory will behave when certain changes are made in the supply pattern or in some other aspect of the operation that can be controlled.

Daniel Seligman comments on the Monte Carlo method in an article titled "The Road to Monte Carlo" (*Fortune,* April 15, 1985, p. 157). Seligman notes that although the Monte Carlo technique is widely used in business schools to study capital budgeting, inventory planning, and management of cash flow, no one seems to have used the procedure to study how well we might do if we were to gamble at Monte Carlo.

To follow up on this thought, Seligman programmed his personal computer to simulate the game of roulette. Roulette consists of a wheel whose rim is divided into 38 pockets. Thirty-six of the pockets are numbered 1 to 36 and are alternately colored red and black. The two remaining pockets are colored green and are marked 0 and 00. To play the game, you bet a certain amount of money on one or more pockets. The wheel is spun and turns until it stops. A ball falls into a slot on the wheel to indicate the winning number. If you have money on that number, you win a specified amount. For example, if you were to play the number 20, the payoff is 35 to 1. If the wheel does not stop at your pocket, you lose your bet. Seligman decided to see how his nightly gains (or losses) would fare if he were to bet $5 on each turn of the wheel and to repeat the process 200 times each night. He repeated the process 365 times, thereby simulating the outcomes of 365 nights at the casino. Not surprisingly, the mean "gain" per $1000 evening for the 365 nights was a loss of $55, the average of the winnings retained by the gambling house. The surprise, according to Seligman, was the extreme variability of the nightly "winnings." Seven times out of the 365 evenings, the fictitious gambler lost the total $1000 stake, and he won a maximum of $1160 only once. One hundred forty-one of the losses exceeded $250.

So much for Monte Carlo and gambling. Our interest in the Monte Carlo procedure is its use in studying the behavior of sample **statistics**. Since we will use sample statistics to make inferences about population parameters, we will want to see how they behave in repeated sampling. This can be done by using the Monte Carlo procedure, sampling, observing the value of a statistic, and then repeating the process over and over again.

In this chapter we will examine the properties of some useful statistics. In Section 5.8 we will note that a night's winnings in Seligman's simulation of Monte Carlo gambling is itself a statistic, the sum of the gains and losses incurred for 200 $5 bets. Then we will use our knowledge of the behavior of a sample sum to decide whether Seligman observed an improbable number of large losses.

5.1   RANDOM SAMPLING

Since probability distributions are theoretical models for population relative frequency distributions, samples selected from populations can be viewed as observations on random variables, and the probability of observing certain sample outcomes will depend upon how the sample is selected. As noted in Section 3.1, these probabilities play an important role in statistical inference.

The least complicated sampling procedure is known as **simple random sampling**. Simple random sampling gives every different sample in the population an equal chance of being selected. To illustrate, suppose that we wish to select a sample of $n = 2$ from a population containing $N = 4$ elements (we are choosing a small value of N to simplify our discussion). If the four elements are identified by the symbols x_1, x_2, x_3, and x_4, then there are six different samples that can be selected from the population:

Sample	Observations in Sample
1	x_1, x_2
2	x_1, x_3
3	x_1, x_4
4	x_2, x_3
5	x_2, x_4
6	x_3, x_4

If the sample was selected so that each of these six samples had an equal chance of selection (probability equal to 1/6), the sample would be called a simple random (or, simply, "random") sample.

It can be shown* that the number of ways of selecting $n = 2$ elements from a set of $N = 4$, denoted by the symbol C_2^4, is

$$C_2^4 = \frac{4!}{2!2!} = \frac{4 \cdot 3 \cdot 2 \cdot 1}{(2 \cdot 1)(2 \cdot 1)} = 6$$

*An understanding of this derivation is not essential to our discussion.

As explained in Section 3.5, the symbol $n!$ (read "n factorial") is used to denote the product $n(n - 1)(n - 2) \cdots 3 \cdot 2 \cdot 1$. Thus $5! = 5 \cdot 4 \cdot 3 \cdot 2 \cdot 1 = 120$. (The quantity $0!$ is defined to be equal to 1.) In general, the number of ways of selecting n elements from a set of N is

$$C_n^N = \frac{N!}{n!(N - n)!}$$

For example, if you wish to conduct an opinion poll of 5000 people based on a sample of $n = 100$, there are C_{100}^{5000} different combinations of people who could be selected in the sample. If the sampling is conducted so that each of these combinations has an equal probability of being selected, the sample is called a simple random sample.

DEFINITION   Let N and n represent the numbers of elements in the population and sample, respectively. If the sampling is conducted so that each of the C_n^N samples has an equal probability of being selected, the sampling is said to be random, and the result is said to be a *simple random sample*.   ■

It is easy to understand what is meant by random sampling, but it is much more difficult to actually select a random sample in a practical situation. A knowledge of the concept of random sampling is necessary for some of the sampling situations in this chapter; however, the problem of actually selecting random samples is deferred to Section 14.2.

SAMPLING DISTRIBUTIONS OF STATISTICS

5.2   Statistics (Section 2.4), computed from the sample measurements, will be used in Chapter 6 to estimate and to make decisions about population parameters. These quantities, like the sample data from which they were computed, vary from sample to sample in a random manner. For example, if you compute the sample means for two different samples selected from the same population, they will almost certainly assume different values. Consequently, sample statistics, such as the sample mean $\bar{x}$ and the sample standard deviation s, are random variables.

If we compute a sample statistic, say the sample mean $\bar{x}$, from a specific set of sample data, how near to the population mean μ is it likely to fall? What is the probability that the sample mean will deviate from μ by more than some specified amount? To answer these questions, we need to know the probability, or **sampling distribution**, of the sample mean.

DEFINITION   The probability distribution for a statistic is called the *sampling distribution* of the statistic.   ■

The sampling distribution of a statistic can be acquired in two ways. It can be derived mathematically, a topic beyond the scope of this text, or it can be approximated by using the Monte Carlo technique described in the Case Study. This approximation is accomplished by simulating repeated sampling of a fixed number n of observations from a given population. Each time a sample is randomly selected from the population, the value of the statistic is calculated. The observations are returned to the population, and the sampling process is repeated. If the sampling process is repeated a very large number of times, the relative frequency distribution of the computed values of the statistic will provide an approximation to its sampling distribution. This approximation will only be valid for the population and sample size used in the Monte Carlo procedure. We will demonstrate the use of the Monte Carlo procedure in the following section.

THE CENTRAL LIMIT THEOREM AND THE SAMPLING DISTRIBUTION OF THE SAMPLE MEAN

5.3

The sampling distribution of the sample mean $\bar{x}$ possesses some unique properties. If a random sample of n observations is drawn from a population with mean μ and standard deviation σ, the sampling distribution of $\bar{x}$ will have a mean μ (the same as the mean of the sampled population) and a standard deviation equal to $\sigma/\sqrt{n}$. (The standard deviation of the sampling distribution of a statistic is sometimes called the **standard error** of the statistic. Thus the standard deviation of the sampling distribution of the sample mean is sometimes called the **standard error of the mean**.) But the most important property is a result known in statistics as the **Central Limit Theorem**.

This theorem (which applies both to the sample mean $\bar{x}$ and the sample sum $\sum_{i=1}^{n} x_i$) states that when the sample size n is large, the sampling distribution of the sample mean (or sum) will possess approximately a normal distribution. Therefore, for most situations the sampling distribution of the sample mean $\bar{x}$ will appear as shown in Figure 5.1. The Central Limit Theorem is stated formally in the box that follows.

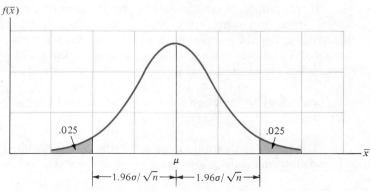

FIGURE 5.1   The Sampling Distribution of the Sample Mean $\bar{x}$

THE CENTRAL LIMIT THEOREM

If random samples of n observations are drawn from a population with finite mean μ and standard deviation σ, then when n is large, the sampling distribution of the sample mean $\bar{x}$ will be approximately a normal distribution with mean equal to μ and standard deviation $\sigma/\sqrt{n}$. The approximation will become more and more accurate as n becomes larger and larger.

  The Central Limit Theorem can be restated to apply to the sum of the sample measurements $\sum\limits_{i=1}^{n} x_i$, which also tends to possess a normal sampling distribution, with mean equal to $n\mu$ and standard deviation $\sigma\sqrt{n}$, as n becomes large.

The mean and standard deviation of the sampling distribution of $\bar{x}$ can be derived and the Central Limit Theorem can be proved mathematically, but the actual proofs are beyond the scope of this text. We can, however, present some Monte Carlo experiments that lend support to our assertions.

Figure 5.2 gives the probability distribution for the number x observed in the toss of a single die. The mean of this distribution is $\mu = 3.5$ (found in Example 3.9), and its standard deviation is $\sigma = 1.71$ (found in Exercise 3.35). Thus Figure 5.2 is the theoretical distribution of a population of die tosses—that is, the distribution of observations obtained if a die were tossed over and over again an infinitely large number of times.

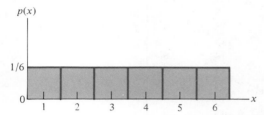

FIGURE 5.2   Probability Distribution for x, the Number Appearing on a Single Toss of a Die

Now suppose that we wish to approximate the sampling distribution for the mean $\bar{x}$ of a sample of $n = 5$ observations selected from the die-tossing population. We can obtain this approximation by conducting a Monte Carlo experiment. As a first step, we draw a sample of $n = 5$ measurements from the population by tossing a die five times and observing the numbers $x = 3, 5, 1, 3,$ and 2. We then repeat this sampling procedure, each time drawing $n = 5$ observations and recording them, for a total of 100 samples. These 100 sets of sample observations, along with the sample sums and means, are recorded in Table 5.1.

The relative frequency histogram for the 100 sample means, shown in Figure 5.3, is an approximation to the sampling distribution for the mean $\bar{x}$ of a random sample of $n = 5$ die tosses. The approximation would have been better (the shape of the histogram more regular) if we had repeated our Monte Carlo procedure a larger number of times, but the results of the 100 sample repetitions illustrate the properties of the sampling distribution of a sample mean. The relative frequency histogram of the 100 die toss means in Figure 5.3 centers over the population mean, $\mu = 3.5$. You can

TABLE 5.1   Sampling from the Population of Die Throws

Sample Number	Sample Measurements	$\sum x_i$	$\bar{x}$	Sample Number	Sample Measurements	$\sum x_i$	$\bar{x}$
1	3, 5, 1, 3, 2	14	2.8	51	2, 3, 5, 3, 2	15	3.0
2	3, 1, 1, 4, 6	15	3.0	52	1, 1, 1, 2, 4	9	1.8
3	1, 3, 1, 6, 1	12	2.4	53	2, 6, 3, 4, 5	20	4.0
4	4, 5, 3, 3, 2	17	3.4	54	1, 2, 2, 1, 1	7	1.4
5	3, 1, 3, 5, 2	14	2.8	55	2, 4, 4, 6, 2	18	3.6
6	2, 4, 4, 2, 4	16	3.2	56	3, 2, 5, 4, 5	19	3.8
7	4, 2, 5, 5, 3	19	3.8	57	2, 4, 2, 4, 5	17	3.4
8	3, 5, 5, 5, 5	23	4.6	58	5, 5, 4, 3, 2	19	3.8
9	6, 5, 5, 1, 6	23	4.6	59	5, 4, 4, 6, 3	22	4.4
10	5, 1, 6, 1, 6	19	3.8	60	3, 2, 5, 3, 1	14	2.8
11	1, 1, 1, 5, 3	11	2.2	61	2, 1, 4, 1, 3	11	2.2
12	3, 4, 2, 4, 4	17	3.4	62	4, 1, 1, 5, 2	13	2.6
13	2, 6, 1, 5, 4	18	3.6	63	2, 3, 1, 2, 3	11	2.2
14	6, 3, 4, 2, 5	20	4.0	64	2, 3, 3, 2, 6	16	3.2
15	2, 6, 2, 1, 5	16	3.2	65	4, 3, 5, 2, 6	20	4.0
16	1, 5, 1, 2, 5	14	2.8	66	3, 1, 3, 3, 4	14	2.8
17	3, 5, 1, 1, 2	12	2.4	67	4, 6, 1, 3, 6	20	4.0
18	3, 2, 4, 3, 5	17	3.4	68	2, 4, 6, 6, 3	21	4.2
19	5, 1, 6, 3, 1	16	3.2	69	4, 1, 6, 5, 5	21	4.2
20	1, 6, 4, 4, 1	16	3.2	70	6, 6, 6, 4, 5	27	5.4
21	6, 4, 2, 3, 5	20	4.0	71	2, 2, 5, 6, 3	18	3.6
22	1, 3, 5, 4, 1	14	2.8	72	6, 6, 6, 1, 6	25	5.0
23	2, 6, 5, 2, 6	21	4.2	73	4, 4, 4, 3, 1	16	3.2
24	3, 5, 1, 3, 5	17	3.4	74	4, 4, 5, 4, 2	19	3.8
25	5, 2, 4, 4, 3	18	3.6	75	4, 5, 4, 1, 4	18	3.6
26	6, 1, 1, 1, 6	15	3.0	76	5, 3, 2, 3, 4	17	3.4
27	1, 4, 1, 2, 6	14	2.8	77	1, 3, 3, 1, 5	13	2.6
28	3, 1, 2, 1, 5	12	2.4	78	4, 1, 5, 5, 3	18	3.6
29	1, 5, 5, 4, 5	20	4.0	79	4, 5, 6, 5, 4	24	4.8
30	4, 5, 3, 5, 2	19	3.8	80	1, 5, 3, 4, 2	15	3.0
31	4, 1, 6, 1, 1	13	2.6	81	4, 3, 4, 6, 3	20	4.0
32	3, 6, 4, 1, 2	16	3.2	82	5, 4, 2, 1, 6	18	3.6
33	3, 5, 5, 2, 2	17	3.4	83	1, 3, 2, 2, 5	13	2.6
34	1, 1, 5, 6, 3	16	3.2	84	5, 4, 1, 4, 6	20	4.0
35	2, 6, 1, 6, 2	17	3.4	85	2, 4, 2, 5, 5	18	3.6
36	2, 4, 3, 1, 3	13	2.6	86	1, 6, 3, 1, 6	17	3.4
37	1, 5, 1, 5, 2	14	2.8	87	2, 2, 4, 3, 2	13	2.6
38	6, 6, 5, 3, 3	23	4.6	88	4, 4, 5, 4, 4	21	4.2
39	3, 3, 5, 2, 1	14	2.8	89	2, 5, 4, 3, 4	18	3.6
40	2, 6, 6, 6, 5	25	5.0	90	5, 1, 6, 4, 3	19	3.8
41	5, 5, 2, 3, 4	19	3.8	91	5, 2, 5, 6, 3	21	4.2
42	6, 4, 1, 6, 2	19	3.8	92	6, 4, 1, 2, 1	14	2.8
43	2, 5, 3, 1, 4	15	3.0	93	6, 3, 1, 5, 2	17	3.4
44	4, 2, 3, 2, 1	12	2.4	94	1, 3, 6, 4, 2	16	3.2
45	4, 4, 5, 4, 4	21	4.2	95	6, 1, 4, 2, 2	15	3.0
46	5, 4, 5, 5, 4	23	4.6	96	1, 1, 2, 3, 1	8	1.6
47	6, 6, 6, 2, 1	21	4.2	97	6, 2, 5, 1, 6	20	4.0
48	2, 1, 5, 5, 4	17	3.4	98	3, 1, 1, 4, 1	10	2.0
49	6, 4, 3, 1, 5	19	3.8	99	5, 2, 1, 6, 1	15	3.0
50	4, 4, 4, 4, 4	20	4.0	100	2, 4, 3, 4, 6	19	3.8

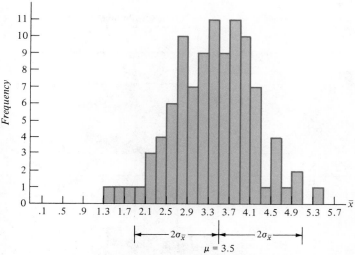

Histogram of Sample Means for the Die-Tossing Experiments in Section 5.3

also see in Figure 5.3 that the interval $(\mu \pm 2\sigma_{\bar{x}})$ (where $\sigma_{\bar{x}} = \sigma/\sqrt{n} = 1.71/\sqrt{5} = .76$) includes most of the sample means. Most surprising is the shape of the sampling distribution. Even though we sampled only $n = 5$ observations from a population with a perfectly flat probability distribution (Figure 5.2), the distribution of sample means in Figure 5.3 is mound-shaped and gives the appearance of being approximately normal.

Figure 5.4 gives the results of some other Monte Carlo sampling experiments. We programmed a computer to select random samples of size $n = 2, 5, 10,$ and 25 from each of three populations, the first possessing a normal probability distribution, the second a uniform probability distribution, and the third a negative exponential probability distribution. These population probability distributions are shown in the top row of Figure 5.4. The computer printouts of the approximations to sampling distributions of the sample mean $\bar{x}$ for sample sizes $n = 2, 5, 10,$ and 25 are shown in rows 2, 3, 4, and 5 of Figure 5.4.

Figure 5.4 illustrates an important theorem of theoretical statistics. The sampling distribution of the sample mean is exactly normally distributed (proof omitted), regardless of the sample size, when we are sampling from a population that possesses a normal distribution. In contrast, the sampling distributions of $\bar{x}$ for samples selected from populations with uniform and negative exponential probability distributions tend to become more nearly normal as the sample size n increases from $n = 2$ to $n = 25$, rapidly for the uniform distribution, and more slowly for the highly skewed exponential distribution. But note that the sampling distribution of $\bar{x}$ is normal or approximately normal for sampling from either the uniform or the exponential probability distributions when the sample size is as large as $n = 25$. This result suggests that for many populations the sampling distribution of $\bar{x}$ will be approximately normal for moderate sample sizes. There are exceptions to this rule. Consequently, we will give the appropriate sample size n for specific applications of the Central Limit Theorem as they are encountered in the text.

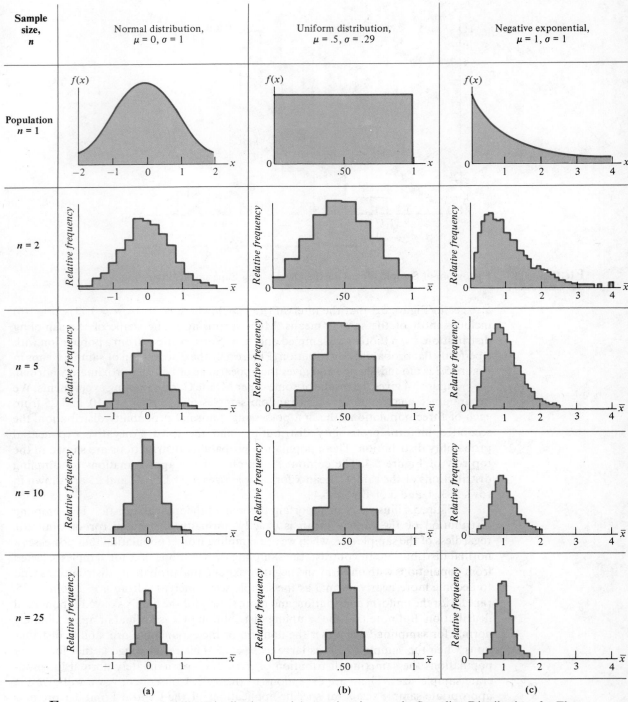

FIGURE 5.4   Probability Distributions and Approximations to the Sampling Distributions for Three Populations

The properties of the sampling distribution of the sample mean are given in the next box.

THE SAMPLING DISTRIBUTION OF THE SAMPLE MEAN $\bar{x}$

(1) If a random sample of n measurements is selected from a population with mean μ and standard deviation σ, the sampling distribution of the sample mean $\bar{x}$ will possess a mean

$$\mu_{\bar{x}} = \mu$$

and a standard deviation

$$\sigma_{\bar{x}} = \frac{\sigma}{\sqrt{n}}$$

(2) If the population possesses a normal distribution, then the sampling distribution of $\bar{x}$ will be exactly normally distributed.

(3) If the population distribution is nonnormal, the sampling distribution of $\bar{x}$ will be, for large samples, approximately normally distributed (by the Central Limit Theorem). Figure 5.4 suggests that the sampling distributions of $\bar{x}$ will be approximately normal for sample sizes as small as $n = 25$ for most populations of measurements.

EXAMPLE 5.1   Suppose that you select a random sample of $n = 25$ observations from a population with mean $\mu = 8$ and $\sigma = .6$.

(a) Find the approximate probability that the sample mean $\bar{x}$ will be less than 7.9.

(b) Find the approximate probability that the sample mean $\bar{x}$ will exceed 7.9.

(c) Find the approximate probability that the sample mean $\bar{x}$ will lie within .1 of the population mean $\mu = 8$.

SOLUTION   (a) Regardless of the shape of the population relative frequency distribution, the sampling distribution of $\bar{x}$ will possess a mean $\mu_{\bar{x}} = \mu = 8$ and a standard deviation

$$\sigma_{\bar{x}} = \frac{\sigma}{\sqrt{n}} = \frac{.6}{\sqrt{25}} = .12$$

For a sample as large as $n = 25$, it is likely (because of the Central Limit Theorem) that the sampling distribution of $\bar{x}$ is approximately normally distributed (we will assume that it is). Therefore, the probability P that $\bar{x}$ will be less than 7.9 is approximated by the shaded area under the normal sampling distribution in Figure 5.5. To find this area, we need to calculate the value of z corresponding to $\bar{x} = 7.9$. This value of z is the distance between $\bar{x} = 7.9$ and $\mu_{\bar{x}} = \mu = 8.0$ expressed in standard deviations of the sampling distribution— that is, in units of

$$\sigma_{\bar{x}} = \frac{\sigma}{\sqrt{n}} = .12$$

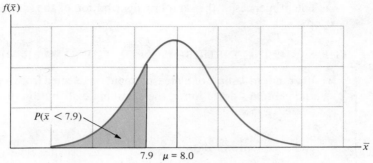

$P(\bar{x} < 7.9)$

7.9 $\mu = 8.0$

FIGURE 5.5   The Probability that $\bar{x}$ Is Less Than 7.9 for Example 5.1

Thus

$$z = \frac{\bar{x} - \mu}{\sigma_{\bar{x}}} = \frac{7.9 - 8.0}{.12} = -.83$$

From Table 4 in the Appendix we find that the area corresponding to $z = .83$ is .2967. Therefore,

$$P = .5 - A = .5 - .2967 = .2033$$

[Note that we must use $\sigma_{\bar{x}}$ (not σ) in the formula for z because we are finding an area under the sampling distribution for $\bar{x}$, not under the sampling distribution for x.]

(b) The event that $\bar{x}$ exceeds 7.9 is the complement of the event that $\bar{x}$ is less than 7.9. Thus the probability that $\bar{x}$ exceeds 7.9 is

$$P(\bar{x} > 7.9) = 1 - P(\bar{x} < 7.9)$$
$$= 1 - .2033$$
$$= .7967$$

(c) The probability that $\bar{x}$ lies within .1 of $\mu = 8$ is the shaded area in Figure 5.6. We found in part (a) that the area A between $\bar{x} = 7.9$ and $\mu = 8.0$ is .2967. Since the

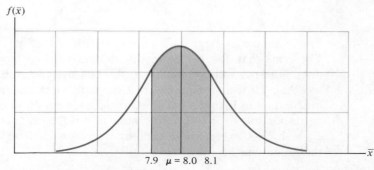

7.9 $\mu = 8.0$ 8.1

FIGURE 5.6   The Probability that $\bar{x}$ Lies Within .1 of $\mu = 8$ for Example 5.1

area under the normal curve between $\bar{x} = 8.1$ and $\mu = 8.0$ is identical to the area between $\bar{x} = 7.9$ and $\mu = 8.0$, it follows that

$$P(7.9 < \bar{x} < 8.1) = 2A$$
$$= 2(.2967)$$
$$= .5934$$ ■

EXAMPLE 5.2   To avoid difficulties with the Federal Trade Commission or state and local consumer protection agencies, a beverage bottler must make reasonably certain that 12-ounce bottles actually contain 12 ounces of beverage. To infer whether a bottling machine is working satisfactorily, one bottler randomly samples 10 bottles per hour and measures the amount of beverage in each bottle. The mean $\bar{x}$ of the 10 fill measurements is used to decide whether to readjust the amount of beverage delivered per bottle by the filling machine. If records show that the amount of fill per bottle possesses a standard deviation of .2 ounce, and if the bottling machine is set to produce a mean fill per bottle of 12.1 ounces, what is the approximate probability that the sample mean $\bar{x}$ of the 10 test bottles is less than 12 ounces?

SOLUTION   The mean of the sampling distribution of the sample mean $\bar{x}$ is identical to the mean of the population of bottle fills, namely, $\mu = 12.1$ ounces, and the standard deviation of the sampling distribution, denoted by the symbol $\sigma_{\bar{x}}$, is

$$\sigma_{\bar{x}} = \frac{\sigma}{\sqrt{n}} = \frac{.2}{\sqrt{10}} = .063$$

(*Note:* σ is the standard deviation of the population of bottle fills and n is the number of bottles in the sample.) Even though n is as small as 10, it is likely, for this type of data, that the sampling distribution of $\bar{x}$ will be approximately normal because of the Central Limit Theorem. Then the sampling distribution of $\bar{x}$ will appear as shown in Figure 5.7.

The probability that $\bar{x}$ will be less than 12 ounces is approximately equal to the shaded area under the normal curve in Figure 5.7. This area will equal $(.5 - A)$, where

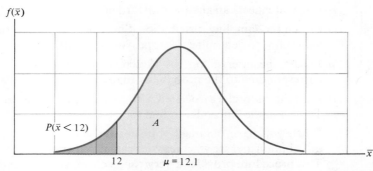

$f(\bar{x})$

$P(\bar{x} < 12)$

A

12    $\mu = 12.1$

$\bar{x}$

FIGURE 5.7   Sampling Distribution of $\bar{x}$, the Mean of the $n = 10$ Bottle Fills, for Example 5.2

A is the area between 12 and the mean, $\mu = 12.1$. Expressing this distance in terms of z yields

$$z = \frac{\bar{x} - \mu}{\sigma_{\bar{x}}} = \frac{12 - 12.1}{.063}$$

$$= \frac{-.1}{.063}$$

$$= -1.59$$

[Note that we must use $\sigma_{\bar{x}}$ (not σ) in the formula for z because we are finding an area under the sampling distribution for $\bar{x}$, not under the sampling distribution for x.] Then the area A is equal to the tabulated area over the interval $0 \leq z \leq 1.59$. This area is given in Table 4 of the Appendix as .4441. Then the probability that $\bar{x}$ will be less than 12 ounces is

$$P(\bar{x} < 12) = .5 - A$$

$$= .5 - .4441$$

$$= .0559$$

$$\approx .056$$

Or if the fill machine is set to produce a mean fill of 12.1 ounces, the mean fill $\bar{x}$ of a sample of 10 bottles will be less than 12 ounces with probability approximately equal to .056. When this danger signal occurs ($\bar{x}$ is less than 12), the bottler takes a larger sample to recheck the setting of the filling machine. Note that the Central Limit Theorem plays a role in the solution of this problem because it justifies the approximate normality of the sampling distribution of the sample mean. ∎

TIPS ON PROBLEM SOLVING

Before attempting to calculate the probability that the statistic $\bar{x}$ falls in some interval, follow these steps:

(1) Calculate the mean and the standard deviation of the sampling distribution of $\bar{x}$.

(2) Sketch the sampling distribution. Show the location of the mean μ, and use the value of $\sigma_{\bar{x}}$ to determine the approximate location of the tails of the distribution.

(3) Locate the interval on the sketch you drew in part 2, and shade the area corresponding to the probability that you wish to calculate.

(4) Find the z score(s) associated with the value(s) of interest in your problem. Use Table 4 in the Appendix to find the probability.

(5) When you have obtained your answer, look at your sketch of the sampling distribution and see whether your calculated answer agrees with the shaded area. This procedure provides a very rough check on your calculations.

EXERCISES

BASIC TECHNIQUES

5.1 Random samples of size n were selected from populations with the following means and variances. Find the mean and standard deviation (standard error) of the sampling distribution of the sample mean.

(a) $n = 25$, $\mu = 10$, $\sigma^2 = 9$ (b) $n = 100$, $\mu = 5$, $\sigma^2 = 4$

(c) $n = 36$, $\mu = 120$, $\sigma^2 = 1$

5.2 Sketch each of the sampling distributions described in Exercise 5.1, locating the mean and the interval ($\mu \pm 2\sigma_{\bar{x}}$) along the $\bar{x}$ axis of the graph.

5.3 Refer to the sampling distribution described in Exercise 5.1(a).

(a) Sketch the sampling distribution for the sample mean, and shade the area under the curve that corresponds to the probability that $\bar{x}$ lies within 1.5 units of the population mean μ.

(b) Find the probability described in part (a).

5.4 Refer to the sampling distribution described in Exercise 5.1(b).

(a) Sketch the sampling distribution for the sample mean, and shade the area under the curve that corresponds to the probability that $\bar{x}$ lies within .15 unit of the population mean μ.

(b) Find the probability described in part (a).

5.5 Refer to the sampling distribution described in Exercise 5.1(c).

(a) Sketch the sampling distribution for the sample mean, and shade the area under the curve that corresponds to the probability that $\bar{x}$ lies within .5 unit of the population mean μ.

(b) Find the probability described in part (a).

5.6 Looking at the histogram of Figure 5.3, guess the value of its mean and standard deviation. (*Hint:* The Empirical Rule states that approximately 95% of the measurements associated with a mound-shaped distribution will lie within two standard deviations of the mean.)

5.7 Let x equal the number of dots observed when a single die is tossed. The mean value of x (Example 3.9) and standard deviation (Exercise 3.103) were found to equal $\mu = 3.5$ and $\sigma = 1.71$, respectively. Suppose that the sampling experiment of Section 5.3 were repeated over and over again an infinitely large number of times, each sample consisting of $n = 5$ measurements. Find the mean and standard deviation for this distribution of sample means. (*Hint:* See the Central Limit Theorem.) Compare this solution with the solution to Exercise 5.6.

5.8 Suppose that you were to experiment by drawing thousands of samples, where each sample involved tossing a die $n = 10$ times. If a histogram were constructed for the sample means, what would be the value for the mean of the distribution? The standard deviation?

5.9 Suppose that a random sample of $n = 5$ observations is selected from a population that is normally distributed with mean equal to 1 and standard deviation equal to .36.

(a) Give the mean and standard deviation of the sampling distribution of $\bar{x}$.

(b) Find the probability that $\bar{x}$ exceeds 1.3.

(c) Find the probability that the sample $\bar{x}$ will be less than .5.

(d) Find the probability that the sample mean will deviate from the population mean $\mu = 1$ by more than .4.

5.10 Suppose that a random sample of $n = 25$ observations is selected from a population that is normally distributed with mean equal to 106 and standard deviation equal to 12.

(a) Give the mean and the standard deviation of the sampling distribution of the sample mean $\bar{x}$.

(b) Find the probability that $\bar{x}$ exceeds 110.

(c) Find the probability that the sample mean will deviate from the population mean $\mu = 106$ by no more than 4.

5.11 The mean and standard deviation of the population normal frequency distribution in Figure 5.4(a) are equal to 0 and 1, respectively. Examine Figure 5.4(a) and visually verify that this is true. Then according to statistical theory, the sampling distributions of the sample mean $\bar{x}$ in Figure 5.4(a) should have a mean equal to $\mu = 0$ and standard deviation equal to

$$\sigma_{\bar{x}} = \frac{\sigma}{\sqrt{n}}$$

or since $\sigma = 1$, $\sigma/\sqrt{n} = 1/\sqrt{n}$.

(a) For $n = 2$, $\sigma_{\bar{x}} = 1/\sqrt{2} = .707$. Examine the sampling distribution of $\bar{x}$, and verify that all or almost all of the sample means fall in the interval $(\mu \pm 3\sigma_{\bar{x}})$.

(b) Repeat the instructions of part (a) for $n = 5$.

(c) Repeat the instructions of part (a) for $n = 10$.

(d) Repeat the instructions of part (a) for $n = 25$.

5.12 The population uniform distribution in Figure 5.4(b) has a mean $\mu = .5$ and standard deviation $\sigma = .29$. Examine Figure 5.4(b) and visually verify that this is true. Then according to statistical theory, the sampling distributions of the sample mean $\bar{x}$ in Figure 5.4(b) should have a mean equal to $\mu = .5$ and a standard deviation equal to

$$\sigma_{\bar{x}} = \frac{\sigma}{\sqrt{n}} = \frac{.29}{\sqrt{n}}$$

(a) For $n = 2$, $\sigma_{\bar{x}} = .29/\sqrt{2} = .205$. Examine the sampling distribution of $\bar{x}$, and verify that all or almost all of the sample means fall in the interval $(\mu \pm 3\sigma_{\bar{x}})$.

(b) Repeat the instructions of part (a) for $n = 5$.

(c) Repeat the instructions of part (a) for $n = 10$.

(d) Repeat the instructions of part (a) for $n = 25$.

5.13 The population negative exponential distribution in Figure 5.4(c) has a mean $\mu = 1$ and standard deviation $\sigma = 1$. Examine Figure 5.4(c) and visually verify that this is true. Then according to statistical theory, the sampling distributions of the sample mean $\bar{x}$ in Figure 5.4(c) should have a mean equal to $\mu = 1$ and

$$\sigma_{\bar{x}} = \frac{\sigma}{\sqrt{n}} = \frac{1}{\sqrt{n}}$$

(a) For $n = 2$, $\sigma_{\bar{x}} = 1/\sqrt{2} = .707$. Examine the sampling distribution of $\bar{x}$, and verify that all or almost all of the sample means fall in the interval $(\mu \pm 3\sigma_{\bar{x}})$.

(b) Repeat the instructions of part (a) for $n = 5$.

(c) Repeat the instructions of part (a) for $n = 10$.

(d) Repeat the instructions of part (a) for $n = 25$.

5.14 A class Monte Carlo experiment: In the Case Study in Chapter 2 we presented data on 227 money market mutual funds. As an experiment, regard the 227 30-day yields in Table 2.2 as a population. Have each member of the class select a random sample of $n = 4$ observations from this population and calculate the sample mean $\bar{x}$. (A procedure for selecting a random sample is described in Section 14.2.) Construct a relative frequency histogram for the sample means calculated by the class members. This relative frequency distribution of sample means provides an approximation to the sampling distribution of $\bar{x}$ for sample size $n = 4$.

(a) Compare your sampling distribution of $\bar{x}$ with the population relative frequency histogram, Figure 2.20.

(b) Calculate the theoretical mean and standard deviation of the sampling distribution of $\bar{x}$. (*Note:* The mean and standard deviation of this "population" of data are given in Figure 2.20 as $\mu = 6.66$ and $\sigma = .53$.) Locate the mean μ and the interval ($\mu \pm 2\sigma_{\bar{x}}$) along the horizontal axis of your relative frequency histogram in part (a). Does μ fall approximately in the center of the histogram? Does the interval ($\mu \pm 2\sigma_{\bar{x}}$) include most of the sample means?

(c) Calculate the mean and standard deviation of the sample means used to construct the relative frequency histogram. Are these values close to the values found for μ and $\sigma_{\bar{x}}$ in part (b)?

5.15 Repeat the instructions of Exercise 5.14, except use a sample size $n = 16$. What is the effect on the sampling distribution of increasing the sample size by a multiple of 4?

5.16 Figure 5.4 and Exercises 5.11, 5.12, and 5.13 demonstrate that the standard deviation of the sampling distribution decreases as the sample size increases. To see this relationship more clearly, suppose that a random sample of n observations is selected from a population with standard deviation $\sigma = 1$. Calculate $\sigma_{\bar{x}}$ for $n = 1, 2, 4, 9, 16, 25,$ and 100. Then plot $\sigma_{\bar{x}}$ versus the sample size n, and connect the points with a smooth curve. Note the manner in which $\sigma_{\bar{x}}$ decreases as n increases.

APPLICATIONS

5.17 The 1985 Scholastic Aptitude Test (SAT) scores showed the largest increase in 21 years. The math and verbal tests, taken by approximately one-third of the nation's high school seniors, showed an increase in the average math score of 4 points, from 471 to 475. The average of the verbal scores increased 5 points, from 426 to 431 (*Wall Street Journal,* September 4, 1985). Why would these very small increases be viewed as a significant improvement in achievement by educators?

5.18 Explain why the shipping weight of a truckload of oranges might be normally distributed.

5.19 Use the Central Limit Theorem to explain why a Poisson random variable, say the number of employee accidents per year in a large manufacturing plant, possesses a distribution that is approximately normal when the mean μ is large. (*Hint:* One year is the sum of 365 days.)

5.20 A lobster fisherman's daily catch x is the total, in pounds, of lobster landed from a fixed number of lobster traps. What kind of probability distribution would you expect the daily catch to possess and why? If the mean catch per trap per day is 30 pounds with $\sigma = 5$ pounds, and the fisherman has 50 traps, give the mean and standard deviation of the probability distribution of the total daily catch x.

5.21 An important expectation of the recent federal income tax reduction is that consumers will save a substantial portion of the money that they receive. Suppose that estimates of the portion of total tax saved, based on a random sampling of 35 economists, possessed a mean of 26% and a standard deviation of 12%.

(a) What is the approximate probability that a sample mean, based on a random sample of $n = 35$ economists, will lie within 1% of the mean of the population of the estimates of all economists?

(b) Is it necessarily true that the mean of the population of estimates of all economists is equal to the percentage tax saving that will actually be achieved?

5.22 To obtain information on the volume of freight shipped by truck over a particular interstate highway, a state highway department monitored the highway for 25 1-hour periods randomly selected throughout a one-month period. The number of truck trailers was counted for each

1-hour period, and $\bar{x}$ was calculated for the sample of 25 individual 1-hour periods. Suppose that the number of heavy-duty trailers per hour is approximately normally distributed, with $\mu = 50$ and $\sigma = 7$.

(a) What is the probability that the sample mean $\bar{x}$ for $n = 25$ 1-hour periods is larger than 55?

(b) Suppose you were to count the truck trailers for each of $n = 4$ randomly selected 1-hour periods. What is the probability that $\bar{x}$ would be larger than 55? (*Hint:* The distribution of the sample means will be normally distributed, regardless of the sample size, for the special case when the population possesses a normal distribution.)

(c) What is the probability that the total number of trucks for a 4-hour period would exceed 180?

5.23 A manufacturer of paper used for packaging requires a minimum strength of 20 pounds per square inch. As a check on the quality of the paper, a random sample of 10 pieces of paper is selected each hour from the previous hour's production, and a strength measurement is recorded for each. The standard deviation σ of the strength measurements, computed by pooling the sum of squares of deviations of many samples, is known to equal 2 pounds per square inch.

(a) What is the approximate probability distribution of the sample mean strength of $n = 10$ test pieces of paper?

(b) If the mean of the population of strength samples is 21 pounds per square inch, what is the probability that $\bar{x} < 20$ for a random sample of $n = 10$ test pieces of paper?

(c) What value would you want for the mean paper strength μ in order that $P(\bar{x} < 20)$ be equal to .001?

THE SAMPLING DISTRIBUTION OF THE PRODUCT OF A CONSTANT AND A STATISTIC

5.4

There are many occasions when we know the sampling distribution of a statistic, call it X, but we are, in fact, interested in the sampling distribution of the product cX, where c is a constant. For example, suppose that the average cost of a sample of 500 automobile insurance claims for a company so far this year is $\bar{x} = \$1869$. If the insurance company anticipates 8000 similar claims for the total year, an estimate of the total cost of claims for the year is 8000 times the cost per claim, or

$$8000\bar{x} = 8000(\$1869) = \$14,952,000$$

In other words, $c = 8000$, and the statistic X is $\bar{x}$.

The insurance company knows that the sampling distribution of the sample mean $\bar{x}$ is approximately normally distributed (by the Central Limit Theorem) with mean μ and standard deviation $\sigma/\sqrt{n}$ (which can be estimated by the mean $\bar{x}$ and standard deviation $s/\sqrt{n}$ of the sample of 500 claims). But what is the sampling distribution of the statistic $8000\bar{x}$ that is used to estimate the total cost of the insurance company's claim?

To answer this question in general, suppose that X is a statistic (or any random variable), c is a constant, and the sampling distribution of X is known. Then the sampling distribution of the product cX will possess the following properties (which we state without proof): The sampling distribution of cX will possess exactly the same shape as the sampling distribution for X. The only difference is that the location of a number, say cX, on the cX axis will be in the same relative location to the frequency distribution as the location of X on the X axis. To illustrate, suppose that X can assume the values $X = 1, 2, 3$ with the sampling distribution shown in Figure 5.8(a). If we multiply X by the constant $c = 4$, then the product $4X$ can assume the values 4, 8, and 12 with the sampling distribution shown in Figure 5.8(b).

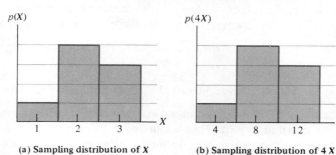

(a) Sampling distribution of X (b) Sampling distribution of $4X$

FIGURE 5.8   The Sampling Distribution of X and $4X$

If X has a mean μ and standard deviation σ, then the mean and standard deviation of the product cX are

$$\mu_{cX} = c\mu \qquad \text{and} \qquad \sigma_{cX} = c\sigma$$

In other words, if you multiply a statistic (or any random variable) by a constant c, the sampling distribution of the product cX will have a mean equal to $c\mu$ and standard deviation equal to $c\sigma$. The properties of the sampling distribution of cX are given in the following box.

PROPERTIES OF THE SAMPLING DISTRIBUTION OF cX

(1) If c is a constant and X is a statistic (or any other random variable), then the sampling distribution of cX will possess the same shape as the sampling distribution of X.

(2) If the mean and standard deviation of the sampling (or probability) distribution of X are μ and σ, respectively, then the mean and standard deviation of the sampling distribution of cX are

$$\mu_{cX} = c\mu \qquad \text{and} \qquad \sigma_{cX} = c\sigma$$

EXAMPLE 5.3   Suppose that x is a normally distributed random variable with mean $\mu = 4$ and standard deviation $\sigma = 3$. Describe the sampling distribution of $10x$.

SOLUTION   From the properties described in the box we know that the sampling distribution of $10x$ will be normally distributed with mean and standard deviation

$$\mu_{10x} = 10\mu = 10(4) = 40$$

and

$$\sigma_{10x} = 10(\sigma) = 10(3) = 30$$

EXAMPLE 5.4

An auto supply company maintains an inventory of 800 different auto parts of varying values. In order to estimate the total value of its inventory, the company randomly selected a sample of 50 parts from its list of 800. A count was made of the number of items in stock for each of the 50 selected parts, and the dollar values were calculated for each auto part. The mean inventory value per part was $\bar{x} = 914$, and the standard deviation of the values was \$637. From these sample statistics the company estimates the total value of its inventory for the 800 different auto parts as

$$T = 800(\text{estimated mean inventory value per part})$$

$$= 800\bar{x}$$

What can you say about the sampling distribution of the statistic T?

SOLUTION

Let μ and σ be the true but unknown mean and standard deviation of the inventory value x of an auto part. Then $\bar{x}$, the mean value per part for the sample of $n = 50$ auto parts, is approximately normally distributed (by the Central Limit Theorem) with mean μ and standard deviation $\sigma/\sqrt{n}$. Then from the properties listed in the box, the statistic

$$T = 800\bar{x}$$

will be approximately normally distributed with mean

$$\mu_T = 800\mu_{\bar{x}} = 800\mu$$

and

$$\sigma_T = 800\sigma_{\bar{x}} = \frac{800\sigma}{\sqrt{n}} = \frac{800\sigma}{\sqrt{50}}$$

How close to the true total value of the company's inventory is T likely to be? This true total value is unknown but it is equal to μ_T, the mean of the sampling distribution for T (see Figure 5.9). The probability that T will lie within

$$2\sigma_T = 2(800)\sigma = 1600\sigma$$

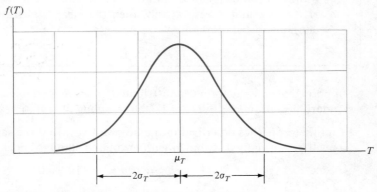

FIGURE 5.9   The Sampling Distribution of T for Example 5.4

of the true total value is (by the Empirical Rule) approximately .95. Since the sample standard deviation s provides an estimate of σ, T will lie within

$$2\sigma_T \approx 1600s = (1600)637 = \$1,019,200$$

of the true total value of the company's inventory with probability near .95.   ∎

EXERCISES

BASIC TECHNIQUES

5.24 If x is a random variable with mean $\mu = 6$ and $\sigma = 5$, find the mean and standard deviation of the sampling distribution of $3x$.

5.25 If x is a random variable with mean $\mu = 14$ and $\sigma^2 = 16$, find the mean and standard deviation of the sampling distribution of $x/10$.

5.26 Suppose that x is a random variable that measures the length of time to complete a job and that it is expressed in minutes. Also assume that x is normally distributed with mean $\mu = 139$ and $\sigma^2 = 36$. Let y be the corresponding measurement expressed in hours. Describe the sampling distribution of y.

5.5   THE SAMPLING DISTRIBUTION OF A SAMPLE PROPORTION

We explained in Chapter 3 that consumer preference or opinion polls provide practical examples of binomial experiments. The objective of these polls is to estimate the proportion p of people in the population who possess some specified characteristic, such as favor a particular issue or consumer product. If a random sample of n persons is selected from the population and if x of these possess the specified characteristic, then the sample proportion,

$$\hat{p} = \frac{x}{n}$$

is used to estimate the population proportion p. (A hat placed over the symbol of a population parameter is often used to denote a statistic used to estimate the population parameter. For example, the symbol $\hat{p}$ is used to denote the sample proportion.)

Since the sample proportion $\hat{p}$ is no more than the binomial random variable x multiplied by the constant $1/n$, its sampling distribution will be the same shape as the binomial probability distribution for x. Like the binomial probability distribution, it will be approximately normal when the sample size n is large.

Since the mean and standard deviation of the binomial random variable x are

$$\mu = np \quad \text{and} \quad \sigma = \sqrt{npq}$$

(where $q = 1 - p$)

it follows (from Section 5.4) that the mean and standard deviation of the product,

$$\hat{p} = \frac{1}{n}(x)$$

are

$$\mu_{\hat{p}} = \frac{1}{n}(\mu_x) = \frac{1}{n}(np) = p \qquad \text{and} \qquad \sigma_{\hat{p}} = \frac{1}{n}\sigma_x = \frac{1}{n}\sqrt{npq} = \sqrt{\frac{pq}{n}}$$

Therefore, for large sample sizes the sampling distribution of $\hat{p}$ appears as shown in Figure 5.10. The properties of the sampling distribution of $\hat{p}$ are given in the box that follows.

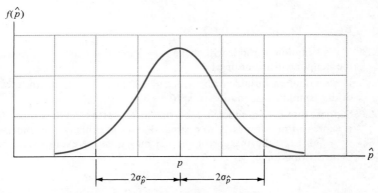

FIGURE 5.10   The Sampling Distribution of the Sample Proportion $\hat{p}$

PROPERTIES OF THE SAMPLING DISTRIBUTION OF THE SAMPLE PROPORTION $\hat{p}$

(1) If a random sample of n observations is selected from a binomial population with parameter p, the sampling distribution of the sample proportion

$$\hat{p} = \frac{x}{n}$$

will possess a mean

$$\mu_{\hat{p}} = p$$

and a standard deviation

$$\sigma_{\hat{p}} = \sqrt{\frac{pq}{n}} \qquad \text{(where } q = 1 - p\text{)}$$

(2) When the sample size n is large, the sampling distribution of $\hat{p}$ will be approximately normal. The approximation will be adequate if

$$\mu_{\hat{p}} - 2\sigma_{\hat{p}} \qquad \text{and} \qquad \mu_{\hat{p}} + 2\sigma_{\hat{p}}$$

fall in the interval 0 to 1.

EXAMPLE 5.5   The *Wall Street Journal* (March 20, 1985) reports on a survey of 313 children, ages 14 to 22 years, from among the children of the nation's top corporate executives. When asked to identify the best aspect of being one of this privileged group, 55% mentioned material and financial advantages. Describe the sampling distribution of the sample proportion $\hat{p}$ of children citing material advantage as being the best aspect of their privileged lives.

SOLUTION   We will assume that the 313 children represent a random sample of the children of all top corporate executives and that the true proportion in the population is equal to some unknown value that we will call p. Then the sampling distribution of $\hat{p}$ will be approximately normally distributed* (because of the Central Limit Theorem) with a mean equal to p (see Figure 5.11) and standard deviation

$$\sigma_{\hat{p}} = \sqrt{\frac{pq}{n}}$$

Examining Figure 5.11, you can see that the sampling distribution of $\hat{p}$ centers over its mean p. Even though we do not know the exact value of p (the sample proportion $\hat{p} = .55$ may be larger or smaller than p), we can calculate an approximate value for the standard deviation of the sampling distribution by using the sample proportion $\hat{p} = .55$ to approximate the unknown value of p. Thus

$$\sigma_{\hat{p}} = \sqrt{\frac{pq}{n}} \approx \sqrt{\frac{\hat{p}\hat{q}}{n}} = \sqrt{\frac{(.55)(.45)}{313}} = .028$$

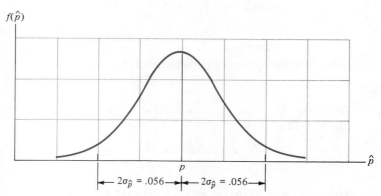

FIGURE 5.11   The Sampling Distribution of $\hat{p}$ Based on a Sample of $n = 313$ Children for Example 5.5 ■

EXAMPLE 5.6   Refer to Example 5.5. Suppose that the proportion p of children in the population is actually equal to .5. What is the probability of observing a sample proportion as large as or larger than the observed value $\hat{p} = .55$?

SOLUTION   Figure 5.12 shows the sampling distribution of $\hat{p}$ when $p = .5$, with the observed value $\hat{p} = .55$ located on the horizontal axis. From Figure 5.12 you can see that the probability of observing a sample proportion $\hat{p}$ equal to or larger than .55 is the shaded

*Checking the conditions for approximate normality (Section 4.4), you will find that $n = 313$ is adequate for values of p near .55.

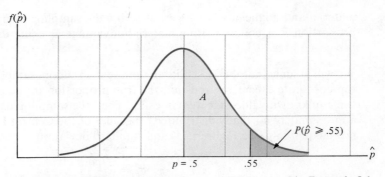

FIGURE 5.12   The Sampling Distribution of $\hat{p}$ for $n = 313$ and $p = .5$ in Example 5.6

area in the upper tail of a normal distribution, with

$$\mu_{\hat{p}} = .5$$

and
$$\sigma_{\hat{p}} = \sqrt{\frac{pq}{n}} = \sqrt{\frac{(.5)(.5)}{313}} = .028$$

To find this shaded area, we need to know how many standard deviations the observed value $\hat{p} = .55$ lies away from the mean of the sampling distribution $p = .5$. This distance is given by the z value,

$$z = \frac{\hat{p} - p}{\sigma_{\hat{p}}} = \frac{.55 - .5}{.028} = 1.79$$

Table 4 in the Appendix gives the area A corresponding to $z = 1.79$ as

$$A = .4633$$

Therefore, the shaded area in the upper tail of the sampling distribution in Figure 5.12 is

$$P(\hat{p} > .55) = .5 - A = .5 - .4633 = .0367$$
$$\approx .04$$

This value tells us that if we were to select a random sample of $n = 313$ observations from a population with proportion p equal to .5, the probability that the sample proportion $\hat{p}$ would be as large or larger than .55 is only .04.   ■

EXERCISES

BASIC TECHNIQUES

5.27 Random samples of size n were selected from binomial populations with the following population parameters p. Find the mean and standard deviation of the sampling distribution of the sample proportion $\hat{p}$.

(a) $n = 100, p = .3$ (b) $n = 400, p = .1$ (c) $n = 250, p = .6$

5.28 Sketch each of the sampling distributions listed in Exercise 5.27. For each, locate the mean p and the interval $(p \pm 2\sigma_{\hat{p}})$ along the $\hat{p}$ axis of the graph.

5.29 Refer to the sampling distribution given in Exercise 5.27(a).

(a) Sketch the sampling distribution for the sample proportion, and shade the area under the curve that corresponds to the probability that $\hat{p}$ lies within .08 of the population proportion p.

(b) Find the probability described in part (a).

5.30 If $n = 1000$ and $p = .1$, find the probability that

(a) $\hat{p} > .12$ \qquad\qquad (b) $\hat{p} < .10$ \qquad\qquad (c) $\hat{p}$ lies within .02 of p

5.31 Calculate $\sigma_{\hat{p}}$ for $n = 100$ and the following values of p.

(a) $p = .01$ \qquad (b) $p = .1$ \qquad (c) $p = .3$ \qquad (d) $p = .5$

(e) $p = .7$ \qquad (f) $p = .9$ \qquad (g) $p = .99$

Plot $\sigma_{\hat{p}}$ versus p on graph paper, and sketch a smooth curve through the points. For what value of p is the standard deviation of the sampling distribution of $\hat{p}$ a maximum? What happens to $\sigma_{\hat{p}}$ when p is near 0 or near 1.0?

5.32 Assuming that p is some fixed value, what is the effect on $\sigma_{\hat{p}}$ of increasing the sample size? Does a change in the sample size n have the same effect on $\sigma_{\hat{p}}$ as on $\sigma_{\bar{x}}$? Explain.

5.33 If $p = .8$ and $n = 400$, find the probability that

(a) $\hat{p} > .83$ \qquad\qquad (b) $.76 \leq \hat{p} \leq .84$

APPLICATIONS

MKTG 5.34 Before making its decision to introduce its "new" Coke in 1985, the Coca-Cola Company introduced new Coca-Cola to approximately 40,000 consumers in 30 cities in the United States. With the brands not identified, 55% chose the new Coke over the old (*Fortune*, May 27, 1985). Assume that the 40,000 consumers in the survey represent a random sample of cola drinkers from a population of cola drinkers in the 30 cities.

(a) Describe the sampling distribution of $\hat{p}$, the proportion in the sample that favor the new Coke. (*Hint:* Use $\hat{p}$ to approximate p when calculating $\sigma_{\hat{p}}$.)

(b) Find the probability that $\hat{p}$ will lie within .005 of the proportion p of cola drinkers in the population who favor the new Coke.

5.35 A survey of purchasing agents from 250 industrial companies found that 25% of the buyers reported higher levels of new orders in January of 1985 than in earlier months (*Wall Street Journal*, February 4, 1985). Assume that the 250 purchasing agents in the sample represent a random sample of company purchasing agents throughout the United States.

(a) Describe the sampling distribution of $\hat{p}$, the proportion of buyers in the United States with higher levels of new orders in January. (*Hint:* Use $\hat{p}$ to approximate p when calculating $\sigma_{\hat{p}}$.)

(b) What is the probability that $\hat{p}$ will differ from p by more than .01?

THE SAMPLING DISTRIBUTION OF THE SUM OF OR THE DIFFERENCE BETWEEN TWO INDEPENDENT STATISTICS

5.6

Many statistical studies involve the comparison of a pair of sample means or proportions. For example, we might want to know whether a difference exists between two population means, and we would use the difference between the sample means to reach a conclusion.

The sampling distribution of the sum of or the difference between a pair of independent statistics (or any pair of independent random variables) possesses some very general properties. Suppose that we let the symbols X_1 and X_2 represent any two independent statistics (such as $\bar{x}_1$ and $\bar{x}_2$ or $\hat{p}_1$ and $\hat{p}_2$), and assume that they possess sampling distributions with means and variances (μ_1, σ_1^2) and (μ_2, σ_2^2), respectively. Then it can be shown (proof omitted) that the sampling distributions of the sums and differences of the two statistics will possess the characteristics listed in the next box.

THE SAMPLING DISTRIBUTIONS OF THE SUM OF OR THE DIFFERENCE BETWEEN TWO INDEPENDENT STATISTICS X_1 AND X_2

Assume that the statistic X_1 and X_2 possess means and variances (μ_1, σ_1^2) and (μ_2, σ_2^2), respectively. Then the sampling distributions of the two statistics $(X_1 + X_2)$ and $(X_1 - X_2)$ will possess the following properties.

(1) The means of the sampling distributions are

$$\mu_{(X_1 + X_2)} = \mu_1 + \mu_2$$

$$\mu_{(X_1 - X_2)} = \mu_1 - \mu_2$$

(2) The variances of the sampling distributions for both the sum and the difference of two independent statistics are equal to the sum of their variances; that is,

$$\sigma_{(X_1 + X_2)}^2 = \sigma_{(X_1 - X_2)}^2 = \sigma_1^2 + \sigma_2^2$$

(3) If X_1 and X_2 are exactly (or approximately) normally distributed, then the sampling distributions of $(X_1 + X_2)$ and $(X_1 - X_2)$ will be exactly (or approximately) normally distributed.

The properties of the sampling distribution of the difference between two independent statistics can be applied to deduce the properties of the sampling distributions of the difference $(\bar{x}_1 - \bar{x}_2)$ between two sample means and the difference $(\hat{p}_1 - \hat{p}_2)$ between two sample proportions.

EXAMPLE 5.7   Describe the sampling distribution of the difference $(\bar{x}_1 - \bar{x}_2)$ between two independent sample means.

SOLUTION   We will assume that $\bar{x}_1$ and $\bar{x}_2$ were calculated from independent random samples of n_1 and n_2 observations from populations with means and variances (μ_1, σ_1^2) and (μ_2, σ_2^2). Then from the properties of the sampling distribution for the difference between two statistics, the mean of the sampling distribution of $(\bar{x}_1 - \bar{x}_2)$ is

$$\mu_{(\bar{x}_1 - \bar{x}_2)} = \mu_{\bar{x}_1} - \mu_{\bar{x}_2} = \mu_1 - \mu_2$$

To find the standard deviation of the sampling distribution of $(\bar{x}_1 - \bar{x}_2)$, we need to find the variances of $\bar{x}_1$ and $\bar{x}_2$. From Section 5.3, you will recall that the standard deviation of the sample mean $\bar{x}$ of a random sample of n observations from a population with variance σ^2 is

$$\sigma_{\bar{x}} = \frac{\sigma}{\sqrt{n}}$$

The variance of $\bar{x}$, the square of $\sigma_{\bar{x}}$, is

$$\sigma_{\bar{x}}^2 = \frac{\sigma^2}{n}$$

Therefore, for our example, the standard deviations and variances of $\bar{x}_1$ and $\bar{x}_2$ are, respectively,

$$\sigma_{\bar{x}_1} = \frac{\sigma_1}{\sqrt{n_1}}, \qquad \sigma_{\bar{x}_1}^2 = \frac{\sigma_1^2}{n_1}$$

$$\sigma_{\bar{x}_2} = \frac{\sigma_2}{\sqrt{n_2}}, \qquad \sigma_{\bar{x}_2}^2 = \frac{\sigma_2^2}{n_2}$$

Then since the variance of the difference between two statistics is equal to the sum of their variances, we have

$$\sigma_{(\bar{x}_1 - \bar{x}_2)}^2 = \sigma_{\bar{x}_1}^2 + \sigma_{\bar{x}_2}^2 = \frac{\sigma_1^2}{n_1} + \frac{\sigma_2^2}{n_2}$$

and the standard deviation is

$$\sigma_{(\bar{x}_1 - \bar{x}_2)} = \sqrt{\frac{\sigma_1^2}{n_1} + \frac{\sigma_2^2}{n_2}}$$

The shape of the sampling distribution of $(\bar{x}_1 - \bar{x}_2)$ will depend upon the nature of the sampled population when the sample sizes n_1 and n_2, are small. When n_1 and n_2 are large, the sampling distribution of $(\bar{x}_1 - \bar{x}_2)$ will be approximately normally distributed, since both $\bar{x}_1$ and $\bar{x}_2$ will be approximately normally distributed when n_1 and n_2 are large because of the Central Limit Theorem. ▪

The sampling distribution of the difference between two sample means is shown in Figure 5.13, and its properties are summarized in the box that follows.

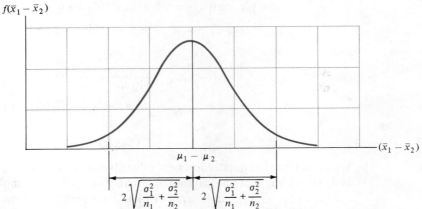

FIGURE 5.13   The Sampling Distribution of the Difference $(\bar{x}_1 - \bar{x}_2)$ Between Two Sample Means

PROPERTIES OF THE SAMPLING DISTRIBUTION OF THE DIFFERENCE $(\bar{x}_1 - \bar{x}_2)$ BETWEEN TWO SAMPLE MEANS

Assume that independent random samples of n_1 and n_2 observations have been selected from populations with means and variances (μ_1, σ_1^2) and (μ_2, σ_2^2), respectively. Then the sampling distribution of the difference $(\bar{x}_1 - \bar{x}_2)$ between the sample means will possess the following properties.

(1) The mean and standard deviation of $(\bar{x}_1 - \bar{x}_2)$ are

$$\mu_{(\bar{x}_1 - \bar{x}_2)} = \mu_1 - \mu_2$$

$$\sigma_{(\bar{x}_1 - \bar{x}_2)} = \sqrt{\frac{\sigma_1^2}{n_1} + \frac{\sigma_2^2}{n_2}}$$

(2) The sampling distribution of $(\bar{x}_1 - \bar{x}_2)$ will be approximately normally distributed when n_1 and n_2 are large.

EXAMPLE 5.8

A survey by the National Education Association, reported in the *New York Times* (April 14, 1985), found that the means of teachers' salaries in the 50 states and the District of Columbia ranged from $15,971 in Mississippi to $39,751 in Alaska. The mean salary in New York State was the second largest at $29,000, followed by the District of Columbia at $28,621. If you were to draw a random sample of 10 teachers from each of the state of New York and the District of Columbia, what is the probability that the sample mean salary $\bar{x}_1$ from New York will exceed the sample mean salary $\bar{x}_2$ from the District of Columbia by $1000 or more? (Assume that the standard deviations for the two population salary distributions are approximately $\sigma_1 = \sigma_2 = \$2500$.)

SOLUTION

From our knowledge of the properties of the sampling distribution of the difference $(\bar{x}_1 - \bar{x}_2)$ in sample means (see the box), it follows that

$$\mu_{(\bar{x}_1 - \bar{x}_2)} = \mu_1 - \mu_2 = 29,000 - 28,621 = 379$$

and

$$\sigma_{(\bar{x}_1 - \bar{x}_2)} = \sqrt{\frac{\sigma_1^2}{n_1} + \frac{\sigma_2^2}{n_2}}$$

$$= \sqrt{\frac{(2500)^2}{10} + \frac{(2500)^2}{10}}$$

$$= 1118.03$$

We expect that the population salary distributions will possess only moderate skewness and, therefore, that the sampling distributions of the sample means and of their difference $(\bar{x}_1 - \bar{x}_2)$ will be approximately normal. Therefore, the sampling distribution of the difference in the two sample mean salaries, each based on $n_1 = n_2 = 10$

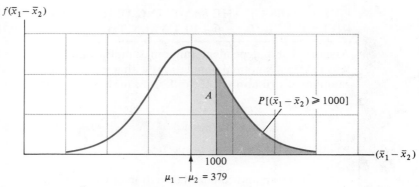

FIGURE 5.14   The Sampling Distribution of $(\bar{x}_1 - \bar{x}_2)$ for Example 5.8

teachers, will appear as shown in Figure 5.14. The probability that $\bar{x}_1$ exceeds $\bar{x}_2$ by $1000 or more is the shaded area in the figure.

The first step in finding the probability that $\bar{x}_1$ exceeds $\bar{x}_2$ by $1000 or more is to find the z value corresponding to $1000. This value is the distance between 1000 and the mean $(\mu_1 - \mu_2) = 379$, expressed in units of $\sigma_{(\bar{x}_1 - \bar{x}_2)}$. Thus

$$z = \frac{(\bar{x}_1 - \bar{x}_2) - (\mu_1 - \mu_2)}{\sigma_{(\bar{x}_1 - \bar{x}_2)}} = \frac{1000 - 379}{1118.03}$$

$$= .56$$

The area A (see Figure 5.14) corresponding to $z = .56$ is given in Table 4 of the Appendix as .2123. Therefore, the shaded area in Figure 5.14 is

$$P[(\bar{x}_1 - \bar{x}_2) \geq 1000] = .5 - A = .5 - .2123$$

$$= .2877$$

This result tells us that the probability that the mean of a random sample of 10 teachers' salaries from New York State exceeds the mean of a sample of 10 teachers' salaries from the District of Columbia by $1000 or more is .2877.   ■

Another common statistical problem involves the comparison of two binomial population proportions p_1 and p_2 based on independent random samples of n_1 and n_2 observations, respectively, selected from the two populations. From the properties of the sampling distribution of the difference in two statistics, it can be shown that the sampling distribution of the difference $(\hat{p}_1 - \hat{p}_2)$ in the sample proportions is approximately normally distributed with mean and standard deviation as shown in the next box. (We leave the derivation of the mean and standard deviation for you as an optional exercise.)

PROPERTIES OF THE SAMPLING DISTRIBUTION OF THE DIFFERENCE $(\hat{p}_1 - \hat{p}_2)$ BETWEEN TWO SAMPLE PROPORTIONS

Assume that independent random samples of n_1 and n_2 observations have been selected from binomial populations with parameters p_1 and p_2, respectively. Then the sampling distribution of the difference in sample proportions

$$\hat{p}_1 - \hat{p}_2 = \frac{x_1}{n_1} - \frac{x_2}{n_2}$$

will possess the following properties.

(1) The mean and standard deviation of $(\hat{p}_1 - \hat{p}_2)$ are

$$\mu_{(\bar{p}_1 - \bar{p}_2)} = p_1 - p_2$$

$$\sigma_{(\bar{p}_1 - \bar{p}_2)} = \sqrt{\frac{p_1 q_1}{n_1} + \frac{p_2 q_2}{n_2}}$$

(2) The sampling distribution of $(\hat{p}_1 - \hat{p}_2)$ will be approximately normally distributed when n_1 and n_2 are large.

EXAMPLE 5.9   One measure of the direction the U.S. economy is moving is apparent in a monthly survey of the purchasing managers of large corporations. The *Wall Street Journal* (February 4, 1985) reports on a survey of 250 purchasing managers that purports to show a rebound in the economy. Of the purchasers surveyed, 25% reported higher new orders in January, compared with 19% in December. Does this difference in sample proportions indicate a real difference in the proportions of all purchasing managers between the months of January and December? To shed some light on this question, find the probability that the sample proportions could differ by as much as 6% when, in fact, there was actually no change in the population proportions from December to January.

SOLUTION   We will assume that the sample sizes for both January and December were 250, that the samples were independently and randomly selected from the population of all purchasing managers, and that the population proportions p_1 and p_2 are equal. Then the probability P that the sample proportions could differ by .06 or more is the shaded area in the tails of the sampling distribution of $(\hat{p}_1 - \hat{p}_2)$, which is shown in Figure 5.15.

From the properties of the sampling distribution given in the box, it follows that the mean and standard deviation of the sampling distribution shown in Figure 5.15 are

$$\mu_{(\bar{p}_1 - \hat{p}_2)} = p_1 - p_2 = 0$$

and

$$\sigma_{(\bar{p}_1 - \hat{p}_2)} = \sqrt{\frac{p_1 q_1}{n_1} + \frac{p_2 q_2}{n_2}}$$

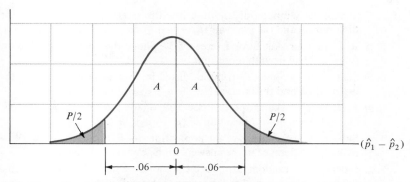

FIGURE 5.15   The Sampling Distribution of the Difference Between Two Sample Proportions for Example 5.9

Since we were not given the exact values of p_1 and p_2, we will have to approximate the value of $\sigma_{(\hat{p}_1 - \hat{p}_2)}$. We will do this by assuming that $p_1 = p_2$ is located approximately halfway between the two observed sample proportions, say $p_1 = p_2 = .22$. [Small changes in the values that we assume for p_1 and p_2 will have little effect on the value of $\sigma_{(\hat{p}_1 - \hat{p}_2)}$.] Then

$$\sigma_{(\hat{p}_1 - \hat{p}_2)} = \sqrt{\frac{p_1 q_1}{n_1} + \frac{p_2 q_2}{n_2}} \approx \sqrt{\frac{(.22)(.78)}{250} + \frac{(.22)(.78)}{250}} = .037$$

The shaded tail areas in Figure 5.15 are equal. Therefore, to find half of the probability that $\hat{p}_1$ and $\hat{p}_2$ differ by as much as .06, we need to determine the upper-tail area $P/2$. The z value corresponding to $(\hat{p}_1 - \hat{p}_2) = .06$ is

$$z = \frac{(\hat{p}_1 - \hat{p}_2) - 0}{\sigma_{(\hat{p}_1 - \hat{p}_2)}} = \frac{.06 - 0}{.037} = 1.62$$

The area A between $z = 0$ and $z = 1.62$, given in Table 4 of the Appendix, is $A = .4474$.

Therefore, $P/2 = .5 - .4474 = .0526$, and $P = .1052$. This value of P tells us that if the proportions of purchasing managers reporting an increase in purchases were the same for January and December, the probability that the sample proportions (based on independent random samples of 250) could differ by as much as .06 is .1052.

EXERCISES

BASIC TECHNIQUES

5.36 Independent random samples of n_1 and n_2 observations were selected from populations with parameters (μ_1, σ_1^2) and (μ_2, σ_2^2). Find the mean and standard deviation of the sampling distribution of the difference $(\bar{x}_1 - \bar{x}_2)$ in sample means for each of the following.

(a) $n_1 = 16, \mu_1 = 10, \sigma_1^2 = 4$ and $n_2 = 20, \mu_2 = 20$, and $\sigma_2^2 = 8$

(b) $n_1 = 100, \mu_1 = 640, \sigma_1^2 = 1$ and $n_2 = 100, \mu_2 = 642$, and $\sigma_2^2 = 3$

5.37 Sketch the sampling distribution listed in Exercise 5.36(a). Locate the mean of the sampling distribution and the interval $[(\mu_1 - \mu_2) \pm 2\sigma_{(\bar{x}_1 - \bar{x}_2)}]$ on the $(\bar{x}_1 - \bar{x}_2)$ axis.

5.38 Refer to your sketch for Exercise 5.37. Shade the area corresponding to the probability that $(\bar{x}_1 - \bar{x}_2)$ will lie within one unit of $(\mu_1 - \mu_2)$.

5.39 Sketch the sampling distribution listed in Exercise 5.36(b). Locate the mean of the sampling distribution and the interval $[(\mu_1 - \mu_2) \pm 2\sigma_{(\bar{x}_1 - \bar{x}_2)}]$ on the $(\bar{x}_1 - \bar{x}_2)$ axis.

5.40 Refer to your sketch for Exercise 5.39. Shade the area corresponding to the probability that $(\bar{x}_1 - \bar{x}_2)$ will lie within .3 unit of $(\mu_1 - \mu_2)$.

5.41 Suppose that the means of the populations for Exercises 5.38 and 5.40 were unknown. Would it make any difference in the answers to the exercises? Explain.

5.42 Independent random samples of n_1 and n_2 were drawn from binomial populations with parameters p_1 and p_2. Find the mean and standard deviation of the sampling distribution of the difference $(\hat{p}_1 - \hat{p}_2)$ in sample proportions for each of the following.

(a) $n_1 = 100, p_1 = .5$ and $n_2 = 300, p_2 = .4$
(b) $n_1 = 400, p_1 = .1$ and $n_2 = 400, p_2 = .6$

5.43 Sketch each of the sampling distributions listed in Exercise 5.42, locating the appropriate mean and the interval $[(p_1 - p_2) \pm 2\sigma_{(\hat{p}_1 - \hat{p}_2)}]$ along the $(\hat{p}_1 - \hat{p}_2)$ axis of each sampling distribution.

5.44 Refer to Exercise 5.43 and the sketch for the sampling distribution of Exercise 5.42(a).

(a) Shade the area under the curve corresponding to the probability that the difference $(\hat{p}_1 - \hat{p}_2)$ will differ from $(p_1 - p_2)$ by less than .06.
(b) Calculate the probability for part (a).

5.45 Refer to Exercise 5.43 and the sketch for the sampling distribution of Exercise 5.42(b).

(a) Shade the area under the curve corresponding to the probability that the difference $(\hat{p}_1 - \hat{p}_2)$ will differ from $(p_1 - p_2)$ by less than .06.
(b) Calculate the probability for part (a).

5.46 Explain how you would conduct a Monte Carlo experiment to obtain an approximation to the sampling distribution for $(\hat{p}_1 - \hat{p}_2)$ if $n_1 = 100, p_1 = .5$ and $n_2 = 300, p_2 = .4$.

APPLICATIONS

5.47 A company wants to sample and compare the mean number of days sick leave per year for two classes of employees, those with less than five years of service versus those with ten or more years of service. The sample sizes are $n_1 = n_2 = 100$ employees, and the standard deviations of the two populations are $\sigma_1 = 8.2$ days and $\sigma_2 = 5.7$ days.

(a) What is the probability that the difference $(\bar{x}_1 - \bar{x}_2)$ between the sample means will differ from the population difference in mean number of days of sick leave by more than 1 day?
(b) Is it possible that $(\bar{x}_1 - \bar{x}_2)$ could deviate from $(\mu_1 - \mu_2)$ by more than 5 days? Explain.

5.48 A sampling of market forecasters was made for two different types of specialists, company managers and company purchasing agents. Random and independent samples of 400 individuals each were selected from the two groups, and each person was asked to forecast the change in economic activity that would occur over the next six months. The difference $(\hat{p}_1 - \hat{p}_2)$ in the sample proportions was to be used to estimate the difference $(p_1 - p_2)$ in population proportions that forecast an upturn in the economy. How close to $(p_1 - p_2)$ would you expect $(\hat{p}_1 - \hat{p}_2)$ to fall? Explain.

5.49 Want to advertise in China? The first Chinese computerized opinion poll was conducted in Peking in 1982. A sample consisting of 2430 Peking residents was randomly chosen by computer, and each person completed a 54-item questionnaire, many of whose items dealt with China's tightly controlled news media. Among various statistics compiled from the survey were the statistics that 38.7% of those surveyed relied on newspapers for their information and 35% relied on the radio (*Orlando Sentinel*, January 30, 1983). Suppose that we wished to use the sample proportions $\hat{p}_1$ and $\hat{p}_2$ to compare the proportion p_1 of Peking residents who rely on newspapers for the information with the proportion p_2 who rely on the radio. Can we use the techniques of Section 5.6 to find the mean and standard deviation of $(\hat{p}_1 - \hat{p}_2)$? Explain.

5.50 A Boston College survey of 320 Michigan workers who were laid off between 1979 and 1984 found that 20% were out of work for at least two years (*Wall Street Journal*, April 2, 1985). Suppose you were to draw another random sample of 320 workers from among all Michigan workers laid off between 1979 and 1984.

(a) What is the probability that your sample percentage of workers out of work for at least two years differs by as much as 5% from that obtained in the Boston College survey?

(b) If the sample percentages differed by as much as 15%, what might you suspect?

THE SAMPLING DISTRIBUTION OF A LINEAR FUNCTION OF RANDOM VARIABLES*

5.7

If $x_1, x_2, \ldots, x_n$ are variables and $a_1, a_2, \ldots, a_n$ are constants, then the variable ℓ

$$\ell = a_1 x_1 + a_2 x_2 + \cdots + a_n x_n$$

is said to be a linear function of the variables $x_1, x_2, \ldots, x_n$. For example, if x_1, x_2, and x_3 are variables, then

$$\ell = 3x_1 + 2x_2 - x_3$$

is a linear function of x_1, x_2, and x_3, where, for this special case, $a_1 = 3$, $a_2 = 2$, and $a_3 = -1$. Similarly,

$$\ell = -5x_1 + 2x_2$$

is a linear function of x_1 and x_2, where $a_1 = -5$ and $a_2 = 2$.

Many statistics used to make inferences are linear functions of random variables. The sample mean

$$\bar{x} = \frac{\sum\limits_{i=1}^{n} x_i}{n} = \frac{x_1 + x_2 + \cdots + x_n}{n} = \left(\frac{1}{n}\right)x_1 + \left(\frac{1}{n}\right)x_2 + \cdots + \left(\frac{1}{n}\right)x_n$$

is a linear function of the sample observations $x_1, x_2, \ldots, x_n$. The constants in the linear function are $a_1 = 1/n$, $a_2 = 1/n, \ldots, a_n = 1/n$. The difference between two statistics, such as the difference between two sample means, $\ell = \bar{x}_1 - \bar{x}_2$, is a linear function of two random variables, $\bar{x}_1$ and $\bar{x}_2$, where the coefficients of the linear function are $a_1 = 1$ and $a_2 = -1$. In the chapter that follows we will encounter many other statistics that are linear functions of the sample observations or of other statistics. For that reason, we present a few properties of the sampling distributions of linear functions of random variables (see the following box). We will state the properties (proof omitted) and will give an illustration of their use. As you can see, the results presented in Section 5.5 are a direct consequence of these properties.

*This section is optional.

THE SAMPLING DISTRIBUTION OF A LINEAR FUNCTION OF RANDOM VARIABLES

Let $x_1, x_2, \ldots, x_n$ be random variables with means and variances $(\mu_1, \sigma_1^2), (\mu_2, \sigma_2^2), \ldots, (\mu_n, \sigma_n^2)$, and let $a_1, a_2, \ldots, a_n$ be constants. Then the sampling distribution of a linear function ℓ

$$\ell = a_1 x_1 + a_2 x_2 + \cdots + a_n x_n$$

will possess the following properties.

(1) The mean value of ℓ is

$$\mu_\ell = E(\ell) = a_1 \mu_1 + a_2 \mu_2 + \cdots + a_n \mu_n$$

that is, the mean value of ℓ is the same linear function with $x_1, x_2, \ldots, x_n$ replaced by their respective means. This property holds regardless of the probability distributions of $x_1, x_2, \ldots, x_n$. (In fact, the random variables may have different probability distributions.) It also applies whether the random variables are dependent or independent—that is, whether the values the random variables assume represent dependent or independent numerical events.

(2) If $x_1, x_2, \ldots, x_n$ are independent random variables, the variance of ℓ is

$$\sigma_\ell^2 = a_1^2 \sigma_1^2 + a_2^2 \sigma_2^2 + \cdots + a_n^2 \sigma_n^2$$

and the standard deviation is

$$\sigma_\ell = \sqrt{a_1^2 \sigma_1^2 + a_2^2 \sigma_2^2 + \cdots + a_n^2 \sigma_n^2}$$

Once again, note that the random variables may possess completely different probability distributions but they must be independent.

(3) If $x_1, x_2, \ldots, x_n$ are normally distributed random variables, then ℓ will possess a normally distributed sampling distribution.

The following example shows how these properties can be applied in a practical situation.

EXAMPLE 5.10   The appraised values of the private homes in a city have become completely obsolete. To assist in determining an approximate value for the city's tax base, the tax appraiser's office divided the city into three residential areas consisting of 22,201 residential homes in area 1, 18,744 in area 2, and 33,675 in area 3. Random samples of 100 properties were selected from each area and appraised, and the sample means and variances, $(\bar{x}_1, s_1^2)$, $(\bar{x}_2, s_2^2)$, and $(\bar{x}_3, s_3^2)$, were calculated. Find a statistic that might be used to estimate the total appraised value of real estate for the three areas, and describe its sampling distribution.

SOLUTION   Assume that the means and variances of the correct appraised values of residential properties from the three regions are (μ_1, σ_1^2), (μ_2, σ_2^2), and (μ_3, σ_3^2). If the mean value of a property in area 1 is μ_1 and if there are 22,201 properties in the area, then the total appraised value of the properties in area 1 is equal to $(22{,}201)\mu_1$. Since $\bar{x}_1$ would seem to provide a good estimate of μ_1, an estimate of the total property value in area 1 is

$(22,201)\bar{x}_1$. Combining estimates from the three areas, we obtain the estimate of the total property value in all three areas:

$$T = (22,201)\bar{x}_1 + (18,744)\bar{x}_2 + (33,675)\bar{x}_3$$

What can we say about the sampling distribution of this statistic T? Since the sample means are all based on independent random samples of $n_1 = n_2 = n_3 = 100$, it follows (by the Central Limit Theorem) that $\bar{x}_1$, $\bar{x}_2$, and $\bar{x}_3$ are (approximately) normally distributed. Therefore (according to property 3), the linear function of $\bar{x}_1$, $\bar{x}_2$, and $\bar{x}_3$,

$$T = (22,201)\bar{x}_1 + (18,744)\bar{x}_2 + (33,675)\bar{x}_3$$

will be (approximately) normally distributed (see Figure 5.16).

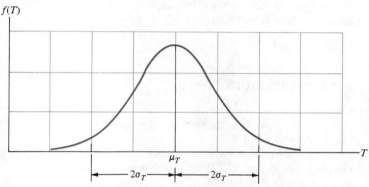

FIGURE 5.16   The Sampling Distribution of the Linear Function T for Example 5.10

Since we know that the expected values of $\bar{x}_1$, $\bar{x}_2$, and $\bar{x}_3$ are μ_1, μ_2, and μ_3, respectively, it follows that the mean of the sampling distribution of the statistic T in Figure 5.16 is

$$\mu_T = (22,201)\mu_1 + (18,744)\mu_2 + (33,675)\mu_3$$

Therefore, the mean of the sampling distribution is the exact sum of the appraised values of all properties in the three areas. This sum is the quantity that we wish to estimate.

Clearly, if T is used to estimate this total value μ_T, sometimes T will be larger than μ_T, sometimes smaller. How close will T be to μ_T? The answer, from the Empirical Rule, is within $2\sigma_T$ of μ_T.

What is the standard deviation σ_T of the statistic T equal to? We know from property 2 (in the box) that

$$\sigma_T^2 = (22,201)^2\sigma_{\bar{x}_1}^2 + (18,744)^2\sigma_{\bar{x}_2}^2 + (33,675)^2\sigma_{\bar{x}_3}^2$$

where the variances of the sample means, based on sample sizes $n_1 = n_2 = n_3 = 100$, are

$$\sigma_{\bar{x}_1}^2 = \frac{\sigma_1^2}{100}, \qquad \sigma_{\bar{x}_2}^2 = \frac{\sigma_2^2}{100}, \qquad \text{and} \qquad \sigma_{\bar{x}_3}^2 = \frac{\sigma_3^2}{100}$$

Then
$$\sigma_T^2 = (22{,}201)^2 \frac{\sigma_1^2}{100} + (18{,}744)^2 \frac{\sigma_2^2}{100} + (33{,}675)^2 \frac{\sigma_3^2}{100}$$

and σ_T is the square root of this quantity,

$$\sigma_T = \sqrt{(22{,}201)^2 \frac{\sigma_1^2}{100} + (18{,}744)^2 \frac{\sigma_2^2}{100} + (33{,}675)^2 \frac{\sigma_3^2}{100}}$$

The unknown variances, $\sigma_1^2, \sigma_2^2,$ and σ_3^2 in the formula for σ_T, can be approximated by the sample variances, $s_1^2, s_2^2,$ and s_3^2. We can then substitute these approximations into the formula to obtain an approximate value of σ_T. Once this value is calculated, we can say, with reasonable confidence, that an estimate T will lie within $2\sigma_T$ of the true total appraised value of the properties in the three areas with probability near .95. Thus knowledge about the sampling distribution of the linear function T enables us to determine how accurately it will estimate the total appraised value μ_T of the properties from the three regions. ∎

EXERCISES

BASIC TECHNIQUES

5.51 Let $\ell = 3x_1 - x_2 + x_3$, where $x_1, x_2,$ and x_3 are independent random variables with $\mu_1 = 5$, $\mu_2 = -4$, $\mu_3 = 0$, $\sigma_1^2 = 3$, $\sigma_2^2 = 9$, $\sigma_3^2 = 2$. Find the mean and standard deviation of the sampling distribution of ℓ.

5.52 From the information given in Exercise 5.51, can you say anything about the shape of the sampling distribution of ℓ? What will be the form of the sampling distribution of ℓ if $x_1, x_2,$ and x_3 are normally distributed?

5.53 Let $\ell = -2x_1 + 5x_2 + x_3 - x_4$, where $x_1, x_2, x_3,$ and x_4 are random variables with $\mu_1 = 5$, $\mu_2 = 0, \mu_3 = -1, \mu_4 = 2, \sigma_1 = 1, \sigma_2 = 1, \sigma_3 = 2, \sigma_4 = 3$.

(a) Find the mean and standard deviation of the sampling distribution of ℓ.

(b) If $x_1, x_2, x_3,$ and x_4 are normally distributed, what is the probability that ℓ will lie within ten units of μ_ℓ?

5.54 Suppose that $\bar{x}_1, \bar{x}_2, \bar{x}_3,$ and $\bar{x}_4$ are the means of independent random samples of $n_1 = 40$, $n_2 = 30, n_3 = 20,$ and $n_4 = 40$ observations from populations with means $\mu_1 = 10, \mu_2 = 4$, $\mu_3 = 5$, and $\mu_4 = -6$ and variances $\sigma_1^2 = 4$, $\sigma_2^2 = 10$, $\sigma_3^2 = 6$, and $\sigma_4^2 = 12$. Then the sum of the observations in all four samples is

$$\ell = n_1\bar{x}_1 + n_2\bar{x}_2 + n_3\bar{x}_3 + n_4\bar{x}_4 = 40\bar{x}_1 + 30\bar{x}_2 + 20\bar{x}_3 + 40\bar{x}_4$$

Describe the sampling distribution of the sum ℓ of the observations in the four samples.

THE SAMPLING DISTRIBUTION OF WINNINGS AT ROULETTE

5.8 In the Case Study that introduces this chapter, we described a Monte Carlo experiment conducted by Daniel Seligman of *Fortune* magazine. Seligman simulated 365 evenings of gambling at Monte Carlo. On each of the 365 evenings Seligman placed 200 bets of $5 each with a payoff of 35 to 1 and with a probability of 1/38 of winning.

To evaluate the results of Seligman's Monte Carlo experiment, we note that each bet results in a gain of $(-\$5)$ if he loses and $\$175$ if he wins. Thus the probability distribution of the gain x on a single $\$5$ bet is

x	$p(x)$
-5	$37/38$
175	$1/38$

Then from Chapter 3 the expected gain $E(x)$ and variance σ_x^2 are

$$E(x) = \mu_x = \sum xp(x) = (-5)\left(\frac{37}{38}\right) + (175)\left(\frac{1}{38}\right) = -.2632$$

$$\sigma_x^2 = \sum(x - \mu)^2 p(x) = \sum x^2 p(x) - \mu^2$$

$$= (-5)^2\left(\frac{37}{38}\right) + (175)^2\left(\frac{1}{38}\right) - (.2632)^2 = 830.1939$$

and

$$\sigma_x = \sqrt{830.1939} = \$28.81$$

Therefore, the mean gain for a $\$5$ bet is a loss of approximately 26¢, and the standard deviation is $\$28.81$. The 26¢ represents the mean amount that you lose to the "house."

The gain for an evening is the sum $S = \sum_{i=1}^{200} x_i$ of the gains or losses for 200 $\$5$ bets. The properties of the sampling distribution for this sum are described in our statement of the Central Limit Theorem (see the box in Section 5.3). When the sample size n is large, the sampling distribution of the sum of the sample measurements will tend to normality. The mean and standard deviation of the sampling distribution are

$$\mu_S = n\mu \qquad \sigma_S = \sigma\sqrt{n}$$

where μ and σ are the mean and standard deviation of the gain x for a single $\$5$ bet. Therefore,

$$\mu_S = (200)(-.2632) = -\$52.64$$
$$\sigma_S = 28.81\sqrt{200} = 407.43$$

Therefore, the total winnings (or losses) for a single evening will vary from $-\$1000$ (if the gambler loses all 200 bets) to $\$35,000$ (if the gambler wins all 200 times), a range of $\$36,000$. The mean gain (actually, a loss) per evening is $-\$52.64$, and most of the nightly gains will fall (from the Empirical Rule) in the interval

$$\mu_S \pm 2\sigma_S, \qquad \text{that is,} \qquad -52.64 \pm (2)(407.43)$$

or

$$-\$867.50 \qquad \text{to} \qquad \$762.22$$

Of course, the loss on any one night cannot exceed $\$1000$. Therefore, most of the large deviations from the mean will be observations in the upper tail of the distribution (improbable large gains).

Now that we know something about the sampling distribution of an evening's winning at roulette, let us examine the results of Daniel Seligman's Monte Carlo experiment. We agree with Seligman that it is surprising that 7 of the 365 evenings resulted in losses of the total $1000 stake. The probability of no wins in 200 (a single evening's betting) is less than .005, and the mean number of times this event would occur in a total of 365 evenings is less than 1.825. Based on a mean equal to 1.825, it can be shown that the observance of 7 evenings resulting in a loss of $1000 is highly improbable.*

The largest evening's winnings, $1160, lies 2.98 standard deviations away from the mean $\mu_S = -52.64$. It is improbable, but it is an event that might occur in one out of 365 evenings.

SUMMARY

5.9

In a practical sampling situation we will draw a *single* random sample of n observations from a population, calculate a single value of a sample statistic, and use it to make an inference about a population parameter. But in order to interpret the statistic, to know how close to the population parameter the computed statistic might be expected to fall, we need to observe the results of many, many samplings. Thus if we were to repeat the sampling process, over and over again an infinitely large number of times, the distribution of values of the statistic produced by this enormous Monte Carlo experiment would be the sampling (or probability) distribution of the statistic.

This chapter describes the properties of the sampling distributions for several useful statistics that we will employ in the following chapters to make inferences about population parameters. Particularly, we learned that sample means, proportions, and differences between a pair of means or proportions possess sampling distributions that are approximately normal when the sample sizes are large. Furthermore, the distributions are centered over their respective population parameters. Thus the mean of the sampling distribution of the sample mean $\bar{x}$ is the population mean μ; the mean of the sampling distribution of the sample proportion $\hat{p}$ is the population proportion p; and so forth.

The third common characteristic of the sampling distributions discussed in this chapter is that the spread of the distributions, measured by their standard deviations, decreases as the sample size increases. As you will subsequently learn in Chapter 6, this property of the sampling distributions plays an important role when we wish to use a sample statistic to estimate its corresponding population parameter. By choosing a larger sample size, we can increase the probability that a sample statistic will fall close to the population parameter.

---

*The number x of evenings in a total of 365 that result in a $1000 loss possesses a binomial probability distribution with $n = 365$ and $p = .005$. Using the Poisson approximation to the binomial probability distribution (Section 3.6), you can show that $x = 7$ lies almost four standard deviations away from the mean $\mu = np = 1.825$.

REFERENCES

Hogg, R. V., and Craig, A. T. *Introduction to Mathematical Statistics*. 4th ed. New York: Macmillan, 1978.

Karalekas, P. C., Jr., Ryan, C.R., and Taylor, F. B. "Control of Lead, Copper and Iron Pipe Corrosion in Boston." *American Water Works Journal,* February 1983.

Mendenhall, W., and Sincich, T. *Statistics for the Engineering and Computer Sciences*. San Francisco: Dellen, 1984.

KEY TERMS

Monte Carlo procedure (page 155)   **Sampling distribution** (page 157)

Statistics (page 155)   **Central Limit Theorem** (page 158)

Simple random sampling (page 156)

SUPPLEMENTARY EXERCISES

5.55 Review the die-tossing experiment of Section 5.3, where we simulated the selection of samples of $n = 5$ observations and obtained an approximation to the sampling distribution for the sample mean. Repeat this experiment, selecting 200 samples of size $n = 3$.

(a) Construct the sampling distribution for $\bar{x}$. Note that the sampling distribution of $\bar{x}$ for $n = 3$ does not achieve the bell shape that you observed for $n = 5$ (Figure 5.4).

(b) The mean and standard deviation of the probability distribution for x, the number of dots that appear when a single die is tossed, are $\mu = 3.5$ and $\sigma = 1.71$. What are the exact values of the mean and standard deviation of the sampling distribution of $\bar{x}$ based on samples of $n = 3$?

(c) Calculate the mean and standard deviation of the simulated sampling distribution of part (a). Are these values close to the corresponding values obtained for part (b)?

5.56 Refer to the sampling experiment of Exercise 5.55. Calculate the median for each of the 200 samples of size $n = 3$.

(a) Use the 200 medians to construct a relative frequency histogram that approximates the sampling distribution of the sample median.

(b) Calculate the mean and standard deviation of the sampling distribution of part (a).

(c) Compare the mean and standard deviation of this sampling distribution with the mean and standard deviation calculated for the sampling distribution of $\bar{x}$ of Exercise 5.55(b). Which statistic, the sample mean or the sample median, appears to fall closer to μ?

5.57 Independent random samples of $n_1 = 10$ and $n_2 = 8$ observations were randomly selected from populations with means and variances $\mu_1 = 4, \sigma_1^2 = 6$ and $\mu_2 = -3, \sigma_2^2 = 12$. Find the mean and standard deviations of the following.

(a) $\bar{x}_1 - \bar{x}_2$ (b) $\bar{x}_1 + \bar{x}_2$

5.58 Refer to Exercise 5.57. Let S_1 and S_2 represent the sum of the observations in samples 1 and 2. Find the mean and standard deviation of the sampling distribution of the following.

(a) $S_1 - S_2$ (b) $S_1 + S_2$

5.59 If random samples of $n_1 = 400$ and $n_2 = 800$ observations are selected from binomial populations, $p_1 = .3$ and $p_2 = .4$, what is the probability that the sample proportions will differ by less than .15?

5.60 The Central Limit Theorem implies that a sample mean $\bar{x}$ is approximately normally distributed for large values of n. Suppose that a sample of size $n = 100$ is drawn from a population with mean $\mu = 40$ and $\sigma = 4$.

(a) What is $E(\bar{x})$?

(b) What is the standard deviation of $\bar{x}$?

(c) What is $P(\bar{x} > 41)$?

 5.61 The length of time required for a local automobile dealer to run a 5000-mile check and service for a new automobile is approximately normally distributed with a mean of 1.4 hours and a standard deviation of .7 hour. Suppose that the service department plans to service 50 automobiles per 8-hour day and that in order to do so, it must spend no more service time than an average of 1.6 hours per automobile. What proportion of all days will the service department have to work over time?

As stated in Chapter 3, probability reasons from a population to a sample. Statistical inference, the reverse of this procedure, infers the nature of a population based on information contained in a sample. Chapters 2 through 5 present the basic concepts of probability, probability distributions, and probability (sampling) distributions of statistics. The objective of this chapter is to show you how sampling distributions can be used to make inferences about a population from the observed values of sample statistics. Thus we present one of two methods for making inferences about population parameters: statistical estimation.

6

LARGE-SAMPLE ESTIMATION

193

CASE STUDY

Sampling: What Will the IRS Allow?

The Internal Revenue Service (IRS) not only uses statistical sampling for examining large volumes of accounting data but also permits the use of statistical sampling and inference by corporations to estimate certain costs and other items when it is impractical to obtain exact data. Writing on this subject, W. L. Felix, Jr., and R. S. Roussey cite an example of a corporation that claimed $6 million in one year and $3.8 in the next for repair expense replacement and other costs ("Statistical Inference and the IRS," *Journal of Accountancy,* June 1985).* These claims were based on samples of 350 items for the first year and 520 items for the second. The IRS did not dispute the use of sampling, the sampling procedure, or the sample sizes; but it did object to lack of information on the "sample error." Analyzing the corporation's sample data, the IRS concluded that the actual expense could have been as low as $3.5 million and $2.8 million for the first and second years, respectively, and therefore disallowed $3.4 million of the total $9.8 million in claims.

This example demonstrates one of the many ways that sampling and statistical inference can be of value in accounting. In this chapter we will study estimators for a number of useful population parameters, and we will use the sampling distribution of an estimator to determine how close to a population parameter an estimate is likely to be. Then in Section 6.10 we will examine the logic for the IRS's $3.4 million disallowance of the claim.

A BRIEF SUMMARY

6.1

The preceding five chapters set the stage for the objective of this text: to develop an understanding of statistical inference and how it can be applied to the solution of practical problems. In Chapter 1 we stated that statistics is primarily concerned with making inferences about populations of measurements based on information contained in samples. We showed you how to phrase an inference—that is, how you describe a set of measurements—in Chapter 2. We discussed probability, the mechanism for making inferences, in Chapter 3; and we followed that with a discussion about probability distributions: discrete probability distributions in Chapter 3 and continuous probability distributions in Chapter 4.

In Chapter 5 we noted that statistics, quantities computed from sample measurements, are used to make inferences about population parameters; and we found an important use for the normal probability distribution of Chapter 4. Particularly, we learned that some of the most important statistics, sample means and proportions, possess sampling distributions (i.e., probability distributions) that are approximately normal when the sample sizes are large (because of the Central Limit Theorem). As you will subsequently see, we will use these statistics to make inferences about population parameters and will use the statistics' sampling distributions to evaluate their reliabilities.

There are two general methods for making an inference about a population parameter. We can estimate the value of a parameter, the topic of Chapter 6, or we can test an hypothesis about its value. The logic involved in a test of an hypothesis will be explained in Chapter 7.

6.2   TYPES OF ESTIMATORS

Estimation procedures can be divided into two types, point estimation and interval estimation. Suppose that an Oldsmobile dealer wants to estimate the mean profit per sale of a new automobile. The estimate might be given as a single number, for instance $935, or we might estimate that the mean profit per sale will fall in an interval $835 to $1035. **The first type of estimate is called a point estimate because the single number, representing the estimate, may be associated with a point on a line. The second type, involving two points and defining an interval on a line, is called an interval estimate.** We will consider each of these methods of estimation.

A point estimation procedure uses information in a sample to arrive at a single number or point that estimates the parameter of interest. The actual estimation is accomplished by an **estimator**.

DEFINITION   An *estimator* is a rule that tells us how to calculate the *estimate* on the basis of information in the sample and is generally expressed as a formula. ∎

For example, the sample mean

$$\bar{x} = \frac{\sum\limits_{i=1}^{n} x_i}{n}$$

is a **point estimator** of the population mean μ and explains exactly how the actual numerical value of the **estimate** may be obtained once the sample values $x_1, x_2, \ldots, x_n$ are known. On the other hand, an **interval estimator** uses the data in the sample to calculate *two* points that are intended to enclose the true value of the parameter estimated.

Many different statistics can be constructed to estimate the same parameter. For example, if we sample $n = 5$ measurements, 2, 7, 0, 1, and 4, from a population, we can estimate the population mean by using the sample mean

$$\bar{x} = \frac{\sum\limits_{i=1}^{n} x_i}{n} = \frac{14}{5} = 2.8$$

by using the sample median $m = 2$, or even by using the average of the smallest and largest measurements in the sample, $(0 + 7)/2 = 3.5$. How can we evaluate the properties of these estimators, compare one with another, and eventually, decide which is "best"?

The answers to these questions are provided by the sampling distribution of the estimators. For example, if we let the symbol θ (Greek letter theta) represent a population parameter (μ, σ, or any parameter) and $\hat{\theta}$ (theta hat)* represent a statistic used to estimate θ (i.e., $\hat{\theta}$ is an estimator of θ), its sampling distribution might appear as shown in Figure 6.1. If the estimator $\hat{\theta}$ is to be a "good" estimator of θ, its sampling distribution will possess two properties. First, we want the sampling distribution to be centered (as shown in Figure 6.1) over the parameter that we are estimating. Thus we prefer that the *mean* of the sampling distribution equal θ. Such an estimator is said to be **unbiased**. One estimate might fall above θ, another below; but if we were to use the estimator many, many times, the mean value of all of the estimates would equal θ.

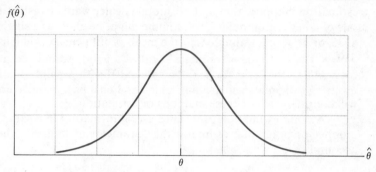

FIGURE 6.1   Distribution of Estimates

DEFINITION   If $\hat{\theta}$ is an estimator of a parameter θ and if the mean of the distribution of $\hat{\theta}$ is θ—that is, if

$$E(\hat{\theta}) = \theta$$

then $\hat{\theta}$ is said to be *unbiased*. Otherwise, $\hat{\theta}$ is said to be *biased*.   ∎

The sampling distributions for an **unbiased estimator** and a **biased estimator** are shown in Figures 6.2(a) and 6.2(b). Note that the sampling distribution for the biased estimator [Figure 6.2(b)] is shifted to the right of θ. This biased estimator is more likely to overestimate θ.

The second desirable property of an estimator is that the spread (measured by the variance) of the sampling distribution of the estimator be as small as possible. This ensures that there is a high probability that an individual estimate will fall close to θ. The sampling distributions for two estimators, one with a small variance and the other with a larger variance, are shown in Figures 6.3(a) and 6.3(b), respectively. (We use the term **variance of an estimator** when in fact we mean the variance of the sampling distribution of the estimator. This contractive expression is used almost universally in statistical texts.) Naturally, we would prefer the estimator with the smaller variance, the

*The estimator of a population parameter is often symbolized by a hat over the symbol for the parameter. Thus the symbol $\hat{\mu}$ means that we are talking about an estimator of μ. Similarly, $\hat{\sigma}$ represents an estimator of σ.

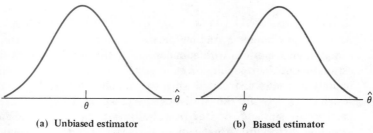

(a) Unbiased estimator   (b) Biased estimator

FIGURE 6.2   Distributions for Unbiased and Biased Estimators

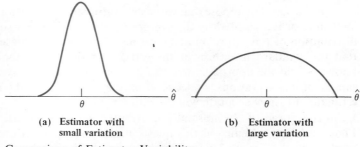

(a) Estimator with   (b) Estimator with
     small variation   large variation

FIGURE 6.3   Comparison of Estimator Variability

sampling distribution shown in Figure 6.3(a), because the estimates tend to lie closer to θ than in the distribution in Figure 6.3(b).

There are often several different statistics that could be used to estimate the same parameter. Among these, we would prefer the estimator with the smallest amount of bias and possessing the smallest variance. The best possible estimator is one that is unbiased and that possesses a variance smaller than that of any other unbiased estimator. This is called a **minimum variance unbiased estimator (MVUE)**.

The goodness of an interval estimator is analyzed in much the same manner as is a point estimator. Samples of the same size are repeatedly drawn from the population, and the interval estimate is calculated on each occasion. This process will generate a large number of intervals rather than points. A good interval estimate will successfully enclose the true value of the parameter a large fraction of the time. This fraction is called the **confidence coefficient** for the estimator; the estimator itself is often called a **confidence interval**.

The selection of a "best" estimator—the proper formula to use in calculating the estimates—involves the comparison of various methods of estimation. This is the task of the theoretical statistician and is beyond the scope of this text. Throughout the remainder of this chapter and succeeding chapters, populations and parameters of interest will be defined and the appropriate estimator indicated along with its expected value and standard deviation.

LARGE-SAMPLE POINT ESTIMATION

6.3

As noted in Chapter 5, sample means, sample totals, and sample proportions possess sampling distributions with common properties. The statistics themselves are unbiased estimators of their population equivalents, and their sampling distributions are approximately normally distributed when the sample sizes are large. This phenomenon is not restricted solely to the statistics discussed in Chapter 5. Many other statistics, particularly statistics derived from business polls (also called sample surveys), possess sampling distributions that cannot be clearly defined for small sample sizes but that possess sampling distributions that are mound-shaped, even approximately normally distributed, when the sample size is large. For this reason, the procedure for evaluating the goodness (i.e., the reliability) of any one of these estimators is the same as for any other estimator.

For example, suppose that we wish to estimate a population parameter θ by using an estimator represented by the symbol $\hat{\theta}$. We will further assume that the sampling distribution of $\hat{\theta}$ is approximately normal, that $\hat{\theta}$ is an unbiased estimator of θ, and that the standard deviation of the estimator* (i.e., of its sampling distribution) is known or can be approximated and is represented by the symbol $\sigma_{\hat{\theta}}$. If a random sample of n observations is selected from the population and $\hat{\theta}$ is used to calculate an estimate of θ, how accurate will the estimate be?

The graph of the normally distributed sampling distribution of $\hat{\theta}$, shown in Figure 6.4, will help answer this question. Suppose that our estimate fell at the point marked by the arrow. This particular estimate lies to the right of θ and therefore overestimates θ by the amount $(\hat{\theta} - \theta)$. The absolute (or unsigned) value of this deviation, denoted by the symbol $|\hat{\theta} - \theta|$, is called the **error of estimation**.

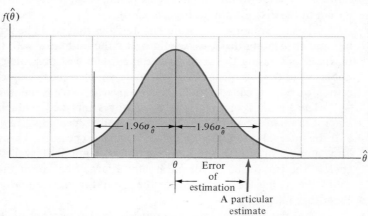

FIGURE 6.4   The Sampling Distribution of an Estimator $\hat{\theta}$

---

*Recall that the expression *standard deviation of an estimator* (also called *the standard error* of the estimator) refers to the standard deviation of the sampling distribution of the estimator.

DEFINITION   If θ is a population parameter and $\hat{\theta}$ is an estimate of θ, then $|\hat{\theta} - \theta|$ is called the *error of estimation.*   ∎

How large is this error likely to be in a practical situation? Since we know that, with probability equal to .95, the error of estimation will be less than $1.96\sigma_{\hat{\theta}}$, the quantity $1.96\sigma_{\hat{\theta}}$ provides a practical upper limit or **bound on the error of estimation**. Thus the bound on the error of estimation provides a practical way of measuring the reliability of a point estimator.

DEFINITION   The *bound on the error of estimation* by an estimator $\hat{\theta}$ is $1.96\sigma_{\hat{\theta}}$.

Note: If $\hat{\theta}$ is normally distributed, the probability that the error of estimation will be less than $1.96\sigma_{\hat{\theta}}$ is approximately .95. If we know only that the distribution of $\hat{\theta}$ is mound-shaped, the probability that the error of estimation will be less than $1.96\sigma_{\hat{\theta}}$ is still (by the Empirical Rule) approximately .95.   ∎

The following example illustrates the use of the bound on the error of estimation.

EXAMPLE 6.1   A marketing research organization was hired to estimate the mean prime lending rate for banks located in the western region of the United States. A random sample of $n = 50$ banks was selected from within the region, and the prime rate was recorded for each. The mean and standard deviation of the 50 prime rates were

$$\bar{x} = 9.1\% \qquad \text{and} \qquad s = .24$$

Estimate the mean prime rate for the region, and evaluate the reliability of the estimate.

SOLUTION   For this example the parameter θ that we wish to estimate is a population mean μ. The point estimator $\hat{\theta}$ is the sample mean $\bar{x}$, and the point estimate of μ is $\bar{x} = 9.1\%$. Since the sample mean satisfies all the properties described in this section—that is, it is an unbiased estimator of μ, and its sampling distribution is approximately normally distributed when the sample size n is large—the bound on the error of estimation is

$$\text{bound on error of estimation} = 1.96\sigma_{\bar{x}} = \frac{1.96\sigma}{\sqrt{n}}$$

where $\sigma_{\bar{x}}$ is the standard deviation of the sampling distribution of $\bar{x}$. Although the population standard deviation σ is unknown, we can use the sample standard deviation s to approximate its value. Therefore, the bound on the error of estimation is approximately

$$\text{bound on error of estimation} = \frac{1.96\sigma}{\sqrt{n}} \approx \frac{1.96s}{\sqrt{n}} = \frac{1.96(.24)}{\sqrt{50}} = .0665 \approx .07$$

Summarizing, the estimate of the mean prime lending rate in the western region of the United States is 9.1%. How accurate is this estimate? We really do not know. It may overestimate or it may underestimate the mean prime lending rate. What we *do*

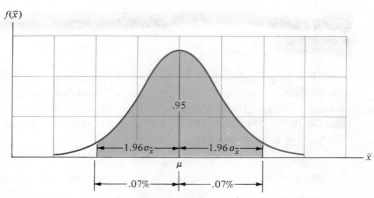

$f(\bar{x})$

.95

$1.96\sigma_{\bar{x}}$ $1.96\sigma_{\bar{x}}$

μ

$\bar{x}$

.07%   .07%

FIGURE 6.5   Bound on the Error of Estimation for Example 6.1

know is that with our estimator the probability that the error will be less than .07% is approximately .95 (see Figure 6.5). Thus the bound on the error of estimation, .07%, provides a measure of reliability for the marketing research organization's estimate.

LARGE-SAMPLE CONFIDENCE INTERVALS (ONE- AND TWO-SIDED)

6.4

Constructing an interval estimate is like attempting to rope an immobile steer. In this case, the parameter that you wish to estimate corresponds to the steer and the interval to the loop formed by the cowboy's lariat. Each time you draw a sample, you construct a **confidence interval** for a parameter and you hope to "rope it"—that is, include it in the interval. You will not be successful for every sample, but a good interval estimator will have a high probability of including the estimated parameter.

To consider a practical example, suppose that you wish to estimate the mean return of AA grade municipal bonds. If we were to draw 10 samples, each containing $n = 30$ interest rates for 30 municipal bonds, and construct a confidence interval for the population mean μ for each sample, the intervals might appear as shown in Figure 6.6. The horizontal line segments represent the 10 intervals, and the vertical line represents the location of the true mean rate of return for AA-rated municipal bonds. Note that the parameter is fixed and that the interval location and width vary from sample to sample. Thus we speak of "the probability that the interval encloses μ," not "the probability that μ falls in the interval," because μ is fixed. The interval is random.

Having grasped the concept of a confidence interval, let us now consider how to find the confidence interval for a population mean μ from a random sample of n observations.

An **interval estimator**, or confidence interval, can be constructed by using any point estimator that satisfies the properties of Section 6.3—that is, one that is unbiased and possesses a sampling distribution that is approximately normal. We will represent the parameter to be estimated as θ and the point estimator as $\hat{\theta}$.

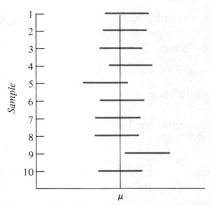

FIGURE 6.6   Ten Confidence Intervals for the Mean Return of AA Grade Municipal Bonds (Based on a Sample of $n = 30$ Observations)

To see how a confidence interval for θ can be constructed, examine the sampling distribution of $\hat{\theta}$ shown in Figure 6.7. Suppose that we were to draw a random sample of n observations from the population and use the sample data to calculate an estimate of θ. We show a particular point estimate, indicated by the arrow in Figure 6.7, that lies within $1.96\sigma_{\hat{\theta}}$ of θ. You can see that the interval $(\hat{\theta} - 1.96\sigma_{\hat{\theta}})$ to $(\hat{\theta} + 1.96\sigma_{\hat{\theta}})$ includes θ. The point estimate $\hat{\theta}$ will fall within $1.96\sigma_{\hat{\theta}}$ of θ with a probability equal to .95. Therefore, the interval

$$\hat{\theta} - 1.96\sigma_{\hat{\theta}} \qquad \text{to} \qquad \hat{\theta} + 1.96\sigma_{\hat{\theta}}$$

should contain θ with probability equal to .95.

Since the interval that we have just described will enclose θ with probability .95, it is called a **95% confidence interval**. The probability that the interval contains θ is

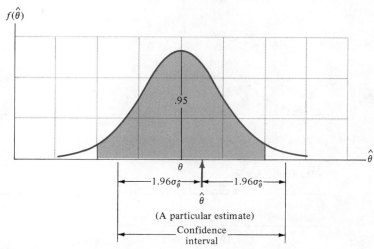

FIGURE 6.7   A Confidence Interval for θ

called the **confidence coefficient** for the confidence interval. The lower and upper boundaries of the confidence interval are called the **lower and upper confidence limits** (LCL and UCL), respectively. Thus

$$\text{lower confidence limit:} \quad \text{LCL} = \hat{\theta} - 1.96\sigma_{\hat{\theta}}$$

and

$$\text{upper confidence limit:} \quad \text{UCL} = \hat{\theta} + 1.96\sigma_{\hat{\theta}}$$

DEFINITION

The probability that a confidence interval will enclose the estimated parameter is called the *confidence coefficient*. ■

The confidence coefficient for a confidence interval can be varied by changing the normal distribution z value used to construct the interval. Thus we used $z_{.025} = 1.96$, the z value that locates .025 in the upper tail of the normal distribution, to form a 95% confidence interval. A 90% confidence interval will locate $z_{.05}$ in the upper tail of the z distribution (see Figure 6.8). With this z value, $z_{.05} = 1.645$ (given in Table 4 of the Appendix), substituted for $z_{.025} = 1.96$, the 90% confidence interval for θ is

$$\hat{\theta} \pm 1.645\sigma_{\hat{\theta}}$$

In general, if we wish the confidence coefficient to equal $(1 - \alpha)$, we use the z value $z_{\alpha/2}$ that places $\alpha/2$ in the upper tail of the z distribution (see Figure 6.8). This value can be found in Table 4 of the Appendix. Then a $(1 - \alpha)100\%$ confidence interval for θ is

$$\hat{\theta} \pm z_{\alpha/2}\sigma_{\hat{\theta}}$$

Some common confidence intervals, confidence coefficients, and their z values are shown in Table 6.1.

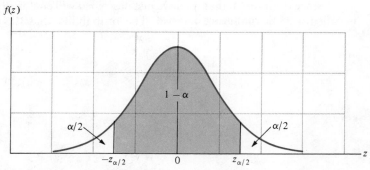

FIGURE 6.8   The Location of $z_{\alpha/2}$ Used for a $(1 - \alpha)100\%$ Confidence Interval

TABLE 6.1   Confidence Limits for θ

Confidence Coefficient	α	z_{α}	LCL	UCL
.90	.10	1.645	$\hat{\theta} - 1.645\sigma_{\hat{\theta}}$	$\hat{\theta} + 1.645\sigma_{\hat{\theta}}$
.95	.05	1.96	$\hat{\theta} - 1.96\sigma_{\hat{\theta}}$	$\hat{\theta} + 1.96\sigma_{\hat{\theta}}$
.99	.01	2.58	$\hat{\theta} - 2.58\sigma_{\hat{\theta}}$	$\hat{\theta} + 2.58\sigma_{\hat{\theta}}$

EXAMPLE 6.2   Find a 90% confidence interval for the mean prime lending rate discussed in Example 6.1.

SOLUTION   We have already noted that the point estimator $\bar{x}$ of the population mean μ possesses a sampling distribution that satisfies the properties of Section 6.3. Therefore, a 90% confidence interval for the mean prime lending rate μ is

$$\bar{x} \pm z_{.05}\sigma_{\bar{x}}$$

or

$$\bar{x} \pm 1.645\frac{\sigma}{\sqrt{n}}$$

Substituting $\bar{x} = 9.1\%$ and $n = 50$ and using $s = .24\%$ to approximate σ, we obtain

$$9.1 \pm (1.645)\frac{.24}{\sqrt{50}}$$

or

$$9.1 \pm .0558$$

Thus we estimate the mean prime lending rate to lie somewhere between 9.0442% and 9.1558%.

   Can we say that this particular interval encloses μ? No, but we are fairly confident that it does. If we use our confidence interval to estimate μ, the probability that an interval will enclose μ is .90.   ∎

   In addition to two-sided confidence intervals (which we will simply call confidence intervals), we can also construct **one-sided confidence intervals** for parameters. A **lower one-sided confidence interval** for a parameter θ will estimate that θ is larger than some lower confidence limit (LCL). An **upper one-sided confidence interval** will estimate θ to be less than some upper confidence limit (UCL). The z-value to be used for a one-sided $(1 - \alpha)100\%$ confidence interval, z_α, locates α in a single tail of the normal distribution, as shown in Figure 6.9. Lower and upper one-sided confidence limits for θ are shown in Table 6.2.

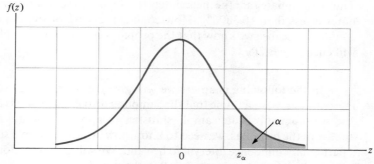

FIGURE 6.9   The Location of z_α for a One-Sided $(1 - \alpha)100\%$ Confidence Interval

TABLE 6.2   One-Sided Confidence Limits for θ

Confidence Coefficient	α	z_α	LCL	UCL
.90	.10	1.28	$\hat\theta - 1.28\sigma_{\hat\theta}$	$\hat\theta + 1.28\sigma_{\hat\theta}$
.95	.05	1.645	$\hat\theta - 1.645\sigma_{\hat\theta}$	$\hat\theta + 1.645\sigma_{\hat\theta}$
.99	.01	2.33	$\hat\theta - 2.33\sigma_{\hat\theta}$	$\hat\theta + 2.33\sigma_{\hat\theta}$

EXAMPLE 6.3   A corporation plans to issue some short-term notes and is hoping that the interest it will have to pay will not exceed 11.5%. To obtain some information on the mean interest rate that the corporation might expect to pay, the corporation marketed 40 notes, one through each of 40 brokerage firms. The mean and standard deviation for the 40 interest rates were $\bar{x} = 10.3\%$ and $s = .31\%$. Since the corporation is only interested in the upper limit on the interest rate that it must pay, find an upper one-sided 95% confidence interval for the mean interest rate that the corporation will have to pay for the notes.

SOLUTION   Since the confidence coefficient is .95, $\alpha = .05$ and $z_{.05} = 1.645$. Therefore (see Table 6.2), the one-sided 95% confidence interval for μ is

$$\bar{x} + z_{.05}\sigma_{\bar{x}}$$

or

$$\bar{x} + 1.645\frac{\sigma}{\sqrt{n}}$$

Substituting $\bar{x} = 10.3$, $n = 40$, and $s = .31$ to approximate σ, we obtain the one-sided confidence interval:

$$\text{UCL} = 10.3 + (1.645)\frac{.31}{\sqrt{40}}$$

 or

$$\text{UCL} = 10.3 + .0806 = 10.3806$$

Thus we estimate that the mean interest rate that the corporation will have to pay on its notes is less than 10.3806%. How confident are we of this conclusion? We are fairly confident because we know that the probability that our one-sided confidence interval will enclose μ is .95. ∎

In the following chapters we will give the formulas for some useful confidence intervals. Since we assume that the sampling distribution of $\hat\theta$ is approximately normal and we often substitute sample statistics to approximate unknown parameters that appear in the formulas, we need to know how large the sample size must be in order for a particular confidence interval to be valid. We will give this information for each of the confidence intervals presented in this chapter.

6.5

ESTIMATING A POPULATION MEAN

Having used estimation of a population mean as an example of the point and interval estimation methods of Sections 6.3 and 6.4, we will summarize the formulas used in those sections and explain when the formulas are appropriate.

While there are always rare exceptions, sample sizes of $n = 30$ or larger will assure the validity of both the bound on the error of estimation and the confidence interval. The sampling distribution for $\bar{x}$ will be approximately normally distributed for $n \geq 30$, and the sample standard deviation s will provide an adequate approximation to the population standard deviation σ. We summarize the formulas for confidence intervals in the box and refer you to Examples 6.2 and 6.3 (Section 6.4) to see how they are used. The calculation for the bound on the error of estimation for a point estimator is demonstrated in Example 6.1 (Section 6.3).

A LARGE SAMPLE $(1 - \alpha)100\%$ CONFIDENCE INTERVAL FOR A POPULATION MEAN μ

$$\bar{x} \pm \frac{z_{\alpha/2}\sigma}{\sqrt{n}}$$

where $z_{\alpha/2}$ = z value corresponding to an area $\alpha/2$ in the upper tail of a standard normal z distribution

$\qquad n$ = sample size

$\qquad \sigma$ = standard deviation of the sampled population

If σ is unknown, it can be approximated by the sample standard deviation s.

Assumption: $n \geq 30$.

EXERCISES

BASIC TECHNIQUES

6.1 Explain what is meant by "bound on the error of estimation."

6.2 Give the bound on the error of estimating a population mean μ for the following.
  (a) $n = 40, \sigma^2 = 4$ (b) $n = 100, \sigma^2 = .9$ (c) $n = 50, \sigma^2 = 12$

6.3 Give the bound on the error of estimating a population mean μ for the following.
  (a) $n = 50, \sigma = .1$ (b) $n = 100, \sigma = 9$ (c) $n = 100, \sigma = .01$

6.4 Find a 95% confidence interval for a population mean μ for the following.
  (a) $n = 36, \bar{x} = 13.1, s^2 = 3.42$ (b) $n = 64, \bar{x} = 2.73, s^2 = .1047$
  (c) $n = 41, \bar{x} = 28.6, s^2 = 1.09$

6.5 Find a 95% confidence interval for a population mean μ for the following.
  (a) $n = 125, \bar{x} = .84, s^2 = .086$ (b) $n = 50, \bar{x} = 21.9, s^2 = 3.44$
  (c) $n = 46, \bar{x} = 907, s^2 = 128$

.90   1.28
1.645
2.33

6.6 Find a $(1 - \alpha)100\%$ confidence interval for a population mean μ for the following.

   (a) $\alpha = .01, n = 38, \bar{x} = 34, s^2 = 12$
   (b) $\alpha = .10, n = 65, \bar{x} = 1049, s^2 = 51$
   (c) $\alpha = .05, n = 89, \bar{x} = 66.3, s^2 = 2.48$

6.7 Find a lower one-sided $(1 - \alpha)100\%$ confidence interval for a population mean μ for the following.

   (a) $\alpha = .10, n = 45, \bar{x} = 22.1, s^2 = 6.8$
   (b) $\alpha = .05, n = 120, \bar{x} = 150, s^2 = 29$
   (c) $\alpha = .05, n = 35, \bar{x} = 1.4, s^2 = .12$

6.8 Find an upper one-sided $(1 - \alpha)100\%$ confidence interval for a population mean μ for the following.

   (a) $\alpha = .01, n = 30, \bar{x} = 147, s^2 = 16$
   (b) $\alpha = .05, n = 49, \bar{x} = 12, s^2 = 25$
   (c) $\alpha = .10, n = 41, \bar{x} = 1472, s^2 = 143$

6.9 A random sample of n measurements is selected from a population with unknown mean μ and known standard deviation $\sigma = 10$. Calculate the width of a 95% confidence interval for μ for the following values of n.

   (a) $n = 100$ (b) $n = 200$ (c) $n = 400$

6.10 Compare the confidence intervals in Exercise 6.9. What is the effect on the width of a confidence interval under the following conditions?

   (a) You double the sample size.
   (b) You quadruple the sample size.

6.11 Refer to Exercise 6.9.

   (a) Calculate the width of a 90% confidence interval for μ when $n = 100$.
   (b) Calculate the width of a 99% confidence interval for μ when $n = 100$.
   (c) Compare the widths of 90%, 95%, and 99% confidence intervals for μ. What effect does increasing the confidence coefficient have on the width of the confidence interval?

APPLICATIONS

6.12 An increase in the rate of consumer savings is frequently tied to a lack of confidence in the economy and is said to be an indicator of a recessional tendency in the economy. A random sampling of $n = 200$ savings accounts in a local community showed a mean increase in savings account values of 7.2% over the past 12 months and a standard deviation of 5.6%. Estimate the mean percentage increase in savings account values over the past 12 months for depositors in the community. Place a bound on your error of estimation.

6.13 Most of the claims on a small company's medical insurance are in the neighborhood of $800 but a few are very large. As a consequence, the distribution of claims is highly skewed to the right and possesses a standard deviation σ equal to $2000. The first 40 claims received this month possess a mean $\bar{x}$ equal to $930. Suppose that we were to regard this group of 40 claims as a random sample from the population of all potential claims and use $\bar{x}$ to estimate the population mean μ.

   (a) What is the bound on the error of estimation?
   (b) Can you make a precise statement about the probability that the error of estimation will be less than the bound in part (a)? Explain.

6.14 A survey of 312 graduating college accounting majors during the 1983–1984 recruiting season provides information on the employment objectives of graduating college accounting majors as well as their thoughts on recruiting by CPA firms (R. A. Scott, E. J. Pavlock, and M. H. Lathan,

"On-Campus Recruiting: The Students Speak Up," *Journal of Accountancy,* January 1985).*
One question was, "What annual salary would these 312 prospective 1984 graduates expect to
receive after being employed 2, 6, and 15 years, respectively?" The responses ranged as follows:

Year 2:	$19,860 to $25,860
Year 6:	$29,664 to $39,440
Year 15:	$53,660 to $87,320

Suppose that you view the 312 salary expectations for one of these lengths of employments, say
the expectations at the end of year 2, as a random sample of the salary expectations at the end of
year 2 for all prospective college accounting graduates in 1984. If you wanted to estimate the
mean salary expectation for this population, what could you say about the approximate value
of the error of estimation? (Scott et al. do not give the sample means for the 312 students in the
survey.) To answer this question, answer parts (a)–(c).

(a) Use the range of the 312 salary expectations at the end of year 2 to find an approximate value
for s. (See Section 2.9 for a range approximation for s.)

(b) Use the values of s found in part (a) to calculate an approximate value for the bound on the
error of estimation.

(c) How does your answer in part (b) provide a measure of the error that you might expect if you
were to use the sample mean salary expectation to estimate the corresponding mean salary
expectation at the end of year 2?

6.15   Follow the instructions of Exercise 6.14 but refer to the data on the salaries that 1984 accounting
graduates expect to receive at the end of year 6.

6.16   Follow the instructions of Exercise 6.14 but refer to the data on the salaries that 1984 accounting
graduates expect to receive at the end of year 15.

6.17   In Exercise 2.36 we commented on a Columbia University survey of the earnings of American
authors, noting in particular that a *New York Times* (June 15, 1981) summary of the study stated
that the "average" American author's writings net less than $5000 per year. The meaning of this
statement is not clear, but let us suppose that the *New York Times* writer was trying to tell us that
the mean income from writing of the 2239 authors included in the survey was less than $5000. If
the standard deviation σ of the distribution of writing incomes is equal to $20,000, how
accurately would the sample mean $\bar{x}$ of the 2239 authors' incomes estimate the population mean
of the writing incomes of all American authors? To answer this question, assume that $\bar{x} = 5000$,
and find a 95% confidence interval for μ.

6.18   If you are renting an apartment and you think that your rent is too high, part of the rent that
you are paying may be caused by the high interest rate on borrowed money. What will be the
prime rate of interest next September 1? A random sample of $n = 32$ economic forecasters
produced a mean $\bar{x} = 11.7\%$ and standard deviation, $s = 2.1\%$. If the forecasters' forecasts are
"unbiased"—that is, if the mean of the population of forecasts of all economic forecasters will
equal the actual interest rate next fall—find a 90% confidence interval for the September 1 prime
interest rate.

6.19   A company personnel officer wants to estimate the mean time between occurrences of personnel
accidents that might provide the potential for liability lawsuits. A random sample of $n = 30$
accidents from the company's records of the time x between an accident and the one preceding
gave a sample mean of $\bar{x} = 42.1$ days and standard deviation of $s = 19.6$ days. Find a 90%
confidence interval for the mean time between occurrences of personnel accidents possessing the
potential for liability lawsuits.

*Copyright © 1985 by American Institute of Certified Public Accountants, Inc.

6.20 A random sampling of a company's monthly operating expenses for a sample of $n = 36$ months produced a sample mean of \$5474 and a standard deviation of \$764. Find an upper one-sided 90% confidence interval for the company's mean monthly expenses.

 6.21 In Exercise 1.4 we described one of many opinion surveys conducted by the Conference Board, a nonprofit economic research institute. The survey involved a sampling of 38 senior business executives to obtain the "best guess" of each executive of the average U.S. inflation rate in the upcoming five-year period. The average of the sample of 38 "best guesses" was a 5.9% inflation per year; the sample standard deviation was not reported (*Wall Street Journal*, April 16, 1984). Suppose that the 38 "best guesses" ranged from 3% to 8% and therefore that the sample standard deviation was approximately 1.25%.

(a) Describe the sampled population.

(b) Find a 95% confidence interval for the mean of the sampled population.

(c) Interpret the interval that you calculated in part (b).

(d) What assumptions must be satisfied in order for your confidence interval to be valid?

ESTIMATING THE DIFFERENCE BETWEEN TWO MEANS

6.6

A problem of equal importance to the estimation of population means is the comparison of two population means. For instance, we might wish to estimate the difference between two states in the mean claim size for a type of automobile insurance. This estimate will be based on independent random samples of claims selected from among those filed in the two states. Or we might wish to compare the average yield in a chemical plant using raw materials furnished by two suppliers, A and B. Samples of daily yield, one for each of the two suppliers, will be recorded and used to make inferences concerning the difference in mean yield.

For each of these examples we postulate two populations, the first with mean and variance μ_1 and σ_1^2, and the second with mean and variance μ_2 and σ_2^2. A random sample of n_1 measurements is drawn from population I and n_2 from population II, where the samples are assumed to have been drawn independently of one another. Finally the estimates of the population parameters $\bar{x}_1$, s_1^2, $\bar{x}_2$, and s_2^2 are calculated from the sample data.

The difference $(\bar{x}_1 - \bar{x}_2)$ in sample means is an unbiased point estimator of the difference between the population means $(\mu_1 - \mu_2)$. As explained in Section 5.6, the sampling distribution of the estimator $(\bar{x}_1 - \bar{x}_2)$ will be approximately normally distributed for large samples (say, n_1 and n_2 both equal to 30 or more), with mean and standard deviation as given in the following box.

MEAN AND STANDARD DEVIATION OF $(\bar{x}_1 - \bar{x}_2)$

$$E(\bar{x}_1 - \bar{x}_2) = \mu_1 - \mu_2$$

$$\sigma_{(\bar{x}_1 - \bar{x}_2)} = \sqrt{\frac{\sigma_1^2}{n_1} + \frac{\sigma_2^2}{n_2}}$$

The bound on the error of the point estimate of $(\mu_1 - \mu_2)$ is

$$\text{bound on error} = 1.96\sigma_{(\bar{x}_1 - \bar{x}_2)} = 1.96\sqrt{\frac{\sigma_1^2}{n_1} + \frac{\sigma_2^2}{n_2}}$$

A (two-sided) confidence interval for $(\mu_1 - \mu_2)$ with confidence coefficient $(1 - \alpha)$ can be obtained by using the formula given in the next box.

A LARGE-SAMPLE $(1 - \alpha)100\%$ CONFIDENCE INTERVAL FOR $(\mu_1 - \mu_2)$

$$(\bar{x}_1 - \bar{x}_2) \pm z_{\alpha/2}\sqrt{\frac{\sigma_1^2}{n_1} + \frac{\sigma_2^2}{n_2}}$$

The sample variances s_1^2 and s_2^2 can be used to estimate σ_1^2 and σ_2^2 when these parameters are unknown.

Assumption: n_1 and n_2 are both greater than or equal to 30.

This approximation will be reasonably good when n_1 and n_2 are equal to 30 or more.

EXAMPLE 6.4 Recognizing that court liability awards vary over time, an insurance company wants to compare the mean level of current personal liability awards with those of a year earlier. A random sample of $n = 30$ cases was selected from among cases tried during each of the two yearly periods. The sample means and variances of the liability awards (in millions of dollars) for each of the two years are shown in Table 6.3. Find a 90% confidence interval for the difference in the mean level of liability awards between the current and preceding year.

TABLE 6.3 Sample Means and Variances for Example 6.4

Year	Sample Size	Sample Mean (Million \$)	Sample Variance (Million \$)^2
Current	$n_1 = 30$	$\bar{x}_1 = 1.32$	$s_1^2 = .9734$
Previous	$n_2 = 30$	$\bar{x}_2 = 1.04$	$s_2^2 = .7291$

SOLUTION Since we want to find a 90% confidence interval for $(\mu_1 - \mu_2)$, $(1 - \alpha) = .90$, $\alpha = .10$, $\alpha/2 = .05$, and $z_{.05} = 1.645$. Substituting $\bar{x}_1$, $\bar{x}_2$, s_1^2, and s_2^2 (the latter as approximations to σ_1^2 and σ_2^2) into the formula for the confidence interval, we obtain

$$(\bar{x}_1 - \bar{x}_2) \pm z_{\alpha/2}\sqrt{\frac{\sigma_1^2}{n_1} + \frac{\sigma_2^2}{n_2}}$$

or

$$(1.32 - 1.04) \pm (1.645)\sqrt{\frac{.9734}{30} + \frac{.7291}{30}}$$

$$.28 \pm .392$$

Rounding to two places, we estimate the difference in mean liability awards to fall between $-\$.11$ million and $\$.67$ million. You can see that this confidence interval is very wide, allowing the possibilities that the mean award this year could have been $\$.67$

million larger than last year or $.11 million smaller. If the insurance company wants to estimate the difference in mean awards with a narrower confidence interval, it will have to obtain more information by increasing the sample sizes n_1 and n_2. ∎

EXERCISES

BASIC TECHNIQUES

6.22 Independent random samples were selected from two populations, 1 and 2. The sample sizes, means, and variances were as shown in Table 6.4. Find a bound on the error of estimating the difference in population means $(\mu_1 - \mu_2)$.

TABLE 6.4   Sample Data for Exercise 6.22

	Population	
	1	2
Sample size	35	49
Sample mean	12.7	7.4
Sample variance	1.38	4.14

6.23 Independent random samples were selected from two populations, 1 and 2. The sample sizes, means, and variances were as shown in Table 6.5. Find a 90% confidence interval for the difference in the population means, and interpret your result.

TABLE 6.5   Sample Data for Exercise 6.23

	Population	
	1	2
Sample size	64	64
Sample mean	2.9	5.1
Sample variance	.83	1.67

6.24 Refer to Exercise 6.23. Find an upper one-sided 90% confidence interval for $(\mu_1 - \mu_2)$.

6.25 Refer to Exercise 6.23. Find a lower one-sided 99% confidence interval for $(\mu_1 - \mu_2)$.

6.26 Independent random samples were selected from two populations, 1 and 2. The sample sizes, means, and variances were as shown in Table 6.6. Find a 99% confidence interval for the difference in the population means and interpret your result.

TABLE 6.6   Sample Data for Exercise 6.26

	Population	
	1	2
Sample size	135	210
Sample mean	183	194
Sample variance	16.1	9.8

6.27 Refer to Exercise 6.26. Find a lower one-sided 99% confidence interval for $(\mu_1 - \mu_2)$.

APPLICATIONS

6.28 A study was conducted to compare the mean number of police emergency calls per 8-hour shift in two districts of a large city. Samples of 100 8-hour shifts were randomly selected from the police records for each of the two regions, and the number of emergency calls was recorded for each shift. The sample statistics are shown in Table 6.7. Find a 90% confidence interval for the difference in the mean number of police emergency calls per shift between the two districts of the city. Interpret the interval.

TABLE 6.7   Sample Data for Exercise 6.28

	Region	
	1	2
Sample size	100	100
Sample mean	2.4	3.1
Sample variance	1.44	2.64

6.29 One method suggested a number of years ago for solving the electric power shortage employed floating nuclear power plants located a few miles offshore in the ocean. Because there was concern about the possibility of a ship collision with the floating (but anchored) plant, an estimate of the density of ship traffic in the area was needed. The number of ships passing within 10 miles of the proposed power plant location per day, recorded for $n = 60$ days during July and August, possessed sample mean and variance equal to

$$\bar{x} = 7.2 \qquad s^2 = 8.8$$

(a) Find a 95% confidence interval for the mean number of ships passing within 10 miles of the proposed power plant location during a one-day time period.

(b) The density of ship traffic was expected to decrease during the winter months. A sample of $n = 90$ daily recordings of ship sightings for December, January, and February gave the following mean and variance:

$$\bar{x} = 4.7 \qquad s^2 = 4.9$$

Find a 90% confidence interval for the difference in mean density of ship traffic between the summer and winter months.

(c) What is the population associated with your estimate in part (b)? What could be wrong with the sampling procedure in parts (a) and (b)?

6.30 An audit was conducted to estimate the difference in mean percentage shrinkage (loss due to theft, damage, etc.) in inventory at two department stores. One hundred items were randomly selected within each store, and the percentage of each item actually on hand, in comparison to the total shown on inventory records, was recorded. The mean and standard deviation of the percentage shrinkage for the 100 items are shown in Table 6.8 for each store. Estimate the

TABLE 6.8   Sample Data for Exercise 6.30

	Department Store	
	1	2
Sample size	100	100
Sample mean	5.3	6.4
Sample standard deviation	2.7	2.9

difference in mean percentage shrinkage between the two department stores, using a 95% confidence interval. Interpret the confidence interval.

 6.31 Based on a Conference Board survey, spending on holiday giving in 1986 was projected to rise by only 5% (*Wall Street Journal,* December 9, 1986). The nationwide survey of 5000 households found the (sample) average expenditure per household to be highest in the New England states, an average of $\bar{x}_1 = \$387$ per household, and lowest in the mountain states of Arizona, Colorado, Idaho, Montana, Nevada, New Mexico, Utah, and Wyoming, an average of $\bar{x}_2 = \$283$ per household. Suppose that approximately 800 households were contacted in each of these two regions and that the sample standard deviations were $s_1 = \$99$ and $s_2 = \$76$.

(a) How accurate are the individual estimates for the two regions? Give bounds on the error of estimation for each region.

(b) Give, for each region, a 95% confidence interval for the mean of the planned holiday spending per household.

(c) Find a 95% confidence interval for the difference in mean planned holiday spending per household between the two regions.

6.32 A bank's loan department found that 57 home loans processed during April had a mean value of $78,100 and a standard deviation of $6300. An analysis of the loans in May, a total of 66, had a mean value of $82,700 with a standard deviation of $7100. Suppose these home loans represent random samples of the values of home loan applications approved in the bank's service area. Find a 90% confidence interval for the difference in the mean level of approved home applications from April to May.

ESTIMATING THE PARAMETER OF A BINOMIAL POPULATION

6.7

The best point estimator of the binomial parameter p is also the estimator that would be chosen intuitively. That is, the estimator $\hat{p}$ equals

$$\hat{p} = \frac{x}{n}$$

the total number of successes divided by the total number of trials. By "best" we mean that $\hat{p}$ is unbiased and possesses a minimum variance compared with other possible unbiased estimators.

Recall from Section 5.5 that the sampling distribution of $\hat{p}$ is approximately normally distributed when n is large. The mean and standard deviation of the sampling distribution of $\hat{p}$ are given in the following box.

MEAN AND STANDARD DEVIATION OF $\hat{p}$

$$E(\hat{p}) = p \qquad \sigma_{\hat{p}} = \sqrt{\frac{pq}{n}}$$

Therefore, the bound on the error of a point estimate will be

$$\text{bound on error of estimation} = 1.96\sigma_{\hat{p}} = 1.96\sqrt{\frac{pq}{n}}$$

and the $(1 - \alpha)100\%$ confidence interval, appropriate for large n, is given in the next box.

A LARGE-SAMPLE $(1 - \alpha)100\%$ CONFIDENCE INTERVAL FOR p

$$\hat{p} \pm z_{\alpha/2}\sqrt{\frac{\hat{p}\hat{q}}{n}}$$

Assumption: The sample size must be large enough so that the sampling distribution of $\hat{p}$ will be approximately normal. These conditions are given in Section 5.5.

The sample size will be considered large when we can assume that $\hat{p}$ is approximately normally distributed. The conditions necessary for the approximate normality of a binomial distribution were discussed in Section 5.5.

The only difficulty encountered in our procedure will be in calculating $\sigma_{\hat{p}}$, which involves p (and $q = 1 - p$), which is unknown. Note that we have substituted $\hat{p}$ for the parameter p in the standard deviation, $\sqrt{pq/n}$. When n is large, little error will be introduced by this substitution. As a matter of fact, the standard deviation changes only slightly as p changes. This fact can be observed in Table 6.9, where $\sqrt{pq}$ is recorded for several values of p. Note that $\sqrt{pq}$ changes very little as p changes, especially when p is near .5.

TABLE 6.9   Some Calculated Values of $\sqrt{pq}$

p	$\sqrt{pq}$
.5	.50
.4	.49
.3	.46
.2	.40
.1	.30

EXAMPLE 6.5   A random sample of $n = 100$ wholesalers who buy polyvinyl plastic pipe indicated that 59 plan to increase their purchases in the coming year. Estimate the proportion p of wholesalers in the population of all polyvinyl pipe wholesalers who plan to increase their purchases next year, and place a bound on the error of estimation. Find a 95% confidence interval for p.

SOLUTION   The point estimate is

$$\hat{p} = \frac{x}{n} = \frac{59}{100} = .59$$

and the bound on the error of estimation is

$$1.96\sigma_{\hat{p}} = 1.96\sqrt{\frac{pq}{n}}$$

$$\approx 1.96\sqrt{\frac{(.59)(.41)}{100}} = .096$$

A 95% confidence interval for p is

$$\hat{p} \pm 1.96 \sqrt{\frac{\hat{p}\hat{q}}{n}}$$

Substituting into this formula, we obtain

$$.59 \pm 1.96(.049)$$

or

$$.59 \pm .096$$

Thus we estimate that the proportion p of wholesalers who plan to increase their purchases lies in the interval .494 to .686, with confidence coefficient .95. ■

EXERCISES

BASIC TECHNIQUES

6.33 A random sample of $n = 900$ observations from a binomial population produced $x = 655$ successes. Find a 99% confidence interval for p, and interpret the interval.

6.34 A random sample of $n = 300$ observations from a binomial population produced $x = 263$ successes. Find a 90% confidence interval for p, and interpret the interval.

6.35 A random sample of $n = 500$ observations from a binomial population produced $x = 140$ successes. Find a 95% confidence interval for p, and interpret the interval.

6.36 Suppose that the number of successes observed in $n = 500$ trials of a binomial experiment is 27. Find a 95% confidence interval for p. Why is the confidence interval narrower than the confidence interval in Exercise 6.35?

APPLICATIONS

 6.37 In Exercise 6.14 we presented data on the salary aspirations of 312 graduating college accounting majors during the 1983–1984 recruiting season (R. A., Scott, E. J., Pavlock, and M. H. Lathan, "On-Campus Recruiting: The Students Speak Up," *Journal of Accountancy*, January 1985).* The survey also produced information on the type of CPA firm that they would prefer to work for. The 312 preferences were distributed as follows:

One of the eight largest firms	52%
A medium- to large-sized firm	25%
A small- to moderate-sized local or regional firm	17%
Do not care	6%
	100%

Suppose the percentages of preferences for these four categories can be viewed as estimates of the percentages of all accounting majors entering the job market in 1984.

(a) How good is the estimate of the percentage that would prefer employment with a "big-eight" firm? Give a 95% confidence interval for the percentage.

(b) Is the width of the confidence interval for the percentage in part (a) different from the width of a 95% confidence interval for one of the other category percentages? Explain.

*Copyright © 1985 by the American Institute of Certified Public Accountants, Inc.

6.38 A survey is conducted twice each year by the National Association of Purchasing Agents to determine the outlook of purchasing agents on the economy and business in general. The results of one of these surveys of 160 purchasing agents, reported in the *Wall Street Journal* (May 6, 1986), found that 48% of agents surveyed "said they were satisfied or optimistic about the economic outlook for the next twelve months," up from 34% in December. What is the approximate bound on the error of these forecasts, assuming that each was based on a random sample of 160 purchasing agents?

 6.39 A Gallup survey for the Urban Land Institute seems to carry undesirable implications for retail businesses located in the inner city. In a sample of 1008 adults polled in the survey, "more than 8 in 10 surveyed said they would not want to move to the downtown nearest them" and "56% said suburban shopping malls offer a better variety of retail outlets than the central city" (*Orlando Sentinel*, May 11, 1986).

(a) Place a bound on the error of estimating the proportion of adults "who would not want to move to the downtown nearest them."

(b) Find a 90% confidence limit for the percentage of adults who found the retail outlets in suburban shopping malls preferable to those in the central city.

 6.40 An article titled "Dreaded Tourists Pretty Well Liked in Vermont, Poll Shows" reports on a poll of 504 Vermonters conducted by the University of Vermont and the State Department of Forests, Parks and Recreation (*New York Times*, July 6, 1986). The random sample, contacted by telephone, answered more than a hundred questions about the respondents' attitudes toward tourists and the impact of tourism on wildlife, recreation, and other factors that affect the quality of life in the state. The survey found, for example, that 63% said tourists were wealthy and 70% said tourists had a good sense of humor. Half believed that tourism would raise the standard of living in Vermont. How accurate are these estimates of the corresponding population percentages? Give an approximate bound on the error of estimation.

 6.41 A study by the General Accounting Office (GAO) of Veterans Administration (VA) hospitals suggests that some of the $8.3 billion spent on the treatment of VA patients in 1984 might have been saved. After evaluating the cases of 800 patients at six VA hospitals in 1984, the GAO concluded that 244, or 31%, of the patients "did not belong in medical and surgical acute care beds and could have been treated in less costly facilities if available" (*Philadelphia Inquirer*, August 8, 1985). If we can regard the cases of the 800 patients as a random sample of all VA patients treated in VA hospitals in 1984, how accurate is the estimate that 31% could have been treated in less costly facilities? Find a bound on the error of estimation.

 6.42 A survey of 415 corporate, government, and accounting executives of the Financial Accounting Foundation (*Wall Street Journal*, June 13, 1980) found that 67% rated cash flow (as opposed to earnings per share, etc.) as the most important indicator of a company's financial health. Assume that these 415 executives can be viewed as a random sample from the population of all executives. Use the data to find a 95% confidence interval for the fraction of all corporate executives who would list cash flow as the most important measure of a company's financial health.

 6.43 In Exercises 2.11 and 2.38 we discussed a study by E. C. Lawrence of the reporting delays for 58 firms filing for bankruptcy ("Reporting Delays for Failed Firms," *Journal of Accounting Research*, Vol. 21, No. 2, 1983). Among the various statistics derived from the study, Lawrence notes that approximately 53% of the failing firms released their annual reports within three months of the end of their firm's year-end. Suppose that we view the 58 time lags as a random sample from a large population of time lags for failing firms. How accurate is the sample estimate 53% of the population percentage of firms that released their annual reports within three months of year-end? Answer this question by giving an approximate bound on the error of estimation.

6.44 A Wall Street Journal (July 23, 1981) report on a survey by Warwick, Welsh & Miller, a New York advertising agency, indicates that matters of taste cannot be ignored in television advertising. In a mail survey of 3440 people, 40% indicated that they found TV commercials to be in poor taste, 55% said that they avoided products whose commercials were judged to be in poor taste, and of this latter group, only 20% ever complained to a TV station or an advertiser about their dissatisfaction.

(a) Find a 95% confidence interval for the percentage of TV viewers who find TV commercials to be in poor taste.

(b) Find a 95% confidence interval for the percentage of TV viewers who avoid products that are promoted by TV commercials they consider to be in poor taste.

(c) Find a 95% confidence interval for the percentage of those who avoid products and who have complained to the TV station or the advertiser about poor taste in a TV commercial.

ESTIMATING THE DIFFERENCE BETWEEN TWO BINOMIAL PARAMETERS

6.8

The fourth and final estimation problem considered in this chapter is estimation of the difference between the parameters of two binomial populations. Assume that the two populations I and II possess parameters p_1 and p_2, respectively. Independent random samples consisting of n_1 and n_2 trials are drawn from their respective populations, and the estimates $\hat{p}_1$ and $\hat{p}_2$ are calculated.

The point estimator of $(p_1 - p_2)$ is the corresponding difference in the estimates $(\hat{p}_1 - \hat{p}_2)$. As we learned in Section 5.6, this estimator is unbiased and has a sampling distribution that is approximately normal for large samples. The mean and standard deviation of the sampling distribution of $(\hat{p}_1 - \hat{p}_2)$ are given in the following box.

MEAN AND STANDARD DEVIATION OF $(\hat{p}_1 - \hat{p}_2)$

$$E(\hat{p}_1 - \hat{p}_2) = (p_1 - p_2)$$

$$\sigma_{(\hat{p}_1 - \hat{p}_2)} = \sqrt{\frac{p_1 q_1}{n_1} + \frac{p_2 q_2}{n_2}}$$

Therefore, the bound on the error of estimating $(p_1 - p_2)$ is

$$\text{bound on error of estimation} = 1.96\sigma_{(\hat{p}_1 - \hat{p}_2)} = 1.96\sqrt{\frac{p_1 q_1}{n_1} + \frac{p_2 q_2}{n_2}}$$

Because p_1 and p_2 are unknown, we use the estimates $\hat{p}_1$ and $\hat{p}_2$ to approximate p_1 and p_2 in this formula.

The $(1 - \alpha)100\%$ confidence interval, appropriate when n_1 and n_2 are large, is given in the next box.

A $(1 - \alpha)100\%$ LARGE-SAMPLE CONFIDENCE INTERVAL FOR $(p_1 - p_2)$

$$(\hat{p}_1 - \hat{p}_2) \pm z_{\alpha/2} \sqrt{\frac{\hat{p}_1 \hat{q}_1}{n_1} + \frac{\hat{p}_2 \hat{q}_2}{n_2}}$$

Assumption: n_1 and n_2 are sufficiently large so that the sampling distributions of $\hat{p}_1$ and $\hat{p}_2$ are approximately normal. (See Section 4.4 for guidelines.)

EXAMPLE 6.6

A large clothing retailer conducted a study to compare the effectiveness of a newspaper advertisement in each of two large cities. A large advertisement was run in the major newspaper in each of the two large cities. Immediately thereafter, a marketing research organization conducted a telephone survey of 1000 randomly selected adults living in a middle- to upper-income suburban area in each of the cities to determine the proportion that had read the retailer's advertisement. The sample proportions were $\hat{p}_1 = .18$ and $\hat{p}_2 = .14$. Find a 95% confidence interval for the difference in the proportions of adults in the two populations who read the advertisement.

SOLUTION

A 95% confidence interval for the difference $(p_1 - p_2)$ in the proportions of adults who read the retailer's advertisement is

$$(\hat{p}_1 - \hat{p}_2) \pm z_{\alpha/2} \sqrt{\frac{\hat{p}_1 \hat{q}_1}{n_1} + \frac{\hat{p}_2 \hat{q}_2}{n_2}}$$

where $\alpha = .05$ and $z_{\alpha/2} = z_{.025} = 1.96$. Substituting this value, along with the estimates $\hat{p}_1 = .18$ and $\hat{p}_2 = .14$, into the formula for the confidence interval, we find the confidence interval to be

$$(.18 - .14) \pm 1.96 \sqrt{\frac{(.14)(.86)}{1000} + \frac{(.18)(.82)}{1000}}$$

or $.04 \pm .0321$

Thus we estimate the difference in the proportions of readers of the advertisement to lie between .0079 and .0721. If we wish to express this difference as a percentage, we multiply each proportion by 100. Then we can say that we estimate the difference in the percentages of adults reading the advertisement in the two marketing regions as between .79% and 7.21%. ∎

EXERCISES

BASIC TECHNIQUES

6.45 Samples of $n_1 = 500$ and $n_2 = 500$ observations were selected from binomial populations 1 and 2, and $x_1 = 120$ and $x_2 = 147$ were observed. Find a bound on the error of estimating the difference in population proportions $(p_1 - p_2)$.

6.46 Samples of $n_1 = 800$ and $n_2 = 640$ observations were selected from binomial populations 1 and 2, and $x_1 = 337$ and $x_2 = 374$ were observed.

(a) Find a 90% confidence interval for the difference $(p_1 - p_2)$ in the two population parameters. Interpret the interval.

(b) What assumptions must you make in order that the confidence interval be valid?

6.47 Samples of $n_1 = 1265$ and $n_2 = 1688$ observations were selected from binomial populations 1 and 2, and $x_1 = 849$ and $x_2 = 910$ were observed.

(a) Find a 99% confidence interval for the difference $(p_1 - p_2)$ in the two population parameters. Interpret the interval.

(b) What assumptions must you make in order that the confidence interval be valid?

6.48 Samples of $n_1 = 314$ and $n_2 = 207$ observations were selected from binomial populations 1 and 2, and $x_1 = 108$ and $x_2 = 102$ were observed.

(a) Find a 95% confidence interval for the difference $(p_1 - p_2)$ in the two population parameters. Interpret the interval.

(b) What assumptions must you make in order that the confidence interval be valid?

APPLICATIONS

6.49 In an effort to forecast the direction of consumer spending, polls are frequently conducted to determine consumers' perceptions of their financial well-being. Typical of these polls was one conducted by the Gallup organization in June 1986 (*New York Times,* August 1, 1986). Based on personal interviews with a sample of 1539 adults, the poll found that 51% of those polled expect to be better off financially one year later. This percentage compares with a finding of 61% in a similar poll conducted in March 1986. Assume that the two surveys were based on random samples of equal size. Find a 95% confidence interval for the difference in the percentage of adults who expect their financial conditions to be better one year following the date of their interviews.

6.50 A bank survey of delinquent credit card payments found that the delinquency rate in a given month for 414 small-business owners was 5.8% versus only 3.6% for 1029 professionals. Assume that the data for these two types of cardholders can be regarded as independent random samples of monthly accounts over a relatively long period of time, say one or two years. Find a 95% confidence interval for the difference in the proportions of delinquencies for these two types of credit card users.

6.51 From a telephone survey of 1675 Canadian adults conducted by Angus Reid Associates for the Montreal *Gazette,* the agency estimated that 66% support the kind of flat-rate income tax system adopted in the United States in 1986 [*Gazette* (Montreal), September 13, 1986]. The sample percentages of adults who regarded a flat-rate tax system as a "good idea" varied somewhat from province to province. For example, in a sample of 403 adults from Quebec province, 68% thought a flat-rate income tax system was a good idea; only 63% of 535 adults in Ontario thought so.

(a) Find a 99% confidence interval for the proportion of all Canadian adults in the sampled population (presumably, those who own telephones) that regard a flat-rate tax system as a good idea.

(b) Find a 95% confidence interval for the difference in proportions between Quebec and Ontario.

(c) Did the sampled populations in the provinces of Quebec and Ontario include all adult Canadians in those two provinces? Explain.

6.52 Does the financial distress associated with bankruptcy motivate firms to change auditors? A study of the association between financial distress and auditor switches found that 35 of 132 bankrupt firms shifted auditors at some time during the four-year period prior to declaring bankruptcy (K. B. Schwartz and K. Menon, "Auditor Switches by Failing Firms," *Accounting*

Review, Vol. 60, No. 2, 1985). In contrast, only 13 of 132 nonbankrupt firms changed auditors during a comparable four-year period. Find a confidence interval for the difference $(p_1 - p_2)$ between the proportions of firms shifting auditors for those facing bankruptcy and those not facing bankruptcy.

6.9 CHOOSING THE SAMPLE SIZE

The design of an experiment is essentially a plan for purchasing a quantity of information that, like any other commodity, may be acquired at varying prices depending upon the manner in which the data are obtained. Some measurements contain a large amount of information concerning the parameter of interest; others may contain little or none. Since the sole product of research is information, we want to make its purchase at minimum cost.

The sampling procedure, or *experimental design* as it is usually called, affects the quantity of information per measurement. This design, along with the sample size n, controls the total amount of relevant information in a sample. With few exceptions we shall be concerned with the simplest sampling situation, random sampling from a relatively large population, and will devote our attention to the selection of the sample size n.

To see how the sample size affects the width of a confidence interval, consider the standard deviation of the sampling distribution for any point estimator considered in this chapter. The value of each is inversely proportional to the square root of the sample size n. For example, the standard deviation of the sample mean $\bar{x}$ is

$$\sigma_{\bar{x}} = \frac{\sigma}{\sqrt{n}}$$

In order to halve the value of $\sigma_{\bar{x}}$—and therefore the width of a confidence interval— we would need to quadruple the sample size. The sampling distributions for the sample mean $\bar{x}$ are shown in Figure 6.10 for three different sample sizes, $n = 5, 20,$ and 80. Note

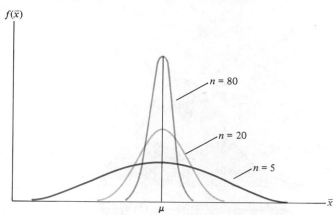

FIGURE 6.10 Sampling Distributions for $\bar{x}$ Based on Random Sampling from a Normal Distribution, $n = 5, 20,$ and 80

that the spread of the sampling distributions decreases as the sample size n increases. We can use this relationship between sample size and standard deviation of a point estimator to control the size of the bound on the error of estimation or the width of a confidence interval.

For instance, suppose that we want to estimate the mean bank prime lending rate (Example 6.1), and we wish the error of estimation to be less than .06% with a probability of .95. Since approximately 95% of the sample means will lie within $1.96\sigma_{\bar{x}}$ of μ in repeated sampling, we are asking that $1.96\sigma_{\bar{x}}$ equal .06% (see Figure 6.11). Then

$$1.96\sigma_{\bar{x}} = .06$$

or

$$\frac{1.96\sigma}{\sqrt{n}} = .06$$

Solving for n, we obtain

$$n = \left(\frac{1.96}{.06}\right)^2 \sigma^2$$

If we know σ, we can substitute its value into this formula and solve for n. If σ is unknown, we use the best approximation available, such as an estimate s, obtained from a previous sample or knowledge of the range in which the measurements will fall. Since the range is approximately equal to 4σ (the Empirical Rule), one-fourth of the range will provide an approximate value for σ. For our example we can use the sample standard deviation of Example 6.1, which provides a reasonably accurate estimate of σ equal to $s = .24$. Then

$$n = \left(\frac{1.96}{.06}\right)^2 \sigma^2$$

$$\approx \left(\frac{1.96}{.06}\right)^2 (.24)^2 = 61.5$$

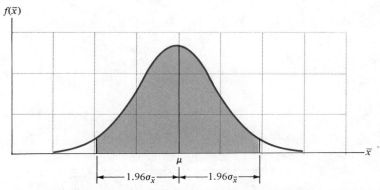

FIGURE 6.11   Approximate Sampling Distribution of $\bar{x}$ for Large Samples

or

$$n = 62$$

Using a sample size $n = 62$, we will be reasonably certain (with probability approximately equal to .95) that our estimate will lie within $1.96\sigma_{\bar{x}} = .06\%$ of the true mean bank prime lending rate.

The solution $n = 62$ is only approximate because we had to use an approximate value for σ in calculating the value of n. Although this may bother you, it is the best method available for selecting the sample size and it is certainly better than guessing.

The method of choosing the sample size for all the large-sample estimation procedures discussed in preceding sections is identical to that described above. The first step is to choose a bound on the error of estimation that we are willing to tolerate and an associated confidence level $(1 - \alpha)$. Then if the parameter is θ and the desired bound is B, we equate

$$z_{\alpha/2}\sigma_{\hat{\theta}} = B$$

where $z_{\alpha/2}$ is the z value defined in the previous sections; that is, it is an upper-tail value for the standard normal distribution such that

$$P(z > z_{\alpha/2}) = \frac{\alpha}{2}$$

The steps in the procedure for choosing n are listed in the next box.

PROCEDURE FOR CHOOSING THE SAMPLE SIZE

Let θ be the parameter to be estimated, and let $\sigma_{\hat{\theta}}$ be the standard deviation of the point estimator. Then proceed according to the following steps.

(1) Choose B, the bound on the error of estimation, and a confidence coefficient $(1 - \alpha)$.

(2) Solve the following equation for the sample size n:

$$z_{\alpha/2}\sigma_{\hat{\theta}} = B$$

Note: For most estimators (all presented in this text) $\sigma_{\hat{\theta}}$ is a function of the sample size n.

We will illustrate the procedure with examples.

EXAMPLE 6.7

In Example 6.5 a survey of 100 purchasing agents produced an estimate of the proportion of polyvinyl pipe wholesalers who plan to increase their purchases in the coming year. The bound on the error of estimation, .096, was relatively large. Suppose that the marketing organization conducting the survey is asked to conduct a new survey and to obtain an estimate correct to within .04 with probability equal to .90. Approximately how many wholesalers would have to be included in the survey?

SOLUTION

For this particular example the bound B on the error of estimation is .04. Since the confidence coefficient is $(1 - \alpha) = .90$, α must equal .10 and $\alpha/2$ is .05. The z value corresponding to an area equal to .05 in the upper tail of the z distribution is $z_{.05} = 1.645$. We then require

$$1.645\sigma_{\hat{p}} = .04$$

or

$$1.645\sqrt{\frac{pq}{n}} = .04$$

In order to solve this equation for n, we must substitute an approximate value of p into the equation. We could use the estimate $\hat{p} = .59$ based on the sample of $n = 100$; or if we want to be certain that the sample size is large enough, we could use $p = .5$ (substituting $p = .5$ will yield the largest possible solution for n). We will substitute $p = .5$. Then

$$1.645\sqrt{\frac{(.5)(.5)}{n}} = .04$$

or

$$\sqrt{n} = \frac{(1.645)(.5)}{.04} = 20.56$$

and

$$n = (20.56)^2 = 422.7$$

Therefore, the marketing organization must include approximately 423 wholesalers in its survey if it wants to estimate the proportion p correct to within .04.   ■

EXAMPLE 6.8   A personnel director wishes to compare the effectiveness of two methods of training industrial employees to perform a certain assembly operation. A number of employees are to be divided into two equal groups, the first receiving training method 1 and the second training method 2. Each will perform the assembly operation, and the length of assembly time will be recorded. It is expected that the measurements for both groups will have a range of approximately 8 minutes. If the estimate of the difference in mean times to assemble is desired correct to within 1 minute with probability equal to .95, how many workers must be included in each training group?

SOLUTION   Equating $1.96\sigma_{(\bar{x}_1 - \bar{x}_2)}$ to $B = 1$ minute, we obtain

$$1.96\sqrt{\frac{\sigma_1^2}{n_1} + \frac{\sigma_2^2}{n_2}} = 1$$

Or since we wish n_1 to equal n_2, we may let $n_1 = n_2 = n$ and obtain the equation

$$1.96\sqrt{\frac{\sigma_1^2}{n} + \frac{\sigma_2^2}{n}} = 1$$

As noted above, the variability (range) of each method of assembly is approximately the same, and hence $\sigma_1^2 = \sigma_2^2 = \sigma^2$. Since the range, equal to 8 minutes, is approximately equal to 4σ, then

$$4\sigma \approx 8$$

and

$$\sigma \approx 2$$

Substituting this value for σ_1 and σ_2 in the above equation, we obtain

$$1.96\sqrt{\frac{(2)^2}{n} + \frac{(2)^2}{n}} = 1$$

or

$$1.96\sqrt{\frac{8}{n}} = 1$$

and

$$\sqrt{n} = 1.96\sqrt{8}$$

Solving, we have $n = 31$. Thus each group should contain approximately $n = 31$ members. ■

EXERCISES

BASIC TECHNIQUES

6.53 Suppose that you wish to estimate a population mean from a random sample of n observations, and that prior experience suggests that $\sigma = 12.7$. If you wish to estimate μ correct to within 1.6 with probability equal to .95, how many observations should be included in your sample?

6.54 Suppose that you wish to estimate a binomial parameter p correct to within .04 with probability equal to .95. If you suspect that p is equal to some value between .1 and .3 and you want to be certain that your sample is large enough, how large should n be? (*Hint:* When calculating $\sigma_{\hat{p}}$, use the value of p in the interval $.1 < p < .3$ that will give the largest sample size.)

6.55 Independent random samples of $n_1 = n_2 = n$ observations are to be selected from each of two populations, 1 and 2. If you wish to estimate the difference between the two population means correct to within .17 with probability equal to .90, how large should n_1 and n_2 be? Assume that you know that $\sigma_1^2 \approx \sigma_2^2 \approx 27.8$.

6.56 Independent random samples of $n_1 = n_2 = n$ observations are to be selected from each of two binomial populations, 1 and 2. If you wish to estimate the difference in the two population binomial parameters correct to within .05 with probability equal to .98, how large should n be? Assume that you have no prior information on the values of p_1 and p_2, but you want to make certain that you have an adequate number of observations in the samples.

APPLICATIONS

6.57 According to the Sheriff's Office in Marion County, Florida, an automobile salesman who rolled back the mileage on a used car by 60,000 miles increased its value by $1375 (*New York*

Times, April 14, 1985). Fraud involving the rollback of odometer readings in used cars is prevalent and costly to society. Suppose that it was possible to positively identify an automobile with an altered odometer reading. If you were to accept an appraiser's statement of the amount of the increase in the car's value produced by the odometer alteration, how would you proceed to estimate the mean loss to odometer fraud per used automobile sold?

(a) Explain how you would select your sample.

(b) Explain how you would decide on the number of used automobile purchases to be included in your sample.

6.58 In Exercise 6.32 we estimated the difference in the mean values of a bank's home loans processed in the month of April versus the month of May. Suppose that the bank desires a more accurate estimate of this difference, say an estimate correct to within $1000 with probability equal to .95. How many home loans would have to be included in each sample? (Assume that the sample sizes for the two months are equal.)

6.59 In earlier exercises we described the results of a government survey of telephone use by federal employees; particularly, we noted that approximately one in three calls is made for personal (i.e., nonbusiness) reasons (*New York Times,* June 23, 1986). The government did not listen in on employee's calls to determine whether an employee's phone call was for business or personal reasons. Rather, it randomly sampled the numbers dialed and checked the source of each number. Suppose that the government wanted to estimate the proportion of nonbusiness calls made by its employees correct to within .02 with probability equal to .99. Approximately how many dialed telephone numbers would have to be included in the sample?

6.60 Hard times in the energy industry? A survey of 43 energy companies by the Wyatt Company, a benefits consulting firm, found that only 44% of those sampled made bonus payments to their executives in 1985, down from 76% in 1984 (*Wall Street Journal,* April 29, 1986). Is the sample size, $n = 43$, too small to obtain a useful estimate of the percentage of all energy companies that made bonus payments to executives last year? Explain.

6.61 In Exercise 6.31 we discussed the results of a survey conducted by the Conference Board to estimate the mean expenditure per household holiday giving in 1986 (*Wall Street Journal,* December 9, 1986). Suppose, in fact, that most of these expenditures are expected to fall within $250 of the mean for any region of the United States. If we wished to estimate the difference in the mean expenditures per household between the New England states region and the mountain states of the West, how many households must be included in each sample if we wish the estimate to lie within $10 of the true difference with probability equal to .95?

6.62 An auditing firm wishes to estimate the mean error per account in accounts receivable for a plumbing supply company correct to within $20 with probability equal to .99. A small prior sample suggests that the error per account possesses a standard deviation approximately equal to $58. If the firm wishes to estimate the mean error per account correct to within $20, how many accounts would have to be sampled? What attribute(s) must the sample possess?

6.63 A food products company has hired a marketing research firm to sample two markets, I and II, to compare the proportions of consumers who prefer the company's frozen dinners over its competitors' products. No prior information is available on the magnitude of the proportions p_1 and p_2. If the food products company wishes to estimate the difference in proportions of consumers preferring its products correct to within .04 with probability equal to .95, how many consumers must be sampled in each market? How must the samples be collected?

6.64 Refer to the biannual survey of purchasing agents discussed in Exercise 6.38. How large would the sample size need to be in order that an estimate of the proportion "who were satisfied or optimistic about the economic outlook" be correct to within .05 with probability .95?

6.65 Refer to the survey of purchasing agents discussed in Exercise 6.38. If the National Association of Purchasing Agents wishes to estimate the change in the proportion of purchasing agents possessing a satisfactory or optimistic outlook on the economy from one biannual survey to another, correct to within .06 with probability equal to .90, how many purchasing agents must be included in each sample? (Assume independent random samples of equal size.)

THE LOGIC BEHIND THE IRS's $3.4 MILLION DISALLOWANCE

6.10

The Case Study in this chapter describes a corporation's claim for repair expense replacement and the disallowance of a large portion of the claim by the Internal Revenue Service (IRS). In the discussion that follows, we will explain the basis for the IRS's disallowance of a portion of the claim. Both the Case Study and the explanation for the disallowance are based on information contained in an article by W. L. Felix, Jr., and R. S. Roussey ("Statistical Inference and the IRS," *Journal of Accountancy,* June 1985).

To review the details of the case: A corporation claimed $6 million in one year and $3.8 million the next for repair expense replacement. These figures were based on "random sampling techniques," specifically, samples of 350 items in the first year and 520 in the second. The IRS did not object to the sampling procedure, the sample sizes, or the use of statistical inference to estimate the total replacement claim. The IRS did, however, "refer to written standards for statistical sampling that would allow a mathematical expression of the margin of error associated with a sample (the calculation of a sample error)." Furthermore, the IRS took the position that the company "could and should have applied the sample error to calculate a lower limit of allowable repair allowance so that management could have said, for example, 'We are 95 percent certain that the allowable repair allowance is at least X dollars.'" The IRS did, in fact, calculate this lower limit and used it as the repair expense replacement that it would allow.

To understand the position of the IRS with regard to the disallowance, we need to translate these two quotations into the language of this chapter. In the first quotation the IRS is stating that the corporation should have provided information on the "sample error." By sample error, we assume that the agency means the error of estimation.

Interpreting the second quotation, we assume the IRS means that management should have located a **95% lower confidence limit on the total repair cost. The IRS performed this calculation and then chose this LCL as the maximum repair expense that it would allow.**

Although Felix and Roussey did not explain the details of the sampling and estimation procedures employed for this Case Study, we will explain how the IRS would have arrived at the lower confidence limit for the repair expense allowance based on random sampling.

We will assume that the total number of repair expenses for the year is N, and for purposes of illustration, we assume that

$$N = 100,000$$

A random sample of $n = 500$ of these repair expenses is selected from among the 100,000 in the population, and the average cost of a repair expense for the $n = 500$ is calculated to be $\bar{x} = \$65$. Then if the estimate of a single repair expense is $65, the estimate of the total repair expense costs for the 100,000 repair expenses incurred during the year is $(100,000)(\$65) = \$6,500,000$. That is, letting $\hat{\tau}$ (Greek letter tau) represent the total repair expense cost, we have

$$\text{estimate of total repair expense cost} = \hat{\tau} = N\bar{x}$$
$$= (100,000)(65)$$
$$= \$6,500,000$$

To find a one-sided lower confidence interval for the total repair expense cost, we need to determine the properties of the sampling distribution of $\hat{\tau} = N\bar{x}$. We know, from the Central Limit Theorem, that the sampling distribution of $\bar{x}$ will be approximately normally distributed. Then since N is a constant, it follows from Section 5.4 that the sampling distribution of $\hat{\tau} = N\bar{x}$ is approximately normally distributed with mean $N\mu$ and standard deviation

$$\sigma_{\hat{\tau}} = N\sigma_{\bar{x}} = N\frac{\sigma}{\sqrt{n}}$$

Since $\hat{\tau}$ is an unbiased estimator of the total repair expense cost and it is approximately normally distributed, it satisfies all of the properties required for the one-sided lower 95% confidence interval given in Section 6.4. That is,

$$\text{LCL} = \hat{\tau} - z_{.05}\sigma_{\hat{\tau}}$$
$$= \hat{\tau} - 1.645\frac{N\sigma}{\sqrt{n}}$$

To illustrate the calculation of the LCL, suppose that the standard deviation s for the sample of 500 repair expenses is $342. Then a one-sided 95% lower confidence interval for the repair expense total for the year is

$$\text{LCL} = \hat{\tau} - z_{.05}\frac{N\sigma}{\sqrt{n}}$$
$$= 6,500,000 - (1.645)(100,000)\frac{(342)}{\sqrt{500}}$$
$$= 6,500,000 - 2,515,979$$
$$= \$3,984,021$$

Therefore, from this illustration the IRS would allow a repair expense replacement of $3,984,021.

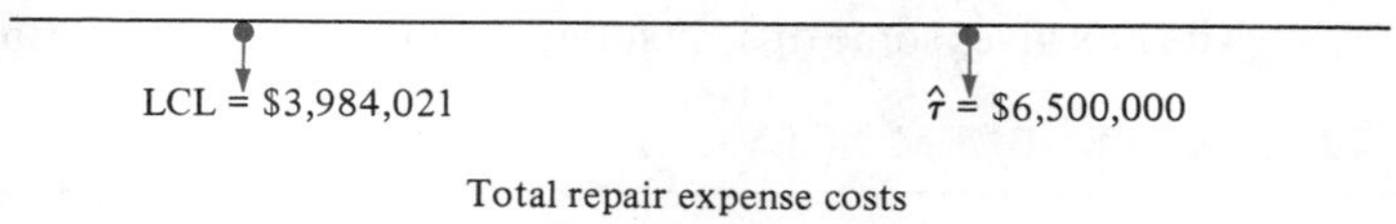

LCL = $3,984,021 $\hat{\tau}$ = $6,500,000

Total repair expense costs

FIGURE 6.12   Location of the LCL with Respect to $\hat{\tau}$

The IRS is certainly not losing money by choosing the lower confidence limit on total repair expense as the maximum repair expense replacement that it will allow. As you can see from Figure 6.12, the unbiased point estimator $\hat{\tau}$ estimates the total repair expense costs to be $6,500,000. By allowing only the LCL (in this case, $3,984,021), the IRS will be allowing less than the actual total expense repair costs 95% of the time. Only 5% of the time will it shortchange the U.S. government. When it does, it will probably be by a small amount.

6.11 SUMMARY

Chapter 6 presents the basic concepts of statistical estimation and demonstrates how these concepts can be applied to the solution of some practical problems.

We learned that estimators are rules (usually formulas) that tell us how to calculate a parameter estimate based on sample data. Point estimators produce a single number (point) that estimates the value of a population parameter. The properties of a point estimator are contained in its sampling distribution. Thus we prefer a point estimator that is unbiased—that is, the mean of its sampling distribution is equal to the estimated parameter. The point estimator should possess a small, preferably a minimum, variance.

The reliability of a point estimator is usually measured by a 1.96 standard deviation (of the sampling distribution of the estimator) bound on the error of estimation. When we use sample data to calculate a particular estimate, the probability that the error of estimation will be less than the bound is approximately .95.

An interval estimator uses the sample data to calculate two points—a confidence interval—that we hope will enclose the estimated parameter. Since we will want to know the probability that the interval will enclose the parameter, we need to know the sampling distribution of the statistic used to calculate the interval.

Four estimators—a sample mean, a proportion, and the differences between pairs of these statistics—were used to estimate their population equivalents and to demonstrate the concepts of estimation developed in this chapter. These estimators were chosen for a particular reason. Generally, they are "good" estimators for the respective population parameters in a wide variety of applications. Fortunately, they all possess, for large samples, sampling distributions that are approximately normal. This fact enabled us to use the same procedure to construct confidence intervals for the four population parameters μ, p, $(\mu_1 - \mu_2)$, and $(p_1 - p_2)$. Thus we were able to demonstrate an important role that the Central Limit Theorem (Chapter 5) plays in statistical inference.

The box gives some tips for solving problems of the type discussed in this chapter.

TIPS ON PROBLEM SOLVING

In solving the exercises in this chapter, you will be required to answer a practical question of interest to a businessperson, a professional person, a scientist, or a layperson. To find the answer to the question, you will need to make an inference about one or more population parameters. Consequently, the first step in solving a problem is in deciding on the objective of the exercise. What parameters do you wish to make an inference about? Answering the following two questions will help you reach a decision.

(1) What *type of data* is involved? The answer to this question will help you decide the type of parameters about which you will wish to make inferences, binomial proportions (p's) or population means (μ's): Check to see whether the data are of the yes-no (two-possibility) variety. If they are, the data are probably binomial, and you will be interested in proportions. If not, the data probably represent measurements on one or more quantitative random variables, and you will be interested in means. To aid you, look for key words such as *proportions* and *fractions,* which indicate binomial data. Binomial data often (but not exclusively) evolve from a sample survey.

(2) Do I wish to make an inference about a *single parameter, p* or μ, or about the *difference between two parameters,* $(p_1 - p_2)$ or $(\mu_1 - \mu_2)$? This is an easy question to answer. Check on the number of samples involved. One sample implies an inference about a single parameter; two samples imply a comparison of two parameters. The answers to questions 1 and 2 identify the parameter.

After identifying the parameter(s) involved in the exercise, you must identify the *exercise objective.* It will be one of these two:

(1) Choosing the sample size required to estimate a parameter with a specified bound on the error of estimation.

(2) Estimating a parameter (or difference between two parameters).

The objective will be very clear if it is 1 because the question will ask for or direct you to find the "sample size." Objective 2 will be clear because the exercise will specifically direct you to estimate a parameter (or the difference between two parameters).

To summarize these tips: your thought process should follow the decision tree shown in Figure 6.13.

Key Terms

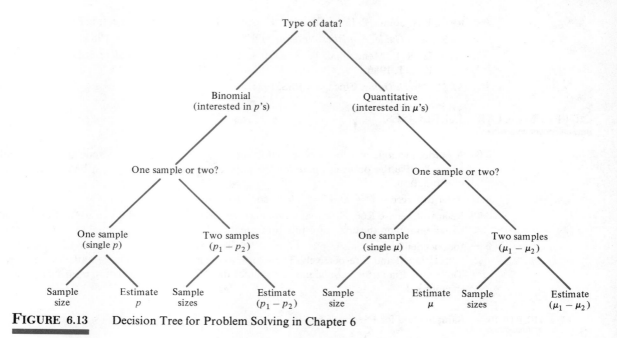

FIGURE 6.13   Decision Tree for Problem Solving in Chapter 6

References

Dixon, W. J., and Massey, F. J., Jr. *Introduction to Statistical Analysis.* 4th ed. New York: McGraw-Hill, 1983.

Dixon, W. J., Brown, M. B., Engelman, L., Frane, J. W., Hill, M. A., Jennich, R. I., and Toporek, J. D. *BMDP Statistical Software.* Berkeley: University of California Press, 1985.

Freund, J. E., and Williams, F. J., revised by B. Perles and C. Sullivan. *Modern Business Statistics.* Englewood Cliffs, N. J.: Prentice-Hall, 1969.

Hamburg, M. *Statistical Analysis for Decision Making.* 2nd ed. New York: Harcourt Brace Jovanovich, 1977.

Mendenhall, W., Scheaffer, R. L., and Wackerly, D. D. *Mathematical Statistics with Applications.* 3rd ed. Boston: PWS-KENT, 1986.

Neter, J., Wasserman, W., and Whitmore, F. A. *Fundamental Statistics for Business and Economics.* 4th ed. Boston: Allyn and Bacon, 1973.

Ryan, T. A., Joiner, B. L., and Ryan, B. F. *Minitab Handbook*. 2nd ed. Boston: PWS-KENT, 1985.

SAS User's Guide: Statistics. Version 5 ed. Cary, N. C.: SAS Institute, 1985.

Scheaffer, R. L., Mendenhall, W., and Ott, L. *Elementary Survey Sampling*. 3rd ed. Boston: PWS-KENT, 1986.

SPSS^x User's Guide. Chicago: SPSS, 1983.

SUPPLEMENTARY EXERCISES

6.66 A random sample of $n = 64$ observations possessed a mean $\bar{x} = 29.1$ and standard deviation $s = 3.9$. Give the point estimate for the population mean μ, and give a bound on the error of estimation.

6.67 Refer to Exercise 6.66, and find a 90% confidence interval for μ.

6.68 Refer to Exercise 6.66. How many observations would be required if you wanted to estimate μ with a bound on the error of estimation equal to .5 with probability equal to .95?

6.69 Independent random samples of $n_1 = 50$ and $n_2 = 60$ observations were selected from populations 1 and 2, respectively. The sample sizes and computed sample statistics are shown in Table 6.10. Find a 90% confidence interval for the difference in population means, and interpret the interval.

TABLE 6.10   Sample Data for Exercise 6.69

	Population	
	1	2
Sample size	50	60
Sample mean	100.4	96.2
Sample standard deviation	.8	1.3

6.70 Refer to Exercise 6.69. Suppose that you want to estimate $(\mu_1 - \mu_2)$ correct to within .2 with probability equal to .95. If you plan to use equal sample sizes, how large should n_1 and n_2 be?

6.71 A random sample of $n = 500$ observations from a binomial population produced $x = 240$ successes.

(a) Find a point estimate for p, and place a bound on your error of estimation.

(b) Find a 90% confidence interval for p.

6.72 Refer to Exercise 6.71. How large a sample would be required if you want to estimate p correct to within .025 with probability equal to .90?

6.73 Independent random samples of $n_1 = 40$ and $n_2 = 80$ observations were selected from binomial populations 1 and 2, respectively. The number of successes in the two samples were $x_1 = 17$ and $x_2 = 23$. Find a 90% confidence interval for the difference between the two binomial population proportions.

6.74 Refer to Exercise 6.73. Suppose that you want to estimate $(p_1 - p_2)$ correct to within .06 with probability equal to .90 and that you plan to use equal sample sizes, that is, $n_1 = n_2$. How large should n_1 and n_2 be?

6.75 State the Central Limit Theorem. Of what value is the Central Limit Theorem in statistical inference?

6.76 A random sample of 400 television tubes was tested and 40 tubes were found to be defective. With confidence coefficient equal to .90, estimate the interval within which the true fraction defective lies.

6.77 Past experience shows that the standard deviation of the yearly income of textile workers in a certain state was $1000. How large a sample of textile workers would one need to take if one wished to estimate the population mean to within $100.00 with a probability of .95 of being correct? Given that the mean of the sample in this problem is $14,800, determine 95% confidence limits for the population mean.

6.78 An experimenter wants to use the sample mean $\bar{x}$ to estimate the mean of a normally distributed population with an error of less than .5 with probability .9. If the variance of the population is equal to 4, how large should the sample be to achieve the accuracy stated above?

6.79 A time study is planned to estimate, correct to within 4 seconds with probability .90, the mean time for a worker to complete an assembly task. If past experience suggests that $\sigma = 16$ seconds measures the worker-to-worker variation in assembly time, how many workers, each performing a single assembly operation, will have to be included in the sample?

6.80 To estimate the proportion of unemployed workers in Panama, an economist selected at random 400 persons from the working class. Of these, 25 were unemployed.

(a) Estimate the true proportion of unemployed workers, and place bounds on the error of estimation.

(b) How many persons must be sampled to reduce the bound on error to .02?

6.81 Sixty of 87 housewives prefer detergent A. If the 87 housewives represent a random sample from the population of all potential purchasers, estimate the fraction of total housewives favoring detergent A. Use a 90% confidence interval.

6.82 A dean of men wishes to estimate the average cost of the freshman year at a particular college correct to within $500.00 with a probability of .95. If a random sample of freshmen is to be selected and requested to keep financial data, how many must be included in the sample? Assume that the dean knows only that the range of expenditure will vary from approximately $4800 to $13,000.

6.83 The percentage of D's and F's awarded to students by two college history professors was duly noted by the dean. Professor I achieved a rate equal to 32% as opposed to 21% for professor II, based upon 200 and 180 students, respectively. Estimate the difference in the percentage of D's and F's awarded by the professors. Place bounds on the error of estimation.

6.84 Suppose you wish to estimate the mean hourly yield for a process manufacturing an antibiotic. The process is observed for 100 hourly periods chosen at random, with the following results:

$$\bar{x} = 34 \text{ ounces per hour} \qquad s = 3$$

Estimate the mean hourly yield for the process, using a 95% confidence interval.

6.85 A quality control engineer wants to estimate the fraction of defectives in a large lot of light bulbs. From previous experience he feels that the actual fraction of defectives should be somewhere around .2. How large a sample should he take if he wants to estimate the true fraction to within .01, using a 95% confidence interval?

6.86 Samples of 400 radio tubes were selected from each of two production lines, A and B. The numbers of defectives in the samples are given in the accompanying table. Estimate the difference in the actual fractions of defectives for the two lines with a confidence coefficient of .90.

Line	Number of Defectives	
A	40	p_1
B	80	p_2

6.87 A sample of $n = 200$ items was taken from each of two binomial populations, where $p_1 = p_2 = .5$. What is the probability that $(\hat{p}_1 - \hat{p}_2)$ is greater than .1 in absolute value?

6.88 The length of time between the billing and the receipt of payment was recorded for a random sample of 100 of a CPA firm's clients. The sample mean and standard deviation for the 100 accounts were 39.1 days and 17.3 days, respectively. Find a 90% confidence interval for the mean time between billing and receipt of payment for all of the CPA firm's accounts. Interpret the interval.

6.89 Refer to Exercise 6.88. A comparison of the mean time between billing and payment was made by selecting random samples of 30 clients each from the population of all individual clients and from the population of business clients. The sample sizes, means, and standard deviations for the two samples are shown in Table 6.11. Find a 95% confidence interval for the difference in mean time to pay between individual and business clients.

TABLE 6.11   Sample Data for Exercise 6.89

	Individual Clients	Business Clients
Sample size	30	30
$\bar{x}$	28.3	47.7
s	15.5	18.9

6.90 Refer to Exercise 6.89. How many clients of each type would have to be sampled (with equal sample sizes) if you wanted to estimate the difference in mean time to pay, correct to within 5 days with probability approximately equal to .95?

6.91 Television advertisers may mistakenly believe that most viewers understand most of the advertising that they see and hear. A recent research study used 2300 viewers above age 13. Each viewer looked at 30-second television advertising excerpts. Of these, 1914 of the viewers misunderstood all or part of the excerpt. Find a 95% confidence interval for the proportion of all viewers (of which the sample is representative) that will misunderstand all or part of the television excerpts used in this study.

As explained in Chapter 6, there are two methods for making inferences about population parameters based on sample data. The first method, statistical estimation, was the topic of Chapter 6. The objective of Chapter 7 is to present a second method for making inferences about population parameters, testing hypotheses about their values. As was the case in Chapter 6, we will demonstrate the procedure for situations where the sample sizes are large enough to produce approximate normality in the sampling distributions of the sample statistics used to make the inferences.

7

LARGE-SAMPLE TESTS OF HYPOTHESES

CASE STUDY

Women in Overseas Management: Why the Scarcity?

A survey of 686 Canadian and American multinational corporations conducted by Nancy J. Adler in an article in *Columbia Journal of World Business* identified 13,338 overseas managers. Of these, only 3% were women. Why are so few women employed in international management? One explanation is that women neither want nor seek international assignments. A second is that North American corporations are resistant to sending female managers overseas. A third belief is that foreigners are prejudiced against women managers, and that they therefore cannot serve effectively in overseas assignments.

How do the academic world and managers themselves perceive these beliefs? To shed light on this question, Adler surveyed the opinions of 60 international personnel managers from 60 different American and Canadian international companies as well as the opinions of 1129 graduating MBA students from Canada, the United States, and Europe. As part of the survey, each person was presented with six reasons why so few women are expatriate managers and was asked to indicate whether he or she agreed or disagreed with each reason. The percentages of MBAs and international personnel managers agreeing with the six reasons are shown in Table 7.1.

Do graduating MBAs and international personnel managers have different perceptions of the reasons why there are so few women in overseas management? For example, one reason posed in the survey concerned the problem of balancing marriage with an international career (identified in the table as "dual-career marriages"). Companies, it is said, are concerned about the impact of a wife's assignment overseas on a husband's career, the unwillingness of husbands to move, and so on. As you can see from the table, 72.8% of the sample of 1129 MBAs perceived this impact to be a major reason why so few women are employed in international management. The corresponding response for the sample of 60 international managers was 69.1%. Does this small percentage difference, 72.8% versus 69.1%, imply a difference in the perceptions of the populations of all graduating MBAs and international managers on this particular "reason"? Or consider the comparison of the percentages in agreement for the reason "women are unqualified." A small 5.6% of the sample of 1129 MBAs agree with this reason,

TABLE 7.1   A Comparison of Managers' and Graduating MBAs' Perceptions of Women in International Management

Reasons Why So Few Women Are Expatriate Managers	Perceptions of (% Agreeing)	
	Graduating MBAs ($n = 1129$)	Personnel Managers ($n = 60$)
Women are		
Unqualified	5.6	18.2
Ineffective	19.1	5.6
Uninterested	21.4	24.5
Not selected by corporations	78.0	53.8
Dual-career marriages	72.8	69.1
Foreigner's prejudice	83.6	72.7

Source: Nancy J. Adler, "Expecting International Success: Female Managers Overseas," *Columbia Journal of World Business,* Fall 1984.

in comparison with 18.2% of the sample of 60 personnel managers. Does this relatively larger percentage difference imply a difference in perceptions of MBAs and personnel managers for this particular reason? The answers to these questions require us to make decisions about two population parameters, the proportions of all MBAs and all international personnel managers who agree with a specific reason for the scarcity of women in international management.

How large must the difference in sample proportions be in order to imply a difference in the corresponding population proportions? And if we make a decision about the population proportions, what is the probability that we will make the wrong decision? We will present the methodology required to answer these questions—the mechanics of a statistical test of an hypothesis—throughout Chapter 7. We will apply this methodology to the Case Study data in Section 7.10.

TESTING HYPOTHESES ABOUT POPULATION PARAMETERS

7.1

Inferences about population parameters can be made in one of two ways. We can estimate the values of parameters (the topic of Chapter 6), or we can make decisions about them. The procedure we use often depends upon the practical circumstances that motivate our inference making.

For example, suppose that a corporation wants to offer early retirement to its employees and wants to know the proportion p of those who would accept the offer. In this situation the corporation would want to survey the opinions of a sample of its employees and estimate the value of p with a specified error of estimation.

In contrast, suppose that the corporation possesses two plans for early employee retirement. It plans to sample its employees and, from the survey results, choose the plan that leads to the higher proportion of plan acceptance. Thus the corporation wants to reach a decision about the difference between two proportions of acceptance. And equally important, it wants to know that its risk of reaching an incorrect decision is relatively small.

In this chapter we will explore the concepts involved in a statistical test of an hypothesis about one or more population parameters. We will identify the elements of a statistical test by using a familiar coin-tossing example. Then we will present some useful large-sample statistical tests based on the sampling distributions of Chapter 5.

THE ELEMENTS OF A TEST OF AN HYPOTHESIS

7.2

The logic underlying a statistical test of an hypothesis can be illustrated with an example. Suppose that we believe that more than 50% of all consumers prefer toothpaste brand A. To determine whether our hypothesis is true, we decide to conduct an experiment. One hundred consumers are randomly selected and 99 state that they prefer brand A. What do you conclude? It is not *impossible* to observe 99 in favor of brand A, if 50% or less in the entire population favor the brand, but it is highly improbable. Thus the observance of a highly improbable or "rare" event leads us to conclude that more than 50% of all consumers favors brand A.

The method employed in reaching a decision in the consumer preference survey can be formalized. Like all statistical tests of hypotheses, it involves a test of an hypothesis about a population parameter. In this particular example we want to determine whether a binomial parameter p exceeds .5. Therefore, our research hypothesis, called an **alternative hypothesis** in statistics and denoted by the symbol H_a, is that p is larger than .5—that is, $p > .5$. We hope to reach this conclusion by showing that the converse of the research hypothesis, the **null hypothesis**, $H_0: p = .5$, is false. Thus we hope to show support for the research (or alternative) hypothesis H_a by showing lack of support for its converse, the null hypothesis H_0.

The decision to reject the null hypothesis and support the alternative hypothesis is based on information contained in a sample of n measurements drawn from a population—for our example, a sample of $n = 100$ observations from a binomial population. The sample values are used to compute a single number corresponding to a point on a line. This number operates as a decision maker and is called the **test statistic**. The entire set of values that the test statistic can assume is divided into two sets or regions, one corresponding to the **rejection region** and the other to the acceptance region (see Figure 7.1). If the test statistic computed from a particular sample assumes a value in the rejection region, the null hypothesis is rejected and you decide in favor of the alternative hypothesis. If the test statistic falls in the acceptance region, the null hypothesis is accepted—that is, you decide in favor of the null hypothesis. Thus a statistical test involves four elements as indicated in the following box.

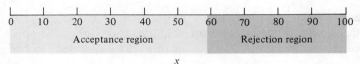

x

FIGURE 7.1   Possible Values for the Test Statistic x

ELEMENTS OF A STATISTICAL TEST

(1) Null hypothesis

(2) Alternative hypothesis

(3) Test statistic

(4) Rejection region

For our consumer preference survey the test statistic is the number x of consumers who prefer brand A in a sample of $n = 100$, selected from a binomial population. The rejection region includes values of x that support the alternative hypothesis (that the proportion p favoring brand A is larger than .5)—that is, very large values of x that would be improbable if p is .5 or less. Values of x that support the null hypothesis—values less than or not too much larger than $\mu = np = 100(.5) = 50$—are assigned to the acceptance region. When we decided (at the beginning of this section) that the proportion of consumers favoring brand A was larger than .5, we did so because we know intuitively that a value of x as large as $x = 99$ is highly improbable, assuming that 50% (or less) of all consumers favor brand A. Therefore, we automatically assigned $x = 99$ to our intuitive rejection region, rejected the null hypothesis, and concluded that p was larger than .5.

How do we decide on the values of the test statistic to assign to the rejection region for a test? For example, should the value $x = 70$ consumers in favor of brand A be assigned to the acceptance or the rejection region? The answer to this question depends upon the risks that we are willing to take. The decision that you make when you test an hypothesis is subject to two types of errors, errors that are prevalent in any two-choice decision problem. We can reject the null hypothesis when, in fact, it is true; or we can accept H_0 when it is false and some *alternative hypothesis* is true. These errors are called **type I and type II errors**, respectively, for the statistical test. The two states for the null hypothesis—that is, true or false—along with the two decisions that the experimenter can make are indicated in the two-way table of Table 7.2. The occurrences of the type I and type II errors are indicated in the appropriate cells.

TABLE 7.2   Decision Table

	Null Hypothesis	
Decision	True	False
Reject H_0	Type I error	Correct decision
Accept H_0	Correct decision	Type II error

The goodness of a statistical test of an hypothesis is measured by the **probabilities of making a type I or a type II error**. These probabilities, denoted by the symbols α and β, respectively, can be calculated if we know the sampling distribution of the test statistic. To illustrate, if the null hypothesis is true for the consumer preference survey, we know that the mean and standard deviation of the number x observed in a sample of $n = 100$ are

$$\mu = np = (100)(.5) = 50$$

and

$$\sigma = \sqrt{npq} = \sqrt{(100)(.5)(.5)} = \sqrt{25} = 5$$

Suppose that we were to define the rejection region for our test as those values of x that lie more than 2σ above $\mu = 50$, say $x = 60, 61, 62, \ldots, 100$ (see Figure 7.2). Then

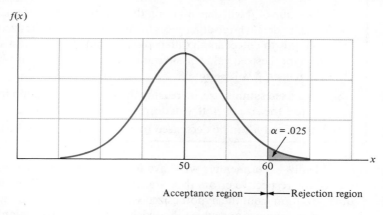

FIGURE 7.2   The Acceptance and Rejection Region for the Consumer Preference Survey

since the sampling distribution of x is approximately normally distributed (see Section 5.4), we know that the probability α that x will lie more than 2σ away from $\mu = 50$ is approximately .025. Therefore, the test statistic will fall into the rejection region, just by chance, approximately 2 1/2% of the time and lead us to the erroneous (type I error) conclusion that p is larger than .5.

The probability of making a type II error, β, varies depending on the true value of the population parameter. For example, suppose that we want to test the null hypothesis that the binomial parameter p is equal to $p_0 = .5$. (We will use a subscript 0 to indicate the parameter value specified in the null hypothesis H_0.) Furthermore, suppose that H_0 is false and that p is really equal to an alternative value, say p_a. What will be more easily detected, $p_a = .5001$ or $p_a = 1.0$? Certainly, if p is really equal to 1.0, every single trial will result in a success, and the sample results will produce strong evidence to support a rejection of $H_0: p_0 = .5$. On the other hand, $p_a = .5001$ lies so close to $p_0 = .5$ that it would be extremely difficult to detect without a very large sample. In other words, the probability β of falsely accepting H_0 will vary depending upon the difference between the true value of p and the hypothesized value p_0. A graph of the probability of a type II error β as a function of the true value of the parameter is called the **operating characteristic curve** for the statistical test. Note that the operating characteristic curves for the lot acceptance sampling plans discussed in Example 3.18 were really graphs expressing β as a function of p. We will show you how β is calculated for a statistical test in Section 7.4.

Since the rejection region is specified and remains constant for a given test, α will also remain constant; and the operating characteristic curve will describe the characteristics of the statistical test. An increase in the sample size n will decrease β and reduce its value for all alternative values of the parameter tested. Thus there is an operating characteristic curve corresponding to each sample size.

The properties of α and β are listed in the next box.

PROPERTIES OF α AND β

(1) The value of α is decided when the rejection region is chosen.

(2) The value of β will depend upon the alternative hypothesis that you choose. It is easier to detect large differences from the (null) hypothesized value of a parameter than it is to detect small differences. If you wish to detect small differences from the hypothesized value of a parameter, β will be large. If you wish to detect large differences, β will be small.

(3) For a fixed sample size, increasing the size of the rejection region (and therefore α) reduces the size of β. If you decrease α, β will increase.

(4) Both α and β can be decreased by increasing the sample size n.

Ideally, experimenters will have in mind some values α and β that measure the risks of the respective errors they are willing to tolerate. They will also have in mind some deviation from the hypothesized value of the parameter, which they consider of *practical* importance and which they wish to detect. The rejection region for the test will then be located in accordance with the specified value of α. Finally, they will choose the sample size necessary to achieve an acceptable value of β for the specified deviation that they wish to detect. This choice can be made by consulting the operating characteristic curves, corresponding to various sample sizes, for the chosen test.

   In a practical situation this ideal procedure is usually not followed. For most statistical tests it is relatively easy to determine the value of α for a specified rejection region, but it may be very difficult to calculate the values of β for different alternative values of the tested parameter. For this reason, we usually decide on the risk α that we are willing to accept and choose the rejection region accordingly. If the test statistic falls in the rejection region (and thereby supports our research hypothesis), we know immediately the risk that we take of making a type I error. However, if the test statistic does not fall into the rejection region, we must proceed with caution. We should not accept the null hypothesis if we do not know the value of β, the probability of making a type II error. The preferable action is to withhold judgment and collect more data.

A Large-Sample Statistical Test

7.3

Many large sample tests of hypotheses concerning population means and proportions are very similar. In fact, when viewed in a certain light, they are equivalent. Seeing this equivalency will make it easier to understand the tests and examples described in the following sections.

   The key to the equivalency lies in the fact that many point estimators (all of those discussed in Chapter 6) are unbiased and possess sampling distributions that for large samples are approximately normal. Therefore, we can use the point estimators as test statistics to test hypotheses about the respective parameters.

   To illustrate, suppose that we use the symbol θ to denote one of the four parameters $\mu, (\mu_1 - \mu_2), p,$ or $(p_1 - p_2)$ that we estimated in Chapter 6; let $\hat{\theta}$ denote the corresponding unbiased point estimator—that is, $\hat{\mu} = \bar{x}$ and so forth. Then when the null hypothesis is true—that is, θ equals some hypothesized value, say θ_0—the sampling distribution of $\hat{\theta}$ will be (for large samples) approximately normal with mean θ_0, as shown in Figure 7.3.

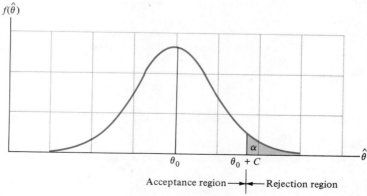

FIGURE 7.3   Distribution of $\hat{\theta}$ When H_0 Is True

Suppose that from a *practical* point of view we are primarily concerned with the rejection of H_0 when θ is greater than θ_0. Then the alternative hypothesis is $H_a : \theta > \theta_0$, and we will reject the null hypothesis when $\hat{\theta}$ is too large. If we let $\sigma_{\hat{\theta}}$ represent the standard deviation of the sampling distribution of $\hat{\theta}$, "too large" will mean too many standard deviations $\sigma_{\hat{\theta}}$ above θ_0. Therefore, the rejection region for the test will be values of $\hat{\theta}$ greater than some number—say $(\theta_0 + C)$, called the **critical value**—as shown in Figure 7.3.

DEFINITION   The value $(\theta_0 + C)$ of the test statistic that separates the rejection and acceptance regions is called the *critical value* of the test statistic.   ■

The probability of rejecting the null hypothesis, assuming it to be true, will equal the area under the normal curve lying above the rejection region. Thus if we desire $\alpha = .05$, we will reject when $\hat{\theta}$ is more than $1.645\sigma_{\hat{\theta}}$ to the right of θ_0. A test rejecting in one tail of the distribution of the test statistic is called a **one-tailed statistical test**.

DEFINITION   A *one-tailed statistical test* is one that locates the rejection region in only one tail of the sampling distribution of the test statistic. To detect $\theta > \theta_0$, place the rejection region in the upper tail of the distribution of $\hat{\theta}$. To detect $\theta < \theta_0$, place the rejection region in the lower tail of the distribution of $\hat{\theta}$.   ■

If we wish to detect departures *either* greater than or less than θ_0, the alternative hypothesis is

$$H_a : \theta \neq \theta_0,$$

that is,

$$\theta > \theta_0 \qquad \text{or} \qquad \theta < \theta_0$$

The probability of a type I error, α, will be equally divided between the two tails of the normal distribution, and we will reject H_0 for values of $\hat{\theta}$ greater than some critical value $(\theta_0 + C)$ or less than $(\theta_0 - C)$. See Figure 7.4. This test is called a **two-tailed statistical test**.

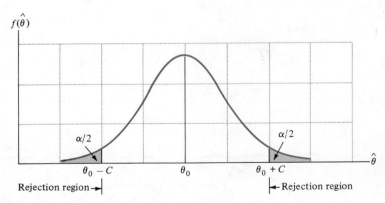

FIGURE 7.4   The Rejection Region for a Two-Tailed Test

DEFINITION

A *two-tailed statistical test* is one that locates the rejection region in both tails of the sampling distribution of the test statistic. Two-tailed tests are used to detect either $\theta > \theta_0$ or $\theta < \theta_0$. ∎

The calculation of β for the one-tailed statistical test described above can be facilitated by considering Figure 7.5. When H_0 is false and $\theta = \theta_a$, the test statistic $\hat{\theta}$ will be normally distributed about a mean θ_a, rather than θ_0. The distribution of $\hat{\theta}$, assuming $\theta = \theta_a$, is shown by the black curve. The hypothesized distribution of $\hat{\theta}$, shown by the colored curve, locates the rejection region and the critical value of $\hat{\theta}$, $(\theta_0 + C)$. Since β is the probability of accepting H_0, given $\theta = \theta_a$, β equals the area under the black curve located above the acceptance region. This area, which is shaded, can be calculated by using the methods described in Chapter 4.

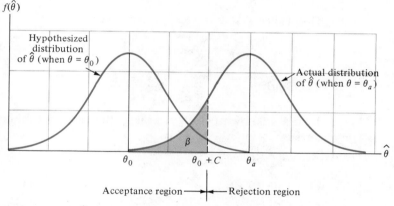

FIGURE 7.5   Distribution of $\hat{\theta}$ When H_0 Is False and $\theta = \theta_a$

The mechanics of testing are simplified by using the standardized normal z variable as a test statistic.

LARGE-SAMPLE TEST STATISTIC

$$z = \frac{\hat{\theta} - \theta_0}{\sigma_{\hat{\theta}}}$$

Note that z is the deviation of a normally distributed random variable $\hat{\theta}$ from θ_0, expressed in units of $\sigma_{\hat{\theta}}$. Thus for a two-tailed test with $\alpha = .05$, we will reject H_0 when $z > 1.96$ or $z < -1.96$.

As we have previously stated, the method of inference used in a given situation will often depend upon the preference of the experimenter. Some people want to express an inference as an estimate; others prefer to test an hypothesis concerning the parameter of interest. The following section will demonstrate the use of the z test in testing an hypothesis concerning a population mean and, at the same time, will illustrate the close relationship between the statistical test and the large-sample confidence intervals discussed in Chapter 6.

Testing an Hypothesis About a Population Mean

7.4   We can apply the large-sample test (Section 7.3) to test an hypothesis about a population mean. The parameter θ to be tested is μ, the point estimator $\hat{\theta}$ is the sample mean $\bar{x}$, and the standard deviation $\sigma_{\hat{\theta}}$ of the sampling distribution of $\bar{x}$ is $\sigma/\sqrt{n}$. A summary of the test is shown in the next box.

LARGE-SAMPLE STATISTICAL TEST FOR μ

(1) *Null Hypothesis: $H_0 : \mu = \mu_0$.*

(2) *Alternative Hypothesis:*

One-Tailed Test

$H_a : \mu > \mu_0$
(or $H_a : \mu < \mu_0$)

Two-Tailed Test

$H_a : \mu \neq \mu_0$

(3) *Test Statistic:* $z = \dfrac{\bar{x} - \mu_0}{\sigma_{\bar{x}}} = \dfrac{\bar{x} - \mu_0}{\sigma/\sqrt{n}}.$

If σ is unknown (which is usually the case), substitute the sample standard deviation s for σ.

(4) *Rejection Region:*

One-Tailed Test

$z > z_\alpha$
(or $z < -z_\alpha$ when the alternative hypothesis is $H_a : \mu < \mu_0$)

Two-Tailed Test

$z > z_{\alpha/2}$ or $z < -z_{\alpha/2}$

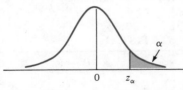   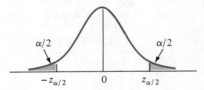

Assumptions: The n observations in the sample were randomly selected from the population and n is large, say $n \geq 30$.

EXAMPLE 7.1   The daily yield at a chemical plant, recorded for $n = 50$ days, possesses a sample mean and standard deviation of $\bar{x} = 871$ tons and $s = 21$ tons. Test the hypothesis that the average daily yield of the chemical is $\mu = 880$ tons per day against the alternative that μ is either greater or less than 880 tons per day.

SOLUTION   We wish to test the null hypothesis

$$H_0 : \mu = 880 \text{ tons}$$

against the alternative hypothesis

$$H_a : \mu \neq 880 \text{ tons}$$

The point estimate for μ is $\bar{x}$. Therefore, the test statistic is

$$z = \frac{\bar{x} - \mu_0}{\sigma_{\bar{x}}} = \frac{\bar{x} - \mu_0}{\sigma/\sqrt{n}}$$

Using s to approximate σ, we obtain

$$z = \frac{871 - 880}{21/\sqrt{50}} = -3.03$$

For $\alpha = .05$ the rejection region is $z > 1.96$ or $z < -1.96$. (See Figure 7.6.) Since the calculated value of z falls in the rejection region, we reject the hypothesis that $\mu = 880$ tons. (In fact, it appears that the mean yield is less than 880 tons per day.) The probability of rejecting H_0, assuming it to be true, is only $\alpha = .05$. Therefore, we are reasonably confident that our decision is correct.

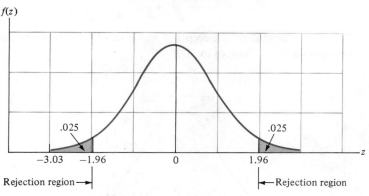

FIGURE 7.6 Location of the Rejection Region in Example 7.1

The statistical test based on a normally distributed test statistic, with given α, and the $(1 - \alpha)100\%$ confidence interval (Section 6.5) are clearly related. The interval $\bar{x} \pm 1.96\sigma/\sqrt{n}$, or approximately 871 ± 5.82 for Example 7.1, is constructed such that in repeated sampling $(1 - \alpha)100\%$ of the intervals will enclose μ. Noting that $\mu = 880$ does not fall in the interval, we would be inclined to reject $\mu = 880$ as a likely value and conclude that the mean daily yield was, indeed, less.

The following example will demonstrate the calculation of β for the statistical test of Example 7.1.

EXAMPLE 7.2 Referring to Example 7.1, calculate the probability β of accepting H_0 if μ is actually equal to 870 tons.

SOLUTION The acceptance region for the test in Example 7.1 is located in the interval $\mu_0 \pm 1.96\sigma_{\bar{x}}$. Substituting numerical values, we obtain

$$880 \pm 1.96\left(\frac{21}{\sqrt{50}}\right)$$

or

$$874.18 \qquad \text{to} \qquad 885.82$$

The probability of accepting H_0 if, in fact, $\mu = 870$ is equal to the area under the sampling distribution for the test statistic $\bar{x}$ above the interval 874.18 to 885.82. Since $\bar{x}$ will be normally distributed with mean equal to 870 and $\sigma_{\bar{x}} = 21/\sqrt{50} = 2.97$, β is equal to the area under the normal curve (Figure 7.7) located to the right of 874.18 (because the area to the right of 885.82 is negligible). Calculating the z value corresponding to 874.18, we obtain

$$z = \frac{\bar{x} - \mu}{\sigma/\sqrt{n}} = \frac{874.18 - 870}{21/\sqrt{50}}$$

$$= 1.41$$

We see from Table 4 in the Appendix that the area between $z = 0$ and $z = 1.41$ is .4207. Therefore,

$$\beta = .5 - .4207 = .0793$$

Thus the probability of accepting H_0, given that μ is really equal to 870, is .0793, or approximately 8 chances in 100.

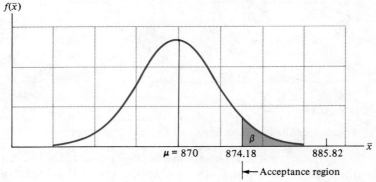

FIGURE 7.7   Calculating β in Example 7.2

EXERCISES

BASIC TECHNIQUES

7.1 A random sample of $n = 35$ observations from a population produced a mean $\bar{x} = 2.4$ and a standard deviation equal to .29. Suppose that you wish to show that the population mean μ exceeds 2.3.

(a) Give the alternative hypothesis for the test.

(b) Give the null hypothesis for the test.

(c) If you wish your probability of (erroneously) deciding that $\mu > 2.3$, when in fact $\mu = 2.3$, to equal .05, what is the value of α for the test?

(d) Before you conduct the test, glance at the data and use your intuition to decide whether the sample mean $\bar{x} = 2.4$ implies that $\mu > 2.3$. Now test the null hypothesis. Do the data provide sufficient evidence to indicate that $\mu > 2.3$? Test using $\alpha = .05$.

7.2 Refer to Exercise 7.1. Suppose that you wish to show that the sample data support the hypothesis that the mean of the population is less than 2.9. Give the null and alternative hypotheses for this test. Would this test be a one- or a two-tailed test? Explain.

7.3 Refer to Exercises 7.1 and 7.2. Suppose that you wish to detect a value of μ that differs from 2.9— that is, a value of μ either greater or less than 2.9. State the null and alternative hypotheses for the test. Would the alternative hypothesis imply a one- or a two-tailed test?

7.4 A random sample of $n = 60$ observations from a population produced a mean $\bar{x} = 83.8$ and a standard deviation equal to .29. Suppose that you wish to show that the population mean μ is less than 84.

(a) Give the alternative hypothesis for the test.

(b) Give the null hypothesis for the test.

(c) If you wish your probability of (erroneously) deciding that $\mu < 84$, when in fact $\mu = 84$, to equal .05, what is the value of α for the test?

(d) Before you conduct the test, glance at the data and use your intuition to decide whether the sample mean $\bar{x} = 83.8$ implies that $\mu < 84$. Now test the null hypothesis. Do the data provide sufficient evidence to indicate that $\mu < 84$? Test using $\alpha = .05$.

7.5 Refer to Exercise 7.4. Suppose that we wish to detect any values of μ that differ from 84—that is, values larger than or less than 84.

(a) Give the null hypothesis for the test.

(b) Give the alternative hypothesis for the test.

(c) Locate the rejection region for the test for $\alpha = .01$.

(d) Conduct the test and state your conclusions.

APPLICATIONS

Starred (*) exercises are optional.

7.6 A new-car dealer calculates that the company must average more than 4.8% profit on the sales of its allotted new cars. A random sampling of $n = 80$ cars gave a mean and standard deviation of the percentage profit per car of $\bar{x} = 4.87\%$ and $s = 3.9\%$. Do the data provide sufficient evidence to indicate that the sales manager's policy in approving sale prices is achieving a mean profit exceeding 4.8% per car?

(a) State the alternative hypothesis that the sales manager wants to show to be true.

(b) Examine the data. From your intuition only, do you think that the data support the alternative hypothesis of part (a)?

(c) State the null hypothesis to be tested.

(d) The company's owner wants to be reasonably certain that the decision is correct if, in fact, the data show that the company is operating at an acceptable profit level. To accomplish this, the owner wants to test the null hypothesis using $\alpha = .01$. Explain how this choice for α will accomplish the owner's objective.

(e) Give the rejection region for the test.

(f) Conduct the test and state your conclusions in a manner that will be understandable to the company's owner. Compare your answer with your intuitive guess in part (b).

7.7 A manufacturer of metal fasteners expects to ship an average of 1200 boxes of fasteners per day. An analysis of the shipments for the past 30 days possessed a mean of $\bar{x} = 1186$ boxes per day and a variance of $s^2 = 2480$ (boxes)^2 per day. Do the data provide sufficient evidence to indicate that the mean daily demand for the fasteners is slipping—that is, is below 1200 boxes per day?

(a) Give the alternative hypothesis that the manufacturer wishes to detect.

(b) Examine the data. From your intuition, do you think that the data support the alternative hypothesis of part (a)?

(c) Give H_0 for the test.

(d) Give the rejection region for the test for $\alpha = .10$.

(e) Conduct the test and state the practical conclusions to be derived from the test. Compare your conclusions with your answer to part (a).

(f) Find a 90% lower one-sided confidence interval for the mean daily demand for the boxes of fasteners.

 7.8 An article in *U.S. News & World Report* (September 28, 1981) states that approximately 21.3 million workers, more than one-fifth of the U.S. work force, works unorthodox schedules. More than 9.3 million are involved in flextime (the worker schedules his or her work hours) or compressed workweek schedules. A company that was contemplating the installation of a flextime schedule estimated that it needed a minimum mean of 7 hours per day per assembly worker in order to operate effectively. Each of a random sample of 80 of the company's assemblers was asked to submit a tentative flextime schedule. If the mean of the number of hours per day for Monday was 6.7 hours and the standard deviation was 2.7 hours, do the data provide sufficient evidence to indicate that the mean number of hours worked per day on Mondays, for all of the company's assemblers, will be less than 7 hours? Test using $\alpha = .05$.

 7.9 The Food and Drug Administration (FDA) and the Environmental Protection Agency (EPA) are responsible for setting the maximum level of toxicants in foods. A *tolerance level* is a regulation that has the force of law. An *action level* is an informal judgment of the level of a toxicant that will not be harmful to human health (H. Babich and D. L. Davis, "Food Tolerances and Action Levels: Do They Adequately Protect Children?" *Bioscience,* Vol. 6, 1981). A particular toxicant in a tank loaded with milk has a specified action level of .3 part per million (ppm). Measurements on milk samples within the tank vary slightly owing to errors in the measuring process, but the mean for a population of samples should equal the mean toxicant level in the milk. Thirty specimens of the milk were selected, stirring between each specimen selection. The sample mean and variance were $\bar{x} = .282$ and $s^2 = .012$. Do the data provide sufficient evidence to indicate that the mean toxicant level in the milk is below the FDA's action level? Test using $\alpha = .01$. If you considered milk safe to use if the toxicant level did not exceed its action level, would you consider this milk safe to use? Explain.

 *7.10 (For students who have covered optional Section 3.8) Japan's All-Nippon Airways has found that painting menacing eyes on its aircraft jet engine intakes frightens birds away and saves maintenance money (*Gainesville Sun,* November 16, 1986). A study of multiengine passenger aircraft over a one-year period found an average of one bird hit per engine as compared with an average of nine bird hits for unpainted engines.

(a) What type of data would you expect the number of bird hits per engine to be? Explain.

(b) Explain why the numbers of hits per engine on the same aircraft might be dependent and thus violate the assumption that the sample was randomly selected.

*7.11 Refer to Exercise 7.10. Suppose that all aircraft in the study contained the same number of jet engines and that x represents the number of engine bird hits per aircraft.

(a) If $n = 40$ aircraft were randomly selected to have their engines painted, would the 40 values of x represent a random sample?

(b) Suppose that the mean value of bird hits per aircraft with unpainted engines is $\mu = 9$. If the sample mean number of bird hits per engine per aircraft is $\bar{x} = 1$, do you have sufficient evidence to indicate that the painted menacing eyes on the engines produced a reduction in the mean number of bird hits per engine per aircraft? Test using $\alpha = .05$. (*Hint:* The number of engine bird hits per aircraft is likely to be a Poisson random variable. Since the standard deviation σ of a Poisson random variable is equal to the square root of its mean μ—that is, $\sigma = \sqrt{\mu}$. It can be estimated by substituting $\bar{x}$ for μ—that is, $\hat{\sigma} = \sqrt{\bar{x}}$.)

TESTING AN HYPOTHESIS ABOUT THE DIFFERENCE BETWEEN TWO POPULATION MEANS

7.5

A test of an hypothesis about the difference $(\mu_1 - \mu_2)$ between two population means μ_1 and μ_2, based on independent random samples of n_1 and n_2 observations, respectively, is illustrated in Example 7.3 and summarized in the box.

LARGE-SAMPLE STATISTICAL TEST FOR $(\mu_1 - \mu_2)$

(1) *Null Hypothesis:* $H_0 : (\mu_1 - \mu_2) = D_0$ where D_0 is some specified difference that you wish to test. For many tests you will wish to hypothesize that there is no difference between μ_1 and μ_2—that is, $D_0 = 0$.

(2) *Alternative Hypothesis:*

One-Tailed Test

$H_a : (\mu_1 - \mu_2) > D_0$

$[\text{or } H_a : (\mu_1 - \mu_2) < D_0]$

Two-Tailed Test

$H_a : (\mu_1 - \mu_2) \neq D_0$

(3) *Test Statistic:* $z = \dfrac{(\bar{x}_1 - \bar{x}_2) - D_0}{\sigma_{(\bar{x}_1 - \bar{x}_2)}} = \dfrac{(\bar{x}_1 - \bar{x}_2) - D_0}{\sqrt{\dfrac{\sigma_1^2}{n_1} + \dfrac{\sigma_2^2}{n_2}}}$.

If σ_1^2 and σ_2^2 are unknown (which is usually the case), substitute the sample variances s_1^2 and s_2^2 for σ_1^2 and σ_2^2, respectively.

(4) *Rejection Region:*

One-Tailed Test

$z > z_\alpha$

or $z < -z_\alpha$ when the alternative hypothesis is $H_a : (\mu_1 - \mu_2) < D_0]$

Two-Tailed Test

$z > z_{\alpha/2}$ or $z < -z_{\alpha/2}$

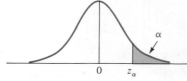

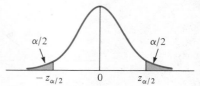

Assumptions: The samples were randomly and independently selected from the two populations, and $n_1 \geq 30$ and $n_2 \geq 30$.

EXAMPLE 7.3   A company employing a new sales-plus-commission compensation plan for its sales personnel wants to compare the annual salary expectations of its female and male sales personnel under the new plan. Random samples of $n_1 = 40$ female and $n_2 = 40$ male sales representatives were asked to forecast their annual incomes under the new plan. Sample means and standard deviations were

$$\bar{x}_1 = \$31{,}083 \qquad \bar{x}_2 = \$29{,}745$$
$$s_1 = \$2312 \qquad s_2 = \$2569$$

Do the data provide sufficient evidence to indicate a difference in mean expected annual income between female and male sales representatives? Test using $\alpha = .10$.

SOLUTION   Since we wish to detect a difference in mean annual income between female and male sales representatives, either $\mu_1 > \mu_2$ or $\mu_1 < \mu_2$, we want to test the null hypothesis

$$H_0 : \mu_1 = \mu_2, \qquad \text{that is, } \mu_1 - \mu_2 = D_0 = 0$$

against the alternative hypothesis

$$H_a : \mu_1 \neq \mu_2, \qquad \text{that is, } D_0 \neq 0$$

We use s_1^2 and s_2^2 to approximate σ_1^2 and σ_2^2, respectively. Substituting these values, along with $\bar{x}_1$ and $\bar{x}_2$, into the formula for the z test statistic, we obtain

$$
\begin{aligned}
z &= \frac{(\bar{x}_1 - \bar{x}_2) - D_0}{\sqrt{\dfrac{\sigma_1^2}{n_1} + \dfrac{\sigma_2^2}{n_2}}} \\[2mm]
&\approx \frac{(31{,}083 - 29{,}745) - 0}{\sqrt{\dfrac{(2312)^2}{40} + \dfrac{(2569)^2}{40}}} \\[2mm]
&= 2.45
\end{aligned}
$$

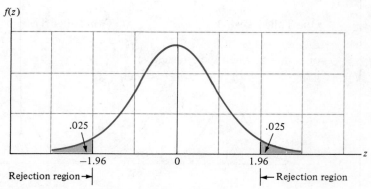

$f(z)$

.025   .025

-1.96 0   1.96 z

Rejection region →| |← Rejection region

FIGURE 7.8   Location of the Rejection Region in Example 7.3

Using a two tailed test with $\alpha = .05$, we will place $\alpha/2 = .025$ in each tail of the z distribution and reject H_0 if $z > 1.96$ or $z < -1.96$ (see Figure 7.8). Since the observed value of z, $z = 2.45$, exceeds 1.96, the test statistic falls in the rejection region. We reject H_0 and conclude that there is a difference in the mean annual salary expectations between female and male sales representatives. We should feel very confident that we have made the correct decision. The probability that our test would lead us to reject H_0, when in fact it is true, is only $\alpha = .05$.   ■

EXERCISES

BASIC TECHNIQUES

7.12 Independent random samples of $n_1 = 80$ and $n_2 = 80$ were selected from populations 1 and 2, respectively. The population parameters and the sample means and variances are shown in Table 7.3.

TABLE 7.3   Parameters and Sample Data for Exercise 7.12

	Population	
Parameters and Statistics	1	2
Population mean	μ_1	μ_2
Population variance	σ_1^2	σ_2^2
Sample size	80	80
Sample mean	11.6	9.7
Sample variance	27.9	38.4

(a) If your research objective is to show that μ_1 is larger than μ_2, state the alternative and the null hypotheses that you would choose for a statistical test.

(b) Is the test in part (a) a one- or a two-tailed test?

(c) Give the test statistic that you would use for the test in parts (a) and (b), and give the rejection region for $\alpha = .10$.

(d) Look at the data. From your intuition, do you think that the data provide sufficient evidence to indicate that μ_1 is larger than μ_2? [We will employ a statistical test to reach this decision in part (e).]

(e) Conduct the test and draw your conclusions. Do the data present sufficient evidence to indicate that $\mu_1 > \mu_2$?

7.13 Refer to Exercise 7.12. Explain the practical conditions that would motivate you to run a one-tailed z test with the rejection region in the lower tail of the z distribution. Give the alternative and null hypotheses for this test.

7.14 Refer to Exercise 7.12.

(a) Explain the practical conditions that would motivate you to run a two-tailed z test.

(b) Give the alternative and null hypotheses.

(c) Use the data of Exercise 7.12 to conduct the test. Do the data provide sufficient evidence to reject H_0 and accept H_a? Test using $\alpha = .05$.

(d) What practical conclusions can be drawn from the test in part (c)?

7.15 Independent random samples of $n_1 = 36$ and $n_2 = 45$ were selected from populations 1 and 2, respectively. The population parameters and the sample means and variances are shown in Table 7.4.

TABLE 7.4   Parameters and Sample Data for Exercise 7.15

Parameters and Statistics	Population 1	Population 2
Population mean	μ_1	μ_2
Population variance	σ_1^2	σ_2^2
Sample size	36	45
Sample mean	1.24	1.31
Sample variance	.0560	.0540

(a) If your research objective is to show that μ_1 and μ_2 are different, state the alternative and the null hypotheses that you would choose for a statistical test.

(b) Is the test in part (a) a one- or a two-tailed test?

(c) Give the test statistic that you would use for the test in parts (a) and (b), and give the rejection region for $\alpha = .05$.

(d) Look at the data. From your intuition, do you think that the data provide sufficient evidence to indicate that μ_1 differs from μ_2? [We will employ a statistical test to reach this decision in part (e).]

(e) Conduct the test and draw your conclusions. Do the data present sufficient evidence to indicate that $\mu_1 \neq \mu_2$?

7.16 Suppose that you wish to detect a difference between μ_1 and μ_2 (either $\mu_1 > \mu_2$ or $\mu_1 < \mu_2$) and that instead of running a two-tailed test, using $\alpha = .10$, you employ the following test procedure: You wait until you have collected the sample data and have calculated $\bar{x}_1$ and $\bar{x}_2$. If $\bar{x}_1$ is larger than $\bar{x}_2$, you choose the alternative hypothesis $H_a : \mu_1 > \mu_2$ and run a one-tailed test, placing $\alpha_1 = .10$ in the upper tail of the z distribution. If, on the other hand, $\bar{x}_2$ is larger than $\bar{x}_1$, you reverse the procedure and run a one-tailed test, placing $\alpha_2 = .10$ in the lower tail of the z distribution. If you use this procedure and if μ_1 actually equals μ_2, what is the probability α that you will conclude that μ_1 is not equal to μ_2 (i.e., what is the probability α that you will incorrectly reject H_0 when H_0 is true)? This exercise demonstrates why statistical tests should be formulated *prior* to observing the data.

APPLICATIONS

Starred (*) exercises are optional.

7.17 To compare the stock-picking abilities of two brokerage firms, we compared the annual gain (excluding brokerage fees) for a $1000 investment in each of 30 stocks listed on each of the two firm's "most recommended" lists of stocks. The means and standard deviations (in dollars) for each of the two samples are shown in Table 7.5. Do the data provide sufficient evidence to indicate a difference between the two brokerage firms in the mean return per recommended stock?

(a) State the alternative hypothesis that will best answer this question.

(b) State H_0.

(c) Give the rejection region for the test for $\alpha = .01$.

(d) Conduct the test and state your conclusions.

TABLE 7.5   Sample Data for Exercise 7.17

	Firm	
Sample Statistic	1	2
Size	30	30
Mean	264	199
Standard deviation	157	111

 7.18 In Exercise 6.32 we described a comparison of the mean level of a bank's approved home loan applications from April to May. The sample sizes, means, and standard deviations for the two months are reproduced in Table 7.6.

TABLE 7.6   Sample Data for Exercise 7.18

Sample Statistic	April	May
Size	57	66
Mean	$78,100	$82,700
Standard deviation	$6,300	$7,100

(a) Do these data provide sufficient evidence to indicate a difference in the mean value of approved home loan applications from April to May? Test using $\alpha = .10$.

(b) What difference does it make if you conduct the test in part (a) using $\alpha = .10$ versus $\alpha = .05$? Explain.

 7.19 A supermarket chain sampled customer opinions on the service provided by the chain's supermarkets both before and after store personnel were exposed to three weekly 10-minute videotape training sessions that were aimed at the improvement of customer relations. Independent random samples of 50 customers each were interviewed before and after the training sessions, and each person was asked to rate the store's service on a scale of 1 (poor) to 10 (excellent). The mean and standard deviation for each sample are shown in the accompanying table. Do the data present sufficient evidence to indicate that the training course was effective in increasing customer service scores?

Before	After
$\bar{x}_1 = 6.82$	$\bar{x}_2 = 8.17$
$s_1 = .95$	$s_2 = .56$

(a) State the alternative hypothesis that will best answer this question.

(b) State H_0.

(c) Give the rejection region for the test for $\alpha = .05$.

(d) Conduct the test and state the practical conclusions to be derived from the test.

(e) Describe the risk that you take in reaching an incorrect conclusion in part (d).

(f) Find a lower one-sided 95% confidence interval for the improvement in the mean service score after exposing personnel to the training program.

7.20 Do soldiers who reenlist enjoy greater job satisfaction than those who do not reenlist? Or do they reenlist because of other factors, such as reenlistment bonuses or a lack of opportunity in civilian life? A study by Chisholm, Gauntner, and Munzenrider of the attitudes of a sample of soldiers stationed in the United States in 1976 addresses this and other questions relating to army life. Each soldier included in the study completed a job satisfaction questionnaire, received a job satisfaction score, and indicated his reenlistment intentions. The sample sizes, means, and standard deviations for the two groups are shown in Table 7.7.

TABLE 7.7   Sample Data and Parameters for Exercise 7.20

	Intention	
Statistics and Parameter	To Reenlist	Not to Reenlist
Sample size	30	297
Sample mean	136.9	108.8
Sample standard deviation	29.8	31.3
Population mean	μ_1	μ_2

Source: Data from R. F. Chisholm, D. E. Gauntner, and R. F. Munzenrider, "Preenlistment Expectations/Perceptions of Army Life, Satisfaction and Reenlistment of Volunteers," *Journal of Political and Military Sociology,* Vol. 8, 1980.

(a) Suppose that you had a preconceived theory that the job satisfaction mean score μ_1 for soldiers intending to reenlist is higher than the mean score μ_2 for soldiers who do not intend to reenlist. Based on this theory, what alternative hypothesis would you choose for a statistical test of the null hypothesis $H_0 : (\mu_1 - \mu_2) = 0$?

(b) Does your alternative hypothesis in part (a) imply a one-tailed or a two-tailed statistical test? Locate the rejection region for the test.

(c) Conduct the test and state your conclusions.

 *7.21 (For students who have covered optional Section 3.8) Refer to the All-Nippon Airways study described in Exercises 7.10 and 7.11 (*Gainesville Sun,* November 16, 1986). All-Nippon found that painting menacing eyes on jet aircraft engine intakes seemed to produce a reduction in the mean number of bird hits per jet engine. (They estimated a maintenance cost reduction of almost $200,000 for the small number of aircraft included in their study.) Suppose that the study had involved independent random samples of aircraft, 40 with painted air intakes and 40 without, and that the sample mean number of bird hits per aircraft was $\bar{x}_1 = 1$ for the aircraft with painted intakes and $\bar{x}_2 = 9$ for those with unpainted intakes. Do these data provide sufficient evidence to indicate that the mean number of bird hits per engine per aircraft is less for aircraft with the painted air intakes? Test by using $\alpha = .05$. (*Hint:* The number of bird hits per engine per aircraft is likely to be a Poisson random variable. Since the standard deviation σ of a Poisson random variable is equal to the square root of its mean μ—that is, $\sigma = \sqrt{\mu}$. It can be estimated by substituting $\bar{x}$ for μ—that is, $\hat{\sigma} = \sqrt{\bar{x}}$.)

TESTING AN HYPOTHESIS ABOUT A POPULATION PROPORTION

7.6   The large-sample statistical test for a population proportion p is summarized in the box. Example 7.4 illustrates its use.

LARGE-SAMPLE TEST FOR A POPULATION PROPORTION p

(1) *Null Hypothesis: $H_0 : p = p_0$.*

(2) *Alternative Hypothesis:*

One-Tailed Test

$H_a : p > p_0$
(or $H_a : p < p_0$)

Two-Tailed Test

$H_a : p \neq p_0$

(3) *Test Statistic:* $z = \dfrac{\hat{p} - p_0}{\sigma_{\hat{p}}} = \dfrac{\hat{p} - p_0}{\sqrt{\dfrac{p_0 q_0}{n}}}$ where $\hat{p} = \dfrac{x}{n}$.

(4) *Rejection Region:*

One-Tailed Test

$z > z_\alpha$
(or $z < -z_\alpha$ when the alternative
hypothesis is $H_a : p < p_0$)

Two-Tailed Test

$z > z_{\alpha/2}$ or $z < -z_{\alpha/2}$

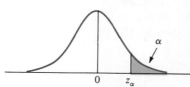

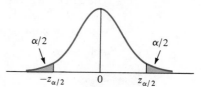

Assumptions: The sampling satisfies the assumptions of a binomial experiment (Section 3.5) and n is large enough so that the sampling distribution of x (and consequently of $\hat{p}$) will be approximately normally distributed. These conditions are given in Section 4.4 (and 5.5).

EXAMPLE 7.4

Approximately 1 in 10 consumers favor cola brand A. After a promotional campaign in a given sales region, 200 cola drinkers were randomly selected from consumers in the market area and were interviewed to determine the effectiveness of the campaign. The result of the survey showed that a total of 26 people expressed a preference for cola brand A. Do these data present sufficient evidence to indicate an increase in the acceptance of brand A in the region?

SOLUTION

We assume that the sample satisfies the requirements of a binomial experiment. The question can be answered by testing the hypothesis

$$H_0 : p = .10$$

against the alternative

$$H_a : p > .10$$

A one-tailed statistical test will be utilized because we are primarily concerned with detecting a value of p greater than .10. For this situation it can be shown that the probability of a type II error, β, is minimized by placing the entire rejection region in the upper tail of the distribution of the test statistic.

The point estimator of p is $\hat{p} = x/n$, and the test statistic is

$$z = \frac{\hat{p} - p_0}{\sigma_{\hat{p}}} = \frac{\hat{p} - p_0}{\sqrt{\dfrac{p_0 q_0}{n}}}$$

Once again, we require a value of p so that $\sigma_{\hat{p}} = \sqrt{pq/n}$, appearing in the denominator of z, can be calculated. Since we have hypothesized that $p = p_0$, it seems reasonable to use p_0 as an approximation for p. Note that this approximation differs from the approximation used for the estimation procedure, where, lacking knowledge of p, we chose $\hat{p}$ as the best approximation. This apparent inconsistency will have a negligible effect on the inference, whether it is the result of a test or of estimation, when n is large.

Choosing $\alpha = .05$, we reject H_0 when $z > 1.645$. See Figure 7.9. Substituting the numerical values into the test statistic, we obtain

$$z = \frac{\hat{p} - p_0}{\sqrt{\dfrac{p_0 q_0}{n}}} = \frac{.13 - .10}{\sqrt{\dfrac{(.10)(.90)}{200}}} = 1.41$$

The calculated value, $z = 1.41$, does not fall in the rejection region, and thus we do not reject H_0. There is insufficient evidence to indicate that the proportion p of consumers who favor cola brand A exceeds .10.

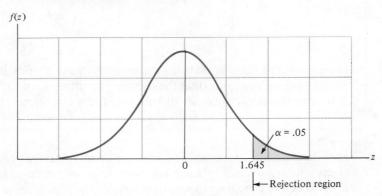

FIGURE 7.9   Location of the Rejection Region in Example 7.4

Do we accept H_0? No, not until we have stated an alternative value of p that is larger than $p_0 = .10$ and considered to be of *practical* significance. The probability of a type II error, β, should be calculated for this alternative. If β is sufficiently small, we would accept H_0 and would do so with the risk of an erroneous decision fully known.

TIPS ON PROBLEM SOLVING

When testing an hypothesis concerning p, use p_0 (not $\hat{p}$) to calculate $\sigma_{\hat{p}}$ in the denominator of the z statistic. The reason you use p_0 is that the rejection region is determined by the distribution of $\hat{p}$ when the null hypothesis is true, namely, when $p = p_0$.

Examples 7.1 and 7.4 illustrate an important point. If the data present sufficient evidence to reject H_0, the probability of an erroneous conclusion, α, is known in advance because α is used in locating the rejection region. Since α is usually small, we are fairly certain that we have made a correct decision. On the other hand, if the data present insufficient evidence to reject H_0, the conclusions are not so obvious. Ideally, following the statistical test procedure outlined in Section 7.3, we would have specified a practically significant alternative p_a in advance and chosen n such that β would be small. Unfortunately, many experiments are not conducted in this ideal manner. Someone chooses a sample size and the experimenter or statistician is left to evaluate the evidence.

The calculation of β is not too difficult for the statistical test procedure outlined in this section but may be extremely difficult, if not beyond the capability of the beginner, in other test situations. A much simpler procedure is to *not reject H_0*, rather than to accept it; then estimate using a confidence interval. The interval will give you a range of possible values for p.

EXERCISES

BASIC TECHNIQUES

7.22 A random sample of $n = 1000$ observations from a binomial population produced $x = 279$.

(a) If your research hypothesis is that p is less than .3, what should you choose for your alternative hypothesis? Your null hypothesis?

(b) Does your alternative hypothesis in part (a) imply a one- or a two-tailed statistical test? Explain.

(c) Do the data provide sufficient evidence to indicate that p is less than .3? Test using $\alpha = .05$.

7.23 A random sample of $n = 2000$ observations from a binomial population produced $x = 1238$.

(a) If your research hypothesis is that p is greater than .6, what should you choose for your alternative hypothesis? Your null hypothesis?

(b) Does your alternative hypothesis in part (a) imply a one- or a two-tailed statistical test? Explain.

(c) Do the data provide sufficient evidence to indicate that p is greater than .6? Test using $\alpha = .05$.

7.24 A random sample of $n = 1400$ observations from a binomial population produced $x = 529$.

(a) If your research hypothesis is that p differs from .4, what should you choose for your alternative hypothesis? Your null hypothesis?

(b) Does your alternative hypothesis in part (a) imply a one- or a two-tailed statistical test? Explain.

(c) Do the data provide sufficient evidence to indicate that p differs from .4? Test using $\alpha = .10$.

7.25 A random sample of 120 observations was selected from a binomial population and 72 successes were observed. Do the data provide sufficient evidence to indicate that p is larger than .5? Test using $\alpha = .05$.

APPLICATIONS

 7.26 The *Wall Street Journal* (August 27, 1985) states that the National Union of Hospital and Health Care Workers won 56 of 80 union representation elections in 1984 compared with an all–health care union rate of 55%. Do the data provide sufficient evidence to indicate that the National Union of Hospital and Health Care Workers is more successful in winning union representation elections than other unions in the health care industry?

(a) State the null and alternative hypotheses that you will use to answer this question.

(b) Give the formula for the test statistic, and substitute the appropriate numbers into it.

(c) Give the rejection region for the test.

(d) Explain how the test will lead you to a decision.

(e) What assumptions must be satisfied in order that the test be valid?

7.27 Refer to Exercise 7.26. Perform the calculations, complete the test, and state your conclusions.

7.28 A check-cashing service has found that approximately 5% of all checks submitted to the service for cashing are bad. After instituting a check verification system to reduce its losses, the service found that only 45 checks were bad in a total of 1124 cashed.

(a) If you wish to conduct a statistical test to determine whether the check verification system reduces the probability that a bad check will be cashed, what should you choose for the alternative hypothesis? The null hypothesis?

(b) Does your alternative hypothesis in part (a) imply a one- or a two-tailed test? Explain.

(c) Noting the data, what does your intuition tell you? Do you think that the check verification system is effective in reducing the proportion of bad checks that were cashed?

(d) Conduct a statistical test of the null hypothesis in part (a), and state your conclusions. Test using $\alpha = .05$. Do the test conclusions agree with your intuition in part (c)?

7.29 From past experience an appliance dealer has found that 10% of her customers who buy on installment pay off their bills before the last (the 24th) monthly installment is due. Suspecting an increase in this percentage, the dealer surveyed 200 installment buyers concerning their intentions. Of these, 33 stated that they planned to pay off their debt before the last installment. Do the data provide sufficient evidence to indicate that the percentage of installment buyers that will pay off their debt before the last installment exceeds 10%?

(a) State the alternative hypothesis for the test.

(b) State the null hypothesis.

(c) Give the rejection region for $\alpha = .05$.

(d) Conduct the test and state your conclusions.

7.30 A publisher of a newsmagazine has found through past experience that 60% of its subscribers renew their subscriptions. Because it was heading into a business recession, the company decided to randomly select a small sample of subscribers and, via telephone questioning, determine whether they planned to renew their subscriptions. One hundred eight of a sample of 200 indicated that they planned to renew their subscriptions.

(a) If you want to detect whether the data provide sufficient evidence of a reduction in the proportion p of all subscribers who will renew, what will you choose for your alternative hypothesis? Your null hypothesis?

(b) Conduct the test using $\alpha = .05$. State the results.

(c) Find a 95% confidence interval for p.

(d) How many subscribers would have to be included in the publisher's sample in order to estimate p to within .01, with 95% confidence?

Testing an Hypothesis About the Difference Between Two Population Proportions

7.7

The large-sample statistical test for the difference between two population proportions is summarized in the box. Example 7.5 illustrates its use.

A LARGE-SAMPLE STATISTICAL TEST FOR $(p_1 - p_2)$

(1) *Null Hypothesis: $H_0 : (p_1 - p_2) = D_0$*, where D_0 is some specified difference that you wish to test. For many tests you will wish to hypothesize that there is no difference between p_1 and p_2—that is, $D_0 = 0$.

(2) *Alternative Hypothesis:*

One-Tailed Test	**Two-Tailed Test**
$H_a : (p_1 - p_2) > D_0$	$H_a : (p_1 - p_2) \neq D_0$
[or $H_a : (p_1 - p_2) < D_0$]	

(3) *Test Statistic:* $z = \dfrac{(\hat{p}_1 - \hat{p}_2) - D_0}{\sigma_{(\hat{p}_1 - \hat{p}_2)}} = \dfrac{(\hat{p}_1 - \hat{p}_2) - D_0}{\sqrt{\dfrac{p_1 q_1}{n_1} + \dfrac{p_2 q_2}{n_2}}}$

where $\hat{p}_1 = \dfrac{x_1}{n_1}$ and $\hat{p}_2 = \dfrac{x_2}{n_2}$

Since p_1 and p_2 are unknown, we will need to approximate their values in order to calculate the standard deviation of $(\hat{p}_1 - \hat{p}_2)$ that appears in the denominator of the z statistic. Approximations are available for two cases.

Case I: If we hypothesize that p_1 equals p_2, that is,

$$H_0 : p_1 = p_2$$

or equivalently, that

$$(p_1 - p_2) = 0$$

then $p_1 = p_2 = p$, and the best estimate of p is obtained by pooling the data from both samples. Thus if x_1 and x_2 are the numbers of successes obtained from the two samples, then the **pooled estimate of** p is

$$\hat{p} = \frac{x_1 + x_2}{n_1 + n_2}$$

The test statistic is

$$z = \frac{(\hat{p}_1 - \hat{p}_2) - 0}{\sqrt{\dfrac{\hat{p}\hat{q}}{n_1} + \dfrac{\hat{p}\hat{q}}{n_2}}}$$

or

$$z = \frac{\hat{p}_1 - \hat{p}_2}{\sqrt{\hat{p}\hat{q}\left(\dfrac{1}{n_1} + \dfrac{1}{n_2}\right)}}$$

Case II: If we hypothesize that D_0 is *not equal* to zero, that is,

$$H_0 : (p_1 - p_2) = D_0$$

where $D_0 \neq 0$, then the best estimates of p_1 and p_2 are $\hat{p}_1$ and $\hat{p}_2$, respectively. The test statistic is

$$z = \frac{(\hat{p}_1 - \hat{p}_2) - D_0}{\sqrt{\dfrac{\hat{p}_1 \hat{q}_1}{n_1} + \dfrac{\hat{p}_2 \hat{q}_2}{n_2}}}$$

(4) *Rejection Region:*

One-Tailed Test

$z > z_\alpha$
[or, $z < -z_\alpha$ when the alternative hypothesis is $H_a : (p_1 - p_2) < D_0$]

Two-Tailed Test

$z > z_{\alpha/2}$ or $z < -z_{\alpha/2}$

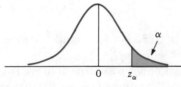
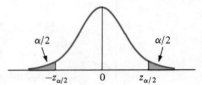

Assumptions: Samples were selected in a random and independent manner from two binomial populations, and n_1 and n_2 are large enough so that the sampling distributions of x_1 and x_2 (and, therefore, of $\hat{p}_1$ and $\hat{p}_2$) will be approximately normally distributed. These conditions are given in Section 5.5.

EXAMPLE 7.5   A hospital administrator suspects that the delinquency rate in the payment of hospital bills has increased over the past year. Hospital records show that the bills of 48 of 1284 persons admitted in the month of April have been delinquent for more than 90 days. This number compares with 34 of 1002 persons admitted during the same month one year ago. Do these data provide sufficient evidence to indicate an increase in the rate of delinquency in payments exceeding 90 days? Test using $\alpha = .10$.

SOLUTION   Let p_1 and p_2 represent the proportions of all potential hospital admissions in April of this year and last year, respectively, that would have allowed their accounts to be delinquent for a period exceeding 90 days; and let the $n_1 = 1284$ admissions this year and the $n_2 = 1002$ admissions last year represent independent random samples from these populations. Since we want to detect an increase in the delinquency rate, if it exists, we will test the null hypothesis

$$H_0 : p_1 = p_2, \quad \text{that is, } p_1 - p_2 = D_0 = 0$$

against the one-sided alternative hypothesis

$$H_a : p_1 > p_2, \quad \text{that is, } p_1 - p_2 > 0$$

To conduct this test, we will use the z test statistic and approximate the value of

$\sigma_{(\hat{p}_1 - \hat{p}_2)}$ by using the pooled estimate of p described in Case I. Since H_a implies a one-tailed test, we will reject H_0 only for large values of z. Thus for $\alpha = .10$ we will reject H_0 if $z > 1.28$ (see Figure 7.10).

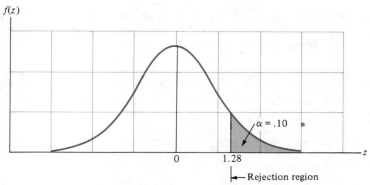

FIGURE 7.10 Location of the Rejection Region in Example 7.5

The estimates of p_1 and p_2 are

$$\hat{p}_1 = \frac{48}{1284} = .0374 \quad \text{and} \quad \hat{p}_2 = \frac{34}{1002} = .0339$$

The pooled estimate of p required for $\sigma_{(\hat{p}_1 - \hat{p}_2)}$ is

$$\hat{p} = \frac{x_1 + x_2}{n_1 + n_2}$$

$$= \frac{48 + 34}{1284 + 1002} = .0359$$

The test statistic is

$$z = \frac{\hat{p}_1 - \hat{p}_2}{\sqrt{\hat{p}\hat{q}\left(\dfrac{1}{n_1} + \dfrac{1}{n_2}\right)}}$$

$$= \frac{.0374 - .0339}{\sqrt{(.0359)(.9641)\left(\dfrac{1}{1284} + \dfrac{1}{1002}\right)}}$$

or

$$z = .45$$

Since the computed value of z does not fall in the rejection region, we cannot reject the null hypothesis that $p_1 = p_2$. The data present insufficient evidence to indicate that the proportion of delinquent accounts in April of this year exceeds the corresponding proportion last year. ∎

EXERCISES

BASIC TECHNIQUES

7.31 Independent random samples of $n_1 = 140$ and $n_2 = 140$ observations were randomly selected from binomial populations 1 and 2, respectively. The number of successes in the samples and the population parameters are shown in Table 7.8.

TABLE 7.8   Sample Data and Parameters for Exercise 7.31

Statistics and Parameter	Population 1	Population 2
Sample size	140	140
Number of successes	74	81
Binomial parameter	p_1	p_2

(a) Suppose that you have no preconceived theory concerning which parameter, p_1 or p_2, is the larger, and that you only wish to detect a difference between the two parameters, if it exists. What should you choose for the alternative hypothesis for a statistical test? The null hypothesis?

(b) Does your alternative hypothesis in part (a) imply a one- or a two-tailed test?

(c) Conduct the test and state your conclusions. Test using $\alpha = .05$.

7.32 Refer to Exercise 7.31. Suppose that for practical reasons you know that p_1 cannot be larger than p_2.

(a) Given this knowledge, what should you choose as the alternative hypothesis for your statistical test? Your null hypothesis?

(b) Will your alternative hypothesis in part (a) imply a one- or a two-tailed test? Explain.

(c) Conduct the test and state your conclusions. Test using $\alpha = .10$.

7.33 Independent random samples of $n_1 = 280$ and $n_2 = 350$ observations were randomly selected from binomial populations 1 and 2, respectively. The number of successes in the samples and the population parameters are shown in Table 7.9.

TABLE 7.9   Sample Data and Parameters for Exercise 7.33

Statistics and Parameter	Population 1	Population 2
Sample size	280	350
Number of successes	132	178
Binomial parameter	p_1	p_2

(a) Suppose that you know that p_1 can never be larger than p_2, and you want to know if p_1 is less than p_2. What should you choose for your null and alternative hypotheses?

(b) Does your alternative hypothesis in part (a) imply a one- or a two-tailed test?

(c) Conduct the test and state your conclusions. Test using $\alpha = .05$.

7.34 Independent random samples of $n_1 = 1200$ and $n_2 = 1000$ observations were randomly selected from binomial populations 1 and 2, respectively. The number of successes in the samples and the population parameters are shown in Table 7.10.

TABLE 7.10   Sample Data and Parameters for Exercise 7.34

Statistics and Parameter	Population	
	1	2
Sample size	1200	1000
Number of successes	462	342
Binomial parameter	p_1	p_2

(a) Suppose that you know that p_1 can never be less than p_2, and you want to know if p_1 is larger than p_2. What should you choose for your null and alternative hypotheses?

(b) Does your alternative hypothesis in part (a) imply a one- or a two-tailed test?

(c) Conduct the test and state your conclusions. Test using $\alpha = .05$.

APPLICATIONS

7.35 A manufacturer modified a production line to reduce the mean fraction defective. To determine whether the modification was effective, the manufacturer randomly sampled 400 items before modification of the production line and 400 items after modification. The percentage defectives in the samples were

before: 5.25%
after: 3.5%

(a) If the modification could not possibly increase the fraction defective, what should the manufacturer choose for an alternative hypothesis? The null hypothesis?

(b) Conduct the test using $\alpha = .05$. Interpret the results.

7.36 In Exercise 6.52 we presented data on the relationship between financial distress and the tendency of firms to shift auditors (K. B. Schwartz and K. Menon, "Auditor Switches by Failing Firms," *Accounting Review*, Vol. 60, No. 2, 1985). Of 132 bankrupt firms included in the study, 35 shifted auditors at some time during the four years prior to declaring bankruptcy. In contrast, only 13 of 132 nonbankrupt firms shifted auditors during comparable periods of time. Does the financial stress associated with bankruptcy increase the likelihood that a firm will shift auditors in the four-year period prior to declaring bankruptcy?

(a) State the alternative hypothesis that will best answer this question.

(b) State the null hypothesis.

(c) Conduct the test using $\alpha = .05$. State your conclusions.

(d) Find a 95% upper one-sided confidence interval for the increase in the probability that a firm under stress will shift auditors.

7.37 A survey by Merrill Lynch Relocation Management, Inc., of more than 600 large industrial and 250 nonindustrial companies found that 73% of the companies reported no difficulties with employee acceptance of job transfers. This percentage was up from 67% in 1984 (*Orlando Sentinel*, May 11, 1986). Suppose that we assume that each of the surveys was based on a random sample of 850 companies. Do the data provide sufficient evidence to indicate a change in the proportion of companies throughout the United States, from 1984 to 1985, that found employee acceptance of job transfers?

(a) State the null hypothesis to be tested.

(b) State the alternative hypothesis.

(c) Suppose that $\alpha = .05$. Give the test statistic and the rejection region for the test.

(d) Conduct the test and state your conclusions.

 7.38 Are consumer product complaints legitimate? A. J. Resnick and R. R. Harmon of Portland State University conducted a study to examine and compare the reactions of consumers and company managers to five different consumer letters containing complaints about well-known consumer products. The total number n of persons examining each letter and the number n_c of those who agreed that the complaint was justified are given for each letter, for samples of consumers and managers, in Table 7.11. Let p_1 and p_2 represent, respectively, the proportions of consumers and managers who view the complaints as legitimate. Do the data present sufficient evidence to indicate that p_1 and p_2 differ for consumer complaint letter 2? Test by using $\alpha = .05$.

TABLE 7.11   Sample Data for Consumers and Managers for Exercise 7.38

	Consumers Letter					Managers Letter				
Number	1	2	3	4	5	1	2	3	4	5
n	120	121	120	120	121	40	39	39	39	36
n_c	114	20	115	50	19	40	5	37	3	4

Source: Data from A. J. Resnick and R. R. Harmon, "Consumer Complaints and Managerial Response: A Holistic Approach," *Journal of Marketing,* Vol. 47, 1983.

7.39 Refer to Exercise 7.38. Do the data present sufficient evidence to indicate that p_1 and p_2 differ for consumer complaint letter 4? Test using $\alpha = .05$.

 7.40 William B. Waegel collected data to investigate the relationship between law and the use of lethal force by police. The data, reproduced in Table 7.12, represent the classification of 459 police shootings in Philadelphia over the period 1970 to 1978. The objective of the study was to see whether restrictive laws governing the use of lethal force, introduced in 1973, produced a change (presumably in reduction) in the proportion of cases where lethal force was justifiably used. Assume that the data in the table represent samples from populations of cases that could have occurred and in which lethal force would have been used, one population corresponding to the

TABLE 7.12   Philadelphia Police Data for Exercise 7.40

Classification of Shooting	Total for Period 1970–1972	1973	Total for Period 1974–1978
Justified	72	30	173
Not justified	11	9	59
Unable to determine	18	7	53
Accidental	10	5	12
Total	111	51	297

Source: Data from William B. Waegel, "The Use of Lethal Force by Police: The Effect of Statutory Change," *Crime and Delinquency,* Vol. 30, No. 1, January 1984.

legal situation existing prior to 1973 and the other to the one after the new restrictive laws were introduced.

(a) Do the data provide sufficient evidence to indicate that the proportion of nonjustified shootings for the 1974–1978 period differs from the corresponding proportion for the 1970–1972 period? Test using $\alpha = .05$.

(b) Presumably, the intent of the 1973 change in the law was to reduce the proportion of cases where the use of lethal force was unjustified. Yet the sample proportion of the total number of shootings over the 1974–1978 period that were classified as unjustified was larger than for the 1970–1972 period. Can you give a possible explanation for this discrepancy?

7.41 Refer to the data of Exercise 7.40 on the Philadelphia police shootings, 1970–1978. Did the new 1973 law that placed greater restrictions on the use of lethal force make it more difficult to classify a shooting?

(a) Suppose that you wanted to answer this question by testing for a difference in the proportions of shootings that could not be classified (i.e., they fell in the "unable to determine" category). State the null and alternative hypotheses that you would employ for the test.

(b) Conduct the test using $\alpha = .05$.

(c) State the practical conclusions to be derived from the test.

ANOTHER WAY TO REPORT THE RESULTS OF STATISTICAL TESTS: *p*-VALUES

7.8

The probability α of making a type I error is often called the significance level of the statistical test, a term that originated in the following way. The probability of the observed value of the test statistic, or some value even more contradictory to the null hypothesis, measures (in a sense) the weight of evidence favoring rejection of H_0. Some experimenters report test results as being significant (we would reject H_0) at the 5% significance level but not at the 1% level. This means that we would reject H_0 if α were .05 but not if α were .01.

The smallest value of α for which test results are statistically significant is often called the **p-value*** or the **observed significance level** for the test. Some statistical computer programs compute *p*-values for statistical tests correct to four or five decimal places. But if you are using statistical tables to determine a *p*-value, you will only be able to approximate its value, because most statistical tables give the critical values of test statistics only for large differential values of α (e.g., .01, .025, .05, .10, etc.). Consequently, the *p*-value reported by most experimenters is the smallest tabulated value of α for which the test remains **statistically significant**. For example, if a test result is statistically significant for $\alpha = .10$ but not for $\alpha = .05$, then the *p*-value for the test would be given as $p = .10$, or more precisely, as $p < .10$.

Many scientific journals require researchers to report the *p*-values associated with statistical tests because these values provide a reader with *more information* than simply stating that a null hypothesis is or is not to be rejected for some value of α chosen by the experimenter. In a sense, it allows the reader of published research to evaluate the extent to which the data disagree with the null hypothesis. Particularly, it enables each reader to choose his or her own personal value for α and then to decide whether or not the data lead to rejection of the null hypothesis.

*Users of statistics often call the observed significance level a "probability or *p*-value." The *p* symbol in the expression has no connection to the binomial parameter *p*.

The procedure for finding the *p*-value for a test is illustrated in the following examples.

EXAMPLE 7.6   Find the *p*-value for the statistical test in Example 7.1. Interpret your results.

SOLUTION   Example 7.1 presents a test of the null hypothesis $H_0 : \mu = 880$ against the alternative hypothesis $H_a : \mu \neq 880$. The value of the test statistic, computed from the sample data, was $z = -3.03$. Therefore, the *p*-value for this two-tailed test is the probability that $z \leq -3.03$ or $z \geq 3.03$ (see Figure 7.11).

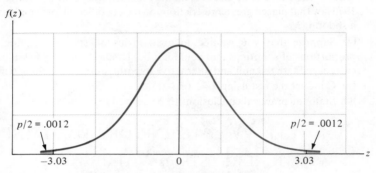

FIGURE 7.11   Determining the *p*-Value for the Test in Example 7.1

From Table 4 in the Appendix you can see that the tabulated area under the normal curve between $z = 0$ and $z = 3.03$ is .4988, and the area to the right of $z = 3.03$ is $.5 - .4988 = .0012$. Then because this was a two-tailed test, the value of α corresponding to a rejection region, $z > 3.03$ or $z < -3.03$, is $2(.0012) = .0024$. Consequently, we report the *p*-value for the test as $p = .0024$.   ■

EXAMPLE 7.7   Find the *p*-value for the statistical test in Example 7.4. Interpret your results.

SOLUTION   Example 7.4 presented a one-tailed test of the null hypothesis $H_0 : p = .10$ against the alternative hypothesis $H_a : p > .10$, and the observed value of the test statistic was

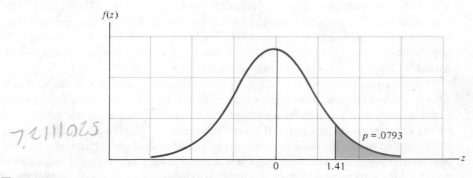

FIGURE 7.12   Finding the *p*-Value for the Test in Example 7.4

$z = 1.41$. Therefore, the p-value for the test is the probability of observing a value of the z statistic larger than 1.41. This value is the area under the normal curve to the right of $z = 1.41$ (the shaded area in Figure 7.12).

From Table 4 in the Appendix the area under the normal curve between $z = 0$ and $z = 1.41$ is .4207. Therefore, the area under the normal curve to the right of $z = 1.41$, the p-value for the test, is $p = .5 - .4207 = .0793$. ∎

To advocate that a researcher report the p-value for a test and leave its interpretation to a reader does not violate the traditional statistical test procedure described in the preceding sections. It simply leaves the decision of whether to reject the null hypothesis (with the potential for a type I or type II error) to the reader. Thus it shifts the responsibility for choosing the value of α, and possibly the problem of evaluating the probability β of making a type II error, to the reader.

EXERCISES

BASIC TECHNIQUES

7.42 Suppose that you tested the null hypothesis $H_0 : \mu = 94$ against the alternative hypothesis $H_a : \mu < 94$. For a random sample of $n = 52$ observations, $\bar{x} = 92.9$ and $s = 4.1$.

(a) Give the observed significance level for the test.

(b) If you wish to conduct your test using $\alpha = .05$, what would be your test conclusions?

7.43 Suppose that you tested the null hypothesis $H_0 : \mu = 94$ against the alternative hypothesis $H_a : \mu \neq 94$. For a random sample of $n = 52$ observations, $\bar{x} = 92.1$ and $s = 4.1$.

(a) Give the observed significance level for the test.

(b) If you wish to conduct your test using $\alpha = .05$, what would be your test conclusions?

7.44 Suppose that you tested the null hypothesis $H_0 : \mu = 15$ against the alternative hypothesis $H_a : \mu \neq 15$. For a random sample of $n = 38$ observations, $\bar{x} = 15.7$ and $s = 2.4$.

(a) Give the observed significance level for the test.

(b) If you wish to conduct your test using $\alpha = .05$, what would be your test conclusions?

APPLICATIONS

7.45 Find the p-value for the test of the mean demand for metal fasteners in Exercise 7.7, and interpret it.

7.46 If only the p-value for the test in Exercise 7.45 were reported to you, how could you use it to conduct the test for $\alpha = .05$?

7.47 Find the p-value for the test in Exercise 7.19, and interpret it.

7.48 Find the p-value for the test in Exercise 7.26, and interpret it.

7.49 Find the p-value for the test in Exercise 7.36, and interpret it.

 7.50 In Exercise 6.51 we presented some results obtained from a Canadian public opinion poll conducted by Angus Reid Associates for the Montreal Gazette [(Montreal) *Gazette*, September 13, 1986]. Among other statistics gleaned from the telephone survey of 1675 Canadian adults was the finding that 66% thought that a flat-rate income tax system, similar to that adopted in the United States in 1986, was a "good idea." Is this sample percentage large enough to indicate that more than 50% of all Canadian adults (those that can be contacted by telephone) favor a flat-rate income tax system?

(a) Test using $\alpha = .01$.

(b) Find the p-value for the test.

7.51 Refer to the Angus Reid survey noted in Exercise 7.50. The researchers found that 68% of a random sample of 403 adults from the province of Quebec favored a flat-rate income tax system, versus only 63% of 535 adults sampled from the province of Ontario [(Montreal) *Gazette,* September 13, 1986].

(a) Do these data provide sufficient evidence to indicate differences in the proportions of adults favoring a flat-rate income tax system between Quebec and Ontario? Test using $\alpha = .05$.

(b) Find the approximate p-value for the test.

SOME COMMENTS ON THE THEORY OF TESTS OF HYPOTHESES

7.9

As outlined in Section 7.2, the theory of a statistical test of an hypothesis is indeed a very clear-cut procedure, enabling the experimenter to either reject or accept the null hypothesis with measured risks α and β. Unfortunately, as we noted, the theoretical framework does not suffice for all practical situations.

The crux of the theory requires that we be able to specify a meaningful alternative hypothesis that permits the calculation of the probability β of a type II error for all alternative values of the parameter(s). This calculation can be done for many statistical tests, including the large-sample test discussed in Section 7.3, although the calculation of β for various alternatives and sample sizes may be difficult in some cases. On the other hand, in some test situations it is difficult to clearly specify alternatives to H_0 that have practical significance. This may occur when we want to test an hypothesis concerning the values of a set of parameters, a situation that we will encounter in Chapter 10 in analyzing enumerative data.

The obstacle that we mention does not invalidate the use of statistical tests. Rather, it urges caution in drawing conclusions when insufficient evidence is available to reject the null hypothesis. The difficulty of specifying meaningful alternatives to the null hypothesis, together with the difficulty encountered in the calculation and tabulation of β for other than the simplest statistical tests, justifies skirting this issue in an introductory text. Thus we can adopt one of two procedures. We can present the p-value associated with a statistical test and leave the interpretation to the reader. Or we can agree to adopt the procedure described in Example 7.4 when tabulated values of β (the operating characteristic curve) are unavailable for the test. When the test statistic falls in the acceptance region, we will "not reject" rather than "accept" the null hypothesis. Further conclusions can be made by calculating an interval estimate for the parameter or by consulting one of several published statistical handbooks for tabulated values of β. We will not be too surprised to learn that these tabulations are inaccessible, if not completely unavailable, for some of the more complicated statistical tests.

Finally, we might comment on the choice between a one- or a two-tailed test for a given situation. We emphasize that this choice is dictated by the practical aspects of the problem and will depend on the alternative value of the parameter, say θ, the experimenter is trying to detect. If we were to sustain a large financial loss if θ were greater than θ_0 but not if it were less, we would concentrate our attention on the detection of values of θ greater than θ_0. Therefore, we would reject in the upper tail of the distribution for the test statistics previously discussed. On the other hand, if we are equally interested in detecting values of θ that are either less than or greater than θ_0, we would employ a two-tailed test.

7.10   WOMEN IN OVERSEAS MANAGEMENT: PERCEPTIONS

This chapter's Case Study concerned research by Nancy J. Adler on reasons why so few women are assigned by multinational U.S. and Canadian companies to overseas management positions. One aspect of the research involved identical surveys of the opinions of a sample of 1129 graduating MBA students and a sample of 60 international personnel managers. Each person in the two surveys was presented six reasons why so few women were assigned as overseas managers and was asked to respond whether he or she agreed that the reason was valid. The percentages of MBAs and personnel managers expressing agreement for each of the six reasons are reproduced in Table 7.13.

TABLE 7.13   A Comparison of Percentages: MBAs Versus Personnel Managers

Reasons Why So Few Women Are Expatriate Managers	Perceptions of (% Agreeing):		z Value	p-Value
	Graduating MBAs ($n = 1129$)	Personnel Managers ($n = 60$)		
Women are				
Unqualified	5.6	18.2	4.04	<.001
Ineffective	19.1	5.6	2.70	.007
Uninterested	21.4	24.5	.79	.430
Not selected				
by corporations	78.0	53.8	4.48	<.001
Dual-career marriages	72.8	69.1	.64	.4966
Foreigner's prejudice	83.6	72.7	2.25	.024

Source: Nancy J. Adler, "Expecting International Success: Female Managers Overseas," *Columbia Journal of World Business,* Fall 1984.

Do these percentages provide sufficient information to indicate differences in the perceptions held by two groups of persons, graduating MBA students and international personnel managers, of the reasons why so few women are employed in international management? The techniques of Section 7.7 enable us to detect differences in the proportions in agreement on a single reason for the scarcity of women managers overseas, but they do not permit us to test the equality of proportions for all six reasons simultaneously. For example, do the data provide sufficient information to indicate differences in the proportions p_1 and p_2 of graduating MBA students and personnel managers, respectively, who perceive dual-career marriages as a reason for the scarcity of women overseas managers? To answer this question, we want to test

$$H_0 : p_1 = p_2$$

against the two-sided alternative hypothesis

$$H_a : p_1 \neq p_2$$

That is, we want to detect any inequality that exists, either $p_1 > p_2$ or $p_1 < p_2$.

The sample percentages in agreement that dual-career marriages are a reason why so few women are in international management are (from Table 7.13) 72.8% for the $n_1 = 1129$ MBAs and 69.1% for the $n_2 = 60$ managers. Therefore, $\hat{p}_1 = .728$, $\hat{p}_2 = .691$, and the numbers of persons in the two samples expressing agreement are $x_1 = n_1\hat{p}_1 = (1129)(.728) = 822$ and $x_2 = n_2\hat{p}_2 = (60)(.691) = 41$. [The numbers calculated (by rounding) for x_1 and x_2 do not reproduce Adler's percentages. The differences are small, and they do not affect the validity of our discussion.]

The test statistic is

$$z = \frac{\hat{p}_1 - \hat{p}_2}{\sqrt{\hat{p}\hat{q}\left(\dfrac{1}{n_1} + \dfrac{1}{n_2}\right)}} \qquad \text{where} \qquad \hat{p} = \frac{x_1 + x_2}{n_1 + n_2} = \frac{822 + 41}{1129 + 60} = .726$$

Substituting $\hat{p}_1, \hat{p}_2, \hat{p}, n_1$, and n_2 into the formula for z, we find the observed value of the test statistics to be

$$z = \frac{.728 - .691}{\sqrt{(.726)(.274)\left(\dfrac{1}{1129} + \dfrac{1}{60}\right)}} = \frac{.037}{.0591} = .63$$

This z value is not nearly large enough to imply differences in the proportions p_1 and p_2. For example, for α as large as .10 the rejection region is $z > 1.645$ or $z < -1.645$. The calculated z value is not even close to this rejection region. Therefore, there is insufficient evidence to indicate differences in the proportions of graduating MBAs and personnel managers in their perceptions of dual-career marriages as a reason for the scarcity of women overseas managers.

The p-value corresponding to a z value of .63 (for a two-tailed test) is the probability that $z \geq .63$ or $z \leq -.63$. This probability is

$$p\text{-value} = 1 - 2A = 1 - (2)(.2357) = .5286$$

where A is the tabulated area in Table 4 in the Appendix corresponding to $z = .63$ (see Figure 7.13).

The z values and p-values for comparing the proportions of MBAs and personnel managers in agreement for each of the other five reasons for the scarcity of women in overseas management are shown in columns 3 and 4, respectively, of Table 7.13. You can see that there is evidence of differences in perceptions between MBAs and personnel managers for four of the six reasons. Each of these four tests would be considered statistically significant (i.e., we would reject H_0) for $\alpha = .05$ because the p-values for each of these tests is less than .05.

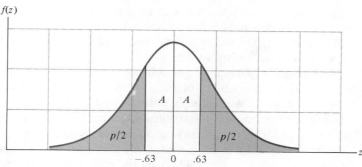

The p-Value for Dual-Career Marriages

So what do we conclude? Do the data provide sufficient evidence to indicate that the perceptions of MBAs and international personnel managers differ about the reasons for the scarcity of women in international management? We stated at the outset that the tools of Section 7.7 enable us to answer this question for one particular reason but they do not provide us with the tools to test the equality of proportions for all six reasons simultaneously. The problem with using the results of six individual tests to answer the question of overall equality of pairs of proportions is that there is a probability α of wrongfully concluding that a difference exists when, in fact, a pair of proportions is equal. The probability of making this error for *at least one* of the six tests is much higher than .05. Even though we do not know α for this overall test, the evidence supporting a difference in overall perceptions of the reasons for a scarcity of women in overseas management appears to be fairly strong. It seems unlikely that we would reject H_0 for four of the six tests if, in fact, there are no differences in the perceptions of MBAs and personnel managers.

SUMMARY

7.11

In this chapter we have presented the basic concepts of a test of an hypothesis and have demonstrated the procedure with four large-sample tests.

The key to a statistical test is the research hypothesis about a population parameter, call it θ. For some practical reason you will want to show that θ is larger than some value, for example 50, or smaller than some value, say 50; or you may want to show that θ is either larger or smaller than some value. This hypothesis is called the alternative hypothesis, H_a.

To gain evidence to support H_a, we define a null hypothesis. This hypothesis is defined in such a way that if we decide to reject it, we are left with only one alternative— that is, support of the research (or alternative) hypothesis. For example, if we wanted to show that a population mean was larger than 50, the alternative hypothesis would be $H_a : \mu > 50$ and the null hypothesis would be $H_0 : \mu = 50$.

To conduct a test, we need a decision maker—that is, a test statistic—which is calculated from the sample data. Then knowing its sampling distribution, we can decide which values (the rejection region) of the test statistic favor acceptance of the alternative hypothesis and which values (the nonrejection region) favor the null hypothesis. For each of the four tests presented in this chapter, we used a point estimator (from Chapter 6) to form a standard normal z test statistic. Values of z contradictory to the null hypothesis were those in the tail (one-tailed test) or tails (two-tailed test) of the z distribution.

Equally important as the test conclusion is a measure of its reliability. This measure is the probability of making an incorrect decision, α, if we reject H_0 and thereby accept the alternative hypothesis, and β, if we accept the null hypothesis. You can present the results of a statistical test either by stating the test conclusions (i.e., the decision) and the accompanying values of α and β or by stating the observed significance level for a test—that is, the probability of observing a value of the test statistic at least as contradictory to the null hypothesis (and as supportive of the alternative hypothesis) as the one calculated from the sample data. This latter procedure enables a reader of the test results to choose his or her own value of α.

Many test statistics possess sampling distributions that are approximately normal when the sample sizes are large and therefore can be expressed in the form of standard normal z statistics. The four tests presented in this chapter—tests of hypotheses about means and proportions—are examples of this phenomenon, as are three other statistical tests presented in Chapter 15. Although these tests concern different parameters, they are conducted in the same way and can be viewed as identical. Thus our large-sample statistical test possesses far greater applicability than the four specific applications presented in this chapter.

When the sample sizes are small, the sampling distributions of most test statistics are nonnormal. One of these nonnormal sampling distributions, the t distribution, will be used in Chapter 8 to obtain confidence intervals and tests of hypotheses for a single population mean and the difference between two population means.

References

Dixon, W. J., and Massey, F. J., Jr. *Introduction to Statistical Analysis*. 4th ed. New York: McGraw-Hill, 1983.

Dixon, W. T., Brown, M. B., Engelman, L., Frane, J. W., Hill, M. A., Jennich, R. I., and Toporek, J. D. *BMDP Statistical Software*. Berkeley: University of California Press, 1985.

Freund, J. E., and Walpole, R. E. *Mathematical Statistics*. 4th ed. Englewood Cliffs, N. J.: Prentice-Hall, 1987.

Mendenhall, W., Scheaffer, R. L., and Wackerly, D. D. *Mathematical Statistics with Applications*. 3rd ed. Boston: PWS-KENT, 1986.

Neter, J., Wasserman, W., and Whitmore, G. A. *Applied Statistics*. 3rd ed. Boston: Allyn and Bacon, 1988.

Ryan, T. A., Joiner, B. L., and Ryan, B. F. *Minitab Handbook*. 2nd ed. Boston: PWS-KENT, 1985.

SAS User's Guide: Statistics. Version 5 ed. Cary, N.C.: SAS Institute, 1985.

Scheaffer, R. L., Mendenhall, W., and Ott, L. *Elementary Survey Sampling*. 3rd ed. Boston: PWS-KENT, 1986.

Sincich, T. *Statistics by Example*. 3rd ed. New York: Macmillan, 1987.

SPSS^x User's Guide. Chicago: SPSS, 1983.

KEY TERMS

Alternative hypothesis (page 236)
Null hypothesis (page 236)
Test statistic (page 236)
Rejection region (page 236)
Type I error (page 237)
Type II error (page 237)
Probability α of a type I error (page 237)
Probability β of a type II error (page 237)

Critical value of test statistic (page 240)
One-tailed statistical test (page 240)
Two-tailed statistical test (page 240)
Pooled estimate of p (page 257)
Observed significance level (page 263)
p-Value for a test (page 263)
Statistically significant (page 263)

SUPPLEMENTARY EXERCISES

Starred (*) exercises are optional.

7.52 Define α and β for a statistical test of an hypothesis.

7.53 What is the observed significance level of a test?

7.54 The daily wages in a particular industry are normally distributed with a mean of $23.20 and a standard deviation of $4.50. A company in this industry employing 40 workers pays these workers an average of $21.20 daily. Based on this sample mean, could these workers be viewed as a random sample from among all workers in the industry?

(a) Find the observed significance level of the test.

(b) If you planned to conduct your test using $\alpha = .01$, what would be your test conclusion?

7.55 High airline occupancy rates on scheduled flights are essential to profitability. Suppose that a scheduled flight must average at least 60% occupancy in order that it be profitable and that an examination of the occupancy rates for 120 10:00 A.M. flights from Atlanta to Dallas showed a mean occupancy rate per flight of 58% and a standard deviation of 11%.

(a) If μ is the mean occupancy per flight and if the company wishes to determine whether this scheduled flight is unprofitable, give the alternative and the null hypotheses for the test.

(b) Does the alternative hypothesis in part (a) imply a one- or a two-tailed test? Explain.

(c) Do the occupancy data for the 120 flights suggest that this scheduled flight is unprofitable? Test using $\alpha = .10$.

7.56 A manufacturer of automatic washers provides a particular model in one of three colors, A, B, or C. Of the first 1000 washers sold, 400 of the washers were of color A. Would you conclude that more than 1/3 of all customers have a preference for color A?

(a) Find the observed significance level of the test.

(b) If you planned to conduct your test using $\alpha = .05$, what would be your test conclusion?

7.57 A manufacturer claimed that at least 20% of the public preferred its product. A sample of 100 persons is taken to check this claim. With $\alpha = .05$, how small would the sample percentage need to be before the claim could be statistically refuted? (Note that this would require a one-tailed test of an hypothesis.)

7.58 Refer to Exercise 7.57. Sixteen people in the sample of 100 consumers expressed a preference for the manufacturer's product. Does this result present sufficient evidence to reject the manufacturer's claim? Test using $\alpha = .10$.

7.59 What conditions must be met in order that the z test may be used to test an hypothesis concerning a population mean μ?

7.60 A manufacturer claimed that at least 95% of the equipment that it supplied to a factory conformed to specification. An examination of a sample of 700 pieces of equipment revealed that 53 were faulty. Test the manufacturer's claim using $\alpha = .05$.

 7.61 In deciding where to place its emphasis in advertising, the market research department for a major automobile manufacturer wished to compare the mean number of automobiles per family in two regions of the United States. Suppose that a preliminary study of the number of cars per family for $n = 200$ families from each of the two regions gave the means and variances for the two samples as shown in Table 7.14.

TABLE 7.14   Sample Data for Exercise 7.61

	Area 1	Area 2
Sample size	200	200
Sample mean	1.30	1.37
Sample variance	.53	.64

(a) Note that a small increase in the mean number of automobiles per family can represent a very large number of automobiles for a region. Do the data provide sufficient evidence to indicate a difference in the mean number of automobiles per family for the two regions?

(b) Picture the data associated with either of the two populations. What values will x assume? Imagine the probability distributions for these two populations. Will their nature violate the conditions necessary in order that the test in part (a) be valid? Explain.

(c) Find a 95% confidence interval for the mean number of automobiles per family for region 2. Interpret the interval.

(d) Find a 90% confidence interval for the difference in the mean number of automobiles for the two regions. Interpret the interval.

 7.62 The mean lifetime of a sample of 100 fluorescent bulbs produced by a company is computed to be 1570 hours, and the standard deviation is 120 hours. If μ is the mean lifetime of all the bulbs produced by the company, test the hypothesis $\mu = 1600$ hours against the alternative hypothesis $\mu < 1600$.

(a) Find the observed significance level of the test.

(b) If you planned to conduct your test using $\alpha = .05$, what would be your test conclusion?

 7.63 Presently 20% of potential customers buy a certain brand of soap, say brand A. To increase sales, the company plans an extensive advertising campaign. At the end of the campaign a sample of 400 potential customers will be interviewed to determine whether the campaign was successful.

(a) State H_0 and H_a in terms of p, the probability that a customer prefers soap brand A.

(b) The company will conclude that the advertising campaign was a success if at least 92 of the 400 customers interviewed prefer brand A. Find α. (Use the normal approximation to the binomial distribution to evaluate the desired probability.)

 7.64 In the past a chemical plant has produced an average of 1100 pounds of chemical per day. The records for the past year, based on 260 operating days, show the following:

$$\bar{x} = 1060 \text{ pounds per day} \qquad s = 340 \text{ pounds per day}$$

The plant manager wishes to test whether the average daily production has dropped significantly over the past year.

(a) Give the appropriate null and alternative hypotheses.

(b) If z is used as a test statistic, determine the rejection region corresponding to $\alpha = .05$.

(c) Do the data provide sufficient evidence to indicate a drop in average daily production?

7.65 In Exercise 6.38 we described a biannual survey of purchasing agents by the National Association of Purchasing Agents (*Wall Street Journal*, May 6, 1986). This survey of 160 purchasing agents found 48% "satisfied or optimistic about the economic outlook for the next twelve months," up from 34% in December. Assume that the surveys were conducted independently and that both were based on random samples of 160 purchasing agents each. Do the data provide sufficient evidence to indicate a change, from December 1985 to mid-1986, in the outlook on the economy of all purchasing agents? Test using $\alpha = .05$.

7.66 Both union and management conducted surveys of worker opinion prior to a vote for or against unionization of a large industrial plant. The union survey, consisting of a sample of 500 workers, was reported to show 54% of the workers in favor of unionization. A corresponding management survey of 400 workers found only 46% in favor of unionization. Is it likely that surveys involving these sample sizes would produce percentages in favor of unionization that differ as much as those presented here? Or is it possible that something was wrong with the survey method or data analysis for either the union, management, or both? Test using $\alpha = .05$.

7.67 A hotel needs a 60% occupancy rate in order to show a profit. A random sampling of 50 days produced a mean occupancy rate of 62% and a standard deviation of 8%. Do these data provide sufficient evidence to indicate that the mean occupancy rate (for the population of days representative of those in the sample) exceeds 60%? Test using $\alpha = .10$.

*7.68 Refer to Example 7.2. Use the procedure described in Example 7.2 to calculate β for several alternative values of μ. (For example, $\mu = 873, 875,$ and 877.) Use the three computed values of β along with the value computed in Example 7.2 to construct an operating characteristic curve for the statistical test. The resulting graph will be similar to that shown in Figure 7.14.

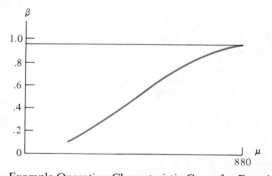

FIGURE 7.14   Example Operating Characteristic Curve for Exercise 7.68

*7.69 Repeat the procedure described in Exercise 7.68 for sample size $n = 25$ (as opposed to $n = 50$ used in Exercise 7.68), and compare the two operating characteristic curves.

The basic concepts of statistical estimation and tests of hypotheses were presented in Chapters 6 and 7 along with summaries of the methodologies for some large-sample estimation and test procedures. Large-sample estimation and test procedures for population means and proportions were used to illustrate concepts as well as to give you some useful tools for solving some practical problems. Because all these techniques rely on the Central Limit Theorem to justify the normality of the estimators and test statistics, they apply only when the sample sizes are large. Consequently, the objective of Chapter 8 is to supplement the results of Chapters 6 and 7 by presenting small-sample statistical test and estimation procedures for population means and variances. These techniques differ substantially from those of Chapters 6 and 7 because they require that the relative frequency distributions of the sampled populations be approximately normal.

8 INFERENCE FROM SMALL SAMPLES

CASE STUDY: Early-Warning Systems for Impending Bank Failure

Early-Warning Systems for Impending Bank Failure

Do some measures of a bank's performance provide an early warning of potential bank failure? We know, intuitively, that certain variables measure bank performances and that these variables may change in their relative importance as indicators of impending danger from one period of time to another. For example, a large proportion of agricultural loans was a signal of possible trouble for banks in the 1980s but was not considered a problem in the 1970s. Similarly, loans to companies in the oil and oil service industries were considered to be secure—until the enormous drop in the price of oil in 1985.

The Federal Deposit Insurance Corporation (FDIC), the Federal Reserve Board (FRB), and the Office of the Controller of the Currency (OCC) have developed early-warning systems to identify potential bank failures. One of these, the FDIC's Integrated Monitoring System (IMS), is the subject of a study by Peter S. Rose and James W. Kolari of the Texas A&M University ("Early Warning Systems as a Monitoring Device for Bank Condition," *Quarterly Journal of Business and Economics,* Vol. 24, No. 1, 1985).

The key feature of the IMS early-warning system is a screening procedure called Just a Warning System (JAWS). The screening procedure examines a set of variables that are believed to measure bank performance. The values of these variables are reported quarterly to a regional FDIC office by each bank, and the observed values are then compared with established critical values. Failure to compare favorably with one or more of these critical values is considered a warning of impending trouble.

In their study Rose and Kolari examine the values of 23 variables (listed in Table 8.18, p. 323) involved in the IMS screening procedure to determine whether the mean values for failing banks differ from the corresponding

means for healthy banks. To compare the mean values of these variables for failing and healthy banks, the researchers selected a sample of failing commercial banks from among all of those that were declared insolvent during the period 1964–1977. Each was matched with a healthy bank of approximately the same size, from the same county location, and possessing the same supervisory authority and regulation. The values of the 23 variables were recorded for each bank a specified length of time before bank failure. For example, observations on the 23 variables were recorded on 24 pairs of banks 8 years prior to failure of the failing bank in each given pair. A test was then conducted for each variable to determine whether the mean value for failing banks differed from the mean for healthy banks.

Since the usefulness of some variables as early-warning indicators might depend upon the length of time between the measurement of a variable and the subsequent time of bank failure, observations on the 23 variables were recorded 7 years prior to bank failure and also for 6, 5, 4, 3, 2, and 1 years. For various reasons the sample sizes (number of pairs of failed and healthy banks) differ depending upon the lag time—that is, the number of years between the time of the observation and the subsequent time of bank failure.

Although each of the tests that we have described involves the comparison of a pair of means, the mean for failed banks versus the mean for healthy banks, the tests cannot be conducted by using the test procedure of Section 7.5. Two of the assumptions required for the test have been violated. First, the sample sizes for observations taken 8 years prior to bank failure were smaller than the minimum number 30 specified in Section 7.5. Second, the samples were not selected independently. Rather, they were selected in matched pairs. In this chapter you will learn how to make inferences about population means based on small sample sizes. In Section 8.5 we will discuss the advantages to be derived from paired sampling. Then in Section 8.9 we will present the results of Rose and Kolari's study of the IMS JAWS variables and see what conclusions we can draw from them.

8.1   INTRODUCTION

Large-sample methods for making inferences concerning population means and the difference between two means were discussed with examples in Chapters 6 and 7. Frequently cost, available time, and other factors limit the size of the sample that may be acquired. In this case large-sample procedures are inadequate, and other tests and estimation procedures must be used. In this chapter we will study several small-sample inferential procedures that are closely related to the large-sample methods presented in Chapters 6 and 7. Specifically, we will consider methods for estimating and testing hypotheses concerning population means, the difference between two means, a population variance, and a comparison of two population variances. Small-sample tests and confidence intervals for binomial parameters will be omitted from our discussion.

8.2   STUDENT'S t DISTRIBUTION

We introduce our topic by considering the following problem: A very costly experiment has been conducted to evaluate a new process for producing synthetic diamonds. Six diamonds have been generated by the new process with recorded weights .46, .61, .52, .48, .57, and .54 carat.

A study of the process costs indicates that the average weight of the diamonds must be greater than .5 carat in order that the process be operated at a profitable level. Do the six diamond weight measurements present sufficient evidence to indicate that the average weight of the diamonds produced by the process is in excess of .5 carat?

Recall that according to the Central Limit Theorem,

$$z = \frac{\bar{x} - \mu}{\sigma/\sqrt{n}}$$

possesses approximately a normal distribution in repeated sampling when n is large. For $\alpha = .05$ we would use a one-tailed statistical test and reject H_0 when $z > 1.645$. To conduct the test, one must assume that σ is known or that a good estimate, s, is available and is based on a reasonably large sample (we have suggested $n \geq 30$). Unfortunately, this latter requirement will not be satisfied for the $n = 6$ diamond weight measurements. How, then, may we test the hypothesis that $\mu = .5$ against the alternative that $\mu > .5$ when we have a small sample?

The problem that we pose is not new; rather, it is one that received serious attention by statisticians and experimenters at the turn of the century. If a sample standard deviation *s* were substituted for σ in *z*, would the resulting quantity possess approximately a standardized normal distribution in repeated sampling? More specifically, would the rejection region $z > 1.645$ be appropriate; that is, would approximately 5% of the values of the test statistic, computed in repeated sampling, exceed 1.645? In order to answer these questions, we need to know the sampling distribution of the statistic

$$\frac{\bar{x} - \mu}{s/\sqrt{n}}$$

for small sample sizes.

The distribution of the test statistic

$$t = \frac{\bar{x} - \mu}{s/\sqrt{n}}$$

for samples drawn from a normally distributed population was discovered by W. S. Gosset and published (1908) under the pen name of Student. He referred to the quantity under study as *t*, and it has since been known as **Student's *t***. We omit the complicated mathematical expression for the density function for *t* but describe some of its characteristics.

The sampling distribution of the *t* test statistic, called a *t* **distribution**, is, like *z*, mound-shaped and perfectly symmetrical about $t = 0$. Unlike *z*, it is much more variable, tailing rapidly out to the right and left, a phenomenon that may readily be explained. The variability of *z* in repeated sampling is due solely to $\bar{x}$; the other quantities appearing in *z* (n, μ, and σ) are nonrandom. On the other hand, the variability of *t* is contributed by *two* random quantities, $\bar{x}$ and *s*, which can be shown to be independent of one another. Thus when $\bar{x}$ is very large, *s* may be very small, and vice versa. As a result, *t* will be more variable than *z* in repeated sampling (see Figure 8.1). Finally, as we might surmise, the variability of *t* decreases as *n* increases because the *s* of

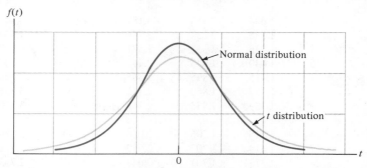

FIGURE 8.1   Standard Normal *z* and a *t* Distribution Based on $n = 6$ Measurements (5 d.f.)

σ will be based upon more and more information. When n is infinitely large, the t and z distributions will be identical. Thus Gosset discovered that the distribution of t depended upon the sample size n.

The divisor of the sum of squares of deviations, $(n - 1)$, that appears in the formula for s^2 is called the number of **degrees of freedom** (d.f.) associated with s^2 and with the statistic t. The term *degrees of freedom* is linked to the statistical theory underlying the probability distribution of s^2, and a discussion of its origin is beyond the scope of this text.

The critical values of t, which separate the rejection and acceptance regions for the statistical test, are presented in Table 5 of the Appendix. Table 5 is partially reproduced in Table 8.1. The tabulated value t_α records the value of t such that an area α lies to its right, as shown in Figure 8.2. The degrees of freedom associated with t, d.f., are shown in the first and last columns of the table (see Table 8.1), and the t_α corresponding

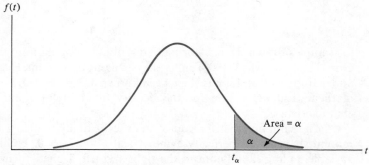

FIGURE 8.2   Tabulated values of Student's t

TABLE 8.1   Format of the Student's t table, Table 5 in the Appendix

d.f.	$t_{.100}$	$t_{.050}$	$t_{.025}$	$t_{.010}$	$t_{.005}$	d.f.
1	3.078	6.314	12.706	31.821	63.657	1
2	1.886	2.920	4.303	6.965	9.925	2
3	1.638	2.353	3.182	4.541	5.841	3
4	1.533	2.132	2.776	3.747	4.604	4
5	1.476	2.015	2.571	3.365	4.032	5
6	1.440	1.943	2.447	3.143	3.707	6
7	1.415	1.895	2.365	2.998	3.499	7
8	1.397	1.860	2.306	2.896	3.355	8
9	1.383	1.833	2.262	2.821	3.250	9
$\vdots$	$\vdots$	$\vdots$	$\vdots$	$\vdots$	$\vdots$	$\vdots$
26	1.315	1.706	2.056	2.479	2.779	26
27	1.314	1.703	2.052	2.473	2.771	27
28	1.313	1.701	2.048	2.467	2.763	28
29	1.311	1.699	2.045	2.462	2.756	29
inf.	1.282	1.645	1.960	2.326	2.576	inf.

to various values of α appear in the top row. Thus if we want to find the value of t such that 5% of the area lies to its right, we use the column marked $t_{.05}$. The critical value of t for our example, found in that $t_{.05}$ column opposite d.f. $= (n - 1) = (6 - 1) = 5$, is $t = 2.015$ (shaded in Table 8.1). Thus we will reject $H_0 : \mu = .5$ in favor of $H_a : \mu > .5$ when $t > 2.015$.

Note that the critical value of t will always be larger than the corresponding critical value of z for a specified α. For example, where $\alpha = .05$, the critical value of t for $n = 2$ (d.f. $= 1$) is $t = 6.314$, which is very large when compared with the corresponding $z_{.05} = 1.645$. Proceeding down the $t_{.05}$ column, we note that the critical value of t decreases, reflecting the effect of a larger sample size (more degrees of freedom) on the estimation of σ. Finally, when n is infinitely large, the critical value of t will equal $z_{.05} = 1.645$.

The reason for choosing $n = 30$ (an arbitrary choice) as the dividing line between large and small samples is apparent. For $n = 30$ (d.f. $= 29$), the critical value of $t_{.05} = 1.699$ is numerically quite close to $z_{.05} = 1.645$. For a two-tailed test based upon $n = 30$ measurements and $\alpha = .05$, we would place .025 in each tail of the t distribution and reject $H_0 : \mu = \mu_0$ when $t > 2.045$ or $t < -2.045$. Note that this tabulated value of t is very close to the $z_{.025} = 1.96$ employed in the z test.

Remember that Student's t and corresponding tabulated critical values are based on the assumption that the sampled population possesses a normal probability distribution. This is a very restrictive assumption because in many sampling situations the properties of the population will be completely unknown and may well be nonnormal. If nonnormality of the population were to seriously affect the distribution of the t statistic, the application of the t test would be very limited. Fortunately, this point is of little consequence, because it can be shown that the distribution of the t statistic possesses nearly the same shape as the theoretical t distribution for populations that are nonnormal but possess a mound-shaped probability distribution. This property of the t statistic and the common occurrence of mound-shaped distributions of data in nature enhance the value of Student's t for use in statistical inference.

Having discussed the origin of Student's t and the tabulated critical values (Table 5 in the Appendix), we now return to the problem of making an inference about the mean diamond weight based upon our sample of $n = 6$ measurements. Prior to considering the solution, you may want to test your built-in inference-making equipment by glancing at the six measurements and arriving at a conclusion concerning the significance of the data.

SMALL-SAMPLE INFERENCES CONCERNING A POPULATION MEAN

8.3

The statistical test of an hypothesis concerning a population mean is stated in the following box. Example 8.1 illustrates its use.

SMALL-SAMPLE TEST OF AN HYPOTHESIS CONCERNING A
POPULATION MEAN

(1) *Null Hypothesis:* $H_0 : \mu = \mu_0$.

(2) *Alternative Hypothesis:*

One-Tailed Test	**Two-Tailed Test**
$H_a : \mu > \mu_0$	$H_a : \mu \neq \mu_0$
(or $H_a : \mu < \mu_0$)	

(3) *Test Statistic:* $t = \dfrac{\bar{x} - \mu_0}{s/\sqrt{n}}$.

(4) *Rejection Region:*

One-Tailed Test

$t > t_\alpha$
(or $t < -t_\alpha$ when the alternative
hypothesis is $H_a : \mu < \mu_0$)

Two-Tailed Test

$t > t_{\alpha/2}$ or $t < -t_{\alpha/2}$

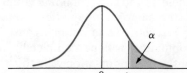   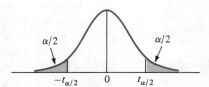

The critical values of t, t_α and $t_{\alpha/2}$, are based on $(n - 1)$ degrees of freedom. These tabulated critical values can be found in Table 5 in the Appendix.

Assumption: The sample has been randomly selected from a normally distributed population.

EXAMPLE 8.1

Do the weights of the six synthetic diamonds, .46, .61, .52, .48, .57, and .54 carat, provide sufficient evidence to indicate that the mean diamond weight produced by the process exceeds .5 carat? Test using $\alpha = .05$.

SOLUTION

Since we want to detect values of $\mu > .5$, we will test the null hypothesis

$$H_0 : \mu = .5$$

against the alternative hypothesis

$$H_a : \mu > .5$$

Using the methods of Chapter 2, you can verify that the sample mean and standard deviation for the six diamond weights are

$$\bar{x} = .53 \quad \text{and} \quad s = .0559$$

Substituting these quantities into the formula for the test statistic, we obtain

$$t = \frac{\bar{x} - \mu_0}{s/\sqrt{n}} = \frac{.53 - .5}{.0559/\sqrt{6}} = 1.31$$

(313) 838-6313 BEEPER 829-9638

Motor City Drop Shop

LOWERING TRUCK, CAR, ANYTHING ON WHEELS

TARGA TOP-SUNROOF-CONVERTIBLE TOP

SOUND SYSTEMS & CUSTOM WORK

RAG TOPS - CUSTOM TARPS - CUSTOM PAINTING

ALL WORK GUARANTEED

AMA

ANGELO

16166 Murray Hill
Detroit, MI 48235

Since we only wish to detect large values of μ, we will conduct an upper one-tailed test. The rejection region for this test for $\alpha = .05$ and $(n - 1) = (6 - 1) = 5$ degrees of freedom is $t > 2.015$. This is the value of t, given in Table 5 of the Appendix, that places $\alpha = .05$ in the upper tail of the t distribution (see Figure 8.3). Noting that the calculated value of the test statistic does not fall in the rejection region, we do not reject H_0. Nonrejection of H_0 implies that the data do not present sufficient evidence to indicate that the mean diamond weight exceeds .5 carat.

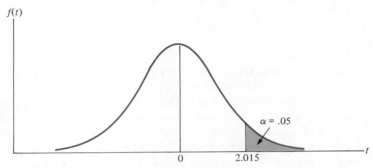

FIGURE 8.3   Rejection Region for the Test in Example 8.1

The calculation of the probability of a type II error, β, for the t test is very difficult and is beyond the scope of this text. Instead, we will obtain an interval estimate for μ, as noted in Section 7.9.

Recall that the large-sample confidence interval for μ is

$$\bar{x} \pm \frac{z_{\alpha/2}\sigma}{\sqrt{n}}$$

where $z_{\alpha/2} = 1.96$ for a confidence coefficient equal to .95. This result assumes that σ is known and simply involves a measurement of $1.96\sigma_{\bar{x}}$ (or approximately $2\sigma_{\bar{x}}$) on either side of $\bar{x}$ in conformity with the Empirical Rule. When σ is unknown and must be estimated by a small-sample standard deviation s, the large-sample confidence interval will not enclose μ 95% of the time in repeated sampling. But this situation can be easily corrected; that is, we can make the confidence coefficient equal .95 if we substitute $t_{.025}$ for $z_{.025}$ in the formula for the large-sample 95% confidence interval. Although we omit the derivation, the corresponding small-sample confidence interval for μ, with confidence coefficient $(1 - \alpha)$, is as shown in the next box.

A $(1 - \alpha)100\%$ SMALL-SAMPLE CONFIDENCE INTERVAL FOR μ

$$\bar{x} \pm \frac{t_{\alpha/2}s}{\sqrt{n}}$$

where s is the sample standard deviation and $s/\sqrt{n}$ is the *estimated* standard deviation of $\bar{x}$.

Assumption: The sampled population is approximately normally distributed.

EXAMPLE 8.2   Find a 95% confidence interval for the mean diamond weight.

SOLUTION   The mean and standard deviation for the six diamond weights, $\bar{x} = .53$ and $s = .0559$, and the value of $t_{.025}$ were given in Example 8.1. Substituting these values into the formula for a 95% confidence interval yields

$$\bar{x} \pm t_{.025}\frac{s}{\sqrt{n}} = .53 + (2.571)\frac{(.0559)}{\sqrt{6}}$$

or

$$.53 \pm .059$$

The interval estimate for μ is therefore .471 to .589 with confidence coefficient equal to .95. If the experimenter wants to detect a small increase in mean diamond weight in excess of .5 carat, the width of the interval must be reduced by obtaining more diamond weight measurements. Increasing the sample size will decrease both $1/\sqrt{n}$ and $t_{\alpha/2}$ and thereby decrease the width of the interval. Or from the standpoint of a statistical test of an hypothesis, more information will be available upon which to base a decision, and the probability of making a type II error will decrease.   ■

EXAMPLE 8.3   A small manufacturer's new system for inventory control is designed to reduce the inventory for a particular electric motor to an average of less than 3000 motors per day. A sampling of the inventory on hand at the end of each of eight randomly selected days is shown in the accompanying table. Do the data present sufficient evidence to indicate that the mean daily number of motors in inventory is less than 3000?

Number of Motors	
2905	2895
2725	3005
2835	2835
3065	2605

SOLUTION   Testing the null hypothesis that $\mu = 3000$ motors per day against the alternative that μ is less than 3000 will result in a one-tailed statistical test. Thus

$$H_0 : \mu = 3000$$

$$H_a : \mu < 3000$$

where μ is the mean daily number of motors in inventory. Using $\alpha = .05$ and placing .05 in the lower tail of the t distribution, we find that the critical value of t for $n = 8$ measurements [or $(n - 1) = 7$ d.f.] is $t = 1.895$. Therefore, we will reject H_0 if $t < -1.895$ (see Figure 8.4).

You can verify that the sample mean and standard deviation for the $n = 8$ measurements in the table are

$$\bar{x} = 2858.75 \quad \text{and} \quad s = 146.77$$

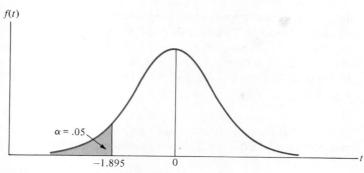

FIGURE 8.4   Rejection Region for Example 8.3

Substituting these values into the formula for the test statistic yields

$$t = \frac{\bar{x} - \mu_0}{s/\sqrt{n}} = \frac{2858.75 - 3000}{146.77/\sqrt{8}} = -2.72$$

Since the observed value of t falls in the rejection region, there is sufficient evidence to indicate that the new system for inventory control reduces the mean number of motors on hand per day to less than 3000. Furthermore, we will be reasonably confident that we have made the correct decision. When we use our procedure, we should erroneously reject H_0 only $\alpha = .05$ of the time in repeated applications of the statistical test.

EXAMPLE 8.4   If you planned to report the results of the statistical test in Example 8.3, what p-value would you report?

SOLUTION   The p-value for this test is the probability of observing a value of the t statistic at least as contradictory to the null hypothesis as the one observed for this set of data, namely, a value of $t \le -2.72$ (see Figure 8.5).

Unlike the table of areas under the normal curve (Table 4 of the Appendix), Table 5 in the Appendix does not give the areas corresponding to various values of t. Rather, it gives the values of t corresponding to upper-tail areas equal to .10, .05, .025, .010, and .005. Since the t distribution is symmetric about its mean, we can use these

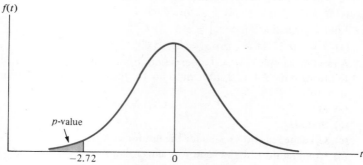

FIGURE 8.5 p-Value for the Test in Example 8.3

upper-tail areas to approximate the probability that $t < -2.72$. Since the t statistic for this test is based on 7 degrees of freedom, we consult the d.f. $= 7$ row of Table 5 and find that 2.72 falls between $t_{.025} = 2.365$ and $t_{.010} = 2.998$. Since the observed value of t, -2.72, is less than $-t_{.025} = -2.365$ but not less than $-t_{.01} = -2.998$, we reject H_0 for $\alpha = .025$ but not for $\alpha = .01$. Therefore, the p-value for the test is reported as $p \leq .025$. ∎

EXAMPLE 8.5

Suppose that the manufacturer in Example 8.3 is concerned about a lower limit for the mean inventory. Find a 95% lower confidence interval for μ.

SOLUTION

The formula for a small-sample $(1 - \alpha)100\%$ lower one-sided confidence interval for a population mean μ is identical to the corresponding large-sample formula, except that z_α is replaced by t_α. In Example 8.3 we found that the mean and standard deviation of the $n = 8$ sample daily inventories were $\bar{x} = 2858.75$ and $s = 146.77$, and the value of $t_{.05}$, based on 7 degrees of freedom, was $t_{.05} = 1.895$. Substituting these values into the formula for the lower confidence interval, we obtain

$$\text{LCL} = \bar{x} - t_{.05}\frac{s}{\sqrt{n}}$$

$$= 2858.75 - (1.895)\frac{(146.77)}{\sqrt{8}}$$

$$= 2760.42$$

Therefore, we estimate the mean daily inventory to be as large or larger than 2760.42 motors per day with confidence coefficient equal to .95. ∎

EXERCISES

BASIC TECHNIQUES

8.1 Find the value of t.
  (a) $t_{.05}$ for 5 degrees of freedom (d.f.)   (b) $t_{.025}$ for 8 d.f.
  (c) $t_{.10}$ for 18 d.f.   (d) $t_{.025}$ for 30 d.f.

8.2 Find t_α given that $P(t > t_\alpha) = \alpha$.
  (a) $\alpha = .10$, 12 d.f.   (b) $\alpha = .01$, 25 d.f.   (c) $\alpha = .05$, 16 d.f.

8.3 A random sample of $n = 4$ observations from a normally distributed population produced the following data: 9.4, 12.2, 10.7, and 11.6. Do the data provide sufficient evidence to indicate that $\mu > 10$?
  (a) State H_a.
  (b) State H_0.
  (c) Give the rejection region for the test for $\alpha = .10$.
  (d) Conduct the test and state your conclusions.
  (e) Give the approximate p-value for the test, and interpret it.

8.4 Find a 90% confidence interval for μ in Exercise 8.3. Interpret the interval.

8.5 A random sample of $n = 6$ observations from a normally distributed population produced the following data: 3.7, 6.4, 8.1, 8.8, 4.9, and 5.0. Do the data provide sufficient evidence to indicate that $\mu < 7$?

(a) State H_a.

(b) State H_0.

(c) Give the rejection region for the test for $\alpha = .10$.

(d) Conduct the test and state your conclusions.

(e) Give the approximate p-value for the test, and interpret it.

8.6 Find a 90% confidence interval for μ in Exercise 8.5. Interpret the interval.

8.7 Test the null hypothesis $H_0 : \mu = 3$ against $H_a : \mu > 3$ for $\alpha = .05$, $n = 12$, $\bar{x} = 3.18$, and $s^2 = .21$.

8.8 Test the null hypothesis $H_0 : \mu = 48$ against $H_a : \mu \neq 48$ for $\alpha = .10$, $n = 25$, $\bar{x} = 47.1$, and $s^2 = 4.7$.

8.9 Find a 90% confidence interval for the mean in Exercise 8.8. Interpret the interval.

8.10 Find a one-sided lower 90% confidence interval for the mean in Exercise 8.8. Interpret the interval.

8.11 Test the null hypothesis $H_0 : \mu = 34$ against $H_a : \mu \neq 34$ for $\alpha = .05$, $n = 3$, $\bar{x} = 36.1$, and $s^2 = 1.7$.

8.12 Find a 95% confidence interval for the mean in Exercise 8.11. Interpret the interval.

8.13 Find a one-sided upper 95% confidence interval for the mean in Exercise 8.11. Interpret the interval.

APPLICATIONS

 8.14 A money manager claims that her common stock selection for investment will, on average, beat the annual change in the Standard & Poor's stock average. A random selection of three of the manager's stock choices found annual increases of 22%, 12%, and 31% in comparison with an increase in the Standard & Poor's average of 19%. Does this sample of three stock picks provide sufficient evidence to indicate that the mean increase in all of the manager's stock selections exceeds 19%?

(a) State H_a.

(b) State H_0.

(c) Give the rejection region for the test for $\alpha = .05$.

(d) Conduct the test and state your conclusions.

(e) Give the approximate p-value for the test, and interpret it.

8.15 Refer to Exercise 8.14. If you were considering the money manager as a possible manager of your investments, you might be concerned about the low side for the mean increase (or decrease) in the value of the money manager's stock selections. Find a one-sided lower 95% confidence interval for the mean change. Interpret the interval.

 8.16 With home mortgage loan rates in a slow downward movement and a mean prevailing rate of 9.8%, a bank decided to survey the mortgage rate expectations of its current applicants. A random sample of the ten latest applicants found that the mean of the ten rate expectations that the applicants wanted to negotiate was 9.6%. The ten individual rate expectations varied from a low of 9.1% to a high of 10.0% with a standard deviation equal to .23%. Do the data provide sufficient evidence to indicate that the mean mortgage rate expectations of the bank's mortgage loan applicants is less than the mean 9.8% rate prevailing in the bank's market area?

(a) State H_a.

(b) State H_0.

(c) Give the rejection region for the test for $\alpha = .10$.

(d) Conduct the test and state your conclusion.

(e) Give the approximate p-value for the test, and interpret it.

8.17 Refer to Exercise 8.16, and find a 90% confidence interval for the mean rate expectation of the bank's home mortgage loan applicants. Interpret this interval.

 8.18 Varying costs, primarily labor, make home building vary from one unit to the next. A builder of standard tract homes needs to make an average profit in excess of $8500 per home in order to achieve an annual profit goal. The profits per home for the builder's most recent five units are $8760, $6370, $9620, $8200, and $10,350. Do the data provide sufficient evidence to indicate that the builder is operating at the desired profit level?

(a) State H_a.

(b) State H_0.

(c) Give the rejection region for the test for $\alpha = .05$.

(d) Conduct the test and state your conclusion.

(e) Give the approximate p-value for the test, and interpret it.

8.19 Refer to Exercise 8.18, and find a 95% confidence interval for the builder's mean profit per unit. Interpret the interval.

 8.20 The tremendous growth of the Florida lobster (called spiny lobster) industry over the past 20 years has made it the state's second most valuable fishery industry. Several years ago, a declaration by the Bahamian government, which prohibited United States lobstermen from fishing on the Bahamian portion of the continental shelf, was expected to produce a dramatic reduction in the landings in pounds per lobster per trap. According to the records, the mean landing per trap is 30.31 pounds. A random sampling of 20 lobster traps since the Bahamian fishing restriction went into effect gave the following results (in pounds):

17.4	18.9	39.6	34.4	19.6
33.7	37.2	43.4	41.7	27.5
24.1	39.6	12.2	25.5	22.1
29.3	21.1	23.8	43.2	24.4

Do these landings provide sufficient evidence to support the contention that the mean landings per trap decreased after imposition of the Bahamian restrictions? Test using $\alpha = .05$.

8.21 Refer to Exercise 8.20, and find a 90% confidence interval for the mean landing per lobster trap (in pounds), and interpret your result.

 8.22 PCBs (polychlorinated biphenyls), used in the manufacture of large electric power transformers and capacitors, are known to be hazardous substances that have serious health effects. *Environment News* (October 1976) reports that federal and state governments are investigating PCB contamination in the Acushnet River in the New Bedford, Massachusetts, area. As part of their investigation, they found that analyses of three clam specimens showed PCB levels of 21, 23, and 53 parts per million (ppm)(the FDA tolerance level for PCBs is 5 ppm). Use these three clam PCB concentration levels to estimate the mean concentration in clams in the Acushnet River area. Use a 90% confidence interval. Interpret your results. What assumptions must be made in order that your inference be valid?

8.23 The U.S. budget deficit projections for fiscal year 1984 by some leading economic forecasting organizations are shown in Table 8.2.

TABLE 8.2 Deficit Projection Data for Exercise 8.23

Forecasting Organization	Forecast (Billion $)
Reagan budget	82.9
Chase Econometrics	90
Morgan Guaranty	150
Townsend-Greenspan	126.5
Aubrey G. Lanston	130
Manufacturers Hanover	90
Bankers Trust	140
Merrill Lynch	145
Data Resources	130.6
Shilling & Co.	100
Bear Stearns	150

Source: Data from the *Wall Street Journal,* February 10, 1982.

Note: We show the midpoint when the forecaster gave the deficit projection as an interval prediction.

(a) If the forecasts represent a random sample of the 1984 budget deficit predictions from among all forecasting organizations, find a 95% confidence interval for the mean forecasted deficit for all forecasting organizations.

(b) Is it likely that the mean forecast deficit will equal the actual U.S. deficit in 1984? Explain.

SMALL-SAMPLE INFERENCES CONCERNING THE DIFFERENCE BETWEEN TWO POPULATION MEANS

8.4

The physical setting for the problem that we consider is identical to that discussed for the large-sample test in Section 7.5. Independent random samples of n_1 and n_2 measurements are drawn from two populations that possess means and variances μ_1, σ_1^2 and μ_2, σ_2^2. Our objective is to make inferences concerning the difference between the two population means $(\mu_1 - \mu_2)$.

The small-sample test for a difference between population means is based on the assumption that both populations are normally distributed and, in addition, that they possess equal variances—that is, $\sigma_1^2 = \sigma_2^2 = \sigma^2$. For this special case the large-sample test statistic for a test $H_0 : \mu_1 - \mu_2 = D_0$ reduces to

$$z = \frac{(\bar{x}_1 - \bar{x}_2)}{\sqrt{\dfrac{\sigma_1^2}{n_1} + \dfrac{\sigma_2^2}{n_2}}} = \frac{(\bar{x}_1 - \bar{x}_2) - D_0}{\sqrt{\dfrac{\sigma^2}{n_1} + \dfrac{\sigma^2}{n_2}}} = \frac{(\bar{x}_1 - \bar{x}_2) - D_0}{\sigma\sqrt{\dfrac{1}{n_1} + \dfrac{1}{n_2}}}$$

For small-sample tests of the hypothesis $H_0: \mu_1 - \mu_2 = D_0$, it seems reasonable to use the test statistic

$$t = \frac{(\bar{x}_1 - \bar{x}_2) - D_0}{s\sqrt{\dfrac{1}{n_1} + \dfrac{1}{n_2}}}$$

that is, we substitute a sample standard deviation s for σ. Surprisingly enough, the sampling distribution of this statistic is a Student's t distribution when the stated assumptions are satisfied, a fact that can be proved mathematically or verified by experimental sampling from two normal populations.

The estimate s to be used in the t statistic could be either s_1 or s_2, the standard deviations for the two samples, although the use of either would be wasteful since both estimate σ. Since we want to obtain the best estimate available, it seems reasonable to use an estimator that pools the information from both samples. This **pooled estimator of σ^2**, using the sums of squares of the deviations about the mean for both samples, is given in the following box.

POOLED ESTIMATOR OF σ^2

$$s^2 = \frac{\displaystyle\sum_{i=1}^{n_1}(x_i - \bar{x}_1)^2 + \sum_{i=1}^{n_2}(x_i - \bar{x}_2)^2}{n_1 + n_2 - 2}$$

Note that the pooled estimator may also be written as

$$s^2 = \frac{(n_1 - 1)s_1^2 + (n_2 - 1)s_2^2}{n_1 + n_2 - 2}$$

because

$$s_1^2 = \frac{\displaystyle\sum_{i=1}^{n_1}(x_i - \bar{x}_1)^2}{n_1 - 1} \quad \text{and} \quad s_2^2 = \frac{\displaystyle\sum_{i=1}^{n_2}(x_i - \bar{x}_2)^2}{n_2 - 1}$$

As for the single sample, the denominator in the formula for s^2, $(n_1 + n_2 - 2)$, is called the **number of degrees of freedom** associated with s^2. It can be proved either mathematically or experimentally that the expected value of the pooled estimator s^2 is equal to σ^2 and therefore that s^2 is an unbiased estimator of the common population variance. Finally, recall that the divisors of the sums of the squares of deviations in s_1^2 and s_2^2, $(n_1 - 1)$ and $(n_2 - 1)$, respectively, are the numbers of degrees of freedom associated with these two independent estimators of σ^2. Note that an estimator that uses the pooled information for both samples possesses $(n_1 - 1) + (n_2 - 1)$, or $(n_1 + n_2 - 2)$, degrees of freedom.

Summarizing, the small-sample statistical test for the difference between two means is as given in the next box.

TEST OF AN HYPOTHESIS CONCERNING THE DIFFERENCE BETWEEN TWO MEANS

(1) *Null Hypothesis:* $H_0 : (\mu_1 - \mu_2) = D_0$, where D_0 is some specified difference that you want to test. For many tests you will want to hypothesize that there is no difference between μ_1 and μ_2—that is, $D_0 = 0$.

(2) *Alternative Hypothesis:*

One-Tailed Test

$H_a : (\mu_1 - \mu_2) > D_0$
[or $H_a : (\mu_1 - \mu_2) < D_0$]

Two-Tailed Test

$H_a : (\mu_1 - \mu_2) \neq D_0$

(3) *Test Statistic:* $t = \dfrac{(\bar{x}_1 - \bar{x}_2) - D_0}{s\sqrt{\dfrac{1}{n_1} + \dfrac{1}{n_2}}}$

where

$$s^2 = \frac{\sum\limits_{i=1}^{n_1}(x_i - \bar{x}_1)^2 + \sum\limits_{i=1}^{n_2}(x_i - \bar{x}_2)^2}{n_1 + n_2 - 2}$$

(4) *Rejection Region:*

One-Tailed Test

$t > t_\alpha$
[or $t < -t_\alpha$ when the alternative hypothesis is $H_a : (\mu_1 - \mu_2) < D_0$]

Two-Tailed Test

$t > t_{\alpha/2}$
(or $t < -t_{\alpha/2}$)

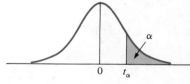
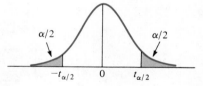

The critical values of t, t_α and $t_{\alpha/2}$, will be based upon $(n_1 + n_2 - 2)$ degrees of freedom. The tabulated values can be found in Table 5 in the Appendix.

Assumption: The samples were randomly and independently selected from normally distributed populations. The variances of the populations, σ_1^2 and σ_2^2, are equal.

EXAMPLE 8.6   An assembly operation in a manufacturing plant requires approximately a one-month training period for a new employee to reach maximum efficiency. A new method of training was suggested and a test was conducted to compare the new method with the standard procedure. Two groups of nine new employees were trained for a period of three weeks, one group using the new method and the other following standard training procedure. The length of time in minutes required for each employee to assemble the device was recorded at the end of the three-week period. These measurements appear in

TABLE 8.3   Assembly Time Data for Example 8.6

Standard Procedure	New Procedure
32	35
37	31
35	29
28	25
41	34
44	40
35	27
31	32
34	31

Table 8.3. Do the data present sufficient evidence to indicate that the mean time to assemble at the end of a three-week training period is less for the new training procedure?

SOLUTION   Let μ_1 and μ_2 equal the mean time to assemble for the standard and the new assembly procedures, respectively. Also, assume that the variability in mean time to assemble is essentially a function of individual differences and that the variability for the two populations of measurements will be approximately equal.

The sample means and sums of squares of deviations are

$$\bar{x}_1 = 35.22 \qquad \sum_{i=1}^{9}(x_i - \bar{x}_1)^2 = 195.56$$

$$\bar{x}_2 = 31.56 \qquad \sum_{i=1}^{9}(x_i - \bar{x}_2)^2 = 160.22$$

Then the pooled estimate of the common variance is

$$s^2 = \frac{\sum_{i=1}^{9}(x_i - \bar{x}_1)^2 + \sum_{i=1}^{9}(x_i - \bar{x}_2)^2}{n_1 + n_2 - 2} = \frac{195.56 + 160.22}{9 + 9 - 2} = 22.24$$

and the standard deviation is $s = \sqrt{22.24} = 4.72$.

The null hypothesis to be tested is

$$H_0 : (\mu_1 - \mu_2) = 0$$

Suppose that we are concerned only with detecting whether the new method reduces the assembly time; therefore the alternative hypothesis is

$$H_a : (\mu_1 - \mu_2) > 0$$

This alternative hypothesis implies that we should use a one-tailed statistical test and that the rejection region for the test will be located in the upper tail of the t distribution. Referring to Table 5 in the Appendix, we note that the critical value of t for $\alpha = .05$ and $(n_1 + n_2 - 2) = 16$ degrees of freedom is 1.746. Therefore, we will reject H_0 when $t > 1.746$ (see Figure 8.6).

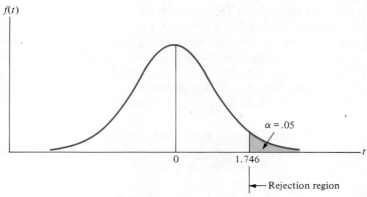

FIGURE 8.6   Rejection Region for Example 8.6

The calculated value of the test statistic is

$$t = \frac{\bar{x}_1 - \bar{x}_2}{s\sqrt{\dfrac{1}{n_1} + \dfrac{1}{n_2}}} = \frac{35.22 - 31.56}{4.72\sqrt{\dfrac{1}{9} + \dfrac{1}{9}}} = 1.64$$

Comparing this value with the critical value, $t = 1.746$, we can see that the calculated value does not fall in the rejection region. Therefore, we conclude that there is insufficient evidence to indicate that the new method of training is superior, at the .05 level of significance. As we will show in Example 8.8, the variability of the data is sufficient to mask a difference in μ_1 and μ_2, if in fact it exists. Consequently, the plant manager may want to increase the number of employees in each sample and repeat the test. ∎

EXAMPLE 8.7   Find the p-value that would be reported for the statistical test in Example 8.6.

SOLUTION   The observed value of t for this one-tailed test was $t = 1.64$. Therefore, the p-value for the test would be the probability that $t > 1.64$ (see Figure 8.7). Since we cannot obtain

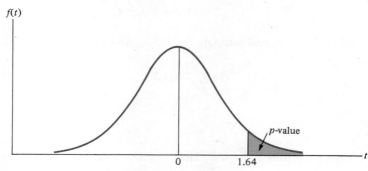

FIGURE 8.7 p-Value for the Test in Example 8.6

this probability from Table 5 in the Appendix, we would report the p-value for the test as the smallest tabulated value for α that leads to the rejection of H_0. Consulting the row in Table 5 corresponding to 16 degrees of freedom, we see that we would reject H_0 for this one-tailed test if t were greater than $t_{.10} = 1.337$ but not for $t_{.05} = 1.746$. Therefore, the p-value for the test would be reported as $p < .10$. Because of the limitations of most t tables, a reader of this reported value would realize that the exact p-value for the test was less than or equal to .10 but larger than .05.   ■

The small-sample confidence interval for $(\mu_1 - \mu_2)$ is based on the same assumption as was the statistical test procedure. This confidence interval, with confidence coefficient $(1 - \alpha)$, is given by the formula in the next box.

A $(1 - \alpha)100\%$ SMALL-SAMPLE CONFIDENCE INTERVAL FOR $(\mu_1 - \mu_2)$

$$(\bar{x}_1 - \bar{x}_2) \pm t_{\alpha/2} s \sqrt{\frac{1}{n_1} + \frac{1}{n_2}}$$

where s is obtained from the pooled estimate of σ^2.

Assumption: The samples were randomly and independently selected from normally distributed populations. The variances of the populations, σ_1^2 and σ_2^2, are equal.

Note the similarity in the procedures for constructing the confidence intervals for a single mean (Section 8.3) and the difference between two means. In both cases the interval is constructed by using the appropriate point estimator and then adding and subtracting an amount equal to $t_{\alpha/2}$ times the *estimated* standard deviation of the point estimator.

EXAMPLE 8.8   Find an interval estimate for $(\mu_1 - \mu_2)$ of Example 8.6, using a confidence coefficient equal to .95.

SOLUTION   Substituting into the formula

$$(\bar{x}_1 - \bar{x}_2) \pm t_{\alpha/2} s \sqrt{\frac{1}{n_1} + \frac{1}{n_2}}$$

we find the interval estimate (or 95% confidence interval) to be

$$(35.22 - 31.56) \pm (2.120)(4.72) \sqrt{\frac{1}{9} + \frac{1}{9}}$$

or

$$3.66 \pm 4.72$$

Thus we estimate the difference in mean time to assemble, $(\mu_1 - \mu_2)$, to fall in the interval -1.06 to 8.38. Note that the interval width is considerable and that it would seem advisable to increase the size of the samples and reestimate. ∎

Before concluding our discussion, we will comment on the two assumptions upon which our inferential procedures are based. Moderate departures from the assumption that the populations possess a normal probability distribution do not seriously affect the properties of the test (the values of α and β) or the confidence coefficient for the corresponding confidence interval. On the other hand, the population variances should be nearly equal in order that the aforementioned procedures be valid. A procedure will be presented in Section 8.7 for testing an hypothesis concerning the equality of two population variances.

If there is reason to believe that the population variances are unequal or that the normality assumptions have been violated, you can test for a shift in location of two population distributions by using the nonparametric Mann-Whitney U test of Chapter 15. The test procedure, which requires fewer assumptions concerning the nature of the population probability distributions, is almost as sensitive in detecting a difference in population means when the conditions necessary for the t test are satisfied. It may be more sensitive when the assumptions are not satisfied.

EXERCISES

BASIC TECHNIQUES

8.24 Give the number of degrees of freedom for s^2, the pooled estimator of σ^2, for the following sample sizes.

(a) $n_1 = 16, n_2 = 8$ (b) $n_1 = 10, n_2 = 12$ (c) $n_1 = 15, n_2 = 3$

8.25 Calculate s^2, the pooled estimator for σ^2, for the following sample data.

(a) $n_1 = 10, n_2 = 4, s_1^2 = 3.4, s_2^2 = 4.9$ (b) $n_1 = 12, n_2 = 21, s_1^2 = 18, s_2^2 = 23$

8.26 You are given the following two independent random samples:

Sample 1	12	3	8	5	
Sample 2	14	7	7	9	6

Calculate s^2, the pooled estimator of σ^2.

8.27 Refer to Exercise 8.26. Test $H_0 : \mu_1 - \mu_2 = 0$ against $H_a : \mu_1 - \mu_2 > 0$ for $\alpha = .05$. State your conclusions.

8.28 Find a 90% confidence interval for $(\mu_1 - \mu_2)$ in Exercise 8.26.

8.29 Independent random samples of $n_1 = 16$ and $n_2 = 13$ observations were selected from two normal populations with equal variances. The sample means and variances are shown in Table 8.4.

TABLE 8.4   Sample Data for Exercise 8.29

	Population	
	1	2
Sample size	16	13
Sample mean	34.6	32.2
Sample variance	4.8	5.9

(a) Suppose that you wish to detect a difference between the population means. State the null and alternative hypotheses that you would use for the test.
(b) Find the rejection region for the test in part (a) for $\alpha = .10$.
(c) Find the value of the test statistic.
(d) Find the approximate observed significance level for the test.
(e) Conduct the test and state your conclusions.

8.30 Refer to Exercise 8.29. Find a 90% confidence interval for $(\mu_1 - \mu_2)$.

8.31 Independent random samples of $n_1 = n_2 = 4$ observations were selected from two normal populations with equal variances. The data are shown below.

Sample 1	12	9	14	14
Sample 2	11	9	10	8

(a) Suppose that you wish to determine whether μ_1 is larger than μ_2. Give the alternative hypothesis for the test.
(b) State H_0.
(c) Give the rejection region for the test for $\alpha = .10$.
(d) Conduct the test and state your conclusions.
(e) Give the approximate p-value for the test, and interpret it.

APPLICATIONS

8.32 An experiment was conducted to compare the mean lengths of time required for two bank employees, A and B, to complete the paperwork for new customer personal checking accounts. Ten customers were randomly assigned to each employee, and the length of servicing time was recorded in minutes for each customer. The means and variances for the two samples are given in the accompanying table.

Employee A	Employee B
$\bar{x}_1 = 22.2$	$\bar{x}_2 = 28.5$
$s_1^2 = 16.36$	$s_2^2 = 18.92$

(a) Do the data provide sufficient evidence to indicate a difference in mean times required to complete the paperwork necessary for a new customer checking account? Test using $\alpha = .10$.
(b) Find the approximate observed significance level for the test, and interpret its value.

8.33 Refer to Exercise 8.32. Find a 95% confidence interval for the difference in mean servicing times.

8.34 Refer to Exercise 8.32. Suppose that you wanted to estimate the difference in mean servicing times correct to within 1 minute with probability approximately equal to .95. Approximately how large a sample would be required for each bank employee (assume that the sample sizes will be equal)? (*Hint:* To solve, use the method of Section 6.9.)

 8.35 An automobile manufacturer recently decided that the primary factor inhibiting sales was not the automobile or its service but the sales approach employed by its salespersons. In a test of this theory 16 salespersons in a large dealership were randomly assigned to two groups of 8 salespersons each. One group employed a hard-sell approach to customers for a one-month period; the other employed a slower-paced, soft-sell approach over the same period of time. The means and standard deviations of the dollar sales per salesperson per month for the two groups are shown in Table 8.5.

TABLE 8.5   Sample Data for Exercise 8.35

Sample Data	Hard Sell	Soft Sell
Sample size	8	8
Sample mean	106,200	111,900
Sample standard deviation	24,400	28,600

(a) Do the data provide sufficient evidence to indicate a difference in the mean level of sales for the two sales approaches? Test using $\alpha = .10$.

(b) Give the approximate p-value for the test, and interpret it.

(c) Find a 90% confidence interval for the difference in the mean level of sales.

 8.36 Ronald C. Curhan (Boston University), Walter J. Salmon, and Robert D. Buzzell (Harvard University) conducted a study of supermarket sales and profitability in the sale of health and beauty aids (HBA) and small-ticket general merchandise (GM). Fifteen supermarket firms were included in the study; 5 used service merchandisers (rack jobbers) to supply their store, and 10 warehoused and supplied the individual stores themselves (direct buyers). A small portion of the data collected in this study was reconstructed from a graph presented in the report and appears in Table 8.6. It gives the (approximate) sales (in dollars) per linear foot of floor space for the 15 supermarket firms. Do these data present sufficient evidence to indicate a difference in mean sales

TABLE 8.6   Dollar Sales Data for Exercise 8.36

Service Merchandisers ($n = 5$)	Direct Buying (In-House Warehousing) ($n = 10$)	
6100	4100	2000
2950	3500	1800
3800	3500	900
2200	2700	1800
2400	2400	1900

Source: Data reconstructed from a graph in R. C. Curhan, W. J. Salmon, and R. D. Buzzell, "Sales and Profitability of Health and Beauty Aids and General Merchandise in Supermarkets," *Journal of Retailing,* Vol. 59, No. 1, 1983.

per foot (in dollars) of HBA products between the two types of supermarket firms, those serviced by rack jobbers and those employing direct buying? Test using $\alpha = .10$.

8.37 Refer to Exercise 8.36. Find a 90% confidence interval for the difference in mean sales per linear foot for the two types of supermarket firms.

8.38 How do corporate executives and stock market analysts compare in their forecasts of increase in the gross national product (GNP) for the next year? Forecasts (in percentages) from five randomly selected corporate executives and five market analysts are shown below.

Corporate Executives	3.4	2.8	3.9	3.7	3.4
Market Analysts	3.3	3.9	3.4	3.8	4.0

(a) Do the data provide sufficient evidence to indicate a difference in the mean forecast GNP increase between corporate executives and stock market analysts? Test using $\alpha = .10$.

(b) Give the approximate p-value for the test, and interpret it.

(c) Find a 90% confidence interval for the difference in mean GNP forecast between corporate executives and stock market analysts. Interpret the interval.

A PAIRED-DIFFERENCE TEST

8.5

A manufacturer wanted to compare the wearing qualities of two different types of automobile tires, A and B. In the comparison a tire of type A and one of type B were randomly assigned and mounted on the rear wheels of each of five automobiles. The automobiles were then operated for a specified number of miles, and the amount of wear was recorded for each tire. These measurements appear in Table 8.7. Do the data present sufficient evidence to indicate a difference in the average wear for the two tire types?

TABLE 8.7   Tire Wear Data

Automobile	Tire A	Tire B
1	10.6	10.2
2	9.8	9.4
3	12.3	11.8
4	9.7	9.1
5	8.8	8.3
	$\bar{x}_1 = 10.24$	$\bar{x}_2 = 9.76$

Analyzing the data, we note that the difference between the two sample means is $(\bar{x}_1 - \bar{x}_2) = .48$, a rather small quantity considering the variability of the data and the small number of measurements involved. At first glance it would seem that there is little evidence to indicate a difference between the population means, a conjecture that we may check by the method outlined in Section 8.4.

The pooled estimate of the common variance σ^2 is

$$s^2 = \frac{\sum\limits_{i=1}^{n_1}(x_i - \bar{x}_1)^2 + \sum\limits_{i=1}^{n_2}(x_i - \bar{x}_2)^2}{n_1 + n_2 - 2}$$

$$= \frac{6.932 + 7.052}{5 + 5 - 2} = 1.748$$

and

$$s = 1.32$$

The calculated value of t used to test the hypothesis that $\mu_1 = \mu_2$ is

$$t = \frac{\bar{x}_1 - \bar{x}_2}{s\sqrt{\dfrac{1}{n_1} + \dfrac{1}{n_2}}}$$

$$= \frac{10.24 - 9.76}{1.32\sqrt{\dfrac{1}{5} + \dfrac{1}{5}}}$$

$$= .57$$

a value that is not nearly large enough to reject the hypothesis that $\mu_1 = \mu_2$. The corresponding 95% confidence interval is

$$(\bar{x}_1 - \bar{x}_2) \pm t_{\alpha/2}s\sqrt{\frac{1}{n_1} + \frac{1}{n_2}}$$

$$= (10.24 - 9.76) \pm (2.306)(1.32)\sqrt{\frac{1}{5} + \frac{1}{5}}$$

or -1.45 to 2.41. Note that the interval is quite wide, considering the small difference between the sample means.

A second glance at the data reveals a marked inconsistency with this conclusion. We note that the wear measurement for the type A tire is larger than the corresponding value for type B for *each* of the five automobiles. These differences, recorded as $d = A - B$, are as follows:

Automobile	$d = A - B$
1	.4
2	.4
3	.5
4	.6
5	.5

$$\bar{d} = .48$$

Suppose that we were to use x, the number of times that A is larger than B, as a test statistic. Then the probability that A would be larger than B on a given automobile, assuming no difference between the wearing quality of the tires, would be $p = 1/2$, and x would be a binomial random variable. If the null hypothesis were true, the expected value of x would be $\mu = np = 5(1/2) = 2.5$.

If we choose the most extreme values of x, $x = 0$ and $x = 5$, as the rejection region for a two-tailed test, then $\alpha = p(0) + p(5) = 2(1/2)^5 = 1/16$. We would then reject $H_0 : \mu_1 = \mu_2$ with a probability of type I error equal to $\alpha = 1/16$. Certainly, this is evidence to indicate that a difference exists in the mean wear of the two tire types.

You will note that we have used two different statistical tests to test the same hypothesis. Is it not peculiar that the t test, which uses more information (the actual sample measurements) than the binomial test, fails to supply sufficient evidence for rejection of the hypothesis $\mu_1 = \mu_2$?

There is an explanation for this seeming inconsistency. The t test described in Section 8.4 is *not* the proper statistical test to be used for our example. The statistical test procedure in Section 8.4 required that the two samples be *independent* and random. Certainly, the independence requirement was violated by the manner in which the experiment was conducted. The (pair of) measurements, an A and B, for a particular automobile are definitely related. A glance at the data will show that the readings are of approximately the same magnitude for a particular automobile but vary from one automobile to another. This, of course, is exactly what we might expect. Tire wear, in a large part, is determined by driver habits, the balance of the wheels, and the road surface. Since each automobile had a different driver, we might expect a large amount of variability in the data from one automobile to another.

The familiarity that we have gained with interval estimation has shown that the width of the large- and small-sample confidence intervals will depend on the magnitude of the standard deviation of the point estimator of the parameter. The smaller its value, the better the estimate and the more likely that the test statistic will reject the null hypothesis if it is, in fact, false. Knowledge of this phenomenon was used in the **design** of the tire wear experiment.

The experimenter would realize that the wear measurements would vary greatly from auto to auto and that this variability could not be separated from the data if the tires were assigned to the ten wheels in a *random* manner. (A random assignment of the tires would have implied that the data be analyzed according to the procedure of Section 8.4.) Instead, a comparison of the wear between the tire types A and B made on each automobile resulted in the five difference measurements. This design, called a **paired-difference experiment**, eliminates the effect of the car-to-car variability and yields more information on the mean difference in the wearing quality for the two tire types.

The proper analysis of the data would use the five difference measurements to test the hypothesis that the average difference μ_d is equal to zero, or equivalently, to test the null hypothesis $H_0 : \mu_d = \mu_1 - \mu_2 = 0$ against the alternative hypothesis $\mu_d = \mu_1 - \mu_2 \neq 0$. The procedure for this **paired-difference test** is given in the following box.

PAIRED-DIFFERENCE TEST FOR $(\mu_1 - \mu_2) = \mu_d$

(1) *Null Hypothesis:* $H_0 : \mu_d = 0$.

(2) *Alternative Hypothesis:*

One-Tailed Test	**Two-Tailed Test**
$H_a : \mu_d > 0$	$H_a : \mu_d \neq 0$
(or $H_a : \mu_d < 0$)	

(3) *Test Statistic:* $t = \dfrac{\bar{d} - 0}{s_d/\sqrt{n}} = \dfrac{\bar{d}}{s_d/\sqrt{n}}$

where $n =$ number of paired differences

$$s_d = \sqrt{\frac{\sum_{i=1}^{n}(d_i - \bar{d})^2}{n - 1}}$$

(4) *Rejection Region:*

One-Tailed Test	**Two-Tailed Test**
$t > t_\alpha$	$t > t_{\alpha/2}$ or $t < -t_{\alpha/2}$
(or $t < -t_\alpha$ when the alternative hypothesis is $H_a : \mu_d < 0$)	

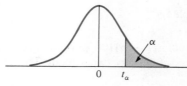
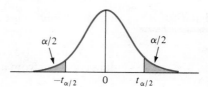

The critical values of t, t_α and $t_{\alpha/2}$, are based on $(n - 1)$ degrees of freedom. These tabulated critical values are given in Table 5 in the Appendix.

Assumptions: The n paired differences are randomly selected from a normally distributed population.

EXAMPLE 8.9   Do the data in Table 8.7 provide sufficient evidence to indicate a difference in mean wear for tire types A and B? Test using $\alpha = .05$.

SOLUTION   You can verify that the average and standard deviation of the five difference measurements are

$$\bar{d} = .48 \qquad \text{and} \qquad s_d = .0837$$

Then

$$H_0 : \mu_d = 0 \qquad \text{and} \qquad H_a : \mu_d \neq 0$$

and

$$t = \frac{\bar{d} - 0}{s_d/\sqrt{n}} = \frac{.48}{.0837/\sqrt{5}} = 12.8$$

The critical value of t for a two-tailed statistical test, $\alpha = .05$ and four degrees of freedom, is 2.776 (see Figure 8.8). Since the observed value of $t = 12.8$ falls far out into the rejection region, there is ample evidence of a difference in the mean amount of wear for tire types A and B.

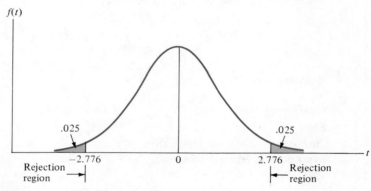

FIGURE 8.8   Rejection Region for Example 8.9

You can also construct a $(1 - \alpha)100\%$ confidence interval for $(\mu_1 - \mu_2)$ based on data collected from a paired-difference experiment. The procedure is shown in the box.

$(1 - \alpha)100\%$ **SMALL-SAMPLE CONFIDENCE INTERVAL FOR**
$(\mu_1 - \mu_2) = \mu_d$ **(BASED ON A PAIRED-DIFFERENCE EXPERIMENT)**

$$\bar{d} \pm t_{\alpha/2} \frac{s_d}{\sqrt{n}}$$

where n = number of paired differences

and

$$s_d = \sqrt{\frac{\sum_{i=1}^{n} (d_i - \bar{d})^2}{n - 1}}$$

Assumptions: The n paired differences are randomly selected from a normally distributed population.

EXAMPLE 8.10   Find a 95% confidence interval for $(\mu_1 - \mu_2) = \mu_d$ (Example 8.9).

SOLUTION   A 95% confidence interval for the difference between the mean wear is

$$\bar{d} \pm \frac{t_{\alpha/2} s_d}{\sqrt{n}} = .48 \pm (2.776)\frac{.0837}{\sqrt{5}}$$

or $.48 \pm .10$ ∎

The statistical design of the tire experiment represents a simple example of a randomized block design and the resulting statistical test is often called a paired-difference test. **Note that the pairing occurred when the experiment was planned and** *not* **after the data were collected.** Comparisons of tire wear were made within relatively homogeneous blocks (automobiles), with the tire types randomly assigned to the two automobile wheels.

An indication of the gain in the amount of information obtained by **blocking** the tire experiment can be observed by comparing the calculated confidence interval for the unpaired (and incorrect) analysis with the interval obtained for the paired-difference analysis. The confidence interval for $(\mu_1 - \mu_2)$ that might have been calculated, had the tires been randomly assigned to the ten wheels (unpaired), is unknown but likely would have been of the same magnitude as the interval -1.45 to 2.41 calculated by analyzing the observed data in an unpaired manner. Pairing the tire types on the automobiles (blocking) and the resulting analysis of the differences produced the interval estimate $.38$ to $.58$. Note the difference in the width of the intervals indicating the very sizable increase in information obtained by blocking in this experiment.

While blocking proved to be very beneficial in the tire experiment, this may not always be the case. The degrees of freedom available for estimating σ^2 are less for the paired than for the corresponding unpaired experiment. If there were actually no difference between the blocks, the reduction in the degrees of freedom would produce a moderate increase in the $t_{\alpha/2}$ employed in the confidence interval and thereby would increase the width of the interval. This, of course, did not occur in the tire experiment because the large reduction in the standard deviation of $\bar{d}$ more than compensated for the loss in degrees of freedom.

Before concluding, we want to reemphasize a point. Once you have used a paired design for an experiment, you no longer have the option of using the unpaired analysis of Section 8.4. The assumptions upon which that test are based have been violated. Your only alternative is to use the correct method of analysis, the paired-difference test (and associated confidence interval) of this section.

EXERCISES

BASIC TECHNIQUES

8.39 A paired-difference experiment was conducted, using $n = 10$ pairs of observations. Test the null hypothesis $H_0 : \mu_1 - \mu_2 = 0$ against $H_a : \mu_1 - \mu_2 \neq 0$ for $\alpha = .05$, $\bar{d} = .3$, and $s_d^2 = .16$. Give the approximate p-value for the test.

8.40 Find a 95% confidence interval for $(\mu_1 - \mu_2)$ in Exercise 8.39.

8.41 How many pairs of observations would you need if you wished to estimate $(\mu_1 - \mu_2)$ in Exercise 8.39 correct to within .1 with probability equal to .95?

8.42 For a paired-difference experiment consisting of $n = 18$ pairs, $\bar{d} = 5.7$ and $s_d^2 = 256$. We wish to detect $\mu_d > 0$.

(a) Give the null and alternative hypotheses for the test.

(b) Conduct the test and state your conclusions.

8.43 For a paired-difference experiment consisting of $n = 12$ pairs of observations, $\bar{d} = .13$ and $s_d^2 = .001$. Find a 90% confidence interval for $(\mu_1 - \mu_2)$.

8.44 A paired-difference experiment was conducted to compare the means of two populations. The data are shown in Table 8.8.

TABLE 8.8   Paired-Difference Data for Exercise 8.44

| | \multicolumn{5}{c}{Pairs} | | | | |
Population	1	2	3	4	5
1	1.3	1.6	1.1	1.4	1.7
2	1.2	1.5	1.1	1.2	1.8

(a) Do the data provide sufficient evidence to indicate that μ_1 differs from μ_2? Test using $\alpha = .05$.

(b) Find the approximate observed significance level for the test, and interpret its value.

(c) Find a 95% confidence interval for $(\mu_1 - \mu_2)$. Compare your interpretation of the confidence interval with your test results in part (a).

(d) What assumptions must you make in order that your inferences be valid?

8.45 A paired-difference experiment was conducted to compare the means of two populations. The data are shown in Table 8.9.

TABLE 8.9   Paired-Difference Data for Exercise 8.45

| | \multicolumn{7}{c}{Pairs} | | | | | | |
Population	1	2	3	4	5	6	7
1	8.9	8.1	9.3	7.7	10.4	8.3	7.4
2	8.8	7.4	9.0	7.8	9.9	8.1	6.9

(a) Do the data provide sufficient evidence to indicate that μ_1 differs from μ_2? Test using $\alpha = .01$.

(b) Find the approximate observed significance level for the test, and interpret its value.

(c) Find a 95% confidence interval for $(\mu_1 - \mu_2)$. Compare your interpretation of the confidence interval with your test results in part (a).

(d) What assumptions must you make in order that your inferences be valid?

APPLICATIONS

 8.46 In response to a complaint that a particular tax assessor (A) was biased, an experiment was conducted to compare the assessor named in the complaint with another tax assessor (B) from the same office. Eight properties were selected, and each was assessed by both assessors. The assessments (in thousands) are shown in Table 8.10.

TABLE 8.10   Assessment Data for Exercise 8.46

Property	Assessor A	Assessor B
1	36.3	35.1
2	48.4	46.8
3	40.2	37.3
4	54.7	50.6
5	28.7	29.1
6	42.8	41.0
7	36.1	35.3
8	39.0	39.1

(a) Do the data provide sufficient evidence to indicate that assessor A tends to give higher assessments than assessor B? Test with $\alpha = .05$.

(b) Estimate the difference in mean assessments for the two assessors.

(c) What assumptions must you make to render the inferences in (a) and (b) valid?

(d) Suppose that assessor A had been compared with a more stable standard, say the average $\bar{x}$ of the assessments given by four assessors selected from the tax office. Thus each property would be assessed by A and also by each of the four other assessors, and $x_A - \bar{x}$ would be calculated. If the test in part (a) is valid, could you use the paired-difference t test to test the hypothesis that the bias, the mean difference between A's assessments and the mean of the assessments of the four assessors, is equal to 0? Explain.

8.47 Persons submitting computing jobs to a computer center are usually required to estimate the amount of computer time required to complete the job. This time is measured in CPUs: the amount of time that a job will occupy a part of the computer's central processing unit's memory. A computer center decided to perform a comparison of the estimated versus actual CPU time for a particular customer. The corresponding times were available for 11 jobs. The sample data are shown in Table 8.11.

TABLE 8.11   CPU Time Data for Exercise 8.47

CPU Time (Minutes)	Job Number										
	1	2	3	4	5	6	7	8	9	10	11
Estimated	.50	1.40	.95	.45	.75	1.20	1.60	2.6	1.30	.85	.60
Actual	.46	1.52	.99	.53	.71	1.31	1.49	2.9	1.41	.83	.74

(a) Why would you expect these pairs of data to be dependent?

(b) Do the data provide sufficient evidence to indicate that, "on the average," the customer tends to underestimate CPU time required for computing jobs? Test using $\alpha = .10$.

(c) Find the observed significance level for the test, and interpret its value.

(d) Find a 90% confidence interval for the difference in mean estimated CPU time versus mean actual CPU time.

8.48 A recent drop in the value of the dollar versus foreign currencies is expected to increase the value of U.S. exports. A comparison of the current year's versus last year's shipments (in thousands of dollars) for each of six U.S. exporters is shown in Table 8.12. Assume that exporters represent a random sample selected from among all U.S. exporters.

TABLE 8.12   Export Shipment Data for Exercise 8.48

	Year	
Exporter	Current	Last
1	4.81	4.27
2	5.03	5.97
3	2.38	2.61
4	4.26	3.96
5	5.14	4.86
6	3.93	3.17

(a) Do the data provide sufficient evidence to indicate an increase in the mean number of cases exported from last year to the current year? Test using $\alpha = .05$.

(b) Find the approximate p-value for the test.

(c) Find a 95% confidence interval for the mean increase in the number of cases shipped.

 8.49 Attempting to motivate customers to make early payment of bills, the manager of a consulting company offered customers an incentive to make early payment, a 2% discount for bills paid within 30 days of issuance of the bill. In order to assess the effect of the new policy on time to payment, the manager randomly sampled 15 accounts and recorded the number of days to payment for the last bill issued under the old system and the first bill issued under the incentive system. The data, in days, are shown in Table 8.13.

TABLE 8.13   Days-to-Payment Data for Exercise 8.49

Bill	Company														
	1	2	3	4	5	6	7	8	9	10	11	12	13	14	15
Old System	92	88	65	85	95	64	65	62	90	89	65	75	84	90	80
Incentive	28	30	29	85	29	28	26	29	88	30	70	30	27	92	29

(a) Find a 95% confidence interval for the decrease in the mean time to payment per account after the incentive was introduced. Interpret the interval.

(b) Find a one-sided 95% lower confidence interval for the decrease in mean time to payment, and interpret the interval in practical terms.

 8.50 When the Securities and Exchange Commission (SEC) believes that investors need additional information on a corporation's financial affairs, it issues a requirement for the disclosure of the pertinent information. Byung T. Ro of Purdue University conducted a study to determine whether SEC requirements concerning the disclosure of replacement cost accounting data produced an increase in the volume of transactions in a corporation's stock. To conduct his study, Ro matched 73 pairs of corporations. One of each pair made the required SEC disclosure on replacement cost data; the other, the control, did not. Change in the volume of transactions was measured for each pair during the week in which an SEC ruling or an SEC Accounting Bulletin was issued that pertained to replacement costs. The paired t values for comparing the mean changes in volume of transactions for reporting versus nonreporting firms for nine of these "critical weeks" are shown next.

Critical Week	1	2	3	4	5	6	7	8	9
Paired t	.340	.731	.866	$-.255$	-1.740	.047	-2.277	$-.822$	$-.881$

Source: Data from Byung T. Ro, "The Disclosure of Replacement Cost Accounting Data and Its Effect on Transaction Volumes," *Accounting Review,* Vol. LVI, No. 1, 1981.

(a) How many degrees of freedom are associated with each of these nine paired-difference t tests?

(b) Do the data provide sufficient evidence to indicate an increase in the mean change in volume of transactions between reporting and nonreporting corporations for any of the critical weeks? Explain.

(c) Suppose that you were to conduct nine independent, paired-difference t tests, each with $\alpha = .05$, and suppose that H_0 is true for all nine tests—that is, that no difference exists in the pairs of population means. Is the probability of rejecting H_0—that is, of committing a type I error—for at least one of the tests larger than .05? Explain.

MKTG 8.51 Does background music affect the behavior of supermarket shoppers? An experiment to answer this question was conducted in a supermarket during the relatively stable summer shopping months. Two days were selected in midweek. One day was randomly assigned to receive no background music. During the second day slow-tempo background music was played. The daily sales (in dollars) for 12 weeks are shown in Table 8.14.

TABLE 8.14   Daily Sales Data for Exercise 8.51

Music	Week											
	1	2	3	4	5	6	7	8	9	10	11	12
None	$14,172	15,485	13,922	12,204	15,501	15,106	14,608	13,946	15,002	14,670	16,202	13,286
Slow tempo	15,917	16,110	13,818	14,709	13,982	16,416	14,727	14,823	14,825	15,949	15,488	14,955

(a) Do the data provide sufficient evidence to indicate a difference in mean daily sales for days when no background music was played versus days when slow-tempo music was played? Test using $\alpha = .10$.

(b) Find a 90% confidence interval for the difference in mean daily sales for no-music days versus slow-tempo days.

8.6   INFERENCES CONCERNING A POPULATION VARIANCE

We have seen in the preceding sections that an estimate of the population variance σ^2 is fundamental to procedures for making inferences about population means. Moreover, there are many practical situations where σ^2 is the primary objective of an experimental investigation; thus it may assume a position of far greater importance than that of the population mean.

Scientific measuring instruments must provide unbiased readings with a very small error of measurement. An aircraft altimeter that measured the correct altitude on the *average* would be of little value if the standard deviation of the error of measurement were 5000 feet. Indeed, bias in a measuring instrument can often be corrected, but the precision of the instrument, measured by the standard deviation of the error of measurement, is usually a function of the design of the instrument itself and cannot be controlled.

Machined parts in a manufacturing process must be produced with minimum variability in order to reduce out-of-size and hence defective products. And, in general, it is desirable to maintain a minimum variance in the measurements of the quality characteristics of an industrial product in order to achieve process control and thereby minimize the percentage of poor-quality product.

The sample variance

$$s^2 = \frac{\sum_{i=1}^{n} (x_i - \bar{x})^2}{n - 1}$$

is an unbiased estimator of the population variance σ^2. Thus the distribution of sample variances generated by repeated sampling will have a probability distribution that commences at $s^2 = 0$ (since s^2 cannot be negative) with a mean equal to σ^2. Unlike the distribution of $\bar{x}$, the distribution of s^2 is nonsymmetrical, the exact form being dependent upon the probability distribution of the population.

For the methodology that follows, we will assume that the sample is drawn from a normal population and that s^2 is based on a random sample of n measurements. Or using the terminology of Section 8.2, we say that s^2 possesses $(n - 1)$ degrees of freedom.

The next and obvious step is to consider the distribution of s^2 in repeated sampling from a specified normal distribution—one with a specific mean and variance—and to tabulate the critical value of s^2 for some of the commonly used tail areas. If this is done, we will find that the sampling distribution of s^2 is independent of the population mean μ but possesses a distribution for each sample size and each value of σ^2. This task is quite laborious, but fortunately it can be simplified by *standardizing*, as was done by using z in the normal tables.

The quantity

$$\chi^2 = \frac{(n - 1)s^2}{\sigma^2}$$

called a **chi-square variable** by statisticians (χ is the Greek letter chi), admirably suits our purposes. Its distribution in repeated sampling is called, as we might suspect, a **chi-square probability distribution**. The equation of the density function for the chi-square distribution is well known to statisticians who have tabulated critical values corresponding to various tail areas of the distribution. These values are presented in Table 6 in the Appendix.

The shape of the chi-square distribution, like that of the t distribution, will vary with the sample size or, equivalently, with the degrees of freedom associated with s^2. Thus Table 6 in the Appendix is constructed in exactly the same manner as the t table, with the degrees of freedom shown in the first and last columns. A partial reproduction of Table 6 in the Appendix is shown in Table 8.15. The symbol χ_α^2 indicates that the

TABLE 8.15   Format of the Chi-square Table, Table 6 in the Appendix

d.f.	$\chi^2_{0.995} \cdots$	$\chi^2_{0.950}$	$\chi^2_{0.900}$	$\chi^2_{0.100}$	$\chi^2_{0.050}$	$\cdots \chi^2_{0.005}$	d.f.
1	0.0000393	0.0039321	0.0157908	2.70554	3.84146	7.87944	1
2	0.0100251	0.102587	0.210720	4.60517	5.99147	10.5966	2
3	0.0717212	0.351846	0.584375	6.25139	7.81473	12.8381	3
4	0.206990	0.710721	1.063623	7.77944	9.48773	14.8602	4
5	0.411740	1.145476	1.61031	9.23635	11.0705	16.7496	5
6	0.675727	1.63539	2.20413	10.6446	12.5916	18.5476	6
⋮	⋮	⋮	⋮	⋮	⋮	⋮	⋮
15	4.60094	7.26094	8.54675	22.3072	24.9958	32.8013	15
16	5.14224	7.96164	9.31223	23.5418	26.2962	34.2672	16
17	5.69724	8.67176	10.0852	24.7690	27.5871	35.7185	17
18	6.26481	9.39046	10.8649	25.9894	28.8693	37.1564	18
19	6.84398	10.1170	11.6509	27.2036	30.1435	38.5822	19
⋮	⋮	⋮	⋮	⋮	⋮	⋮	⋮

tabulated χ^2 value is such that an area α lies to its right. (See Figure 8.9.) Stated in probabilistic terms,

$$P(\chi^2 > \chi^2_\alpha) = \alpha$$

Thus 99% of the area under the χ^2 distribution lies to the right of $\chi^2_{.99}$. We note that the extreme values of χ^2 must be tabulated for both the lower and the upper tails of the distribution because it is nonsymmetrical.

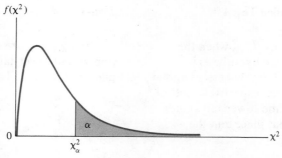

FIGURE 8.9   A Chi-square Distribution

You can check your ability to use the table by verifying the following statements. The probability that χ^2, based upon $n = 16$ measurements (d.f. $= 15$), will exceed 24.9958 is .05. For a sample of $n = 6$ measurements (d.f. $= 5$), 95% of the area under the χ^2 distribution will lie to the right of $\chi^2 = 1.145476$. These values of χ^2 are shaded in Table 8.15.

The statistical test of a null hypothesis concerning a population variance,

$$H_0 : \sigma^2 = \sigma_0^2$$

will employ the test statistic

$$\chi^2 = \frac{(n-1)s^2}{\sigma_0^2}$$

If σ^2 is really greater than the hypothesized value σ_0^2, then the test statistic will tend to be large and will likely fall toward the upper tail of the distribution. If $\sigma^2 < \sigma_0^2$, the test statistic will tend to be small and will likely fall toward the lower tail of the χ^2 distribution. As in the other statistical tests, we can use either a one- or two-tailed statistical test, depending upon the alternative hypothesis that we choose. The procedure for the chi-square test is given in the box.

TEST OF AN HYPOTHESIS CONCERNING A POPULATION VARIANCE (CHI-SQUARE TEST)

(1) *Null Hypothesis:* $H_0 : \sigma^2 = \sigma_0^2$.

(2) *Alternative Hypothesis:*

One-Tailed Test

$H_a : \sigma^2 > \sigma_0^2$
(or $H_a : \sigma^2 < \sigma_0^2$)

Two-Tailed Test

$H_a : \sigma^2 \neq \sigma_0^2$

(3) *Test Statistic:* $\chi^2 = \dfrac{(n-1)s^2}{\sigma_0^2}$.

(4) *Rejection Region:*

One-Tailed Test

$\chi^2 > \chi_\alpha^2$
[(or $\chi^2 < \chi_{(1-\alpha)}^2$) when the alternative hypothesis is $H_a : \sigma^2 < \sigma_0^2$), where χ_α^2 and $\chi_{(1-\alpha)}^2$ are, respectively, the upper- and lower-tail values of χ^2 that place α in the tail areas]

Two-Tailed Test

$\chi^2 > \chi_{\alpha/2}^2$ or $\chi^2 < \chi_{(1-\alpha/2)}^2$, where $\chi_{\alpha/2}^2$ and $\chi_{(1-\alpha/2)}^2$ are, respectively, the upper- and lower-tail values of χ^2 that place $\alpha/2$ in the tail areas

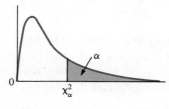
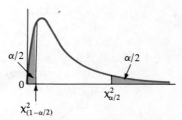

The critical values of χ^2 are based on $(n-1)$ degrees of freedom. These tabulated values are given in Table 6 in the Appendix.

Assumption: The sample has been randomly selected from a normal population.

EXAMPLE 8.11   A cement manufacturer claimed that concrete prepared from his product would possess a relatively stable compressive strength and that the strength measured in kilograms per square centimeter would lie within a range of 40 kilograms per square centimeter. A sample of $n = 10$ measurements produced a mean and variance equal to, respectively,

$$\bar{x} = 312 \quad \text{and} \quad s^2 = 195$$

Do these data present sufficient evidence to reject the manufacturer's claim?

SOLUTION   As stated, the manufacturer claimed that the range of the strength measurements would equal 40 kilograms per square centimeter. We will suppose that he meant that the measurements would lie within this range 95% of the time and, therefore, that the range would equal approximately 4σ and that $\sigma = 10$. We then want to test the null hypothesis

$$H_0 : \sigma^2 = (10)^2 = 100$$

against the alternative

$$H_a : \sigma^2 > 100$$

The alternative hypothesis requires a one-tailed statistical test, with the entire rejection region located in the upper tail of the χ^2 distribution. The critical value of χ^2 for $\alpha = .05$ and $(n - 1) = 9$ degrees of freedom is $\chi^2 = 16.9190$, which implies that we will reject H_0 if the test statistic exceeds this value.

Calculating, we obtain

$$\chi^2 = \frac{(n - 1)s^2}{\sigma_0^2}$$

$$= \frac{1755}{100}$$

$$= 17.55$$

Since the value of the test statistic falls in the rejection region, we conclude that the null hypothesis is false and that the range of concrete strength measurements will exceed the manufacturer's claim.   ∎

EXAMPLE 8.12   Find the approximate observed significance level for the test in Example 8.11.

SOLUTION   Examining the row corresponding to 9 degrees of freedom in Table 6 in the Appendix, you will see that the observed value of chi-square, $\chi^2 = 17.55$, is larger than the tabulated value, $\chi^2_{.05} = 16.9190$, and less than $\chi^2_{.025} = 19.0228$. Therefore, the observed significance level (p-value) for the test lies between .025 and .05. We would report the observed significance level for the test as $p < .05$. This tells us that we would reject the null hypothesis for any value of α equal to .05 or larger.   ∎

A confidence interval for σ^2 with a $(1 - \alpha)$ confidence coefficient is given in the next box.

A $(1 - \alpha)100\%$ CONFIDENCE INTERVAL FOR σ^2

$$\frac{(n-1)s^2}{\chi^2_{\alpha/2}} < \sigma^2 < \frac{(n-1)s^2}{\chi^2_{(1-\alpha/2)}}$$

where $\chi^2_{\alpha/2}$ and $\chi^2_{(1-\alpha/2)}$ are the upper and lower χ^2 values, respectively, which would locate one-half of α in each tail of the chi-square distribution.

Assumptions: The sample has been randomly selected from a normal population.

EXAMPLE 8.13   Find a 90% confidence interval for σ^2 in Example 8.11.

SOLUTION   The tabulated values of $\chi^2_{.95}$ and $\chi^2_{.05}$ corresponding to $(n - 1) = 9$ degrees of freedom are

$$\chi^2_{(1-\alpha/2)} = \chi^2_{.95} = 3.32511$$

$$\chi^2_{\alpha/2} = \chi^2_{.05} = 16.9190$$

Substituting these values and $s^2 = 195$ into the formula for the confidence interval,

$$\frac{(n-1)s^2}{\chi^2_{\alpha/2}} < \sigma^2 < \frac{(n-1)s^2}{\chi^2_{(1-\alpha/2)}}$$

yields the interval estimate for σ^2:

$$\frac{9(195)}{16.9190} < \sigma^2 < \frac{9(195)}{3.32511}$$

or

$$103.73 < \sigma^2 < 527.80$$

EXAMPLE 8.14   A company's quality control manager was convinced that a scale for weighing raw materials possessed a variability measured by a standard deviation $\sigma = 2$. In a test of the equipment a 107-pound test weight was weighed, and the measurements 104.1, 105.2, 110.2 were recorded. Do these data disagree with the manager's assumption? Test the hypothesis $H_0 : \sigma = 2$, or $\sigma^2 = 4$. Then place a 90% confidence interval on σ^2.

SOLUTION   The calculated sample variance is $s^2 = 10.57$. Since we want to detect $\sigma^2 > 4$ as well as $\sigma^2 < 4$, we should use a two-tailed test. When we use $\alpha = .10$ and place .05 in each tail, we will reject H_0 when $\chi^2 > 5.99147$ or $\chi^2 < .102587$.

The calculated value of the test statistic is

$$\chi^2 = \frac{(n-1)s^2}{\sigma_0^2} = \frac{2(10.57)}{4} = 5.29$$

Since the test statistic does not fall in the rejection region, the data do not provide sufficient evidence to reject the null hypothesis $H_0 : \sigma^2 = 4$.

The corresponding 90% confidence interval for σ^2 is

$$\frac{(n-1)s^2}{\chi^2_{\alpha/2}} < \sigma^2 < \frac{(n-1)s^2}{\chi^2_{(1-\alpha/2)}}$$

The values of $\chi^2_{(1-\alpha/2)}$ and $\chi^2_{\alpha/2}$ are

$$\chi^2_{(1-\alpha/2)} = \chi^2_{.95} = .102587$$
$$\chi^2_{\alpha/2} = \chi^2_{.05} = 5.99147$$

Substituting these values into the formula for the interval estimate, we obtain

$$\frac{2(10.57)}{5.99147} < \sigma^2 < \frac{2(10.57)}{.102587}$$

or

$$3.53 < \sigma^2 < 206.07$$

Thus we estimate the population variance to fall in the interval 3.53 to 206.07. This very wide confidence interval indicates how little information on the population variance is obtained in a sample of only three measurements. Consequently, it is not surprising that there was insufficient evidence to reject the null hypothesis $\sigma^2 = 4$. To obtain more information on σ^2, the manager needs to increase the sample size. ■

EXERCISES

BASIC TECHNIQUES

8.52 A random sample of $n = 25$ observations from a normal population produced a sample variance equal to 21.4. Do these data provide sufficient evidence to indicate that $\sigma^2 > 15$? Test using $\alpha = .05$.

8.53 A random sample of $n = 15$ observations was selected from a normal population. The sample mean and variance were $\bar{x} = 3.91$ and $s^2 = .3214$. Find a 90% confidence interval for the population variance σ^2.

8.54 A random sample of $n = 22$ observations was selected from a normal population. The sample mean and variance were $\bar{x} = 41.3$ and $s^2 = 14.14$. Do the data provide sufficient evidence to indicate that $\sigma^2 < 25$? Test using $\alpha = .05$.

8.55 Find a 90% confidence interval for the population variance in Exercise 8.54.

APPLICATIONS

8.56 Refer to the comparison of the estimated versus actual CPU times for computer jobs submitted by the customer in Exercise 8.47. The data are given in Table 8.16. Find a 90% confidence interval for the variance of the differences between estimated and actual CPU times.

TABLE 8.16   CPU Time Data for Exercise 8.56

CPU Time (Minutes)	Job Number										
	1	2	3	4	5	6	7	8	9	10	11
Estimated	.50	1.40	.95	.45	.75	1.20	1.60	2.6	1.30	.85	.60
Actual	.46	1.52	.99	.53	.71	1.31	1.49	2.9	1.41	.83	.74

8.57 Refer to Exercise 8.56. Suppose that the computer center expects customers to estimate CPU time correct to within .2 minute most (say 95%) of the time.

(a) Do the data provide sufficient evidence to indicate that the customer's error in estimating job CPU time exceeds the computer center's expectation? Test using $\alpha = .10$.

(b) Find the approximate observed significance level for the test, and interpret its value.

8.58 In 1978 the Environmental Protection Agency (EPA) set a maximum noise level for heavy trucks at 83 decibels. This limit could be interpreted in several ways. One way to apply the limit would be to require all trucks to conform to the noise limit. A second but less satisfactory method would be to require the truck fleet's mean noise level to be less than the limit. If the latter were the rule, variation in the noise level from truck to truck would be important because a large value of σ^2 would imply many trucks exceeding the limit, even if the mean fleet level was 83 decibels. The data for six trucks, in decibels, were

$$82.4, \ 83.8, \ 83.1, \ 82.3, \ 81.8, \ 83.0$$

Use these data to construct a 90% confidence interval for σ^2, the variance of the truck noise emission readings. Interpret your results.

8.59 A precision instrument is guaranteed to read accurately to within 2 units. A sample of four instrument readings on the same object yielded the measurements 353, 351, 351, and 355. Test the null hypothesis that $\sigma = .7$ against the alternative $\sigma > .7$. Conduct the test at the $\alpha = .05$ level of significance.

8.60 Find a 90% confidence interval for the population variance in Exercise 8.59.

8.61 A manufacturer of hard safety hats for construction workers is concerned about the mean and the variation of the forces helmets transmit to wearers when subjected to a standard external force. The manufacturer desires the mean force transmitted by helmets to be 800 pounds (or less), well under the legal 1000-pound limit, and σ to be less than 40. A random sample of $n = 40$ helmets was tested, and the sample mean and variance were found to be equal to 825 pounds and 2350 (pounds)^2, respectively.

(a) If $\mu = 800$ and $\sigma = 40$, is it likely that any helmet, subjected to the standard external force, will transmit a force to a wearer in excess of 1000 pounds? Explain.

(b) Do the data provide sufficient evidence to indicate that when the helmets are subjected to the standard external force, the mean force transmitted by the helmets exceeds 800 pounds?

(c) Do the data provide sufficient evidence to indicate that σ exceeds 40?

8.7   COMPARING TWO POPULATION VARIANCES

The need for statistical methods to compare two population variances is readily apparent from the discussion in Section 8.6. We may frequently wish to compare the precision of one measuring device with that of another, the stability of one manufacturing process with that of another, or even the variability in the grading procedure of one college professor with that of another.

Intuitively, we might compare two population variances, σ_1^2 and σ_2^2, using the ratio of the sample variances s_1^2/s_2^2. If s_1^2/s_2^2 is nearly equal to 1, we would find little evidence to indicate that σ_1^2 and σ_2^2 are unequal. On the other hand, a very large or very small value for s_1^2/s_2^2 would provide evidence of a difference in the population variances.

How large or small must s_1^2/s_2^2 be in order that sufficient evidence exists to reject the null hypothesis $H_0 : \sigma_1^2 = \sigma_2^2$? The answer to this question may be acquired by studying the sampling distribution of s_1^2/s_2^2.

When independent random samples are drawn from two normal populations with equal variances—that is, $\sigma_1^2 = \sigma_2^2$—then s_1^2/s_2^2 possesses a sampling distribution that is known to statisticians as an **F distribution**. We need not concern ourselves with the equation of the probability distribution for F. It is well known, and the critical values have been tabulated. These values appear in Tables 7, 8, 9, 10, and 11 in the Appendix.

The shape of the F distribution is nonsymmetrical and will depend on the number of degrees of freedom associated with s_1^2 and s_2^2. We will represent these quantities as v_1 and v_2, respectively. This fact complicates the tabulation of critical values for the F distribution and necessitates the construction of a table for each value that we may choose for a tail area α. Thus Tables 7, 8, 9, 10, and 11 in the Appendix present critical values corresponding to $\alpha = .10, .05, .025, .01,$ and $.005$, respectively. A typical F probability distribution ($v_1 = 10$ and $v_2 = 10$) is shown in Figure 8.10.

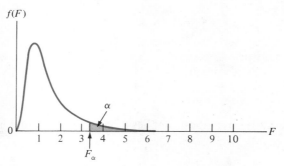

FIGURE 8.10   An F Distribution with $v_1 = 10$ and $v_2 = 10$

A partial reproduction of Table 8 in the Appendix is shown in Table 8.17. Table 8 records the value $F_{.05}$ such that the probability that F will exceed $F_{.05}$ is .05. Another way of saying this is that 5% of the area under the F distribution lies to the right of $F_{.05}$. The degrees of freedom for s_1^2, v_1, are indicated across the top of the table, and the degrees of freedom for s_2^2, v_2, appear in the first column on the left.

Referring to Table 8.17, we note that $F_{.05}$ for sample sizes $n_1 = 7$ and $n_2 = 10$ (that is, $v_1 = 6, v_2 = 9$) is 3.37. Likewise, the critical value $F_{.05}$ for sample sizes $n_1 = 9$ and $n_2 = 16$ ($v_1 = 8, v_2 = 15$) is 2.64. These values of F are shaded in Table 8.17.

In a similar manner, the critical values for a tail area $\alpha = .01$ are presented in Table 10 in the Appendix. Thus

$$P(F > F_{.01}) = .01$$

The statistical test of the null hypothesis

$$H_0 : \sigma_1^2 = \sigma_2^2$$

TABLE 8.17   Format of the F Table, Table 8 in the Appendix, for $\alpha = .05$

v_2 (d.f.)	1	2	3	4	5	6	7	8	9	... 60	120	∞	v_2 (d.f.)
1	161.4	199.5	215.7	224.6	230.2	234.0	236.8	238.9	240.5	252.2	253.3	254.3	1
2	18.51	19.00	19.16	19.25	19.30	19.33	19.35	19.37	19.38	19.48	19.49	19.50	2
3	10.13	9.55	9.28	9.12	9.01	8.94	8.89	8.85	8.81	8.57	8.55	8.53	3
4	7.71	6.94	6.59	6.39	6.26	6.16	6.09	6.04	6.00	5.69	5.66	5.63	4
5	6.61	5.79	5.41	5.19	5.05	4.95	4.88	4.82	4.77	4.43	4.40	4.36	5
6	5.99	5.14	4.76	4.53	4.39	4.28	4.21	4.15	4.10	3.74	3.70	3.67	6
7	5.59	4.74	4.35	4.12	3.97	3.87	3.79	3.73	3.68	3.30	3.27	3.23	7
8	5.32	4.46	4.07	3.84	3.69	3.58	3.50	3.44	3.39	3.01	2.97	2.93	8
9	5.12	4.26	3.86	3.63	3.48	3.37	3.29	3.23	3.18	2.79	2.75	2.71	9
:	:	:	:	:	:	:	:	:	:	:	:	:	:
15	4.54	3.68	3.29	3.06	2.90	2.79	2.71	2.64	2.59	2.16	2.11	2.07	15
16	4.49	3.63	3.24	3.01	2.85	2.74	2.66	2.59	2.54	2.11	2.06	2.01	16
17	4.45	3.59	3.20	2.96	2.81	2.70	2.61	2.55	2.49	2.06	2.01	1.96	17
18	4.41	3.55	3.16	2.93	2.77	2.66	2.58	2.51	2.46	2.02	1.97	1.92	18
19	4.38	3.52	3.13	2.90	2.74	2.63	2.54	2.48	2.42	1.98	1.93	1.88	19
:	:	:	:	:	:	:	:	:	:	:	:	:	:

The column group header above columns 1–∞ is v_1 (d.f.).

utilizes the F **statistic**

$$F = \frac{s_1^2}{s_2^2}$$

When the alternative hypothesis implies a one-tailed test, that is,

$$H_a : \sigma_1^2 > \sigma_2^2$$

we can use the tables directly. However, when the alternative hypothesis requires a two-tailed test

$$H_a : \sigma_1^2 \neq \sigma_2^2$$

the rejection region will be divided between the lower and upper tails of the F distribution, and you can see that tables of critical values for the lower tail are conspicuously missing. The reason for their absence is explained as follows: We are at liberty to identify either of the two populations as population I. If the population with the larger sample variance is designated as population II, then $s_2^2 > s_1^2$ and we will be concerned with rejection in the lower tail of the F distribution. Since the identification of the populations was arbitrary, we can avoid this difficulty by designating the population with the larger sample variance as population I. In other words, always place the larger sample variance in the numerator of

$$F = \frac{s_1^2}{s_2^2}$$

and designate that population as I. Then since the area in the right-hand tail will represent only $\alpha/2$, we double this value to obtain the correct value for the probability of a type I error, α. Hence if we use Table 8 in the Appendix for a two-tailed test, the probability of a type I error will be $\alpha = .10$. The procedure for the F test is given in the following box. We illustrate it with examples.

TEST OF AN HYPOTHESIS CONCERNING THE EQUALITY OF TWO POPULATION VARIANCES

(1) *Null Hypothesis:* $H_0 : \sigma_1^2 = \sigma_2^2$.

(2) *Alternative Hypothesis:*

One-Tailed Test

$H_a : \sigma_1^2 > \sigma_2^2$
(or $H_a : \sigma_2^2 > \sigma_1^2$)

Two-Tailed Test

$H_a : \sigma_1^2 \neq \sigma_2^2$

(3) *Test Statistic:*

One-Tailed Test

$F = \dfrac{s_1^2}{s_2^2}$

$\left(\text{or } F = \dfrac{s_2^2}{s_1^2} \text{ for } H_a : \sigma_2^2 > \sigma_1^2 \right)$

Two-Tailed Test

$F = \dfrac{s_1^2}{s_2^2}$, where s_1^2 is the larger sample variance

(4) *Rejection Region:*

One-Tailed Test

$F > F_\alpha$

Two-Tailed Test

$F > F_{\alpha/2}$

When $F = s_1^2/s_2^2$, the critical values, F_α and $F_{\alpha/2}$, are based on $v_1 = n_1 - 1$ and $v_2 = n_2 - 1$ degrees of freedom. These tabulated critical values, for $\alpha = .10, .05, .025, .01,$ and $.005$, can be found in Tables 7, 8, 9, 10, and 11, respectively, in the Appendix.

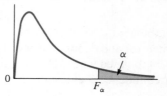
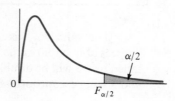

Assumptions: The samples were randomly and independently selected from normally distributed populations.

EXAMPLE 8.15   Two samples consisting of 10 and 8 measurements each were observed to possess sample variances equal to $s_1^2 = 7.14$ and $s_2^2 = 3.21$, respectively. Do the sample variances present sufficient evidence to indicate that the population variances are unequal?

SOLUTION   Assume that the populations possess probability distributions that are reasonably mound-shaped and thus will satisfy, for all practical purposes, the assumption that the populations are normal.

We want to test the null hypothesis

$$H_0 : \sigma_1^2 = \sigma_2^2$$

against the alternative

$$H_a : \sigma_1^2 \neq \sigma_2^2$$

Using Table 8 in the Appendix, and doubling the tail area, we will reject H_0 when $F > 3.68$ with $\alpha = .10$.

The calculated value of the test statistic is

$$F = \frac{s_1^2}{s_2^2} = \frac{7.14}{3.21} = 2.22$$

Noting that the test statistic does not fall in the rejection region, we do not reject $H_0 : \sigma_1^2 = \sigma_2^2$. Thus there is insufficient evidence to indicate a difference in the population variances.   ■

The confidence interval, with confidence coefficient $(1 - \alpha)$, for the ratio of two population variances is given in the next box.

A CONFIDENCE INTERVAL FOR σ_1^2/σ_2^2

$$\frac{s_1^2}{s_2^2}\frac{1}{F_{v_1,v_2}} < \frac{\sigma_1^2}{\sigma_2^2} < \frac{s_1^2}{s_2^2}F_{v_2,v_1}$$

where $v_1 = n_1 - 1$ and $v_2 = n_2 - 1$.

Assumptions: The samples were randomly and independently selected from normally distributed populations.

The value F_{v_1,v_2} is the tabulated critical value of F corresponding to v_1 and v_2 degrees of freedom in the numerator and denominator of F, respectively. As in the two-tailed test, α will be double the tabulated value. Thus F values extracted from Tables 8 and 9 will be appropriate for confidence coefficients equal to .90 and .95, respectively.

EXAMPLE 8.16   Refer to Example 8.15, and find a 90% confidence interval for σ_1^2/σ_2^2.

SOLUTION   The 90% confidence interval for σ_1^2/σ_2^2 in Example 8.15 is

$$\frac{s_1^2}{s_2^2}\frac{1}{F_{v_1,v_2}} < \frac{\sigma_1^2}{\sigma_2^2} < \frac{s_1^2}{s_2^2}F_{v_2,v_1}$$

where

$$s_1^2 = 7.14 \qquad s_2^2 = 3.21$$

$$v_1 = (n_1 - 1) = 9 \qquad v_2 = (n_2 - 1) = 7$$

$$F_{v_1,v_2} = F_{9,7} = 3.68 \qquad F_{v_2,v_1} = F_{7,9} = 3.29$$

Substituting these values into the formula for the confidence interval, we obtain

$$\left(\frac{7.14}{3.21}\right)\frac{1}{3.68} < \frac{\sigma_1^2}{\sigma_2^2} < \frac{(7.14)(3.29)}{3.21}$$

or

$$.60 < \frac{\sigma_1^2}{\sigma_2^2} < 7.32$$

The calculated interval estimate, .60 to 7.32, includes 1.0, the value hypothesized in H_0. This indicates that it is quite possible that $\sigma_1^2 = \sigma_2^2$ and therefore agrees with our test conclusions. Do not reject $H_0 : \sigma_1^2 = \sigma_2^2$.   ∎

EXAMPLE 8.17   The variability in the amount of impurities present in a batch of chemical used for a particular process depends upon the length of time the process is in operation. A manufacturer using two production lines, 1 and 2, has made a slight adjustment to process 2, hoping to reduce the variability as well as the average amount of impurities in the chemical. Samples of $n_1 = 25$ and $n_2 = 25$ measurements from the two batches yield means and variances as follows:

$$\bar{x}_1 = 3.2 \qquad s_1^2 = 1.04$$

$$\bar{x}_2 = 3.0 \qquad s_2^2 = .51$$

Do the data present sufficient evidence to indicate that the process variability is less for process 2? Test the null hypothesis $H_0 : \sigma_1^2 = \sigma_2^2$.

SOLUTION   The practical implications of this example are illustrated in Figure 8.11. We believe that the mean levels of impurities in the two production lines are nearly equal (in fact, that they may be equal) but that there is a possibility that the variation in the level of impurities is substantially less for line 2. Then distributions of impurity measurements for the two production lines would have nearly the same mean level, but they would

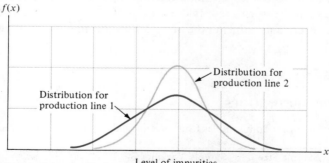

FIGURE 8.11   Distributions of Impurity Measurements for Two Production Lines in Example 8.17

differ in their variation. A large variance for the level of impurities increases the probability of producing shipments of chemical with an unacceptably high level of impurities. Consequently, we hope to show that the process change in line 2 has made σ_2^2 less than σ_1^2.

Testing the null hypothesis

$$H_0 : \sigma_1^2 = \sigma_2^2$$

against the alternative

$$H_a : \sigma_1^2 > \sigma_2^2$$

at an $\alpha = .05$ significance level, we will reject H_0 when F is greater than $F_{.05} = 1.98$; that is, we shall employ a one-tailed statistical test.

The calculated value of the F test statistic,

$$F = \frac{s_1^2}{s_2^2} = \frac{1.04}{.51} = 2.04$$

falls in the rejection region. Therefore, we conclude that the variability of process 2 is less than that for process 1.

The 90% confidence interval for the ratio σ_1^2 / σ_2^2 is

$$\frac{s_1^2}{s_2^2} \frac{1}{F_{v_1, v_2}} < \frac{\sigma_1^2}{\sigma_2^2} < \frac{s_1^2}{s_2^2} F_{v_2, v_1}$$

$$\frac{1.04}{(.51)(1.98)} < \frac{\sigma_1^2}{\sigma_2^2} < \frac{(1.04)(1.98)}{.51}$$

or

$$1.03 < \frac{\sigma_1^2}{\sigma_2^2} < 4.04$$

Thus we estimate the reduction in the variance of the amount of impurities to be as large as 4.04 to 1 or as small as 1.03 to 1. The actual reduction would likely be somewhere between these two extremes. This result suggests that the adjustment is quite effective in reducing the variation in the amount of impurities in the chemical.

EXERCISES

BASIC TECHNIQUES

8.62 Independent random samples from two normal populations produced the following variances:

Sample Size	Sample Variance
16	55.7
20	31.4

(a) Do the data provide sufficient evidence to indicate that σ_1^2 differs from σ_2^2? Test using $\alpha = .05$.

(b) Find the approximate observed significance level for the test, and interpret its value.

8.63 Refer to Exercise 8.62, and find a 95% confidence interval for σ_1^2/σ_2^2.

8.64 Independent random samples from two normal populations produced the following variances:

Sample Size	Sample Variance
10	1.48
9	.54

(a) Do the data provide sufficient evidence to indicate that σ_1^2 differs from σ_2^2? Test by using $\alpha = .10$.

(b) Find the approximate observed significance level for the test, and interpret its value.

8.65 Refer to Exercise 8.64, and find a 90% confidence interval for σ_1^2/σ_2^2.

8.66 Independent random samples from two normal populations produced the following variances:

Population	Sample Size	Sample Variance
1	13	18.3
2	13	7.9

(a) Do the data provide sufficient evidence to indicate that $\sigma_1^2 > \sigma_2^2$? Test using $\alpha = .05$.

(b) Find the approximate observed significance level for the test, and interpret its value.

APPLICATIONS

8.67 The stability of measurements of the characteristics of a manufactured product is important in maintaining product quality. In fact, it is sometimes better to possess small variation in the measured value of some important characteristic of a product and have the process mean slightly off target than to suffer wide variation with a mean value that perfectly fits requirements. The latter situation may produce a higher percentage of defective product than the former. A manufacturer of light bulbs suspected that one of her production lines was producing bulbs with a high variation in length of life. To test this theory, she compared the lengths of life of $n = 50$ bulbs randomly sampled from the suspect line and $n = 50$ from a line that seemed to be "in control." The sample means and variances for the two samples were as follows:

Suspect Line	Line in Control
$\bar{x}_1 = 1520$	$\bar{x}_2 = 1476$
$s_1^2 = 92{,}000$	$s_2^2 = 37{,}000$

(a) Do the data provide sufficient evidence to indicate that bulbs produced by the suspect line possess a larger variance in length of life than those produced by the line that is assumed to be in control? Use $\alpha = .05$.

(b) Find the approximate observed significance level for the test, and interpret its value.

8.68 Obtain a 90% confidence interval for the variance ratio in Exercise 8.67.

8.69 A personnel manager planning to use a Student's t test to compare the mean number of monthly absences for two categories of employees noticed a possible difficulty. The variation in the numbers of absences per month seemed to differ for the two groups. As a check, the personnel manager randomly selected five months and counted the number of absences for each group. The data are shown in the table.

Category A	20	14	19	22	25 x^2
Category B	37	29	51	40	26 x_1

(handwritten above Category A row: 17 15 32 13 1)

(a) About which assumption necessary for use of the t test was the personnel manager concerned?

(b) Do the data provide sufficient evidence to indicate that the variances differ for the populations of absences for the two employee categories? Test with $\alpha = .10$, and interpret the results of the test.

8.70 A pharmaceutical manufacturer purchases a particular material from two different suppliers. The mean level of impurities in the raw material is approximately the same for both suppliers, but the manufacturer is concerned about the variability of the impurities from shipment to shipment. If the level of impurities tends to vary excessively for one source of supply, it could affect the quality of the pharmaceutical product. To compare the variation in percentage impurities for the two suppliers, the manufacturer selects ten shipments from each of the two suppliers and measures the percentage of impurities in the raw material for each shipment. The sample means and variances are shown in the table.

Supplier A	Supplier B
$\bar{x}_1 = 1.89$	$\bar{x}_2 = 1.85$
$s_1^2 = .273$	$s_2^2 = .094$
$n_1 = 10$	$n_2 = 10$

(a) Do the data provide sufficient evidence to indicate a difference in the variability of the shipment impurity levels for the two suppliers? Test using $\alpha = .10$. Based on the results of your test, what recommendation would you make to the pharmaceutical manufacturer?

(b) Find a 90% confidence interval for σ_2^2, and interpret your results.

8.71 The mean percentage (or dollar) profit per project is not the only concern of a real estate developer (or any type of investor). The developer must be concerned with a large variation in gain, because a large negative gain (a loss) could put the developer out of business. A particular developer plans projects so as to achieve a mean profit per project of 12% with a range no larger than 25%. A sampling of the percentage profit per project for the last 25 of the developer's projects produced a sample mean and standard deviation equal to 11.1% and 5.2%, respectively.

(a) Suppose that the developer wants to be fairly certain that the range of the percentage profit per project is no more than 25%. What value of σ will achieve this goal? (*Hint:* Almost all of the observations in a population will fall within 3σ of the population mean μ.)

(b) Do the data for the 25 projects provide sufficient evidence to indicate that the mean profit level is less than 12%? Test using $\alpha = .05$.

(c) Do the data provide sufficient evidence to indicate that the variation in percentage profit per job is greater than the value of σ specified in part (a)? Test using $\alpha = .05$.

8.72 Refer to Exercise 8.71. Find a 95% confidence interval for the variance of the percentage profit per job for the developer, and interpret the interval.

ASSUMPTIONS

8.8

As noted earlier, the tests and confidence intervals based on the Student's t, the chi-square, and the F statistic require that the data satisfy specific assumptions in order that the error probabilities (for the tests) and the confidence coefficients (for the confidence intervals) be equal to the values that we have specified. For example, if the assumptions are violated by selecting a sample from a nonnormal population, and the data are used to construct a 95% confidence interval for μ, the actual confidence coefficient might (unknown to us) be equal to .85 instead of .95. The assumptions are summarized in the box for your convenience.

ASSUMPTIONS

(1) For all tests and confidence intervals described in this chapter, we assume that samples are randomly selected from normally distributed populations.

(2) When two samples are selected, we assume that they are selected in an independent manner, except in the case of the paired-difference experiment.

(3) For tests or confidence intervals concerning the difference between two population means μ_1 and μ_2, based on independent random samples, we assume that $\sigma_1^2 = \sigma_2^2$.

In a practical sampling situation you never know everything about the probability distribution of the sampled population. If you did, there would be no need for sampling or statistics. Furthermore, it is highly unlikely that a population would possess, exactly, the characteristics described above. Consequently, to be useful, the inferential methods described in this chapter must give good inferences when moderate departures from the assumptions are present. For example, if the population possesses a mound-shaped distribution that is nearly normal, we would like a 95% confidence interval constructed for μ to be one with a confidence coefficient close to .95. Similarly, if we conduct a t test of the null hypothesis $\mu_1 = \mu_2$, based on independent random samples from normal populations, where σ_1^2 and σ_2^2 are not exactly equal, we want the probability of incorrectly rejecting the null hypothesis, α, to be approximately equal to the value we used in locating the rejection region.

A statistical method that is insensitive to departures from the assumptions upon which the method is based is said to be *robust*. The t tests are quite robust to moderate departures from normality. In contrast, the chi-square and F tests are sensitive to departures from normality. The t test for comparing two means is moderately robust to departures from the assumption $\sigma_1^2 = \sigma_2^2$ when $n_1 = n_2$. However, the test becomes sensitive to departures from this assumption as n_1 becomes large relative to n_2 (or vice versa).

If you are concerned that your data do not satisfy the assumptions prescribed for one of the statistical methods described in this chapter, you may be able to use a nonparametric statistical method to make your inference. These methods, which require few or no assumptions about the nature of the population probability distributions, are particularly useful for testing hypotheses, and some nonparametric methods have been developed for estimating population parameters. Tests of hypotheses concerning the location of a population distribution or a test for the equivalence of two population distributions are presented in Chapter 15. If you can select relatively large samples, you can use the large-sample estimation or test procedures of Chapters 6 and 7.

8.9   AN ANALYSIS OF JAWS

In the Case Study of this chapter we described the JAWS early-warning system employed by the FDIC to detect banks that might be headed for failure. The system employs 23 variables that measure bank performance. Measurements on these variables for a given bank are compared with a set of established critical values. Failure of one or more of these variables to compare favorably with their critical values is viewed as undesirable and an early warning of possible bank failure.

In their study of the JAWS early-warning system, Rose and Kolari selected a sample of banks that failed during the period 1964–1977 and matched each with a bank of the same size, in the same county location, and with identical supervisory authority and regulation. The values of the 23 screening variables were recorded for each bank 1, 2, . . . , 8 years prior to failure of the failing bank in each matched pair. Then the means for failing and healthy banks for each screening variable were compared for each time interval, using a paired-difference t test. The 23 screening variables are listed in Table 8.18, and the results of the paired t tests are shown in Table 8.19.

The 23 screening variables are listed along the left side of Table 8.19. The sample means for failing and nonfailing banks and the corresponding t values (in parentheses) are shown to the right of each variable for samples taken at 1, 2, 3, . . . , 6 years prior to bank failure. The number of matched pairs varied depending upon the number of years to failure. The sample size for each year is shown immediately below the "Fail Nfail" headings for each of the columns. Test results for 7 and 8 years prior to failure were omitted by Rose and Kolari because they showed little or no evidence of differences in mean value and therefore little evidence of usefulness as early-warning indicators.

If a bank performance variable is to be of any value as an early-warning indicator of bank failure, the mean value for failed banks must differ from the mean for unfailed banks, the greater the difference the better. The objective of the paired-difference t tests is to detect differences if they exist. As an example, growth in equity capital, variable 1, dropped an average of 11.6% one year before bank failure for failed banks, as compared with an average increase of 10.0% for unfailed banks. The t value for the paired t test, based on $(n - 1) = (71 - 1) = 70$ degrees of freedom, is $t = -4.3$. Because the number n of pairs is so large, the critical value of the t test is essentially the same as the critical value for the large-sample z test—namely, $t_{.025} \approx 1.96$—and the rejection region for $\alpha = .05$ is $t < -1.96$ or $t > 1.96$. Since the observed value of t falls far out into the rejection region, there is strong evidence to indicate a difference in the mean level of "percentage growth in equity capital" between failed and nonfailed banks.

You can see from Table 8.19 that there is evidence to indicate differences in mean levels of failed versus nonfailed banks for 14 of the 23 screening variables for

TABLE 8.18   Financial Variables Derived from the FDIC's Integrated Monitoring System (IMS)

Capital Adequacy

1. Percentage growth in equity capital from previous years
2. Equity capital/total assets
3. Capital and reserves/total assets
4. Cash dividends/net income

Liquidity

5. Net borrowings excluding mortgages/cash and due from banks plus U.S. securities
6. Net liquid assets/total assets

Deposit Mix and Growth

7. Percentage growth in other time deposits from previous year
8. Percentage growth in total deposits from previous year
9. Percentage growth in other time deposits/percentage growth in total deposits from previous year

Loan Mix and Growth

10. Percentage growth in total loans from previous year
11. Percentage growth in total loans/percentage growth in total deposits from previous year
12. Gross loans/total deposits
13. Real estate loans/total loans

Borrowings

14. Time deposits of $100,000 or more plus net borrowings/total loans

Security Holdings

15. Municipal securities including trading accounts/total assets

Earnings and Expenses

16. Net operating income/total assets
17. Total operating income/total assets
18. Net after-tax income/total assets
19. Interest expense on deposits and federal funds purchase/total operating income
20. Operating expenses/total operating income
21. Salaries, occupancy, and other expenses/total operating income
22. Interest on deposits/total operating income
23. Provision for loan losses/total operating income

Source: P. S. Rose and J. W. Kolari, "Early Warning Systems as a Monitoring Device for Bank Condition," *Quarterly Journal of Business and Economics,* Vol. 24, No. 1, 1985.

observations made one year prior to bank failure. Tests for differences in means for some of these variables (e.g. the percentage of total assets that are liquid, variable 6), are also statistically significant for observations taken 2, 3, . . . , 6 years prior to bank failure, suggesting that these variables may be good indicators of possible bank failure. Growth in equity capital (variable 1) may be a good indicator of possible bank failure

TABLE 8.19   Means and *t* Tests of Failed Versus Nonfailed Banks' Financial Ratios

Bank Performance Measure: Number of Pairs:	Years Before Bank Failure											
	1		2		3		4		5		6	
	Fail	Nfail	Fail	Nfail	Fail	Nfail	Fail	Nfail	Fail	Nfail	Fail	Nfail
	71		63		58		53		42		32	
Capital Adequacy												
1. Growth in equity capital	−11.6 (−4.3***)	10.00	5.0 (−1.08)	8.3	5.0 (−1.37)	9.2	54.1 (.090)	15.0	9.7 (1.14)	−8.7	11.8 (0.07)	11.6
2. Equity capital/total assets	6.6 (−3.21***)	8.5	8.4 (0.22)	8.5	8.9 (0.53)	8.5	9.5 (1.34)	8.3	9.2 (1.74**)	8.0	10.0 (2.43**)	8.1
3. Capital and reserves/ total assets	6.9 (−3.74***)	9.0	8.6 (−0.76)	9.0	9.2 (0.42)	8.9	9.8 (1.25)	8.7	9.2 (1.29)	8.5	10.2 (2.54**)	8.2
4. Cash dividends/net income	12.3 (1.05)	23.9	23.5 (−0.62)	29.0	25.1 (−0.44)	28.0	32.7 (−0.07)	34.1	12.2 (−2.06**)	26.4	75.1 (0.95)	29.2
Liquidity												
5. Net borrowings/cash and U.S. governments	32.7 (2.70***)	13.2	26.9 (3.26***)	11.1	19.1 (2.76***)	11.4	14.0 (2.04**)	9.1	12.5 (0.03)	12.3	8.3 (−0.33)	9.0
6. Net liquid assets/assets	22.4 (−3.72***)	29.7	26.0 (−4.36***)	32.5	29.0 (−2.12**)	32.3	31.4 (−2.50**)	34.9	30.7 (−1.99*)	34.4	31.9 (−2.40**)	37.5
Deposits												
7. % growth in other time deposits	72.1 (1.31)	18.8	37.0 (0.07)	35.7	46.8 (0.93)	29.4	42.2 (−0.91)	114.5	72.4 (1.96*)	19.8	53.1 (0.81)	31.0
8. % growth in total deposits	1.3 (−2.28**)	9.7	6.0 (−1.03)	9.4	10.7 (0.58)	9.0	12.8 (0.65)	11.3	17.9 (2.83**)	9.7	12.1 (0.11)	11.7
9. % growth in time deposits/ % growth in total deposits	1160.4 (1.11)	198.2	181.6 (−1.14)	2518.7	362.3 (0.66)	136.5	185.5 (−1.29)	1470.7	279.6 (1.77*)	−32.4	−3.7 (−0.41)	91.9
Loan Mix and Growth												
10. % growth in total loans	−155.5 (−1.21)	39.0	86.9 (0.68)	66.7	101.2 (2.15**)	−76.7	−28.4 (−1.26)	45.0	17.7 (−1.06)	68.1	65.04 (−1.17)	119.7
11. % growth in total loans/ % growth in total deposits (in 100s)	−30.2 (−0.54)	13.1	29.6 (−0.58)	52.9	24.2 (0.61)	−118.3	48.2 (0.51)	25.5	2.8 (−0.03)	3.1	10.6 (−0.97)	22.4
12. Gross loans/total deposits	71.3 (5.68***)	57.6	68.9 (5.51***)	56.5	65.7 (5.16***)	56.4	63.6 (3.66***)	54.9	63.7 (3.07***)	55.5	61.4 (3.06***)	52.2
13. Real estate loans/ total loans	21.7 (−1.85*)	26.1	23.1 (−1.49)	26.5	23.9 (−0.10)	24.1	25.4 (0.49)	23.9	26.5 (−0.01)	26.6	28.9 (0.79)	25.9
Borrowings												
14. Large time deposits + net borrowings/loans	47.0 (0.94)	43.2	46.5 (−0.34)	48.2	46.2 (0.31)	44.6	44.7 (0.52)	42.1	45.6 (−0.31)	47.7	44.9 (−0.60)	49.8
Securities												
15. Municipal/total assets	4.5 (−4.96***)	9.6	5.5 (−3.32***)	9.3	6.1 (−3.16***)	9.8	6.9 (−2.05***)	9.4	6.0 (−3.02***)	9.6	6.5 (−1.92*)	9.0
Earnings and Expenses												
16. Net operating income/assets	−0.3 (−5.60***)	1.2	0.5 (−3.57***)	1.2	0.6 (−3.89***)	1.4	0.8 (−2.38**)	1.2	0.7 (−1.64)	1.0	0.8 (−2.90***)	1.3

TABLE 8.19   (*Continued*)

Bank Performance Measure: Number of Pairs:	Years Before Bank Failure											
	1		2		3		4		5		6	
	Fail 71	Nfail	Fail 63	Nfail	Fail 58	Nfail	Fail 53	Nfail	Fail 42	Nfail	Fail 32	Nfail
Earnings and Expenses												
17. Total operating income/ total assets	6.9 (0.99)	6.7	6.8 (1.13)	6.6	6.5 (1.52)	6.3	6.1 (1.03)	5.9	6.2 (2.22**)	5.8	6.0 (1.00)	5.7
18. Net after-tax income/ total assets	−1.3 (−4.03***)	0.9	0.2 (−3.58***)	0.9	0.2 (−3.88***)	1.0	0.6 (−2.49***)	0.9	0.4 (−1.80**)	0.7	0.6 (−2.11**)	0.9
19. Interest expense on deposits and federal funds/ operating income	38.1 (4.47***)	30.1	36.7 (4.15***)	30.3	34.4 (3.70***)	28.1	31.9 (1.67)	28.8	31.7 (0.23)	31.2	31.0 (0.58)	29.6
20. Operating expenses/ operating income	213.3 (1.27)	107.0	114.7 (1.28)	91.0	183.0 (−0.20)	209.1	176.0 (−0.14)	191.6	109.9 (0.08)	107.8	91.5 (0.26)	84.4
21. Salaries, occupancy, and other expenses/operating income	62.7 (4.08***)	48.0	52.8 (2.07**)	47.2	53.4 (2.44**)	46.3	51.7 (1.44)	48.1	55.3 (2.09**)	48.2	54.4 (2.61**)	45.1
22. Interest on deposits/ operating income	39.8 (5.19***)	30.5	38.3 (4.76***)	30.9	35.5 (4.13***)	28.5	32.9 (2.11**)	28.9	32.6 (0.56)	31.4	31.4 (0.69)	29.8
23. Provision for loan losses/ operating income	187.1 (−1.26)	216.4	178.0 (−1.23)	211.6	190.8 (−1.16)	222.3	183.2 (−1.63)	231.6	209.2 (0.21)	202.9	214.5 (1.16)	174.1

*Asterisks indicate those t tests that are significant at levels of 10% (*), 5% (**), and 1% (***).

Source: P. S. Rose and J. W. Kolari, "Early Warning Systems as a Monitoring Device for Bank Condition," *Quarterly Journal of Business and Economics,* Vol. 24, No. 1, 1985.

when observed one year prior to bank failure but there is no evidence to indicate that it is of value if observed 2 or more years prior to bank failure.

When the paired t tests for a variable are statistically significant for observations taken 1, 2, 3, ..., 6 years prior to bank failure, we can be fairly certain that the variable will be useful in identifying future bank failure. Variables 5, 6, 12, 15, 16, 18, 19, 21, and 22 fall in this category.

Other test results must be viewed with caution. Table 8.19 contains the results for $(23)(6) = 138$ paired-difference tests. If the probability of concluding that one pair of means differ, when in fact they are equal, is $\alpha = .05$, just imagine the probability of concluding that *one or more* pairs of means differ in 138 tests! It is very large. Therefore, it is very likely that some of the test results that indicate differences in means in Table 8.19 are due solely to chance. For example, look at the percentage of total assets represented by equity capital (variable 2). The sample mean (6.6) for failed banks one year prior to bank failure is less than the corresponding value for nonfailed banks (8.5), and the t value, $t = -3.2$, is highly significant. For 6 years prior to bank failure the sample mean for failed banks (10.0) is *larger* than the mean for unfailed banks (8.1) and this t value, $t = 2.4$, is also statistically significant. Statistically significant? Yes, but completely reversed in direction. There may be a practical explanation for this phenomenon, but more likely, it is the result of pure chance.

Before we conclude, note that the paired-difference tests of Table 8.19 could have been conducted using the single large-sample z test of Section 7.4. Each involves a test of a single mean, $\mu_d = \mu_1 - \mu_2$, that is based on a large number n of pairs of observations (except for 7 and 8 years prior to failure). Consequently, $\bar{d}$ will be approximately normally distributed, and s_d^2 will provide a good estimate of σ_d^2. As noted earlier, when the sample sizes are large, the z and t tests are (for all practical purposes) equivalent, and they lead to the same test results and conclusions.

SUMMARY

8.10

The t, χ^2, and F statistics employed in the small-sample statistical methods discussed in the preceding sections are based upon the assumption that the sampled populations possess a normal probability distribution. This requirement will be adequately satisfied for many types of experimental measurements.

You will observe the very close relationship connecting Student's t and the z statistic and, therefore, the similarity of the methods for testing hypotheses and constructing confidence intervals. The χ^2 and F statistics employed in making inferences concerning population variances do not, of course, follow this pattern, but the reasoning employed in the construction of the statistical tests and confidence intervals is identical for all the methods we have presented.

TIPS ON PROBLEM SOLVING

To help you decide whether the techniques of this chapter are appropriate for the solution of a problem, ask yourself the following questions:

(1) Does the problem imply that an inference should be made about a population mean or the difference between two means? Are the samples small, say $n < 30$? If the answers to both questions are yes, you may be able to use one of the methods of Sections 8.2, 8.4, or 8.5. If the sample sizes are large ($n \geq 30$), you can use the methods of Chapters 6 and 7. In practice, you would also need to verify that the assumptions underlying each procedure are satisfied. Are the population distributions nearly normal, and have the sampling procedures conformed to those prescribed for the statistical method?

(2) When you are comparing population means, were the observations from the two populations selected in a paired manner? If they were, you must use the paired-difference analysis of Section 8.5. If the samples were selected independently and in a random manner, use the methods of Section 8.4.

(3) Is data variation the primary objective of the problem? If it is, you may be required to make an inference about a population variance σ^2 (Section 8.6), or to compare two population variances σ_1^2 and σ_2^2 (Section 8.7).

Note: The tips on problem solving at the end of Section 6.11 will also be helpful in solving problems in this chapter.

REFERENCES

BMDPC: User's Guide to BMDP on the IBM PC. Los Angeles: BMDP Statistical Software.

Dixon, W. J., Brown, M. B., Engelman, L., Frane, J. W., Hill, M. A., Jennrich, R. I., and Toporek, J. D. *BMDP Statistical Software.* Berkeley: University of California Press, 1985.

Freund, J. E., and Williams, F. J.; revised by B. Perles and C. Sullivan. *Modern Business Statistics.* Englewood Cliffs, N.J.: Prentice-Hall, 1969.

Hill, MaryAnn, ed. *BMDP User's Digest.* 2nd ed. Los Angeles: BMDP Statistical Software, 1982.

Hoel, P. G., and Jessen, R. J. *Basic Statistics for Business and Economics.* 3rd ed. New York: Wiley, 1982.

Norusis, M. J. *SPSS/PC+: SPSS for the IBM PC/XT/AT.* Chicago: SPSS, 1986.

Norusis, M. J. *The SPSS Guide to Data Analysis.* Chicago: SPSS, 1986.

Ryan, T. A., Joiner, B. L., and Ryan, B. F. *Minitab Reference Manual.* University Park, Pa.: Minitab Project, 1985.

Ryan, T. A., Joiner, B. L., and Ryan, B. F. *Minitab Handbook.* 2nd ed. Boston: PWS-KENT, 1985.

SAS Procedures Guide for Personal Computers. Version 6 ed. Cary, N.C.: SAS Institute, 1986.

SAS Statistics Guide for Personal Computers. Version 6 ed. Cary, N.C.: SAS Institute, 1986.

SAS User's Guide: Basics. Version 5 ed. Cary, N.C.: SAS Institute, 1985.

SAS User's Guide: Statistics. Version 5 ed. Cary, N.C.: SAS Institute, 1985.

SPSS^x User's Guide. Chicago: SPSS, 1983.

KEY TERMS

Student's t statistic (page 277)

t distribution (page 277)

Degrees of freedom (page 278)

Pooled estimator of σ^2 (page 288)

Number of degrees of freedom (page 288)

Design of an experiment (page 298)

Paired-difference experiment (page 298)

Paired-difference test (page 298)

Blocking (page 301)

Chi-square variable (page 306)

Chi-square probability distribution (page 306)

F distribution (page 313)

F statistic (page 314)

SUPPLEMENTARY EXERCISES

8.73 What assumptions are made when Student's t test is used to test an hypothesis concerning a population mean?

8.74 A manufacturer can tolerate a small amount (.05 milligram per liter) of impurities in a raw material needed for manufacturing its product. Because the laboratory test for the impurities is subject to experimental error, the manufacturer tests each batch ten times. Assume that the mean value of the experimental error is 0 and thus that the mean value of the ten test readings is an unbiased estimate of the true amount of the impurities in the batch. For a particular batch of the raw material the mean of the ten test readings is .058 milligram per liter (mg/l), and the standard deviation is .012 mg/l. Do the data provide sufficient evidence to indicate that the amount of impurities in the batch exceeds .05 mg/l? Find the approximate p-value for the test, and interpret its value.

8.75 A coin-operated soft-drink machine was designed to discharge, on the average, 7 ounces of beverage per cup. In a test of the machine ten cupfuls of beverage were drawn from the machine and measured. The mean and standard deviation of the ten measurements were 7.1 and .12 ounces, respectively. Do these data present sufficient evidence to indicate that the mean discharge differs from 7 ounces? Test at the 10% level of significance.

8.76 Find a 90% confidence interval for the mean discharge in Exercise 8.75.

8.77 Two random samples, each containing 11 measurements, were drawn from normal populations possessing means μ_1 and μ_2, respectively, and a common variance σ^2. The sample means and variances are as follows:

Population I	Population II
$\bar{x}_1 = 60.4$	$\bar{x}_2 = 65.3$
$s_1^2 = 31.40$	$s_2^2 = 44.82$

Do the data present sufficient evidence to indicate a difference between the population means? Test at the $\alpha = .10$ level of significance.

8.78 Find a 90% confidence interval for the difference between the population means in Exercise 8.77.

 8.79 The temperature of operation of two paint-drying ovens associated with two manufacturing production lines was recorded for 20 days. (Pairing was ignored.) The means and variances of the two samples are

$$\bar{x}_1 = 164 \qquad \bar{x}_2 = 168$$

$$s_1^2 = 81 \qquad s_2^2 = 172$$

Do the data present sufficient evidence to indicate a difference in temperature variability for the two ovens? Test the hypothesis that $\sigma_1^2 = \sigma_2^2$ at the $\alpha = .10$ level of significance.

 8.80 A production plant has two extremely complex fabricating systems, with one being twice the age of the other. Both systems are checked, lubricated, and maintained once every 2 weeks. The number of finished products fabricated daily by each of the systems is recorded for 30 working days. The results are given in the table. Do these data present sufficient evidence to conclude that the variability in daily production warrants increased maintenance of the older fabricating system? Use a 5% level of significance.

New system	Old system
$\bar{x}_1 = 246$	$\bar{x}_2 = 240$
$s_1 = 15.6$	$s_2 = 28.2$

 8.81 A random sampling of bank customer-checking overdrafts at a local bank produced the following data (to the nearest dollar):

302	512	97	316
69	16	133	701
107	156	401	14
465	72	128	68

Suppose that the general level of the bank's overdrafts is expected to remain stable in the immediate future. Use the sample data to find a 90% confidence interval for the mean size of the bank's checking overdrafts.

8.82 Suppose that an experiment has been designed to estimate the difference between two population means $(\mu_1 - \mu_2)$. Independent random samples of size n_1 and n_2 have been selected from the two populations and the statistic $(\bar{x}_1 - \bar{x}_2)$ is used as the estimator. Would the amount of information extracted from the data be increased by pairing successive observations and analyzing the differences? Is this an appropriate method of analysis?

8.83 When should one employ a paired-difference analysis in making inferences concerning the difference between two means?

8.84 A utility company collected data to compare the length of time required to process an electric utility bill using two different processing methods. Eight billing clerks were each given a single utility bill and asked to process the bill by using both procedures 1 and 2. The processing times (in seconds) are shown in Table 8.20. Do the data present sufficient evidence to indicate a difference in mean processing time for the two processing methods?

TABLE 8.20   Processing Time Data for Exercise 8.84

Processor	Process 1	Process 2
1	3	4
2	1	2
3	1	3
4	2	1
5	1	2
6	2	3
7	3	3
8	1	3

(a) Find the approximate observed significance level for the test.

(b) Test using $\alpha = .05$.

8.85 Place a 95% confidence interval on the difference in mean processing time for the two processing methods in Exercise 8.84.

8.86 A condominium apartment's monthly water consumption has been averaging 48,000 gallons per month over the past five years. The mean and standard deviation of the monthly consumption for the current 12 months is $\bar{x} = 51,102$ gallons and $s = 5127$ gallons. Do the data provide sufficient evidence to indicate that some unusual factor is causing a larger-than-expected water consumption for the condominium—that is, a consumption exceeding a mean of 48,000 gallons per month?

(a) State the alternative hypothesis that you would want to use in order to detect an unusually high consumption of water.

(b) State H_0.

(c) Is it reasonable to choose a large or a small value of α for this test? Explain.

(d) Give the rejection region for $\alpha = .05$.

(e) Conduct the test and state your conclusions.

8.87 An industrial psychologist wanted to compare two methods, A and B, for indoctrinating new employees with the company's personnel policies. Twenty new employees were given a general intelligence test and were then matched, according to test scores, in ten pairs. From each pair one employee was randomly assigned to indoctrination method A and the second to method B.

Each employee was tested at the end of a four-week period. The achievement scores shown in Table 8.21 were recorded.

TABLE 8.21   Achievement Score Data for Exercise 8.87

Pair	Method A	Method B
1	36	35
2	37	35
3	41	40
4	42	41
5	36	36
6	35	34
7	42	40
8	33	31
9	40	39
10	38	37

(a) Do the data provide sufficient evidence to indicate that the mean achievement scores differ for the two indoctrination methods? (Use $\alpha = .05$.)

(b) Estimate the mean difference in achievement scores using a 98% confidence interval.

 8.88 A manufacturer of a machine to package soap powder claimed that the machine could load cartons at a given weight with a range of no more than two-fifths of an ounce. The mean and variance of a sample of eight 3-pound boxes were found to equal 3.1 and .018, respectively. Test the hypothesis that the variance of the population of weight measurements is $\sigma^2 = .01$ against the alternative $\sigma^2 > .01$. Use an $\alpha = .05$ level of significance.

8.89 Find a 90% confidence interval for σ^2 in Exercise 8.88.

8.90 Under what assumptions can the F distribution be used in making inferences about the ratio of population variances?

 8.91 The closing prices of two common stocks were recorded for a period of 15 days. The means and variances are

$$\bar{x}_1 = 40.33 \qquad \bar{x}_2 = 42.54$$
$$s_1^2 = 1.54 \qquad s_2^2 = 2.96$$

Do these data present sufficient evidence to indicate a difference in variability of closing prices of the two stocks? Give the approximate p-value for the test, and interpret its value.

 8.92 A chemical manufacturer claims that the purity of his product never varies more than 2%. Five batches were tested and gave purity readings of 98.2%, 97.1%, 98.9%, 97.7%, 97.9%. Do the data provide sufficient evidence to contradict the manufacturer's claim? (*Hint:* To be generous, let a range of 2% equal 4σ.)

8.93 Refer to Exercise 8.92. Find a 90% confidence interval for σ^2.

 8.94 A cannery prints "weight 16 ounces" on its label. The quality control supervisor selects nine cans at random and weighs them. She finds $\bar{x} = 15.7$ and $s = .5$. Do the data present sufficient evidence to indicate that the mean weight is less than that claimed on the label? (Use $\alpha = .05$.)

8.95 A car dealer decided to compare the mean monthly sales of two salespersons, call them A and B. Because the strength of sales varies with the season and with people's opinions about the economy, the car dealer decided to make the comparison on a monthly basis. The data shown in

Table 8.22 give the monthly sales (to the nearest thousands of dollars) for the two salespersons.

TABLE 8.22 Monthly Sales Data for Exercise 8.95

Month	Salesperson A	Salesperson B
January	130	105
February	141	109
March	163	147
April	176	159
May	147	150
June	160	134
July	145	123
August	129	130
September	104	91
October	139	124
November	163	141
December	151	147

(a) Do the data provide sufficient evidence to indicate a difference in mean sales for the two salespersons? Test with $\alpha = .05$.

(b) Find a 95% confidence interval for $(\mu_A - \mu_B)$, and interpret your results.

8.96 How much combustion efficiency should a homeowner expect from an oil furnace? The EPA (*Environment News*, January 1977) states that 80% or above is excellent, 75% to 79% is good, 70% to 74% is fair, and below 70% is poor. A home-heating contractor who sells two makes of oil heaters (call them A and B) decided to compare their mean efficiencies. An analysis was made of the efficiencies for 8 heaters of type A and 6 of type B. The efficiency ratings, in percentages, for the 14 heaters are shown in the table.

Type A	72	78	73	69	75	74	69	75
Type B	78	76	81	74	82	75		

(a) Do the data provide sufficient evidence to indicate a difference in mean efficiencies for the two makes of home heaters? Find the approximate p-value for the test, and interpret its value.

(b) Find a 90% confidence interval for $(\mu_A - \mu_B)$, and interpret the result.

8.97 Now that energy conservation is so important, some scientists think we should give closer scrutiny to the cost (in energy) of producing various forms of food. One recent study compares the mean amount of oil required to produce 1 acre of different types of crops. For example, suppose that we want to compare the mean amount of oil required to produce 1 acre of corn versus 1 acre of cauliflower. The readings in barrels of oil per acre, based on 20-acre plots, seven for each crop, are shown in the table. Use these data to find a 90% confidence interval for the difference in the mean amount of oil required to produce these two crops.

Corn	5.6	7.1	4.5	6.0	7.9	4.8	5.7
Cauliflower	15.9	13.4	17.6	16.8	15.8	16.3	17.1

8.98 In an earlier exercise we mentioned the Bureau of Labor Statistics surveys of consumer spending habits, particularly focusing on the estimate of the mean number of automobiles per family in the United States. Suppose that you were to run a very small survey for your community. You randomly sample $n = 20$ households and for each you record the number of automobiles per household. Suppose that $\bar{x} = 1.75$ and $s = .55$. Is it valid to use the t statistic to form a 90% confidence interval for the mean number of automobiles per household for the community? Explain.

 8.99 One way to compare the relative prices of two common stocks is to compare their price-earnings ratios, the ratios of a stock's price per share to the amount of money earned by the company per share per year. For example, Table 8.23 lists the price-earnings ratios (P/E's) for ten randomly selected electric power companies versus ten nonutility blue-chip stocks in November 1986.

TABLE 8.23   P/E Ratio Data for Exercise 8.99

Electric Utility	P/E	Nonutility Blue Chip	P/E
Carolina Power & Light	10	IBM	14
Minnesota Power & Light	12	Abbot Labs	19
TECO Energy	14	Minnesota Mining	16
Duke Power	14	Safeway Stores	19
Wisconsin Electrical Power	12	RJR Nabisco	13
Pacific Gas & Electric	9	Monsanto	14
Montana Power	11	NCNB Corp.	9
Houston Industries	9	Hilton Hotels	18
Illinois Power	8	Pillsbury	16
Pennsylvania Power & Light	14	Textron	9

Source: Data from *Standard and Poor's Stock Guide*, November 1986.

(a) Do the data provide sufficient evidence to indicate a difference in the mean P/E ratio between electric utility common stocks and nonutility blue-chip stocks? Test using $\alpha = .10$.

(b) Give the approximate p-value for the test, and interpret its value.

8.100 Refer to Exercise 8.99. Do the data present sufficient evidence to indicate differences in variability of the P/E ratios between electric utility common stocks and nonutility blue-chip common stocks?

(a) Test using $\alpha = .05$.

(b) Find the approximate p-value for the test, and interpret it.

 8.101 Owing to the variability of trade-in allowance, the profit per new car sold by an automobile dealer varies from car to car. The profit per sale (in hundreds of dollars), tabulated for the past week, was as follows:

6.3	9.4
6.2	7.7
4.4	8.3

Do these data present sufficient evidence to indicate that the average profit per sale is less than $7.80? Test at an $\alpha = .05$ level of significance.

 8.102 A manufacturer of television sets claimed that his product possessed an average defect-free life of 3 years. Three households in a community have purchased the sets and all three sets are observed to fail before 3 years, with failure times equal to 2.5, 1.9, and 2.9 years, respectively. Do these data present sufficient evidence to contradict the manufacturer's claim? Test at an $\alpha = .05$ level of significance.

8.103 Calculate a 90% confidence interval for the mean life of the television sets in Exercise 8.102.

8.104 Refer to Exercises 8.102 and 8.103. Approximately how many observations would be required to estimate the mean life of the television sets correct to within .2 year with probability equal to .90?

8.105 An experiment is conducted to compare two new automobile designs. Twenty people are randomly selected, and each person is asked to rate each design on a scale of 1 (poor) to 10 (excellent). The resulting ratings will be used to test the null hypothesis that the mean level of approval is the same for both designs against the alternative hypothesis that one of the automobile designs is preferred. Would these data satisfy the assumptions required for the Student's t test of Section 8.4? Explain.

8.106 The data in Table 8.24 were collected on lost-time accidents (the figures given are mean man-hours lost per month over a period of one year) both before and after an industrial safety program was put into effect. Data were recorded for six industrial plants. Do the data provide sufficient evidence to indicate whether the safety program was effective in reducing lost-time accidents? (Use $\alpha = .10$.)

TABLE 8.24   Lost-Time Data for Exercise 8.106

Data Collected	Plant Number					
	1	2	3	4	5	6
Before program	38	64	42	70	58	30
After program	31	58	43	65	52	29

8.107 To compare the demand for two different entrees, the manager of a cafeteria recorded the number of purchases for each entree on seven consecutive days. The data are shown in Table 8.25. Do the data provide sufficient evidence to indicate a greater mean demand for one of the entrees?

TABLE 8.25   Entree Purchase Data for Exercise 8.107

Day	A	B
Mon.	420	391
Tues.	374	343
Wed.	434	469
Thurs.	395	412
Fri.	637	538
Sat.	594	521
Sun.	679	625

8.108 The EPA limit on the allowable discharge of suspended solids into rivers and streams is 60 milligrams per liter (mg/l) per day. A study of water samples selected from the discharge at a phosphate mine shows that over a long period of time the mean daily discharge of suspended solids is 48 mg/l but the day-to-day discharge readings are very variable. State inspectors measured the discharge rates of suspended solids for $n = 20$ days and found $s^2 = 39$ (mg/l)^2. Find a 90% confidence interval for σ^2. Interpret your results.

8.109 A manufacturer of electric motors compared the productivity of assembly workers for two types of 40-hour weekly work schedules, four 10-hour days (schedule 1) and the standard five 8-hour days (schedule 2). Twenty workers were assigned to each work schedule, and the number of units assembled was recorded for a one-week period. The sample means (in hundreds of units) and variances for the two schedules are shown in Table 8.26.

TABLE 8.26   Sample Data for Exercise 8.109

	Schedule	
Statistic	1	2
Sample mean	43.1	44.6
Sample variance	4.28	3.89

(a) Do the data provide sufficient evidence to indicate a difference in the mean productivity for the two work schedules? Test using $\alpha = .05$.

(b) Give the approximate p-value for the test, and interpret it.

(c) Find a 95% confidence interval for the difference in the mean productivity for the two work schedules, and interpret the interval.

8.110 Suppose that the manufacturer of Exercise 8.109 wants to estimate the difference in mean weekly productivity for the two work schedules correct to within one unit. How many workers would have to be included in each sample? (*Hint:* To solve, use the method of Section 6.9.)

8.111 The data shown in Table 8.27 give the annual operating cost comparisons for automatic and stick-shift versions of four different makes of automobiles. If the data represent a random sampling of the comparative costs of operating automobiles, find a 90% confidence interval for the mean difference in operating costs between automatic and stick-shift versions of the same type of automobile.

TABLE 8.27   Cost Data for Exercise 8.111

	Annual Operating Cost*	
Automobile Make	Automatic	Manual
Ford Tempo	$1520	$1440
Plymouth Reliant	1240	1150
AMC Encore S	1380	1150
Chevrolet Cavalier	1150	1100

*Operating costs: oil, maintenance, tires, and fuel.
Source: Runzheimer and Co., Inc., data from *USA Today*, January 10, 1985.

Methods for comparing two population means, based on independent random samples and on a paired-difference experiment, were presented in Chapter 8. Chapter 9 extends these analyses to the comparison of any number of population means, using a technique called an analysis of variance. In this chapter we will explain the logic of an analysis of variance and give the analyses for three experimental designs.

9
THE ANALYSIS OF VARIANCE

A Comparison of Car Insurance Costs for Different Locales

In an article titled "Sure-Fire Ways to Save on Car-Insurance Costs" (*Family Circle,* February 20, 1979), Barbara Gilder Quint notes that some of us are paying more in car insurance than our vehicles are worth. In addition to providing helpful hints on how to save, she provides some data on the costs of $50,000/$100,000/$10,000 liability and $50 deductible comprehensive insurance on a standard Chevrolet Citation. The costs of the same type of policy (excluding claim-handling reliability, etc.) for six different insurance companies were acquired for four different locales in the United States. The data are shown in Table 9.1.

You can see that the differences in mean car insurance costs appear to be substantial. But how can we tell for certain, and how can we place a confidence interval on the difference between any pair of locale means?

You will notice that this sampling situation is similar to the paired-difference experiment of Section 8.5. The major difference is that we are now comparing four population means, in contrast to two in the paired-difference

experiment. The pairing, in this case *matching,* occurs because the insurance costs for the four locales are compared within individual insurance companies. Since procedures for establishing rates may vary substantially from one company to another, comparing locale rates *within* a single company, and repeating the procedure for the six companies, enables us to remove *between*-company variation from the comparison. This experimental procedure for comparing more than two population means—an extension of the paired-difference experiment—is called a *randomized block design.* The populations being compared, the locales, are called *treatments;* the relatively homogeneous matched blocks of experimental units (observations within the same insurance company) are called *blocks.*

In this chapter we will extend the methods of Chapter 8 to the comparison of more than two population means. The method that we will employ is called *an analysis of variance.*

TABLE 9.1   A Comparison of Car Insurance Costs for a Standard Policy

	Policy Cost			
Insurance Company	Big City: Chicago (Business District)	Middle-Sized City: Topeka, KS	Rural: Dillsboro, IN	Suburban: Seattle (Suburbs)
Allstate	$597	$280	$245	$339
Continental	768	260	240	275
Home (Gold Key Package)	776	284	257	304
Nationwide	739	334	262	317
State Farm	562	338	250	335
Travelers	696	315	330	350

Source: Adapted from Barbara Gilder Quint, "Sure-Fire Ways to Save on Car-Insurance Costs," *Family Circle,* February 20, 1979. © 1979 THE FAMILY CIRCLE, INC.

THE MOTIVATION FOR AN ANALYSIS OF VARIANCE

9.1

Suppose that you want to compare the mean size of health insurance claims submitted by five groups of policyholders. Ten claims were randomly selected from among the claims submitted for each group. The data are shown in Table 9.2. Do the data contained in the five samples provide sufficient evidence to indicate a difference in the mean levels of claims among the five health groups?

To answer this question, we might think of comparing the means in pairs by using repeated applications of the Student's t test of Section 8.4. If we were to detect a difference between any pair of means, then we would conclude that there is evidence of at least one difference among the means and it would appear that we would have answered our question. The problem with this procedure is that there are $C_2^5 = 10$ different pairs of means that have to be tested. Even if all of the means are identical, we have a probability α of rejecting the null hypothesis that a particular pair of means are equal. When this test procedure is repeated ten times, the probability of incorrectly concluding that at least one pair of means differ is quite high. Because the risk of an erroneous decision may be quite large, we look for a single test of the null hypothesis, that the five group means $\mu_1, \mu_2, \ldots \mu_5$ are equal, against the alternative hypothesis, that at least one pair of means differ.

The procedure for comparing more than two population means is known as an **analysis of variance**. The logic underlying an analysis of variance can be seen by examining the dot diagrams for two sets of *sample* data for two different cases, (a) and (b). In case (a) the first sample contains $n_1 = 3$ measurements, 1, 8, and 3. The second sample contains $n_2 = 2$ measurements, 2 and 10. The dot diagrams for these two samples appear as shown in Figure 9.1(a). For case (b) the first sample contains $n_1 = 3$ measurements, 4.5, 3, and 4.5. The second sample contains two measurements, 5.5 and 6.5. The dot diagrams for case (b) are shown in Figure 9.1(b). Examining the dot

TABLE 9.2   Insurance Claims Submitted by Five Health Groups

Group 1	Group 2	Group 3	Group 4	Group 5
$ 763	$1335	$ 596	$3742	$1632
4365	1262	1448	1833	5078
2144	217	1183	375	3010
1998	4100	3200	2010	671
5412	2948	630	743	2145
957	3210	942	867	4063
1286	867	1285	1233	1232
311	3744	128	1072	1456
863	1635	844	3105	2735
1499	643	1683	1767	767
$\bar{x}_1 = 1959.8$	$\bar{x}_2 = 1996.1$	$\bar{x}_3 = 1193.9$	$\bar{x}_4 = 1674.7$	$\bar{x}_5 = 2278.9$

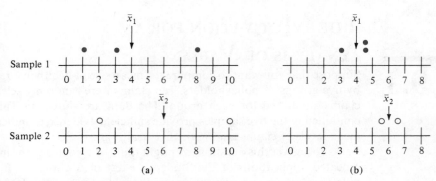

FIGURE 9.1   Dot Diagrams for Comparing Sample Means

diagrams, you can see that for both cases, $\bar{x}_1 = 4$ and $\bar{x}_2 = 6$. Which case, do you think, suggests a difference between population means μ_1 and μ_2?

From a visual observation of the dot diagrams and your intuition, we think that you will agree with us. Case (b) suggests a difference between the population means; case (a) does not. To arrive at this conclusion, we compared the *variation* (difference) *between the sample means* with the *variation within the samples*. Although $\bar{x}_1 - \bar{x}_2 = -2$ for both cases, this difference is small in case (a) in comparison to the large amount of variation within the two samples. In contrast, the difference in sample means in case (b) is very large in comparison to the variation within the two samples.

An analysis of variance to compare more than two population means formalizes the visual comparison of the variation between means with the variation within samples. This comparison of two sources of variation will lead us to the analysis of variance *F* test in Section 9.3.

THE ASSUMPTIONS FOR AN ANALYSIS OF VARIANCE

9.2

The assumptions upon which the test and estimation procedures for an analysis of variance are based are similar to those required for the Student's *t* statistic of Chapter 8. Regardless of the sampling procedure employed to collect the data, we assume that the observations within each sampled population are normally distributed with a common variance σ^2.

In this chapter we will describe the analysis of variance for three different experimental designs. Two are based on independent random sampling from the respective populations. The third is an extension of the matched-pairs design of Chapter 8 and involves the random assignment of treatments within matched sets of observations. The sampling procedure for each of these designs will be restated in their respective sections.

The assumptions for an analysis of variance are given in the following box.

ASSUMPTIONS UNDERLYING ANALYSIS OF VARIANCE TEST AND ESTIMATION PROCEDURES

(1) The observations within each population are normally distributed with a common variance σ^2.

(2) Assumptions regarding the sampling procedure are specified for each design in the sections that follow.

COMPARING MORE THAN TWO POPULATION MEANS: AN ANALYSIS OF VARIANCE FOR INDEPENDENT RANDOM SAMPLES

9.3

The methodology, an analysis of variance, derives its name from the manner in which the quantities used to measure variation are acquired. Suppose that we want to compare k population means $\mu_1, \mu_2, \ldots, \mu_k$, based on independent random samples of $n_1, n_2, \ldots, n_k$ observations selected from populations $1, 2, \ldots, k$, respectively. Thus for the health claims data in Table 9.2 we want to compare the means for $k = 5$ insurance groups based on random samples of $n_1 = n_2 = \cdots = n_5 = 10$ claims per group. Then it can be shown (proof omitted) that the sum of squares of deviations of all $n = n_1 + n_2 + \cdots + n_5 = 50$ x-values about their overall mean $\bar{x}$, often called the **total sum of squares** (or Total SS),

$$\text{Total SS} = \text{SS}_x = \sum_{i=1}^{n} (x_i - \bar{x})^2$$

can be partitioned into two components. The first component, called the **sum of squares for treatments (SST)** is used to calculate a measure of the variation between sample means. For our example, the **treatments** are the five insurance groups. The second component, called **sum of squares for error (SSE)**, is used to measure the variation within samples. Thus

$$\text{Total SS} = \text{SST} + \text{SSE}$$

This partitioning of the Total SS into relevant components that measure sources of variation explains why the procedure is called an analysis of variance.

It is not difficult to calculate the sums of squares needed in an analysis of variance, but it is tedious. Since most statistical computer program packages contain programs to conduct analyses of variance for various experimental designs, we will discuss the procedure while explaining and interpreting the SAS printout for an analysis of variance of the health insurance claims data in Table 9.2. Corresponding Minitab and SPSS[x] printouts will also be presented so that you can compare the outputs for an analysis of variance for the same set of data. The computing formulas, which will enable you to perform the analysis of variance by using a pocket calculator, are presented in optional Section 9.4.

EXAMPLE 9.1   Interpret the SAS analysis of variance printout and present corresponding Minitab and SPSS[x] printouts for the comparison of mean health insurance claims for the five health groups (see Table 9.2).

SOLUTION   The SAS, Minitab, and SPSS[x] computer printouts for an analysis of variance of the health insurance claims data are shown in Tables 9.3, 9.4, and 9.5, respectively. Since the three printouts are similar, we will shade and explain the meanings of the various quantities that appear in the SAS printout in Table 9.3 and will shade (where available) the corresponding quantities in the Minitab and SPSS[x] printouts in Tables 9.4 and 9.5.

(1) The table in shaded area ① in the SAS printout is called an **analysis of variance, or ANOVA, table**. This table contains three rows and five columns. The three sources of variation are listed under SOURCE in column 1:

MODEL: This source, sometimes identified as TREATMENTS, represents variation among the sample means. Minitab calls it FACTOR, and SPSS[x] identifies it as MAIN EFFECTS GROUP.

ERROR: This source measures the variation within samples.

CORRECTED TOTAL: This source measures the variation of all x values about the overall mean of all $n = 50$ x values.

(2) The sums of squares of deviations corresponding to the three sources of variation are shown in column 3 of shaded area ①. The sum of squares corresponding to MODEL, the sum of squares for treatments (or, for this example, insurance groups), SST, is

$$SST = 6742554.48000000$$

The formula for computing SST is given in optional Section 9.4. The sum of squares corresponding to ERROR is a measure of the variability of the x-values within samples. Thus

$$SSE = 77411264.40000000$$

SSE is the pooled sum of squares of deviations of the observations about their respective sample means; that is,

$$SSE = \sum_{i=1}^{n_1}(x_i - \bar{x}_1)^2 + \sum_{i=1}^{n_2}(x_i - \bar{x}_2)^2 + \cdots + \sum_{i=1}^{n_5}(x_i - \bar{x}_5)^2$$

This computing formula is given later in optional Section 9.4. Finally, the sum of squares of deviations corresponding to the CORRECTED TOTAL is what we have called Total SS or SS_x, that is,

$$\text{Total SS} = \sum_{i=1}^{50}(x_i - \bar{x})^2 = 84153818.88$$

You can verify that

$$SST + SSE = \text{Total SS}$$

TABLE 9.3   SAS Computer Printout for an Analysis of Variance of the Health Insurance Data of Table 9.2

ANALYSIS OF VARIANCE PROCEDURE

DEPENDENT VARIABLE: COST

SOURCE	DF	SUM OF SQUARES	MEAN SQUARE	F VALUE	PR > F	R-SQUARE	C.V.
MODEL	4	6742554.48000000	1685638.62000000	0.98	0.4281	0.080122	72.0381
ERROR	45	77411264.40000000	1720250.32000000		ROOT MSE		COST MEAN
CORRECTED TOTAL	49	84153818.88000000			1311.58313499		1820.68000000

SOURCE	DF	ANOVA SS	F VALUE	PR > F
GROUP	4	6742554.48000000	0.98	0.4281

TABLE 9.4   Minitab Computer Printout for an Analysis of Variance of the Health Insurance Data of Table 9.2

ANALYSIS OF VARIANCE

SOURCE	DF	SS	MS	F
FACTOR	4	6742554	1685638	0.98
ERROR	45	77411264	1720250	
TOTAL	49	84153816		

INDIVIDUAL 95 PCT CI'S FOR MEAN
BASED ON POOLED STDEV

LEVEL	N	MEAN	STDEV
C1	10	1960	1659
C2	10	1996	1384
C3	10	1194	839
C4	10	1675	1066
C5	10	2279	1447

```
                    ------+---------+---------+---------+
                          (----------*----------)
                          (----------*----------)
                (----------*----------)
                     (---------*----------)
                          (---------*----------)
                    ------+---------+---------+---------+
                      750      1500      2250      3000
```

POOLED STDEV =   1312

TABLE 9.5   SPSS[x] Computer Printout for an Analysis of Variance of the Health Insurance Data of Table 9.2

* * * A N A L Y S I S   O F   V A R I A N C E * * *

COST
BY   GROUP

SOURCE OF VARIATION	SUM OF SQUARES	DF	MEAN SQUARE	F	SIGNIF OF F
MAIN EFFECTS	6742554.480	4	1685638.620	0.980	0.428
GROUP	6742554.480	4	1685638.620	0.980	0.428
EXPLAINED	6742554.480	4	1685638.620	0.980	0.428
RESIDUAL	77411264.400	45	1720250.320		
TOTAL	84153818.880	49	1717424.875		

that is,

$$6742554.48 + 77411264.40 = 84153818.88$$

(3) Each sum of squares of deviations, divided by the appropriate number of degrees of freedom, will provide an estimate of σ^2 when the null hypothesis is true, in other words, when

$$\mu_1 = \mu_2 = \cdots = \mu_5$$

These degrees of freedom are shown in column 2.

(a) The degrees of freedom for the CORRECTED TOTAL (Total SS) will always be $(n - 1)$, or for this example, $50 - 1 = 49$.

(b) The degrees of freedom for MODEL (or insurance groups) will always equal one less than the number k of populations, in this case, $(k - 1) = 5 - 1 = 4$.

(c) The number of degrees of freedom for ERROR will always equal $n_1 + n_2 + \cdots + n_k - k = n - k$, or for this example, $50 - 5 = 45$. Note that the sum of the numbers of degrees of freedom for MODEL and ERROR will always equal the number of degrees of freedom for the CORRECTED TOTAL; that is, $4 + 45 = 49$.

(4) Column 4 of the ANOVA table, headed MEAN SQUARE, gives the estimates of σ^2 based on the variation among the sample means (in the row corresponding to MODEL) and the variation within samples (in the row corresponding to ERROR) when the null hypothesis is true—that is, when $\mu_1 = \mu_2 = \mu_3 = \cdots = \mu_5$. These estimates are calculated by dividing a sum of squares by its corresponding degrees of freedom. Thus the **mean square for treatments** (MODEL), denoted as MST and shown in column 4, is

$$\text{MST} = \frac{\text{SST}}{k - 1} = \frac{6742554.48}{4} = 1685638.62$$

Similarly, the **mean square for error**, denoted as MSE or s^2 and shown in column 4, is

$$\text{MSE} = s^2 = \frac{\text{SSE}}{n - k} = \frac{77411264.4}{45} = 1720250.32$$

This quantity, s^2, is the pooled estimate of σ^2 based on the sum of squares of deviations of the x-values about their respective sample means and is an extension (since it is based on $k = 5$ samples) of the pooled estimate of σ^2 given in Section 8.4.

(5) The final step in testing $H_0 : \mu_1 = \mu_2 = \cdots = \mu_k$ is comparing the two estimates of σ^2: MST, which is based on the variation of the sample means about $\bar{x}$, and MSE $= s^2$, which is based on the variation of the x-values about their respective sample means. We use the F statistic of Section 8.7. Thus when H_0 is true, the sampling distribution of

$$F = \frac{\text{MST}}{\text{MSE}}$$

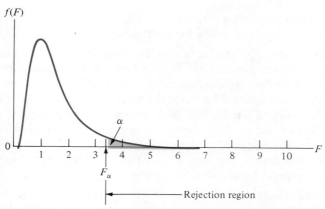

FIGURE 9.2   Rejection Region for the Analysis of Variance F Test

will be an F distribution with $v_1 = k - 1$ (for our example, $k - 1 = 5 - 1 = 4$) numerator degrees of freedom and $v_2 = n - k$ (for our example, $n - k = 45$) denominator degrees of freedom. If H_0 is false—that is, if $\mu_1, \mu_2, \ldots, \mu_k$ are not all equal—the estimate of σ^2 based on MST will be overly large, and the calculated value of F will be larger than expected. Consequently, we reject H_0 for large values of F; that is, values of F larger than some critical value F_α (see Figure 9.2). The critical values of F corresponding to various values of v_1 and v_2 and for $\alpha = .10, .05, .025, .01,$ and $.005$ are shown, respectively, in Tables 7, 8, 9, 10, and 11 of the Appendix. (The use of these tables is explained in Section 8.7.)

For example, if we want to test

$$H_0 : \mu_1 = \mu_2 = \mu_3 = \mu_4 = \mu_5$$

for $\alpha = .05$, we consult Table 8 in the Appendix and look for the F value corresponding to $v_1 = 4$ and $v_2 = 45$. Table 8 does not give this F value, but it does give the F value for $v_1 = 4$ and $v_2 = 40$ as 2.61 and the F value for $v_1 = 4$ and $v_2 = 60$ as 2.53. Consequently, we will reject H_0 if the computed value of F is larger than 2.61 (or actually a number slightly smaller). The computed value of F,

$$F = \frac{\text{MST}}{\text{MSE}} = .98$$

is shown in column 5 of the ANOVA table. You can see that this computed value of F, .98, does not exceed the critical value and therefore does not fall in the rejection region. Consequently, there is not sufficient evidence to indicate that the mean claim size differs among the five insurance groups.

(6) The observed significance level, the probability of observing a value of the F statistic as large or larger than .98, is shown in shaded area ② of the SAS printout. The p-value for the test is

$$p\text{-value} = .4281$$

This large p-value is consistent with the results of the F test (step 5). For $\alpha = .05$ we will reject H_0 when the p-value is less than or equal to .05.

(7) An analysis of variance can be conducted (as you will see in the following sections) to partition the Total SS into sums of squares corresponding to two or more sources of variation in addition to SSE. The SAS analysis of variance table in shaded area 1 always combines these sources into a single source designated as MODEL. Then the MODEL source is partitioned and shown in shaded area ③. For our example there is only one source in addition to SSE, namely, the sum of squares of deviations corresponding to treatments (insurance groups). Consequently, the sum of squares for MODEL is identical to the sum of squares for (insurance) GROUPS.

(8) The standard deviation s, shown in shaded area ④ is used to construct a confidence interval for a single mean or for the difference between a pair of means. Thus

$$s = \sqrt{\text{MSE}} = \sqrt{1720250.32} = 1311.58313499$$

For example, if we want to find a $(1 - \alpha)100\%$ confidence interval for a population mean, say that the mean size of a claim μ_4 for health group 4, we use the formula (given in Section 8.3)

$$\bar{x}_4 \pm t_{\alpha/2}\frac{s}{\sqrt{n_4}}$$

where $\bar{x}_4$ is the sample mean for insurance group 4, $s = 1311.58313499$, $n_4 = 10$, and $t_{\alpha/2}$ is based on $(n - k) = 50 - 5 = 45$ degrees of freedom, the number of degrees of freedom associated with MSE, that is, s^2. The t table, Table 5 in the Appendix, does not give the t values for 45 degrees of freedom, but you can see that the value $t_{.025}$ will be close to 2.0. Therefore, the 95% confidence interval for μ_4, the mean claim for health insurance group 4, is

$$\bar{x}_4 \pm t_{\alpha/2}\frac{s}{\sqrt{n_4}}$$

$$1674.7 \pm (2.0)\frac{(1311.6)}{\sqrt{10}} \qquad \text{or} \qquad \$845.2 \text{ to } \$2504.2$$

If we want to estimate the difference in the size of the mean claims between health insurance groups 1 and 3 by using a $(1 - \alpha)100\%$ confidence interval, we use the formula (Section 8.4)

$$(\bar{x}_1 - \bar{x}_3) \pm t_{\alpha/2}s\sqrt{\frac{1}{n_1} + \frac{1}{n_3}}$$

For a 95% confidence interval the value of $t_{.025}$ for d.f. = 45 will be approximately 2.0, $s = 1311.6$, and the values of $\bar{x}_1$ and $\bar{x}_3$ were shown in

Table 9.2. Then the 95% confidence interval for $(\mu_1 - \mu_3)$ is

$$(\bar{x}_1 - \bar{x}_3) \pm t_{.025} s \sqrt{\frac{1}{n_1} + \frac{1}{n_3}}$$

$$(1959.8 - 1193.9) \pm (2.0)(1311.6) \sqrt{\frac{1}{10} + \frac{1}{10}}$$

$$765.9 \pm 1173.1$$

or from $-\$407.2$ to $\$1939.0$. Thus we estimate the difference in mean claims for groups 1 and 3 to be in the interval $-\$407.2$ to $\$1939.0$. Because this interval includes 0 as a possible value, a t test of $H_0 : \mu_1 = \mu_3$ would not lead to rejection of H_0. There is not sufficient evidence to indicate that μ_1 and μ_3 differ.

(9) The mean of the $n = 50$ observations is shown in shaded area ⑤ as

$$\bar{x} = 1820.68$$

This value is of little use to us.

(10) The quantity identified as R-SQUARE is related to a multiple regression analysis. The significance of R^2 will be explained in Section 12.3.

Now that we have explained the SAS output, compare the SAS output with the Minitab and the SPSS outputs in Tables 9.4 and 9.5. You will be able to locate the relevant sources of variation, degrees of freedom, sums of squares of deviations, and mean squares on the Minitab and SPSS printouts, and you will see the quantities necessary to conduct the F test for comparing the $k = 5$ population means. ∎

The typical ANOVA table for an analysis of variance for k independent random samples is shown in the first box that follows. The other two boxes summarize the analysis of variance F test and give the confidence intervals for treatment means.

ANOVA TABLE FOR k INDEPENDENT RANDOM SAMPLES

Source	d.f.	SS	MS	F
Treatments	$k - 1$	SST	MST $= $ SST$/(k - 1)$	MST/MSE
Error	$n - k$	SSE	MSE $= $ SSE$/(n - k)$	
Total	$n - 1$	Total SS		

F TEST FOR COMPARING k POPULATION MEANS

(1) *Null Hypothesis:* $H_0 : \mu_1 = \mu_2 = \cdots = \mu_k$.

(2) *Alternative Hypothesis:* H_a: one or more pairs of population means differ.

(3) *Test Statistic:* $F = $ MST/MSE, where F is based on $v_1 = (k - 1)$ and $v_2 = (n - k)$ degrees of freedom.

(4) *Rejection Region:* Reject if $F > F_\alpha$, where F_α lies in the upper tail of the F distribution (with $v_1 = k - 1$ and $v_2 = n - k$) and satisfies the expression $P(F > F_\alpha) = \alpha$.

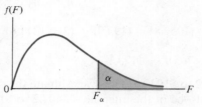

Assumptions:

(1) The samples have been randomly and independently selected from their respective populations.

(2) The populations are normally distributed with means $\mu_1, \mu_2, \ldots, \mu_k$ and equal variances, $\sigma_1^2 = \sigma_2^2 = \cdots = \sigma_k^2 = \sigma^2$.

INDEPENDENT RANDOM SAMPLES:
$(1 - \alpha)100\%$ CONFIDENCE INTERVALS FOR A SINGLE TREATMENT
MEAN AND THE DIFFERENCE BETWEEN TWO TREATMENT MEANS

A Single Treatment Mean:

$$\bar{x}_i \pm t_{\alpha/2} \frac{s}{\sqrt{n_i}}$$

Difference Between Two Treatment Means:

$$(\bar{x}_i - \bar{x}_j) \pm t_{\alpha/2} s \sqrt{\frac{1}{n_i} + \frac{1}{n_j}}$$

where

$$s = \sqrt{s^2} = \sqrt{\text{MSE}} = \sqrt{\frac{\text{SSE}}{n_1 + n_2 + \cdots + n_k - k}}$$

$$n = n_1 + n_2 + \cdots + n_k$$

and $t_{\alpha/2}$ is based upon $(n - k)$ degrees of freedom.

COMPUTING FORMULAS: COMPARING TWO OR MORE POPULATION MEANS*

9.4

Suppose that we want to compare k population means $\mu_1, \mu_2, \ldots, \mu_k$, based on independent random samples, n_1 observations from population 1, n_2 from population

*This section is optional.

2, . . . , and n_k observations from population k. We will employ the symbols given in the following box for the quantities used to perform an analysis of variance of the data.

NOTATION

Statistic	Population			
	1	2	$\cdots$	k
Sample size	n_1	n_2	$\cdots$	n_k
Total of all observations in the sample	T_1	T_2	$\cdots$	T_k
Sample mean	$\bar{x}_1$	$\bar{x}_2$	$\cdots$	$\bar{x}_k$

$$T = \text{total of all } n = n_1 + n_2 + \cdots + n_k \text{ observations} = \sum_{i=1}^{n} x_i$$
$$= T_1 + T_2 + \cdots + T_k$$

The computing formulas for the analysis of variance follow. Along with each formula, we show the numerical substitutions for the data in Table 9.2.
For Table 9.2, $k = 5, n_1 = n_2 = \cdots = n_5 = 10, n = 50$, and

$$T = (19{,}598) + (19{,}961) + (11{,}939) + (16{,}747) + (22{,}789) = 91{,}034$$

Correction for the mean $= \text{CM} = \dfrac{(T)^2}{n}$

For Table 9.2, $\text{CM} = \dfrac{(T)^2}{n} = \dfrac{(91{,}034)^2}{50} = 165{,}743{,}783.12$

Total sum of squares of deviations $=$ Total SS

where

$$\text{Total SS} = \text{SS}_x = \sum_{i=1}^{n} x_i^2 - \text{CM} = (\text{sum of squares of all } x\text{-values}) - \text{CM}$$
$$= (763)^2 + (4365)^2 + \cdots + (767)^2 - 165{,}743{,}783.12$$
$$= 84{,}153{,}818.88$$

Sum of squares for treatments $=$ SST

where

$$\text{SST} = \sum_{i=1}^{k} \frac{T_i^2}{n_i} - \text{CM}$$

and where

$$T_i = \text{total of all observations receiving treatment } i$$

and

$$n_i = \text{number of observations receiving treatment } i$$

Then

$$SST = \frac{T_1^2}{n_1} + \frac{T_2^2}{n_2} + \cdots + \frac{T_k^2}{n_k} - CM$$

$$= \frac{(19,598)^2}{10} + \frac{(19,961)^2}{10} + \cdots + \frac{(22,789)^2}{10} - 165,743,783.12$$

$$= 172,486,337.6 - 165,743,783.12$$

$$= 6,742,554.48$$

$$SSE = \text{Total SS} - SST$$

$$= 84,153,818.88 - 6,742,554.48$$

$$= 77,411,264.4$$

$$\text{Mean square treatments} = MST = \frac{SST}{k-1} = \frac{6,742,554.48}{4}$$

$$= 1,685,638.62$$

$$\text{Mean square error} = MSE = s^2 = \frac{SSE}{n-k} = \frac{77,411,264.4}{45}$$

$$= 1,720,250.32$$

The F test for testing

$$H_0 : \mu_1 = \mu_2 = \cdots = \mu_k$$
$$H_a : \text{at least two of the means differ}$$

uses the F statistic,

$$F = \frac{MST}{MSE} = \frac{1,685,638.62}{1,720,250.32} = .98$$

where F is based on $v_1 = k - 1$ and $v_2 = n - k$ degrees of freedom. For this example $v_1 = k - 1 = 5 - 1 = 4$ and $v_2 = n - k = 50 - 5 = 45$.

If we choose $\alpha = .05$, then $F_{.05} \approx 2.59$. Since the computed value of F is less than this value, there is insufficient evidence to indicate that differences exist among the mean insurance claims for the five health insurance groups.

The sources of variation, the degrees of freedom, the sums of squares, the mean squares, and the value of the F statistic for this analysis of variance are summarized in

TABLE 9.6   ANOVA Table for the Health Insurance Data of Table 9.2

Source	d.f.	SS	MS	F
Treatments	4	6,742,554.48	1,685,638.62	.98
Error	45	77,411,264.40	1,720,250.32	
Total	49	84,153,818.88		

the ANOVA table in Table 9.6. You can see that the information contained in Table 9.6 agrees with the SAS, Minitab, and SPSS[x] printouts, Tables 9.3, 9.4, and 9.5.

A summary of the computing formulas is given in the following box.

SUMMARY OF COMPUTING FORMULAS: ANALYSIS OF VARIANCE FOR AN INDEPENDENT RANDOM SAMPLES DESIGN, k TREATMENTS

$$CM = \frac{(T)^2}{n}$$

$$\text{Total SS} = \sum_{i=1}^{n} x_i^2 - CM$$

$$= \text{sum of squares of all } x \text{ values} - CM$$

where

$$n = n_1 + n_2 + \cdots + n_k$$

and

$$T = \text{total of all } n \text{ observations}$$

$$SST = \sum_{i=1}^{k} \frac{T_i^2}{n_i} - CM \qquad MST = \frac{SST}{k-1}$$

$$SSE = \text{Total SS} - SST \qquad MSE = \frac{SSE}{n-k}$$

EXERCISES

Starred (*) exercises are optional.

BASIC TECHNIQUES

9.1 Suppose that you wish to compare the means of six populations based on independent random samples, each of which contains ten observations. Insert, in an ANOVA table, the sources of variation and their respective degrees of freedom.

9.2 The values of Total SS and SSE for the experiment in Exercise 9.1 are Total SS = 21.4 and SSE = 16.2.

(a) Complete the ANOVA table for Exercise 9.1.

(b) How many degrees of freedom are associated with the F statistic for testing $H_0: \mu_1 = \mu_2 = \cdots = \mu_6$?

(c) Give the rejection region for the test in part (b) for $\alpha = .05$.

(d) Do the data provide sufficient evidence to indicate differences among the population means?

9.3 The sample means corresponding to populations 1 and 2 in Exercise 9.1 are $\bar{x}_1 = 3.07$ and $\bar{x}_2 = 2.52$.

(a) Find a 95% confidence interval for μ_1.

(b) Find a 95% confidence interval for the difference $(\mu_1 - \mu_2)$.

9.4 Suppose that you wish to compare the means of four populations based on independent random samples, each of which contains six observations. Insert, in an ANOVA table, the sources of variation and their respective degrees of freedom.

9.5 The values of Total SS and SST for the experiment in Exercise 9.4 are Total SS = 473.2 and SST = 339.8.

(a) Complete the ANOVA table for Exercise 9.4.

(b) How many degrees of freedom are associated with the F statistic for testing $H_0 : \mu_1 = \mu_2 = \mu_3 = \mu_4$?

(c) Give the rejection region for the test in part (b) for $\alpha = .10$.

(d) Do the data provide sufficient evidence to indicate differences among the population means?

9.6 The sample means corresponding to populations 1 and 2 in Exercise 9.4 are $\bar{x}_1 = 88.0$ and $\bar{x}_2 = 83.9$.

(a) Find a 90% confidence interval for μ_1.

(b) Find a 90% confidence interval for the difference $(\mu_1 - \mu_2)$.

9.7 A portion of the ANOVA table for a completely randomized design is shown in Table 9.7.

TABLE 9.7   ANOVA Table for Exercise 9.7

Source	d.f.	SS	MS	F
Treatments	4	26.3		
Error		52.8		
Total	29			

(a) How many independent random samples were selected in this experiment?

(b) Does the ANOVA table provide the information necessary to determine the sample sizes?

(c) How many observations were involved in the complete design?

(d) Fill in the blanks in the ANOVA table.

(e) Give the rejection region for the analysis of variance F test.

(f) Do the data provide sufficient evidence to indicate a difference among at least two of the population means? Test using $\alpha = .05$.

*9.8 The following data are observations collected by using a completely randomized design.

Sample 1	Sample 2	Sample 3
3	4	2
2	3	0
4	5	2
3	2	1
2	5	

(a) Calculate CM and Total SS.

(b) Calculate SST and MST.

(c) Calculate SSE and MSE.

(d) Construct an ANOVA table for the data.

(e) State the null and alternative hypotheses for an analysis of variance F test.

(f) Give the rejection region for the test, using $\alpha = .05$.

(g) Conduct the test and state your conclusions.

*9.9 Refer to Exercise 9.8. Do the data provide sufficient evidence to indicate a difference between μ_2 and μ_3? Test using the t test of Section 8.4 with $\alpha = .05$.

*9.10 Refer to Exercise 9.8.

(a) Find a 90% confidence interval for μ_1.

(b) Find a 90% confidence interval for $(\mu_1 - \mu_3)$.

*9.11 The following data are observations collected by using a completely randomized design.

Sample 1	Sample 2	Sample 3	Sample 4
2	6	3	3
4	2	0	6
0	5	5	4
	4	2	
		3	

(a) Calculate CM and Total SS.

(b) Calculate SST and MST.

(c) Calculate SSE and MSE.

(d) Construct an ANOVA table for the data.

(e) State the null and alternative hypotheses for an analysis of variance F test.

(f) Give the rejection region for the test using $\alpha = .05$.

(g) Conduct the test and state your conclusions.

*9.12 Refer to Exercise 9.11. Do the data provide sufficient evidence to indicate a difference between μ_1 and μ_2? Test using the t test of Section 8.4 with $\alpha = .05$.

*9.13 Refer to Exercise 9.11.

(a) Find a 90% confidence interval for μ_3.

(b) Find a 90% confidence interval for $(\mu_1 - \mu_3)$.

APPLICATIONS

9.14 An experiment was conducted to compare the price of a loaf of bread (a particular brand) at four city locations. Four stores were randomly sampled in locations 1, 2, and 3 but only two were selected from location 4 (only two carried the brand). Note that a completely randomized design was employed. Conduct an analysis of variance for the data shown in Table 9.8. An SAS computer printout of the analysis of variance for the data is shown in Table 9.9. Use the information in the printout to answer the following questions.

(a) Do the data provide sufficient evidence to indicate a difference in mean price of the bread in stores located in the four areas of the city?

(b) Suppose that prior to seeing the data, we wanted to compare the mean prices between locations 1 and 4. Estimate the difference in means, using a 95% confidence interval.

TABLE 9.8   Cost Data for Exercise 9.14

Location	Price (cents)			
1	59	63	65	61
2	58	61	64	63
3	54	59	55	58
4	69	70		

TABLE 9.9   SAS Printout for Exercise 9.14

ANALYSIS OF VARIANCE PROCEDURE

DEPENDENT VARIABLE: PRICE

SOURCE	DF	SUM OF SQUARES	MEAN SQUARE	F VALUE	PR > F	R-SQUARE	C.V.
MODEL	3	228.71428571	76.23809524	13.03	0.0009	0.796319	3.9420
ERROR	10	58.50000000	5.85000000		ROOT MSE		PRICE MEAN
CORRECTED TOTAL	13	287.21428571			2.41867732		61.35714286

SOURCE	DF	ANOVA SS	F VALUE	PR > F
LOCATION	3	228.71428571	13.03	0.0009

9.15 An experiment was conducted to compare the effectiveness of three training programs, *A, B,* and *C,* in training assemblers of a piece of electronic equipment. Fifteen employees were randomly assigned, 5 each, to the three programs. After completion of the courses, each person was required to assemble four pieces of the equipment, and the average length of time required to complete the assembly was recorded. Owing to resignation from the company, only 4 employees completed program *A* and only 3 completed *B.* The data are shown in Table 9.10. An SAS computer printout of the analysis of variance for the data is shown in Table 9.11. Use the information in the printout to answer the following questions.

TABLE 9.10   Assembly Time Data for Exercise 9.15

Training Program	Average Assembly Time (Minutes)				
A	59	64	57	62	
B	52	58	54		
C	58	65	71	63	64

TABLE 9.11   SAS Printout for Exercises 9.15

ANALYSIS OF VARIANCE PROCEDURE

DEPENDENT VARIABLE: TIME

SOURCE	DF	SUM OF SQUARES	MEAN SQUARE	F VALUE	PR > F	R-SQUARE	C.V.
MODEL	2	170.45000000	85.22500000	5.70	0.0251	0.559005	6.3802
ERROR	9	134.46666667	14.94074074		ROOT MSE		TIME MEAN
CORRECTED TOTAL	11	304.91666667			3.86532544		60.58333333

SOURCE	DF	ANOVA SS	F VALUE	PR > F
PROGRAM	2	170.45000000	5.70	0.0251

(a) Do the data provide sufficient evidence to indicate a difference in mean assembly times for people trained by the three programs?

(b) Find a 90% confidence interval for the difference in mean assembly times between persons trained by programs *A* and *B*.

(c) Find a 90% confidence interval for the mean assembly time for persons trained by program *A*.

(d) Do you think the data will satisfy (approximately) the assumption that they have been selected from normal populations? Why?

 9.16 Larry R. Smeltzer (Louisiana State University) and Kittie W. Watson (Tulane University) conducted an experiment to investigate the effect of four different instructional approaches for improving learning. The treatments are listed next:

(1) No instruction on listening.

(2) A 45-minute lecture on listening skills.

(3) A 30-minute video model on effective listening skills.

(4) Both of the educational exposures described in treatments 2 and 3.

Ninety-nine subjects were randomly assigned to receive the treatments: 19 to the control group (treatment 1), 31 to treatment 2, 27 to treatment 3, and 22 to treatment 4. The educational messages presented in treatments 2, 3, and 4 emphasized the importance of asking questions and taking notes during discussions. After the treatments were applied, the students were scored on the basis of the numbers of questions asked. The analysis of variance table for the data is shown in Table 9.12.

TABLE 9.12   ANOVA Table for Exercise 9.16

Source	d.f.	SS	MS	F
Between groups	3	63.21	21.07	8.11*
Within groups	95	350.55	3.69	
Total	98	413.76		

Source: L. R. Smeltzer and K. W. Watson, "A Test of Instructional Strategies for Listening Improvement in a Simulated Business Setting," *Journal of Business Communication*, Vol. 22, No. 2, 1985.
*Significant at the .01 level.

(a) Why is "no instruction on listening" called the "control group"?

(b) Do the data present sufficient evidence to indicate differences in the mean number of questions asked among the four treatment groups? Test using $\alpha = .05$.

(c) The mean number of questions asked for each of the four treatments is shown in Table 9.13.

TABLE 9.13   Sample Data for Exercise 9.16

Treatment	Sample Size	Mean
1. Control group	19	1.36
2. Lecture group	31	1.87
3. Video role model	27	2.97
4. Lecture plus video role model	22	3.18

Compare the most intensive educational treatment, treatment 4, with the control, treatment 1. Do the data present sufficient evidence to indicate a difference in mean number of questions asked? Test using $\alpha = .05$.

*9.17 Perform the analysis of variance calculations for Exercise 9.14, and present them in an analysis of variance table. Compare your answers with those given in the computer printout in Table 9.9. Interpret the results of the analysis of variance.

*9.18 Perform the analysis of variance calculations for Exercise 9.15, and present them in an analysis of variance table. Compare your answers with those given in the computer printout in Table 9.11. Interpret the results of the analysis of variance.

9.5 RANDOMIZED BLOCK DESIGNS

You will recall that the paired-difference design of Section 8.5 was used to compare two treatment means within matched pairs of experimental units. By eliminating the variation *among* the matched pairs from the comparison, we greatly reduced the standard deviation of the error of estimating the difference between the two population means.

A **randomized block design** is an extension of the paired-difference design. If we wish to compare three treatments, we make the comparison within matched sets (or **blocks**), each of which contains three experimental units. In general, a randomized block design conducted to compare k treatments will utilize blocks of k matched experimental units, one and only one experimental unit for each treatment. The design is said to be randomized because the treatments are randomly assigned to the k experimental units within each block. If a randomized block design involves a comparison of k treatments within each of b blocks, the total number of observations collected in the experiment is $n = bk$.

Suppose that the chief executive of a large construction corporation employs three experienced construction engineers to perform the time-consuming cost analyses, estimates, and bids for the work on large construction projects. Do those "estimators" tend to estimate at the same mean level, or does one or another tend to always submit a high (or a low) bid on projects? To answer this question, the executive can select independent random samples of projects estimated by each of the three estimators and compare the three means. This procedure will be valid but will require very large sample sizes to detect differences in means because of the large amount of variation in the cost levels of the individual projects.

A much easier method for detecting differences in the mean level of estimates for the three estimators is to conduct an experiment. Each of the three estimators will be required to analyze, estimate, and provide a bid price for the same project for each of a set of b (say $b = 5$) projects. Then the bid prices of the three estimators can be compared for the same project, thereby eliminating the project-to-project variation in bid prices.

As a second example of the use of blocking to increase the information in an experiment, suppose that a production superintendent wants to compare the mean time for an assembly line operator to perform a job by using one of three methods, A, B, and C. Each of the $b = 5$ operators is to perform the job by using each of the methods A, B, and C. The objective of the blocking is to eliminate the variation in time to assemble caused by operator-to-operator differences in manual dexterity, motivation, and so on. Since the sequence in which the operator performs the three assembly operations may be important (e.g., fatigue may be a factor), each assembly operator should be assigned a random sequencing of the three methods. For example, operator 1 might be assigned to perform method C first, followed by A and B. Operator 2 might be assigned to perform method A first, then C and B.

Matching (or blocking) can take place in many different ways. As we have illustrated, comparisons of treatments are often made within blocks of time, within blocks of people, or within similar external environments. The exercises and the Case Study in Section 9.13 will provide other examples of the use of randomized block designs.

An Analysis of Variance for a Randomized Block Design

9.6

An analysis of variance for a randomized block design partitions the total sum of squares of deviations of all x-values about the overall mean $\bar{x}$ into three parts, the first measuring the variation among treatment means, the second measuring the variation among block means, and the third measuring the variation of the differences among the treatment observations *within* blocks (which measures experimental error). Thus

$$\text{Total SS} = \text{SST} + \text{SSB} + \text{SSE}$$

where

$$\text{Total SS} = \sum_{i=1}^{n}(x_i - \bar{x})^2$$

$\quad$ SST = sum of squares for treatments

$\qquad$ = b (sum of squares of deviations of the treatment means about $\bar{x}$)

$\quad$ SSB = sum of squares for blocks

$\qquad$ = k(sum of squares of deviations of the block means about $\bar{x}$)

$\quad$ SSE = sum of squares for error = Total SS − SST − SSB

$\qquad$ = unexplained variation

In order to avoid distracting you with computational formulas and computations, we will explain how to perform an analysis of variance by explaining and interpreting an SAS analysis of variance printout for an example. We will present corresponding Minitab and SPSS[x] printouts in case you have access to these program packages. The computing formulas and the hand calculator computations for the example are given in optional Section 9.7.

EXAMPLE 9.2   Refer to the comparison of the mean project bid price levels for the three construction project estimators described in Section 9.5. Each of the three estimators was required to analyze and determine a bid price for each of $b = 5$ projects. The data are shown in Table 9.14, and the SAS, Minitab, and SPSS[x] analysis of variance printouts are shown in Tables 9.15, 9.16, and 9.17. Describe and interpret the SAS printout.

TABLE 9.14   Bid Price Data (Million $) for Three Estimators for Each of Five Projects for Example 9.2

	Project					
Estimator	1	2	3	4	5	Total
1	3.52	4.71	3.89	5.21	4.14	21.47
2	3.39	4.79	3.82	4.93	3.96	20.89
3	3.64	4.92	4.19	5.10	4.20	22.05
Total	10.55	14.42	11.90	15.24	12.30	64.41

TABLE 9.15   SAS ANOVA Printout for Example 9.2

```
                              ANALYSIS OF VARIANCE PROCEDURE

DEPENDENT VARIABLE: PRICE

SOURCE            DF    SUM OF SQUARES    MEAN SQUARE     F VALUE    PR > F    R-SQUARE        C.V.

MODEL              6       5.02352000      0.83725333      99.32     0.0001    0.986753      2.1382
                                                      ①
ERROR              8       0.06744000      0.00843000                ROOT MSE            PRICE TIME

CORRECTED TOTAL   14       5.09096000                               0.09181503  ③      4.29400000


SOURCE            DF       ANOVA SS     F VALUE    PR > F

ESTIMATOR          2       0.13456000      7.98    0.0124  ②
PROJECT            4       4.88896000    144.99    0.0001
```

TABLE 9.16   Minitab ANOVA Printout for Example 9.2

```
ANALYSIS OF VARIANCE  PRICE

SOURCE      DF        SS        MS
ESTIMATR     2   0.13456   0.06728
PROJECT      4   4.88896   1.22224
ERROR        8   0.06744   0.00843
TOTAL       14   5.09096
```

SOLUTION   (1) The SAS printout for an analysis of variance always presents the information for an ANOVA table in two stages. The first stage, shaded area ① in Table 9.15, shows only two sources of variation, MODEL and ERROR. The source MODEL *includes all sources of variation other than ERROR.*

TABLE 9.17   SPSS^x ANOVA Printout for Example 9.2

```
              * * * A N A L Y S I S   O F   V A R I A N C E * * *

                PRICE
         BY     ESTIMATR
                PROJECT

                        SUM OF              MEAN                  SIGNIF
SOURCE OF VARIATION      SQUARES    DF      SQUARE        F       OF F

MAIN EFFECTS             5.024      6       0.837      99.318     0.000
   ESTIMATR              0.135      2       0.067       7.981     0.012
   PROJECT               4.889      4       1.222     144.987     0.000

EXPLAINED                5.024      6       0.837      99.318     0.000

RESIDUAL                 0.067      8       0.008

TOTAL                    5.091     14       0.364
```

(2) The source MODEL is broken down into its components, ESTIMATOR (treatments) and PROJECT (blocks), in the table in shaded area ②. This table gives the number of degrees of freedom for ESTIMATOR (treatments) and PROJECT (blocks). The number of degrees of freedom for treatments will always be one less than the number k of treatments, that is $(k - 1)$. For our example there were $k = 3$ estimators (treatments). Therefore, $(k - 1) = 3 - 1 = 2$. This number appears in the DF column in shaded area ② opposite ESTIMATOR. Similarly, if there are b blocks, the number of degrees of freedom for blocks is $(b - 1)$. For our example there were $b = 5$ blocks. Therefore, the number of degrees of freedom for blocks is $(b - 1) = 5 - 1 = 4$. This number appears in the DF column in shaded area 2 opposite PROJECT. The number of degrees of freedom for error will always equal $(n - b - k + 1)$. This number, $(n - b - k + 1) = 15 - 5 - 3 + 1 = 8$, is shown in the DF column in shaded area ① opposite ERROR. The number of degrees of freedom corresponding to Total SS is always equal to $(n - 1) = 15 - 1 = 14$. This number appears under DF in the row corresponding to CORRECTED TOTAL. Note that the sum of the numbers of degrees of freedom corresponding to ESTIMATOR, PROJECT, and ERROR always equals the number of degrees of freedom corresponding to CORRECTED TOTAL; that is, $(2 + 4 + 8) = 14$.

   The traditional ANOVA format combines shaded areas ① and ② into a single table by replacing the source MODEL in shaded area ① with the sources in shaded area ②. This traditional format is shown in the first box at the end of this section.

(3) Column 3 of shaded areas ① and ②, labeled SUM OF SQUARES and ANOVA SS, respectively, shows the sums of squares for the sources of variation. Thus SSE, shown in shaded area ①, is

$$\text{SSE} = .06744000$$

The Total SS is also shown in shaded area ① in the row corresponding to

CORRECTED TOTAL. Thus

$$\text{Total SS} = 5.09096000$$

The sums of squares for ESTIMATOR (treatments) and PROJECT (blocks) are shown in shaded area ②. Thus

$$\text{SST} = \text{SS(ESTIMATOR)} = .13456000$$

and

$$\text{SSB} = \text{SS(PROJECT)} = 4.88896000$$

(4) Each mean square is obtained by dividing a sum of squares by its respective degrees of freedom. For example,

$$\text{MSE} = s^2 = \frac{\text{SSE}}{n - b - k + 1}$$

The mean squares for the sources of variation are shown in column 4 of shaded areas ① and ②. Thus

$$\text{MSE} = s^2 = .00843000$$
$$\text{MST} = \text{MS(ESTIMATOR)} = .06728000$$

and

$$\text{MSB} = \text{MS(PROJECT)} = 1.22224000$$

(5) Under the null hypotheses that there are no differences among treatment means or that there are no differences among block means, the mean squares for treatments (MST), blocks (MSB), and error (MSE) provide independent estimates of the common population variance σ^2.

(a) To test H_0: no differences among the k treatment means, we use $F = \text{MST/MSE}$ as the test statistic; and we reject H_0 if $F > F_\alpha$, where F is based on the number of degrees of freedom associated with MST and MSE, namely, $v_1 = k - 1$ and $v_2 = n - b - k + 1$. The computed value of the F statistic, $F = \text{MST/MSE}$, is shown in column 5 of shaded area ② as $F = 7.98$. For $\alpha = .05$ the critical value of $F_{.05}$ for $v_1 = k - 1 = 2$ and $v_2 = n - b - k + 1 = 8$ is 4.46. Since the computed value of F, 7.98, exceeds this value, there is sufficient evidence to indicate a difference among at least two of the treatment means. The observed significance level (p-value) for the test is shown in column 6 of shaded area ② as .0124. Thus the probability of observing an F value as large as or larger than $F = 7.98$, assuming H_0 true, is only .0124.

(b) To test H_0: no difference among the b block means, we use $F = \text{MSB/MSE}$ as the test statistic; and we reject H_0 if $F > F_\alpha$, where F is based on the number of degrees of freedom associated with MSB and MSE, namely $v_1 = b - 1 = 4$ and $v_2 = n - b - k + 1 = 8$. The computed value of the F statistic, $F = \text{MSB/MSE}$, is shown in column 5 of shaded area ② as $F = 144.99$. For $\alpha = .05$ the critical value of F for $v_1 = 4$ and $v_2 = 8$ degrees of freedom is 3.84. Since the observed value of F, 144.99, greatly exceeds this critical value, there is ample evidence to indicate differences among the block means. Since the sizes of the construction projects (in dollars) were known to vary over a wide range, we are not surprised to find differences in the mean values of the construction project bids.

(6) The standard deviation, $s = \sqrt{\text{MSE}} = .09181503$, is shown in shaded area 3. It can be used to construct a confidence interval for the difference between a pair of treatment means* or between a pair of block means, and it can also be used to test for differences between pairs of means. The formulas and procedures are the same as those used for independent random samples. Since each treatment mean appears in each block, there are b observations per treatment. Therefore, a $(1 - \alpha)100\%$ confidence interval for the difference between a pair of treatment means, say i and j, is

$$(\bar{x}_i - \bar{x}_j) \pm t_{\alpha/2} s \sqrt{\frac{1}{b} + \frac{1}{b}}$$

or

$$(\bar{x}_i - \bar{x}_j) \pm t_{\alpha/2} s \sqrt{\frac{2}{b}}$$

where $t_{\alpha/2}$ is based on the number of degrees of freedom associated with s^2.

Similarly, since each block contains k treatments, each block mean will be based on k observations. And a $(1 - \alpha)100\%$ confidence interval for the difference between a pair of block means, say ℓ and m, is

$$(\bar{x}_\ell - \bar{x}_m) \pm t_{\alpha/2} s \sqrt{\frac{2}{k}}$$

To illustrate, suppose that we want to construct a 95% confidence interval for the difference between the mean estimates for treatments (estimators) 3 and 1. The means for these treatments are $\bar{x}_1 = 4.294$ and $\bar{x}_3 = 4.410$ and, from the printout in Table 9.15, $s = .09181503 \approx .0918$. Since s^2 is based upon 8 degrees of freedom, $t_{\alpha/2} = t_{.025} = 2.306$, and the 95% confidence interval for $(\mu_3 - \mu_1)$ is

$$(\bar{x}_3 - \bar{x}_1) \pm t_{\alpha/2} s \sqrt{\frac{2}{b}}$$

$$(4.410 - 4.294) \pm (2.306)(.0918) \sqrt{\frac{2}{5}}$$

or $.116 \pm .134$. Therefore, we estimate the difference in mean level of estimates between estimators 3 and 1 to be from $-\$.018$ to $\$.250$ million. (*Note:* Since this interval includes 0, there is not sufficient evidence to indicate a difference between μ_3 and μ_1.) ∎

---

*You cannot construct a confidence interval for a single mean unless the blocks have been randomly selected from among the population of all blocks. The procedure for constructing confidence intervals for single means is beyond the scope of this text.

The typical ANOVA table for k treatments in b blocks is shown in the first box that follows. The other two boxes summarize the analysis of variance F tests for comparing treatment and block means and give the confidence intervals for the differences between pairs of treatment and pairs of block means.

ANOVA TABLE FOR A RANDOMIZED BLOCK DESIGN, k TREATMENTS AND b BLOCKS

Source	d.f.	SS	MS	F
Treatments	$k - 1$	SST	$MST = SST/(k - 1)$	MST/MSE
Blocks	$b - 1$	SSB	$MSB = SSB/(b - 1)$	MSB/MSE
Error	$n - b - k + 1$	SSE	$MSE = SSE/(n - b - k + 1)$	
Total	$n - 1$			

TESTS FOR A RANDOMIZED BLOCK DESIGN

For Comparing Treatment Means:

(1) *Null Hypothesis:* H_0: the treatment means are equal.

(2) *Alternative Hypothesis:* H_a: at least two of the treatment means differ.

(3) *Test Statistic:* $F = MST/MSE$, where F is based on $v_1 = k - 1$ and $v_2 = n - b - k + 1$ degrees of freedom.

(4) *Rejection region:* Reject if $F > F_\alpha$, where F_α lies in the upper tail of the F distribution (see the figure).

For Comparing Block Means:

(1) *Null Hypothesis:* the block means are equal.

(2) *Alternative Hypothesis:* at least two of the block means differ.

(3) *Test Statistic:* $F = MSB/MSE$, where F is based on $v_1 = b - 1$ and $v_2 = n - b - k + 1$ degrees of freedom.

(4) *Rejection Region:* Reject if $F > F_\alpha$, where F_α lies in the upper tail of the F distribution (see the figure).

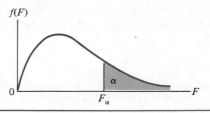

$(1 - \alpha)100\%$ CONFIDENCE INTERVALS FOR THE DIFFERENCE BETWEEN PAIRS OF TREATMENT AND BLOCK MEANS: A RANDOMIZED BLOCK DESIGN

Difference Between Treatment Mean i and j:

$$(\bar{x}_i - \bar{x}_j) \pm t_{\alpha/2}s\sqrt{\frac{2}{b}}$$

Difference Between Block Means ℓ and m

$$(\bar{x}_\ell - \bar{x}_m) \pm t_{\alpha/2}s\sqrt{\frac{2}{k}}$$

where

k = number of treatments

b = number of blocks

$s = \sqrt{\text{MSE}}$

and $t_{\alpha/2}$ is based on $(n - b - k + 1)$ degrees of freedom.

COMPUTING FORMULAS: THE ANALYSIS OF VARIANCE FOR A RANDOMIZED BLOCK DESIGN*

9.7

We will use the notation given in the following box when conducting an analysis of variance for a randomized block design.

NOTATION

k = number of treatments

b = number of blocks

$n = bk$ = total number of observations in the experiment

$T = \sum_{i=1}^{n} x_i$ = total of all observations in the experiment

$\bar{x} = \dfrac{T}{n}$ = mean of all observations in the experiment

T_i = total of all observations receiving treatment i, $i = 1, 2, \ldots, k$

B_j = total of all observations in block j, $j = 1, 2, \ldots, b$

---

*This section is optional.

The computing formulas for the analysis follow. To demonstrate their use, we show the numerical substitutions and calculations for an analysis of the data in Example 9.2. Treatment and block totals for Example 9.2 are given in Table 9.14.

For Example 9.2, $b = 5$ and $k = 3$. Therefore, $n = bk = (5)(3) = 15$, and

$$T = \text{sum of all } n = bk \text{ observations}$$
$$= T_1 + T_2 + \cdots + T_k$$

For Example 9.2

$$T = T_1 + T_2 + T_3 = 21.47 + 20.89 + 22.05 = 64.41$$

Correction for the mean $= \text{CM} = \dfrac{(T)^2}{n} = \dfrac{(64.41)^2}{15} = 276.57654$

Total sum of squares of deviations $=$ Total SS

$$\text{Total SS} = \sum_{i=1}^{n} (x_i - \bar{x})^2 = \sum_{i=1}^{n} x_i^2 - \text{CM}$$
$$= (3.52)^2 + (3.39)^2 + (3.64)^2 + \cdots + (4.20)^2 - \text{CM}$$
$$= 281.66750 - 276.57654$$
$$= 5.09096$$

Sums of squares for treatments $=$ SST

$$\text{SST} = \sum_{i=1}^{k} \frac{T_i^2}{b} - \text{CM}$$
$$= \frac{(21.47)^2 + (20.89)^2 + (22.05)^2}{5} - 276.57654$$
$$= .13456$$

Sum of squares for blocks $=$ SSB

$$\text{SSB} = \sum_{j=1}^{b} \frac{B_j^2}{k} - \text{CM}$$
$$= \frac{(10.55)^2 + (14.42)^2 + \cdots + (12.30)^2}{3} - 276.57654$$
$$= 4.88896$$

Sum of squares for error $=$ SSE

$$\text{SSE} = \text{Total SS} - \text{SST} - \text{SSB}$$
$$= 5.09096 - .13456 - 4.88896$$
$$= .06744$$

Mean square for treatments $= \text{MST} = \dfrac{\text{SST}}{k-1} = \dfrac{.13456}{2} = .06728$

where $k - 1 = 2 =$ number of degrees of freedom for MST

$$\text{Mean square for blocks} = \text{MSB} = \frac{\text{SSB}}{b-1} = \frac{4.88896}{4} = 1.22224$$

where $\quad b - 1 = 4 =$ number of degrees of freedom for MSB

$$\text{Mean square for error} = \text{MSE} = s^2 = \frac{\text{SSE}}{n-b-k+1} = \frac{.06744}{8}$$

$$= .00843$$

where $\quad n - b - k + 1 = 8 =$ number of degrees of freedom for MSE

The sources of variation, degrees of freedom, sums of squares, mean squares, and F values for testing differences among treatment means and block means are summarized in the ANOVA table in Table 9.18. You can verify that the numbers presented in Table 9.18 are the same as those shown in the SAS printout in Table 9.15.

TABLE 9.18   ANOVA Table for the Randomized Block Data of Example 9.2

Source	d.f.	SS	MS	F
Treatments (estimators)	2	.13456	.06728	7.98
Blocks (projects)	4	4.88896	1.22224	144.99
Error	8	.06744	.00843	
Total	14			

A summary of the computing formulas is given in the next box.

SUMMARY OF COMPUTING FORMULAS: ANALYSIS OF VARIANCE FOR A RANDOMIZED BLOCK DESIGN, k TREATMENTS IN b BLOCKS

$$\text{CM} = \frac{(T)^2}{n}$$

where $\quad n = bk$

and $\quad T =$ sum of all n observations

$$\text{Total SS} = \sum_{i=1}^{n} x_i^2 - \text{CM}$$

$$= \text{sum of squares of all } x\text{-values} - \text{CM}$$

$$\text{SST} = \sum_{i=1}^{k} \frac{T_i^2}{b} - \text{CM} \qquad \text{MST} = \frac{\text{SST}}{k-1}$$

$$\text{SSB} = \sum_{j=1}^{b} \frac{B_j^2}{k} - \text{CM} \qquad \text{MSB} = \frac{\text{SSB}}{b-1}$$

EXERCISES

Starred (*) exercises are optional.

BASIC TECHNIQUES

9.19 A randomized block design was conducted to compare the means of three treatments within six blocks. Construct an analysis of variance table showing the sources of variation and their respective degrees of freedom.

9.20 Suppose that the analysis of variance calculations for Exercise 9.19 gave SST = 11.4, SSB = 17.1, and Total SS = 42.7. Complete the analysis of variance table, showing all sums of squares, mean squares, and pertinent F values.

9.21 Do the data of Exercise 9.20 provide sufficient evidence to indicate differences among the treatment means? Test using $\alpha = .05$.

9.22 Find a 95% confidence interval for the difference between a pair of treatment means A and B if $\bar{x}_A = 21.9$ and $\bar{x}_B = 24.2$.

9.23 Do the data of Exercise 9.20 provide sufficient evidence to indicate that blocking increased the amount of information in the experiment about the treatment means? Justify your answer.

9.24 A randomized block design was conducted to compare the means of six treatments within four blocks. Construct an analysis of variance table showing the sources of variation and their respective degrees of freedom.

9.25 Suppose that the analysis of variance calculations for Exercise 9.24 gave SST = 6.1, SSB = 2.2, and Total SS = 12.2. Complete the analysis of variance table, showing all sums of squares, mean squares, and pertinent F values.

9.26 Do the data of Exercise 9.24 provide sufficient evidence to indicate differences among the treatment means? Test using $\alpha = .10$.

9.27 Find a 90% confidence interval for the difference between a pair of treatment means A and B if $\bar{x}_A = 291.2$ and $\bar{x}_B = 289.7$.

9.28 Do the data of Exercise 9.24 provide sufficient evidence to indicate that blocking increased the amount of information in the experiment about the treatment means? Justify your answer.

9.29 The partially completed ANOVA table for a randomized block design is shown in Table 9.19.

TABLE 9.19   ANOVA Table for Exercise 9.29

Source	d.f.	SS	MS	F
Treatments	4	14.2		
Blocks		18.9		
Error	24			
Total	34	41.9		

(a) How many blocks were involved in the design?
(b) How many observations are in each treatment total?
(c) How many observations are in each block total?
(d) Fill in the blanks in the ANOVA table.

(e) Do the data present sufficient evidence to indicate differences among the treatment means? Test using $\alpha = .10$.

(f) Do the data present sufficient evidence to indicate differences among the block means? Test using $\alpha = .10$.

*9.30 The data shown in Table 9.20 are observations collected from an experiment that compared four treatments, A, B, C, and D, within each of three blocks by using a randomized block design.

TABLE 9.20   Randomized Block Data for Exercise 9.30

| Block | Treatment | | | | Total |
	A	B	C	D	
1	6	10	8	9	33
2	4	9	5	7	25
3	12	15	14	14	55
Total	22	34	27	30	113

(a) Calculate CM and Total SS.

(b) Calculate SST and MST.

(c) Calculate SSB and MSB.

(d) Calculate SSE and MSE.

(e) Construct an ANOVA table for the data.

(f) Do the data present sufficient evidence to indicate differences among the treatment means? Test using $\alpha = .05$.

(g) Do the data present sufficient evidence to indicate differences among the block means? Test using $\alpha = .05$.

(h) Does it appear that the use of a randomized block design for this experiment was justified? Explain.

*9.31 Refer to Exercise 9.30. Find a 90% confidence interval for the difference $(\mu_A - \mu_B)$.

*9.32 The data shown in Table 9.21 are observations collected from an experiment that compared three treatments, A, B, and C, within each of five blocks by using a randomized block design.

TABLE 9.21   Randomized Block Data for Exercise 9.32

| Treatment | Block | | | | | Total |
	1	2	3	4	5	
A	2.1	2.6	1.9	3.2	2.7	12.5
B	3.4	3.8	3.6	4.1	3.9	18.8
C	3.0	3.6	3.2	3.9	3.9	17.6
Total	8.5	10.0	8.7	11.2	10.5	48.9

(a) Calculate CM and Total SS.

(b) Calculate SST and MST.

(c) Calculate SSB and MSB.

(d) Calculate SSE and MSE.

(e) Construct an ANOVA table for the data.

(f) Do the data present sufficient evidence to indicate differences among the treatment means? Test using $\alpha = .05$.

(g) Do the data present sufficient evidence to indicate differences among the block means? Test using $\alpha = .05$.

(h) Does it appear that the use of a randomized block design for this experiment was justified? Explain.

*9.33 Find a 99% confidence interval for the difference $(\mu_C - \mu_A)$.

APPLICATIONS

 9.34 In Exercise 8.51 we described a paired-difference experiment conducted to compare mean daily sales at a supermarket for days when no background music was present versus days when the supermarket provided a slow-tempo background music. A follow-up experiment employed three treatments, no music, slow-tempo background music, and fast-tempo background music. Three midweek days, Tuesday, Wednesday, and Thursday, were selected for the experiment. The three treatments were randomly assigned, one to each of these three days, for each of four weeks, and the daily sales were recorded. They are shown in Table 9.22. Table 9.23 shows an SAS analysis of variance printout for the data.

TABLE 9.22   Sales Data for Exercise 9.34

Treatment	Week 1	2	3	4
No music	14,140	13,991	14,772	13,266
Slow tempo	15,029	14,546	15,029	14,783
Fast tempo	12,874	13,165	13,140	11,245

TABLE 9.23   SAS Printout for Exercise 9.34

```
                              ANALYSIS OF VARIANCE PROCEDURE

DEPENDENT VARIABLE: SALES

SOURCE            DF      SUM OF SQUARES     MEAN SQUARE      F VALUE       PR > F    R-SQUARE           C.V.

MODEL              5     12734149.83333340   2546829.96666669    10.89       0.0057   0.900704        3.4971

ERROR              6      1403850.83333337    233975.13888890                ROOT MSE            SALES MEAN

CORRECTED TOTAL   11     14138000.66666680                                 483.70976720        13831.66666667


SOURCE            DF              ANOVA SS    F VALUE      PR > F

WEEK               3      2426156.66666663       3.46      0.0916
TRTMENT            2     10307993.16666680      22.03      0.0017
```

(a) Explain how the design of this experiment might increase the information on the differences in mean daily sales for the three treatments.

(b) Do the data present sufficient evidence to indicate a difference in mean daily sales for the three treatments? Test using $\alpha = .05$.

(c) Do the data indicate a difference in the mean daily sales for days when slow-tempo music was played versus days when the background music was fast tempo? Test using $\alpha = .05$.

MKTG   9.35 A fast-food chain wants to compare daily sales during three types of sales promotions. The sales promotions were employed in three different cities over a six-week period, two weeks for each promotion. The promotions were randomly assigned to the two-week time periods within each city, and the amount of sales (in thousands of dollars) for one outlet in each city was measured for the last two days of the two-week period (to avoid carryover effects of the promotions). The data are shown in Table 9.24. An SAS analysis of variance printout is shown in Table 9.25.

TABLE 9.24   Sales Data for Exercise 9.35

| City | Promotion | | |
	A	B	C
1	4.65	5.21	4.62
2	4.32	4.69	4.27
3	4.14	4.68	4.25

TABLE 9.25   SAS Printout for Exercise 9.35

ANALYSIS OF VARIANCE PROCEDURE

DEPENDENT VARIABLE: SALES

SOURCE	DF	SUM OF SQUARES	MEAN SQUARE	F VALUE	PR > F	R-SQUARE	C.V.
MODEL	4	0.85640000	0.21410000	46.54	0.0013	0.978967	1.4950
ERROR	4	0.01840000	0.00460000		ROOT MSE		SALES MEAN
CORRECTED TOTAL	8	0.87480000			0.06782330		4.53666667

SOURCE	DF	ANOVA SS	F VALUE	PR > F
CITY	2	0.38580000	41.93	0.0021
PROMO	2	0.47060000	51.15	0.0014

(a) Identify the treatments and blocks in this experiment.

(b) How were the experimental units matched within blocks?

(c) Explain why you might expect the blocking for this experiment to increase the information available for comparing treatment means.

(d) Do the data provide sufficient evidence to indicate differences among mean sales for the three types of promotions? Test using $\alpha = .10$.

(e) Find a 90% confidence interval for the difference in mean sales for promotions A and C.

(f) Explain why you can or cannot construct confidence intervals for the mean sales for the individual promotions.

9.36 A service station manager wants to estimate the mean summer weekly demand for three types of gasoline, leaded, unleaded, and super unleaded. Data (in thousands of gallons) collected over an eight-week period are shown in Table 9.26. A Minitab analysis of variance printout for the data is shown in Table 9.27.

TABLE 9.26   Demand Data for Exercise 9.36

Gasoline Type	Week							
	1	2	3	4	5	6	7	8
Leaded	2.4	2.6	2.7	2.8	3.0	2.6	2.7	2.4
Unleaded	18.2	19.7	21.3	22.4	21.5	19.7	18.0	18.8
Super unleaded	4.3	4.6	4.7	5.5	5.0	4.8	4.6	5.0

TABLE 9.27   Minitab ANOVA Printout for Exercise 9.36

```
ANALYSIS OF VARIANCE   DEMAND

SOURCE      DF       SS        MS
TYPE         2   1421.628   710.814
WEEK         7      9.810     1.401
ERROR       14      9.919     0.709
TOTAL       23   1441.356
```

(a) Explain why the sampling procedure employed in collecting these data is or is not a randomized block design.

(b) Would it be valid to analyze these data as though the data for the three gasolines represent independent random samples? Explain.

(c) Find a 95% confidence interval for the difference between unleaded and super unleaded mean weekly sales.

 9.37 The data shown in Table 9.28 give the prices for six different items at five different supermarkets in Gainesville, Florida. The items were randomly selected from a list of those contained in a Kash n' Karry advertisement in the *Gainesville Sun*, January 3, 1985. The SAS analysis of variance printout for the data is shown in Table 9.29.

TABLE 9.28   Price Data for Exercise 9.37

Item	Supermarket				
	Kash n' Karry	Publix	Winn-Dixie	Albertsons	Food 4 Less
Celery	.33	.34	.69	.59	.58
Colgate toothpaste	1.28	1.49	1.44	1.37	1.28
Campbell's beef soup	1.05	1.19	1.23	1.19	1.10
Crushed pineapple	.83	.95	.95	.87	.84
Mueller's spaghetti	.68	.79	.83	.69	.69
Heinz catsup	1.41	1.69	1.79	1.65	1.49

TABLE 9.29   SAS Printout for Exercise 9.37

```
                              ANALYSIS OF VARIANCE PROCEDURE
DEPENDENT VARIABLE: PRICE

SOURCE            DF       SUM OF SQUARES      MEAN SQUARE     F VALUE      PR > F     R-SQUARE          C.V.

MODEL              9          4.39130000        0.48792222       83.14      0.0001     0.973969       7.3423

ERROR             20          0.11736667        0.00586833                  ROOT MSE               PRICE MEAN

CORRECTED TOTAL   29          4.50866667                                   0.07660505              1.04333333


SOURCE            DF           ANOVA SS     F VALUE      PR > F

ITEM               5          4.21866667     143.78      0.0001
SUPRMKT            4          0.17263333       7.35      0.0008
```

(a) Is this a randomized block design? If so, identify the blocks and treatments.

(b) Assume that the items listed in Table 9.28 were randomly selected from among all items sold by the supermarkets. Based on this assumption, do the data present sufficient evidence to indicate differences in the mean per-item price for the five supermarkets? Test using $\alpha = .05$.

(c) Find a 90% confidence interval for the difference in the mean per-item prices between the Kash n' Karry and the Albertsons supermarkets.

*9.38 Perform the analysis of variance calculations for Exercise 9.34, and present them in an analysis of variance table. Compare your answers with those given in the computer printout in Table 9.23. Interpret the results of the analysis of variance.

*9.39 Perform the analysis of variance calculations for Exercise 9.35, and present them in an analysis of variance table. Compare your answers with those given in the computer printout in Table 9.25. Interpret the results of the analysis of variance.

*9.40 Perform the analysis of variance calculations for Exercise 9.36, and present them in an analysis of variance table. Compare your answers with those given in the computer printout in Table 9.27. Interpret the results of the analysis of variance.

*9.41 Perform the analysis of variance calculations for Exercise 9.37, and present them in an analysis of variance table. Compare your answers with those given in the computer printout in Table 9.29. Interpret the results of the analysis of variance.

FACTORIAL EXPERIMENTS

9.8

Suppose the manager of a manufacturing plant suspects that the output (in number of units produced per 8-hour shift) of a production line depends upon two qualitative variables, the foreman supervising the line (of which there are two, A_1 and A_2) and the shift on which the production is measured. We will denote the three shifts, 8:00 A.M. to 4:00 P.M., 4:00 P.M. to 12:00 P.M., and 12:00 P.M. to 8:00 A.M., as B_1, B_2, and B_3.

These two qualitative independent variables, "foreman" and "shift," are called **factors** in the language of statistics. The different settings for a given factor are called **levels**. Thus in this experiment the plant manager wants to investigate the effect of the first factor, "foreman," at two levels, A_1 and A_2, one level corresponding to each foreman. Similarly, the manager wants to investigate the effect of the second factor at three levels, B_1, B_2, and B_3, one level corresponding to each of the three shifts. What combination of the two factor levels should be included in the experiment?

One way to conduct the experiment is to hold one factor constant, say "foreman," and vary the shift. For example, we might use foreman A_1 on each of the three shifts B_1, B_2, and B_3. Thus we will collect output counts for each of three treatments, one corresponding to each of the factor level combinations, A_1B_1, A_1B_2, and A_1B_3. If the output counts for these three treatments are 600, 500, and 450, respectively (as represented by the plotted points in Figure 9.3), the data will lead us to believe that the first (8:00 A.M. to 4:00 P.M.) shift seems to be the most productive and that productivity decreases for the second and third shifts.

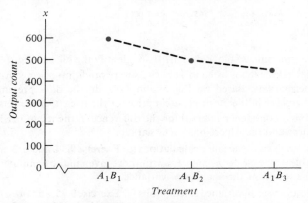

FIGURE 9.3   Output Counts for Three Shifts Using Foreman A_1

Similarly, we might hold the second factor, "shift," constant and vary the foremen to see which foreman seems to be associated with the greater productivity. For example, we might use both foreman A_1 and foreman A_2 on day shift B_1, thus observing the output for the factor level combinations A_1B_1 and A_2B_1. Since we have already collected an observation for the factor level combination A_1B_1, we only need to collect one more observation, one corresponding to the factor level combination, A_2B_1. Suppose that this combination gave an output count of 480 units. Comparing the outputs for A_1B_1 and A_2B_1 (see Figure 9.4), we may conclude that foreman A_1 achieves a greater productivity than foreman A_2.

In the preceding discussion we have investigated the effect of two factors on the output count x by using only four treatments, the factor level combinations A_1B_1, A_1B_2, A_1B_3, and A_2B_1. We concluded that the greatest output occurs when foreman A_1 manages the day shift B_1. Is there a flaw in our logic?

There are $2 \times 3 = 6$ possible combinations of levels of the two factors: A_1B_1, A_1B_2, A_1B_3, and A_2B_1, A_2B_2, A_2B_3. Suppose that we were to run the remaining two factor level combinations, A_2B_2 and A_2B_3, and found the outputs to be 380 and 330, respectively. A plot of all six outputs is shown in Figure 9.5.

Figure 9.5 shows how the outputs would plot *if* the two factors "foreman" and "shift" affect output count *independently* of each other. They show, for example, that the output when A_1 is foreman is always 120 units higher than when A_2 is foreman,

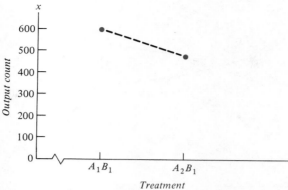

FIGURE 9.4   Output Counts for One Shift Using Foremen A_1 and A_2

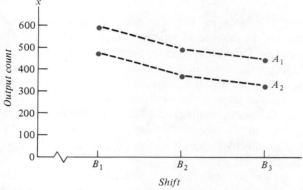

FIGURE 9.5   Plots Indicating That the Factors Affect Output Independently of Each Other

regardless of the shift. Similarly, they show that shift B_1 always produces 100 units more than shift 2 and 150 more than shift 3, regardless of who is the foreman. Of course, we have based this whole discussion on a single observation per treatment, and in practical situations we would select larger samples. Nevertheless, our example makes a point. If the two factors affect output x in an independent manner, we need to compare the means of only four treatments to reach this conclusion.

However, suppose that the output counts for the factor level combinations A_2B_2 and A_2B_3 were 600 and 650, respectively. A plot of the data (see Figure 9.6) leads us to a completely different conclusion. Although foreman A_1 achieves the larger output on the first shift, foreman A_2 (a night person) is superior on shifts B_2 and B_3. Thus we cannot generalize and say that one foreman is better than the other or that the output of one particular shift is best. The output *depends* upon the particular factor level combination that is employed. When this situation occurs, we say that the two factors **interact**, or that **interaction** exists between the two **factors**.

Multifactor experiments are conducted to determine which, if any, of the factors affect the mean response; and if they do, whether they do so independently or whether

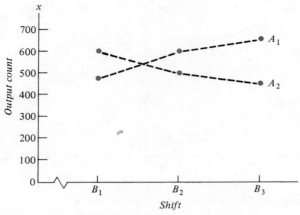

FIGURE 9.6   Output Counts Indicating Factor Interaction

they interact. Therefore, the first step in an analysis of variance is to test the complete model—that is, to determine whether there is evidence of differences among the treatment means. This test appears at the top of the SAS analysis of variance printout. (For example, see the F test in the SAS analysis of variance printout in Table 9.3 in the line corresponding to MODEL.) If there is evidence of differences among the treatment means, the second step in the analysis is to test for factor interaction. If present, we ignore the factors themselves and focus our attention on the means for the individual factor level combinations. If factor interaction seems to be negligible, we can investigate the effect of the factors on the response x as if they affected x in an independent manner.

One safe way to detect factor interactions is to conduct a **factorial experiment**, one that collects sample data for every combination of factor levels. For example, a factorial experiment conducted to investigate the effect of two factors on a response— one at two levels A_1, A_2 and the second at three levels B_1, B_2, and B_3—acquires data for each of the $2 \times 3 = 6$ treatments that correspond to factor level combinations A_1B_1, A_1B_2, A_1B_3, A_2B_1, A_2B_2, A_2B_3. Likewise, a two-factor experiment with one factor at 3 levels and one at 4 levels involves 12 treatments corresponding to the 3×4 factor level combinations. The first experiment is called a 2×3 factorial experiment and indicates that there are two factors, one at 2 levels and the other at 3 levels. A 3×4 factorial experiment is also a two-factor experiment, with one factor at 3 levels and the other factor at 4 levels.

Factorial experiments can also be employed to investigate the effects of three or more factors on a response. A $2 \times 2 \times 3$ factorial experiment involves three factors, two each at 2 levels and the third at 3 levels. The total number of treatments is $2 \times 2 \times 3 = 12$, one for each combination of the levels of the three factors. The factors in a three-factor factorial experiment may affect the response independently; one or more pairs of the factors may interact, or all three factors may interact. Thus the objective of experiments involving three or more factors is to test for factor interactions. If they exist, we know that we should examine treatment means individually. If factor interactions are negligible, we can study the effect of each factor on the response as if the factor affected the response independently of the levels of the other factors.

      When comparing treatment means for a factorial experiment (or for any other experiment), we usually need more than one observation per treatment. For example, if we obtain two observations for each of the treatments of a complete factorial experiment, we say that we have two **replications** of the complete factorial. For all further discussions in this text we will assume that the treatment samples are independent random samples of equal sample size and that the number r of replications is at least equal to 2. One can, under some circumstances, draw practical conclusions from a single replication of a factorial experiment when the number of factors is equal to 3 or larger, but that topic is beyond the scope of this text.

THE ANALYSIS OF VARIANCE FOR A FACTORIAL EXPERIMENT

9.9

An analysis of variance for a replicated, two-factor factorial experiment partitions the total sum of squares of deviations into four parts, the first two representing the variation of the factor level means, the third representing factor interaction, and the fourth measuring the variation of the observations *within* a treatment about the treatment mean. Representing the factors as A and B, we have

$$\text{Total SS} = \text{SS}A + \text{SS}B + \text{SS}(AB) + \text{SSE}$$

where

$$\text{Total SS} = \text{SS}_x = \sum_{i=1}^{n}(x_i - \bar{x})^2$$

$$\text{SS}A = \text{sum of squares for factor } A$$

$$\text{SS}B = \text{sum of squares for factor } B$$

Sums of squares $\text{SS}A$ and $\text{SS}B$ are often called **main-effect** sums of squares for the respective factors to distinguish them from the interaction sum of squares $\text{SS}(AB)$. To continue,

$$\text{SS}(AB) = \text{sum of squares measuring the interaction between factors } A \text{ and } B$$

$$\text{SSE} = \text{Total SS} - \text{SS}A - \text{SS}B - \text{SS}(AB)$$

$$= \text{unexplained variation}$$

As the following example will demonstrate, these sums of squares play the same role here as in the analyses of variance presented in earlier sections.

      Once again, we will explain how to conduct an analysis of variance for a two-factor factorial experiment by describing and interpreting a computer output for an example. The computing formulas are presented in optional Section 9.10.

EXAMPLE 9.3   The manager of the manufacturing plant (see Section 9.8) conducted $r = 3$ replications of a 2×3 factorial experiment to investigate the effect of "foreman" (2 levels) and "shift" (3 levels) on the output of a production line. The observations are given in

TABLE 9.30   Output per Shift for the 2×3 Factorial Experiment of Example 9.3

| Foreman (Factor A) | Shift (Factor B) | | | Total |
	B_1 (8 A.M.–4 P.M.)	B_2 (4 A.M.–12 P.M.)	B_3 (12 P.M.–8 A.M.)	
A_1	570 610 625	480 475 540	470 430 450	4650
A_2	480 515 465	625 600 580	630 680 660	5235
Total	3265	3300	3320	9885

TABLE 9.31   SAS ANOVA Printout for Example 9.3

```
                              ANALYSIS OF VARIANCE PROCEDURE

DEPENDENT VARIABLE: OUTPUT

SOURCE            DF      SUM OF SQUARES      MEAN SQUARE    F VALUE      PR > F    R-SQUARE          C.V.

MODEL              5     100179.16666667    20035.83333333     27.85      0.0001    0.920659        4.8842
                                                                       ①
ERROR             12       8633.33333333      719.44444444             ROOT MSE              OUTPUT MEAN

CORRECTED TOTAL   17     108812.50000000                             26.82246157  ③       549.16666667


SOURCE            DF          ANOVA SS    F VALUE     PR > F

FOREMAN            1     19012.50000000      26.43     0.0002  ②
SHIFT              2       258.33333333       0.18     0.8379
SHIFT*FOREMAN      2     80908.33333333      56.23     0.0001
```

TABLE 9.32   Minitab ANOVA Printout for Example 9.3

```
ANALYSIS OF VARIANCE   OUTPUT

SOURCE       DF       SS        MS
FACTORA       1    19013     19013
FACTORB       2      258       129
INTERACTION   2    80908     40454
ERROR        12     8633       719
TOTAL        17   108813
```

Table 9.30; the SAS, Minitab, and SPSS[x] printouts are shown in Tables 9.31, 9.32, and 9.33. Describe and interpret the SAS printout.

SOLUTION   (1) As noted in our discussion of the analysis of variance for a randomized block design, the SAS output for an analysis of variance presents the ANOVA table in two stages. The first stage, shaded area ① in Table 9.31, separates the total variation of the x-values into two sources, MODEL and ERROR. The portion

TABLE 9.33   SPSS[x] ANOVA Printout for Example 9.3

```
                    * * * A N A L Y S I S   O F   V A R I A N C E * * *

                    OUTPUT
              BY    FOREMAN
                    SHIFT

                                SUM OF                 MEAN               SIGNIF
   SOURCE OF VARIATION           SQUARES     DF       SQUARE         F     OF F

   MAIN EFFECTS                 19270.833     3      6423.611     8.929    0.002
      FOREMAN                   19012.500     1     19012.500    26.427    0.000
      SHIFT                       258.333     2       129.167     0.180    0.838

   2-WAY INTERACTIONS           80908.333     2     40454.167    56.230    0.000
      FOREMAN SHIFT             80908.333     2     40454.167    56.230    0.000

   EXPLAINED                   100179.167     5     20035.833    27.849    0.000

   RESIDUAL                      8633.333    12       719.444

   TOTAL                       108812.500    17      6400.735
```

for MODEL combines the three sources corresponding to main-effect factor A (foreman), main-effect factor B (shift), and the AB (foreman by shift) interaction. These three sources are shown in shaded area ② in the table.

(2) The degrees of freedom for the respective sources are shown in column 2 of the tables. If factor A is at a levels and factor B is at b levels, then the number of degrees of freedom for the main effects A and B will always equal $(a - 1)$ and $(b - 1)$, respectively, and the number of degrees of freedom for interaction will be $(a - 1)(b - 1)$. These numbers—$(a - 1) = (2 - 1) = 1$, $(b - 1) = (3 - 1) = 2$, and $(a - 1)(b - 1) = (1)(2) = 2$—are shown in the DF column in shaded area 2. Note that the sum of these degrees of freedom, 5, is equal to the number of degrees of freedom for MODEL (shown in shaded area ①), the source which was partitioned to form sources A, B, and AB.

If the experiment is replicated r times—that is, there are r observations for each combination of factor levels (for our example, $r = 3$)—then the total number of observations in the experiment is $n = abr$, and the number of degrees of freedom associated with Total SS is $(n - 1) = (abr - 1)$. For our example, $(n - 1) = (abr - 1) = (2)(3)(3) - 1 = 17$. The number of degrees of freedom for ERROR will always equal $ab(r - 1)$—that is, $(r - 1)$ degrees of freedom for each of the ab factor level combinations. For our example, $ab(r - 1) = (2)(3)(3 - 1) = 12$. These numbers of degrees of freedom, for the CORRECTED TOTAL and for ERROR, are shown in column 2 in shaded area ①.

(3) Column 3 of shaded areas ① and ②, labeled SUM OF SQUARES and ANOVA SS, respectively, shows the sums of squares for the sources of variation. Thus SSE, shown in shaded area ①, is

$$SSE = 8633.33333$$

The Total SS is shown in shaded area ① in the row corresponding to

CORRECTED TOTAL:

$$\text{Total SS} = 108812.500000$$

The sums of squares for main effects A and B and for the AB interaction are shown in shaded area ② as

$$SSA = 19012.5000$$
$$SSB = 258.3333$$
$$SS(AB) = 80908.3333$$

(4) Each mean square is obtained by dividing a source sum of squares by its degrees of freedom. These quantities have been calculated and appear in column 4 of the tables opposite their respective sources. Thus

$$MSE = s^2 = 719.44444$$
$$MSA = 19012.5000$$
$$MSB = 129.1667$$
$$MS(AB) = 40454.1667$$

(5) The F values for testing the hypotheses of "no interaction between factors A and B," "no main-effect factor A," and "no main-effect factor B" are shown in column 5; and the observed significance levels (p-values) for the three tests are shown in column 6 of shaded area ②. The numerator number (v_1) of degrees of freedom for an F value will equal the number of degrees of freedom of the mean square appearing in the numerator of the F statistic. The denominator number (v_2) of degrees of freedom will always equal the number of degrees of freedom of the mean square appearing in the denominator of F, namely, MSE. For example, the F statistic used to test for AB interaction is

$$F = \frac{MS(AB)}{MSE}$$

This F value for our example possesses $v_1 = 2$ and $v_2 = 12$ degrees of freedom, the degrees of freedom associated with $MS(AB)$ and MSE, respectively.

The small p-value ($p = .0002$) indicates that there is sufficient evidence to indicate differences in the mean levels of factor B—that is, differences in the mean output per shift. But this fact is overshadowed by the fact that there is strong evidence ($p = .0001$) of an AB interaction. This implies that the mean output for a given shift depends upon the supervising foreman. You can see this result by examining the means for the six factor level combinations shown in Table 9.34. The three largest mean outputs occur when foreman A_1 is on the day shift and when foreman A_2 is on one of the two night shifts. The largest mean output appears to occur when foreman A_2 is supervising the early-morning shift. The practical implications of these comparisons suggest that foreman A_1 should be scheduled for the day shift and foreman A_2 for the early-morning shift.

(6) The standard deviation, $s = \sqrt{MSE} = 26.822462$, is shown in shaded area ③. It can be used to test or to construct confidence intervals for the individual

TABLE 9.34   Means of the Factor Level Combinations

Foreman (Factor A)	Shift (Factor B)		
	B_1 (8 A.M.–4 P.M.)	B_2 (4 P.M.–12 P.M.)	B_3 (12 P.M.–8 A.M.)
A_1	601.67	498.33	450.00
A_2	486.67	601.67	656.67

treatment (factor level combination) means or for the difference between a pair of means. The formulas and procedures are the same as those used for the independent random sampling design. Since we obtained r observations for each treatment, $(1 - \alpha)100\%$ confidence intervals for a single treatment mean or the difference between two means are

and

$$\bar{x}_i \pm t_{\alpha/2}\frac{s}{\sqrt{r}}$$

$$(\bar{x}_i - \bar{x}_j) \pm t_{\alpha/2}\sqrt{\frac{2}{r}}$$

For example, suppose that we want to construct a 95% confidence interval for the difference in mean output for foremen A_1 and A_2 on the second shift (B_2). We will denote these factor level combinations, A_1B_2 and A_2B_2, as μ_1 and μ_2, respectively. The sample means for these treatments are $\bar{x}_1 = 498.33$ and $\bar{x}_2 = 601.67$, and $s = 26.822462$. Since s^2 is based on 12 degrees of freedom, the tabulated value of t (Table 5 in the Appendix) is $t_{\alpha/2} = t_{.025} = 2.179$; and the confidence interval is

$$(\bar{x}_i - \bar{x}_j) \pm t_{\alpha/2}s\sqrt{\frac{2}{r}}$$

$$(498.33 - 601.67) \pm (2.179)(26.822)\sqrt{\frac{2}{3}}$$

$$-103.34 \pm 47.72$$

or $-151.06 \quad$ to $\quad -55.62$

Therefore, we estimate the difference in mean output between foremen A_1 and A_2 on shift B_2 to be between -151.06 to -55.62 units. Thus we estimate the mean output on the second shift to be 55.62 to 151.06 higher when foreman A_2 is supervising the shift. ∎

The typical ANOVA table for r replications of a two-factor factorial experiment, factor A at a levels and factor B at b levels, is shown in the first box that follows. The other two boxes summarize the analysis of variance F tests and give the confidence intervals for an individual treatment mean and for the difference between a pair of treatment means.

ANOVA TABLE FOR r REPLICATIONS OF A TWO-FACTOR FACTORIAL EXPERIMENT; FACTOR A AT a LEVELS AND FACTOR B AT b LEVELS

Source	d.f.	SS	MS	F
A	$a - 1$	SSA	$\text{MS}A = \dfrac{\text{SS}A}{a - 1}$	$\dfrac{\text{MS}A}{\text{MSE}}$
B	$b - 1$	SSB	$\text{MS}B = \dfrac{\text{SS}B}{b - 1}$	$\dfrac{\text{MS}B}{\text{MSE}}$
AB	$(a - 1)(b - 1)$	SS(AB)	$\text{MS}(AB) = \dfrac{\text{SS}(AB)}{(a - 1)(b - 1)}$	$\dfrac{\text{MS}(AB)}{\text{MSE}}$
Error	$ab(r - 1)$	SSE	$\text{MSE} = \dfrac{\text{SSE}}{ab(r - 1)}$	
Total	$abr - 1$	Total SS		

TESTS FOR A FACTORIAL EXPERIMENT

Testing for Interaction:

(1) *Null Hypothesis:* H_0: factors A and B do not interact.

(2) *Alternative Hypothesis:* H_a: factors A and B interact.

(3) *Test Statistic:* $F = \text{MS}(AB)/\text{MSE}$, where F is based on $v_1 = (a - 1)(b - 1)$ and $v_2 = ab(r - 1)$ degrees of freedom.

(4) *Rejection Region:* Reject H_0 if $F > F_\alpha$, where F_α lies in the upper tail of the F distribution (see the figure).

Testing for Main Effects, Factor A:

(1) *Null Hypothesis:* H_0: There are no differences among the factor A means.

(2) *Alternative Hypothesis:* H_a: at least two of the factor A means differ.

(3) *Test Statistic:* $F = \text{MS}A/\text{MSE}$, where F is based on $v_1 = a - 1$ and $v_2 = ab(r - 1)$ degrees of freedom.

(4) *Rejection Region:* Reject H_0 if $F > F_\alpha$ (see the figure).

Testing for Main Effects, Factor B:

(1) *Null Hypothesis:* H_0: there are no differences among the factor B means.

(2) *Alternative Hypothesis:* H_a: at least two of the factor B means differ.

(3) *Test Statistic:* $F = \text{MS}B/\text{MSE}$, where F is based on $v_1 = b - 1$ and $v_2 = ab(r - 1)$ degrees of freedom.

(4) *Rejection Region:* Reject H_0 if $F > F_\alpha$ (see the figure).

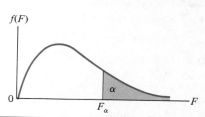

$(1 - \alpha)100\%$ CONFIDENCE INTERVALS FOR A SINGLE TREATMENT MEAN OR THE DIFFERENCE BETWEEN A PAIR OF TREATMENT MEANS: A TWO-FACTOR FACTORIAL EXPERIMENT

Single Treatment Mean: $\bar{x}_i \pm t_{\alpha/2} \dfrac{s}{\sqrt{r}}$

Difference Between Two Treatment Means: $(\bar{x}_i - \bar{x}_j) \pm t_{\alpha/2} s \sqrt{\dfrac{2}{r}}$

where r = number of replications (observations per treatment)

$s = \sqrt{\text{MSE}}$

and $t_{\alpha/2}$ is based on $ab(r - 1)$ degrees of freedom.

COMPUTING FORMULAS: THE ANALYSIS OF VARIANCE FOR A TWO-FACTOR FACTORIAL EXPERIMENT*

9.10

We will use the symbols given in the next box when conducting an analysis of variance for a two-factor factorial experiment.

The computing formulas for the analysis of variance follow. To demonstrate their use, we show the numerical substitutions and calculations for the data in Example 9.3.

The totals for the factor levels and for the factor level combinations are shown in Table 9.35.

For Example 9.3, $a = 2$, $b = 3$, $r = 3$, and $n = abr = (2)(3)(3) = 18$. Then

$$T = \text{total of all } n = abr \text{ observations}$$
$$= 570 + 610 + 625 + 480 + \cdots + 660$$
$$= 9885$$

*This section is optional.

NOTATION

a = number of levels of factor A

b = number of levels of factor B

r = number of replications, that is, the number of observations for each factor level combination (treatment)

$n = abr$ = total number of observations

A_i = total of all observations at the ith level of factor A, $i = 1, 2, \ldots, a$

B_j = total of all observations at the jth level of factor B, $j = 1, 2, \ldots, b$

$(AB)_{ij}$ = total of the r observations at the ith level of factor A and the jth level of factor B

TABLE 9.35   Table of Totals for the Data of Example 9.3

| Foreman (Factor A) | Shift (Factor B) | | | Total |
	B_1 (8 A.M.–4 P.M.)	B_2 (4 P.M.–12 P.M.)	B_3 (12 P.M.–8 A.M.)	
A_1	1805	1495	1350	4650
A_2	1460	1805	1970	5235
Total	3265	3300	3320	9885

$$CM = \frac{(T)^2}{n} = \frac{(9885)^2}{18} = 5{,}428{,}512.5$$

Total sum of squares of deviations = Total SS

$$\text{Total SS} = SS_x = \sum_{i=1}^{n} (x_i - \bar{x})^2 = \sum_{i=1}^{n} x_i^2 - CM$$

$$= (570)^2 + (610)^2 + (625)^2 + (480)^2 + \cdots + (660)^2 - CM$$

$$= 5{,}537{,}325 - 5{,}428{,}512.5$$

$$= 108{,}812.5$$

Sum of squares, main effects A = SSA

$$SSA = \sum_{i=1}^{a} \frac{A_i^2}{br} - CM = \frac{(4650)^2 + (5235)^2}{9} - 5{,}428{,}512.5$$

$$= 19{,}012.5$$

Sum of squares, main effects $B = SSB$

$$SSB = \sum_{j=1}^{b} \frac{B_j^2}{ar} - CM = \frac{(3265)^2 + (3300)^2 + (3320)^2}{6} - 5,428,512.5$$

$$= 258.3333$$

Sum of squares, interaction $AB = SS(AB)$

$$SS(AB) = \sum_{j=1}^{b} \sum_{i=1}^{a} \frac{(AB)_{ij}^2}{r} - SSA - SSB - CM$$

$$= \frac{(1805)^2 + (1460)^2 + \cdots + (1970)^2}{3} - 19012.5 - 129.1667 - 5,428,512.5$$

$$= 80,908.3333$$

Sum of squares for error $= SSE$

$$SSE = \text{Total SS} - SSA - SSB - SS(AB)$$

$$= 108,812.5 - 19,012.5 - 129.1667 - 40,454.1667$$

$$= 8633.3333$$

Mean square for $A = MSA = \dfrac{SSA}{a-1} = \dfrac{19,012.5}{1} = 19,012.5$

Mean square for $B = MSB = \dfrac{SSB}{b-1} = \dfrac{258.3333}{2} = 129.1667$

Mean square for $AB = MS(AB) = \dfrac{SS(AB)}{(a-1)(b-1)} = \dfrac{80,908.3333}{(1)(2)}$

$$= 40,454.1667$$

The sources of variation, degrees of freeedom, sums of squares, mean squares and F values are summarized in the ANOVA table in Table 9.36. You can verify that the numbers shown in Table 9.36 are the same as those shown in the SAS printout in Table 9.31.

TABLE 9.36   ANOVA Table for the Two-Factor Factorial Experiment of Example 9.3

Source	d.f.	SS	MS	F
A	1	19,012.5	19,012.5	26.43
B	2	258.3333	129.1667	.18
AB	2	80,908.3333	40,454.1667	56.23
Error	12	8,633.3333	719.4444	
Total	17	108,812.5		

A summary of the computing formulas is given in the next box.

SUMMARY OF COMPUTING FORMULAS: ANALYSIS OF VARIANCE FOR A TWO-FACTOR FACTORIAL EXPERIMENT

$$CM = \frac{(T)^2}{n} \qquad\qquad \text{Total SS} = \sum_{i=1}^{n} x_i^2 - CM$$

$$SSA = \sum_{i=1}^{a} \frac{A_i^2}{br} - CM \qquad\qquad SSB = \sum_{j=1}^{b} \frac{B_j^2}{ar} - CM$$

$$SS(AB) = \sum_{j=1}^{b} \sum_{i=1}^{a} \frac{(AB)_{ij}^2}{r} - SSA - SSB - CM$$

$$MSA = \frac{SSA}{a-1} \qquad\qquad MSB = \frac{SSB}{b-1}$$

$$MS(AB) = \frac{SS(AB)}{(a-1)(b-1)} \qquad MSE = s^2 = \frac{SSE}{ab(r-1)}$$

EXERCISES

Starred (*) exercises are optional.

BASIC TECHNIQUES

9.42 Suppose that you were to conduct a two-factor factorial experiment, factor A at 4 levels and factor B at 5 levels, with 3 replications per treatment.

(a) How many treatments will be involved in the experiment?

(b) How many observations will be involved?

(c) List the sources of variation and their respective degrees of freedom.

9.43 Suppose that you were to conduct a two-factor factorial experiment, factor A at 4 levels and factor B at 2 levels, with r replications per treatment.

(a) How many treatments will be involved in the experiment?

(b) How many observations will be involved?

(c) List the sources of variation and their respective degrees of freedom.

9.44 The analysis of variance table for a 3×4 factor factorial experiment, factor A at 3 levels and factor B at 4 levels, with 2 observations per treatment, is shown in Table 9.37.

TABLE 9.37   ANOVA Table for Exercise 9.44

Source	d.f.	SS	MS	F
	2	5.3		
	3	9.1		
	6			
	12	24.5		
Total	23	43.7		

(a) Fill in the missing items in the table.

(b) Do the data present sufficient evidence to indicate that factors A and B interact? Test using $\alpha = .05$. What are the practical implications of your answer?

(c) Do the data present sufficient evidence to indicate that the factors A and B affect the response variable x? Explain.

9.45 Refer to Exercise 9.44. The means of the factor level combinations $A_1 B_1$ and $A_1 C_1$ are $\bar{x}_1 = 12.4$ and $\bar{x}_2 = 6.3$, respectively. Find a 95% confidence interval for the difference between the two corresponding population means.

9.46 The analysis of variance table for a 2×3 factorial experiment, factor A at 2 levels and factor B at 3 levels, with 5 observations per treatment, is shown in Table 9.38.

TABLE 9.38   ANOVA Table for Exercise 9.46

Source	d.f.	SS	MS	F
A		1.14		
B		2.58		
AB		.49		
Error				
Total		8.41		

(a) Do the data present sufficient evidence to indicate interaction between factors A and B? Test using $\alpha = .05$. What are the practical implications of your answer?

(b) Give the approximate p-value for the test in part (a).

(c) Do the data present sufficient evidence to indicate that factor A affects the response? Test using $\alpha = .05$.

(d) Do the data present sufficient evidence to indicate that factor B affects the response? Test using $\alpha = .05$.

9.47 Refer to Exercise 9.46. The means of all observations at the factor A levels A_1 and A_2 were $\bar{x}_1 = 3.7$ and $\bar{x}_2 = 1.4$, respectively. Find a 95% confidence interval for the difference in mean response for factor levels A_1 and A_2.

*9.48 Table 9.39 gives data for a 3×3 factorial experiment, two replications per treatment.

TABLE 9.39   Sample Data for Exercise 9.48

Levels of Factor B	Levels of Factor A		
	1	2	3
1	5, 7	9, 7	4, 6
2	8, 7	12, 13	7, 10
3	14, 11	8, 9	12, 15

(a) Perform an analysis of variance for the data, and present the results in an analysis of variance table.

(b) What do we mean when we say that factors A and B interact?

(c) Do the data provide sufficient evidence to indicate interaction between factors A and B? Test using $\alpha = .05$.

(d) Find the approximate p-value for the test in part (c).

(e) Find a 95% confidence interval for the mean for the factor level combination $A_2 B_2$.

(f) Find a 95% confidence interval for the difference in means for factor level combinations $A_1 B_3$ and $A_3 B_1$.

*9.49 Table 9.40 gives data for a 2×2 factorial experiment, four replications per treatment.

TABLE 9.40   Sample Data for Exercise 9.49

Levels of Factor B	Levels of Factor A 1	2
1	2.1, 2.7, 2.4, 2.5	3.7, 3.2, 3.0, 3.5
2	3.1, 3.6, 3.4, 3.9	2.9, 2.7, 2.2, 2.5

(a) Perform an analysis of variance for the data, and present the results in an analysis of variance table.

(b) What do we mean when we say that factors A and B interact?

(c) Do the data provide sufficient evidence to indicate interaction between factors A and B? Test using $\alpha = .05$.

(d) Find the approximate p-value for the test in part (c).

(e) Find a 95% confidence interval for the mean for the factor level combination $A_2 B_2$.

(f) Find a 95% confidence interval for the difference in means for factor level combinations $A_1 B_2$ and $A_2 B_1$.

APPLICATIONS

 9.50 A builder of speculative houses uses one of three designs and assigns each house to the supervision of one of four foremen. Noticing variation in profit per house, the builder decided to investigate the effect of the two factors, "house design" and "foreman," on profit per house. The builder used each foreman as supervisor for each house design and for three houses for each

TABLE 9.41   Profit Data for Exercise 9.50

Design	Foreman A_1	A_2	A_3	A_4
B_1	12.8 9.4 10.3	9.2 7.8 10.9	11.6 12.9 9.6	8.7 7.4 8.5
B_2	9.2 7.4 8.6	11.4 9.6 8.3	8.7 7.5 9.0	10.3 10.9 11.7
B_3	13.7 12.0 14.6	10.7 10.2 11.1	10.1 8.7 9.1	7.3 8.6 6.9

TABLE 9.42   SAS Printout for Exercise 9.50

ANALYSIS OF VARIANCE PROCEDURE

DEPENDENT VARIABLE: PROFIT

SOURCE	DF	SUM OF SQUARES	MEAN SQUARE	F VALUE	PR > F	R-SQUARE	C.V.
MODEL	11	91.86972222	8.35179293	6.11	0.0001	0.736787	11.8687
ERROR	24	32.82000000	1.36750000		ROOT MSE		PROFIT MEAN
CORRECTED TOTAL	35	124.68972222			1.16940156		9.85277778

SOURCE	DF	ANOVA SS	F VALUE	PR > F
DESIGN	2	4.60055556	1.68	0.2072
FOREMAN	3	17.72750000	4.32	0.0143
DESIGN*FOREMAN	6	69.54166667	8.48	0.0001

foreman-design combination. The data (in thousands of dollars profit per house) is shown in Table 9.41. The SAS analysis of variance printout for the data is shown in Table 9.42.

(a) What would be the practical implications if factors A and B interact?

(b) Do the data present sufficient evidence to indicate interaction between factors A and B? Test using $\alpha = .05$.

(c) Give the approximate p-value for the test in part (b). Interpret the results.

(d) Find a 95% confidence interval for the difference in mean profit between foremen A_1 and A_2 for houses built using plan B_1.

 9.51 A chain of jewelry stores conducted an experiment to investigate the relationship between price and location on the demand for its diamonds. Six small-town stores were selected for the study as well as six stores located in large suburban city malls. Two stores in each of these location categories were assigned to each of three item percentage markups. The percentage gain (or loss) in sales for each store was recorded at the end of one month. The data are shown in Table 9.43. The SAS analysis of variance printout for the data is shown in Table 9.44.

(a) Do the data present sufficient evidence to indicate an interaction between markup and location? Test using $\alpha = .05$.

(b) What are the practical implications of your test in part (a)?

(c) Find a 95% confidence interval for the difference in mean change in sales for stores in small towns versus those in suburban malls if the stores are using price markup A_3.

TABLE 9.43   Percentage Gain (Loss) Data for Exercise 9.51

Location	Markup		
	A_1	A_2	A_3
Small towns, B_1	10 4	−3 7	−10 −24
Suburban malls, B_2	14 18	8 3	−4 3

TABLE 9.44   SAS Printout for Exercise 9.51

```
                              ANALYSIS OF VARIANCE PROCEDURE

DEPENDENT VARIABLE: PCTGAIN

SOURCE              DF      SUM OF SQUARES     MEAN SQUARE     F VALUE      PR > F     R-SQUARE          C.V.

MODEL                5       1200.66666667    240.13333333        6.83     0.0183     0.850531      273.6992

ERROR                6        211.00000000     35.16666667                 ROOT MSE              PCTGAIN MEAN

CORRECTED TOTAL     11       1411.66666667                              5.93014896               2.16666667


SOURCE              DF             ANOVA SS    F VALUE     PR > F

LOCATION             1       280.33333333        7.97     0.0302
MARKUP               2       835.16666667       11.87     0.0082
MARKUP*LOCATION      2        85.16666667        1.21     0.3616
```

 9.52 Helena F. Barsam and Zita M. Simutis, at the U.S. Army Research Institute for the Behavior and Social Sciences, conducted a study to determine the effect of two factors on terrain visualization training for soldiers. During the training programs participants viewed contour maps of various terrains and then were permitted to view a computer reconstruction of the terrain as it would appear from a specified angle. The two factors investigated in the experiment were the participants' spatial abilities (abilities to visualize in three dimensions) and the viewing procedure, active or passive. Active participation permitted participants to view the computer-generated reconstructions of the terrain from any and all angles. Passive participation gave the participants a set of preselected reconstructions of the terrain. Participants were tested according to spatial ability, and from the test scores, 20 were categorized as possessing high spatial ability, 20 medium, and 20 low. Then 10 participants within each of these groups were assigned to each of the two training modes, active or passive. Table 9.45 shows the analysis of variance table computed by Barsam and Simutis, and Table 9.46 shows the six treatment means.

(a) Explain how the authors arrived at the degrees of freedom shown in the ANOVA table.

(b) Are the F values correct?

(c) Interpret the test results. What are their practical implications?

(d) Use Tables 7, 8, 9, 10, and 11 in the Appendix to approximate the p-values for the F statistics shown in the ANOVA table.

TABLE 9.45   ANOVA Table for Exercise 9.52

Source	d.f.	MS	error d.f.	F	p
Main effects:					
Training condition	1	103.7009	54	3.66	.061
Ability	2	760.5889	54	26.87	.0005
Interaction:					
Training condition × ability	2	124.9905	54	4.42	.017
Within cells	54	28.3015			

TABLE 9.46 Treatment Means for Exercise 9.52

	Training Condition	
Spatial Ability	Active	Passive
High	17.895	9.508
Medium	5.031	5.648
Low	1.728	1.610

Source: H. F. Barsam and Z. M. Simutis, "Computer-Based Graphics for Terrain Visualization Training," *Human Factors,* Vol. 26, 1984. Copyright 1984, by the Human Factors Society, Inc. and reproduced by permission.
Note: Maximum score = 36.

*9.53 Perform the analysis of variance calculations for the data in Exercise 9.50, and display the results in an ANOVA table. Compare your table with the SAS printout in Table 9.42.

*9.54 Perform the analysis of variance calculations for the data in Exercise 9.51, and display the results in an ANOVA table. Compare your table with the SAS printout in Table 9.44.

9.11 RANKING POPULATION MEANS

Many experiments are exploratory in nature. Thus we have no preconceived notions about the results and have not decided (before conducting the experiment) to make specific treatment comparisons. Rather, we are searching for the treatment that possesses the largest treatment mean, possesses the smallest mean, or satisfies some other set of comparisons. When this situation occurs, we will want to rank the treatment means, determine which means differ, and identify sets of means for which no evidence of differences exists.

One way to achieve this goal is to order the sample means from the smallest to the largest and then to conduct t tests for adjacent means in the ordering. If two means differ by more than

$$t_{\alpha/2} s \sqrt{\frac{1}{n_1} + \frac{1}{n_2}}$$

you conclude that the pair of population means differ. The problem with this procedure is that the probability of making a type I error—that is, concluding that two means differ when, in fact, they are equal—is α for each test. If you compare a large number of pairs of means, the probability of detecting at least one difference in means, when, in fact, none exists, is quite large.

A simple way to avoid the high risk of proclaiming differences in multiple comparisons when they do not exist is to use the **studentized range**, the difference between the smallest and the largest in a set of k sample means, as the yardstick for determining whether there is a difference in a pair of population means. This method, often called **Tukey's method for paired comparisons**, makes the probability of declaring that a difference exists between at least one pair in a set of k treatment means, when no difference exists, equal to α.

Tukey's method for making paired comparisons is based on the usual analysis of variance assumptions. **In addition, it assumes that the sample means are independent and based upon samples of equal size.** The yardstick that determines whether a difference exists between a pair of treatment means is the quantity ω (Greek letter omega), which is presented in the following box.

YARDSTICK FOR MAKING PAIRED COMPARISONS

$$\omega = q(k, v)\frac{s}{\sqrt{n_t}}$$

where

k = number of treatments

s^2 = estimator of the common variance σ^2 (calculated in an analysis of variance)

v = number of degrees of freedom for s^2

n_t = common sample size, that is, the number of observations in each of the k treatment means

$q_\alpha(k, v)$ = tabulated value from Tables 16 and 17 in the Appendix, for α = .05 and .01, respectively, and for various combinations of k and v

Rule: Two population means are judged to differ if the corresponding sample means differ by ω or more.

As noted in the box, the values of $q(k, v)$ are listed in Tables 16 and 17 in the Appendix for α = .05 and .01, respectively. A portion of Table 16 in the Appendix is reproduced in Table 9.47. To illustrate the use of Tables 16 and 17, suppose that you want to make pairwise comparisons of $k = 5$ means with α = .05 for an analysis of variance, where s^2 possesses $v = 9$ degrees of freedom. The tabulated value for $k = 5$, $v = 9$, and α = .05, shaded in Table 9.47, is $q_{.05}(5, 9) = 4.76$.

The following example will illustrate the use of Tables 16 and 17 in the Appendix in making paired comparisons.

EXAMPLE 9.4

In Example 9.3 we performed an analysis of variance for three replications of a 2×3 factorial experiment. The six cell means are shown in Table 9.48. Rank the $k = 6$ treatment means, make paired comparisons, and determine which treatment mean(s), if any, is (are) the largest.

SOLUTION

For this example there are $k = 6$ treatment means, each based on a sample of $n_t = 3$ observations. The standard deviation s, obtained from the SAS analysis of variance printout in Table 9.31, is based on $v = 12$ degrees of freedom and is equal to 26.822462. Therefore, from Table 16 in the Appendix, $q_{.05}(k, v) = q_{.05}(6, 12) = 4.75$, and the

TABLE 9.47   A Partial Reproduction of Table 16 in the Appendix; Upper 5% Points

v	2	3	4	5	6	7	8	9	10	11	12	...
						k						
1	17.97	26.98	32.82	37.08	40.41	43.12	45.40	47.36	49.07	50.59	51.96	
2	6.08	8.33	9.80	10.88	11.74	12.44	13.03	13.54	13.99	14.39	14.75	
3	4.50	5.91	6.82	7.50	8.04	8.48	8.85	9.18	9.46	9.72	9.95	
4	3.93	5.04	5.76	6.29	6.71	7.05	7.35	7.60	7.83	8.03	8.21	
5	3.64	4.60	5.22	5.67	6.03	6.33	6.58	6.80	6.99	7.17	7.32	
6	3.46	4.34	4.90	5.30	5.63	5.90	6.12	6.32	6.49	6.65	6.79	
7	3.34	4.16	4.68	5.06	5.36	5.61	5.82	6.00	6.16	6.30	6.43	
8	3.26	4.04	4.53	4.89	5.17	5.40	5.60	5.77	5.92	6.05	6.18	
9	3.20	3.95	4.41	4.76	5.02	5.24	5.43	5.59	5.74	5.87	5.98	
10	3.15	3.88	4.33	4.65	4.91	5.12	5.30	5.46	5.60	5.72	5.83	
11	3.11	3.82	4.26	4.57	4.82	5.03	5.20	5.35	5.49	5.61	5.71	
12	3.08	3.77	4.20	4.51	4.75	4.95	5.12	5.27	5.39	5.51	5.61	
⋮	⋮	⋮	⋮	⋮	⋮	⋮	⋮	⋮	⋮	⋮	⋮	

TABLE 9.48   Treatment Means for the Factorial Experiment in Example 9.3

Foreman (Factor A)	Shift (Factor B)		
	B_1 (8 A.M.–4 P.M.)	B_2 (4 P.M.–12 P.M.)	B_3 (12 P.M.–8 A.M.)
A_1	601.67	498.33	450.00
A_2	486.67	601.67	656.67

yardstick for detecting a difference between a pair of treatment means is

$$\omega = q_{.05}(6, 12)\frac{s}{\sqrt{n_t}} = (4.75)\frac{(26.82)}{\sqrt{3}} = 73.55$$

The six treatment means are arranged in order from the smallest, 450.00, to the largest, 656.67, in Figure 9.7. The appropriate treatment (factor level combination) is shown above its mean. The next step is to check the difference between each pair of means. If the means differ by ω or more, there is sufficient evidence to indicate a difference between the corresponding population means. If there is no evidence to indicate a difference between a pair of means, that fact is indicated by drawing a line under the means.

You can see that the three largest means in the ranking in Figure 9.7 differ by less than $\omega = 73.55$. Therefore, there is no evidence of differences among these three means, and this fact is indicated by the line drawn beneath them. Similarly, there is insufficient evidence to indicate differences among the three smallest means, which is also indicated by underlining. In contrast, each of the three largest means differs by

			Treatment			
A_1B_3	A_2B_1	A_1B_2	A_1B_1	A_2B_2	A_2B_3
450.00	486.67	498.33	601.67	601.67	656.67

Means

FIGURE 9.7   A Ranking of Treatment Means

more than $\omega = 73.55$ from the three smallest. Therefore, we conclude that there is sufficient evidence to indicate that the three largest means differ from the three smallest. The probability that we will make at least one error in making all of these multiple comparisons is only $\alpha = .05$.   ∎

EXERCISES

Starred (*) exercises are optional.

BASIC TECHNIQUES

9.55   Suppose that you wish to use Tukey's method of paired comparisons to rank a set of population means. In addition to the analysis of variance assumptions, what other property must the treatment means satisfy?

9.56   Consult Tables 16 and 17 in the Appendix, and find the values of $q_\alpha(k, v)$:
(a) $\alpha = .05, k = 5, v = 7$ (b) $\alpha = .05, k = 3, v = 10$
(c) $\alpha = .01, k = 4, v = 8$ (d) $\alpha = .01, k = 7, v = 5$

9.57   If the sample size for each treatment is n_t and if s^2 is based on 12 degrees of freedom, find ω.
(a) $\alpha = .05, k = 4, n_t = 5$ (b) $\alpha = .01, k = 6, n_t = 8$.

9.58   An independent random sampling design was employed to compare the means of six treatments based on samples of four observations per treatment. The pooled estimator σ^2 is 9.12, and the sample means follow:

$$\bar{x}_1 = 101.6 \qquad \bar{x}_2 = 98.4 \qquad \bar{x}_3 = 112.3$$
$$\bar{x}_4 = 92.9 \qquad \bar{x}_5 = 104.2 \qquad \bar{x}_6 = 113.8$$

(a) Give the value of ω that you would use to make pairwise comparisons of the treatment means for $\alpha = .05$.

(b) Rank the treatment means using pairwise comparisons.

*9.59   Use Tukey's pairwise comparison procedure to rank the means for the 3×3 factorial experiment in Exercise 9.48.

*9.60   Use Tukey's pairwise comparison procedure to rank the means for the 2×2 factorial experiment in Exercise 9.49.

APPLICATIONS

9.61   Refer to Exercise 9.50. Rank the mean profits per house for the four foremen for house design B_1, and make pairwise comparisons for $\alpha = .05$. Which, if any, of the foremen appears to achieve the largest profit when building house design B_1? (*Note:* When calculating ω, use the value of s^2 calculated by using the complete data set.)

9.62 Refer to Exercise 9.50. Rank the mean profits per house for the four foremen for house design B_2, and make pairwise comparisons for $\alpha = .05$. Which, if any, of the foremen appears to achieve the largest profit when building house design B_2?

9.63 Refer to Exercise 9.50. Rank the mean profits per house for the four foremen for house design B_3, and make pairwise comparisons for $\alpha = .05$. Which, if any, of the foremen appears to achieve the largest profit when building house design B_3?

9.64 Rank the mean percentage gains in sales for the six markup price and location combinations and make paired comparisons for the data in Exercise 9.51, using $\alpha = .05$. What are the practical implications of your comparisons?

9.65 The means for the 2×3 factorial experiment conducted by Barsam and Simutis, discussed in Exercise 9.52, are shown in Table 9.49. Use Tukey's procedure to make paired comparisons of the treatment means, using $\alpha = .05$. What are the practical implications of your comparison?

TABLE 9.49   Treatment Means for Exercise 9.65

| | Training Condition | |
Spatial Ability	Active	Passive
High	17.895	9.508
Medium	5.031	5.648
Low	1.728	1.610

Source: H. F. Barsam, and Z. M. Simutis, "Computer-Based Graphics for Terrain Visualization Training," *Human Factors,* Vol. 26, 1984. Copyright 1984, by the Human Factors Society, Inc. and reproduced by permission.

Note: Maximum score = 36.

SATISFYING THE ASSUMPTIONS FOR AN ANALYSIS OF VARIANCE: VARIANCE-STABILIZING TRANSFORMATIONS

9.12

As with all statistical methods, the validity of the analysis of variance tests of hypotheses and confidence intervals is based on the assumptions specified in Section 9.2, namely, that the populations are normally distributed with common variance σ^2 and that the samples have been selected according to certain specific designs (e.g., independent random samples, a randomized block design, etc.). In the real world we rarely know for certain if these assumptions of normality and a common variance have been satisfied. Therefore, we must know when the analysis of variance tests and confidence intervals will possess the theoretical properties that we expect.

Nonnormality does not seriously affect the methodology as long as the population distributions are not badly skewed. If the populations possess unequal variances, that is a more serious problem. If population variances do not differ greatly and the treatment sample sizes are equal, the properties of the statistical tests and confidence intervals will be approximately the same as if the assumptions were true. If the population variances differ substantially, we can **transform the data** before we conduct the analysis of variance.

For example, one way to transform the data is to take the square root of each value of x. Or we might take the logarithm of each value of x. The type of transformation to be employed depends upon the type of data involved in the experiment. Once the data are transformed, we perform the analysis of variance on the transformed data. Tests results for differences in transformed treatment means and the like apply to the original untransformed treatment means.

The two most common types of data that violate the analysis of variance assumptions are those for which x represents the number of occurrences of some event or x is a sample proportion (or percentage).

Count data often are generated by a random variable x that possesses a Poisson probability distribution. As explained in optional Section 3.8, the variance of a Poisson random variable is equal to its mean—that is, $\sigma^2 = \mu$. Therefore, the variances of populations of Poisson data are likely to vary from one treatment to another. The variance of sample proportions derived from binomial experiments will also vary with the mean. Thus if x is a sample proportion, the mean value of the sample proportion is p, and its variance is

$$\sigma^2 = \frac{p(1 - p)}{n}$$

A formula for transforming Poisson type data so that the different treatment populations possess approximately the same variance is

$$y = \sqrt{x}$$

where x is the original Poisson observation and y is the new transformed observation. The following example will illustrate the transformation procedure.

EXAMPLE 9.5   A manufacturer wishes to compare the mean number of accidents per month on $k = 5$ different production lines. Since the data for this experiment represent observations on five different Poisson random variables, the observations will be transformed by using $y = \sqrt{x}$, where the x values are the original Poisson counts of the number of accidents per month for a given production line and the y values are the new variance-stabilized observations. If three of the original x values are 2, 5, and 4, find the corresponding transformed observations that will be used in the analysis of variance.

SOLUTION   Since $y = \sqrt{x}$, the original and transformed observations are

$$y_1 = \sqrt{2} = 1.414$$
$$y_2 = \sqrt{5} = 2.236$$
$$y_3 = \sqrt{4} = 2.000$$

■

If x is a sample proportion calculated from a binomial experiment, the variances of a set of different binomial populations can be stabilized by using the transformation

$$y = \sin^{-1} \sqrt{x}$$

where x is the original sample proportion and y, the new transformed observation, is equal to the angle (in radians) with a trigonometric sine equal to $\sqrt{x}$. To make this transformation easy for you, we give corresponding values of y and $\sqrt{x}$ in Table 18 in the Appendix. We will illustrate the transformation for binomial sample proportions in the following example.

EXAMPLE 9.6   A company plans to promote a new product by using one of three advertising plans. To investigate the extent of product recognition by consumers, 15 market areas were selected, and 5 were randomly assigned to each advertising plan. After the advertising plans were employed in the assigned market areas, random samples of 400 adults were selected from each area, and the proportion x who were familiar with the new product was recorded for each sample. The data are shown in Table 9.50. Transform the data by using the transformation $y = \sin^{-1}\sqrt{x}$.

TABLE 9.50   Proportion of 400 Adults per Marketing Area Familiar with the New Product; Data for Example 9.6

Advertising Plan 1	Advertising Plan 2	Advertising Plan 3
.33	.28	.21
.29	.41	.30
.21	.34	.26
.32	.39	.33
.25	.27	.31

SOLUTION   Table 18 in the Appendix gives values of y corresponding to the square root of the proportion x. Consequently, the first step in the transformation is to calculate $\sqrt{x}$ for each value of x. These values are shown in Table 9.51.

TABLE 9.51 $\sqrt{x}$ for the x Values in Table 9.50

Advertising Plan 1	Advertising Plan 2	Advertising Plan 3
.574	.529	.458
.539	..640	.548
.458	.583	.510
.566	.624	.574
.500	.520	.557

The final step in the transformation is to find the value of y that corresponds to each value of $\sqrt{x}$. These values can be found in Table 18 in the Appendix. For example, the tabulated value of $\sqrt{x}$ that is closest to .574 is .57287, which corresponds to $y = .61$. Similarly, the tabulated value of $\sqrt{x}$ closest to .539 is .53963. This value corresponds to $y = .57$. You can verify that the remaining transformed values for x are as shown in Table 9.52.

TABLE 9.52   Transformed x Values for the Data in Table 9.50: $y = \sin^{-1} \sqrt{x}$

Advertising Plan 1	Advertising Plan 2	Advertising Plan 3
.61	.56	.48
.57	.69	.58
.48	.62	.54
.60	.67	.61
.52	.55	.59

To determine whether differences exist among the means for the three advertising plans, we would perform an analysis of variance on the transformed data in Table 9.52. We will leave that project as an exercise for you (see Exercises 9.75 and 9.76). ■

In the preceding discussion we have explained how to transform Poisson counts and binomial proportions so that they satisfy the assumptions of an analysis of variance. Transformations can be developed for other types of data where the variance σ^2 of a population is some function of the population mean μ. The procedure for determining an appropriate transformation for a specific relationship between σ^2 and μ is explained in Mendenhall (1968).

In conclusion, the use of a transformation is not without its drawbacks. It is often difficult to assign a practical interpretation to the transformed variable and to the various treatment means. Consequently, many applied statisticians do not use transformations unless there is evidence to suggest sizable differences among the treatment population variances.

The following box gives some useful transformations for data.

SOME USEFUL DATA TRANSFORMATIONS

Relation Between Variance and Mean of a Population	Application	Transformation
$\sigma^2 = \mu$	Poisson data	$y = \sqrt{x}$
$\sigma^2 = \mu(1 - \mu), (0 < \mu < 1)$	Binomial sample proportions: equal sample sizes	$y = \sin^{-1} \sqrt{x}$
$\sigma^2 = \mu^2$	Sample variances, for quantitative data: equal sample sizes	$y = \ln x$

AN ANALYSIS OF THE DIFFERENCE IN CAR INSURANCE COSTS FOR FOUR LOCALES

9.13

We mentioned in the Case Study that a randomized block design was used for this experiment. An insurance quote for a standard policy was obtained for each of the four locales for the same insurance company. The reasoning was that a single company has an established rate-setting policy and that differences in quotes between locales would be more stable *within* companies than *among* companies. We can determine whether this logic is reasonable by testing the block (company) means.

The SAS printout for the analysis of variance is shown in Table 9.53. The key portions of the analysis of variance for this randomized block design are shaded and marked.

TABLE 9.53   SAS ANOVA Printout for the Car Insurance Data in Table 9.1

ANALYSIS OF VARIANCE PROCEDURE

DEPENDENT VARIABLE: PRICE

SOURCE	DF	SUM OF SQUARES	MEAN SQUARE	F VALUE	PR > F	R-SQUARE	C.V.
MODEL	8	720641.33333333	90080.16666667	30.42	0.0001	0.941935	13.8166
ERROR	15	44423.29166667	2961.55277778		ROOT MSE		PRICE MEAN
CORRECTED TOTAL	23	765064.62500000			54.42015048		393.87500000

SOURCE	DF	ANOVA SS	F VALUE	PR > F
LOCALE	3	709736.45833333	79.88	0.0001
COMPANY	5	10904.87500000	0.74	0.6077

(1) The ANOVA table, marked as shaded area ①, shows the Total SS as CORRECTED TOTAL, with 23 d.f.; it is 765064.62500000. SSE, with 15 d.f., is 44423.29166667. The sum of squares for MODEL is equal to the sum of the sums of squares for both treatments and blocks, as indicated in shaded area ②.

(2) Shaded area ② gives a breakdown of the sum of squares for MODEL into its two components: sum of squares for treatments (LOCALE), with 3 d.f.; and sum of squares for blocks (COMPANY), with 5 d.f. These sums of squares are, respectively,

$$SST = 709736.45833333$$

$$SSB = 21094.87500000$$

The F values for testing equality of treatment means or block means and their observed significance levels are shown under the columns marked F VALUE and PR > F:

	F	p-Value
Locale	79.88	.0001
Company	.74	.6077

The analysis of variance in Table 9.53 shows that there is a substantial difference in the mean car insurance rates from one locale to another. There is insufficient evidence to indicate a difference in the mean car insurance rates among the six insurance companies.

(3) Shaded area ③ gives the standard deviation, $s = 54.42015048$. This quantity would be needed to construct a confidence interval for the difference between a pair of treatment means.

Suppose that we want a 95% confidence interval for the difference in mean rates between Chicago and Topeka. The interval is

$$(\bar{x}_C - \bar{x}_T) \pm t_{.025} s \sqrt{\frac{2}{b}}$$

where $t_{.025}$ is based on the d.f. associated with SSE, that is, d.f. $= 15$. Then

$$(\$690 - \$301.83) \pm (2.131)(54.42)\sqrt{\frac{2}{6}}$$

$$\$388.17 \pm 66.95$$

Thus we estimate the difference in mean rates between Chicago and Topeka to be between $321.22 and $455.12.

Summary

9.14

This chapter introduces you to the methodology of an analysis of variance, the notion of partitioning the total sum of squares of deviations of the x-values about their overall mean $\bar{x}$ into components pertinent to one or more qualitative variables and to a within-sample source of variation, SSE. The mean squares for these sources of variation can then be compared with the mean square for error, MSE, using the F test. If there is evidence to indicate that a particular source mean square is overly large compared with MSE, we conclude that there are differences in the population means associated with that source.

The analysis of variance not only enables us to test the equivalence of a set of population means but also enables us to place confidence intervals on the difference between pairs of means and, in some cases, on the individual means themselves. Tukey's method for paired comparisons enables us to compare any and all pairs of means, to rank them, and to group means for which no evidence of differences exists.

The validity of an analysis of variance is based on the assumption that the sampled populations are normally distributed (at least approximately) with a common variance σ^2. It is further assumed that the data have been collected according to a specific design. If data from a designed experiment have been lost or destroyed, the standard analysis of variance formulas will give incorrect answers for the sums of squares. In this situation the sums of squares can be calculated and the analysis of variance F tests conducted by using a procedure known as a multiple regression analysis. Although this procedure requires much more computation than the standard analyses of variance, it can be performed on a computer by using Minitab, SAS, SPSS^x, or other computer programs.

REFERENCES

Dixon, W. J., Brown, M. B., Engelman, L., Frane, J. W., Hill, M. A., Jennrich, R. I., and Toporek, J. D. *BMDP Statistical Software*. Berkeley: University of Californial Press, 1985.

Guenther, W. C. *Analysis of Variance*. Englewood Cliffs, N. J.: Prentice-Hall, 1964.

Hicks, C. R. *Fundamental Concepts in the Design of Experiments*. 3rd ed. New York: Holt, Rinehart and Winston, 1982.

Hill, MaryAnn, ed. *BMDP User's Digest*. 2nd ed. Los Angeles: BMDP Statistical Software, 1982.

Mendenhall, W. *An Introduction to Linear Models and the Design and Analysis of Experiments*. Boston: PWS-KENT, 1968. Chapters 10–13.

Mendenhall, W., and Sincich, T. *A Second Course in Business Statistics: Regression Analysis*. 2nd ed. San Francisco: Dellen, 1986.

Neter, J., and Wasserman, W. *Applied Linear Statistical Models*. 2nd ed. Homewood, III.: Irwin, 1985. Chapters 13–24.

Quint, B. G. *Family Circle*, February 20, 1979.

Ryan, T. A., Joiner, B. L., and Ryan, B. F. *Minitab Reference Manual*. University Park, Pa.: Minitab Project, 1985.

Ryan, T. A., Joiner, B. L., and Ryan, B. F. *Minitab Handbook*. 2nd ed., Boston: PWS-KENT, 1985.

SAS User's Guide: Basics. Version 5 ed. Cary, N.C.: SAS Institute. 1985.

SAS User's Guide: Statistics. Version 5 ed. Cary, N.C.: SAS Institute, 1985.

SPSS^x User's Guide. Chicago: SPSS, 1983.

KEY TERMS

Analysis of variance (page 337)

Total sum of squares (page 339)

Sum of squares for treatments (page 339)

Treatments (page 339)

Sum of squares for error (page 339)

ANOVA table (page 341)

Mean square for treatments (page 342)

Mean square for error (page 342)

Randomized block design (page 354)

Factor interaction (page 371)

Factorial experiment (page 372)

Tukey's method for paired comparisons (page 387)

Transformation of data (page 392)

SUPPLEMENTARY EXERCISES

Starred (*) exercises are optional.

 9.66 Four chemical plants, producing the same product and owned by the same company, discharge effluents into streams in the vicinity of their locations. To check on the extent of the pollution created by the effluents and to determine if it varies from plant to plant, the company collected random samples of liquid waste, five specimens for each of the four plants. The data are shown in Table 9.54. An SAS computer printout of the analysis of variance for the data is shown in Table 9.55. Use the information in the printout to answer the following questions.

(a) Do the data provide sufficient evidence to indicate a difference in the mean amount of effluents discharged by the four plants? 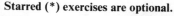 *yes*

TABLE 9.54   Pollution Data for Exercise 9.66

Plant	Polluting Effluents (Pounds per Gallon of Waste)				
A	1.65	1.72	1.50	1.37	1.60
B	1.70	1.85	1.46	2.05	1.80
C	1.40	1.75	1.38	1.65	1.55
D	2.10	1.95	1.65	1.88	2.00

(handwritten annotations: 7.348, 1.568, 1.916, 1.568 − 1.916 ± t₀/₂ S√(1/5 + 1/5), 2/120, 2/10, .4, .2314588)

TABLE 9.55   SAS Printout for Exercise 9.66

ANALYSIS OF VARIANCE PROCEDURE

DEPENDENT VARIABLE: WASTE

SOURCE	DF	SUM OF SQUARES	MEAN SQUARE	F VALUE	PR > F	R-SQUARE	C.V.
MODEL	3	0.46489500	0.15496500	5.20	0.0107	0.493679	10.1515
ERROR	16	0.47680000	0.02980000		ROOT MSE		WASTE MEAN
CORRECTED TOTAL	19	0.94169500			0.17262677		1.70050000

SOURCE	DF	ANOVA SS	F VALUE	PR > F
PLANT	3	0.46489500	5.20	0.0107

(b) If the maximum mean discharge of effluents is 1.5 pounds per gallon, do the data provide sufficient evidence to indicate that the limit is exceeded at plant *A*? *No.*

(c) Estimate the difference in the mean discharge of effluents between plants *A* and *D*, using a 95% confidence interval.

 9.67 An investment advisor decided to compare the 1986 annual returns for three types of common stocks, (1) small-capitalization growth stocks, (2) high-capitalization, investment-grade, blue-chip stocks, and (3) electric utility stocks. The returns (in percentages) on random samples of eight stocks selected from among each of the stock-type populations are shown in Table 9.56. A Minitab analysis of variance printout is shown in Table 9.57.

TABLE 9.56   Stock Return Data for Exercise 9.67

Growth Stock	Blue-Chip Stock	Utilities
59	25	27
31	14	−6
120	40	36
−61	17	42
14	53	31
92	54	35
8	27	26
−51	35	32

TABLE 9.57   Minitab Printout for Exercise 9.67

```
ANALYSIS OF VARIANCE
SOURCE      DF        SS        MS        F
FACTOR       2       196        98      0.07
ERROR       21     31376      1494
TOTAL       23     31571

                                  INDIVIDUAL 95 PCT CI'S FOR MEAN
                                  BASED ON POOLED STDEV
LEVEL        N      MEAN     STDEV   -+---------+---------+---------+-----
GROWTH       8     26.50     63.55   (-------------*-------------)
BLUECHIP     8     33.13     15.17       (-------------*-------------)
UTILITY      8     27.88     14.61   (-------------*-------------)
                                     -+---------+---------+---------+-----
POOLED STDEV =     38.65            0        20        40        60
```

(a) Do the data present sufficient evidence to indicate differences in the mean annual returns for the three types of stock? Test using $\alpha = .05$.

(b) Find a 95% confidence interval for the difference in mean annual return between growth and utility stocks.

*9.68 Consider the accompanying one-way classification consisting of three treatments, *A*, *B*, and *C*, where the number of observations per treatment varies from treatment to treatment. The observations were randomly and independently selected from their respective treatment populations.

A	B	C
24.2	24.5	26.0
27.5	22.7	
25.9		
24.7		

(a) Use the formulas of optional Section 9.4 to perform the analysis of variance for these data.

(b) Do the data present sufficient evidence to indicate a difference among the treatment means?

(c) Find a 90% confidence interval for the mean for treatment *B*.

(d) Find a 90% confidence interval for the difference between the means for treatments *A* and *C*.

 *9.69 A company wanted to study the differences among four sales-training programs on the sales abilities of their sales personnel. Thirty-two people were randomly divided into four groups of equal size, and the groups were then subjected to the different sales-training programs. Because there were some dropouts (illness, etc.) during the training programs, the number of trainees completing the programs varied from group to group. At the end of the training programs each salesperson was randomly assigned a sales area from a group of sales areas that were judged to have equivalent sales potentials. The numbers of sales made by each of the four groups of salespeople during the first week after completing the training program are listed in Table 9.58.

(a) Use the formulas of optional Section 9.4 to perform the analysis of variance for these data.

(b) Do the data present sufficient evidence to indicate a difference in the mean achievement for the four training programs?

TABLE 9.58   Sales Data for Exercise 9.69

| | Training Program | | | |
	1	2	3	4
	78	99	74	81
	84	86	87	63
	86	90	80	71
	92	93	83	65
	69	94	78	86
	73	85		79
		97		73
		91		70
Total	482	735	402	588

(c) Find a 90% confidence interval for the difference in the mean numbers of sales that would be expected for persons subjected to training programs 1 and 4. Interpret the interval.

(d) Find a 90% confidence interval for the mean number of sales by persons subjected to training program 2.

9.70 An experiment was conducted to compare the effect of four different chemicals, A, B, C, and D, in producing water resistance in textiles. A strip of material, randomly selected from a bolt, was cut into four pieces, and the pieces were randomly assigned to receive one of the four chemicals A, B, C, or D. This process was replicated three times, thus producing a randomized block design. The design, with moisture resistance measurements, is as shown (low readings indicate low moisture penetration). An SAS computer printout of the analysis of variance for the data is presented in Table 9.59. Use the information in the printout to answer the following questions.

TABLE 9.59   SAS Printout for Exercise 9.70

```
                              ANALYSIS OF VARIANCE PROCEDURE

DEPENDENT VARIABLE: MOISTURE

SOURCE          DF     SUM OF SQUARES     MEAN SQUARE    F VALUE      PR > F    R-SQUARE           C.V.

MODEL           5       12.37166667       2.47433333     27.75       0.0004    0.958549         2.5023

ERROR           6        0.53500000       0.08916667                 ROOT MSE          MOISTURE MEAN

CORRECTED TOTAL 11      12.90666667                                  0.29860788         11.93333333


SOURCE          DF          ANOVA SS     F VALUE       PR > F

BLOCKS          2        7.17166667       40.21        0.0003
TRTMENTS        3        5.20000000       19.44        0.0017
```

(a) Do the data provide sufficient evidence to indicate a difference in the mean moisture penetration for fabric treated with the four chemicals? Yes

(b) Do the data provide evidence to indicate that blocking increased the amount of information in the experiment? Yes

(c) Find a 95% confidence interval for the difference in mean moisture penetration for fabrics treated by chemicals A and D. Interpret the interval.

Blocks (Bolt Samples)		
1	2	3
C	D	B
9.9	13.4	12.7
A	B	D
10.1	12.9	12.9
B	A	C
11.4	12.2	11.4
D	C	A
12.1	12.3	11.9

[handwritten:] 12.3

[handwritten:] 11.9

[handwritten:] $(11.4 + 12.8) \pm t_{\alpha/2, n+k-b+2}$

[handwritten:] $-1.4 \pm (\quad \chi_{.9.5} \, S \sqrt{\frac{1}{n_1} + \frac{1}{n}}$

[handwritten:] $2.447 \, (.12190c$

*9.71 A building contractor employs three construction engineers, A, B, and C, to estimate and bid on jobs. To determine whether one tends to be a more conservative (or liberal) estimator than the others, the contractor selects four projected construction jobs and has each estimator independently estimate the cost (dollars per square foot) of each job. The data are shown in Table 9.60.

[handwritten:] .2983039

TABLE 9.60   Cost Estimate Data for Exercise 9.71

Estimator (Treatments)	Construction Job (Blocks)				Total
	1	2	3	4	
A	35.10	34.50	29.25	31.60	130.45
B	37.45	34.60	33.10	34.40	139.55
C	36.30	35.10	32.45	32.90	136.75
Total	108.85	104.20	94.80	98.90	406.75

(a) Do the data provide sufficient evidence to indicate a difference in the mean building costs estimated by the three estimators? Test using $\alpha = .05$.

(b) Find a 90% confidence interval for the difference in the mean of the estimates produced by estimators A and B. Interpret the interval.

(c) Do the data support the contention that the mean estimate of the cost per square foot varies from job to job?

*9.72 A production superintendent wants to compare the mean time to assemble a piece of electronic equipment for three different methods of assembly, A_1, A_2, and A_3. Six assemblers were chosen for the experiment. Each person was assigned to assemble one piece of equipment for each method of assembly, and the average assembly time (in minutes) was recorded for each. The methods of assembly were randomly assigned in sequence for each assembler. The data are shown in Table 9.61.

(a) What type of experimental design is this? Explain.

(b) Explain how the design may increase the amount of information in the experiment on treatment mean differences.

(c) Perform an analysis of variance for the data.

(d) Do the data provide sufficient evidence to indicate differences in the mean time to assemble for the three methods of assembly? Test using $\alpha = .05$.

TABLE 9.61   Assembly Time Data for Exercise 9.72

Sequence of Assembly	Assembler					
	1	2	3	4	5	6
A_1	20.2	22.6	19.2	22.5	18.7	21.5
A_2	23.7	24.1	22.6	24.3	20.2	21.5
A_3	21.4	23.0	22.9	22.0	19.8	20.1

MKTG *9.73 A large food products company conducted an experiment to investigate the effects of two factors, package wrapper material and color of wrapper, on sales of one of the company's products. Two types of wrapping material were employed, a waxed paper and a plastic, in three colors. Eighteen supermarkets were selected for the experiment, and three were assigned to each of the six factor level combinations. After the product had been in the supermarkets for one week, the company recorded the percentage change in weekly sales over each supermarket's average weekly sales of the product for the past year. The data are shown in Table 9.62.

TABLE 9.62   Weekly Sales Data for Exercise 9.73

Wrapping Material	Package Color		
	A_1	A_2	A_3
	6	−3	7
B_1	−2	7	3
	4	−2	10
	5	3	12
B_2	2	6	7
	5	4	10

(a) Perform an analysis of variance for the data, and display the results in an ANOVA table.

(b) Find the approximate p-values for the F tests.

(c) What practical conclusions do you derive from the F test results?

9.74 A study was conducted to compare automobile gasoline mileage for three brands of gasoline, A, B, and C. Four automobiles, all of the same make and model, were employed in the experiment, and each gasoline brand was tested in each automobile. Using each brand within the same automobile has the effect of eliminating (blocking out) automobile-to-automobile variability. Table 9.63 gives the data (in miles per gallon) for the 12 brand-automobile combinations, and the Minitab analysis of variance for the data is shown in Table 9.64.

TABLE 9.63   Mileage Data for Exercise 9.74

Gasoline Brand	Automobile			
	1	2	3	4
A	20.7	22.0	22.3	21.1
B	22.2	23.1	22.9	22.7
C	21.1	22.5	21.8	22.8

TABLE 9.64   Minitab Analysis of Variance Printout for Exercise 9.74

```
ANALYSIS OF VARIANCE   MPG

SOURCE       DF      SS      MS
BRAND         2    2.895   1.448
AUTOTYPE      3    2.520   0.840
ERROR         6    1.345   0.224
TOTAL        11    6.760
```

(a) Do the data provide sufficient evidence to indicate a difference in mean mileage per gallon for the three gasolines?

(b) Is there evidence of a difference in mean mileage for the four automobiles?

(c) Suppose that *prior to looking at the data,* we had decided to compare the mean mileage per gallon for gasoline brands A and B. Find a 90% confidence interval for this difference.

 *9.75 In Example 9.6 we presented data representing consumer response to three different market advertising plans based on independent random samples, five observations per sample. Because the data represent sample proportions, we transformed each observation by using a $\sin^{-1} \sqrt{x}$ transformation. The transformed data of Table 9.52 are reproduced below.

Advertising Plan 1	Advertising Plan 2	Advertising Plan 3
.61	.56	.48
.57	.69	.58
.48	.62	.54
.60	.67	.61
.52	.55	.59

(a) Perform an analysis of variance on the transformed data, and present the results in an ANOVA table.

(b) Do the data present sufficient evidence to indicate differences in mean responses to the three advertising plans? Test using $\alpha = .05$.

* 9.76 The original untransformed sample proportions for Example 9.6 are shown in the table below.

Advertising Plan 1	Advertising Plan 2	Advertising Plan 3
.33	.28	.21
.29	.41	.30
.21	.34	.26
.32	.39	.33
.25	.27	.31

(a) Perform an analysis of variance for the data.

(b) Do the data present sufficient evidence to indicate differences in mean responses to the three advertising plans? Test using $\alpha = .05$.

(c) Did the analysis of the transformed data lead to conclusions that differ from the analysis of the corresponding untransformed data?

Observations that can be classified, each observation falling into one (and only one) of k categories, yield a set of counts, each count representing the number of observations falling in a particular category. The objective of this chapter is to provide methods for testing hypotheses about the category probabilities and, as a particular application, to test the equivalence of more than two binomial proportions. Thus Chapters 9 and 10 are natural extensions of the methodologies in Chapters 7 and 8 for comparing pairs of population means and proportions.

10 THE CHI-SQUARE GOODNESS-OF-FIT TEST

CASE STUDY

No Wine Before Its Time

In an article titled "They Will Can No Wine Before Its Time," *Washington Post* Staff Writer, Nicholas D. Kristof, surveys industry response to a novel method for packaging wine—canning! (*Washington Post,* August 23, 1981.)

Both the Geyser Creek Winery (of California) and Wine Spectrum, a subsidiary of Coca-Cola, envision great sales prospects for this new method of marketing wine. Packaged in six-packs, similar to beer, the cans are more compact, lighter in weight, and less susceptible to damage than bottles. For example, a case of wine in bottles weighs 48 pounds, while an equivalent amount packed in aluminum cans weighs 22 pounds and occupies 30% less space. This feature is particularly appealing to the airlines, where weight and space play an important role in a flight's profit equation.

But what of the concept and the taste? Will it be appealing to consumers? "Très, très, tacky," is the reported response of Jean-Jacques Moreau, a wine connoisseur and producer of fine wines in the Chablis region of France. Moreau is further quoted as saying, "C'est ridicule, ça ne va pas. Ça n'a pas de sens d'acheter du bon vin en autre chose qu'une bouteille de verre. Ça ne marcherait pas en Europe," which Kristof translates to mean, "Canned wine is gauche."

But what does the consumer say? Reynolds Metals Company, which makes the aluminum cans, claims that the cans are coated on the inside to prevent the wine from acquiring a metallic taste. They claim to have conducted a blind taste test, one in which the participants were given two identical glasses of the same wine, one wine from a can and the other from a bottle. Fifty percent of their participants preferred the glass containing wine from a can, 39% preferred the wine from a bottle, and 11% could detect no difference between the two.

How can we use the Reynolds Metals Company taste test data to determine whether consumers can detect a difference in taste between canned and bottled wine? Because we want to test $H_0 : p_1 = p_2$, where p_1 and p_2 are the proportions of consumers who prefer canned and bottled wine, respectively, we might think of using the large-sample z test of Chapter 7. But you can see that the z test is inappropriate because it is based on independent random samples, selected from two different binomial populations. Further examination will reveal that the Reynolds taste test was analogous to a binomial experiment, the difference being that the response of each person fell in one of three, rather than two categories, namely, (1) favor the canned wine, (2) favor the bottled wine, and (3) have no preference. We call this a *multinomial experiment.*

This chapter will introduce you to the analysis of data obtained from a multinomial experiment. We will reexamine the data from canned versus bottled wine taste test data in Section 10.5.

10.1 A MULTINOMIAL EXPERIMENT

Many consumer and business surveys produce categorical data. Each observation can fall in one and only one of a fixed number, say k, of categories. If a total of n persons are included in a survey, the data summary gives the numbers of responses, $n_1, n_2, \ldots, n_k$, falling in the 1st, the 2nd, . . . , and the kth categories, respectively, where $n_1 + n_2 + \cdots + n_k = n$.

The survey that we have described exhibits, to a reasonable degree of approximation, the following characteristics. These characteristics define a **multinomial experiment**.

CHARACTERISTICS OF A MULTINOMIAL EXPERIMENT

(1) The experiment consists of n identical trials.

(2) The outcome of each trial falls into one of k categories or cells.

(3) The probability that the outcome of a single trial will fall in a particular cell, say cell i, is p_i $(i = 1, 2, \ldots, k)$, and remains the same from trial to trial. Note that

$$p_1 + p_2 + p_3 + \cdots + p_k = 1$$

(4) The trials are independent.

(5) We are interested in $n_1, n_2, n_3, \ldots, n_k$, where n_i $(i = 1, 2, \ldots, k)$ is equal to the number of trials in which the outcome falls in cell i. Note that $n_1 + n_2 + n_3 + \cdots + n_k = n$.

The above experiment is analogous to tossing n balls at k boxes, where each ball must fall in one of the boxes. The boxes are arranged such that the probability that a ball will fall in a box varies from box to box but remains the same for a particular box in repeated tosses. Finally, the balls are tossed in such a way that the trials are independent. At the conclusion of the experiment we observe n_1 balls in the first box, n_2 in the second, $\ldots$, and n_k in the kth. The total number of balls is equal to

$$\sum_{i=1}^{k} n_i = n$$

Note the similarity between the binomial and multinomial experiments and, in particular, that the binomial experiment represents the special case for the multinomial experiment when $k = 2$. The two cell probabilities, p and q, of the binomial experiment are replaced by the k cell probabilities, $p_1, p_2, \ldots, p_k$, of the multinomial experiment. The objective of this chapter is to make inferences about the cell probabilities $p_1, p_2, \ldots, p_k$. The inferences will be expressed in terms of a statistical test of an hypothesis concerning their specific numerical values or their relationship, one to another.

10.2   THE CHI-SQUARE GOODNESS-OF-FIT TEST

The simplest hypothesis about multinomial cell probabilities is one that specifies numerical values for each. For example, if the multinomial experiment involves $k = 4$ cells, we might want to test the hypothesis

$$H_0 : p_1 = .2, \quad p_2 = .4, \quad p_3 = .1, \quad \text{and } p_4 = .3$$

against the alternative hypothesis that at least two of the cell probabilities differ from the values specified at H_0.

The following example illustrates a common application of the **chi-square goodness-of-fit test** and shows how the test is conducted.

EXAMPLE 10.1

Suppose that customers can purchase one of three brands of milk at a supermarket. In a study to determine whether one brand is preferred over another, a record is made of a sample of $n = 300$ milk purchases. The data are shown in Table 10.1. Do the data provide sufficient evidence to indicate a preference for one or more brands?

TABLE 10.1 Milk Purchases Data for Example 10.1

Brand 1	Brand 2	Brand 3
78	117	105

SOLUTION

If all of the brands are *equally* preferred, then the probability that a purchaser will choose any one brand is the same as the probability of choosing any other—that is, $p_1 = p_2 = p_3 = 1/3$. Therefore, the null hypothesis of "no preference" is

$$H_0 : p_1 = p_2 = p_3 = 1/3$$

If p_1, p_2, and p_3 are not all equal, the brands are not equally preferred; in other words, the purchasers must have a preference for one (or possibly two) brands. The alternative hypothesis is

$$H_a : p_1, p_2, \text{ and } p_3 \text{ are not all equal}$$

Therefore, we seek a test statistic that will detect a **lack of fit** of the observed **cell counts**, or **frequencies**, to our hypothesized (null) expected cell counts based on the hypothesized cell probabilities.

If the observed cell counts fit the hypothesized cell probabilities, they should be close to their expected values. These expected values, for a multinomial experiment, are

$$E(n_1) = np_1, \qquad E(n_2) = np_2, \qquad \ldots, \qquad E(n_k) = np_k$$

For $p_1 = p_2 = p_3 = 1/3$, the expected cell counts are

$$E(n_1) = np_1 = (300)\left(\frac{1}{3}\right) = 100$$

$$E(n_2) = np_2 = (300)\left(\frac{1}{3}\right) = 100$$

$$E(n_3) = np_3 = (300)\left(\frac{1}{3}\right) = 100$$

The observed cell counts are shown along with their respective expected counts (in parentheses) in Table 10.2.

The test statistic for comparing the observed and expected cell counts (and, consequently, testing $H_0 : p_1 = p_2 = p_3 = 1/3$) is the X^2 statistic:

$$X^2 = \sum_{i=1}^{k} \frac{[n_i - E(n_i)]^2}{E(n_i)} = \sum_{i=1}^{k} \frac{d_i^2}{E(n_i)}$$

TABLE 10.2   Observed and Expected Cell Counts for Milk Purchases in Example 10.1

Brand 1	Brand 2	Brand 3
78	117	105
(100)	(100)	(100)

where

$$n_i = \text{observed count for cell } i$$

$$E(n_i) = np_i = \text{expected count for cell } i$$

$$d_i = n_i - E(n_i)$$

$$= \text{difference between the observed and expected counts for cell } i$$

The computation of X^2 for our example can be accomplished by using Table 10.3. The observed n_i and expected $E(n_i)$ cell counts are shown in columns 2 and 3, the difference $d_i = n_i - E(n_i)$ is shown in column 4, and d_i^2 is shown in column 5. The final step in calculating X^2 is performed in column 6, where we calculate $d_1^2/E(n_1)$, $d_2^2/E(n_2)$, and $d_3^2/E(n_3)$. The sum of these column 6 entries is X^2.

TABLE 10.3   Table for Calculating X^2 for Example 10.1

i	n_i	$E(n_i)$	d_i	d_i^2	$d_i^2/E(n_i)$
1	78	100	-22	484	4.84
2	117	100	17	289	2.89
3	105	100	5	25	.25
Total	300	300			$X^2 = 7.98$

If the null hypothesis is true, the statistic X^2 will possess, approximately, the chi-square probability distribution that we encountered in Section 8.6. The larger the sample size n, the better the approximation will be, but n should always be large enough so that all expected cell counts are larger than or equal to 5. When the null hypothesis is false, the differences d_1, d_2, and d_3 between the observed and expected cell counts will be large and will make the X^2 statistic larger than expected. Consequently, we will reject H_0 for large values of X^2, those that exceed χ_α^2, a value of χ^2 that places α in the upper tail of the chi-square distribution (see Figure 10.1).

One last point needs to be clarified before we conclude our test. You may recall from Section 8.6 that the shape of the chi-square probability distribution depends on a single parameter, the degrees of freedom for the chi-square statistic. We will give you the number of degrees of freedom for the approximating chi-square distribution for all applications in this chapter. As a general rule, the degrees of freedom (d.f.) for the chi-square statistic will equal the number k of categories less one degree of freedom for every linear restriction placed on the category counts. For example, you will always lose one degree of freedom because the sum of the category counts will equal the

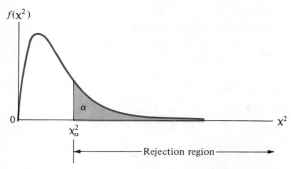

$f(\chi^2)$

α

0

χ^2_α

χ^2

— Rejection region —

FIGURE 10.1   Rejection Region for the Chi-square Test of Goodness of Fit

sample size n; that is,

$$n_1 + n_2 + \cdots + n_k = n$$

You will also lose one degree of freedom for each category probability that must be estimated to calculate the expected category frequencies. For the test described in this section, all of the cell probabilities are specified. Therefore, the number of degrees of freedom for this chi-square statistic will always be $(k - 1)$.

The number k of cells for our example is 3. Therefore, the degrees of freedom for the approximating chi-square will be

$$\text{d.f.} = k - 1 = 3 - 1 = 2$$

Consulting Table 6 in the Appendix for d.f. $= 2$, we find $\chi^2_{.05} = 5.99147$. Consequently, we will reject the hypothesis of "no preference" in the milk brand study if

$$\text{rejection region: } X^2 > 5.99147$$

Because the computed value of X^2, $X^2 = 7.98$ (see Table 10.3), exceeds the critical value, $\chi^2_{.05} = 5.99147$, we reject $H_0 : p_1 = p_2 = p_3 = 1/3$ and conclude that the three brands of milk are not equally preferred.   ∎

A summary of the chi-square test of specific values of the cell probabilities is given in the box.

CHI-SQUARE TEST OF SPECIFIED VALUES FOR THE CELL PROBABILITIES

(1) *Null Hypothesis:* $H_0 : p_1, p_2, \ldots, p_k$ possess specified values.

(2) *Alternative Hypothesis:* H_a: at least two of the cell probabilities differ from the values specified in H_0.

(3) *Test Statistic:* $X^2 = \sum\limits_{i=1}^{k} \dfrac{[n_i - E(n_i)]^2}{E(n_i)} = \sum\limits_{i=1}^{k} \dfrac{d_i^2}{E(n_i)},$

where n_i = observed count for cell i

and $E(n_i) = np_i, \quad i = 1, 2, \ldots, k$

(4) *Rejection Region:* $X^2 > \chi_\alpha^2$, where χ_α^2 is based upon d.f. $= k - 1$ degrees of freedom (see Table 6 in the Appendix).

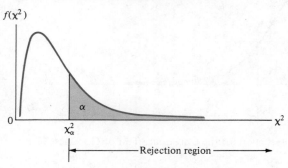

Assumption: All expected cell counts are greater than or equal to 5.

EXERCISES

BASIC TECHNIQUES

10.1 Give the value of χ_α^2.
   (a) $\alpha = .05$, d.f. $= 3$
   (b) $\alpha = .01$, d.f. $= 8$
   (c) $\alpha = .10$, d.f. $= 15$
   (d) $\alpha = .10$, d.f. $= 11$

10.2 Give the rejection region for a chi-square test of specified cell probabilities if the experiment involves k cells:
   (a) $k = 7$, $\alpha = .10$
   (b) $k = 10$, $\alpha = .01$
   (c) $k = 14$, $\alpha = .05$
   (d) $k = 3$, $\alpha = .05$

10.3 List the characteristics of a multinomial experiment.

10.4 Suppose that a response can fall in one of $k = 5$ categories with probabilities $p_1, p_2, \ldots, p_5$, respectively, and that $n = 300$ responses produced the following category counts:

Category	1	2	3	4	5
Observed Count	47	63	74	51	65

(a) If you were to test $H_0 : p_1 = p_2 = \cdots = p_5$, using the chi-square test, how many degrees of freedom would the test statistic possess?
(b) If $\alpha = .05$, find the rejection region for the test.
(c) What is your alternative hypothesis?

(d) Conduct the test in part (a), using $\alpha = .05$. State your conclusions.

(e) Find the approximate observed significance level for the test, and interpret its value.

10.5 Suppose that a response can fall in one of $k = 3$ categories with probabilities p_1, p_2, and p_3, respectively, and that $n = 300$ responses produced the following category counts:

Category	1	2	3
Observed Count	130	98	72

(a) If you were to test $H_0 : p_1 = p_2 = p_3$, using the chi-square test, how many degrees of freedom would the test statistic possess?

(b) If $\alpha = .05$, find the rejection region for the test.

(c) What is your alternative hypothesis?

(d) Conduct the test in part (a), using $\alpha = .05$. State your conclusions.

(e) Find the approximate observed significance level for the test, and interpret its value.

APPLICATIONS

10.6 A city expressway using four lanes in each direction was studied to see whether drivers preferred to drive on the inside lanes. A total of 1000 automobiles was observed during the heavy early-morning traffic, and their respective lanes were recorded. The results were as follows:

Lane	1	2	3	4
Observed Count	294	276	238	192

Do the data present sufficient evidence to indicate that some lanes are preferred over others? Test using $\alpha = .05$.

10.7 An occupant traffic study was conducted to aid in the remodeling of an office building that contains three entrances. The choice of entrance was recorded for a sample of 200 persons entering the building. Do the data shown in the table indicate that there is a difference in preference for the three entrances? Find a 90% confidence interval for the proportion of persons favoring entrance 1. (*Hint:* Use the method of Section 6.8.)

	Entrance		
	1	2	3
Number Entering	83	61	56

10.8 Officials in a particular community are seeking a federal program that they hope will boost local income levels. As justification, the city claims that its local income distribution differs substantially from the national distribution and that incomes tend to be lower than expected. A random sample of 2000 family incomes was classified and compared with the corresponding national percentages. They are shown in Table 10.4. Do the data provide sufficient evidence to indicate that the distribution of family incomes within the city differs from the national distribution? Test with $\alpha = .05$.

TABLE 10.4   Income Data for Exercise 10.8

Income	National Percentages	City Salary Class Frequency
More than $50,000	2	27
$25,000 to $50,000	16	193
$20,000 to $25,000	13	234
$15,000 to $20,000	19	322
$10,000 to $15,000	20	568
$5,000 to $10,000	19	482
Below $5,000	11	174
Total	100	2000

 10.9 College and university faculty members are expected (in most cases, required) to write and publish scholarly articles. A. R. Fowler and colleagues conducted a study of 897 management-oriented articles published by college and university faculty members to examine the relationship between the status of a school and the publishing activity of its faculty members. Schools in which the authors were employed were rated as possessing high, moderate, or low status. The number of schools in each of these categories is shown in column 2 of Table 10.5. The percentage of the total number of schools for each category is shown in column 3 (e.g., the 24 high-status schools represent 11.8% of the total number of 204 schools), and the numbers of authors associated with the school status categories are shown in column 4.

TABLE 10.5   Authors and School Status Data for Exercise 10.9

School Status	Number of Schools	Percentage	Number of Actual Authors	Number of Expected Authors
High	24	11.8	261	106
Moderate	30	14.7	213	132
Low	150	73.5	423	659
Total	204	100	897	897

Source: A. R. Fowler, Jr., S. C. Bushardt, and S. A. Brooking, "An Analysis of the Authorship in Management-Oriented Journals: The Relationship Between School Status, Article Type, Publication Outlet, and Author Academic Position," *Journal of Business Communication,* Vol. 22, No. 3, 1985.

(a) Fowler and associates theorize that if there are no differences in publication outputs of faculty from the three school status categories, then the proportions of authors (see column 3) associated with the three status categories should be $p_1 = .118, p_2 = .147,$ and $p_3 = .735$. Based on these hypothesized probabilities, verify that the expected numbers of authors for the three categories are as shown in column 5 of the table.

(b) Test

$$H_0 : p_1 = .118; \quad p_2 = .147; \quad p_3 = .735$$

against H_a: at least two of the proportions $p_1, p_2,$ and p_3 differ from the values specified in H_0. Test using $\alpha = .05$.

(c) Does it appear that the number of authors depends upon the status of the school? Explain, and include any qualifications that you would make in your conclusions.

CONTINGENCY TABLES

10.3

A problem frequently encountered in the analysis of count data concerns the independence of two methods of classification of observed events. For example, we might want to classify defects found on furniture produced in a manufacturing plant, first, according to the type of defect and, second, according to the production shift. Ostensibly, we want to investigate a contingency—that is, a dependence between the two classifications. Do the proportions of various types of defects vary from shift to shift?

A total of $n = 309$ furniture defects was recorded, and the defects were classified according to one of four types: A, B, C, or D. At the same time each piece of furniture was identified according to the production shift in which it was manufactured. These counts are presented in Table 10.6, which is known as a **contingency table**. (*Note:* Numbers in parentheses are the expected cell frequencies.)

Let p_A equal the unconditional probability that a defect will be of type A. Similarly, define p_B, p_C, and p_D as the probabilities of observing the three other types of defects. Then these probabilities, which we will call the column probabilities of Table 10.6, will satisfy the requirement

$$p_A + p_B + p_C + p_D = 1$$

In like manner, let p_i ($i = 1$, 2, or 3) equal the row probability that a defect will have occurred on shift i, where

$$p_1 + p_2 + p_3 = 1$$

Then, if the two classifications are independent of each other, a cell probability will equal the product of its respective row and column probabilities, in accordance with the multiplicative law of probability. For example, the probability that a particular defect will occur on shift 1 and be of type A is $(p_1)(p_A)$. Thus we observe that the numerical values of the cell probabilities are unspecified in the problem under consideration. The null hypothesis specifies only that each cell probability will equal the product of its respective row and column probabilities and therefore imply independence of the two classifications.

The contingency table in Table 10.6 contains $r = 3$ rows and $c = 4$ columns and consequently is called an $r \times c$ (in this case, a 3×4) contingency table. Similarly, a 2×5 contingency table contains 2 rows and 5 columns. We will denote the four column

TABLE 10.6   Contingency Table

Shift	Type of Defect				Total
	A	*B*	*C*	*D*	
1	15 (22.51)	21 (20.99)	45 (38.94)	13 (11.56)	94
2	26 (22.99)	31 (21.44)	34 (39.77)	5 (11.81)	96
3	33 (28.50)	17 (26.57)	49 (49.29)	20 (14.63)	119
Total	74	69	128	38	309

totals, proceeding from left to right, as c_1, c_2, c_3, and c_4, and the three row totals, proceeding from top to bottom, as r_1, r_2, and r_3. Thus $c_1 = 74$ and $r_1 = 94$. Note that the sum of the column totals equals $n = 309$. Similarly, the sum of the row totals equals 309. These row and column totals will be used to estimate the unspecified cell probabilities and, consequently, the expected cell frequencies. In fact, it can be shown (proof omitted) that the appropriate estimate of the expected frequency for the cell in the ith row and jth column of a contingency table is as given in the following box.

EXPECTED FREQUENCY FOR CELL IN THE ith ROW AND jth COLUMN

$$\hat{E}(n_{ij}) = \frac{r_i c_j}{n}$$

For example, the estimated expected cell frequency for the cell corresponding to Shift 1, Defect A (row 1, column 1) is

$$\hat{E}(n_{11}) = \frac{r_1 c_1}{n} = \frac{(94)(74)}{309} = 22.51$$

Similarly,

$$\hat{E}(n_{23}) = \frac{r_2 c_3}{n} = \frac{(96)(128)}{309} = 39.77$$

The X^2 statistic is calculated in exactly the same manner as indicated in Section 10.2. Thus

$$X^2 = \sum_{j=1}^{4} \sum_{i=1}^{3} \frac{[n_{ij} - \hat{E}(n_{ij})]^2}{\hat{E}(n_{ij})} = \sum_{j=1}^{4} \sum_{i=1}^{3} \frac{d_{ij}^2}{\hat{E}(n_{ij})}$$

The approximating chi-square distribution for X^2 will always possess d.f. = $(r - 1)(c - 1)$ degrees of freedom.

CHI-SQUARE DEGREES OF FREEDOM FOR A CONTINGENCY TABLE

$$\text{d.f.} = (r - 1)(c - 1)$$

where

$$r = \text{number of rows}$$

$$c = \text{number of columns}$$

The chi-square test is summarized in the next box.

EXAMPLE 10.2   Refer to the data in Table 10.6. Do the data provide sufficient evidence to indicate that the proportions of the four types of defects vary from shift to shift? Test using $\alpha = .05$.

SOLUTION   The first step is to compute the expected frequencies and insert them (as we have done in

CHI-SQUARE CONTINGENCY TABLE ANALYSIS

(1) *Null Hypothesis:* $H_0 : p_{ij} = p_i p_j$ for all i and j

where p_{ij} = probability that an observation falls in row i and column j

p_i = probability that an observation falls in row i

p_j = probability that an observation falls in column j

(2) *Alternative Hypothesis:* $H_a : p_{ij} \neq p_i p_j$ for at least one cell of the table.

(3) *Test Statistic:* $X^2 = \displaystyle\sum_{j=1}^{c} \sum_{i=1}^{r} \frac{[(n_{ij} - \hat{E}(n_{ij})]^2}{\hat{E}(n_{ij})} = \sum_{j=1}^{c} \sum_{i=1}^{r} \frac{d_{ij}^2}{\hat{E}(n_{ij})},$

where n_{ij} = frequency for cell in row i and column j,

r_i = total for row i

c_j = total for column j

n = total of all observations

$$\hat{E}(n_{ij}) = \frac{r_i c_j}{n}$$

(4) *Rejection Region:* $X^2 > \chi_\alpha^2$, where χ_α^2 is based on d.f. = $(r - 1)(c - 1)$ degrees of freedom (see Table 6 in the Appendix).

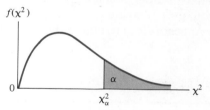

Assumption: All estimated expected cell frequencies are greater than or equal to 5.

Table 10.6) into the contingency table. Then calculate

$$X^2 = \sum_{j=1}^{4} \sum_{i=1}^{3} \frac{[n_{ij} - \hat{E}(n_{ij})]^2}{\hat{E}(n_{ij})} = \sum_{j=1}^{4} \sum_{i=1}^{3} \frac{d_{ij}^2}{\hat{E}(n_{ij})}$$

$$= \frac{(15 - 22.51)^2}{22.51} + \frac{(26 - 22.99)^2}{22.99} + \cdots + \frac{(20 - 14.63)^2}{14.63}$$

$$= 19.18$$

The final step in our test is to locate the rejection region and complete the test. The number of degrees of freedom for this chi-square statistic is

$$\text{d.f.} = (r - 1)(c - 1) = (3 - 1)(4 - 1) = 6$$

If we choose $\alpha = .05$ for our test, the tabulated value of $\chi_{.05}^2$ corresponding to d.f. = 6 in Table 6 in the Appendix is $\chi^2_{.05} = 12.5916$. Therefore, we will reject the hypothesis of independence between the row and column classifications if

$$X^2 > 12.5916$$

Since the computed value, $X^2 = 19.18$, exceeds this value, we reject the null hypothesis and conclude that there is sufficient evidence to indicate that the proportions of the various types of defects vary from shift to shift. ∎

    The calculation of X^2 for a contingency table analysis is tedious (at best). The easy way to perform a contingency table analysis is to use the appropriate program contained in a statistical computer program package and let the computer do the work.

    The SAS, Minitab, and SPSS[x] computer printouts for a contingency table analysis of the data in Table 10.6 are shown in Tables 10.7, 10.8, and 10.9, respectively. Examine the SAS printout in Table 10.7, and you can see the contingency table showing the observed and the computed expected cell frequencies. The computed value of X^2 is shown directly below the table in the row corresponding to CHI-SQUARE as 19.178 with DF = 6 degrees of freedom. The observed significance level is shown as .0039. The quantities printed below the value of CHI-SQUARE are irrelevant to our discussion.

    The Minitab printout in Table 10.8 also gives the contingency table; the observed and expected frequencies are shown in each cell of the table. The value of the test statistic, $X^2 = 19.18$, is shown below the table along with the degrees of freedom for X^2, d.f. = 6. The Minitab printout does not give the observed significance level for the test. Consequently, you must compare the observed value of X^2 with the tabulated value in Table 6 in the Appendix to determine if the X^2 statistic is large enough to reject

TABLE 10.7   SAS Contingency Table Analysis of Table 10.6

```
                         TABLE OF SHIFT BY TYPE

        SHIFT           TYPE

        FREQUENCY
        EXPECTED     A        B        C        D        TOTAL

           1           15       21       45       13        94
                      22.5     21.0     38.9     11.6

           2           26       31       34        5        96
                      23.0     21.4     39.8     11.8

           3           33       17       49       20       119
                      28.5     26.6     49.3     14.6

        TOTAL          74       69      128       38       309

                    STATISTICS FOR 2-WAY TABLES

        CHI-SQUARE                    19.178   DF=      6     PROB=0.0039
        PHI                            0.249
        CONTINGENCY COEFFICIENT        0.242
        CRAMER'S V                     0.176
        LIKELIHOOD RATIO CHISQUARE    20.336   DF=      6     PROB=0.0024
```

TABLE 10.8 Minitab Contingency Table Analysis of Table 10.6

```
      EXPECTED FREQUENCIES ARE PRINTED BELOW OBSERVED
                      FREQUENCIES
```

	A	B	C	D	TOTALS
1	15	21	45	13	94
	22.5	21.0	38.9	11.6	
2	26	31	34	5	96
	23.0	21.4	39.8	11.8	
3	33	17	49	20	119
	28.5	26.6	49.3	14.6	
TOTALS	74	69	128	38	309

TOTAL CHI SQUARE =

$$2.51 + 0.00 + 0.94 + 0.18 +$$
$$0.39 + 4.27 + 0.84 + 3.92 +$$
$$0.71 + 3.45 + 0.00 + 1.97$$

$$= 19.18$$
DEGREES OF FREEDOM = $(3 - 1) \times (4 - 1) = 6$

TABLE 10.9 SPSS^x Contingency Table Analysis of Table 10.6

```
- - - - - - - - - -  C R O S S T A B U L A T I O N   O F  - - - - - - - -
        SHIFT
BY  TYPE
```

		TYPE				ROW TOTAL
	COUNT ROW PCT COL PCT TOT PCT	1	2	3	4	
SHIFT						
1		15	21	45	13	94
		16.0	22.3	47.9	13.8	30.4
		20.3	30.4	35.2	34.2	
		4.9	6.8	14.6	4.2	
2		26	31	34	5	96
		27.1	32.3	35.4	5.2	31.1
		35.1	44.9	26.6	13.2	
		8.4	10.0	11.0	1.6	
3		33	17	49	20	119
		27.7	14.3	41.2	16.8	38.5
		44.6	24.6	38.3	52.6	
		10.7	5.5	15.9	6.5	
COLUMN TOTAL		74 23.9	69 22.3	128 41.4	38 12.3	309 100.0

CHI-SQUARE	D.F.	SIGNIFICANCE	MIN E.F.	CELLS WITH E.F.< 5
19.17797	6	0.0039	11.560	NONE

the null hypothesis of *independence* of the two qualitative variables, shift and type of defect.

The SPSS^x printout in Table 10.9 also shows the contingency table, but each cell contains four numbers. The one at the top is the cell frequency. The second, third, and fourth are, respectively, the cell frequency as a percentage of the row total, the cell frequency as a percentage of the column total, and the cell frequency as a percentage of the total number of observations n. The expected cell frequency is not shown. The value of X^2 is shown directly below the table as CHI-SQUARE = 19.17797 with 6 DEGREES OF FREEDOM. The observed significance level is given as SIGNIFICANCE = .0039.

To summarize, the SAS and SPSS^x printouts in Tables 10.7 and 10.9 provide the observed significance levels and therefore enable you to decide whether there is sufficient evidence to indicate a *contingency*—that is, a dependence—between the qualitative variables "shift" and "type of defect." The Minitab printout provides the value of X^2 and its degrees of freedom, but you must then compare this value with the tabulated critical value of χ^2.

EXERCISES

BASIC TECHNIQUES

10.10 Calculate the value and give the number of degrees of freedom for X^2 for the following contingency tables.

(a)

Row	Column			
	1	2	3	4
1	120	70	55	16
2	79	108	95	43
3	31	49	81	140

(b)

Row	Column		
	1	2	3
1	35	16	84
2	120	92	206

10.11 Suppose that a consumer survey summarizes the responses of $n = 307$ people in a contingency table that contains three rows and five columns. How many degrees of freedom will be associated with the chi-square test statistic?

10.12 A survey of 400 respondents produced the cell counts given in Table 10.10 in a 2 × 3 contingency table.

(a) If you wish to test the null hypothesis of "independence"—that the probability that a response falls in any one row is independent of the column it will fall in—and you plan to use a chi-square test, how many degrees of freedom will be associated with the χ^2 statistic?

(b) Find the value of the test statistic.

TABLE 10.10   Contingency Table Data for Exercise 10.12

	Column			
Row	1	2	3	Total
1	37	34	93	164
2	66	57	113	236
Total	103	91	206	400

(c) Find the rejection region for $\alpha = .10$.

(d) Conduct the test and state your conclusions.

(e) Find the approximate observed significance level for the test, and interpret its value.

APPLICATIONS

10.13 A carpet company was interested in comparing the fraction of new-home builders favoring carpet over other floor coverings for homes in three different areas of a city. The objective was to decide how to allocate sales effort to the areas. A survey was conducted, and the data are shown in Table 10.11.

TABLE 10.11   Preference Data for Exercise 10.13

	Areas		
Floor Covering	1	2	3
Carpet	69	126	16
Other material	78	99	27

(a) Do the data indicate a difference in the percentage favoring carpet from one area of the city to another?

(b) Estimate the difference in the fractions of new-home builders who favor carpet between areas 1 and 2. Use a 95% confidence interval. (*Hint:* Use the procedure of Section 6.8.)

10.14 The data in Table 10.12 represent a small portion of a telephone survey conducted by Jerry R. Lynn to determine the characteristics of the small-town, rural, and farm Tennessee newspaper

TABLE 10.12   Readership Data for Exercise 10.14

	Readership		
Community	Readers	Nonreaders	Total
Urban	529	121	650
Rural	373	137	510
Farm	237	89	326
Total	1139	347	1486

Source: Jerry R. Lynn, "Newspaper Ad Impact in Nonmetropolitan Markets," *Journal of Advertising Research,* Vol. 21, No. 4, 1981.

readership and the impact of advertising on that market. A sample of 1486 persons was selected from among the small towns, rural areas, and farms of Tennessee. One survey question asked whether the respondent did or did not read a newspaper. The numbers of respondents in the six community-readership categories are shown in Table 10.12.

(a) Do the data provide sufficient evidence to indicate that the proportions of readers differ among the three community groups? Test using $\alpha = .05$.

(b) Find the approximate p-value for the test, and interpret its value.

 10.15 A telephone opinion poll of 1675 Canadians was conducted in 1986 by Angus Reid Associates, Inc., for the Montreal *Gazette*. One question asked was whether a respondent favored the new flat income tax structure passed by the U.S. Congress in 1986. The question in the *Gazette* was phrased as follows: "Recently in the United States a bill was passed that made a flat tax system in that country. Americans earning over $30,000 a year will pay a flat tax rate of 28 per cent, Americans earning less than this will pay a rate of 15 per cent. What would you think about a similar flat tax system being implemented in Canada? Do you think it would be a good or bad idea?" Responses were categorized according to the region in which the respondent lived and according to whether the respondent supported the new tax structure (good idea), opposed the new tax structure (bad idea), or had no opinion (don't know). The numbers of respondents in the six regions of Canada and the percentages falling in the opinion categories for each region are shown in Table 10.13.

TABLE 10.13   Opinion Data for Exercise 10.15

Response	Total	B.C.	Alberta	Man.-Sask.	Ontario	Quebec	Atlantic
(Base)	(1675)	(171)	(304)	(122)	(535)	(403)	(140)
Good idea	66%	65%	64%	65%	63%	68%	73%
Bad idea	23%	26%	24%	26%	24%	21%	17%
(Don't know or not stated)	12%	9%	12%	9%	13%	11%	10%

Source: (Montreal) *Gazette*, September 7, 1986. Copyright 1986 by Angus Reid Associates, Inc.

(a) Use the number of respondents and the opinion category percentages for each region to calculate the approximate number of respondents in each of the $3 \times 6 = 18$ cells of the table.

(b) Do the data provide sufficient evidence to indicate that more than 60% of all Canadians support the income tax structure passed by the U.S. Congress in 1986. Test using $\alpha = .05$. (Do you need to qualify your conclusions?)

(c) Do the data provide sufficient evidence to indicate that the distribution of opinions among the three categories depends upon the region in which the respondents live? Test using $\alpha = .05$. State your conclusions.

 10.16 How do women fare in comparison to men in reaching managerial positions in department store retailing? A sampling of 321 retail department store chains by Gable, Gillespie, and Topol may help to answer this question. Table 10.14 gives the numbers and percentages of managers at the upper, middle, and lower levels of management for 10,141 males and 7913 females. Do the data provide sufficient evidence to indicate differences between males and females in the proportions of each sex in the three levels of management? Test using $\alpha = .05$, and state your conclusions.

TABLE 10.14 Management Data for Exercise 10.16

Management Level	Male		Female	
	Number	Percent	Number	Percent
Upper	3,361	85.0	592	15.0
Middle	3,448	72.7	1294	27.3
Lower	3,332	35.6	6027	64.4
Total	10,141		7913	

Chi-square: 3,472.03
Probability: <.01

Source: M. Gable, K. R. Gillespie, and M. Topol, "The Current Status of Women in Department Store Retailing: An Update," *Journal of Retailing,* Vol. 60, 1984.

10.17 In the study of women in retail department store managerial positions (Exercise 10.16), Gable, Gillespie, and Topol provide data on similar studies conducted in 1976 and 1983. As part of the comparison of 1976 and 1983 data, they give data on the numbers of men and women in the most senior managerial positions, chairman of the board, president (or general manager), and vice president (senior or executive). Of 777 persons in these positions in 1976, only 16 were female. In contrast, 26 females out of a total of 923 persons occupied these positions in 1983. Do these sample data provide sufficient evidence to indicate a change in the proportions of women in these top-level positions from 1976 to 1983? Test using $\alpha = .05$, and state your conclusions.

10.18 Refer to the Gable, Gillespie, and Topol data in Exercise 10.17. Suppose that you want to determine only whether the proportion of women in the top-level positions increased from 1976 to 1983 (a one-sided alternative hypothesis). Explain how this test should be conducted. Conduct the test using $\alpha = .05$, and state your conclusions.

10.19 In Exercises 6.52 and 7.36 we presented data on the relationship between financial distress and the tendency of failed firms to shift auditors (K. B. Schwartz and K. Menon, "Auditor Switches by Failing Firms," *Accounting Review,* Vol. 60, No. 2, 1985). One question arising in this study was whether the inclusion of qualified opinions in a financially distressed company's audit increases the likelihood that the company will shift CPA firms. (A financially distressed firm is one observed during the four-year period preceding bankruptcy.) Of 77 financially distressed firms that received audit qualifications, 14 switched CPA firms in the year following receipt of the qualification. In contrast, 17 of 51 financially distressed firms that did not receive audit qualifications switched CPA firms.

(a) Schwartz and Menon state that the null hypothesis to be tested is, "A switch in auditors by a failing firm is not associated with a qualified opinion obtained in the year prior to the switch." Do you agree? Explain.

(b) Schwartz and Menon analyze the data by using a contingency table analysis. They give $X^2 = 3.83$ for their chi-square test, with a *p*-value of .05. Verify the value of X^2 and the *p*-value for the test.

(c) Do the data provide sufficient evidence to reject the null hypothesis? Explain.

(d) Does rejection of H_0 in part (c) imply that failing firms who have received a qualified opinion are more likely to switch CPA firms the following year? Explain.

10.20 Refer to Exercise 10.19.

(a) Express the null hypothesis in part (a) of Exercise 10.19 as an hypothesis about the difference between two proportions (see Section 7.7).

(b) If it is believed that the receipt of a qualified audit would annoy a financially distressed firm and increase the probability that it would switch its CPA firm, state the appropriate alternative hypothesis.

(c) Based on the null and alternative hypotheses in parts (a) and (b), explain why a visual examination of the data leads immediately to the test conclusion.

 10.21 According to one theory, people with type A behavior—hard-driving, impatient, competitive people—are much more prone to heart problems than those classified as low-key, type B individuals. In a study conducted by Robert B. Case and colleagues, 516 heart attack patients were administered the Jenkins Activity Survey (JAS), a questionnaire that purports to provide an approximate measure of individual type A behavior. The scores ranged from a low of -21 (type B behavior) to a high of 23 (type A behavior). The higher the score, the greater is the level of type A behavior in an individual. Each of the 516 patients was categorized according to whether the patient's JAS score was less than -5 (type B), -5 to 5 (neutral), or greater than 5 (type A). The number of patients in each of the three classes along with the number who died during a three-year follow-up period are shown in Table 10.15. The authors used the chi-square test to test for a dependence between the follow-up mortality rate and the level of type A behavior as measured by the JAS score. They give the computed value of X^2 to be 2.56, with a p-value equal to .28.

TABLE 10.15   JAS Score Data for Exercise 10.21

	JAS Score		
Category	Less Than -5	-5 to 5	Greater Than 5
Total number of patients	180	171	165
Number dying in 3-year follow-up	21	17	11

Source: R. B. Case et al., "Type A Behavior and Survival After Acute Myocardial Infarction," *New England Journal of Medicine,* Vol. 312, No. 12, March 21, 1985. Copyright 1985 Massachusetts Medical Society.

(a) Confirm that the computed value of X^2 is correct.

(b) Using Table 6 in the Appendix, would you conclude that the p-value for the test is larger than .10?

(c) From the data in the table, what do you think the authors concluded about the dependence between the mortality rate of heart attack patients and their JAS scores?

$r \times c$ TABLES WITH FIXED ROW OR COLUMN TOTALS

10.4

In the previous section we described the analysis of an $r \times c$ contingency table, using examples that, for all practical purposes, fit the multinomial experiment described in Section 10.1. Although the methods of collecting data in many surveys may adhere to the requirements of a multinomial experiment, other methods do not. For example, we might not want to sample randomly the population described in Example 10.1 because we might find that, owing to chance, one category is completely missing.

To illustrate, suppose that we want to determine whether differences exist among three different product markets in their attitudes to a particular form of product advertising. Say we were to randomly sample $n = 600$ persons, and just by chance, one of the groups, say Hispanics, does not appear in the sample. To ensure against this possibility, we might survey a random sample of $n = 200$ persons from each market group. A summary of the responses might appear as shown in Table 10.16.

TABLE 10.16   Consumer Response to a Form of Product Advertising for Three Product Markets ($k = 2$ Possible Opinions)

Opinion	Product Market			Total
	1	2	3	
Favor	124	111	137	372
Do Not Favor or Have No Opinion	76	89	63	228
Total	200	200	200	600

Table 10.16 contains the results of three independent binomial experiments, one corresponding to each product market ($n = 200$, $k = 2$). The objective of the experiments is to test the equivalence of the binomial probabilities (proportions) p_1, p_2, and p_3. When these probabilities are equal, a person's inclination to favor the form of advertising is independent of the market from which the person is selected. When unequal, a person's opinion will depend upon the market. **Therefore, the equivalence of a set of binomial probabilities can be tested by using the contingency table analysis of Section 10.3.**

Suppose that each opinion in the market surveys was classified into one of three categories, "favor" the form of product advertising, "do not favor," and "no opinion," and that the results of the surveys are as shown in Table 10.17. Table 10.17 contains the outcomes for three independent multinomial experiments, one corresponding to each market ($n = 200$, $k = 3$). If the distribution of opinions into the three categories is the same for all markets—that is, *opinion* is independent of *market*—the multinomial probabilities p_1, p_2, and p_3 will be the same for all three markets. Therefore, as in the comparison of binomial population proportions, we can compare multinomial populations by using a contingency table analysis. **The analysis of an $r \times c$ contingency table in which the column totals (or row totals) have been fixed is identical to the analysis of Section 10.3.**

TABLE 10.17   Consumer Response to a Form of Product Advertising for Three Product Markets

Opinion	Product Market			Total
	1	2	3	
Favor	124	111	137	372
Do Not Favor	55	44	38	137
No Opinion	21	45	25	91
Total	200	200	200	600

EXAMPLE 10.3   Do the data in Table 10.17 provide sufficient evidence to indicate that the proportions of responses in the "favor," "do not favor," and "no opinion" categories differ among the three product markets?

SOLUTION   The SAS computer printout for a contingency table analysis of the data in Table 10.17 is shown in Table 10.18. You can verify that the degrees of freedom for the chi-square statistic is, as shown on the printout, d.f. $= (r - 1)(c - 1) = (3 - 1)(3 - 1) = 4$. You can also see that the computed value of the X^2 statistic is $X^2 = 16.882$ and that the observed level of significance is .0020. Thus we would reject the hypothesis of *independence* of the qualitative variables "consumer response" and "product market" for all values of α larger than .0020. In other words, there is ample evidence to indicate that the consumer response differs among the three markets.

TABLE 10.18   SAS Computer Printout for Table 10.17 and Example 10.3

```
                    TABLE OF OPINION BY MARKET

        OPINION          MARKET

        FREQUENCY                                   TOTAL
        EXPECTED        1        2        3

        FAVOR           124      111      137       372
                        124.0    124.0    124.0

        DO NOT FAVOR    55       44       38        137
                        45.7     45.7     45.7

        NO OPINION      21       45       25        91
                        30.3     30.3     30.3

        TOTAL           200      200      200       600

                    STATISTICS FOR 2-WAY TABLES

        CHI-SQUARE                  16.882   DF=    4    PROB=0.0020
        PHI                         0.168
        CONTINGENCY COEFFICIENT     0.165
        CRAMER'S V                  0.119
        LIKELIHOOD RATIO CHISQUARE  16.332   DF=    4    PROB=0.0026
```

EXERCISES

BASIC TECHNIQUES

10.22   Random samples of 200 observations were selected from each of three populations, and then each observation was classified according to whether it fell into one of three mutually exclusive categories. The cell counts are shown in Table 10.19. Do the data provide sufficient evidence to indicate that the proportions of observations in the three categories depend upon the population from which they were drawn?

(a) Give the value of X^2 for the test.

(b) Give the rejection region for the test for $\alpha = .10$.

(c) State your conclusions.

(d) Find the approximate *p*-value for the test, and interpret its value.

TABLE 10.19   Count Data for Exercise 10.22.

	Category			
Population	1	2	3	Total
1	108	52	40	200
2	87	51	62	200
3	112	39	49	200

10.23 Suppose that you want to test the null hypothesis that three binomial parameters p_A, p_B, and p_C are equal against the alternative that at least two of the parameters differ. Independent random samples of 100 observations were selected from each of the populations. The data are shown in Table 10.20.

TABLE 10.20   Binomial Data for Exercise 10.23

	Population			
Category	A	B	C	Total
Number of Successes	24	19	33	76
Number of Failures	76	81	67	224
Total	100	100	100	300

(a) Find the value of X^2, the test statistic.
(b) Give the rejection region for the test for $\alpha = .05$.
(c) State your test conclusions.
(d) Find the approximate observed significance level for the test, and interpret its value.

APPLICATIONS

10.24 A study of the purchase decisions for three stock portfolio managers, A, B, and C, was conducted to compare the rates of stock purchases that resulted in profits over a time period that was less than or equal to one year. One hundred randomly selected purchases obtained for each of the managers gave the results shown in Table 10.21. Do the data provide evidence of differences among the rates of successful purchases for the three managers?

TABLE 10.21   Profit Data for Exercise 10.24

	Manager		
Purchase Result	A	B	C
Profit	63	71	55
No Profit	37	29	45
Total	100	100	100

10.25 According to the *Wall Street Journal* (October 23, 1981), "most bosses shun symbols of status, help take care of household tasks." The *Wall Street Journal*–Gallup survey finds that 49% of the 307 heads of the nation's largest firms included in the survey sometimes do grocery shopping.

Compare this 49% to 47% of the executives of 309 medium-sized firms and 45% of the executives of 208 small companies. Do the percentages suggest a difference in the proportions of the chief executives of small, medium, and large firms who sometimes do grocery shopping?

(a) Do the data provide sufficient evidence to indicate that the proportions of chief executives who sometimes do grocery shopping differ for the three categories of company size? Test using $\alpha = .05$. (*Hint:* Construct a 2×3 contingency table showing the numbers of executives in each of the six cell categories.)

(b) Suppose that prior to observing the data, you had planned to compare the proportions of executives of large corporations and small corporations who sometimes do grocery shopping. Do the data provide sufficient evidence to indicate a difference in proportions for these two groups? Test using $\alpha = .05$.

MKTG   10.26   Refer to Exercise 10.14. Another interesting set of data provided in Lynn's study (of advertising impact in nonmetropolitan areas) concerned the source that a respondent would select for specific types of product information. The data shown in Table 10.22 are classified according to three types and four sources of product information.

TABLE 10.22   Source Data for Exercises 10.26

Type of Product Information	Media Preference				
	Newspapers	TV	Radio	Magazines	Don't Know or Other
New product information	288	463	26	191	170
Costs of products	703	106	25	67	235
Where to shop	844	65	50	16	162

Source: Jerry R. Lynn, "Newspaper Ad Impact in Nonmetropolitan Markets," *Journal of Advertising Research,* Vol. 21, No. 4, 1981.

(a) Do the data provide sufficient evidence to indicate that a respondent's choice of the source of product information desired (newspapers, television, radio, or magazines) depends on the type of information desired?

(b) Find the approximate *p*-value for the test, and interpret its value.

10.27   In Exercise 6.60 we referred to a Wyatt Company survey that suggested hard times in the energy industry (*Wall Street Journal,* April 29, 1986). The survey found that of 43 energy companies sampled, only 44% made bonus payments to their executives in 1985, compared with 76% in 1984. Assume that the 43 energy companies were randomly and independently selected from among all energy companies in each of the two years.

(a) Do the data present sufficient evidence to indicate a change from 1984 to 1985 in the percentage of energy companies offering executive bonuses? Test using $\alpha = .05$.

(b) Suppose that the 43 energy companies questioned in 1985 were the same companies included in the random sample of 1984 (i.e., the samples were not independent). Would the chi-square test of part (a) be valid? Explain.

10.28   A manufacturer of buttons wanted to determine whether the fraction of defective buttons produced by three machines varied from machine to machine. Samples of 400 buttons were selected from each of the three machines, and the number of defectives were counted for each sample. The results are as follows:

Machine Number	1	2	3
Number of Defectives	16	24	9

Do these data present sufficient evidence to indicate that the fraction of defective buttons varies from machine to machine? Test with $\alpha = .05$.

10.5   WINE PREFERENCES: CANNED OR BOTTLED?

Now that we understand the basic concepts involved in a chi-square test about the probabilities associated with a multinomial experiment, let us reexamine the Case Study, the Reynolds Metals Company taste test data for comparing consumer preferences for canned versus bottled wine. Thus we will compare the observed and expected cell counts, but as you will subsequently see, this application does not fit the stereotypes of the preceding sections.

For this particular experiment each taste tester's response fell in one of $k = 3$ categories, as shown in Table 10.23. The theoretical cell frequencies, p_1, p_2, and p_3 ($p_1 + p_2 + p_3 = 1$), are shown at the tops of the category boxes in the table, and the observed frequencies, corresponding to the preference percentages, are shown at the bottom.

TABLE 10.23   The $k = 3$ Categories for the Wine Taste Test

p_1 Prefer canned wine .50	p_2 Prefer bottled wine .39	p_3 No preference .11

We want to test the null hypothesis $H_0 : p_1 = p_2$—that is, that the proportion of consumers preferring the glasses containing the canned wine is equal to the proportion preferring the glasses containing the bottled wine. The alternative hypothesis is that one of the two types of wines, canned or bottled, is preferred, $H_a : p_1 \neq p_2$. Do the data provide sufficient evidence to indicate that $p_1 \neq p_2$?

To answer this question, we need to know the numbers of responses, n_1, n_2, and n_3, that fell in the three categories of Table 10.23. Kristof's article reports the observed cell relative frequencies, $n_1/n = .50$, $n_2/n = .39$, and $n_3/n = .11$, but fails to give us the total number n of taste testers. Consequently, we can conduct the chi-square test only if we supply a value for n. For example, if $n = 100$ taste testers were involved in the experiment, then $n_1 = (.50)n = (.50)(100) = 50$. Similarly, $n_2 = (.39)n = 39$, and $n_3 = (.11)n = 11$.

The next step is to estimate the values of p_1, p_2, and p_3 and calculate the estimated expected cell frequencies. It can be shown (proof omitted) that the estimates* are

$$\hat{p}_1 = \hat{p}_2 = \frac{1}{2}\left(\frac{n_1 + n_2}{n}\right) \quad \text{and} \quad \hat{p}_3 = 1 - \hat{p}_1 - \hat{p}_2$$

or

$$\hat{p}_1 = \hat{p}_2 = \frac{1}{2}\left(\frac{50 + 39}{100}\right) = .445 \quad \text{and} \quad \hat{p}_3 = 1 - \hat{p}_1 - \hat{p}_2 = .11$$

The resulting expected cell frequencies are

$$\hat{E}(n_1) = \hat{E}(n_2) = n\hat{p}_1 = (100)(.445) = 44.5$$

and

$$\hat{E}(n_3) = n\hat{p}_3 = (100)(.11) = 11$$

These values, along with the observed cell frequencies, are shown in Table 10.24.

TABLE 10.24   The Observed and Estimated Expected Cell Frequencies for the Wine-Tasting Experiment

Frequency	Prefer Canned	Prefer Bottled	No Preference
Observed	50	39	11
Estimated expected	44.5	44.5	11

We have placed two linear restrictions on the cell counts; that is, we have estimated one parameter p_1 (and consequently, p_2, since we are hypothesizing that $p_1 = p_2$), and the sum of the cell counts equals n, i.e., $n_1 + n_2 + n_3 = n$. Therefore, the chi-square test statistic will be based on

d.f. = k − (number of linearly independent restrictions on n_1, n_2, and n_3)
    = 3 − 2 = 1

For $\alpha = .05$, we will reject the null hypothesis $H_0 : p_1 = p_2$ if the computed value of X^2 exceeds the tabulated value of $\chi^2_{.05}$ in Table 6 in the Appendix, namely, $\chi^2_{.05} = 3.84146$.
    Using the observed and estimated expected values of the cell counts, we find the computed value of the statistic to be

$$X^2 = \frac{\sum\limits_{i=1}^{k}[n_i - \hat{E}(n_i)]^2}{\hat{E}(n_i)} = \frac{\sum\limits_{i=1}^{3}(n_i - n\hat{p}_i)^2}{n\hat{p}_i}$$

$$= \frac{(50 - 44.5)^2}{44.5} + \frac{(39 - 44.5)^2}{44.5} + \frac{(11 - 11)^2}{11}$$

$$= 1.36$$

---

*These are known as maximum likelihood estimates. They represent the values of p_1, p_2, and p_3 that give the highest probability of observing this particular set of sample data. Maximum likelihood estimates often agree with our intuition. Thus if we assume that $p_1 = p_2$, it seems reasonable to find the estimate of p_1 by letting it equal 1/2 of the estimated probability for the *combined* two cells, i.e., 1/2 of $(n_1 + n_2)/n$.

Since this computed value is less than the critical value, $\chi^2_{.05} = 3.84146$, there is not sufficient evidence to indicate a difference in the proportions p_1 and p_2 that favor the canned and bottled wines.

A conclusion of "not sufficient evidence to show a difference between wine preferences" may disagree with your intuition, because the observed percentage of taste testers in favor of the canned wine, 50%, seems to be much different from the percentage, 39%, favoring the bottled wine. Failure to detect a difference in preferences for the two types of wine may have resulted because there really is no difference in preferences or because the sample size,* $n = 100$ taste testers, is not large enough to detect a difference.

Summary

10.6

The preceding material has been concerned with a test of an hypothesis regarding the cell probabilities associated with a multinomial experiment. When the number of observations n is large, the test statistic X^2 can be shown to possess, approximately, a chi-square probability distribution in repeated sampling, the number of degrees of freedom being dependent on the particular application. In general, we assume that n is large and that the minimum expected cell frequency is equal to or is greater than 5.

Several words of caution concerning the use of the X^2 statistic as a method of analyzing enumerative-type data are appropriate. The determination of the correct number of degrees of freedom associated with the X^2 statistic is very important in locating the rejection region. If the number is incorrectly specified, erroneous conclusions may result. Also, note that nonrejection of the null hypothesis does not imply that it should be accepted. We would have difficulty in stating a meaningful alternative hypothesis for many practical applications and, therefore, would lack knowledge of the probability of making a type II error. For example, we hypothesize that the two classifications of a contingency table are independent. A specific alternative would have to specify some measure of dependence, which may or may not possess practical significance to the experimenter. Finally, if parameters are missing and the expected cell frequencies must be estimated, the estimators of missing parameters should be of a particular type in order that the test be valid. In other words, the application of the chi-square test for other than the applications outlined in Sections 10.2, 10.3, 10.4, and 10.5 will require experience beyond the scope of this introductory presentation of the subject.

References

Cochran, W. G. "The χ^2 Test of Goodness of Fit." *Annals of Mathematical Statistics,* Vol. 23, 1952, pp. 315–345.

Dixon, W. J., Brown, M. B., Engelman, L., Frane, J. W., Hill, M. A., Jennrich, R. I., and Toporek, J. D. *BMDP Statistical Software.* Berkeley: University of California Press, 1985.

*Recall that we did not know how many taste testers were involved in the Reynolds Metals Company taste test experiment. For purposes of explanation we assumed that $n = 100$.

Dixon, W. J., and Massey, F. J., Jr. *Introduction to Statistical Analysis*. 4th ed. New York: McGraw-Hill, 1983.

Hill, MaryAnn, ed. *BMDP User's Digest*. 2nd ed. Los Angeles: BMDP Statistical Software, 1982.

McClave, J. T., and Benson, G. P. *Statistics for Business and Economics*. 4th ed. San Francisco: Dellen, 1988.

Pierce, A. *Fundamentals of Nonparametric Statistics*. Belmont, Calif.: Dickenson Publishing, 1970.

Ryan, T. A., Joiner, B. L., and Ryan, B. F. *Minitab Reference Manual*. University Park, Pa.: Minitab Project, 1985.

Ryan, T. A., Joiner, B. L., and Ryan, B. F. *Minitab Handbook*. 2nd ed. Boston: PWS-KENT, 1985.

SAS User's Guide: Basics. Version 5 ed. Cary, N.C.: SAS Institute, 1985.

SAS User's Guide: Statistics. Version 5 ed. Cary, N.C.: SAS Institute, 1985.

Sincich, T. *Statistics by Example*. 3rd ed. New York: Macmillan, 1987.

SPSS[x] User's Guide. Chicago: SPSS, 1983.

Key Terms

Multinomial experiment (page 406)
Cell counts (or frequencies) (page 407)
Chi-square goodness-of-fit test (page 407)
Lack of fit (page 407)
X^2 statistic (page 407)

Chi-square probability distribution (page 408)
Contingency table (page 413)
Contingency table analysis (page 423)

Supplementary Exercises

10.29 A die was rolled 600 times, with the following results:

Observed Number	1	2	3	4	5	6
Frequency	89	113	98	104	117	79

Do these data present sufficient evidence to indicate that the die is unbalanced? Test using $\alpha = .05$.

10.30 After inspecting the data in Exercise 10.29, one might want to test the hypothesis that the probability of a "6" is 1/6 against the alternative that this probability is less than 1/6.

(a) Carry out the test, using $\alpha = .05$.

(b) What tenet of good statistical practice is violated in the test of part (a)?

 10.31 Suppose that a government regulation on hiring requires that the proportions of workers of various races employed by a company be consistent with the corresponding racial proportions in the work force at large. In a particular region the workers fall into one of four racial categories in the proportions $p_1 = .2$, $p_2 = .05$, $p_3 = .03$, and $p_4 = .72$. A company employs 300 workers who are racially distributed as follows: $n_1 = 45$, $n_2 = 21$, $n_3 = 8$, and $n_4 = 224$. Do these data disagree with the company's contention that the deviations of these numbers from the expected numbers (based on the distribution of the labor force) are solely due to random variation?

(a) State H_0.

(b) State H_a.

(c) Calculate X^2.

(d) Give the rejection region for the test for $\alpha = .10$.

(e) Conduct the test and state your conclusions.

 10.32 An analysis of industrial plant accident data was made to determine whether the distribution of numbers of fatal accidents differed among three departments of the plant. The data for 346 accidents are shown in Table 10.25. Do the data indicate that the frequency of fatal accidents is dependent on the plant department? Test using $\alpha = .05$.

TABLE 10.25   Accident Data for Exercise 10.32

Accident Type	Plant Department		
	1	2	3
Fatal	67	26	16
Not fatal	128	63	46

 10.33 A radio station conducted a survey to study the relationship between the number of radios per household and family income. The survey, based on $n = 1000$ interviews, produced the results shown in Table 10.26. Do the data present sufficient evidence to indicate that the number of radios per household is dependent on family income? Test at the $\alpha = .10$ level of significance.

TABLE 10.26   Radios-Income Data for Exercise 10.33

Number of Radios per Household	Family Income			
	Less Than $9000	$9000–12,000	$12,000–15,000	More Than $15,000
1	126	362	129	78
2	29	138	82	56

 10.34 A trucking company claims that 30% of its trucks carry produce, 45% carry local freight, and 25% carry the bottled produce from neighboring vineyards. A group of investors who are interested in purchasing the trucking company decides to check this claim. The group randomly samples the bills of lading of 100 trucks and checks their cargos. The survey produced the following counts on the number of trucks carrying specific cargos:

produce: 21   local freight: 39   wine: 40

Do these data disagree with the trucking company's claim? Test using $\alpha = .10$.

10.35 Do the types of articles published by management faculty members in management journals depend on the status of the author's academic institution? Fowler, Bushardt, and Brooking classified 897 management faculty articles (see Exercise 10.9) according to the author's school's status (high, moderate, or low) and to the type of article published (empirical or nonempirical). The distribution of the articles in the six classes of a contingency table are shown in Table 10.27.

(a) Fowler, Bushardt, and Brooking state that $X^2 = 278.08$ "is significant far beyond the .05 critical value of 5.99." What are the practical implications of this statement?

(b) Verify that, in fact, $X^2 = 278.08$.

TABLE 10.27   Type of Article and Type of Journal Data for Exercise 10.35

Type of Journal	Type of Article		Total
	Empirical	Nonempirical	
Academic	182	143	325
Professional	28	494	522
Academic/professional	10	40	50
Total	220	677	897

Source: A. R. Fowler, Jr., S. C. Bushardt, and S. A. Brooking, "An Analysis of the Authorship in Management-Oriented Journals: The Relationship Between School Status, Article Type, Publication Outlet, and Author Academic Position," *Journal of Business Communication,* Vol. 22, No. 3, 1985.

 10.36 Are the journals selected by management faculty for their publications dependent on the status of a faculty member's school? Fowler, Bushardt and Brooking (see Exercises 10.9 and 10.35) classified 897 management articles according to the type of journal in which an article was published: journals publishing primarily academic articles (academic), those publishing primarily professional articles (professional), and those that publish a combination of both. Each article was also classified according to the school status of the author. The number of articles in each of the six type-status categories is shown in Table 10.28.

(a) Calculate the value of X^2 for the contingency table.

(b) Test the null hypothesis

$$H_0 : \text{journal choice is independent of school status}$$

against the alternative hypothesis

$$H_a : \text{journal choice is dependent upon school status}$$

Use $\alpha = .05$. State your conclusions.

(c) Give the approximate p-value for the test, and interpret it.

TABLE 10.28   School Status and Journal Type Data for Exercise 10.36

School Status	Where Published			Total
	Acad.	Prof.	Acad/Prof.	
High	110	135	16	261
Moderate	83	120	10	213
Low	132	267	24	423
Total	325	522	50	897

Source: A. R. Fowler, Jr., S. C. Bushardt, and S. A. Brooking, "An Analysis of the Authorship in Management-Oriented Journals: The Relationship Between School Status, Article Type, Publication Outlet, and Author Academic Position," *Journal of Business Communication,* Vol. 22, No. 3, 1985.

 10.37 In Exercise 7.38 we presented data on the reactions of consumers and managers to five different letters containing consumer complaints about well-known consumer products. The total number n of persons examining each letter and the number n_c of those who agreed that the complaint was justified are given for each letter for samples of consumers and managers. The results are shown in Table 10.29.

TABLE 10.29 Letter Response Data for Exercise 10.37

			Consumers					Managers		
Number	Letter 1	Letter 2	Letter 3	Letter 4	Letter 5	Letter 1	Letter 2	Letter 3	Letter 4	Letter 5
n	120	121	120	120	121	40	39	39	39	36
n_c	114	20	115	50	19	40	5	37	3	4

Source: A. J. Resnick and R. R. Harmon, "Consumer Complaints and Managerial Response: A Holistic Approach," *Journal of Marketing,* Vol. 47, 1983.

(a) Construct a 2×2 contingency table for each letter, showing the number n_c of persons who view the complaint as legitimate and the number who do not (or have no opinion) for both consumers and managers.

(b) Calculate the expected cell counts for all of the contingency tables in part (a). Do any of the expected cell counts violate the assumptions of the chi-square contingency table test? Explain.

10.38 Refer to Exercise 10.37, and let p_1 and p_2 represent, respectively, the proportions of consumers and managers who view the complaint in a particular letter as legitimate. Conduct a contingency table test for each letter where the test is valid. Test using $\alpha = .05$. Describe the results of your test.

 10.39 A survey was conducted by an auto repairman to determine whether various auto ills were dependent on the make of the auto. His survey, restricted to this year's model, produced the results shown in Table 10.30. Do these data present sufficient evidence to indicate a dependency between auto makes and type of repair for these new-model cars? Note that the repairman was not using all the information available when he conducted his survey. When one conducts a study of this type, what other factors should be recorded?

TABLE 10.30 Repair Data for Exercise 10.39

	Type of Repair		
Make	Electrical	Fuel Supply	Other
A	17	19	7
B	14	7	9
C	6	21	12
D	33	44	19
E	7	9	6

 10.40 By tradition, U. S. labor unions have been content to leave the management of the company to the managers and corporate executives. But in Europe, worker participation in management decision making is an accepted idea and one that is continually spreading. In a study of the effect of worker satisfaction with worker participation in managerial decision making, 100 workers were interviewed in each of two separate West German manufacturing plants. One plant had active worker participation in managerial decision making; the other did not. Each selected worker was asked whether he or she generally approved of the managerial decisions made within the firm. The results of the interviews are shown in Table 10.31.

TABLE 10.31   Interview Data for Exercise 10.40

Response	Participative Decision Making	No Participative Decision Making
Generally approve of the firm's decisions	73	51
Do not approve of the firm's decisions	27	49

(a) Do the data provide sufficient evidence to indicate that approval or disapproval of management's decisions depends on whether workers participate in decision making? Test using the X^2 test statistic. Use $\alpha = .05$.

(b) Do these data support the hypothesis that workers in a firm with participative decision making more generally approve of the firm's managerial decisions than those employed by firms without participative decision making? Test by using the z test presented in Section 7.7. This problem requires a one-tailed test. Why?

10.41 The computer, which at its advent was expected to play its primary role in scientific computation, has become essential in banking, in the recording of personal data, in merchandising, and in many areas of our daily lives. Along with this growth in computer applications have come numerous cases of computer abuse, financial fraud, theft of information, and so on. The data in Table 10.32 give four different types of computer abuse that were reported and verified for the years 1970 to 1973. The frequency of computer abuses would be expected to increase as the years go by unless safeguards are found to prevent their occurrence. But are the proportions of the four types of abuses changing over time? Test using $\alpha = .10$.

TABLE 10.32   Computer Abuse Data for Exercise 10.41

Year	Financial Fraud	Theft of Information or Property	Unauthorized Use	Vandalism	Total
1970	7	5	9	8	29
1971	22	18	6	6	52
1972	12	15	6	12	45
1973	21	15	16	9	61
Total	62	53	37	35	187

Source: Data from D. B. Parker, S. Nycum, and S. S. Oura, *Computer Abuse,* Menlo Park, Calif.: Stanford Research Institute, 1973.

We presented methods for making inferences about population means based on large random samples in Chapters 6 and 7; and we presented small-sample methods for comparing two or more population means in Chapters 8 and 9. The object of this chapter is to extend this methodology to consider the case in which the mean value of a variable y is related to another variable, call it x. By making simultaneous observations on y and the x variable, we can use information contained in the x measurements to estimate the mean value of y and to predict particular values of y for preassigned values of x. This chapter will be devoted to the case where y is a linear function of one predictor variable x. The general case, where y is related to one or more predictor variables, say $x_1, x_2, \ldots x_k$, will be discussed in Chapter 12.

11

LINEAR REGRESSION AND CORRELATION

CASE STUDY

Does It Pay to Save?

Does it pay to save? If you had or were to acquire some extra money, should you put it aside for a rainy day (just in case Social Security would no longer be with us in the future)? What is the effect of government taxation on your incentive to put your savings in the bank, a savings and loan, a money fund, real estate, or some other investment? This question is addressed by Dr. Srully Blotnick, a practicing psychologist and columnist for *Forbes* magazine (*Forbes,* May 25, 1981).

The essence of Dr. Blotnick's article is that we are inclined to save and invest if we are allowed to keep some of the rewards. However, the greater the amount of government taxation on the return (interest, dividends, capital gains, etc.) from our savings and/or investments, the less we tend to save and invest. Data suggest that if saving and investment produce low return, people spend their money on entertainment, material goods, and so forth; if they have large amounts available for investment, they place their funds in tax shelters (tax-exempt investments). Thus according to one theory, heavy taxation

decreases capital formation, which is necessary for research investment, for the modernization of industry, for the revitalization of our economy, and ultimately, for our own individual economic welfare.

To support his argument, Dr. Blotnick examines the relationship between the tax rate on *invested income*—that is, income from invested savings or the sales of investments—and the *savings rate* of a country. Suppose, for example, that you received $50,000 annual income as interest, dividends, or capital gains on investment—that is, on income from invested savings. Table 11.1 shows, for each of eight countries, the personal savings rate—that is, the percentage of total national earned income that is saved—and the approximate percentage of investment income that must be paid in taxes (the percentage investment income tax liability was based on an investment income of $49,000). Although based on the tax laws in effect prior to 1981, the data are as pertinent today as they were in 1981. If Blotnick's theory is correct, countries that show low taxation of invested income should show a

TABLE 11.1   A Comparison of Personal Savings Rate and Taxation Rates on Investment Income

Country	Personal Savings Rate (%)	Investment Income Tax Liability (%)
Italy	23.1	6.4
Japan	21.5	14.4
France	17.2	7.3
W. Germany	14.5	11.8
United Kingdom	12.2	32.5
Canada	10.3	30.0
Sweden	9.1	52.7
United States	6.3	33.5

Source: New York Stock Exchange, with the assistance of Price Waterhouse.

high percentage of savings of earned income. Conversely, if the taxation rate is high, the savings rate should be low. The data are shown in Table 11.1.

An examination of Table 11.1 motivates some comments and some questions. In preceding chapters each measurement resulted from one observation on a single experimental unit. The data shown in Table 11.1 are very different. Two observations, the savings rate y and the taxation rate x, are made on each country (the experimental unit). Note also, for the data shown, that the taxation rate of invested income for the United States is nearly the highest and the savings rate is the lowest. Is the savings rate y of a country related to the taxation rate x of invested income? Can we, knowing the taxation rate x, predict the percentage y of national income that will be saved?

Chapter 11 presents an extension of the methodology of Chapters 1 to 9. In those chapters we made a single measurement on each experimental unit, and were interested in the mean, standard deviation, and other features of the relative frequency distribution for the population of measurements. In this chapter we will take pairs of observations (x, y) on each experimental unit. We want to determine whether y and x are related and whether knowledge of the value of x will enable us to get a better estimate of the mean value of y or a better prediction of some future value of y. The techniques we develop will be applied in Section 11.10 to the savings rate/taxation rate data of this Case Study.

11.1   INTRODUCTION

In many practical situations a random variable y may be related to one or more predictor variables, say $x_1, x_2, \ldots x_k$. When this is true, we should be able to use the values of the predictor variables to more accurately estimate the mean value of y or to predict (forecast) some future value of y. For example, an automaker could estimate the weekly demand y for a new automobile, based on an independent random sample of the weekly demands for 30 weeks. We could obtain a much more accurate prediction of demand by determining the relationship between the mean weekly demand $E(y)$ and the price x_1 of the automobile, the prevailing interest rate x_2, and so on. High automobile prices and high interest rates imply lower demand; the converse implies higher demand. Therefore, if we know what the price of the automobile will be next week and we know the prevailing interest rate, we should be able to obtain a more accurate prediction of next week's demand than we could obtain from the random sample of 30 weekly demands.

Practical examples of prediction problems are numerous in business, industry, and the sciences. The stockbroker wants to predict stock market behavior as a function of a number of "key indices," which are observable and serve as the predictor variables $x_1, x_2, x_3, \ldots$. The manager of a manufacturing plant would like to relate yield of a chemical to a number of process variables. The manager would then use the prediction equation to find settings for the controllable process variables that would provide the maximum yield of the chemical. The personnel director of a corporation, like the admissions director of a university, wants to test and measure individual characteristics so that the corporation may hire the person best suited for a particular job. The biologist would like to relate body characteristics to the amounts of various glandular secretions. The political scientist may wish to relate success in a political campaign to the characteristics of a candidate, the nature of the opposition, and various campaign issues and promotional techniques. Certainly, all these prediction problems are, in many respects, one and the same.

In this chapter we will be primarily concerned with the *reasoning* involved in acquiring a prediction equation based on one or more predictor variables. Thus we will restrict our attention to the simple problem of predicting y as a *linear* function of a *single* variable and observe that the solution for the multivariable problem—for example, predicting the weekly demand for a new automobile—will consist of a generalization of our technique. We will show you how to fit a simple linear model to a set of data, a process called a **regression analysis**, and we will show you how to use the model for estimation and prediction. The methodology for finding the multivariable predictor, called a multiple regression analysis, will be discussed in Chapter 12.

11.2   A SIMPLE LINEAR PROBABILISTIC MODEL

We will introduce our topic by considering the problem of predicting the success rating that a management trainee will receive after five years of company employment; this prediction is based on the trainee's rating at the end of a training course. The success rating y is the average of the subjective ratings of five managers, scored from 0 (bad) to 100 (good). The trainee's rating x is the score (0 to 100) acquired on a combination achievement and personality test given at the end of a management training course. The company would like to use the management trainee's score x to predict management success rating y as a tool for eliminating poor management prospects from among their management trainees.

Ten managers currently in the company for a period of five years were randomly selected. Their success ratings and management trainee scores are shown in Table 11.2. Our initial approach to analyzing these data is to plot the data as points on a graph, representing the manager success rating as y and the corresponding trainee test score as x. The graph is shown in Figure 11.1. You can see that y appears to increase as x increases. Do you think this arrangement of the points could have occurred due to chance even if x and y were unrelated?

TABLE 11.2   Management Success Ratings and Trainee Scores for Ten Company Managers

Manager	Management Trainee Score, x	Management Success Rating, y
1	39	65
2	43	78
3	21	52
4	64	82
5	57	92
6	47	89
7	28	73
8	75	98
9	34	56
10	52	75

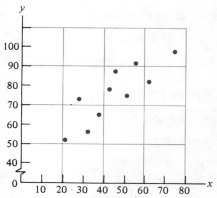

FIGURE 11.1   Plot of the Data in Table 11.2

One method of obtaining a prediction equation relating y to x is to place a ruler on the graph and move it about until it seems to pass through the points and provide what we might regard as the "best fit" to the data. Indeed, if we were to draw a line through the points, it would appear that our prediction problem were solved. We can now use the graph to predict a manager's success rating as a function of the management trainee score. In doing so, we have chosen a **mathematical model** that expresses the supposed functional relation between y and x.

You should recall several facts concerning the graphing of mathematical functions. First, the mathematical **equation of a straight line** is

$$y = \beta_0 + \beta_1 x$$

where β_0 is the y **intercept of the line**, the value of y when $x = 0$, and β_1 is the **slope of the line**, the change in y for a one-unit change in x (see Figure 11.2.) Second, the line that we may graph corresponding to any linear equation is unique. Each equation will correspond to only one line and vice versa. Thus when we draw a line through the

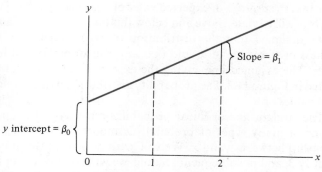

FIGURE 11.2   The y Intercept and Slope for a Line

points, we have automatically chosen a mathematical equation

$$y = \beta_0 + \beta_1 x$$

where β_0 and β_1 have unique numerical values. See the following box.

EQUATION OF A STRAIGHT LINE

$$y = \beta_0 + \beta_1 x$$

$\beta_0 = y$ intercept

= value of y when $x = 0$

β_1 = slope of the line

= change in y for a one-unit increase in x

The linear model

$$y = \beta_0 + \beta_1 x$$

is said to be a **deterministic mathematical model**, because when a value of x is substituted into the equation, the value of y is determined and no allowance is made for error. Deterministic models are suitable for prediction only when the errors of prediction are small. When they are large, which is generally the case in business forecasting, we need to take the error of prediction into account and, particularly, to give some indication of its magnitude. We do so by constructing a **probabilistic mathematical model**, one that contains one or more random components that are added to the deterministic portion of the model to account for the random and unexplained error of prediction. Thus a probabilistic model relating success rating y to management trainee score x is given by the expression

$$y = \beta_0 + \beta_1 x + \varepsilon$$

where ε is assumed to be a random error variable with expected value equal to zero and variance equal to σ^2. In addition, we will assume that any pair of random errors ε_i and ε_j corresponding to two observations y_i and y_j are independent. In other words, we assume that the *average* or expected value of y is linearly related to x and that observed values of y will deviate above and below this line by a random amount ε. Furthermore, we have assumed that the distribution of errors about the line will be identical, regardless of the value of x, and that any pair of errors will be independent of one another. The assumed line, giving the expected value of y for a given value of x, is indicated in Figure 11.3. The probability distribution of the random error ε is shown for several values of x.

The straight-line or linear probabilistic model—the topic of this chapter—is only one of many types of probabilistic models that could be used to express the relationship between y and x. We will learn how to fit this model to a set of data in Section 11.3, and in subsequent sections we will see how it can be used for estimation and prediction. The procedure for choosing and fitting more complicated models is the topic of Chapter 12.

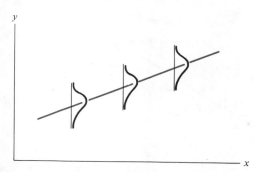

FIGURE 11.3   Linear Probabilistic Model

EXERCISES

BASIC TECHNIQUES

11.1 Graph the line corresponding to the equation $y = 2x + 1$ by graphing the points corresponding to $x = 0, 1$, and 2. Give the y intercept and slope for the line.

11.2 Graph the line corresponding to the equation $y = -2x + 1$ by graphing the points corresponding to $x = 0, 1$, and 2. Give the y intercept and slope for the line. Give the similarities and differences between this line and the line of Exercise 11.1.

11.3 Graph the line corresponding to the equation $2y = -3x + 4$.

11.4 How is the line $2y = 3x + 4$ related to the line of Exercise 11.3?

11.5 Give the equation and graph for a line with a y intercept equal to 3 and a slope equal to -1.

11.6 Give the equation and graph for a line with a y intercept equal to -3 and a slope equal to 1.

11.7 What is the difference between deterministic and probabilistic mathematical models?

11.3 THE METHOD OF LEAST SQUARES

The statistical procedure for finding the "best-fitting" straight line for a set of points would seem, in many respects, a formalization of the procedure used to fit a line by eye. For instance, when we visually fit a line to a set of data, we move the ruler until we think that we have minimized the deviations of the points from the prospective line. If we denote the predicted value of y obtained from the fitted line as $\hat{y}$, the prediction equation is

$$\hat{y} = \hat{\beta}_0 + \hat{\beta}_1 x$$

where $\hat{\beta}_0$ and $\hat{\beta}_1$ represent estimates of the parameters β_0 and β_1. This line for the data of Table 11.2 is shown in Figure 11.4. The vertical lines drawn from the prediction line to each point represent the deviations of the points from the predicted value of y. Thus the **deviation** of the ith point is

$$y_i - \hat{y}_i, \qquad \text{where} \qquad \hat{y}_i = \hat{\beta}_0 + \hat{\beta}_1 x_i$$

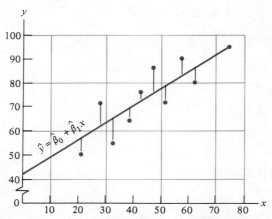

FIGURE 11.4   Linear Prediction Equation for the Data in Table 11.2

Having decided that in some manner or other we will attempt to minimize the deviations of the points in choosing the best-fitting line, we must now define what we mean by "best." That is, we want to define a criterion for "best fit" that will seem intuitively reasonable, that is obective, and that under certain conditions will give the best prediction of y for a given value of x.

We will use a criterion of goodness that is known as the **principle of least squares** and which may be stated as follows: **Choose as the best-fitting line the line that minimizes the sum of squares of the deviations of the observed values of** y **from those predicted.*** Expressed mathematically, we want to choose values for $\hat{\beta}_0$ and $\hat{\beta}_1$ that minimize

$$SSE = \sum_{i=1}^{n} (y_i - \hat{y}_i)^2$$

The symbol SSE represents the sum of squares of deviations or, as commonly called, the sum of squares for error.

Substituting for $\hat{y}_i$ in SSE, we obtain

$$SSE = \sum_{i=1}^{n} [y_i - (\hat{\beta}_0 + \hat{\beta}_1 x_i)]^2$$

The method for finding the numerical values of $\hat{\beta}_0$ and $\hat{\beta}_1$ that minimize SSE uses the differential calculus and therefore is beyond the scope of this text. We simply state that the least-squares solutions for $\hat{\beta}_0$ and $\hat{\beta}_1$ are given by the formulas shown in the following box.

---

*The deviations of the points about the least-squares line satisfy another property. The sum of the deviations will always equal 0, that is, $\sum_{i=1}^{n} (y_i - \hat{y}_i) = 0$ (proof omitted). Many other lines can be found that satisfy this property.

LEAST-SQUARES ESTIMATORS OF β_0 AND β_1

where

$$\hat{\beta}_1 = \frac{SS_{xy}}{SS_x} \quad \text{and} \quad \hat{\beta}_0 = \bar{y} - \hat{\beta}_1 \bar{x}$$

and

$$SS_x = \sum_{i=1}^{n} (x_i - \bar{x})^2 = \sum_{i=1}^{n} x_i^2 - \frac{\left(\sum_{i=1}^{n} x_i\right)^2}{n}$$

$$SS_{xy} = \sum_{i=1}^{n} (x_i - \bar{x})(y_i - \bar{y}) = \sum_{i=1}^{n} x_i y_i - \frac{\left(\sum_{i=1}^{n} x_i\right)\left(\sum_{i=1}^{n} y_i\right)}{n}$$

Note that SS_x (sum of squares for x) is computed by using the familiar shortcut formula for calculating sums of squares of deviations that was presented in Chapter 2. The sum of squares SS_{xy} is computed by using a very similar formula and therefore should be easy to remember. Once $\hat{\beta}_0$ and $\hat{\beta}_1$ have been computed, substitute their values into the equation of a line to obtain the **least-squares prediction line,**

$$\hat{y} = \hat{\beta}_0 + \hat{\beta}_1 x$$

There is one important point to note here. Rounding errors can greatly affect the answer you obtain in calculating SS_x and SS_{xy}. If you must round a number, it is recommended that you carry six or more significant figures in the calculations. (Note also that in the exercises rounding errors might cause some slight discrepancies between your answers and the answers given in the back of the text.)

EXAMPLE 11.1   Obtain the least-squares prediction line for the data of Table 11.2.

SOLUTION   The calculation of $\hat{\beta}_0$ and $\hat{\beta}_1$ for the data of Table 11.2 is simplified by the use of Table 11.3.

Substituting the appropriate sums from Table 11.3 into the least-squares equations, we obtain

$$SS_x = \sum_{i=1}^{n} x_i^2 - \frac{\left(\sum_{i=1}^{n} x_i\right)^2}{n} = 23{,}634 - \frac{(460)^2}{10} = 2474$$

$$SS_{xy} = \sum_{i=1}^{n} x_i y_i - \frac{\left(\sum_{i=1}^{n} x_i\right)\left(\sum_{i=1}^{n} y_i\right)}{n} = 36{,}854 - \frac{(460)(760)}{10} = 1894$$

$$\bar{y} = \frac{\sum_{i=1}^{n} y_i}{n} = \frac{760}{10} = 76 \quad \text{and} \quad \bar{x} = \frac{\sum_{i=1}^{n} x_i}{n} = \frac{460}{10} = 46$$

TABLE 11.3 Calculations for the Data in Table 11.2 for Example 11.2

	y_i	x_i	x_i^2	$x_i y_i$	y_i^2
	65	39	1,521	2,535	4,225
	78	43	1,849	3,354	6,084
	52	21	441	1,092	2,704
	82	64	4,096	5,248	6,724
	92	57	3,249	5,244	8,464
	89	47	2,209	4,183	7,921
	73	28	784	2,044	5,329
	98	75	5,625	7,350	9,604
	56	34	1,156	1,904	3,136
	75	52	2,704	3,900	5,625
Sum	760	460	23,634	36,854	59,816

Therefore,

$$\hat{\beta}_1 = \frac{SS_{xy}}{SS_x} = \frac{1894}{2474} = .7655618 \approx .77$$

and

$$\hat{\beta}_0 = \bar{y} - \hat{\beta}_1 \bar{x} = 76 - (.7655618)(46) = 40.78416 \approx 40.78$$

Then according to the principle of least squares, the best-fitting straight line relating the manager success rating to trainee test score is

$$\hat{y} = \hat{\beta}_0 + \hat{\beta}_1 x$$

or

$$\hat{y} = 40.78 + .77x$$

The graph of this equation is shown in Figure 11.4. Note that the y intercept, 40.78, is the value of $\hat{y}$ when $x = 0$. The slope of the line, .77, gives the estimated change in y for a one-unit increase in x.

We can now predict y for a given value of x by referring to Figure 11.4 or by substituting into the prediction equation. For example, if a management trainee scored $x = 50$ on the trainee test, the trainee's predicted management rating would be

$$\hat{y} = \hat{\beta}_0 + \hat{\beta}_1 x = 40.78 + (.77)(50) = 79.28$$

How accurate will this prediction be? To answer this question, we will want to place a bound on our error of prediction. We will consider this and related problems in subsequent sections. ∎

TIPS ON PROBLEM SOLVING

(1) Be careful of rounding errors. Carry at least six significant figures in computing sums of squares of deviations or the sums of cross products of deviations.

(2) Always plot the data points and graph your least-squares line. If the line does not provide a reasonable fit to the data points, you may have committed an error in your calculations.

EXERCISES

BASIC TECHNIQUES

11.8 Given five points whose coordinates are shown in the following table:

x	-2	-1	0	1	2
y	1	1	3	5	5

(a) Find the least-squares line for the data.

(b) As a rough check on the calculations in part (a), plot the five points and graph the line. Does the line appear to provide a good fit to the data points?

11.9 Given six points whose coordinates are shown in the following table:

x	-5	-3	-1	1	3	5
y	-2	-1	1	2	2	3

(a) Find the least-squares line for the data.

(b) As a rough check on the calculations in part (a), plot the six points and graph the line. Does the line appear to provide a good fit to the data points?

11.10 Given the points whose coordinates are shown in the following table:

x	1	2	3	4	5	6
y	5.6	4.6	4.5	3.7	3.2	2.7

(a) Find the least-squares line for the data.

(b) As a rough check on the calculations in part (a), plot the six points and graph the line. Does the line appear to provide a good fit to the data points?

APPLICATIONS

11.11 A manufacturer of soap powder conducted an experiment to investigate the effect of price per box on demand. Each of six different sales regions was assigned a wholesale unit price per box for sale to wholesalers or large supermarket chains in the region. After a one-month period the percentage y of increase (or decrease) over the preceding month in unit sales per region was calculated. The unit prices assigned to the regions and the percentage increases in sales are shown in the following table.

Unit Price, x ($)	6.40	6.45	6.50	6.55	6.60	6.65
Increase in Sales, y (%)	9.8	7.6	6.3	4.5	4.2	1.7

(a) Plot the data points on graph paper.
(b) Find the least-squares line for the data.
(c) Graph the least-squares line to see how well it fits the data.
(d) Use the least-squares line to estimate the mean change in unit sales for a unit price of $6.60 per unit.
[To simplify your calculations, let $x = $ (unit price $- 6.40$)/.05.]

11.12 The number of salespersons employed by an auto dealership has varied from a low of four salespersons to a high of eight. How does the number y of new cars sold depend on the number x of salespersons? To shed some light on this question, the sales manager examined sales records for the past four months and located eight weeks during which no special incentive programs were employed. The number y of cars sold per week and the number x of salespersons employed are shown in Table 11.4.

TABLE 11.4   Salespersons and Car Sales Data for Exercise 11.12

Variables	Week							
	1	2	3	4	5	6	7	8
Salespersons, x	5	6	5	4	7	6	5	8
Cars sold, y	10	20	18	10	21	15	13	22

(a) Plot the data points on graph paper.
(b) Find the least-squares line for the data.
(c) Graph the least-squares line to see how well it fits the data.
(d) Use the least-squares line to estimate the mean number of cars sold per week if the dealer employs six salespersons.

11.13 In a study of the relationship between strike activity and productivity growth, Dennis R. Maki collected data on productivity and man-days lost per employee due to strikes for 20 OECD (Organization for Economic Cooperation and Development) countries during the period 1967–1975. A plot of the data is shown in Figure 11.5. The coordinates (x, y) for a point give Maki's calculated rate y of productivity growth for a particular country and the corresponding calculated man-days lost due to strikes per employee. For example, Japan had the highest rate of productivity growth, $y \approx .029$ with $x \approx .15$ man-day lost per employee. The least-squares regression line is shown on the graph in Figure 11.5.

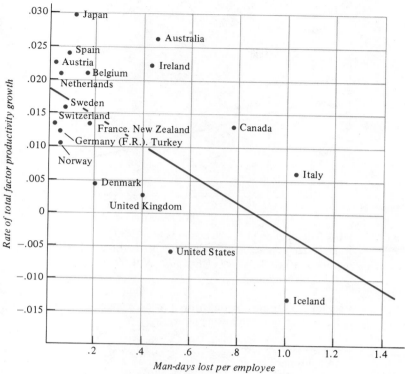

FIGURE 11.5   Productivity and Man-days Lost Data for Exercise 11.13 (*Source:* D. R. Maki, "Strike Activity and Productivity Growth: Evidence from Twenty Countries," *Columbia Journal of World Business,* Summer 1983.)

(a) If the equation of the regression line is $\hat{y} = \hat{\beta}_0 + \hat{\beta}_1 x$, examine the graph and find the approximate value of $\hat{\beta}_0$.

(b) Examine the graph and find the approximate value of $\hat{\beta}_1$.

(c) Use the values of $\hat{\beta}_0$ and $\hat{\beta}_1$ found in parts (a) and (b) to find the equation of the regression line.

11.14   Refer to Exercise 11.13. Examine the graph and determine the approximate coordinates of the 20 plotted points.

(a) Fit a least-squares line to your data.

(b) Compare your least-squares equation in part (a) with your answer obtained in part (c) of Exercise 11.13.

(c) Using the exact values of x and y obtained from his calculations, Maki gives the equation of the least-squares line as $\hat{y} = .019 - .018x$. Compare your answer in part (a) with Maki's equation.

11.15   An article by Curhan, Salmon, and Buzzell describes a study of supermarket sales and profitability for two types of supermarket firms, those whose stores are supplied by service merchandisers (job rackers) and those that warehoused and serviced the individual stores themselves (direct buyers). The graph in Figure 11.6 gives a plot of the health and beauty aids (HBA) sales y per linear foot of shelf space versus the number x of linear feet of shelf space per store for the 15 supermarket firms. The values of sales y per linear foot and HBA linear feet x per

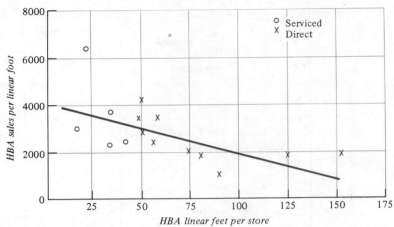

FIGURE 11.6   HBA Sales and Shelf Space Data for Exercise 11.15 (*Source:* R. C. Curhan, W. J. Salmon, and R. D. Buzzell, "Sales and Profitability of Health and Beauty Aids and General Merchandise in Supermarkets," *Journal of Retailing*, Vol. 59, No. 1, 1983.)

store for the 10 direct-buying firms have been approximated from the plotted points in the graph and are given in the following table:

HBA Sales per Linear Foot (in $100)	41	35	35	23	27	20	18	9	18	19
HBA Linear Feet per Store	48	47	58	55	48	72	80	90	124	152

(a) Think about a linear relationship between HBA sales y per linear foot and the linear feet x assigned to HBA products per store. If the principle of diminishing returns is applicable, would you expect the slope of the line to be positive or negative?

(b) Fit a least-squares line to the data.

(c) From your least-squares line, how much (in dollars) would you expect the mean $E(y)$ HBA sales per linear foot to increase or decrease for each one-foot increase in HBA linear feet x per store?

CALCULATING S^2, AN ESTIMATOR OF σ^2

11.4

Recall that we constructed a probabilistic model for y in Section 11.2,

$$y = \beta_0 + \beta_1 x + \varepsilon$$

where ε is a random error with mean value equal to 0 and variance equal to σ^2. Thus each observed value of y is subject to a random error ε, which will enter into the computations of $\hat{\beta}_0$ and $\hat{\beta}_1$ and will introduce errors in these estimates. Furthermore, if we use the least-squares line

$$\hat{y} = \hat{\beta}_0 + \hat{\beta}_1 x$$

to predict some future value of y, the random errors will affect the error of prediction. Consequently, the variability of the random errors, measured by σ^2, plays an important role when estimating or predicting using the least-squares line.

The first step toward acquiring a bound on a prediction error requires that we estimate σ^2, the variance of the random error ε. For this purpose it would seem reasonable to use SSE, the sum of squares of deviations (sum of squares for error) about the predicted line. Indeed, it can be shown that

$$\hat{\sigma}^2 = s^2 = \frac{\text{SSE}}{n-2}$$

provides a good estimator for σ^2, one that is unbiased and based on $(n-2)$ degrees of freedom. See the box.

ESTIMATOR OF σ^2

$$\hat{\sigma}^2 = s^2 = \frac{\text{SSE}}{n-2}$$

where

$$n = \text{number of data points}$$

$$\text{SSE} = \sum_{i=1}^{n}(y_i - \hat{y}_i)^2$$

The sum of squares of deviations, SSE, can be calculated directly by using the prediction equation to calculate $\hat{y}$ for each point, then calculating the deviations $(y_i - \hat{y}_i)$, and finally calculating

$$\text{SSE} = \sum_{i=1}^{n}(y_i - \hat{y}_i)^2$$

This procedure tends to be very tedious and is rather poor from a computational point of view because the numerous subtractions tend to introduce computational rounding errors. An easier and computationally better procedure is to use the formula given in the next box.

EXAMPLE 11.2

Calculate an estimate of σ^2 for the data of Table 11.2.

SOLUTION

SS_{xy} and $\hat{\beta}_1$ were computed in Example 11.1. There we found $\text{SS}_{xy} = 1894$ and $\hat{\beta}_1 = .7655618$. To find SS_y, we need the values of $\sum_{i=1}^{n} y_i$ and $\sum_{i=1}^{n} y_i^2$ given in Table 11.3. Substituting these values into the formula for SS_y, we have

$$\text{SS}_y = \sum_{i=1}^{n} y_i^2 - \frac{\left(\sum_{i=1}^{n} y_i\right)^2}{n} = 59,816 - \frac{(760)^2}{10} = 2056$$

METHOD FOR COMPUTING SSE

$$SSE = SS_y - \hat{\beta}_1 SS_{xy}$$

where

$$SS_y = \sum_{i=1}^{n} (y_i - \bar{y})^2 = \sum_{i=1}^{n} y_i^2 - \frac{\left(\sum_{i=1}^{n} y_i\right)^2}{n}$$

and

$$SS_{xy} = \sum_{i=1}^{n} x_i y_i - \frac{\left(\sum_{i=1}^{n} x_i\right)\left(\sum_{i=1}^{n} y_i\right)}{n}$$

(Note that SS_{xy} was used in the calculation of $\hat{\beta}_1$ and therefore has already been computed.)

Then

$$\begin{aligned}
SSE &= SS_y - \hat{\beta}_1 SS_{xy} \\
&= 2056 - (.7655618)(1894) \\
&= 606.03
\end{aligned}$$

Then since the number of data points is $n = 10$,

$$s^2 = \frac{SSE}{n - 2} = \frac{606.03}{8} = 75.754$$

      How can you interpret these values of SSE and s^2? Refer to Figure 11.4 and note the deviations of the $n = 10$ points from the least-squares line (shown as the vertical line segments between the points and the line). The quantity SSE = 606.03 is equal to the sum of squares of the numerical values of these deviations. This quantity is then used to calculate $s^2 = 75.754$ and $s = \sqrt{75.754} = 8.70$, estimates of σ^2 and σ.

      The practical interpretation that can be given to s ultimately rests on the meaning of σ. Since σ measures the spread of the y values about the line of means, $E(y) = \beta_0 + \beta_1 x$ (see Figure 11.3), we would expect (from the Empirical Rule) approximately 95% of the y values to fall within 2σ of that line. Since we do not know σ, $2s$ provides an approximate value for the half width of this interval. Now refer to Figure 11.4 and note the location of the data points about the least-squares line. Since we used the $n = 10$ data points to fit the least-squares line, you will not be too surprised to find that most of the points fall within $2s = 2(8.7) = 17.40$ of the line. If you check Figure 11.4, you will see that all 10 points fall within $2s$ of the least-squares line. **You will find that, in general, most of the data points used to fit the least-squares line will fall within $2s$ of the line. This provides you with a rough check for your calculated value of s.**

But s will play a much more important role in this chapter than the application described. As mentioned at the beginning of this section, the less the variability of the y values about the line of means (i.e., the smaller the value of σ), the closer the least-squares line will be to the line of means. Consequently, s will play an important role in evaluating the goodness of all of the inferential methods described in this chapter.

TIPS ON PROBLEM SOLVING

(1) To reduce rounding error, always carry at least six significant figures when calculating SS_y and SSE. You can round when you obtain the answer for SSE if you desire.

(2) As a check on your calculated value of s, remember that s measures the spread of the points about the least-squares line. Therefore, you would expect (by the Empirical Rule) most of the points to fall within $2s$ of the least-squares line. For example, if the points appear to fall in a band roughly equal to 4 units in width on the scale of the y variable and if your calculated value of s is 10, your value of s is too large. You have made an error. Perhaps you forgot to divide SSE by $(n - 2)$.

EXERCISES

BASIC TECHNIQUES

11.16 Calculate SSE and s^2 for the data in Exercise 11.8.

11.17 Calculate SSE and s^2 for the data in Exercise 11.9.

11.18 Calculate SSE and s^2 for the data in Exercise 11.10.

11.19 Calculate SSE and s^2 for the data in Exercise 11.11.

11.20 Calculate SSE and s^2 for the data in Exercise 11.12.

11.21 Calculate SSE and s^2 for the data in Exercise 11.14.

11.22 Calculate SSE and s^2 for the data in Exercise 11.15.

11.5 INFERENCES CONCERNING THE SLOPE OF THE LINE, β_1

The initial inference desired in studying the relationship between y and x concerns the existence of the relationship. Does x contribute information for the prediction of y? That is, do the data present sufficient evidence to indicate that y increases (or decreases) linearly as x increases over the region of observation? Or is it possible that the points fall on the graph in a manner similar to that observed in Figure 11.1 when y and x are completely unrelated?

The practical question we pose concerns the value of β_1, which is the average change in y for a one-unit increase in x. Stating that y does not increase (or decrease) linearly as x increases is equivalent to saying that $\beta_1 = 0$. Thus we want to test an hypothesis that $\beta_1 = 0$ against the alternative that $\beta_1 \neq 0$. As we might suspect, the estimator $\hat{\beta}_1$ is extremely useful in constructing a test statistic to test this hypothesis. Therefore, we want to examine the distribution of estimates $\hat{\beta}_1$ that would be obtained when samples, each containing n points, were repeatedly drawn from the population of interest. If we assume that the random error ε is normally distributed, in addition to the previously stated assumptions, it can be shown that the sampling distribution of $\hat{\beta}_1$ will be normally distributed and that the expected value and variance of $\hat{\beta}_1$ will be

$$E(\hat{\beta}_1) = \beta_1 \qquad \sigma_{\hat{\beta}_1}^2 = \frac{\sigma^2}{SS_x}$$

Thus $\hat{\beta}_1$ is an unbiased estimator of β_1, we know its standard deviation, and therefore we can construct a z statistic in the manner described in Section 7.3. Then

$$z = \frac{\hat{\beta}_1 - \beta_1}{\sigma_{\hat{\beta}_1}} = \frac{\hat{\beta}_1 - \beta_1}{\sigma/\sqrt{SS_x}}$$

will possess a standardized normal sampling distribution. Since the actual value of σ^2 is unknown, we wish to obtain the estimated standard deviation of $\hat{\beta}_1$, which is $s/\sqrt{SS_x}$. Substituting s for σ in the formula for z, we obtain, as in Chapter 8, a test statistic

$$t = \frac{\hat{\beta}_1 - \beta_1}{s/\sqrt{SS_x}} = \frac{\hat{\beta}_1 - \beta_1}{s}\sqrt{SS_x}$$

which can be shown to possess a Student's t distribution with $(n-2)$ degrees of freedom. **Note that the number of degrees of freedom associated with s^2 determines the number of degrees of freedom associated with t.** Thus the test of an hypothesis that β_1 equals some particular numerical value, say $\beta_{1,0}$, is the familiar t test encountered in Chapter 8. The test procedure is given in the box.

EXAMPLE 11.3

Use the data of Table 11.2 to determine whether a linear relationship exists between a management trainee's test score x and his or her five-year manager success rating y.

SOLUTION

We want to test the null hypothesis

$$H_0 : \beta_1 = 0 \qquad \text{against} \qquad H_a : \beta_1 \neq 0$$

for the manager rating/trainee test score data in Table 11.2. The test statistic is

$$t = \frac{\hat{\beta}_1 - 0}{s}\sqrt{SS_x}$$

and if we choose $\alpha = .05$, we will reject H_0 when $t > 2.306$ or $t < -2.306$. The critical value of t is obtained from the t table, using $(n-2) = 8$ degrees of freedom. Substituting into the test statistic, we obtain

$$t = \frac{\hat{\beta}_1}{s}\sqrt{SS_x} = \frac{.7655618}{8.70}\sqrt{2474}$$

or

$$t = 4.38$$

TEST OF AN HYPOTHESIS CONCERNING THE SLOPE OF A LINE

(1) *Null Hypothesis:* $H_0 : \beta_1 = \beta_{1,0}$.

(2) *Alternative Hypothesis:*

One-Tailed Test

$H_a : \beta_1 > \beta_{1,0}$
(or $\beta_1 < \beta_{1,0}$)

Two-Tailed Test

$H_a : \beta_1 \neq \beta_{1,0}$

(3) *Test Statistic:* $t = \dfrac{\hat{\beta}_1 - \beta_{1,0}}{s} \sqrt{SS_x}$, where

$$SS_x = \sum_{i=1}^{n} (x_i - \bar{x})^2 = \sum_{i=1}^{n} x_i^2 - \frac{\left(\sum_{i=1}^{n} x_i \right)^2}{n}$$

When the assumptions noted below are satisfied, the test statistic will possess a Student's t distribution with $(n - 2)$ degrees of freedom.

(4) *Rejection Region:*

One-Tailed Test

$t > t_\alpha$
(or $t < -t_\alpha$ when the
alternative hypothesis is
$H_a : \beta_1 < \beta_{1,0}$)

Two-Tailed Test

$t > t_{\alpha/2}$
or $t < -t_{\alpha/2}$

Values of t_α and $t_{\alpha/2}$ are given in Table 5 of the Appendix. Use the values of t corresponding to $(n - 2)$ degrees of freedom.

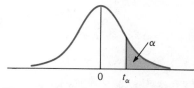
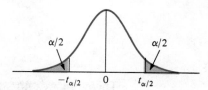

Assumptions: The assumptions are those associated with the linear probabilistic model of Section 11.2. They are summarized and discussed in Section 11.9.

Observing that the test statistic exceeds the critical value of t, we will reject the null hypothesis $\beta_1 = 0$ and conclude that β_1 differs from 0; that is, that there is evidence to indicate that the trainee test score x contributes information for the prediction of the manager success rating y. ■

Once we have decided that x contributes information for the prediction of y, we will be interested in examining the linear relationship in detail. If x increases by one unit, what is the predicted change in y, and how much confidence can be placed in the estimate? In other words, we require an estimate of the slope β_1. You will not be surprised to observe a continuity in the procedures of Chapters 8 and 11. That is, the confidence interval for β_1, with confidence coefficient $(1 - \alpha)$, can be shown to be

$$\hat{\beta}_1 \pm t_{\alpha/2}(\text{estimated } \sigma_{\hat{\beta}_1})$$

The formula is given in the box.

A $(1 - \alpha)100\%$ CONFIDENCE INTERVAL FOR β_1

$$\hat{\beta}_1 \pm \frac{t_{\alpha/2} s}{\sqrt{\text{SS}_x}}$$

where $t_{\alpha/2}$ is based on $(n - 2)$ degrees of freedom and

$$\text{SS}_x = \sum_{i=1}^{n} (x_i - \bar{x})^2 = \sum_{i=1}^{n} x_i^2 - \frac{\left(\sum_{i=1}^{n} x_i\right)^2}{n}$$

EXAMPLE 11.4   Find a 95% confidence interval for β_1 based on the data of Table 11.2.

SOLUTION   The 95% confidence interval for β_1, based on the data of Table 11.2, is

$$\hat{\beta}_1 \pm \frac{t_{.025} s}{\sqrt{\text{SS}_x}}$$

Substituting, we obtain

$$.77 \pm \frac{(2.306)(8.70)}{\sqrt{2474}}$$

or

$$.77 \pm .40$$

Therefore, we estimate the mean increase in the management success rating score for a one-unit increase in trainee score to be contained in the interval .37 to 1.17.   ∎

Several points concerning the interpretation of our results deserve particular attention. As we have noted, β_1 is the slope of the assumed line over the region of observation and indicates the *linear* change in y for a one-unit increase in x. Even though we do not reject the null hypothesis $\beta_1 = 0$, x and y may be related. In the first place, we must be concerned with the probability of committing a type II error—that is, accepting the null hypothesis that the slope β_1 equals 0 when this hypothesis is false. Second, it is possible that x and y might be *perfectly* related in a curvilinear but not in a linear manner. For example, Figure 11.7 depicts a curvilinear relationship between y and x over the domain of x, $a \leq x \leq f$. Note that a straight line would provide a good predictor of y if fitted over a small interval in the x domain, say $b \leq x \leq c$. The resulting line would be line 1. On the other hand, if we attempt to fit a line over the

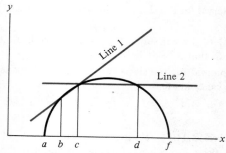

FIGURE 11.7   Curvilinear Relation

region $c \leq x \leq d$, β_1 will equal zero and the best fit to the data will be the horizontal line 2. This would occur even though *all* the points fell perfectly on the curve. Thus we must take care in drawing conclusions if we do not find evidence to indicate that β_1 differs from zero. Perhaps we have chosen the wrong type of probabilistic model for the physical situation.

Note that these comments contain a second implication. If the data provide values of x in an interval $b \leq x \leq c$, then the calculated prediction equation is appropriate only over this region. You can see that extrapolation in predicting y for values of x outside the region $b \leq x \leq c$ for the situation indicated in Figure 11.7 would result in a serious prediction error.

Finally, if the data present sufficient evidence to indicate that β_1 differs from zero, we do not conclude that the true relationship between y and x is linear. Undoubtedly, y is a function of a number of variables that demonstrate their existence to a greater or lesser degree in terms of the random error ε that appears in the model. This, of course, is why we have been obliged to use a probabilistic model in the first place. Large errors of prediction imply either curvatures in the true relation between y and x, the presence of other important variables that do not appear in the model, or, as most often is the case, both. All we can say is that we have evidence to indicate that y changes as x changes and that we may obtain a better prediction of y using x and the linear predictor than simply using $\bar{y}$ and ignoring x. Note that this *does not* imply a *causal* relationship between x and y. A third variable may have caused the change in both x and y, producing the relationship that we have observed.

EXERCISES

BASIC TECHNIQUES

11.23 Do the data in Exercise 11.8 present sufficient evidence to indicate that y and x are linearly related? (Test the hypothesis that $\beta_1 = 0$; use $\alpha = .05$.)

11.24 Find a 90% confidence interval for the slope of the line in Exercise 11.8. Interpret this interval estimate.

11.25 Do the data in Exercise 11.9 present sufficient evidence to indicate that y and x are linearly related? (Test the hypothesis that $\beta_1 = 0$; use $\alpha = .05$.)

11.26 Find a 95% confidence interval for the slope of the line in Exercise 11.9. Interpret this interval estimate.

11.27 Do the data in Exercise 11.10 present sufficient evidence to indicate that y and x are linearly related? (Test the hypothesis that $\beta_1 = 0$; use $\alpha = .05$.)

11.28 Find a 90% confidence interval for the slope of the line in Exercise 11.10. Give a practical interpretation to this interval estimate.

APPLICATIONS

11.29 Refer to the data in Exercise 11.11 relating the percentage y of increase in sales to a manufacturer's wholesale price for a box of soap powder. Do the data provide sufficient information to indicate that the coded price per unit (over the range employed in this study) contributes information for the prediction of the percentage increase in sales? Test using $\alpha = .05$.

11.30 Refer to Exercise 11.29. Find a 90% confidence interval for the mean percentage change in sales for a 5¢ increase in the wholesale price. Interpret the interval.

11.31 Refer to the data in Exercise 11.12 relating the number y of new cars sold per week by an automobile dealer to the number x of salespersons employed. Do the data provide sufficient information to indicate that the number of salespersons contributes information for the prediction of the number of cars sold per week? Test using $\alpha = .05$.

11.32 Refer to Exercise 11.31. Find a 90% confidence interval for the increase (or decrease) in the mean number of cars sold per week for an increase of one salesperson. Interpret the interval.

11.33 Refer to the Maki study of the relationship between rate y of productivity growth and number x of man-days lost due to strikes in Exercises 11.13 and 11.14 (D. R. Maki, "Strike Activity and Productivity Growth: Evidence from Twenty Countries," *Columbia Journal of World Business*, Summer 1983). Does the number x of man-days lost contribute information for the prediction of the rate y of productivity growth? Test using $\alpha = .05$.

11.34 Refer to the data in Exercise 11.15 relating the sales y per linear foot of shelf space to the number x of linear feet of shelf space per store. Do the data provide sufficient evidence to indicate that x contributes information for the prediction of y? Test using $\alpha = .05$.

11.35 Refer to Exercise 11.34. Find a 95% confidence interval for the mean change in sales y per linear foot of shelf space for a one linear foot increase in shelf space.

 11.36 Consider the following management problem. Do football coaches get better with age? If Coach Bear Bryant, the legendary football coach for the University of Alabama, is typical of other football coaches, universities may wish to hire old coaches for their teams. In his thirties Coach Bryant had 59 wins, 23 losses, and 5 ties. In his forties his record improved to 73 wins, 24 losses, and 8 ties. In his fifties it was 88–22–3; and in his sixties it was 95–12–1. The percentage wins in a given ten-year age interval and the midpoint x of a ten-year age interval are given in the table for Coach Bryant.

Midpoint Age Interval	35	45	55	65
Percentage Wins	67.8	69.5	77.9	88.0

Source: Data from *Sports Illustrated*, Vol. 57, No. 11, 1982.

(a) Find the least-squares line for the data.

(b) Plot the data points and graph the least-squares line.

(c) Calculate s^2 for the simple linear regression analysis.

11.37 The win-loss record for Coach Bryant given in Exercise 11.36 is just a sample of what he could have done had he coached and played more games over his long career in coaching. Do the data provide sufficient evidence to indicate that Coach Bryant's probability of winning increased with his age? Test using $\alpha = .05$.

11.38 Our test in Exercise 11.37 is based on the assumption that the variance of the random error ε is constant and equal to σ^2 for all values of x.

(a) Explain why this assumption is not satisfied for the data of Exercise 11.36. (*Hint:* In Section 6.5 we learned that $\sigma_{\hat{p}}^2 = pq/n$.)

(b) Consider an alternative method of answering the question in Exercise 11.37. Use the data in Exercise 11.36 and the method of Section 8.7 to show that Coach Bryant's probability p_1 of winning in his sixties exceeds the probability p_2 of winning in his thirties.

MKTG 11.39 A marketing research experiment was conducted to study the relationship between the length of time necessary for a buyer to reach a decision and the number of alternative package designs of a product presented. Brand names were eliminated from the packages to reduce the effects of brand preferences. The buyers made their selections by using the manufacturer's product descriptions on the packages as the only buying guide. The length of time necessary to reach a decision is recorded for 15 participants in the marketing research study.

Length of Decision Time, y (seconds)	5, 8, 8, 7, 9	7, 9, 8, 9, 10	10, 11, 10, 12, 9
Number of Alternatives, x	2	3	4

(a) Find the least-squares line appropriate for these data.
(b) Plot the points and graph the line as a check on your calculations.
(c) Calculate s^2.
(d) Do the data present sufficient evidence to indicate that the length of decision time is linearly related to the number of alternative package designs? (Test at the $\alpha = .05$ level of significance.)
(e) Find the approximate observed significance level for the test, and interpret its value.

ESTIMATING THE EXPECTED VALUE OF y FOR A GIVEN VALUE OF x

11.6

In Chapters 6 and 8 we studied methods for estimating a population mean μ and encountered numerous practical applications of these methods in the examples and exercises. Now let us consider a generalization of this problem.

Estimating the mean value of y for a given value of x [i.e., estimating $E(y\,|\,x)$] can be a very important practical problem. If a corporation's profit y is linearly related to advertising expenditures x, the corporation may want to estimate the mean profit for a given expenditure x. Similarly, a personnel executive might want to estimate the mean success rating for a manager at the end of five years based on his or her management trainee score of 50. Let us see how our least-squares prediction equation can be used to obtain these estimates.

Assume that x and y are linearly related according to the probabilistic model defined in Section 11.2 and therefore that $E(y \mid x) = \beta_0 + \beta_1 x$ represents the **expected value of y for a given value of x**. Since the fitted line

$$\hat{y} = \hat{\beta}_0 + \hat{\beta}_1 x$$

attempts to estimate the true linear relation (i.e., we estimate β_0 and β_1), then $\hat{y}$ would be used to estimate the *expected* value of y as well as a *particular* value of y for a given value of x. It would seem quite reasonable to assume that the errors of estimation and prediction would differ for these two cases. In this situation we consider the estimation of the expected value of y for a given value of x.

Observe that two lines are drawn in Figure 11.8. The first line represents the line of means for the true relationship,

$$E(y \mid x) = \beta_0 + \beta_1 x$$

and the second is the fitted prediction equation

$$\hat{y} = \hat{\beta}_0 + \hat{\beta}_1 x$$

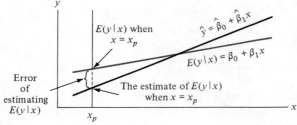

FIGURE 11.8   Estimating $E(y \mid x)$ When $x = x_p$

You can see that the error of estimating the expected value of y when $x = x_p$ will be the deviation between the two lines above the point x_p and that this error will increase as we move to the endpoints of the interval over which x has been measured. It can be shown that the predicted value

$$\hat{y} = \hat{\beta}_0 + \hat{\beta}_1 x$$

is an unbiased estimator of $E(y \mid x)$—that is, $E(\hat{y}) = \beta_0 + \beta_1 x$—and that it will be normally distributed with variance

$$\sigma_{\hat{y}}^2 = \sigma^2 \left[\frac{1}{n} + \frac{(x_p - \bar{x})^2}{SS_x} \right]$$

The corresponding estimated variance of $\hat{y}$ uses s^2 to replace σ^2 in the above expression.

The results just outlined can be used to test an hypothesis concerning the mean or expected value of y for a given value of x, say x_p. (This, of course, would also enable us to test an hypothesis concerning the y intercept, β_0, which is the special case where $x_p = 0$.) The null hypothesis is

$$H_0 : E(y \mid x = x_p) = E_0$$

where E_0 is the hypothesized numerical value of $E(y)$ when $x = x_p$. Once again, it can be shown that the quantity

$$t = \frac{\hat{y} - E_0}{\text{estimated } \sigma_{\hat{y}}} = \frac{\hat{y} - E_0}{s\sqrt{\dfrac{1}{n} + \dfrac{(x_p - \bar{x})^2}{SS_x}}}$$

possesses a Student's t distribution with $(n - 2)$ degrees of freedom. Thus the statistical test is conducted in exactly the same manner as the other t tests previously discussed. The test procedure is given in the next box.

A TEST CONCERNING THE EXPECTED VALUE OF y WHEN $x = x_p$

(1) *Null Hypothesis:* $H_0 : E(y \mid x = x_p) = E_0$.

(2) *Alternative Hypothesis:*

One-Tailed Test	**Two-Tailed Test**
$H_a : E(y \mid x = x_p) > E_0$	$H_a : E(y \mid x = x_p) \neq E_0$
$[\text{or } E(y \mid x = x_p) < E_0]$	

(3) *Test Statistic:* $t = \dfrac{\hat{y} - E_0}{s\sqrt{\dfrac{1}{n} + \dfrac{(x_p - \bar{x})^2}{SS_x}}}$, where

$$SS_x = \sum_{i=1}^{n}(x_i - \bar{x})^2 = \sum_{i=1}^{n} x_i^2 - \frac{\left(\sum_{i=1}^{n} x_i\right)^2}{n}$$

(4) *Rejection Region:*

One-Tailed Test	**Two-Tailed Test**
$t > t_\alpha$	$t > t_{\alpha/2}$
$[\text{or } t < -t_\alpha \text{ when the}$	$\text{or } t < -t_{\alpha/2}$
alternative hypothesis is	
$H_a : E(y \mid x = x_p) < E_0]$	

The values of t_α and $t_{\alpha/2}$ are given in Table 5 of the Appendix. Use the values of t corresponding to $(n - 2)$ degrees of freedom.

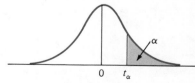   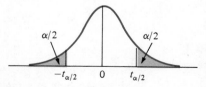

Assumptions: The assumptions are those associated with the linear probabilistic model in Section 11.2. They are summarized and discussed in Section 11.9.

The corresponding confidence interval, with confidence coefficient $(1 - \alpha)$, for the expected value of y, given $x = x_p$, is shown in the next box.

A $(1 - \alpha)100\%$ CONFIDENCE INTERVAL FOR $E(y|x)$ WHEN $x = x_p$

$$\hat{y} \pm t_{\alpha/2} s \sqrt{\frac{1}{n} + \frac{(x_p - \bar{x})^2}{SS_x}}$$

where $t_{\alpha/2}$ is based on $(n - 2)$ degrees of freedom and

$$SS_x = \sum_{i=1}^{n} (x_i - \bar{x})^2 = \sum_{i=1}^{n} x_i^2 - \frac{\left(\sum_{i=1}^{n} x_i\right)^2}{n}$$

EXAMPLE 11.5

Find a 95% confidence interval for the expected value of y, the manager success rating, given that the trainee test score is $x = 50$.

SOLUTION

To estimate the mean manager success rating for trainees whose trainee test score was $x_p = 50$, we use

$$\hat{y} = \hat{\beta}_0 + \hat{\beta}_1 x_p$$

to calculate $\hat{y}$, the estimate of $E(y|x = 50)$. Then

$$\hat{y} = 40.78 + (.77)(50) = 79.28$$

The formula for the 95% confidence interval is

$$\hat{y} \pm t_{.025} s \sqrt{\frac{1}{n} + \frac{(x_p - \bar{x})^2}{SS_x}}$$

Substituting into this expression, we find that the 95% confidence interval for the expected (mean) manager success rating, given a trainee test score of 50, is

$$79.28 \pm (2.306)(8.70) \sqrt{\frac{1}{10} + \frac{(50 - 46)^2}{2474}}$$

or

$$79.28 \pm 6.55$$

Thus we estimate that the mean manager success rating for the population of all trainees with trainee test scores of $x = 50$ will fall in the interval 79.28 ± 6.55, or 72.73 to 85.83.   ∎

EXERCISES

BASIC TECHNIQUES

11.40 Refer to Exercise 11.8. Estimate the expected value of y when $x = 1$, using a 90% confidence interval.

11.41 Refer to Exercise 11.9. Estimate the expected value of y when $x = -1$, using a 90% confidence interval.

11.42 Refer to Exercise 11.10. Find a 90% confidence interval for the mean value of y when $x = 2$.

11.43 Given the following data:

x	-3	-2	-1	0	1	2	3
y	0	1	3	3	5	7	7

(a) Fit a least-squares line to the data.

(b) Calculate SSE and s^2.

(c) Find a 90% confidence interval for the mean value of y when $x = 1$.

APPLICATIONS

11.44 Refer to Exercise 11.12 and find a 90% confidence interval for the mean number of new cars that would be sold per week if the automobile dealer employed seven salespersons.

11.45 Table 11.5 gives the catches in Peruvian anchovies (millions of metric tons) and the prices of fish meal (current dollars per ton) for the years 1965 to 1978.

TABLE 11.5   Price and Catch Data for Exercise 11.45

Variable							Year							
	1965	1966	1967	1968	1969	1970	1971	1972	1973	1974	1975	1976	1977	1978
Price of fish meal, y	190	160	134	129	172	197	167	239	542	372	245	376	454	410
Anchovy catch, x	7.23	8.53	9.82	10.26	8.96	12.27	10.28	4.45	1.78	4.0	3.3	4.3	0.8	0.5

Source: John E. Bardach and Regina M. Santerre, "Climate and the Fish in the Sea," *BioScience*, Vol. 31, No. 3 (March 1981), pp. 206ff. Copyright © 1981 by the American Institute of Biological Sciences.

(a) Find the least-squares line appropriate for these data.

(b) Plot the points and graph the line as a check on your calculations.

(c) Calculate s^2.

(d) Do the data present sufficient evidence to indicate that the size of the anchovy catch x contributes information for the prediction of the price y of fish meal? Test using $\alpha = .10$.

(e) Find the approximate observed significance level for the test in part (d), and interpret its value.

(f) Find a 90% confidence interval for the mean price per ton of fish meal when the anchovy catch is 5 million metric tons.

11.46 If you try to rent an apartment or buy a house, you will find that real estate representatives establish apartment rents and house prices on the basis of the square footage of the heated floor space. The data in Table 11.6 give the square footages and sale prices of $n = 12$ houses randomly selected from those sold in a small city.

TABLE 11.6   Footage and Price Data for Exercise 11.46

Square Feet, x	Price, y	Square Feet, x	Price y
1460	$58,700	1977	$75,400
2108	79,300	1610	67,000
1743	71,400	1530	62,400
1499	61,100	1759	68,200
1864	72,400	1821	74,300
2391	84,900	2216	81,700

(a) Estimate the mean increase in the price for an increase of 1 square foot for houses sold in the city. Use a 90% confidence interval. Interpret your estimate.

(b) Suppose that you are a real estate salesperson, and you desire an estimate of the mean sale price of houses with a total of 2000 square feet of heated space. Use a 95% confidence interval and interpret your estimate.

(c) Calculate the price per square foot for each house, and then calculate the sample mean. Why is this estimate of the mean cost per square foot not equal to the answer in part (a)? Should it? Explain.

 11.47 A property insurer conducted a study to investigate the annual payout y for property damage claims (in millions of dollars) in Florida as a function of the number x of hurricanes hitting the Florida coast. A linear regression model, fit to data over a ten-year period, produced the following equation:

$$\hat{y} = 22.4 + 15.8x$$

with $\bar{x} = 1.5$, $SS_x = 4.95$, and $s^2 = 41.2$.

(a) Do the data provide sufficient evidence to indicate that the number x of hurricanes contributes information for the prediction of the insurer's annual property damage claims? Test using $\alpha = .05$.

(b) Find a 90% confidence interval for the mean annual payout if one hurricane hits the Florida coast in a given year. Interpret the interval.

PREDICTING A PARTICULAR VALUE OF y FOR A GIVEN VALUE OF x

11.7

Although the expected value of y for a particular value of x is of interest for our example in Table 11.2, we are primarily interested in *using* the prediction equation $\hat{y} = \hat{\beta}_0 + \hat{\beta}_1 x$, based on our observed data, to predict the manager success rating for some specific management trainee selected from the population of interest. That is, we want to use the prediction equation obtained for the ten measurements in Table 11.2 to predict the manager success rating (to be recorded five years from now) for a new trainee selected from the population. If the trainee's test score was x_p, we intuitively see that the error of prediction (the deviation between $\hat{y}$ and the actual success rating y that the manager will have obtained) is composed of two elements.

Since the trainee's grade will equal

$$y = \beta_0 + \beta_1 x_p + \varepsilon$$

$(y - \hat{y})$ will equal the deviation between $\hat{y}$ and the expected value of y, described in Section 11.6 (and shown in Figure 11.8), *plus* the random amount ε which represents the deviation of the manager's success rating from the expected value (see Figure 11.9). Thus the variability in the error for predicting a single value of y will exceed the variability for estimating the expected value of y.

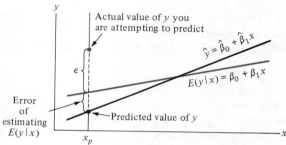

FIGURE 11.9   Error in Predicting a Particular Value of y

It can be shown that the variance of the error of predicting a particular value of y when $x = x_p$—that is, $(y - \hat{y})$—is

$$\sigma_{\text{error}}^2 = \sigma^2 \left[1 + \frac{1}{n} + \frac{(x_p - \bar{x})^2}{SS_x} \right]$$

When n is very large, the second and third terms in the brackets will become small and the variance of the prediction error will approach σ^2. These results can be used to construct the prediction interval for y, given $x = x_p$, as shown in the following box. The confidence coefficient for the prediction interval is $(1 - \alpha)$.

A $(1 - \alpha)100\%$ PREDICTION INTERVAL FOR y WHEN $x = x_p$

$$\hat{y} \pm t_{\alpha/2} s \sqrt{1 + \frac{1}{n} + \frac{(x_p - \bar{x})^2}{SS_x}}$$

where $t_{\alpha/2}$ is based on $(n - 2)$ degrees of freedom and

$$SS_x = \sum_{i=1}^{n} (x_i - \bar{x})^2 = \sum_{i=1}^{n} x_i^2 - \frac{\left(\sum_{i=1}^{n} x_i \right)^2}{n}$$

EXAMPLE 11.6   Refer to Example 11.1, and predict the manager success rating for a trainee who scored $x = 50$ on the trainee test.

SOLUTION   The predicted value of y is

$$\hat{y} = \hat{\beta}_0 + \hat{\beta}_1 x_p$$

or

$$\hat{y} = 40.78 + (.77)(50) = 79.28$$

and the 95% prediction interval for the five-year manager success rating is

$$79.28 \pm (2.306)(8.70)\sqrt{1 + \frac{1}{10} + \frac{(50 - 46)^2}{2474}}$$

or

$$79.28 \pm 21.10$$

Note that in a practical situation we would likely possess the manager success ratings and trainee test scores for many more than the $n = 10$ managers indicated in Table 11.2 and that this would reduce somewhat the width of the prediction interval. ■

Again, note the distinction between the confidence interval for $E(y \mid x)$ discussed in Section 11.6 and the prediction interval presented in this section. The term $E(y \mid x)$ is a mean, a parameter of a population of y values, and y is a random variable that oscillates in a random manner about $E(y \mid x)$. The mean value of y when $x = 50$ is vastly different from some value of y chosen at random from the set of all y values for which $x = 50$. To make this distinction when making inferences, we always *estimate*

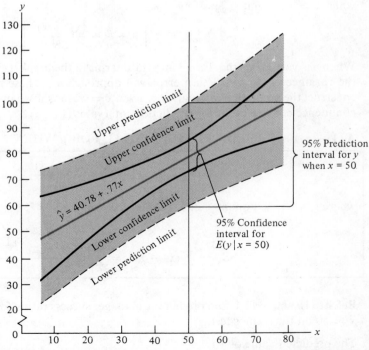

FIGURE 11.10   Confidence Intervals for $E(y \mid x)$ and Prediction Intervals for y Based on Data of Table 11.2

the value of a parameter and *predict* the value of a random variable. As noted in our earlier discussion and as shown in Figures 11.8 and 11.9, the error of predicting y is different from the error of estimating $E(y|x)$. This is evident in the difference in widths of the two prediction and confidence intervals.

A graph of the confidence interval for $E(y|x)$ and the prediction interval for a particular value of y for the data of Table 11.2 is shown in Figure 11.10. The plot of the confidence interval is shown by solid lines; the prediction interval is identified by dashed lines. Note how the widths of the intervals increase as you move to the right or left of $\bar{x} = 46$. Particularly, see the confidence interval and prediction interval for $x = 50$, which were calculated in Examples 11.5 and 11.6.

EXERCISES

BASIC TECHNIQUES

11.48 Refer to Exercise 11.8. Find a 90% prediction interval for some value of y to be observed in the future when $x = 1$.

11.49 Refer to Exercise 11.9. Find a 90% prediction interval for some value of y to be observed in the future when $x = -1$.

11.50 Refer to Exercise 11.10. Find a 90% prediction interval for some value of y to be observed in the future when $x = 2$.

11.51 Refer to Exercise 11.43. Find a 90% prediction interval for y when $x = 1$.

APPLICATIONS

11.52 Suppose that the anchovy catch described in Exercise 11.45 in a given year is 7 million metric tons. Find a 90% prediction interval for the price (dollars per ton) of fish meal.

11.53 Refer to Exercise 11.46. Suppose that a house containing 1780 square feet of heated floor space is offered for sale. Give a 90% prediction interval for the price at which the house will sell. Interpret this prediction.

11.54 The property insurer of Exercise 11.47 is concerned about how large (or small) the payments might be for a given year. Find a 90% prediction interval for the annual payout if two hurricanes hit the Florida coast in a given year. Interpret the interval.

11.55 Colin W. Clark, in an article titled "Bioeconomics of the Ocean," discusses the problem of the overexploitation of ocean resources. As part of the article, Clark presents data on the Peruvian Anchoveta Fishery, a fishery "that developed in the 1960's into the world's largest single fishery." Data showing the growth and the eventual depletion of the anchoveta catch are shown in Table 11.7. The increase in the size of the fishing fleet from 1959 to 1973 can be seen in the second column of the table, and you can also see the reduction in fishing days and the rise and fall in the catch over the same period of time. The column labeled "fishing effort," the product of the number of boats and the number of fishing days, is a measure of the amount of effort (money, time, etc.) expended to obtain the catch.

(a) Find the least-squares prediction equation relating catch y and the fishing effort x. (Delete years in which data are missing.)

(b) Do the data provide sufficient evidence to indicate that, with the straight-line linear model, x contributes information for the prediction of y? Test using $\alpha = .10$.

(c) Plot the data points (x, y). Does the distribution of plotted points appear to agree with your conclusions in part (b)?

TABLE 11.7   Growth and Depletion of Anchoveta Data for Exercise 11.55

Year	Number of Boats	Number of Fishing Days	Fishing Effort [(Number of Boats) × (Number of Fishing Days)] (in Units of 10,000 Boat-days)	Catch (Million Tons)
1959	414	294	12.2	1.91
1960	667	279	18.6	
1961	756	298	22.5	4.58
1962	1069	294	31.4	6.27
1963	1655	269	44.5	6.42
1964	1744	297	51.8	8.86
1965	1623	265	43.0	7.23
1966	1650	190	31.4	8.53
1967	1569	170	26.7	9.82
1968	1490	167	24.9	10.26
1969	1455	162	23.6	8.96
1970	1499	180	27.0	12.27
1971	1473	89	13.1	10.28
1972	1399	89	12.5	4.45
1973	1256	27	3.39	1.78
1974				4.00
1975				3.30
1976				4.30
1977				.80
1978				.50

Source: C. W. Clark, "Bioeconomics of the Ocean," *BioScience,* Vol. 30, No. 3 (March 1981), pp. 231–237. Copyright © 1981 by the American Institute of Biological Sciences.

(d) Find a 90% confidence interval for the mean catch when the fishing effort is equal to 300,000 boat-days.

(e) Find a 90% prediction interval for the catch when the fishing effort is equal to 300,000 boat-days.

A COEFFICIENT OF CORRELATION

11.8

Sometimes, we wish to obtain an indicator of the strength of the linear relationship between two variables y and x that will be independent of their respective scales of measurement. We will call this a **measure of the linear correlation between y and x**.

The measure of linear correlation commonly used in statistics is called the **Pearson product-moment coefficient of correlation**. This quantity, denoted by the symbol r, is defined as shown in the following box.

We will show you how to compute the Pearson product-moment coefficient of correlation for the management success rating and trainee score data in Table 11.2, and then we will explain how it measures the strength of the relationship between y and x.

PEARSON PRODUCT MOMENT COEFFICIENT OF CORRELATION

$$r = \frac{SS_{xy}}{\sqrt{SS_x SS_y}}$$

EXAMPLE 11.7   Calculate the coefficient of correlation for the manager success rating/trainee test score data of Table 11.2.

SOLUTION   The coefficient of correlation for the manager success rating/trainee test score data in Table 11.2 may be obtained by using the formula for r and the quantities

$$SS_{xy} = 1894 \qquad SS_x = 2474 \qquad SS_y = 2056$$

which were computed previously. Then

$$r = \frac{SS_{xy}}{\sqrt{SS_x SS_y}} = \frac{1894}{\sqrt{2474(2056)}} = .84 \qquad \blacksquare$$

A study of the coefficient of correlation r yields rather interesting results and explains the reason for its selection as a measure of linear correlation. Note that the denominators used in calculating r and $\hat{\beta}_1$ will always be positive, since they both involve sums of squares of numbers. Since the numerator used in calculating r is identical to the numerator of the formula for the slope $\hat{\beta}_1$, the coefficient of correlation r will assume exactly the same sign as $\hat{\beta}_1$ and will equal zero when $\hat{\beta}_1 = 0$. **Thus $r = 0$ implies no linear correlation between y and x. A positive value for r will imply that the line slopes upward to the right; a negative value indicates that it slopes downward to the right** (see Figure 11.11).

The interpretation of nonzero values of r may be obtained by comparing the errors of prediction for the prediction equation

$$\hat{y} = \hat{\beta}_0 + \hat{\beta}_1 x$$

with the predictor of y, $\bar{y}$, that would be employed if x were ignored. Figures 11.12(a) and 11.12(b) show the lines $\hat{y} = \hat{\beta}_0 + \hat{\beta}_1 x$ and $\hat{y} = \bar{y}$ fit to the same set of data. Certainly, if x is of any value in predicting y, then SSE, the sum of squares of deviations of y about the linear model, should be less than the sum of squares about the predictor $\bar{y}$, which is

$$SS_y = \sum_{i=1}^{n} (y_i - \bar{y})^2$$

You can see that SSE can *never* be larger than

$$SS_y = \sum_{i=1}^{n} (y_i - \bar{y})^2$$

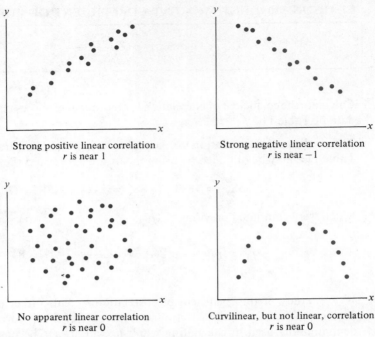

Strong positive linear correlation
r is near 1

Strong negative linear correlation
r is near -1

No apparent linear correlation
r is near 0

Curvilinear, but not linear, correlation
r is near 0

FIGURE 11.11   Some Typical Scatter Diagrams with Approximate Values of r

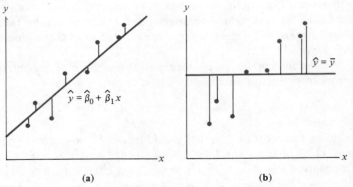

(a)

(b)

FIGURE 11.12   Two Models Fit to the Same Data

because

$$\text{SSE} = \text{SS}_y - \hat{\beta}_1 \text{SS}_{xy} = \text{SS}_y - \left(\frac{\text{SS}_{xy}}{\text{SS}_x}\right)\text{SS}_{xy}$$

$$= \text{SS}_y - \frac{(\text{SS}_{xy})^2}{\text{SS}_x}$$

Therefore, SSE is equal to SS_y minus a positive quantity.

Furthermore, with the aid of a bit of algebraic manipulation, we can show that

$$r^2 = 1 - \frac{SSE}{SS_y}$$

$$= \frac{SS_y - SSE}{SS_y}$$

In other words, r^2 will lie in the interval

$$0 \leq r^2 \leq 1$$

and r will equal $+1$ or -1 only when all the points fall exactly on the fitted line—that is, when SSE equals zero. Actually, we see that r^2 is equal to the ratio of the reduction in the sum of squares of deviations obtained by using the linear model to the total sum of squares of deviations about the sample mean $\bar{y}$, which would be the predictor of y if x were ignored. Thus r^2, called the **coefficient of determination**, would seem to give a more meaningful interpretation of the strength of the relation between y and x than would the correlation coefficient r. The formula for r^2 is given in the box.

THE COEFFICIENT OF DETERMINATION

$$r^2 = \frac{SS_y - SSE}{SS_y} = \frac{\sum_{i=1}^{n} (y_i - \bar{y})^2 - SSE}{\sum_{i=1}^{n} (y_i - \bar{y})^2}$$

A test of an hypothesis that the population correlation coefficient ρ (Greek letter rho) equals 0 can be conducted in two ways. Since $\rho = 0$ if and only if the slope β_1 of the regression line equals 0, a test of the hypothesis $H_0 : \rho = 0$ is equivalent to the test $H_0 : \beta_1 = 0$ of Section 11.5. If the data provide sufficient evidence to indicate $\beta_1 > 0$, then we have evidence to indicate that $\rho > 0$. Similarly, support for the alternative hypothesis $\beta_1 < 0$ is equivalent to supporting the alternative hypothesis $\rho < 0$.

The Student's t statistic,

$$t = \frac{r\sqrt{n - 2}}{\sqrt{1 - r^2}}$$

can also be used to test the null hypothesis $H_0 : \rho = 0$. The test is given in the next box, and its use is illustrated in Example 11.8.

EXAMPLE 11.8   Refer to Example 11.7. Do the data provide sufficient evidence to indicate that success rating y and trainee score x are positively correlated? Test using $\alpha = .05$.

SOLUTION   We want to test $H_0 : \rho = 0$ against the alternative hypothesis $H_a : \rho > 0$, using a one-tailed statistical test. The t statistic will be based on $(n - 2) = 10 - 2 = 8$ degrees of freedom, and we will reject H_0 if $t \geq t_{.05}$, or $t \geq 1.86$ (from Table 5 in the Appendix).

A TEST CONCERNING THE POPULATION SIMPLE COEFFICIENT OF CORRELATION ρ

(1) *Null Hypothesis: $H_0 : \rho = 0$.*

(2) *Alternative Hypothesis:*

One-Tailed Test	**Two-Tailed Test**
$H_a : \rho > 0$ (or $\rho < 0$)	$H_a : \rho \neq 0$

(3) *Test Statistic:* $t = \dfrac{r\sqrt{n-2}}{\sqrt{1-r^2}}$.

(4) *Rejection Region:*

One-Tailed Test	**Two-Tailed Test**
$t > t_\alpha$ (or $t < -t_\alpha$ when the alternative hypothesis is $H_a : \rho < 0$)	$t > t_{\alpha/2}$ or $t < -t_{\alpha/2}$

The values of t_α and $t_{\alpha/2}$ are given in Table 5 of the Appendix. Use the values of t corresponding to $(n - 2)$ degrees of freedom.

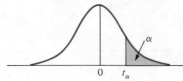   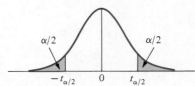

Assumptions: The assumptions are those associated with the linear probabilistic model of Section 11.2. They are summarized and discussed in Section 11.9.

Using the value of r calculated in Example 11.7, we find that the value of the test statistic is

$$t = \frac{r\sqrt{n-2}}{\sqrt{1-r^2}} = \frac{.84\sqrt{10-2}}{\sqrt{1-(.84)^2}} = 4.38$$

Since this value of t exceeds the critical value of t, $t_{.05} = 1.86$, there is sufficient evidence to indicate a correlation between a manager's success rating and trainee test score. (Note that this computed t value is the same as the value computed in the test for β_1 in Example 11.3.) ∎

The coefficient of simple correlation, r, provides a nice measure of the goodness of fit of the least-squares line to the fitted data, but its use in making inferences concerning ρ would seem to be of dubious practical value in many situations. It would seem unlikely that a phenomenon y, observed in business and economics, would be a function of a single variable. Thus the correlation coefficient between a manager's success rating and any one variable likely would be quite small and of questionable value. A larger reduction in SSE could possibly be obtained by constructing a predictor of y based upon a set of variables $x_1, x_2, \ldots$.

One further reminder concerning the interpretation of r is worthwhile. It is not uncommon for researchers in some fields to speak proudly of sample correlation coefficients r in the neighborhood of .5 (and in some cases as low as .1) as indicative of a "relation" between y and x. Certainly, even if these values were *accurate* estimates of ρ, only a very weak relation would be indicated. A value $r = .5$ would imply that the use of x in predicting y reduced the sum of squares of deviations about the prediction line by only $r^2 = .25$, or 25%. A correlation coefficient $r = .1$ would imply only an $r^2 = .01$, or 1%, reduction in the total sum of squares of deviations that could be explained by x.

If the linear coefficients of correlation between y and each of two variables x_1 and x_2 were calculated to be .4 and .5, respectively, it does not follow that a predictor using both variables would account for a $[(.4)^2 + (.5)^2] = .41$, or a 41%, reduction in the sum of squares of deviations. Actually, x_1 and x_2 might be highly correlated and therefore contribute the same information for the prediction of y.

Finally, we remind you that r is a measure of *linear* correlation and that x and y could be perfectly related by some curvilinear function when the observed value of r is equal to zero.

EXERCISES

BASIC TECHNIQUES

11.56 How does the coefficient of correlation measure the strength of the linear relationship between two variables y and x?

11.57 Describe the significance of the algebraic sign and the magnitude of r.

11.58 What value does r assume?

(a) If all the sample points fall on the same straight line and if the line has positive slope.

(b) If all the sample points fall on the same straight line and if the line has negative slope.

11.59 Given the following data:

x	-2	-1	0	1	2
y	2	2	3	4	4

(a) Find the least-squares line for the data.

(b) Plot the data points and graph the least-squares line. From your graph, what will be the sign of the sample correlation coefficient?

(c) Calculate r and r^2 and interpret their values.

11.60 Given the following data:

x	1	2	3	4	5	6
y	7	5	5	3	2	0

(a) Find the least-squares line.

(b) Sketch the least-squares line on graph paper, and plot the six points.

(c) Calculate the sample coefficient of correlation r and interpret.

(d) By what percentage was the sum of squares of deviations reduced by using the least-squares predictor $\hat{y} = \hat{\beta}_0 + \hat{\beta}_1 x$ rather than $\bar{y}$ as a predictor of y?

11.61 Reverse the slope of the line of Exercise 11.60 by reordering the y observations:

x	1	2	3	4	5	6
y	0	2	3	5	5	7

Repeat the steps of Exercise 11.60. Notice the change in sign of r and the relation between the values of r^2 of Exercise 11.60 and this exercise.

APPLICATIONS

11.62 Refer to the data of Exercise 11.11 relating the percentage y of increase in sales x to a manufacturer's coded wholesale price for a box of soap powder.

(a) Calculate the coefficient of correlation between y and x, and interpret its value.

(b) Calculate the coefficient of determination, and interpret its value.

11.63 Refer to the data of Exercise 11.12 relating the number y of new cars sold per week by an automobile dealer to the number x of salespersons employed.

(a) Calculate the coefficient of correlation between y and x, and interpret its value.

(b) Calculate the coefficient of determination, and interpret its value.

11.64 How well does the straight-line model in Exercise 11.47 fit the data relating the annual property damage payout y to the number of hurricanes that hit the Florida coast per year? Justify your answer.

 11.65 An experiment was conducted in a supermarket to observe the relation between the amount of display space allotted to a brand of coffee (brand A) and its weekly sales. The amount of space allotted to brand A was varied over 3-, 6-, and 9-square-feet displays in a random manner over 12 weeks; the space allotted to competing brands was maintained at a constant 3 square feet for each. The data in Table 11.8 were observed.

(a) Find the least-squares line appropriate for the data.

(b) Calculate r and r^2. Interpret.

(c) Find a 90% confidence interval for the mean weekly sales given that 6 square feet is allotted for display.

(d) Use a 90% prediction interval to predict the weekly sales at some time in the future if 6 square feet is allotted for display.

(e) By what percentage was the sum of squares of deviations reduced by using the least-squares predictor $\hat{y} = \hat{\beta}_0 + \hat{\beta}_1 x$ rather than $\bar{y}$ as a predictor of y for these data?

(f) Would you expect the relation between y and x to be linear if x were varied over a wider range (say $x = 1$ to $x = 30$)?

TABLE 11.8 Sales and Space Data for Exercise 11.65

Weekly Sales, y (Dollars)	Space Allotted, x (Square Feet)	Weekly Sales, y (Dollars)	Space Allotted, x (Square Feet)
526	6	434	6
421	3	443	3
581	6	590	9
630	9	570	6
412	3	346	3
560	9	672	9

11.66 Geothermal power could be an important source of energy in future years. Since the amount of energy contained in a pound of water is a function of its temperature, you might wonder whether water obtained from deeper wells contains more energy per pound. The data in Table 11.9 are reproduced from an article on geothermal systems by A. J. Ellis.

TABLE 11.9 Water Well Data for Exercise 11.66

Location of Well	Average (Max.) Drill Hole Depth (Meters), x	Average (Max.) Temperature (°C) y
El Tateo, Chile	650	230
Ahuachapan, El Salvador	1000	230
Namafjall, Iceland	1000	250
Larderello (region), Italy	600	200
Matsukawa, Japan	1000	220
Cerro Prieto, Mexico	800	300
Wairakei, New Zealand	800	230
Kizildere, Turkey	700	190
The Geysers, United States	1500	250

Source: Data from A. J. Ellis, "Geothermal Systems," *American Scientist,* September–October 1975.

(a) Find the least-squares line.

(b) Sketch the least-squares line on graph paper, and plot the nine points.

(c) Calculate the sample coefficient of correlation r, and interpret it.

(d) Do the data provide sufficient evidence to indicate a correlation between average temperature y and drill hole depth x? Test using $\alpha = .10$.

(e) By what percentage was the sum of squares of deviations reduced by using the least-squares predictor $\hat{y} = \hat{\beta}_0 + \hat{\beta}_1 x$ rather than $\bar{y}$?

11.67 Refer to the Peruvian Anchoveta Fishery data in Exercise 11.55.

(a) Calculate the sample coefficient of correlation between the catch y and the fishing effort x. Interpret its value. (Delete years in which data are missing.)

(b) Do the data provide sufficient evidence to indicate a correlation between catch y and fishing effort x? Test using $\alpha = .05$.

(c) Calculate the coefficient of determination and interpret its value.

(d) Noting the values of r and r^2 calculated in parts (a) and (b), reexamine your plot of the data points and your graph of the least-squares line in Exercise 11.55, part (c). Do you think that r and r^2 adequately describe how well the least-squares line fits the data?

11.68 Refer to the Peruvian Anchoveta Fishery data in Exercise 11.55.

(a) Calculate the sample coefficient of correlation r between the catch y and the number of fishing boats x. Interpret its value. (Delete years in which data are missing.)

(b) Do the data provide sufficient evidence to indicate a correlation between catch y and the number of fishing boats x? Test using $\alpha = .05$.

(c) Find the coefficient of determination and interpret its value.

(d) Plot the data points. Do they suggest a linear relationship between y and x? Does the plot agree with your interpretation for r and r^2?

11.69 In Exercise 2.12 we described a study conducted to investigate the relationship between a company's success and its use of modern marketing methods (Tom Griffin, "Linking the Use of Modern Marketing Methods to Company Success," *Columbia Journal of World Business,* Fall 1982). Forty-nine Puerto Rican food manufacturers responded to each of two questionnaires, one designed to measure the extent to which a company used modern marketing methods and the other designed to measure the company's success. The correlation coefficient computed for the 49 pairs of scores was $r = .37$.

(a) Is this value of r large enough to indicate correlation between a company's success score and its marketing score? Test using $\alpha = .05$.

(b) Find the approximate p-value for the test and interpret it.

(c) Suppose that the correlation between a company's success score and its marketing score was actually equal to .37. Would this value imply a strong relationship between the two scores? Explain.

ASSUMPTIONS

11.9

The assumptions for a regression analysis are given in the following box.

ASSUMPTIONS FOR A REGRESSION ANALYSIS

> (1) The response y can be represented by the probabilistic model
> $$y = \beta_0 + \beta_1 x + \varepsilon$$
> (2) x is measured without error.
> (3) ε is a random variable such that, for a given value of x,
> $$E(\varepsilon) = 0 \qquad \sigma_\varepsilon^2 = \sigma^2$$
> and all pairs, $\varepsilon_i, \varepsilon_j$, are independent in a probabilistic sense.
> (4) ε possesses a normal probability distribution.

At first glance, you might forget assumption 1 or fail to catch its significance. Models, deterministic or otherwise, are, as the name implies, only models for real relationships that occur in nature. Consequently, there will always be some error (slight, if we are careful) due to the fact that there is curvature in the response curve. If you have obtained a good fit to the data, then the only difficulty that inherent lack of fit can cause is some problem if you attempt to use the model to predict y for some value of x outside the range of values used to fit the least-squares equation. Of course, this problem will always occur if x is time and you attempt to forecast y at some point in the future. But then this problem occurs with any kind of model for future time predictions. Consequently, you make the forecast but keep the limitations in mind.

The assumption that the variance of the ε's (and consequently y) is constant and equal to σ^2 will not be true for some types of data. Similarly, if x is time, say year, it is possible that y values measured over adjacent years will tend to be dependent (an overly large value of y in 1982 might signal a large value of y in 1983). Substantial departure from either of these assumptions will affect the confidence coefficients and significance levels associated with interval estimates and tests described in this chapter.

Like unequal variances and correlation of the random errors, if the normality assumption (4) is not satisfied, the confidence coefficients and significance levels for interval estimates and tests will not be what we expect them to be. But modest departures from normality will not seriously disturb these values.

A COMPUTER ANALYSIS OF THE PERSONAL SAVINGS RATE/INVESTMENT TAX LIABILITY DATA

11.10

Most regression analyses are performed on a computer, using one of many multiple regression computer program packages. Consequently, while exploring the relationship between personal savings rate y and investment tax liability x (see the Case Study), we will familiarize you with the computer printout for one of the more popular multiple regression program packages. A comparison of the printouts for several different multiple regression packages is given in Section 12.4, but this comparison is not essential to our discussion.

Do the data in Table 11.1 of the Case Study support Dr. Blotnick's theory that the national personal savings rate decreases as the tax on investment income increases? A plot of the data points, one corresponding to each of the eight countries included in Table 11.1, is shown in Figure 11.13.

The computer printout for the Statistical Analysis System (SAS) GLM multiple regression program package is shown in Table 11.10.

(1) The least-squares estimates, shown in shaded area ①, appear in the column under ESTIMATE. Thus $\hat{\beta}_0 = 21.18093677$, $\hat{\beta}_1 = -.29293475$, and the least-squares prediction equation relating personal savings rate y and investment tax rate x is

$$\hat{y} = 21.18 - .29x$$

(2) The t value for testing $H_0 : \beta_1 = 0$ is shown in shaded area ②, on the same line as $\hat{\beta}_1$, as $t = -3.25$. Since we want to detect a negative value of β_1 (i.e., personal savings decrease as the investment tax increases), the alternative hypothesis

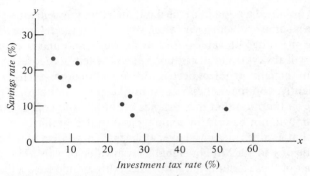

FIGURE 11.13   Plot of the Data Points for the Case Study

TABLE 11.10   Regression Analysis SAS GLM Computer Printout for the Savings Rate/Investment Income Data

```
                    Y = PERSONAL SAVINGS RATE    X = TAXATION RATE
                         GENERAL LINEAR MODELS PROCEDURE

DEPENDENT VARIABLE: Y

SOURCE              DF    SUM OF SQUARES   MEAN SQUARE    F VALUE    PR > F    R-SQUARE             C.V.
                                                                                       ⑧
MODEL               1    158.78381752    158.78381752    10.54      0.0175    0.637238           27.1901

ERROR               6     90.39118248    15.06519708  ⑤            ROOT MSE        ⑥      Y MEAN
                       ⑦                                                3.88139113            14.27500000
CORRECTED TOTAL     7    249.17500000


SOURCE              DF     TYPE I SS    F VALUE    PR > F    DF    TYPE IV SS    F VALUE    PR > F

X                   1    158.78381752    10.54     0.0175    1    158.78381752    10.54     0.0175


                                 T FOR HO:      PR > |T|     STD ERROR OF
PARAMETER          ESTIMATE    PARAMETER = 0               ESTIMATE
                                              ②            ③                   ④
INTERCEPT    ①  21.18093677       8.37         0.0002        2.53142243
X               -0.29293475      -3.25         0.0175        0.09023088
```

is $H_a : \beta_1 < 0$, and we place the rejection region in the lower tail of the t distribution.

(3) The observed significance level for the test in step 2 is shown in shaded area ③ under the column PR > |T| and in the line corresponding to $\hat{\beta}_1$ as .0175. This portion of the SAS printout always gives the observed significance level appropriate for a two-tailed test. The observed significance level for a one-tailed test will be half this value, or

$$p\text{-value} = \frac{.0175}{2} = .00875$$

Therefore, we would reject $H_0 : \beta_1 = 0$ and accept $H_a : \beta_1 < 0$ for a value of α greater than or equal to .00875. Since this test is equivalent to a test of the hypothesis $H_0 : \rho = 0$ and $H_a : \rho < 0$, there is ample evidence to reject H_0 and conclude that the personal savings rate and the investment tax rate are negatively correlated; in other words, the personal savings rate decreases as the investment tax rate increases.

(4) The standard error of the estimator $\hat{\beta}_1$ is shown in shaded area ④ in the line corresponding to $\hat{\beta}_1$ as

$$s_{\hat{\beta}_1} = \frac{s}{\sqrt{SS_x}} = .09023088$$

This quantity is useful for constructing a confidence interval for β_1. Thus a 95% confidence interval for β_1 is

$$\hat{\beta}_1 \pm t_{\alpha/2} s_{\hat{\beta}_1}$$

Since s is based on 6 degrees of freedom, $t_{.025} = 2.447$, and the confidence interval is

$$-.29 \pm (2.447)(.0902)$$

or

$$-.29 \pm .22$$

(5) The values of SSE and s^2 are shown in shaded area ⑤ in the row corresponding to **ERROR** and in the columns headed **SUM OF SQUARES** and **MEAN SQUARE**, respectively. Thus

$$SSE = 90.39118248$$
$$s^2 = 15.06519708$$

(6) The value of s is shown in shaded area ⑥ under **ROOT MSE** as

$$s = 3.88139113$$

(7) SS_y (sometimes called the total sum of squares) is shown in shaded area ⑦, in the row corresponding to **CORRECTED TOTAL** and in the **SUM OF SQUARES** column:

$$SS_y = 249.1750$$

(8) The value of $r^2 = .637238$ is shown in shaded area 8. Because the slope $\hat{\beta}_1$ is negative, r is negative; that is, $r = -\sqrt{r^2} = -.80$.

We have already stated that there is ample evidence to indicate that the personal savings rate y decreases as the tax investment rate increases. But can we use the prediction equation to predict the personal savings rate for a given investment tax rate, say $x = 20$? The answer is "yes," but the prediction error would be quite large. You can see that $r^2 = .637238$ and, therefore, that the straight-line model accounts for only (approximately) 64% of the variability of y about its mean. Thus, as we would expect, there are many other variables, in addition to the investment income tax rate, that contribute information for the prediction of y.

You can see from the printout (shaded area 6) in Table 11.10 that $s = 3.88139113$ and, therefore, that $s \approx 3.88$. A 95% prediction interval for y when $x = x_p$ is

$$\hat{y} \pm t_{.025}s \sqrt{1 + \frac{1}{n} + \frac{(x_p - \bar{x})^2}{\displaystyle\sum_{i=1}^{n}(x_i - \bar{x})^2}}$$

where $t_{.025} = 2.447$, $n = 8$, $\bar{x} = 23.575$, and $\displaystyle\sum_{i=1}^{8}(x_i - \bar{x})^2 = 1850.395$. (Note that $\bar{x}$ and SS_x are calculated from the original data and are not shown on the printout.) The prediction intervals for several values of x_p are given in Table 11.11. These wide prediction intervals confirm our earlier expectation. The personal savings rate does decrease as the investment income tax increases, but the investment tax rate alone does not contribute sufficient information to obtain accurate predictions of the personal savings rate.

TABLE 11.11   Prediction Intervals for the Savings Rate/Investment Income Data

x_p	Lower Prediction Limit		Upper Prediction Limit
6.4	8.54	to	30.07
20.0	5.22	to	25.43
30.0	2.22	to	22.57

Our analysis of the relationship between savings rate y and investment tax rate x aptly illustrates the mechanics of a regression analysis, but you may wonder whether the data satisfy the assumptions upon which the methodology is based. The savings rate y and tax rate x are percentages, and it is possible (as in the case of a binomial sample proportion $\hat{p}$) that the variance of y depends on the value of x. If true, our data would violate the assumptions of the regression model (Sections 11.2 and 11.9).

If you are concerned about the validity of our conclusion—that savings rate y and investment tax rate x are negatively correlated—we can employ a nonparametric statistical test for correlation, one that does not require the assumptions of Section 11.2. We will explain the mechanics of this test in Chapter 15, and we will apply it to the savings rate/tax rate data in Section 15.8. Other methods for coping with departures from the model assumptions are discussed in the references.

SUMMARY

11.11

You will observe that the prediction of a particular value of a random variable was considered for the most elementary situation in Chapters 6 and 8. Thus if we possessed no information concerning independent variables related to a response variable y, the sole information available for predicting y would be provided by its probability distribution. As we noted in Chapter 3, the probability that a random variable y will fall between two specific values, say y_1 and y_2, will equal the area under the probability distribution curve over the interval $y_1 \leq y \leq y_2$. And if we were to select randomly one member of the population, we would most likely choose μ, or some other measure of central tendency, as the most likely value of y to be observed. Thus we would want to estimate μ, and this, of course, was considered in Chapters 6 and 8.

Chapter 11 is concerned with the problem of predicting y when auxiliary information is available on other variables, say x_1, x_2, x_3, . . . , that are related to y and therefore assist in its prediction. We have concentrated on the problem of predicting y as a linear function of a single variable x, which provides the simplest extension of the prediction problem beyond that considered in Chapters 6 and 8. We will consider the multivariable prediction problem in Chapter 12.

REFERENCES

BMDPC: User's Guide to BMDP on the IBM PC. Los Angeles: BMDP Statistical Software.

Dixon, W. J., Brown, M. B., Engelman, L., Frane, J. W., Hill, M. A., Jennrich, R. I., and Toporek, J. D. *BMDP Statistical Software*. Berkeley: University of California Press, 1985.

Draper, N. R., and Smith, H. *Applied Regression Analysis*. 2nd ed. New York: Wiley, 1981.

Freund, J. E., and Walpole, R. E. *Mathematical Statistics*. 4th ed. Englewood Cliffs, N.J.: Prentice-Hall, 1987.

Hill, MaryAnn, ed. *BMDP User's Digest*. 2nd ed. Los Angeles: BMDP Statistical Software, 1982.

Kleinbaum, D., and Kupper, L. *Applied Regression Analysis and Other Multivariable Methods*. Boston: PWS-KENT, 1978.

Mendenhall, W. *An Introduction to Linear Models and the Design and Analysis of Experiments*. Boston: PWS-KENT, 1968.

Mendenhall, W., Scheaffer, R. L., and Wackerly, D. D. *Mathematical Statistics with Applications*. 3rd ed. Boston: PWS-KENT, 1986.

Mendenhall, W., and Sincich, T. *A Second Course in Business Statistics: Regression Analysis*. 2nd ed. San Francisco: Dellen, 1986.

Neter, J., and Wasserman, W. *Applied Linear Statistical Models*. 2nd ed. Homewood, Ill.: Irwin, 1985.

Norusis, M. J. *SPSS/PC+: SPSS for the IBM PC/XT/AT*. Chicago: SPSS, 1986.

Norusis, M. J. *The SPSS Guide to Data Analysis*. Chicago: SPSS, 1986.

Ryan, T. A., Joiner, B. L., and Ryan, B. F. *Minitab Reference Manual*. University Park, Pa.: Minitab Project, 1985.

Ryan, T. A., Joiner, B. L., and Ryan, B. F. *Minitab Handbook*. 2nd ed. Boston: PWS-KENT, 1985.

SAS Procedures Guide for Personal Computers. Version 6 ed. Cary, N.C.: SAS Institute, 1986.

SAS Statistics Guide for Personal Computers. Version 6 ed. Cary, N.C.: SAS Institute, 1986.

SAS User's Guide: Basics. Version 5 ed. Cary, N.C.: SAS Institute, 1985.

SAS User's Guide: Statistics. Version 5 ed. Cary, N.C.: SAS Institute, 1985.

SPSS^x User's Guide. Chicago: SPSS, 1983.

Younger, M. S. *A First Course in Linear Regression*. 2nd ed. Boston: PWS-KENT, 1985.

KEY TERMS

Regression analysis (page 438)
Mathematical model (page 439)
Equation of a straight line (page 439)
y intercept of a line (page 439)
Slope of a line (page 439)
Deterministic mathematical model (page 440)
Probabilistic mathematical model (page 440)
Deviation (page 441)
Principle of least squares (page 442)

Least-squares prediction line (page 443)
Expected value of y for a given value of x
   (page 458)
Pearson product-moment coefficient of
   correlation (page 466)
Measure of the linear correlation between
   y and x (page 466)
Coefficient of determination (page 469)

SUPPLEMENTARY EXERCISES

11.70 Graph the line corresponding to the equation $y = 3x + 2$ by locating points corresponding to $x = 0, 1,$ and 2.

11.71 Given the linear equation $2x + 3y + 6 = 0$,
   (a) Give the y intercept and slope for the line.
   (b) Graph the line corresponding to the equation.

11.72 Follow the instructions given in Exercise 11.71 for the linear equation: $2x - 3y - 5 = 0$.

11.73 Follow the instructions given in Exercise 11.71 for the linear equation $x/y = 1/2$.

11.74 Given the following data for corresponding values of two variables, y and x

y	0	0	1	1	3
x	-2	-1	0	1	2

   (a) Find the least-squares line for the data.
   (b) As a check on the calculations in (a), plot the five points and graph the line.

11.75 Given the following data for corresponding values of two variables, y and x

y	2	1.5	1	2.5	2.5	4	5
x	-3	-2	-1	0	1	2	3

   Follow the instructions of Exercise 11.74.

11.76 Calculate s^2 for the data in Exercise 11.74.

11.77 Calculate s^2 for the data in Exercise 11.75.

11.78 Do the data in Exercise 11.74 present sufficient evidence to indicate that y and x are linearly related? (Test the hypothesis that $\beta_1 = 0$, using $\alpha = .05$.)

11.79 Do the data in Exercise 11.75 present sufficient evidence to indicate that y and x are linearly related? (Test the hypothesis that $\beta_1 = 0$, using $\alpha = .05$.)

11.80 For what configurations of sample points will s^2 be zero?

11.81 For what parameter is s^2 an unbiased estimator? Explain how this parameter enters into the description of the probabilistic model $y = \beta_0 + \beta_1 x + \varepsilon$.

11.82 Find a 90% confidence interval for the slope of the line in Exercise 11.74.

11.83 Find a 95% confidence interval for the slope of the line in Exercise 11.75.

11.84 Refer to Exercise 11.74. Obtain a 90% confidence interval for the expected value of y when $x = 1$.

11.85 Refer to Exercise 11.75. Obtain a 95% confidence interval for the expected value of y when $x = -1$.

11.86 Refer to Exercise 11.75. Given that $x = 2$, find an interval estimate for a particular value of y. Use a confidence coefficient equal to .90.

11.87 Calculate the coefficient of correlation r for the data in Exercise 11.74. What is the significance of this particular value of r?

11.88 Calculate the coefficient of correlation for the data in Exercise 11.75.

11.89 By what percentage was the sum of squares of deviations reduced by using the least-squares predictor $\hat{y} = \hat{\beta}_0 + \hat{\beta}_1 x$ rather than $\bar{y}$ as a predictor of y for the data in Exercise 11.75?

 11.90 A psychological experiment was conducted to study the relationship between the length of time necessary for a human being to reach a decision and the number of alternatives presented. The questions presented to the participants required a classification of an object into two or more classes, similar to the situation that one might encounter in grading potatoes. Five individuals classified one item each for a two-class, two-decision situation. Five each were also allotted to three-class and four-class categories. The length of time necessary to reach a decision is recorded for the 15 participants.

Length of Reaction Time, y (Seconds)	1, 3, 3, 2, 4	2, 4, 3, 4, 5	5, 6, 5, 7, 4
Number of Alternatives, x	2	3	4

(a) Find the least-squares line appropriate for these data.

(b) Plot the points and graph the line as a check on your calculations.

(c) Calculate s^2.

11.91 Do the data in Exercise 11.90 present sufficient evidence to indicate that the length of reaction time y and number of alternatives x are correlated? (Test at the $\alpha = .05$ level of significance.)

 11.92 An experiment was conducted to investigate the effect of a training program on the length of time for a production worker to assemble an electronic timing mechanism. Nine workers were placed in the program. The reduction y in time to complete the assembly was measured for three workers at the end of two weeks, for three at the end of four weeks, and for three at the end of six weeks of training. The data are shown in the table.

Reduction in Time, y (Seconds)	1.6, .8, 1.0	2.1, 1.6, 2.5	3.8, 2.7, 3.1
Length of Training, x (Weeks)	2	4	6

(a) Find the least-squares line for these data.

(b) Estimate the mean reduction in assembly time after four weeks of training. Use a 90% confidence interval.

11.93 Refer to Exercise 11.92. Suppose that only three workers had been employed in the experiment and that the reduction in assembly time was measured for each worker at the end of two, four, and six weeks. Would the assumptions required for the confidence interval in Exercise 11.92(b) be satisfied? Explain.

 11.94 Is the per capita consumption of cheese growing in the United States? A cheese importer would tell you that it depends upon the type. The data shown in Table 11.12 give the per capita consumption of two types of cheeses, Swiss and the combination of Dutch cheeses, Edam and Gouda, for the period 1965 to 1976.

TABLE 11.12   Cheese Consumption Data for Exercise 11.94

Year	$x = $ Year $- 1970$	Per Capita Consumption (Pounds)	
		Swiss	Edam and Gouda
1965	−5	.73	.07
1966	−4	.80	.10
1967	−3	.81	.10
1968	−2	.93	.15
1969	−1	.85	.10
1970	0	.90	.11
1971	1	.95	.10
1972	2	1.08	.11
1973	3	1.08	.12
1974	4	1.21	.11
1975	5	1.12	.11
1976	6	1.28	.11

Source: Dairy Situation, Economic Research Service, U.S. Department of Agriculture, September 1977.

(a) Let y represent the per capita consumption of Swiss cheese. Find a least-squares line appropriate for the data.

(b) Plot the points and graph the line, as a check on your calculations.

(c) Calculate s^2.

(d) Do the data provide sufficient evidence to indicate that the mean annual change β_1 in the per capita consumption of Swiss cheese differs from 0? Test using $\alpha = .10$.

(e) Find a 90% confidence interval for the mean annual change in the consumption rate. Interpret this interval estimate.

(f) If you were a Swiss cheese importer, how much of an increase would you expect in the mean per capita consumption of Swiss cheese in 1978 over 1977?

11.95 Refer to Exercise 11.94. Find a 95% prediction interval for the per capita Swiss cheese consumption in the United States for the year 1977. Interpret your prediction interval. Are there any qualifications that you would place on your prediction? Explain.

11.96 Refer to Exercises 11.94 and 11.95, and perform the same type of data analysis for the per capita consumption measurements for the Dutch (Edam and Gouda) cheese.

 11.97 How closely do the values assigned to properties by appraisers agree with the actual market value of the properties? Table 11.13 gives the tax office appraised values and the sale prices of 12 residential properties sold in a mid-sized Florida city in 1983.

TABLE 11.13   Appraisal and Sales Data for Exercise 11.97

Appraised Value, x	Sale Price, y	Appraised Value, x	Sale Price, y
45.5	60.0	66.4	109.0
42.6	57.5	69.1	96.7
51.2	66.2	73.0	85.0
40.5	51.9	41.7	58.5
61.5	75.0	56.4	109.0
84.7	110.0	102.8	155.0

Source: Data from W. Mendenhall and T. Sincich, *A Second Course in Business Statistics: Regression Analysis,* 2nd ed. (San Francisco: Dellen, 1986).

(a) Plot the data points on graph paper.

(b) Fit a least-squares line to the data.

(c) Find SSE and s^2.

(d) Does the appraised value x contribute information for the prediction of y?

(e) Find r^2 and interpret its value.

(f) Find a 90% confidence interval for the mean sale price of a property with an appraised value of $60,000. Interpret the interval.

(g) Find a 90% prediction interval for the sale price of a property with an appraised value of $70,000. Interpret the interval.

 11.98 Soybean meal production, a major source of protein, varies with the weather, rainfall, and the production of competing products. The data in Table 11.14 show the annual U.S. production (in 100,000 tons) for the years 1960 to 1977.

TABLE 11.14   Soybean Data for Exercise 11.98

Year	Year − 1960, x	Soybean Production, y	Year	Year − 1960, x	Soybean Production, y
1960	0	9.45	1969	9	17.6
1961	1	10.3	1970	10	18.0
1962	2	11.1	1971	11	17.0
1963	3	10.6	1972	12	16.7
1964	4	11.3	1973	13	19.7
1965	5	12.9	1974	14	16.7
1966	6	13.5	1975	15	20.8
1967	7	13.7	1976	16	18.5
1968	8	14.6	1977	17	20.1

Source: Data from *Fats and Oils Situation* (Washington, D.C.: U.S. Department of Agriculture, Economic Research Service, October 1977).

(a) Fit a least-squares line to the data.

(b) Forecast the U.S. soybean meal production for 1978, using a 90% prediction interval.

(c) Notice that you have forecast a value of y outside the range of the x values used to develop the prediction equation. How might this affect the interpretation of your prediction interval?

 11.99 One of the objectives of a study by Scott K. Powers and associates was to investigate the relationship between "running economy" and distance-running performance for trained, competitive male runners. "Running economy" for a runner is defined to be the runner's steady-state oxygen consumption for a standardized running speed. The study involved nine trained runners. Each runner competed in two 10-kilometer races, and the best of the two finish times was recorded. In addition, a measure of each runner's running economy was recorded. These data, along with the number of years of competitive running experience, are shown in Table 11.15 for each runner.

TABLE 11.15   Runners' Data for Exercise 11.99

Runner	Years Competitive Running	Running Economy	10-Kilometer Finish Time (Minutes)
1	9	46.2	33.15
2	13	43.2	33.33
3	5	46.7	33.50
4	7	48.9	33.55
5	12	47.1	33.73
6	6	50.5	33.86
7	4	53.5	33.90
8	5	46.3	34.15
9	3	50.5	34.90

Source: S. K. Powers et al., "Ventilatory Threshold, Running Economy and Distance Running Performance of Trained Athletes, *Research Quarterly for Exercise and Sport,* Vol. 54, No. 3, 1983.

(a) Find the least-squares line relating a runner's running economy x to his finish time y for a 10-kilometer race.

(b) Plot the data points and graph the least-squares line. Does it seem to provide a good fit to the data points?

11.100 Refer to the data in Exercise 11.99 relating the time y to finish a 10-kilometer race to a runner's running economy. Do the data provide sufficient evidence to indicate that the measure of a runner's running economy contributes information for the prediction of finish time? Test using $\alpha = .05$.

11.101 In Exercises 11.99 and 11.100 we analyzed data relating the running time to complete a 10-kilometer race to a measure of a runner's "running economy." If a runner's running economy is found to be 47.0, find a 90% prediction interval for the length of time for the runner to complete a 10-kilometer race.

11.102 A large retailer employs computer-operated record keeping from point of sale through customer billing. Theoretically, the only errors that can enter the system are caused by incorrect entries made for each sale by the salesperson making the sale. Does lack of sleep increase the incidence of incorrect entries by salespersons? A total of ten salespersons participated in a study designed to provide information on this question. Two each were assigned to each of five sleep deprivation periods. Following the assigned period of sleep deprivation, each salesperson worked for an 8-hour shift, and the number of incorrect computer entries was recorded. The data follow.

Number of Errors, y	8, 6	6, 10	8, 14	14, 20	16, 12
Number of Hours Without Sleep	8	12	16	20	24

(a) Plot the data on graph paper.

(b) Fit a least-squares line to the data.

(c) Calculate s^2.

(d) Do the data provide sufficient evidence to indicate that the mean number of errors increases as the number of hours of sleep deprivation increases? Test using $\alpha = .05$.

11.103 Refer to Exercise 11.102. How well does the straight-line, least-squares model fit the data? Justify your answer.

11.104 Refer to Exercise 11.102. Find a 90% confidence interval on the mean number of entry errors that a salesperson might make in an 18-hour day following a sleep deprivation period of 12 hours.

 11.105 Do personal savings increase in proportion to disposable personal income? The data in Table 11.16 may shed some light on this question. They give the total annual savings y and the total disposable income x (in billions of dollars) for the United States for the years 1975 through 1982.

TABLE 11.16 Savings and Income Data for Exercise 11.105

	Year							
Variable	1975	1976	1977	1978	1979	1980	1981	1982
Annual savings, y	94.3	82.5	78.0	89.4	96.7	106.2	130.2	142.7
Disposable personal income, x	1096.1	1194.4	1314.0	1474.0	1650.2	1824.1	2029.1	2173.4

Source: Data from *National Food Review* (Washington, D.C.: U.S. Department of Agriculture, Spring 1983).

(a) Plot the data points on graph paper.

(b) Fit a least-squares line to the data.

(c) Graph the line on your plot for part (a). Does the least-squares line seem to provide a good fit to the data?

11.106 Refer to Exercise 11.105. Does disposable personal income x provide information for the prediction of annual savings y? Test using $\alpha = .05$.

11.107 Calculate r and r^2 for the data of Exercise 11.105, and interpret their values.

 11.108 The earnings y per share (EPS) for Wendy's International (the fast-food company) for the years 1977 through 1985 are shown in Table 11.17; the SAS regression analysis printout is shown in Table 11.18. To simplify calculations, we have coded the year variable by subtracting 1976 from each year; that is, $x =$ year $- 1976$.

TABLE 11.17 Earnings Data for Exercise 11.108

	Actual Year								
Variable	1977	1978	1979	1980	1981	1982	1983	1984	1985
Coded year, x	1	2	3	4	5	6	7	8	9
EPS (Dollars), y	.27	.42	.39	.50	.57	.64	.76	.93	1.03

TABLE 11.18   SAS Printout for Exercise 11.108

DEP VARIABLE: Y

ANALYSIS OF VARIANCE

SOURCE	DF	SUM OF SQUARES	MEAN SQUARE	F VALUE	PROB>F
MODEL	1	0.49504167	0.49504167	165.693	0.0001
ERROR	7	0.02091389	0.002987698		
C TOTAL	8	0.51595556			

ROOT MSE	0.05465984	R-SQUARE	0.9595	
DEP MEAN	0.6122222	ADJ R-SQ	0.9537	
C.V.	8.928105			

PARAMETER ESTIMATES

VARIABLE	DF	PARAMETER ESTIMATE	STANDARD ERROR	T FOR H0: PARAMETER=0	PROB > |T|
INTERCEP	1	0.15805556	0.03970946	3.980	0.0053
X	1	0.09083333	0.007056555	12.872	0.0001

OBS	ID	ACTUAL	PREDICT VALUE	STD ERR PREDICT	LOWER95% PREDICT	UPPER95% PREDICT	RESIDUAL
1	1	0.2700	0.2489	0.0336	0.0972	0.4006	0.0211
2	2	0.4200	0.3397	0.0279	0.1946	0.4849	0.0803
3	3	0.3900	0.4306	0.0230	0.2903	0.5708	-0.0406
4	4	0.5000	0.5214	0.0195	0.3841	0.6586	-0.0214
5	5	0.5700	0.6122	0.0182	0.4760	0.7485	-0.0422
6	6	0.6400	0.7031	0.0195	0.5658	0.8403	-0.0631
7	7	0.7600	0.7939	0.0230	0.6536	0.9342	-0.0339
8	8	0.9300	0.8847	0.0279	0.7396	1.0299	0.0453
9	9	1.0300	0.9756	0.0336	0.8238	1.1273	0.0544

SUM OF RESIDUALS   6.33378E-16
SUM OF SQUARED RESIDUALS   0.02091389

(a) Locate $\hat{\beta}_0$ and $\hat{\beta}_1$ on the printout, and give the equation of the least-squares line.

(b) Plot the data points on graph paper and graph the least-squares line.

(c) Find r^2 on the printout and interpret its value.

(d) Does x contribute information for the prediction of y? Explain.

(e) Find a 95% confidence interval for the mean change in earnings per year.

11.109 Fit a least-squares line to the Wendy's International data in Exercise 11.108.

(a) Find $\hat{\beta}_0$, $\hat{\beta}_1$, and the equation of the least-squares line.

(b) Calculate s^2.

(c) Calculate r^2.

(d) Compare the values in parts (a), (b), and (c) with those given on the SAS printout in Table 11.18.

In Chapter 11 we introduced the concepts of simple linear regression and correlation, the ultimate goal being to estimate the mean value of y or to predict a value of y by using information contained in a single independent (predictor) variable x. In this chapter we expand this idea and will relate the mean value of y to one or more independent variables $x_1, x_2, \ldots x_k$ in models that are more flexible than the straight-line model of Chapter 11. The process of finding the least-squares prediction equation, testing the adequacy of the model, and conducting tests about and estimating the values of the model parameters is called a multiple regression analysis.

12 MULTIPLE REGRESSION ANALYSIS

CASE STUDY: Predicting Worker Absenteeism

Predicting Worker Absenteeism

If you have ever been responsible for managing a high school or college function, a recreational facility, or worked in business or industry, you have probably experienced one of the major problems facing business managers, namely, worker absenteeism. Can you imagine being responsible for the planning and production of college homecoming activities when the participants, seemingly at random, miss the organizational and functional meetings? Or can you imagine coaching a professional football team in which the players, the quarterback, the center, linebackers, and so on, seemingly at random, were absent at games or practice sessions? Or consider being responsible for an automobile assembly line where various members of the assembly team may be absent on any given day. As worker absenteeism increases, the productivity of an operating group, office force, manufacturing plant, and the like decreases, and usually the quality of the product also decreases. Consequently, business managers try to identify the causes of worker absenteeism so that they can take action to control or reduce it.

Regression analysis is one method of determining variables that are related to worker absenteeism. The first step would be to define a measure, y, of worker absenteeism, say, the number of worker absences per month, the number of absences for a given worker per month, or some other suitable criterion. The next step would be to define a set of independent variables that we think might be related to y. Finally, we would relate y to the independent variables, using a multiple regression model, and would fit the model to a set of data. If the resulting least-squares prediction equation provided a good fit to the data—that is, if it enabled us to predict a measure y of absenteeism with a small error of prediction—we would conclude that at least one of the independent variables contributes information for the prediction of y. This would not tell us which of the independent variables contributed the most information for the prediction of y, and it would not imply that any of the independent variables *caused* y to increase or decrease. It would only identify a set of variables important for the prediction of y. To conclude our study, we would need to don our detective's hat and attempt to guess or determine which, if any, of the variables were causally related to the absenteeism measure y.

K. Constas and R. P. Vichas use a multiple regression analysis in an attempt to identify variables related to worker absenteeism at two different types of overseas industrial plants ("An Interpretative Policy-Making Model of Absenteeism with Reference to the Marginal Worker in Overseas Plants," *Journal of Management Studies,* Vol. 17, 1980). They confine their attention to independent variables that characterize a worker's "life space," that is, variables that personally characterize the worker as opposed to variables that characterize the work space (the working conditions to which the worker is exposed). We will learn how to interpret the computer printout for a multiple regression analysis in this chapter, and we will specifically examine the Constas and Vichas regression analysis in Section 12.12.

THE OBJECTIVES OF A MULTIPLE REGRESSION ANALYSIS

12.1

The objective of a multiple regression analysis is to relate a response variable y to a set of predictor variables by using a multiple regression model. Ultimately, we want to be able to estimate the mean value of y and/or predict particular values of y to be observed in the future when the predictor variables assume specific values.

To illustrate, we might want to relate a company's regional sales y of a product to the amount x_1 of the company's television advertising expenditures, to the amount x_2 of newspaper advertising expenditures, and to the number x_3 of sales representatives assigned to the region. Thus we would want to use data collected on y, x_1, x_2, and x_3 to obtain a mathematical prediction equation relating y to x_1, x_2, and x_3. We would use this prediction equation to predict the regional sales of a product for specific advertising expenditures (values of x_1 and x_2) and a specific number of sales representatives. If we are successful in developing a good prediction equation, one that makes accurate sales predictions, we can (by examining the equation) obtain a better understanding of the manner in which these controllable predictor variables x_1, x_2, and x_3 affect the product's sales.

This chapter is intended to be a brief introduction to multiple regression analysis, to help you understand what it is and aid you in interpreting the results of a multiple regression computer printout. We do not intend to cover all of the topics usually covered in a discussion of multiple regression analysis, nor do we intend to spend much time discussing the difficult task of formulating the regression model. For additional information on multiple regression, we recommend the references listed at the end of the chapter.

THE MULTIPLE REGRESSION MODEL AND ASSOCIATED ASSUMPTIONS

12.2

The **general linear model** for a multiple regression analysis will take the form shown in the box.

THE GENERAL LINEAR MODEL AND ASSUMPTIONS

$$y = \beta_0 + \beta_1 x_1 + \beta_2 x_2 + \cdots + \beta_k x_k + \varepsilon$$

where the assumptions are as follows:

(1) $y =$ the response variable that you want to predict.

(2) $\beta_0, \beta_1, \beta_2, \ldots, \beta_k$ are constants.

(3) $x_1, x_2, \ldots, x_k$ are independent **predictor variables** that are measured without error.

(4) ε is a random error that for any given set of values for $x_1, x_2, \ldots, x_k$ is normally distributed with mean 0 and variance equal to σ^2.

(5) The random errors, say ε_i and ε_j, associated with any pair of y values are independent.

With these assumptions, it follows that the mean value of y for a given set of values for $x_1, x_2, \ldots, x_k$ is equal to

$$E(y) = \beta_0 + \beta_1 x_1 + \beta_2 x_2 + \cdots + \beta_k x_k$$

The variables $x_1, x_2, \ldots, x_k$ that appear in the general linear model need not represent *different* predictor variables. Our assumption only requires that when we observe a value of y, the values of $x_1, x_2, \ldots, x_k$ can be recorded without error. For example, if we want to relate the mean measure $E(y)$ of worker absenteeism to two predictor variables, say

$$x_1 = \text{worker age}$$

$$x_2 = \text{worker hourly wage rate}$$

we can construct any of a number of models. One possibility is

$$E(y) = \beta_0 + \beta_1 x_1 + \beta_2 x_2$$

This model graphs as a *plane*, a surface in the three-dimensional space defined by y, x_1, and x_2. Or if we suspect that the response surface relating $E(y)$ to x_1 and x_2 possesses curvature, we might use the model

$$E(y) = \beta_0 + \beta_1 x_1 + \beta_2 x_2 + \beta_3 x_1 x_2$$

or

$$E(y) = \beta_0 + \beta_1 x_1 + \beta_2 x_2 + \beta_3 x_1 x_2 + \beta_4 x_1^2 + \beta_5 x_2^2$$

In addition to containing the *first-order terms*, those involving only x_1 or x_2, these models include *second-order terms*, such as x_1^2, x_2^2, and the two-variable cross product $x_1 x_2$.* Thus all three of these models relate $E(y)$ to only two predictor variables, x_1 and x_2, but the number of terms and interpretations of the models differ.

Choosing a good model relating y to a set of predictor variables is a difficult and important task, much more difficult than fitting the model to a set of data (this is usually done automatically by a computer). Even if your model includes all of the important predictor variables, it still may provide a poor fit to your data if the form of the model is not properly specified.

For example, suppose that $E(y)$ is *perfectly* related to a single predictor variable x_1 by the relation

$$E(y) = \beta_0 + \beta_1 x_1 + \beta_2 x_1^2$$

If you fit the first-order (straight-line) model

$$E(y) = \beta_0 + \beta_1 x_1$$

to the data, you will obtain the *best-fitting, least-squares line,* but it may still provide a poor fit to your data and may be of little value for estimation or prediction [see Figure 12.1(a)]. In contrast, if you fit the model

$$E(y) = \beta_0 + \beta_1 x_1 + \beta_2 x_1^2$$

you obtain a perfect fit to the data [see Figure 12.1(b)].

---

*The *order* of a term is determined by the sum of the exponents of variables making up that term. Terms involving x_1 or x_2 are first-order. Terms involving x_1^2, x_2^2, or $x_1 x_2$ are second-order.

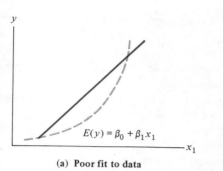
$$E(y) = \beta_0 + \beta_1 x_1$$

(a) **Poor fit to data**

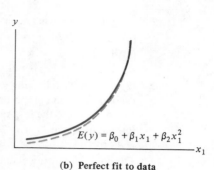
$$E(y) = \beta_0 + \beta_1 x_1 + \beta_2 x_1^2$$

(b) **Perfect fit to data**

FIGURE 12.1   Two Models, Each Using One Predictor Variable

The lesson is quite clear. Including all of the important predictor variables in the model as first-order terms, that is, $x_1, x_2, \ldots, x_k$, may not (and probably will not) produce a model that provides a good fit to your data. You may have to include second-order terms, such as $x_1^2, x_2^2, x_3^2, x_1 x_2, x_1 x_3$.

This discussion of linear models is purposely brief. We want you to understand the importance of model selection as a step that precedes a multiple regression analysis. Second, we want to help you to understand the logic used in selecting the model for the multiple regression analysis that follows in Section 12.3. Although we offer a few additional comments on model formulation in optional Section 12.8, we have no intention of covering this complex topic in a short introductory chapter on regression analysis. Our aim is to help you understand the output of a multiple regression analysis and to understand some of the problems that can be solved by using this statistical methology. For a more thorough discussion of model building, we refer you to Mendenhall and Sincich (1986).

EXERCISES

BASIC TECHNIQUES

12.1 Graph the following equations over the interval $0 \le x \le 4$.

(a) $E(y) = 3 + 2x$. What type of curve is this?

(b) $E(y) = 3 + 2x + x^2$. Compare the graphs of the curves in parts (a) and (b). What effect does the addition of the x^2 term have on the relationship between y and x? What type of curve is this?

(c) $E(y) = 3 - 2x + x^2$. Compare the graphs in parts (b) and (c). What effect does the coefficient of x have on the graph of a parabola?

(d) $E(y) = 3 + 2x - x^2$. Compare the graphs in parts (b) and (d). What effect does the sign of the coefficient of x^2 have on the graph of a parabola?

12.2 Examine the graphs of the equations in Exercise 12.1.

(a) What is the interpretation of the constant β_0 in the equation of a straight line: $E(y) = \beta_0 + \beta_1 x$?

(b) What is the interpretation of the constant β_0 in the equation of a parabola: $E(y) = \beta_0 + \beta_1 x + \beta_2 x^2$?

12.3 Graph the following equations (they graph as parabolas).

(a) $E(y) = 2x^2$

(b) $E(y) = 1 + 2x^2$

(c) $E(y) = -1 + 2x^2$

(d) $E(y) = -2x^2$

(e) How does the sign of the coefficient of x^2 affect the graph of a parabola?

12.4 (a) Graph the following equation: $E(y) = 2x^2 - 4x + 2$.

(b) Compare the graph in part (a) with the graph of Exercise 12.3, part (a). What effect does the inclusion of the first-order term $(-4x)$ have on the graph?

(c) Suppose that $E(y) = 2x^2 + 4x + 2$. Can you deduce the effect on the parabola of replacing $-4x$ by $+4x$?

12.5 Graph the following equations on the same sheet of graph paper.

(a) $y = (x - 2)^2 = x^2 - 4x + 4$

(b) $y = (x + 2)^2 = x^2 + 4x + 4$

(c) Compare the two parabolas that you have graphed. What is the effect of changing the sign of the coefficient of x on the graph of a parabola?

12.6 Graph the following equations on the same sheet of graph paper.

(a) $y = (x - 2)^2 = x^2 - 4x + 4$

(b) $y = -(x - 2)^2 = -x^2 + 4x - 4$

(c) Compare the two parabolas that you have graphed. What is the effect of changing the signs of the terms in the equation of a parabola?

12.7 Graph the following equations.

(a) $y = (x - 2)^2 + 5 = x^2 - 4x + 9$

(b) $y = (x - 2)^2 - 5 = x^2 - 4x - 1$

(c) Compare the graphs in parts (a) and (b) with the graph in Exercise 12.5(a). What is the effect of changing the constant in the equation of a parabola?

12.8 Suppose that $E(y)$ is related to two predictor variables x_1 and x_2 by the equation

$$E(y) = 3 + x_1 - 2x_2$$

(a) Graph the relationship between $E(y)$ and x_1 when $x_2 = 2$. Repeat for $x_2 = 1$ and for $x_2 = 0$.

(b) What relationship do the lines in part (a) have to each other?

12.9 Refer to Exercise 12.8.

(a) Graph the relationship $E(y)$ and x_2 when $x_1 = 0$. Repeat for $x_1 = 1$ and for $x_1 = 2$.

(b) What relationship do the lines in part (a) have to each other?

(c) Suppose that in a practical situation you wanted to model the relationship between $E(y)$ and two predictor variables x_1 and x_2. What would be the implication of using the first-order model $E(y) = \beta_0 + \beta_1 x_1 + \beta_2 x_2$?

12.10 Suppose that $E(y)$ is related to two predictor variables x_1 and x_2 by the equation

$$E(y) = 3 + x_1 - 2x_2 + x_1 x_2$$

(a) Graph the relationship between $E(y)$ and x_1 when $x_2 = 0$. Repeat for $x_2 = 2$ and for $x_2 = -2$.

(b) Note that the equation for $E(y)$ is exactly the same as the equation in Exercise 12.8 except that we have added the term $x_1 x_2$. How does the addition of the $x_1 x_2$ term affect the graphs of the three lines?

(c) What flexibility is added to the first-order model $E(y) = \beta_0 + \beta_1 x_1 + \beta_2 x_2$ by the addition of the term $\beta_3 x_1 x_2$, using the model $E(y) = \beta_0 + \beta_1 x_1 + \beta_2 x_2 + \beta_3 x_1 x_2$?

12.3 A MULTIPLE REGRESSION ANALYSIS

A multiple regression analysis is performed somewhat like a simple linear regression analysis. A multiple regression model, say,

$$E(y) = \beta_0 + \beta_1 x_1 + \beta_2 x_2 + \cdots + \beta_k x_k$$

is fitted to a set of data by using the method of least squares, a procedure that finds the prediction equation

$$\hat{y} = \hat{\beta}_0 + \hat{\beta}_1 x_1 + \hat{\beta}_2 x_2 + \cdots + \hat{\beta}_k x_k$$

that minimizes SSE, the sum of squares of deviations of the observed values of y from their predicted values. The major differences between a simple and a multiple regression analysis are that the multiple regression model contains more parameters, and the computation required for a multiple regression analysis is so complicated and time-consuming that it is usually performed on an electronic computer. In this section we will present two sets of data, formulate models for each, and present printouts for two different SAS multiple regression procedures (REG and GLM). Although these printouts differ somewhat, both contain the same essential information.

EXAMPLE 12.1 In a study of variables affecting productivity in the retail grocery trade, W. S. Good uses value added per man-hour to measure the productivity of retail grocery outlets. He defines "value added" as "the surplus [money generated by the business] available to pay for labor, furniture and fixtures, and equipment" (W. S. Good, "Productivity in the Retail Grocery Trade," *Journal of Retailing,* Vol. 60, No. 3, 1984). Data consistent with the relationship between value added per man-hour (y) and the size (x) of a grocery outlet described in Good's article are shown in Table 12.1 for ten fictitious grocery outlets. Choose a linear model to relate y to x.

TABLE 12.1 Value Added per Man-Hour Versus Size of Store

Variable	Store									
	1	2	3	4	5	6	7	8	9	10
Value added per man-hour (dollars), y	4.08	3.40	3.51	3.09	2.92	1.94	4.11	3.16	3.75	3.60
Size of store (thousands of square feet), x	21.0	12.0	25.2	10.4	30.9	6.8	19.6	14.5	25.0	19.1

SOLUTION The first step in choosing a model to describe the data is to plot the data points (see Figure 12.2). The relationship suggested by the data is one that depicts productivity rising as the size of a grocery outlet increases, until an optimal size is reached. Above that size, productivity tends to decrease. Since the relationship that we have described suggests curvature, we will fit a second-order model,

$$E(y) = \beta_0 + \beta_1 x + \beta_2 x^2$$

to the data.

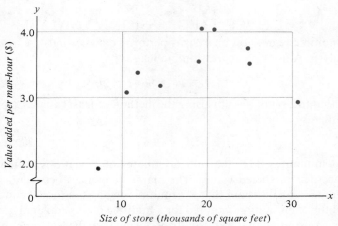

FIGURE 12.2   Plot of the Data Points for Example 12.1

A second-order model,

$$E(y) = \beta_0 + \beta_1 x + \beta_2 x^2$$

always graphs as a parabola (see Figure 12.3). If the coefficient β_2 is negative, the curve will open downward [see Figure 12.3(a)]. If β_2 is positive, the curve will open upward [see Figure 12.3(b)].

The least-squares procedure chooses the best-fitting, second-order model for our data. Since the plot of our data rises and falls as x increases, we would expect the value of β_2 in the fitted model to be negative. The segment of the parabola that passes through our data points should appear as shown in Figure 12.4.

Keep in mind that in choosing a second-order model to fit to our data, we are not saying that the true relationship between the mean value of y and the value x is

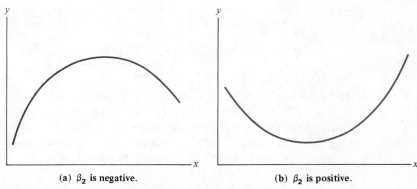

(a) β_2 is negative.   (b) β_2 is positive.

FIGURE 12.3   How the Sign of β_2 Affects the Shape of a Parabola

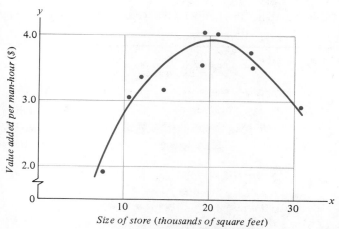

FIGURE 12.4   Graph of the Portion of a Second-Order Model That May Fit the Plot of Our Data Points for Example 12.1

defined by an equation of the type

$$E(y) = \beta_0 + \beta_1 x + \beta_2 x^2$$

Rather, we have chosen this equation to *model* the relationship. Presumably, it will provide a better description of the relationship than a first-order model (that graphs as a straight line), and it will enable us to estimate the mean productivity of a grocery retail outlet as a function of the outlet size.

EXAMPLE 12.2   Refer to the data on grocery retail outlet productivity and outlet size given in Example 12.1.

(a) Fit a second-order model to the data, using a SAS REG* computer program package.

(b) Graph the second-order prediction curve, along with the plotted data points.

SOLUTION   (a) The SAS REG computer printout is shown in Table 12.2. You will see that this printout is similar to the SAS printout in Table 11.10, Section 11.10, but that it contains more entries. The relevant portions of the printout are shaded and numbered.

(1) The value of

$$R^2 = 1 - \frac{\text{SSE}}{\sum_{i=1}^{n}(y_i - \bar{y})^2} = 1 - \frac{\text{SSE}}{\text{SS}_y}$$

the multiple coefficient of determination, provides a measure of how well the model fits the data. As you can see, the value for R^2 is .8794. Therefore, 87.9% of

*SAS provides two multiple regression computer program packages, SAS GLM and SAS REG. The outputs for both packages (which are similar) are described in this chapter.

TABLE 12.2   SAS REG Computer Printout for the Regression Analysis of Example 12.2

DEPENDENT VARIABLE: Y

ANALYSIS OF VARIANCE

SOURCE	DF	SUM OF SQUARES	MEAN SQUARE	F VALUE	PR > F	R-SQUARE	C.V.
MODEL	2	3.19889499	1.59944750	25.530	0.0006	0.8794 ①	7.458236
ERROR	7	0.43854501	0.06264929 ⑦		ROOT MSE	ADJ R-SQ	Y MEAN
CORRECTED TOTAL	9	3.63744000 ⑨			0.2502984 ⑧	0.8450	3.356

② above F VALUE / PR > F area

PARAMETER ESTIMATES

VARIABLE	DF	PARAMETER ESTIMATE ③	T FOR H0: PARAMETER=0 ④	PR > |T| ⑤	STD ERROR
INTERCEP	1	-0.15935613	-0.318	0.7595	0.50058011 ⑥
X	1	0.39193078	6.757	0.0003	0.05800604
XSQ	1	-0.009494814	-6.188	0.0005	0.001534502

OBSERVATION	ACTUAL	PREDICT VALUE	STD ERR PREDICT	LOWER 95% PREDICT	UPPER 95% PREDICT	RESIDUAL
1	4.0800	3.8840	0.1087	3.2387	4.5293	0.1960
2	3.4000	3.1766	0.1074	2.5325	3.8206	0.2234
3	3.5100	3.6877	0.1094	3.0418	4.3337	-0.1777
4	3.0900	2.8898	0.1217	2.2317	3.5478	0.2002 ⑩
5	2.9200	2.8856	0.2227	2.0933	3.6778	0.0344
6	1.9400	2.0667	0.2021	1.3060	2.8274	-0.1267
7	4.1100	3.8750	0.1108	3.2277	4.5222	0.2350
8	3.1600	3.5274	0.1048	2.8857	4.1690	-0.3674
9	3.7500	3.7047	0.1084	3.0597	4.3496	0.0453
10	3.6000	3.8627	0.1112	3.2151	4.5103	-0.2627

SUM OF RESIDUALS   7.77156E-15
SUM OF SQUARED RESIDUALS   0.438545

the sum of squares of deviations of the y values about $\bar{y}$ is explained by the model. The coefficient R^2 assumes practical significance when the number of data points exceeds the number of parameters in the model by a reasonable number, say, at least 5 or more (i.e., the degrees of freedom for SSE is d.f. ≥ 5). That is, a linear model containing three parameters will always fit a data set better than a model containing two parameters; and, in general, a model containing $k + 1$ parameters will fit better than one containing k parameters. If the number of parameters in the model equals the number of data points, the fitted model will pass through all of the data points and you will obtain a perfect fit.

② If the model contributes information for the prediction of y, at least one of the model parameters, β_1 or β_2, will differ from 0. Consequently, we wish to test the null hypothesis $H_0: \beta_1 = \beta_2 = 0$ against the alternative hypothesis H_a: at least one of the parameters β_1 or β_2 differs from 0. The test statistic for this test, an F statistic with $v_1 =$ (the number of parameters in H_0) $= 2$ and $v_2 = n -$ (number of parameters in the model) $= 10 - 3 = 7$, is shown in shaded area ② to be 25.530. Since this value exceeds the tabulated value for F [with $v_1 = 2$, $v_2 = 7$, and $\alpha = .05$, $F = 4.74$ (from Table 8 in the Appendix)] we reject H_0 and conclude that at least one of the parameters β_1 or β_2 differs from 0. There is evidence to indicate that the model contributes information for the prediction of y. The observed significance level (p-value) for the test, **PROB > F**, shown to the right of the value of the F statistic, is equal to .0006. The F statistic used for this test is related to R^2 by the formula

$$F = \frac{R^2/k}{(1 - R^2)/[n - (k + 1)]}$$

where n = number of data points and k = number of terms in the linear model not including β_0. For this example $k = 2$.

(3) The estimates of the three model parameters are shown in shaded area ③ under the heading **PARAMETER ESTIMATE**: $\beta_0 = -.15935613$, $\hat{\beta}_1 = .39193078$, and $\hat{\beta}_2 = -.009494814$. If we round these estimates, the prediction equation is

$$\hat{y} = -.15936 + .39193x - .00949x^2$$

(4) Tests of hypotheses concerning each of the individual model parameters can be conducted by using Student t tests. The test statistic is similar* to the t statistic used for the test $H_0 : \beta_1 = 0$, for the slope β_1 in a simple linear model:

$$t = \frac{\text{parameter estimate}}{\text{estimated standard deviation of the estimator}}$$

The computed value of the t statistic for each of the model parameters is shown in shaded area ④ under the column **T FOR H_0 : PARAMETER = 0**. For example, the value of the t statistic for the test $H_0 : \beta_2 = 0$ is -6.188. The number of degrees of freedom for SSE, s^2, and therefore, t will always be based on $v = n - $ (number of parameters in the model) degrees of freedom. For our example this will be $v = 10 - 3 = 7$ degrees of freedom. For $\alpha = .05$ the tabulated value of t, $t_{.025}$, for a two-tailed test, given in Table 5 in the Appendix, is 2.365. Since the computed t value corresponding to β_2 is less than -2.365, there is evidence to indicate that β_2 differs from 0.

(5) The observed significance levels (p-values) for the t tests described in part (4) are shown in shaded area ⑤ under the column headed **PROB > |T|**. **These values are calculated for two-tailed tests. If you wish to conduct a one-tailed test, the p-value is half of the value shown in the printout.** For example, the observed significance level for a test of the hypothesis $H_0 : \beta_2 = 0$, $H_a : \beta_2 \neq 0$ is .0005 for this two-tailed test. If the alternative hypothesis is $H_a : \beta_2 > 0$—that is, you wish to conduct a one-tailed test of H_0—then the p-value is equal to $(.0005)/2 = .00025$. If you were to test H_0 using $\alpha = .05$, these small p-values would imply rejection of H_0.

(6) The estimated standard deviations of the estimators are shown in shaded area ⑥ under the heading **STANDARD ERROR**. For example,

$$s_{\hat{\beta}_1} = .05800604$$

*The test statistic looks the same, but the standard deviation in the denominator is calculated in a different and more complicated manner.

This quantity is useful in calculating $(1 - \alpha)100\%$ confidence intervals for the model parameters. For example, a $(1 - \alpha)100\%$ confidence interval for β_1 is equal to

$$\hat{\beta}_1 \pm t_{\alpha/2} s_{\hat{\beta}_1}$$

Therefore, a 95% confidence interval for β_1 is

$$.3919 \pm (2.365)(.0580)$$

or

$$.3919 \pm .1372$$

Confidence intervals for the other model parameters are constructed in the same way. Thus a $(1 - \alpha)100\%$ confidence interval for β_2 is

$$\hat{\beta}_2 \pm t_{\alpha/2} s_{\hat{\beta}_2}$$

where $t_{\alpha/2}$ is based on $v = n -$ (number of parameters in the model) $= 10 - 3 = 7$ degrees of freedom.

(7) The values of SSE $= .43854501$ and $s^2 = .06264929$ are shown in shaded area ⑦ in the row corresponding to ERROR and under the columns headed, respectively, SUM OF SQUARES and MEAN SQUARE.

(8) The standard deviation $s = .2502984$ is shown in shaded area ⑧, labeled ROOT MSE.

(9) The total sum of squares of deviations SS_y of the y values about the mean is shown in shaded area ⑨ to be 3.63744000. You can verify that the tabulated value of R^2 is equal to $1 - SSE/SS_y$.

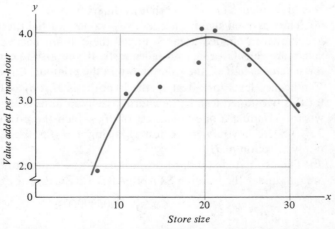

FIGURE 12.5   A Graph of the Least-Squares Prediction Equation for the Second-Order Model of Example 12.2

(10) The predicted value of y for each of the ten observed values of x is shown in shaded area ⑩ under PREDICT VALUE. The observed values of y are shown in the column headed ACTUAL. The 95% prediction intervals for y for these ten values of x are given in the columns headed LOWER 95% PREDICT and UPPER 95% PREDICT. The RESIDUAL, shown in the last column, gives the deviation between the observed and predicted values. For example, when $x = 21$, the observed value of y is 4.0800, the predicted value is 3.8840, the residual is $(4.0800 - 3.8840) = .1960$. The 95% prediction interval for y when $x = 0$ is 3.2387 to 4.5293.

(b) A graph of the second-order prediction curve is shown in Figure 12.5, along with the plotted data points. You can see that the prediction curve provides a good fit to the data.

EXAMPLE 12.3

From the fitted second-order model in Example 12.2, estimate the size of a grocery retail outlet that yields the maximum productivity (measured by the value added per man-hour).

SOLUTION

A visual examination of the graph of $\hat{y}$ in Figure 12.5 shows that $\hat{y}$ reaches a maximum at approximately $x = 20.3$ thousand square feet (see Figure 12.6).

To find the exact value of $\hat{y}$, we employ the methods of calculus to locate a maximum or a minimum—that is, we will differentiate $\hat{y}$ with respect to x, set the derivative equal to 0, and solve for x. Thus

$$\hat{y} = -.15936 + .3913x - .00949x^2$$

$$\frac{d\hat{y}}{dx} = .3913 - 2(.00949)x$$

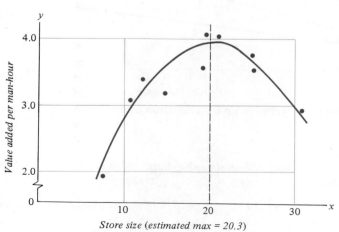

FIGURE 12.6   Estimated Store Size for Example 12.3 for Which Productivity Is a Maximum

Setting $d\hat{y}/dx$ equal to 0 and solving for x yields

$$\frac{d\hat{y}}{dx} = .3913 - .01898x = 0$$

So the value of x for which productivity $\hat{y}$ is a maximum is

$$x = \frac{.3913}{.01898} = 20.6 \text{ thousand square feet}$$

You can see that this is very close to the value obtained from our visual examination of Figure 12.6.*

EXAMPLE 12.4

A study was conducted to examine the relationship between university salary y, the number of years of experience of the faculty member, and the sex of the faculty member. If we expect a straight-line relationship between mean salary and years of experience for both males and females, write the model relating mean salary to the two predictor variables:

(1) Years of experience (quantitative).
(2) Sex of the professor (qualitative).

SOLUTION

Since we may suspect the mean salary lines for females and males to be different, we want to construct a model for mean salary $E(y)$ that may appear as shown in Figure 12.7.

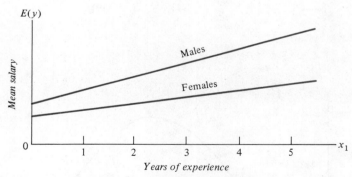

FIGURE 12.7   Hypothetical Relationship Between Mean Salary $E(y)$, Years of Experience (x_1), and Sex (x_2) for Example 12.4

A straight-line relationship between $E(y)$ and years of experience x_1 implies the model

$$E(y) = \beta_0 + \beta_1 x_1 \qquad \text{(graphed as a straight line)}$$

*The procedure required to find a confidence interval for $\hat{x}$ is beyond the scope of this text.

The qualitative variable* sex can only assume two "values," male and female. Therefore, we can enter the predictor variable sex into the model by using one **dummy** (or **indicator**) **variable**, x_2, as

$$E(y) = \beta_0 + \beta_1 x_1 + \beta_2 x_2 \qquad \text{(graphs as two parallel lines)}$$

$$x_2 = \begin{cases} 1, & \text{if male} \\ 0, & \text{if female} \end{cases}$$

The fact that we want to allow the slopes of the two lines to differ means that we think that the two predictor variables **interact** — that is, the change in $E(y)$ corresponding to a change in x_1 depends on whether the professor is male or female. To allow for this interaction (difference in slopes), we introduce the interaction term $x_1 x_2$ into the model. The complete model that characterizes the graph in Figure 12.7 is

dummy variable
for sex
↓

$$E(y) = \beta_0 + \beta_1 x_1 + \beta_2 x_2 + \beta_3 x_1 x_2$$

↑
years of   interaction
experience

where

$$x_1 = \text{years of experience}$$

$$x_2 = \begin{cases} 1, & \text{if a male} \\ 0, & \text{if a female} \end{cases}$$

The interpretation of the model parameters can be seen by assigning values to the dummy variable x_2. Thus when you want to acquire the line for females, the dummy variable $x_2 = 0$ (according to our coding), and

$$E(y) = \beta_0 + \beta_1 x_1 + \beta_2(0) + \beta_3 x_1(0) = \beta_0 + \beta_1 x_1$$

Therefore, β_0 is the y intercept for the females' line, and β_1 is the slope of the line relating expected salary to years of experience for *females only*.

Similarly, the line for males is obtained by letting $x_2 = 1$. Then

$$E(y) = \beta_0 + \beta_1 x_1 + \beta_2(1) + \beta_3 x_1(1)$$
$$= \underbrace{(\beta_0 + \beta_2)}_{y \text{ intercept}} + \underbrace{(\beta_1 + \beta_3) x_1}_{\text{slope}}$$

The y intercept of the males' line is $(\beta_0 + \beta_2)$, and the slope, the coefficient of x_1, is equal to $(\beta_1 + \beta_3)$.

Because the slope of the males' line is $(\beta_1 + \beta_3)$ and the slope of the females' line is β_1, it follows that $(\beta_1 + \beta_3) - \beta_1 = \beta_3$ is the difference in the slopes of the two lines. Similarly, β_2 is equal to the difference in the y intercepts for the two lines. ∎

*Qualitative data, observations on a qualitative variable, were discussed in Section 2.1. We will have more to say about qualitative variables in optional Section 12.8.

EXAMPLE 12.5　Random samples of six female and six male assistant professors were selected from among the assistant professors in a college of arts and sciences. The data on salary and years of experience are shown in Table 12.3. Note that both samples contained two professors with 3 years of experience but no male professor had 2 years of experience.

TABLE 12.3　Salary Versus Sex and Years of Experience

Years of Experience, x_1	1	2	3	4	5
Salary, y (males)	20,710		23,160 23,210	24,140	25,760 25,590
Salary, y (females)	19,510	20,440	21,340 21,760	22,750	23,200

(a) Explain the output of the SAS GLM multiple regression computer printout.

(b) Graph the predicted salary lines.

SOLUTION　(a) The SAS GLM multiple regression computer printout for the data in Table 12.3 is shown in Table 12.4. The explanation of this printout is similar to the explanation of the SAS REG computer printout given in Example 12.2. The relevant portions of the printout are shaded and numbered.

(1) The value of

$$R^2 = 1 - \frac{\text{SSE}}{\sum_{i=1}^{n}(y_i - \bar{y})^2} = 1 - \frac{\text{SSE}}{\text{SS}_y}$$

TABLE 12.4　The SAS GLM Multiple Regression Analysis Computer Printout for Example 12.5

```
DEPENDENT VARIABLE: Y
                                                                    ②              ①
SOURCE              DF          SUM OF SQUARES     MEAN SQUARE    F VALUE   PR > F   R-SQUARE            C.V.

MODEL               3          42108777.02898556  14036259.00966185  346.24  0.0001  0.992357          0.8897

ERROR               8           324314.63768142    40539.32971018 ⑦          ROOT MSE                Y MEAN
                                                                                      ⑧
CORRECTED TOTAL    11          42433091.66666698 ⑨                          201.34380971       22630.83333333


SOURCE              DF              TYPE I SS    F VALUE   PR > F   DF      TYPE IV SS  F VALUE   PR > F

X1                  1          33294036.23595509   821.28   0.0001   1   9389610.00000008  231.62  0.0001
X2                  1           8452796.51598297   208.51   0.0001   1    326808.74399183    8.06  0.0218
X1*X2               1            361944.27704750     8.93   0.0174   1    361944.27704750    8.93  0.0174


                                PARAMETER ESTIMATES
                                      ④
                        ③        T FOR H0:        ⑤        ⑥
VARIABLE              ESTIMATE   PARAMETER=0   PR > |T|   STD ERROR

INTERCEPT        18593.00000000      89.41      0.0001   207.94699250
X1                 969.00000000      15.22      0.0001    63.67050315
X2                 866.71014493       2.84      0.0218   305.25678646
X1*X2              260.13043478       2.99      0.0174    87.05798112
```

Note: The computer uses a star to indicate multiplication. Thus $x_1 x_2$ is printed as X1*X2.

the **multiple coefficient of determination**, provides a measure of how well the model fits the data. As you can see, 99.2% of the sum of squares of deviations of the y values about $\bar{y}$ is explained by all of the terms in the model.

(2) If the model contributes information for the prediction of y, at least one of the model parameters, $\beta_1, \beta_2,$ or β_3, will differ from 0. Consequently, we want to test the null hypothesis $H_0 : \beta_1 = \beta_2 = \beta_3 = 0$ against the alternative hypothesis H_a: at least one of the parameters, $\beta_1, \beta_2,$ or β_3, differs from 0. The test statistic for this test, an F statistic with $v_1 =$ (the number of parameters in H_0) = 3 and $v_2 = n -$ (number of parameters in the model) $= 12 - 4 = 8$, is shown in shaded area ② to be 346.24. Since this value exceeds the tabulated value for F—with $v_1 = 3, v_2 = 8,$ and $\alpha = .05, F = 4.07$ (from Table 8 of the Appendix)—we reject H_0 and conclude that at least one of the parameters $\beta_1, \beta_2, \beta_3$ differs from 0. There is evidence to indicate that the model contributes information for the prediction of y. The observed significance level (p-value) for the test, $PR > F$, shown to the right of the value of the F statistic, is equal to .0001.

(3) The estimates of the four model parameters are shown under the heading ESTIMATE. Thus $\hat{\beta}_0 = 18593.00000000, \hat{\beta}_1 = 969.00000000, \hat{\beta}_2 = 866.71014493,$ and $\hat{\beta}_3 = 260.13043478$; and rounding these estimates, we obtain the prediction equation

$$\hat{y} = 18593.0 + 969.0x_1 + 866.7x_2 + 260.1x_1x_2$$

(4) The computed value of the t statistic for each of the model parameters is shown in shaded area ④ under the column T FOR H_0: PARAMETER = 0. For example, the value of the t statistic for the test $H_0 : \beta_1 = 0$ is 15.22. The number of degrees of freedom for SSE, s^2, and therefore, t will always equal $v = n -$ (number of parameters in the model). For our example this will be $v = 12 - 4 = 8$ degrees of freedom. For $\alpha = .05$ the tabulated value of t, $t_{.025}$, for a two-tailed test is given in Table 5 of the Appendix as 2.306. Since the computed t value corresponding to β_1 exceeds this value, there is evidence to indicate that β_1 differs from 0.

(5) The observed significance levels (p-values) for the t tests described in part (4) are shown in shaded area ⑤ under the column headed $PR > |T|$. These values are calculated for two-tailed tests. The p-value for a one-tailed test is half of the value shown in the printout. For example, the observed significance level for a test of the hypothesis $H_0 : \beta_2 = 0, H_a : \beta_2 \neq 0$ is .0218 for this two-tailed test. If the alternative hypothesis is $H_a : \beta_2 > 0$—that is, you want to conduct a one-tailed test—then the p-value is equal to $(.0218)/2 = .0109$. If you were to test H_0 using $\alpha = .05$, these small p-values would imply rejection of H_0.

(6) The estimated standard deviations of the estimators are shown in shaded area ⑥ under the heading STD ERROR. For example,

$$s_{\hat{\beta}_1} = 63.67050315$$

This quantity is useful in calculating $(1 - \alpha)100\%$ confidence intervals for the model parameters. For example, a $(1 - \alpha)100\%$ confidence interval for β_1 is equal to

$$\hat{\beta}_1 \pm t_{\alpha/2} s_{\hat{\beta}_1}$$

Therefore, a 95% confidence interval for β_1 is

$$969.0 \pm (2.306)(63.67)$$

or

$$969.0 \pm 146.8$$

Confidence intervals for the other model parameters are constructed in the same way. Thus a $(1 - \alpha)100\%$ confidence interval for β_2 is

$$\hat{\beta}_2 \pm t_{\alpha/2} s_{\hat{\beta}_2}$$

where $t_{\alpha/2}$ is based on $v = n -$ (number of parameters in the model) $= 12 - 4 = 8$ degrees of freedom.

(7) The values of SSE = 324314.63768142 and s^2 = 40539.32971018 are shown in shaded area ⑦ in the row corresponding to ERROR and under the columns headed, respectively, SUM OF SQUARES and MEAN SQUARE.

(8) The standard deviation s = 201.34380971 is shown in shaded area ⑧, labeled ROOT MSE.

(9) The total sum of squares of deviations, SS_y, of the y values about the mean is shown in shaded area ⑨ to be 42433091.66666698. You can verify that the value of R^2 is equal to $1 - (SSE/SS_y)$.

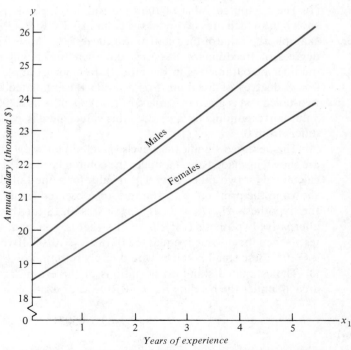

FIGURE 12.8   A Graph of the Faculty Salary Prediction Lines for Example 12.5

(b) A graph of the two salary lines is shown in Figure 12.8. Note that the salary line corresponding to the male faculty members appears to be rising at a more rapid rate than the salary line for females. Is this real, or could it be due to chance? The following example will answer this question. ∎

EXAMPLE 12.6   Refer to Example 12.5. Do the data provide sufficient evidence to indicate that the annual rate of increase in male junior faculty salaries exceeds the annual rate of increase for women junior faculty salaries? Thus we want to know whether the data provide sufficient evidence to indicate that the slope of the men's faculty salary line exceeds the slope of the women's faculty salary line.

SOLUTION   Since β_3 measures the difference in slopes, the slopes of the two lines will be identical if $\beta_3 = 0$. Therefore, we want to test

$$H_0 : \beta_3 = 0, \quad \text{that is, the slopes of the two lines are identical}$$

against the alternative hypothesis

$$H_a : \beta_3 > 0, \quad \text{that is, the slope of the male faculty salary line is greater}$$
$$\text{than the slope of the female faculty salary line}$$

The calculated value of t corresponding to β_3, shown in shaded area 4 of the computer printout (Table 12.4), is 2.99. Since we want to detect values $\beta_3 > 0$, we will conduct a one-tailed test and reject H_0 if $t > t_\alpha$. The tabulated t value from Table 5 of the Appendix, for $\alpha = .05$ and $v = 8$ degrees of freedom, is $t_{.05} = 1.860$. The calculated value of t exceeds this value, and thus there is evidence to indicate that the annual rate of increase in men's faculty salaries exceeds the corresponding annual rate of increase in faculty salaries for women.* ∎

Some computer program multiple regression packages (SAS is one of them) can be instructed to print confidence intervals for the mean value of y and/or prediction intervals for y for specific values of the independent variables. You can also instruct some programs to print a test statistic for testing an hypothesis that each parameter in a subset of the model parameters, say β_2 and β_3, simultaneously equal 0; that is, $H_0 : \beta_2 = \beta_3 = 0$. This latter topic is addressed in optional Section 12.9.

12.4   A COMPARISON OF COMPUTER PRINTOUTS

Several popular statistical program packages contain multiple regression programs. Three of these, Minitab, SAS, and SPSS[x] computer program packages, are referenced at the end of this chapter. Some programs can be used only on specific computers; others are more versatile. If you plan to conduct a multiple regression analysis, you will want to determine the statistical program packages available at your computer center so that you can become familiar with their output.

---

*If we want to determine whether the data provide sufficient evidence to indicate that the male faculty members start at higher salaries, we test $H_0: \beta_2 = 0$ against the alternative hypothesis $H_a: \beta_2 > 0$.

TABLE 12.5   SAS, Minitab, and SPSS[x] Printouts for the Data of Example 12.5

(a) SAS Printout

DEPENDENT VARIABLE: Y

SOURCE	DF	SUM OF SQUARES	MEAN SQUARE	F VALUE	PR > F	R-SQUARE	C.V.
MODEL	3	42108777.02898556	14036259.00966185	346.24 ②	0.0001	0.992357 ①	0.8897
ERROR	8	324314.63768142 ⑦	40539.32971018		ROOT MSE		Y MEAN
CORRECTED TOTAL	11	42433091.66666698 ⑨			201.34380971 ⑧		22630.83333333

SOURCE	DF	TYPE I SS	F VALUE	PR > F	DF	TYPE IV SS	F VALUE	PR > F
X1	1	33294036.23595509	821.28	0.0001	1	9389610.00000008	231.62	0.0001
X2	1	8452796.51598297	208.51	0.0001	1	326808.74399183	8.06	0.0218
X1*X2	1	361944.27704750	8.93	0.0174	1	361944.27704750	8.93	0.0174

PARAMETER ESTIMATES

VARIABLE	ESTIMATE ③	T FOR H0: PARAMETER=0 ④	PR > |T| ⑤	STD ERROR ⑥
INTERCEPT	18593.00000000	89.41	0.0001	207.94699250
X1	969.00000000	15.22	0.0001	63.67050315
X2	866.71014493	2.84	0.0218	305.25678646
X1*X2	260.13043478	2.99	0.0174	87.05798112

(b) Minitab Printout

THE REGRESSION EQUATION IS
Y = 18593. + 969.X1 + 867.X2
    + 260.X3

	COLUMN	COEFFICIENT	ST. DEV. OF COEF.	T-RATIO = COEF/S.D.
	-	18593.0	207.9	89.41
X1	YEARS	968.99 ③	63.67 ⑥	15.21 ④
X2	SEX	866.7	305.2	2.83
X3	YR*SEX	260.13	87.05	2.98

THE ST. DEV. OF Y ABOUT REGRESSION LINE IS
S = 201.3
WITH (12 - 4) = 8 DEGREES OF FREEDOM   ⑧

R-SQUARED = 99.2 PERCENT   ①
R-SQUARED = 98.9 PERCENT   ADJUSTED FOR D.F.

ANALYSIS OF VARIANCE

DUE TO	DF	SS	MS = SS/DF
REGRESSION	3	42108770	14036259
RESIDUAL	8	324314	40539 ⑦
TOTAL	11	42433090 ⑨	

FURTHER ANALYSIS OF VARIANCE
SS EXPLAINED BY EACH VARIABLE WHEN ENTERED IN THE ORDER GIVEN

DUE TO	DF	SS
REGRESSION	3	42108770
YEARS	1	33294010
SEX	1	8452821
YR*SEX	1	361944

ROW	X1 YEARS	Y SALARY	PRED. Y VALUE	ST. DEV. PRED. Y	RESIDUAL	ST. RES
1	1.00	20710.0	20688.8	169.6	21.1	0.19 X

X DENOTES AN OBS. WHOSE X VALUE GIVES IT LARGE INFLUENCE

DURBIN-WATSON STATISTIC = 2.24

TABLE 12.5 *(Continued)*

(c) SPSS^x Printout

```
********************************* MULTIPLE REGRESSION *******************      VARIABLE LIST  1
                                                                              REGRESSION LIST  1

EQUATION NUMBER 1    DEPENDENT VARIABLE..    SALARY

VARIABLE(S) ENTERED ON STEP NUMBER 1..    X1X2
                                     2..    X1
                                     3..    X2

MULTIPLE R              .99617

R SQUARE                .99236  ①

ADJUSTED R SQUARE       .98949

STANDARD ERROR      201.34381  ⑧

                        ANALYSIS OF VARIANCE

                        DF          SUM OF SQUARES         MEAN SQUARE

Regression               3          42108777.02899      14036259.00966
Residual                 8           324314.63768          40539.32971  ⑦

F =     346.23806      Signif F =  .0001  ②


--------------VARIABLES IN THE EQUATION--------------     ----------VARIABLES NOT IN THE EQUATION--------
               ③            ⑥                                ④       ⑤
VARIABLE              B          SE B       BETA          T     SIG T

X1X2           260.130435   87.057981   .277388      2.988   .0174
X1             969.000000   63.670503   .701676     15.219   .0000
X2             866.710145  305.256786   .230453      2.839   .0218
(Constant)   18593.000000  207.946993               89.412   .0000
```

% Minitab-1   Current outfile closed

We presented and described the output for two SAS multiple regression computer packages in Section 12.3. Most other computer outputs are similar. They vary somewhat in the format in which the output is presented and, in some cases, the type of output that can be requested. In this section we will present the output of three multiple regression computer packages, SAS GLM, Minitab, and SPSS^x, for the same set of data: the data of Example 12.5. The three computer printouts for this set of data are shown in Table 12.5.

Corresponding output is shaded and marked with the same number on each printout. For example, parameter estimates on the Minitab printout appear under the column heading COEFFICIENT and appear under the column heading B on the SPSS^x printout.

The Minitab printout does not give the value of F for testing the complete model. You can calculate this directly by using the formula

$$F = \frac{\text{mean square for regression}}{s^2}$$

The denominator, s^2 (the estimator of σ^2), is shown in shaded area ⑦. The value of the quantity called **mean square for regression** appears under the column heading

MS $=$ SS/DF, and in the REGRESSION row, as 14036259. Therefore,

$$F = \frac{\text{mean square for regression}}{s^2} = \frac{14036259}{40539}$$

$$= 346.24$$

You can see that this value of F is identical to the values shown on the SAS and the SPSS[x] printouts.

Both the Minitab and the SPSS[x] printouts give a value of R^2 that is adjusted for the number of degrees of freedom associated with SSE. It appears as R-SQUARED ADJUSTED FOR D.F. on the Minitab printout and ADJUSTED R SQUARE on the SPSS[x] printout. We have not used this quantity in our analysis of the data in Section 12.3 and will therefore omit it from our discussion.

The computer printouts for the Minitab, SAS, SPSS[x], and other multiple regression computer program packages are very similar. Once you can read one, it is likely that you will be able to read the output of the computer program available at your computer center. If you have difficulty understanding the output, consult the package instruction manual.

EXERCISES

BASIC TECHNIQUES

12.11 Suppose that you were to fit the model

$$E(y) = \beta_0 + \beta_1 x_1 + \beta_2 x_2 + \beta_3 x_3$$

to 15 data points and found R^2 equal to .94.

(a) Interpret the value of R^2.

(b) Do the data provide sufficient evidence to indicate that the model contributes information for the prediction of y? Test using $\alpha = .05$.

12.12 The computer output for the multiple regression analysis for Exercise 12.11 provides the following information:

$$\hat{\beta}_0 = 1.04 \qquad \hat{\beta}_1 = 1.29 \qquad \hat{\beta}_2 = 2.72 \qquad \hat{\beta}_3 = .41$$

$$s_{\hat{\beta}_1} = .42 \qquad s_{\hat{\beta}_2} = .65 \qquad s_{\hat{\beta}_3} = .17$$

Which, if any, of the independent variables x_1, x_2, and x_3 contribute information for the prediction of y? Test using $\alpha = .05$.

12.13 Refer to Exercise 12.11.

(a) Give the least-squares prediction equation.

(b) On the same sheet of graph paper, graph y versus x_1 when $x_2 = 1$ and $x_3 = 0$ and when $x_2 = 1$ and $x_3 = .5$. What relationship do the two lines have to each other?

(c) What is the practical interpretation of the parameter β_1?

12.14 Refer to Exercise 12.11. Find a 90% confidence interval for β_1 and interpret it.

12.15 Suppose that you were to fit the model

$$E(y) = \beta_0 + \beta_1 x + \beta_2 x^2$$

to 20 data points and found $R^2 = .762$.

(a) What type of model have you chosen to fit the data?

(b) How well does the model fit the data? Explain.

(c) Do the data provide sufficient evidence to indicate that the model contributes information for the prediction of y? Test using $\alpha = .05$.

12.16 The computer output for the multiple regression analysis for Exercise 12.15 provides the following information:

$$\hat{\beta}_0 = 1.21 \qquad \hat{\beta}_1 = 7.60 \qquad \hat{\beta}_2 = -.94$$
$$s_{\hat{\beta}_0} = .62 \qquad s_{\hat{\beta}_1} = 1.97 \qquad s_{\hat{\beta}_2} = .33$$

(a) Give the prediction equation.

(b) Graph the prediction equation over the interval $0 \le x \le 6$.

12.17 Refer to Exercise 12.16.

(a) What is your estimate of the mean value of y when $x = 0$?

(b) Do the data provide sufficient evidence to indicate that the mean value of y differs from 0 when $x = 0$? Test using $\alpha = .10$.

(c) Find a 90% confidence interval for $E(y)$ when $x = 0$.

12.18 Refer to Exercise 12.16.

(a) Suppose that the relationship between $E(y)$ and x is a straight line. What would you know about the value of β_2?

(b) Do the data provide sufficient evidence to indicate curvature in the relationship between y and x?

12.19 Refer to Exercise 12.16. Suppose that y is the profit for some business and x is the amount of capital invested, and you know that the rate of increase in profit for a unit increase in capital invested can only decrease as x increases. Do the data provide sufficient evidence to indicate a decreasing rate of increase in profit as the amount of capital invested increases?

(a) The circumstances that we have described imply a one-tailed statistical test. Why?

(b) Conduct the test for $\alpha = .05$. State your conclusions.   1.645

APPLICATIONS

12.20 A publisher of college textbooks conducted a study to relate profit per text to cost of sales over a six-year period when its sales force (and sales costs) were growing rapidly. The following inflation-adjusted data (in thousands of dollars) were collected:

Profit per Text, y	16.5	22.4	24.9	28.8	31.5	35.8
Sales Cost per Text, x	5.0	5.6	6.1	6.8	7.4	8.6

Expecting profit per book to rise and then plateau, the publisher fitted the model $E(y) = \beta_0 + \beta_1 x + \beta_2 x^2$ to the data.

TABLE 12.6 SAS Output for Exercise 12.20

```
DEPENDENT VARIABLE: Y
```

SOURCE	DF	SUM OF SQUARES	MEAN SQUARE	F VALUE	PR > F	R-SQUARE	C.V.
MODEL	2	234.95514252	117.47757126	332.53	0.0003	0.995509	2.2303
ERROR	3	1.05985748	0.35328583		ROOT MSE		Y MEAN
CORRECTED TOTAL	5	236.01500000			0.59437852		26.65000000

SOURCE	DF	TYPE I SS	F VALUE	PR > F	DF	TYPE IV SS	F VALUE	PR > F
X	1	227.81864814	644.86	0.0001	1	15.20325554	43.03	0.0072
X*X	1	7.13649437	20.20	0.0206	1	7.13649437	20.20	0.0206

```
                    PARAMETER ESTIMATES
```

VARIABLE	ESTIMATE	T FOR H0: PARAMETER=0	PR > |T|	STD ERROR
INTERCEPT	-44.19249551	-5.33	0.0129	8.28688218
X	16.33386317	6.56	0.0072	2.48991042
X*X	-0.81976920	-4.49	0.0206	0.18239471

OBSERVATION	OBSERVED VALUE	PREDICTED VALUE	RESIDUAL	LOWER 95% CL FOR MEAN	UPPER 95% CL FOR MEAN
1	16.50000000	16.98259044	-0.48259044	15.33066719	18.63451369
2	22.40000000	21.56917626	0.83082374	20.56714686	22.57120566
3	24.90000000	24.94045805	-0.04045805	23.93483233	25.94608377
4	28.80000000	28.97164643	-0.17164643	27.81528749	30.12800537
5	31.50000000	31.78753079	-0.28753079	30.65188830	32.92317327
6	35.80000000	35.64859804	0.15140196	33.81460946	37.48258661
7*		27.34236657		26.23203462	28.45269852

```
* OBSERVATION WAS NOT USED IN THIS ANALYSIS

     SUM OF RESIDUALS                   -0.00000000
     SUM OF SQUARED RESIDUALS            1.05985748
     SUM OF SQUARED RESIDUALS-ERROR SS  -0.00000000
     PRESS STATISTIC                    12.11621807
     FIRST ORDER AUTOCORRELATION        -0.39797399
     SURBIN-WATSON D                     2.55457960
```

(a) What sign would you expect the actual value of β_2 to assume? The SAS computer printout is shown in Table 12.6. Find the value of $\hat{\beta}_2$ on the printout and see whether the sign agrees with your answer.

(b) Find SSE and s^2 on the printout.

(c) How many degrees of freedom do SSE and s^2 possess? Show that

$$s^2 = \frac{\text{SSE}}{\text{degrees of freedom}}$$

(d) Do the data provide sufficient evidence to indicate that the model contributes information for the prediction of y? Test using $\alpha = .05$.

(e) Find the observed significance level for the test in part (d), and interpret its value.

(f) Do the data provide sufficient evidence to indicate curvature in the relationship between $E(y)$ and x (i.e., evidence to indicate that β_2 differs from 0)? Test using $\alpha = .05$.

(g) Find the observed significance level for the test in part (f), and interpret its value.

(h) Find the prediction equation, and graph the relationship between $\hat{y}$ and x.

(i) Find R^2 on the printout and interpret its value.

(j) Use the prediction equation to estimate the mean profit per text when the sales cost per text is $6500. (Express the sales cost in thousands of dollars before substituting into the prediction equation.) We instructed the SAS program to print this confidence interval. The confidence interval when $x = 6.5$, 26.23203462 to 28.45269852, is shown at the bottom of the printout.

12.21 Refer to Example 12.5. The t value for testing the hypothesis $H_0 : \beta_1 = 0$ is

$$t = \frac{\hat{\beta}_1 - 0}{s_{\hat{\beta}_1}} = \frac{\hat{\beta}_1}{s_{\hat{\beta}_1}}$$

where $\hat{\beta}_1$ is the estimate of β_1 and $s_{\hat{\beta}_1}$ is the estimated standard deviation (or standard error) of $\hat{\beta}_1$. Both of these quantities are shown on the SAS, Minitab, and SPSS[x] printouts in Table 12.5. Examine the printouts and verify that the corresponding printed values for $\hat{\beta}_1$ and $s_{\hat{\beta}_1}$ are identical except for rounding errors. Calculate $t = \hat{\beta}_1/s_{\hat{\beta}_1}$. Verify that your calculated value of t is equal to the value printed on the printouts; that is, $t = 15.22$.

12.22 The t test of Exercise 12.21 can also be conducted by using an F test (the test is described in optional Section 12.9). We can use an F test because the square of a t statistic with v degrees of freedom is equal to an F statistic with $v_1 = 1$ and $v_2 = v$ degrees of freedom; that is,

$$F_{1,v} = t_v^2$$

(a) To convince yourself that this relationship is valid, find the value $t_{.025}$ (Table 5 in the Appendix) that is used to locate the rejection regions for the two-tailed ($\alpha = .05$) t tests of Exercise 12.21.

(b) Show that $t_{.025}^2$ [found in part (a)] is equal to the tabulated value $F_{.05}$ (Table 8 in the Appendix) for $v_1 = 1$ and $v_2 = 8$ degrees of freedom.

12.23 When will an F statistic equal the square of a t statistic?

12.24 The waiting time y that elapses between the time a computing job is submitted to a large computer and the time at which the job is initiated (computing commences) is a function of many variables, including the priority assigned to the job, the number and sizes of the jobs already on the computer, the size of the job being submitted, and so on. A study was initiated to investigate the relationship between waiting time y (in hours) for a job and x_1, the estimated CPU time (in seconds) for the job, and x_2, the CPU utilization factor. The estimated CPU time x_1 is an estimate of the amount of time that a job will occupy a portion of the computer's central processing unit's memory. The CPU utilization factor x_2 is the percentage of the memory bank of the central processing unit that is occupied at the time that the job is submitted. We would expect the waiting time y to increase as the size of the job x_1 increases and as the CPU utilization factor x_2 increases. In the study, 15 jobs of varying sizes were submitted to the computer at randomly assigned times throughout the day. The job waiting time y, estimated CPU time x_1, and CPU utilization factor x_2 were recorded for each job.* The data are shown in Table 12.7. A second-order model, $E(y) = \beta_0 + \beta_1 x_1 + \beta_2 x_2 + \beta_3 x_1 x_2 + \beta_4 x_1^2 + \beta_5 x_2^2$, was selected to model mean waiting time $E(y)$. The SAS multiple regression analysis for the data is shown in the printout in Table 12.8.

---

*Waiting time data frequently violate the assumptions required for significance tests and confidence intervals in a regression analysis. The probability distribution for waiting times is often skewed, and its variance increases as the mean waiting time increases. Methods for coping with this problem are discussed in Section 9.12 and in Mendenhall and Sincich (1986).

TABLE 12.7   Waiting Time and CPU Data for Exercise 12.24

Job	1	2	3	4	5	6	7	8	9	10	11	12	13	14	15
x_1	2.0	9.3	5.6	3.7	12.4	18.1	13.5	26.6	34.2	38.8	56.1	60.3	4.4	2.6	20.9
x_2	45	80	23	25	67	30	55	21	79	40	22	37	50	66	42
y	.001	1.140	.030	.001	.780	.300	.600	.200	2.240	.440	.001	.320	.160	.290	.490

TABLE 12.8   SAS Output for Exercise 12.24

```
DEPENDENT VARIABLE: Y

SOURCE              DF          SUM OF SQUARES      MEAN SQUARE   F VALUE    PR > F   R-SQUARE              C.V.

MODEL                5              4.74848837       0.94969767    159.23    0.0001   0.988822          16.5655

ERROR                9              0.05367803       0.00596423              ROOT MSE               Y MEAN

CORRECTED TOTAL     14              4.80216640                              0.07722840            0.46620000


SOURCE              DF          TYPE I SS    F VALUE   PR > F    DF     TYPE IV SS    F VALUE   PR > F

X1                   1          0.08032055     13.47   0.0052     1     0.00448637      0.75    0.4083
X2                   1          3.21553051    539.14   0.0001     1     0.13905895     23.32    0.0009
X1*X2                1          0.96272106    161.42   0.0001     1     0.48988534     82.14    0.0001
X1*X1                1          0.22455767     37.65   0.0002     1     0.16181969     27.13    0.0006
X2*X2                1          0.26535859     44.49   0.0001     1     0.26535859     44.49    0.0001


                                    PARAMETER ESTIMATE

                                  T FOR H0:
VARIABLE         ESTIMATE       PARAMETER=0    PR > |T|     STD ERROR

INTERCEPT        0.43806816        2.71         0.0239      0.16147813
X1               0.00526474        0.87         0.4083      0.00607025
X2              -0.03017242       -4.83         0.0009      0.00624867
X1*X2            0.00068770        9.06         0.0001      0.00007588
X1*X1           -0.00037952       -5.21         0.0006      0.00007286
X2*X2            0.00040726        6.67         0.0001      0.00006106
```

(a) Find the values of SSE and s^2.

(b) Find the prediction equation.

(c) Find R^2 and interpret its value.

(d) Do the data provide sufficient evidence to indicate that the model contributes information for the prediction of y? Test using $\alpha = .10$.

(e) Find the observed significance level for the test in part (d), and interpret its value.

(f) Note that the observed significance level for the test $H_0 : \beta_1 = 0$ is large (p-value $= .4083$). Does this mean that there is little evidence to indicate that x_1 contributes information for the prediction of y?

(g) Predict the waiting time when the estimated CPU time for a job is 30 seconds and the CPU utilization factor is 55%.

(h) Graph the estimated mean waiting time as a function of estimated CPU time x_1 for CPU utilization $x_2 = 30\%$. Also graph the curves for $x_2 = 50\%$ and $x_2 = 70\%$. Observe the behavior of the estimated mean waiting time as x_1 and x_2 increase in value.

12.25 The German system of industrial relations is based upon codetermination, or, equivalently, worker participation in management. In a study of the German worker's perception of this system, Dworkin and associates interviewed a sample of 135 workers, 113 male and 22 female. Each worker responded to ten job satisfaction statements, rating each statement from 1 (least satisfaction) to 5 (most satisfaction). One aspect of the study involved an examination of some variables that might be predictors of job satisfaction. The dependent variable y used to measure a worker's job satisfaction was the average of a worker's responses to the ten job satisfaction questions. These observations, along with the recorded values of nine independent variables (listed in Table 12.9), were recorded for 135 workers. The results obtained after fitting a first-order model to the data are shown in Table 12.9.

$n = 135$
$m = 113$
$w = 22$

TABLE 12.9 Job Satisfaction Data for Exercise 12.25

Independent Variable	Description	Parameter Estimate, $\hat{\beta}_i$	Standard Error, $s_{\hat{\beta}_i}$
x_1	Sex of worker	$-.153$	.201
x_2	Job rank of worker	.398	.142
x_3	Level of education	$-.026$	.080
x_4	Union member (yes or no)	.239	.166
x_5	Union official (yes or no)	$-.002$	.120
x_6	Worker active in codetermination system (yes or no)	$-.264$	.189
x_7	(Identification omitted)	$-.308$	.131
x_8	(Identification omitted)	.072	.062
x_9	Monthly salary of worker	.110	.052

Source: J. B. Dworkin, C. J. Hobson, E. Frieling, and D. M. Oakes, "How German Workers View Their Jobs," *Columbia Journal of World Business,* Summer 1983.

(a) Give the equation of the model used in the regression analysis.

(b) How many degrees of freedom are associated with SSE and s^2?

(c) Examine the table and identify those variables that were entered into the model by using dummy variables.

(d) The value of R^2 for the regression analysis was .281. Interpret the value of R^2, and comment on its relevance to the regression analysis.

(e) Do the data provide sufficient information to indicate that at least one variable in the model contributes information for predicting worker job satisfaction? (*Hint:* Test the usefulness of the complete model with an F test. Test using $\alpha = .05$.)

12.26 Refer to the worker job satisfaction study in Exercise 12.25. Use the information in Table 12.9 to determine which, if any, of the variables contribute information for the prediction of worker job satisfaction. Test each and indicate those with p-values less than or equal to .10.

12.27 In Exercise 11.15 we discussed a study of supermarket firm sales and profitability in the sale of health and beauty aids (HBA) and small-ticket general merchandise (GM) for two types of firms, those that used service merchandisers to supply HBA products and service to their stores and

TABLE 12.10   Summary of Regression Analysis for Supermarkets for Exercise 12.27

Dependent Variable	Intercept	Average per-Store Weekly Customer Count	Category Annual Sales per Firm (Thousand $)	Per-Store Average Linear Feet of Shelf Space	Category Percentage of Sales Purchased Direct	R^2	F Ratio
HBA sales per linear foot	555	$+.31$ $(2.708)^\dagger$	$-\$.003$ $(.104)$	-10.42 (1.028)	-6.90% $(.842)$	.65	4.590*
HBA contribution per linear foot	220	$+.06$ $(2.847)^*$	$\$.007$ (1.401)	-3.98 $(2.143)^\dagger$	-1.73% (1.157)	.72	6.345‡
GM sales per linear foot	1124	$+.06$ $(1.605)^\S$	$+\$.02$ $(1.525)^\S$	-4.36 $(2.174)^\dagger$	-8.07% $(1.394)^\S$	.69	4.904‡
GM contribution per linear foot	466	$+.02$ (1.187)	$-\$.009$ $(1.811)^\S$	-1.90 $(2.589)^\dagger$	-2.88% $(1.357)^\S$	.71	5.389‡

Source: R. C. Curhan, W. J. Salmon, and R. D. Buzzell, "Sales and Profitability of Health and Beauty Aids and General Merchandise in Supermarkets," *Journal of Retailing,* Vol. 59, No. 1, 1983.

Note: t-statistics are shown in parentheses.

*.01 < p < .05.

$\dagger$.05 < p < .10.

$\ddagger$p < .01.

$\S$.10 < p < .20.

those (direct buyers) that buy HBA products, warehouse them, and service the stores themselves. A portion of this study involved multiple regression analyses on data from $n = 15$ supermarket firms for each of four dependent variables. The results are shown in Table 12.10. As you can see from the table, the four dependent variables are listed in column 1. The four independent variables,

$$x_1 = \text{average per-store weekly customer count}$$

$$x_2 = \text{category annual sales per firm (\$1000)}$$

$$x_3 = \text{per-store average linear feet of shelf space}$$

$$x_4 = \text{category percentage of sales purchased directly}$$

appear in columns 3, 4, 5, and 6. A first-order model was used to relate each dependent variable y to these four independent variables. The numbers appearing in the four independent variable columns are the estimates of the regression coefficients. The t value for each parameter estimate is shown in parentheses below it. The y intercept for each of the four multiple regressions is shown in column 2 of the table.

(a) Write the equation of the multiple regression model used in the regression analyses.

(b) Examine the regression analysis for $y =$ HBA sales per linear foot. Find the F value in the table for testing the complete model. Do the data provide sufficient evidence to indicate that the model contributes information for the prediction of y? Test using $\alpha = .05$.

(c) Find the approximate p-value for the test in part (b).

(d) Which, if any, of the independent variables appear to contribute information for the prediction of y? Explain.

(e) Refer to part (b). Use the value of R^2 to calculate the value of the F statistic used to test the complete model. Does your calculated value agree with the value shown in the table [and used in the test in part (b)]?

(f) Interpret the value of R^2 given for the analysis.

(g) Does the first-order model used in this regression analysis provide a good fit to the data? Explain. Can you suggest possible improvements to the model?

12.28 Answer the questions of Exercise 12.27, except refer to the multiple regression analysis for y = HBA contribution (to profit) per linear foot.

12.29 Answer the questions of Exercise 12.27, except refer to the multiple regression analysis for y = GM sales per linear foot.

12.30 Answer the questions of Exercise 12.27, except refer to the multiple regression analysis for y = GM contribution (to profit) per linear foot.

RESIDUAL ANALYSIS

12.5

The deviations between the observed values of y and their predicted values are called **residuals**. For example, the first three columns of Table 12.11 reproduce the data of Table 11.2; and the ten predicted values of y, obtained from the prediction equation (Example 11.1)

$$\hat{y} = 40.78 + .77x$$

are shown in column 4. The predicted value of y for $x_1 = 39$ is $\hat{y}_1 = 40.78 + .77x = 40.78 + (.77)(39) = 70.81$, and the residual is $e_1 = y_1 - \hat{y}_1 = 65 - 70.81 = -5.81$. The ten residuals, one for each x value, appear in column 5 of Table 12.11 and are displayed graphically as the vertical line segments in Figure 12.9.

DEFINITION

The *residual* corresponding to the data point (x_i, y_i) is

$$e_i = y_i - \hat{y}_i$$

TABLE 12.11 Management Data of Table 11.2 with Predicted Values and Residuals

Manager	Management Trainee Score, x	Management Success Rating, y	$\hat{y} = 40.78 + .77x$	$e = y - \hat{y}$
1	39	65	70.81	−5.81
2	43	78	73.89	4.11
3	21	52	56.95	−4.95
4	64	82	90.06	−8.06
5	57	92	84.67	7.33
6	47	89	76.97	12.03
7	28	73	62.34	10.66
8	75	98	98.53	−0.53
9	34	56	66.96	−10.96
10	52	75	80.82	−5.82

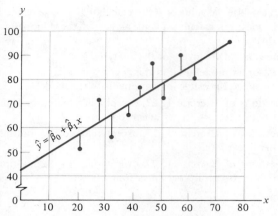

FIGURE 12.9   Residuals for the Least-Squares Line $\hat{y} = 40.78 + .77x$

In **residual analysis**, plots of the residuals against $\hat{y}$ or against the individual independent variables often indicate departures from the assumptions required for an analysis of variance, and they also may suggest changes in the underlying model. Plots of the residuals against $\hat{y}$ are particularly useful for detecting nonuniformity in the variance of y for different values of $E(y)$. We gave three examples of these types of data in Section 9.12 and gave transformations that could be used to stabilize the variance.

For example, the variance of some types of data—Poisson data, in particular—increases with the mean. A plot of the residuals for this type of data might appear as shown in Figure 12.10(a). Note that the range of the residuals increases as $\hat{y}$ increases, thus indicating that the variance of y is increasing as the mean value of y, $E(y)$, increases.

The variances for percentages and proportions calculated from binomial data also increase for values of $p = 0$ to $p = .5$ and then decrease from $p = .5$ to $p = 1.0$. Plots of residuals versus $\hat{y}$ for this type of data would appear as shown in Figure 12.10(b). Therefore, if the data were small percentages, the plot of residuals would show

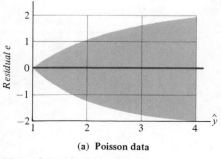

(a) **Poisson data**

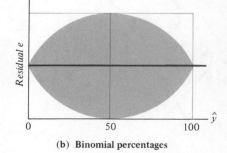

(b) **Binomial percentages**

FIGURE 12.10   Plots of Residuals Against $\hat{y}$

the range of the residuals *increasing* as $\hat{y}$ increases. If the data were large percentages, the range of the residuals would appear to *decrease* as $\hat{y}$ increases.

If the range of the residuals increases as $\hat{y}$ increases and you know that the data are measurements on Poisson variables, you can stabilize the variance of the response by running the regression analysis on $y^* = \sqrt{x}$. Or if percentages are calculated from binomial data, you can use the arc sin transformation, $y = \sin^{-1}\sqrt{x}$. Both of these transformations were discussed in Section 9.2.[†] If you have no prior reason to explain why the range of the residuals increases as $\hat{y}$ increases, you can still use a transformation on y that affects larger values of y more than smaller values, say $y^* = \sqrt{y}$ or $y^* = \ln y$. These transformations have a tendency to both stabilize the variance of y^* and to make the distribution of y^* more nearly normal when the distribution of y is highly skewed.

Plots of the residuals against the individual independent variables often indicate the problems with models selection. In theory, the residuals should vary in size and sign (positive or negative) in a random manner about $\hat{y}$ if the equation that you have selected for $E(y)$ is a good approximation to the true relationship between $E(y)$ and the independent variables. For example, if $E(y)$ and a single independent variable x are linearly related; that is,

$$E(y) = \beta_0 + \beta_1 x$$

and you fit a straight line to the data, then the observed y values should vary in a random manner about $\hat{y}$, and a plot of the residuals against x will appear as shown in Figure 12.11.

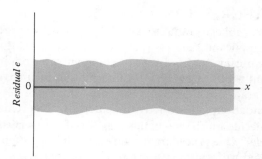

FIGURE 12.11   Residual Plot When the Model Provides a Good Approximation to Reality

In contrast, suppose that you fit the straight-line model

$$E(y) = \beta_0 + \beta_1 x$$

to the points plotted in Figure 12.12(a). You can see from the plotted points in Figure 12.12(a) that the relationship between y and x appears to be curvilinear. As a consequence, the residuals for small values of x tend to be negative; then they change to positive and back to negative. This particular type of nonrandom behavior in the

[†]In Chapter 9 and earlier chapters we represented the response variable by the symbol x. In the chapters on regression analysis, Chapters 11 and 12, the response variable is represented by the symbol y.

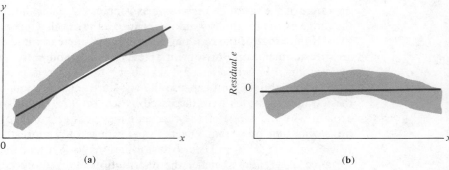

FIGURE 12.12   Data and Residual Plots for a Model That Does Not Agree with Reality

residuals suggests what is apparent from Figures 12.12(a) and 12.12(b). A straight line does not provide a good approximation to the relationship between y and x.

Most computer multiple regression analysis printouts give the predicted values of y and the residuals for each value of x (see shaded area 10 of the SAS printout in Table 12.2). In addition, you can request plots of the residuals versus $\hat{y}$ or versus the individual independent variables. Examine the plots and look for nonrandomness in the behavior of the residuals. If nonrandomness is observed, seek an explanation for the behavior and attempt to correct it.

STEPWISE REGRESSION ANALYSIS

12.6

A company that hires college graduates as sales personnel wants to construct a model to predict a hired applicant's success (measured by the sales that the applicant will subsequently make during the third year of employment) from information acquired during the applicant's job interview. This information includes the applicant's high school and college grades, achievement test scores, ratings of personal interviews and letters of recommendation, outside activities, interests, achievements, and so on. **How does the company decide which among this long list of independent variables should be included in the model? One procedure for answering this question is to use a computer program package that performs a stepwise regression analysis**.

Suppose that we have data available on y and a number of possible independent variable, $x_1, x_2, \ldots x_k$. A **stepwise regression analysis** commences by fitting the model

$$E(y) = \beta_0 + \beta_1 x$$

for each of the k independent variables. The best-fitting of these k prediction equations is chosen (for most programs) as the one with the largest t values for β_1. We will denote this independent variable as x_1.

The second step in a stepwise regression analysis is to fit all possible two-variable models. Most computer programs retain x_1 and fit only models of the type

$$E(y) = \beta_0 + \beta_1 x_1 + \beta_2 x_2$$

where x_2 is one of the $(k - 1)$ remaining variables. For these programs the variable to be denoted as x_2 and retained in the model is again the one with the largest t value for β_2. Other programs try all possible two-variable models because **it is conceivable that the best two-variable model will not include x_1, the variable entered in step 1.** These programs usually choose as the best two-variable model the one with the largest value of R^2.

The third and succeeding steps in a stepwise regression analysis are identical to the second step. The third step fits the model

$$E(y) = \beta_0 + \beta_1 x_1 + \beta_2 x_2 + \beta_3 x_3$$

The variable x_3 chosen to be retained in the model is either the one for which the t value for β_3 is the largest or the value for which R^2 is the largest (depending upon the computer program). The procedure stops when the t value for the entering value is less than some predetermined value that would imply statistical significance (or when R^2 exceeds some predetermined value).

A stepwise regression analysis is an easy way to locate some variables that contribute information for the prediction of y, but it is not a foolproof method for finding a good model. Stepwise regression procedures almost always fit first-order models composed of the variables entered into the computer—that is, models of the type

$$E(y) = \beta_0 + \beta_1 x_1 + \beta_2 x_2 + \cdots + \beta_k x_k$$

If you want to introduce second-order terms to account for curvature in the response surface, you will have to enter them into the computer as though they were new variables. In other words, if you had three independent variables, x_1, x_2, and x_3, you could enter these variables into the computer along with $x_4 = x_1^2, x_5 = x_2^2, x_6 = x_3^2, x_7 = x_1 x_2$, and so on.

If the number of independent variables is large, the total number of first-order and second-order terms may be unmanageable. One alternative, when this situation occurs, is to perform a stepwise regression analysis on the original set of independent variables, thereby acquiring a small set of information-contributing variables. If the model requires improvement, a second stepwise regression analysis could be performed, using these variables as well as their squares and cross products. This procedure is unlikely to yield the best second-order model to fit the data, but it is a reasonable alternative to the massive task involved in fitting all possible second-order models.

The computer printout for a stepwise regression analysis is a sequence of individual regression analyses, one for each step in the procedure. Most will be easy to read. They will differ, depending upon the computer program that you use, but the printout for each step will be similar to the printout for a standard multiple regression analysis.

MISINTERPRETATIONS IN A REGRESSION ANALYSIS

12.7

Several misinterpretations of the output of a regression analysis are common. We have already mentioned the importance of model selection. If a model does not fit a set of data, it does not mean that the variables included in the model contribute little or no information for the prediction of y. The variables may be very important contributors of information, but you may not have entered the variables into the model in an appropriate way. For example, a second-order model in the variables might provide a very good fit to the data when a first-order model appears to be completely useless in describing the response variable y.

Second, you must be careful not to deduce that a causal relationship exists between a response y and a variable x. Just because a variable x contributes information for the prediction of y, it does not imply that changes in x *cause* changes in y. It is possible to *design* an experiment to detect causal relationships. For example, if you randomly assign experimental units to each of two levels of a variable x, say $x = 5$ and $x = 10$, and the data show that the mean value of y is larger when $x = 10$, then you could say that the change in the level of x caused a change in the mean value of y. But in most regression analyses, where the experiments are not designed, there is no guarantee that an important predictor variable, say x_1, caused y to change. It is quite possible that some variable that is not even in the model caused *both* y and x_1 to change.

A third common misinterpretation concerns the magnitude of the regression coefficients. Neither the size of a regression coefficient nor its t value indicates the importance of the associated variable as an information contributor. For example, suppose that you wish to predict a college student's calculus grade y as a function of the student's high school average mathematics grade x_1 and the student's score x_2 on a college mathematics placement test. A regression analysis, using the first-order model $E(y) = \beta_0 + \beta_1 x_1 + \beta_2 x_2$, would likely show that both x_1 and x_2 contribute information for the prediction of y. However, it is conceivable that the t value associated with one of the regression coefficients would not be statistically significant, because much of the information contained in x_1 is the same information contained in x_2. When this occurs, the one-variable model

$$E(y) = \beta_0 + \beta_1 x_1 \qquad \text{or} \qquad E(y) = \beta_0 + \beta_2 x_2$$

may be almost as useful in predicting y as the model

$$E(y) = \beta_0 + \beta_1 x_1 + \beta_2 x_2$$

When two or more of the independent variables are related and, therefore, contribute overlapping information for the prediction of y, we say that **multicollinearity** exists in the independent variables—that is, they are correlated. Since multicollinearity exists in most regression analyses, the individual terms in the model should be viewed as information contributors. The primary decision to be made is whether one or more of the terms contribute sufficient information for the prediction of y and whether they should be retained in the model.

How to Write a Linear Model☆

12.8

The variables in a regression analysis can be one of two types, quantitative or qualitative. For example, the age of a person is a **quantitative variable** because its values express the quantity or amount of something—in this case, age. In contrast, the nationality of a person is a **qualitative variable** that varies from person to person, but

☆This section is optional.

the values of the variable cannot be quantified; they can only be classified. For the methods we present, the response variable y must always be (according to the assumptions of Section 12.2) a quantitative variable. In contrast, predictor variables may be either quantitative or qualitative. For example, suppose that we want to predict the annual income of a person. Both the age and the nationality of the person could be important predictor variables, and there are probably many others.

DEFINITION   A *quantitative variable* is one whose values correspond to the quantity or the amount of something.   ■

DEFINITION   A *qualitative variable* is one that assumes values that cannot be quantifed. They can only be categorized.   ■

As noted in Section 12.2, quantitative predictor variables, say x_1, x_2, and so forth, are usually entered into a model by using first-order terms, those involving $x_1, x_2, x_3, \ldots$, and second-order terms, those involving $x_1^2, x_2^2, x_3^2, x_1 x_2, x_1 x_3,$ $x_2 x_3, \ldots$. In general, the second-order terms allow for curvature in the relationship between $E(y)$ and the dependent variables, but the cross product, second-order terms possess a special significance. They are often used to model the **interaction** between two predictor variables in their effect on the response variable.

To understand the concept of interaction, consider the **first-order (planar) model**.

FIRST-ORDER MODEL IN TWO INDEPENDENT VARIABLES

$$E(y) = \beta_0 + \beta_1 x_1 + \beta_2 x_2$$

If you were to graph $E(y)$ as a function of x_1 with x_2 held constant, you would obtain a straight line. Repeating this process for other values of x_2, you would obtain a set of parallel lines (with slopes β_1 but intercepts depending on the particular value of x_2) that might appear as shown in Figure 12.13. [Graphs of $E(y)$ versus x_2 for various values of x_1 would also produce a set of parallel lines but with common slope β_2.]

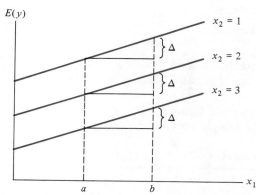

FIGURE 12.13   No Interaction Between x_1 and x_2

Figure 12.13 shows that regardless of the value of x_2, a change in x_1, say from $x_1 = a$ to $x_1 = b$, will always produce the same change, Δ, in $E(y)$. When this situation occurs—that is, when the change in $E(y)$ for a change in one variable does not depend on the value of the second variable—we say that the variables **do not interact**.

In contrast, consider the **second-order (interaction) model**.

SECOND-ORDER INTERACTION MODEL IN TWO INDEPENDENT VARIABLES

$$E(y) = \beta_0 + \beta_1 x_1 + \beta_2 x_2 + \beta_3 x_1 x_2$$

If you were to again graph $E(y)$ versus x_1 for various values of x_2, you would obtain a set of lines, but they would not be parallel (see Figure 12.14). In Figure 12.14 you can see that $E(y)$ rises very slowly as x_1 increases when $x_2 = 1$; more rapidly when $x_2 = 2$; and even more rapidly when $x_2 = 3$. Therefore, the effect on $E(y)$ of a change in x_1 **depends** on the value of x_2. When this situation occurs, we say that the predictor variables **interact**. If you attempt to fit the noninteractive first-order model to data that graph as shown in Figure 12.14, you would obtain a very poor fit to your data. The warning is clear. You may need interaction terms in your model to obtain a good fit to a set of data.

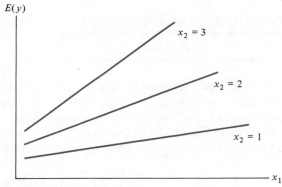

FIGURE 12.14   Interaction Between x_1 and x_2

DEFINITION   Two predictor variables are said to *interact* if the change in $E(y)$ corresponding to a change in one predictor variable depends upon the value of the other variable.   ∎

If the second-order terms $\beta_3 x_1 x_2$, $\beta_4 x_1^2$, and $\beta_5 x_2^2$ are added to a first-order model, we obtain a complete second-order model.

COMPLETE SECOND-ORDER MODEL IN TWO INDEPENDENT VARIABLES

$$E(y) = \beta_0 + \beta_1 x_1 + \beta_2 x_2 + \overbrace{\beta_3 x_1 x_2 + \beta_4 x_1^2 + \beta_5 x_2^2}^{\text{second-order terms}}$$

First-order, second-order interaction, and complete second-order models for three or more independent variables are extensions of the corresponding two-variable models. These models, for three independent variables, are shown next.

FIRST-ORDER MODEL IN THREE INDEPENDENT VARIABLES

$$E(y) = \beta_0 + \beta_1 x_1 + \beta_2 x_2 + \beta_3 x_3$$

SECOND-ORDER INTERACTION MODEL IN THREE INDEPENDENT VARIABLES

$$E(y) = \beta_0 + \beta_1 x_1 + \beta_2 x_2 + \beta_3 x_3 + \beta_4 x_1 x_2 + \beta_5 x_1 x_3 + \beta_6 x_2 x_3$$

COMPLETE SECOND-ORDER MODEL IN THREE INDEPENDENT VARIABLES

$$E(y) = \beta_0 + \beta_1 x_1 + \beta_2 x_2 + \beta_3 x_3 + \beta_4 x_1 x_2 +$$
$$\beta_5 x_1 x_3 + \beta_6 x_2 x_3 + \beta_7 x_1^2 + \beta_8 x_2^2 + \beta_9 x_3^2$$

Graphs of linear models in two or more independent variables are called **response surfaces**. For example, a graph of a first-order model in two independent variables traces a plane in a three-dimensional space (see Figure 12.15). The second-order interaction model graphs as a twisted plane (see Figure 12.16), and the complete second-order model graphs as a paraboloid (see Figure 12.17). Models containing

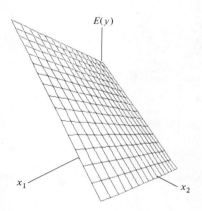

$E(y) = 30 + x_1/3 - x_2$

$0 \leqslant x_1 \leqslant 25$
$0 \leqslant x_2 \leqslant 25$

FIGURE 12.15   Response Surface for a First-Order Model in Two Independent Variables

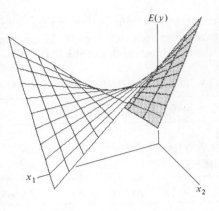

$$E(y) = 5 + x_1 + 2x_2 - x_1x_2/15$$

$$0 \leqslant x_1 \leqslant 50$$
$$0 \leqslant x_2 \leqslant 30$$

FIGURE 12.16   Response Surface for a Second-Order Interaction Model in Two Independent Variables

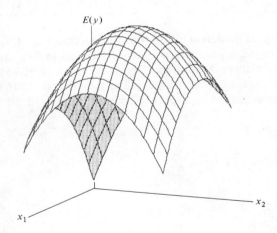

$$E(y) = 1 + 2x_1 + 2.5x_2 - .02x_1x_2 - .05x_1^2 - .06x_2^2$$

$$0 \leqslant x_1 \leqslant 32$$
$$0 \leqslant x_2 \leqslant 32$$

FIGURE 12.17   Response Surface for a Complete Second-Order Model in Two Independent Variables

three (or more) independent variables would have to be graphed in a four- (or more) dimensional space. We cannot visualize response surfaces in four dimensions, but we can imagine that graphs of these models would possess the same types of shapes as their two-independent-variable counterparts.

In contrast to quantitative predictor variables, qualitative predictor variables are entered into a model by using **dummy (indicator) variables**. For example, suppose that you were attempting to relate the mean salary of a group of employees to a set of predictor variables and that one of the variables that you want to include is the employee's race. If each employee included in your study belongs to one of three races, say A, B, or C, you will want to enter the qualitative predictor variable "race" into your model as follows:

$$E(y) = \beta_0 + \beta_1 x_1 + \beta_2 x_2$$

where

$$x_1 = \begin{cases} 1, & \text{if race B} \\ 0, & \text{if not} \end{cases} \qquad x_2 = \begin{cases} 1, & \text{if race C} \\ 0, & \text{if not} \end{cases}$$

If you want to find $E(y)$ for race A, you examine the coding for the dummy variables x_1 and x_2 and note that $x_1 = 0$ and $x_2 = 0$. Therefore, for race A

$$E(y) = \beta_0 + \beta_1 x_1 + \beta_2 x_2 = \beta_0 + \beta_1(0) + \beta_2(0) = \beta_0$$

The value of $E(y)$ for race B is obtained by letting $x_1 = 1$ and $x_2 = 0$; that is, for race B

$$E(y) = \beta_0 + \beta_1 x_1 + \beta_2 x_2 = \beta_0 + \beta_1(1) + \beta_2(0) = \beta_0 + \beta_1$$

Similarly, the value of $E(y)$ for race C is obtained by letting $x_1 = 0$ and $x_2 = 1$. Therefore, for race C

$$E(y) = \beta_0 + \beta_1 x_1 + \beta_2 x_2 = \beta_0 + \beta_1(0) + \beta_2(1) = \beta_0 + \beta_2$$

Models with qualitative predictor variables that may assume, say, k values can be constructed in a similar manner, by using $(k - 1)$ terms involving dummy variables. These terms can be added to models containing other predictor variables, quantitative or qualitative, and you can also include terms involving the cross products (interaction terms) of the dummy variables with other variables that appear in the model. For an example, see Example 12.9, Section 12.10.

This optional section introduced two important aspects of model formulation: the concept of predictor variable interaction (and how to cope with it) and, second, the method for introducing qualitative predictor variables into a model. Clearly, this is not enough to make you proficient in model formulation, but it will help you to understand why and how some terms are included in regression models, and it may help you to avoid some pitfalls encountered in model construction. An elementary but fairly complete discussion of this topic can be found in Mendenhall and Sincich (1986).

12.9   TESTING SETS OF MODEL PARAMETERS*

In the preceding sections we found it useful to test a complete linear model to determine whether the model contributes information for the prediction of y. We also were able to test an hypothesis about an individual β parameter, using a Student's t test. In addition to these two important tests, we may want to test hypotheses about sets of parameters. For example, suppose that you suspect that the demand y for some product is

*This section is optional.

related to two independent variables x_1 and x_2. Recall that a first-order model

$$E(y) = \beta_0 + \beta_1 x_1 + \beta_2 x_2$$

implies that each of the variables x_1 and x_2 affects $E(y)$ independently of the values of the other variable, and the relationship is a straight line. Thus a first-order model implies no curvature in the relationship between $E(y)$ and the independent variables x_1 and x_2, and furthermore, it implies no interaction* between x_1 and x_2. In contrast, the complete second-order model

$$E(y) = \beta_0 + \beta_1 x_1 + \beta_2 x_2 + \beta_3 x_1 x_2 + \beta_4 x_1^2 + \beta_5 x_2^2$$

makes allowance for both curvature and interaction in the relationship between the response variable y and the independent variables x_1 and x_2. Which model should we use to relate product demand to x_1 and x_2, the first-order model or the complete second-order model?

To answer this question, we need to know whether the second-order terms $\beta_3 x_1 x_2$, $\beta_4 x_1^2$, and $\beta_5 x_2^2$ contribute information for the prediction of y. If they do, we will want to use the second-order model to relate $E(y)$ to x_1 and x_2. If not, we can use the simpler first-order model.

If the second-order terms contribute no information about y, then they would not appear in the model—that is, $\beta_3 = \beta_4 = \beta_5 = 0$. Therefore, we will want to test

H_0: $\beta_3 = \beta_4 = \beta_5 = 0$—that is, the second-order terms contribute no information for the prediction of y

against the alternative hypothesis

H_a: at least one of the parameters β_3, β_4, or β_5 differs from 0—that is, at least one of the second-order terms contributes information for the prediction of y

Thus in deciding whether the second-order model is preferable to the first-order model in predicting demand, we are led to a test of an hypothesis about a set of three parameters, β_3, β_4, and β_5.

To explain how to test an hypothesis concerning a set of model parameters, we will define two models:

Model 1 (Reduced Model)

$$E(y) = \beta_0 + \beta_1 x_1 + \beta_2 x_2 + \cdots + \beta_k x_k$$

Model 2 (Complete Model)

$$E(y) = \underbrace{\beta_0 + \beta_1 x_1 + \beta_2 x_2 + \cdots + \beta_k x_k}_{\text{terms in Model 1}} + \underbrace{\beta_{k+1} x_{k+1} + \beta_{k+2} x_{k+2} + \cdots + \beta_r x_r}_{\text{additional terms in Model 2}}$$

Suppose that we were to fit both models to the data set and calculate the sum of squares for error for both regression analyses. If Model 2 contributes more information for the prediction of y than Model 1, then the errors of prediction for Model 2 should be

---

*The concept of variable interaction is discussed in Section 9.8 and in optional Section 12.8.

smaller than the corresponding errors for Model 1, and SSE_2 should be smaller than SSE_1. In fact, the greater the difference between SSE_1 and SSE_2, the greater is the evidence to indicate that Model 2 contributes more information for the prediction of y than Model 1.

The test of the null hypothesis

$$H_0: \beta_{k+1} = \beta_{k+2} = \cdots = \beta_r = 0$$

against the alternative hypothesis

$H_a:$ at least one of the parameters $\beta_{k+1}, \beta_{k+2}, \cdots, \beta_r$ differs from zero

uses the test statistic

$$F = \frac{(SSE_1 - SSE_2)/(k - r)}{MSE_2}$$

where F is based on $v_1 = k - r$ and $v_2 = n - (r + 1)$ degrees of freedom. Note that the $(k - r)$ parameters involved in H_0 are those added to Model 1 to obtain Model 2. The numerator number v_1 of degrees of freedom will always equal $(k - r)$, the number of parameters involved in H_0. The denominator number v_2 of degrees of freedom is the number of degrees of freedom associated with the sum of squares for error, SSE_2, for the complete model.

The rejection region for the test is identical to the rejection region for all of the analysis of variance F tests, namely,

$$F > F_\alpha$$

We will demonstrate this test in the following section.

PERFORMING AN ANALYSIS OF VARIANCE WHEN DATA ARE MISSING[☆]

12.10

The formulas given for calculating the sums of squares necessary to compare treatment means for randomized block designs and factorial experiments in Chapter 9 are valid only if the data are collected exactly as prescribed by the design. (This statement is true for formulas used in the analysis of variance for many other experimental designs.) For example, if you use a randomized block design to compare $k = 3$ treatments within $b = 5$ blocks and if the observation for treatment A_2 located in block 1 is lost, then the formulas for the analysis of variance for the data given in Section 9.6 will be invalid. Similarly, if the number of observations per treatment are unequal for the six treatment combinations of a 2×3 two-factor factorial experiment, the formulas for the analysis of variance given in Section 9.9 will be invalid.

A multiple regression analysis can be used to calculate the analysis of variance sums of squares for the experimental designs of Chapter 9 (as well as for many other experimental designs), and it can also be used to compute the appropriate sums of squares when some of the observations in a designed experiment have been lost. The technique is illustrated by the following examples.

☆This section is optional.

EXAMPLE 12.7   Use multiple regression analyses to calculate the sum of squares for treatments for the randomized block design of Example 9.2. The data, which give bid prices for three project cost estimators for each of five projects, are reproduced in Table 12.12.

TABLE 12.12   Data for the Comparison of Estimator Project Bid Prices in Example 9.2

Estimator	Project					Total
	1	2	3	4	5	
1	3.52	4.71	3.89	5.21	4.14	21.47
2	3.39	4.79	3.82	4.93	3.96	20.89
3	3.64	4.92	4.19	5.10	4.20	22.05
Total	10.55	14.42	11.90	15.24	12.30	64.41

SOLUTION   In order to use a regression analysis to calculate an ANOVA sum of squares, we must write a linear model for y by using the method of optional Section 12.8. For this experiment the estimated bid price for a construction project is dependent upon two qualitative variables, estimators (treatments) and the project (blocks) for which the observation was recorded. Since the variable "estimator" can take one of three levels (corresponding to the three estimators), "estimator" is entered into the model by using *two* dummy (indicator) variables. Similarly, the qualitative variable "project" can assume one of five levels (corresponding to the five projects included in the randomized block design). Therefore, the qualitative variable "project" is entered into the model by using four dummy variables. (Note that the number of dummy variables for a qualitative variable is always equal to one less than the number of levels that the variable can assume in the experiment.) The resulting model is

$$E(y) = \beta_0 + \overbrace{\beta_1 x_1 + \beta_2 x_2}^{\text{treatment terms}} + \overbrace{\beta_3 x_3 + \beta_4 x_4 + \beta_5 x_5 + \beta_6 x_6}^{\text{block terms}}$$

where

$$x_1 = \begin{cases} 1, & \text{if the bid price is given by estimator 2} \\ 0, & \text{if not} \end{cases}$$

$$x_2 = \begin{cases} 1, & \text{if the bid price is given by estimator 3} \\ 0, & \text{if not} \end{cases}$$

$$x_3 = \begin{cases} 1, & \text{if the bid price is on project 2} \\ 0, & \text{if not} \end{cases}$$

$$x_4 = \begin{cases} 1, & \text{if the bid price is on project 3} \\ 0, & \text{if not} \end{cases}$$

$$x_5 = \begin{cases} 1, & \text{if the bid price is on project 4} \\ 0, & \text{if not} \end{cases}$$

$$x_6 = \begin{cases} 1, & \text{if the bid price is on project 5} \\ 0, & \text{if not} \end{cases}$$

An understanding of the coding is necessary so that you will know how to enter values of x into a computer for each of the $n = 15$ y values of Table 12.12. For example, if an observation y is the estimated bid price given by estimator 3 for project 4, then $x_1 = 0$, $x_2 = 1$, $x_3 = 0$, $x_4 = 0$, $x_5 = 1$, and $x_6 = 0$. For this combination of estimator and project,

$$E(y) = \beta_0 + \beta_1(0) + \beta_2(1) + \beta_3(0) + \beta_4(0) + \beta_5(1) + \beta_6(0)$$
$$= \beta_0 + \beta_2 + \beta_5$$

Similarly, if the observation y is the estimated bid price given by estimator 1 for project 1, then according to the coding described above, $x_1 = x_2 = \cdots = x_6 = 0$ and $E(y) = \beta_0$.

You will recall (Section 12.8) that the $(1, 0)$ coding that we have used for the dummy (indicator) variables makes it easy to interpret the model parameters. If we denote the three treatment means as μ_1, μ_2, and μ_3, respectively, then

$$\beta_1 = \mu_2 - \mu_1 \qquad \text{and} \qquad \beta_2 = \mu_3 - \mu_1$$

Therefore, the null hypothesis

$$H_0 : \beta_1 = \beta_2 = 0$$

is equivalent to saying that the treatment means are equal—that is, $\mu_1 = \mu_2 = \mu_3$. Therefore, to conduct the ANOVA test of $H_0 : \mu_1 = \mu_2 = \mu_3$, we can use the method of Section 12.9.

To calculate SST, the sum of squares needed to test

$$H_0 : \beta_1 = \beta_2 = 0$$

that is, there are no differences among the treatment means, we first fit the complete model (Model 2) to the data by using a regression analysis and calculate SSE_2:

Complete Model (2)

$$E(y) = \beta_0 + \overbrace{\beta_1 x_1 + \beta_2 x_2}^{\text{treatment terms}} + \overbrace{\beta_3 x_3 + \beta_4 x_4 + \beta_5 x_5 + \beta_6 x_6}^{\text{block terms}}$$

Next, we write the reduced model (Model 1) for y by deleting the two treatment terms from the complete model:

Reduced Model (1)

$$E(y) = \beta_0 + \overbrace{\beta_3 x_3 + \beta_4 x_4 + \beta_5 x_5 + \beta_6 x_6}^{\text{block terms}}$$

We fit this model to the data and calculate SSE_1. The difference between SSE_1 and SSE_2 is (proof omitted) the sum of squares for treatments SST; that is,

$$SST = SSE_1 - SSE_2$$

In order to perform these calculations, we must list the values of y (given in Table 12.12) and the corresponding values of $x_1, x_2, \ldots, x_6$ so that they can be entered into a computer. These values are shown in Table 12.13.

TABLE 12.13   Values of y and $x_1, x_2, \ldots, x_6$ for the Data of Table 12.12

y	x_1	x_2	x_3	x_4	x_5	x_6
3.52	0	0	0	0	0	0
3.39	1	0	0	0	0	0
3.64	0	1	0	0	0	0
4.71	0	0	1	0	0	0
4.79	1	0	1	0	0	0
4.92	0	1	1	0	0	0
3.89	0	0	0	1	0	0
3.82	1	0	0	1	0	0
4.19	0	1	0	1	0	0
5.21	0	0	0	0	1	0
4.93	1	0	0	0	1	0
5.10	0	1	0	0	1	0
4.14	0	0	0	0	0	1
3.96	1	0	0	0	0	1
4.20	0	1	0	0	0	1

The SAS multiple regression printouts for the complete and reduced models are shown in Tables 12.14 and 12.15. The values of SSE_2 and SSE_1 from the printouts are $SSE_2 = .06744$ and $SSE_1 = .20200$. Then

$$SST = .20200 - .06744 = .13456$$

You can verify that this is exactly the value obtained for SST by using the analysis of variance, Table 9.15. The sum of squares for error needed for the F test is SSE_2, the value calculated for the complete model. You can verify that this value,

$$SSE_2 = .06744$$

is also the same as the value shown in the ANOVA printout in Table 9.15. The remaining steps necessary for testing $H_0 : \beta_1 = \beta_2 = 0$—that is $\mu_1 = \mu_2 = \mu_3$—are exactly the same as those described for that ANOVA F test in Section 9.3 and for the F test in Section 12.9. The two tests are equivalent.

The sum of squares for blocks, SSB, can be calculated in a similar manner. The reduced model for these calculations is obtained by deleting the block terms from the complete model. This reduced model is

Reduced Model (1)

$$E(y) = \beta_0 + \beta_1 x_1 + \beta_2 x_2$$

Fitting this model to the data, we obtain a new value for SSE_1, and

$$SSB = SSE_1 - SSE_2$$

We omit the calculations.

TABLE 12.14   SAS Output Using the Complete Model for the Randomized Block Design of Example 12.7

```
Model: MODEL2
Dep Variable: Y
```

Analysis of Variance

Source	DF	Sum of Squares	Mean Square	F Value	Prob>F
Model	6	5.02352	0.83725	99.318	0.0001
Error	8	0.06744	0.00843		
C Total	14	5.09096			

Root MSE	0.09182	R-Square	0.9868
Y Mean	4.29400	Adj R-Sq	0.9768
C.V.	2.13822		

Parameter Estimates

Variable	DF	Parameter Estimate	T for H0: Parameter=0	Prob > |T|	Std Error
INTERCEP	1	3.516667	56.068	0.0001	0.06272161
X1	1	-0.116000	-1.998	0.0808	0.05806892
X2	1	0.116000	1.998	0.0808	0.05806892
X3	1	1.290000	17.208	0.0001	0.07496666
X4	1	0.450000	6.003	0.0003	0.07496666
X5	1	1.563333	20.854	0.0001	0.07496666
X6	1	0.583333	7.781	0.0001	0.07496666

TABLE 12.15   SAS Output Using the Reduced Model for the Randomized Block Design of Example 12.7

```
Model: MODEL1
Dep Variable: Y
```

Analysis of Variance

Source	DF	Sum of Squares	Mean Square	F Value	Prob>F
Model	4	4.88896	1.22224	60.507	0.0001
Error	10	0.20200	0.02020		
C Total	14	5.09096			

Root MSE	0.14213	R-Square	0.9603
Y Mean	4.29400	Adj R-Sq	0.9445
C.V.	3.30989		

Parameter Estimates

Variable	DF	Parameter Estimate	T for H0: Parameter=0	Prob > |T|	Std Error
INTERCEP	1	3.516667	42.856	0.0001	0.08205689
X3	1	1.290000	11.116	0.0001	0.11604597
X4	1	0.450000	3.878	0.0031	0.11604597
X5	1	1.563333	13.472	0.0001	0.11604597
X6	1	0.583333	5.027	0.0005	0.11604597

You may be wondering why we would want to go through all of the steps in Example 12.7 to obtain the analysis of variance sums of squares when we can obtain them so easily from a computer program package for an analysis of variance. Of course, you are correct. Analyzing the set of data in Table 12.12 can be accomplished much easier by using an analysis of variance computer program package.

Now suppose something happened to disrupt the design. For example, suppose that estimator 1 was sick and unable to obtain bid price estimates for projects 1 and 2. Then the observations for treatment 1 in blocks 1 and 2 would be missing and the formulas given for the calculation of SST, SSB, and SSE in Section 9.7 would be invalid. One easy way to calculate the sum of squares for treatment for this unbalanced design (a randomized block design with missing observations) is to fit complete and reduced models by using a multiple regression analysis. The following example illustrates the procedure.

EXAMPLE 12.8   Find SST and SSE for the data of Example 12.7 if the observations for estimator 1, projects 1 and 2 ($y = 3.52$ and 4.71), are missing. Do the data provide sufficient evidence to indicate differences in mean bid price estimation levels for the three construction project estimators? Test using $\alpha = .05$. The data are reproduced in Table 12.16.

TABLE 12.16   Project Bid Price Estimation Data with Two Missing Observations for Example 12.8

Estimator	Project 1	Project 2	Project 3	Project 4	Project 5	Total
1	Deleted	Deleted	3.89	5.21	4.14	13.24
2	3.39	4.79	3.82	4.93	3.96	20.89
3	3.64	4.92	4.19	5.10	4.20	22.05
Total	7.03	9.71	11.90	15.24	12.30	56.18

SOLUTION   The complete and reduced models for calculating SST are exactly the same as in Example 12.7. The SAS multiple regression printouts for fitting these two models to the $n = 13$ data points of Table 12.16 are shown in Tables 12.17 and 12.18, respectively. Examining these printouts, you can see that

$$\text{SSE}_1 = .18797 \quad \text{and} \quad \text{SSE}_2 = .04905$$

Therefore,

$$\text{SST} = \text{SSE}_1 - \text{SSE}_2 = .18797 - .04905 = .13892$$

$$\text{MST} = \frac{\text{SST}}{2} = \frac{.13892}{2} = .06946$$

$$\text{MSE} = s^2 = \frac{\text{SSE}_2}{n - (\text{number of parameters in the complete model})}$$

$$= \frac{.04905}{13 - 7} = .00818$$

TABLE 12.17   SAS Output Using the Complete Model for the Unbalanced Randomized Block Design for Example 12.8

```
Model: MODEL2
Dep Variable: Y
                            Analysis of Variance

                          Sum of        Mean
         Source      DF   Squares      Square      F Value     Prob>F

         Model        6   4.25992      0.70999     86.847      0.0001
         Error        6   0.04905      0.00818
         C Total     12   4.30897

              Root MSE     0.09042     R-Square     0.9886
              Y Mean       4.32154     Adj R-Sq     0.9772
              C.V.         2.09223


                           Parameter Estimates

                      Parameter     T for H0:
     Variable     DF   Estimate     Parameter=0     Prob > |T|     Std Error

     INTERCEPT     1   3.561667       39.392         0.0001       0.09041673
     X1            1  -0.162667       -2.323         0.0592       0.07003650
     X2            1   0.069333        0.990         0.3604       0.07003650
     X3            1   1.340000       14.820         0.0001       0.09041673
     X4            1   0.436111        5.116         0.0022       0.08524571
     X5            1   1.549444       18.176         0.0001       0.08524571
     X6            1   0.569444        6.680         0.0005       0.08524571
```

TABLE 12.18   SAS Output Using the Reduced Model for the Unbalanced Randomized Block Design for Example 12.8

```
Model: MODEL1
Dep Variable: Y
                            Analysis of Variance

                          Sum of        Mean
         Source      DF   Squares      Square      F Value     Prob>F

         Model        4   4.12100      1.03025     43.848      0.0001
         Error        8   0.18797      0.02350
         C Total     12   4.30897

              Root MSE     0.15328     R-Square     0.9564
              Y Mean       4.32154     Adj R-Sq     0.9346
              C.V.         3.54697


                           Parameter Estimates

                      Parameter     T for H0:
     Variable     DF   Estimate     Parameter=0     Prob > |T|     Std Error

     INTERCEP      1   3.515000       32.430         0.0001       0.10838781
     X3            1   1.340000        8.742         0.0001       0.15328351
     X4            1   0.451667        3.228         0.0121       0.13992806
     X5            1   1.565000       11.184         0.0001       0.13992806
     X6            1   0.585000        4.181         0.0031       0.13992806
```

Then to test

H_0: $\beta_1 = \beta_2 = 0$—that is, there are no differences among the
treatment means

against the alternative hypothesis

H_a: at least one of the parameters β_1 or β_2 differs from zero—that is,
at least two of the treatment means differ

we calculate the test statistic

$$F = \frac{MST}{MSE} = \frac{.06946}{.00818} = 8.49$$

where F possesses $v_1 = $ number of parameters in $H_0 = 2$

and $v_2 = n - $ (number of parameters in the complete model) $= 13 - 7 = 6$

degrees of freedom. The rejection region for the test is $F > F_\alpha$. The tabulated value for
$\alpha = .05$, given in Table 8 of the Appendix, for $v_1 = 2$ and $v_2 = 6$ degrees of freedom is

$$F_{.05} = 5.14$$

Since the calculated value of the F test statistic, $F = 8.49$ exceeds $F_{.05} = 5.14$, there is
strong evidence to indicate a difference between at least two of the treatment means.

$\blacksquare$

EXAMPLE 12.9   In Example 9.3 we presented data (Table 9.30) for three replications of a 2×3 factorial
experiment. The first factor, "foreman," was at $a = 2$ levels; the second factor, "shift,"
was at $b = 3$ levels. The objective of the experiment was to investigate the effects of the
two factors, foreman and shift, on the output count y of a production line for an 8-hour
shift. Suppose that two of the observations were missing because foreman 1 was sick
and absent on one of the 8 A.M.–4 P.M. shifts and foreman 2 was absent for one of the
12 P.M.–8 A.M. shifts. The remaining 16 observations of Table 9.30 are shown in
Table 12.19. Do the data provide sufficient information to indicate an interaction between foremen and shifts? Test using $\alpha = .05$.

TABLE 12.19   Output per Shift for a 2×3 Factorial Experiment with an Unequal Number of Observations
per Treatment (Example 12.9)

Foreman (Factor A)	Shift (Factor B)		
	B_1 (8 A.M.–4 P.M.)	B_2 (4 P.M.–12 P.M.)	B_3 (12 P.M.–8 A.M.)
A_1	—	480	470
	610	475	430
	625	540	450
A_2	480	625	—
	515	600	680
	465	580	660

SOLUTION We can no longer find the sum of squares SS(AB) for the interaction of factors A and B by using the analysis of variance formulas of Section 9.10 because the numbers of observations for the factor level combinations (the treatments) are not equal. But we can calculate SS(AB) by fitting complete and reduced models to the data, models that do and do not, respectively, contain the terms that imply interaction between the factors.

The complete model for the experiment is

Complete Model (2)

$$E(y) = \beta_0 + \overbrace{\beta_1 x_1}^{\substack{\text{main effects,}\\ \text{factor } A}} + \overbrace{\beta_2 x_2 + \beta_3 x_3}^{\substack{\text{main effects,}\\ \text{factor } B}} + \overbrace{\beta_4 x_1 x_2 + \beta_5 x_1 x_3}^{\substack{\text{interaction of}\\ A \text{ and } B}}$$

where

$$x_1 = \begin{cases} 1, & \text{if factor } B \\ 0, & \text{if not} \end{cases}$$

$$x_2 = \begin{cases} 1, & \text{if shift 2} \\ 0, & \text{if not} \end{cases}$$

$$x_3 = \begin{cases} 1, & \text{if shift 3} \\ 0, & \text{if not} \end{cases}$$

Note that no term is included in the model for $x_2 x_3$ because x_2 and x_3 are dummy variables for the *same* main effect, and a main effect does not interact with itself.

The reduced model for calculating SS(AB) contains all of the terms of the complete model (with the same coding for x_1, x_2 and x_3, except that the interaction terms are deleted). Thus the reduced model is

Reduced Model (1)

$$E(y) = \beta_0 + \overbrace{\beta_1 x_1}^{\substack{\text{main effects,}\\ \text{factor } A}} + \overbrace{\beta_2 x_2 + \beta_3 x_3}^{\substack{\text{main effects,}\\ \text{factor } B}}$$

The SAS multiple regression printouts for fitting Models 1 and 2 to the data are shown in Tables 12.20 and 12.21.

The sum of squares of error for the reduced and complete models, given in Tables 12.20 and 12.21, are

$$\text{SSE}_1 = 83{,}098.97436 \quad \text{and} \quad \text{SSE}_2 = 6062.50000$$

Then the sum of squares SS(AB) to test the null hypothesis that the interaction terms contribute no information for the prediction of y, that is,

$$H_0 : \beta_4 = \beta_5 = 0$$

is

$$\text{SS}(AB) = \text{SSE}_1 - \text{SSE}_2 = 83{,}098.97436 - 6062.50000 = 77036.47$$

TABLE 12.20   SAS Output Using the Complete Model for the 2×3 Factorial Experiment with Missing Data, for Example 12.9

```
Model: MODEL2
Dep Variable: Y
                              Analysis of Variance

                          Sum of         Mean
       Source     DF      Squares       Square      F Value      Prob>F

       Model       5    95135.93750   19027.18750    31.385       0.0001
       Error      10     6062.50000     606.25000
       C Total    15   101198.43750

              Root MSE       24.62214     R-Square      0.9401
              Y Mean        542.81250     Adj R-Sq      0.9101
              C.V.            4.53603


                              Parameter Estimates

                          Parameter      T for H0:
       Variable    DF      Estimate     Parameter=0    Prob > |T|     Std Error

       INTERCEP     1     617.500000       35.467        0.0001      17.41048535
       X1           1    -130.833333       -5.821        0.0002      22.47683993
       X2           1    -119.166667       -5.302        0.0003      22.47683993
       X3           1    -167.500000       -7.452        0.0001      22.47683993
       X1X2         1     234.166667        7.765        0.0001      30.15584520
       X1X3         1     350.833333       11.037        0.0001      31.78705187
```

TABLE 12.21   SAS Output Using the Reduced Model for the 2×3 Factorial Experiment with Missing Data, for Example 12.9

```
Model: MODEL1
Dep Variable: Y
                              Analysis of Variance

                          Sum of         Mean
       Source     DF      Squares       Square      F Value      Prob>F

       Model       3    18099.46314    6033.15438     0.871        0.4829
       Error      12    83098.97436    6924.91453
       C Total    15   101198.43750

              Root MSE       83.21607     R-Square      0.1789
              Y Mean        542.81250     Adj R-Sq     -0.0264
              C.V.           15.33054


                              Parameter Estimates

                          Parameter      T for H0:
       Variable    DF      Estimate     Parameter=0    Prob > |T|     Std Error

       INTERCEP     1     498.692308       11.084        0.0001      44.99117453
       X1           1      67.179487        1.594        0.1369      42.13809571
       X2           1      17.717949        0.350        0.7321      50.56571485
       X3           1      12.435897        0.233        0.8194      53.30094348
```

And

$$MS(AB) = \frac{SS(AB)}{(\text{number of parameters in } H_0)}$$

$$= \frac{77036.47436}{2}$$

$$= 38{,}518.237$$

The mean square for error for the complete model is

$$MSE = \frac{SSE_2}{n - (\text{number of parameters in the complete model})}$$

$$= \frac{6062.5}{10} = 606.25$$

The F statistic for testing

H_0: $\beta_4 = \beta_5 = 0$—that is, there is no interaction between factors A and B
is

$$F = \frac{MST}{MSE} = \frac{38{,}518.237}{606.25} = 63.5$$

The rejection region for the test for $\alpha = .05$ is $F > F_{.05}$, where the degrees of freedom for the F statistic are

$$v_1 = \text{number of parameters in } H_0 = 2$$
$$v_2 = n - (\text{number of parameters in the complete model})$$
$$= 16 - 6 = 10$$

Consulting Table 8 in the Appendix, we find $F_{.05} = 4.10$. Since the calculated value of the F statistic ($F = 63.5$) greatly exceeds $F_{.05} = 4.10$, there is strong evidence to indicate an interaction between factors A and B. The practical implications of this result were explained in Example 9.3. ∎

    To conclude this section, we want to remind you why we are using a regression analysis to analyze data that seem to be more appropriately analyzed by using an analysis of variance. The analysis of variance formulas of Chapter 9 are only valid if the data are collected according to a specific design. If any observations are lost, the formulas of Chapter 9 cannot be used. There are methods available to determine values for the missing observations so that the analysis of variance formulas can be used. But with computers so accessible, it seems (to the author) that it is easier to feed the data into a computer and to fit complete and reduced models to obtain the desired sums of squares. The remaining steps of the test are identical to those described in the analysis of variance of Chapter 9 or as given in optional Section 12.9.

Steps to Follow When Building a Linear Model

12.11

The preceding sections describe most of the statistical tests and estimation procedures associated with a multiple regression analysis. Ultimately, the objective is to develop a model that will predict y as a function of a set of independent variables $x_1, x_2, \ldots, x_k$ and to do so with a small error of prediction. The procedure for developing this model is summarized in the following steps.

(1) Select the independent variables to be included in the model. Presumably, you have some understanding of the physical, biological, or social mechanisms that affect y. This knowledge should enable you to list some of the independent variables that may be important information contributors. Since some of these variables may contribute overlapping information, the list may be reduced by running a stepwise regression analysis (see Section 12.6) on the data. You will want to keep the number of independent variables to a minimum so that the number of terms in your linear model does not become too large and the model unmanageable. Remember that the number of observations in your data set must exceed the number of terms in your linear model by at least five or more—the greater the excess, the better.

(2) Write a model relating y to the independent variables that you have selected in step 1. If the independent variables are qualitative, it is best to include terms representing factor interactions. Similarly, if the independent variables are quantitative, it is best to start with a complete second-order model to allow for curvature in the response curve (or surface). Unnecessary terms can be deleted later if their information contribution is negligible.

(3) Fit the model to the data set. Check the F value to see whether the complete model contributes information for the prediction of y. Also note the value of R^2 to see how well the model fits the data set.

(4) Test individual parameters and sets of parameters to detect factor interaction, curvature, and so on. If some terms appear to contribute little information for the prediction of y, you may wish to simplify the model by eliminating them. If you do eliminate terms, refit the model and recheck the model F value and the value of R^2.

(5) Examine plots of the residuals as a final check to detect flaws in your model construction (see Section 12.5).

A Multiple Regression Analysis for the Worker Absenteeism Case Study

12.12

As noted in the Case Study, Constas and Vichas (1980) investigated the relationship between worker absenteeism and four life space predictor variables, those that characterized the worker rather than the work space. The measure of worker absenteeism was the number of days the worker was absent from his or her job during a one-year period of time. The predictor variables and their type, qualitative or quantitative, and the symbols that represent them are given in the following list.

(1) Sex (qualitative):

$$\text{coding:} \quad x_1 = 0, \quad \text{if male}$$
$$x_1 = 1, \quad \text{if female}$$

This variable was selected because (according to Constas and Vichas) "women tend to manifest higher absence rates—both in frequency and duration—than men in comparable working situations."

(2) Marital status (qualitative):

$$\text{coding:} \quad x_2 = 0, \quad \text{if married or divorced}$$
$$x_2 = 1, \quad \text{if single}$$

Marital status was viewed as a measure of a worker's responsibilities. The suggestion is that workers with strong family ties and responsibilities might be less prone to absenteeism than workers with fewer responsibilities. You can see that marital status can actually assume any one of three values corresponding to the three categories single (unmarried), married, and divorced. If the researchers use only one dummy variable and combine the *married* and *divorced* categories of workers, categories that may represent *greater* and *lesser* family responsibilities, respectively, the usefulness of marital status as a predictor variable could be nullified.

(3) Age of the employee (quantitative):

$$\text{coding:} \quad x_3 = \text{age of the employee}$$

Age is probably related to absenteeism, but the nature of the relationship is in debate. Most researchers agree that young employees, those younger than age 25, might be expected to have higher rates of absenteeism and that this rate might decrease as the worker approaches age 40. Some researchers theorize that the relationship between absenteeism and worker age can be characterized by an "envelope-shaped curve, decreasing to age mid-forties, then gradually rising." If this latter theory were true, we would expect to enter both first- and second-order terms, those involving x_3 and x_3^2, into the model to allow for curvature in the relationship between $E(y)$ and x_3.

(4) Number of dependents (quantitative):

$$\text{coding:} \quad x_4 = \text{number of dependents}$$

The expectation, in introducing this predictor variable, is that the number of dependents is a measure of the worker's responsibilities. If correct, we would expect absenteeism to decrease as the number of dependents increases.

(5) Automobile ownership (qualitative):

$$\text{coding:} \quad x_5 = 0, \quad \text{if employee owns a vehicle}$$
$$x_5 = 1, \quad \text{if not}$$

The logic of including this variable is that car ownership may be associated with the difficulty the worker may have in traveling to the workplace.

The data for the Constas-Vichas study consist of observations on 50 workers randomly selected from among the work force of an electronics assembly plant and observations on 120 workers at a petrochemical plant, both located in southern Puerto Rico. The authors fit separate first-order regression models

$$E(y) = \beta_0 + \beta_1 x_1 + \beta_2 x_2 + \cdots + \beta_5 x_5$$

to each of the two sets of data. The sample sizes, their computed values of R^2, and F values for tests of the complete models are shown in Table 12.22. The parameter estimates, their estimated standard deviations (standard errors), and the computed values of the t statistics are presented in Table 12.23.

TABLE 12.22   Results of Two Multiple Regression Analyses for the Case Study Data

Parameter	Plant A	Plant B
Sample size, n	50	120
Coefficient of determination, R^2	.452	.282
F	2.266	1.969

Does the model contribute information for the prediction of worker absenteeism y for plants A and B? The F statistics for testing the complete model, 2.266 for plant A and 1.969 for plant B, are based on $v_1 = 5$ and $v_2 = n - 6$ ($v_2 = 44$ for plant A and 114 for plant B). The corresponding critical (upper-tail) F values for $\alpha = .10$ are, approximately, 1.99 and 1.90, respectively. Since the computed values of the F statistics exceed the corresponding critical values, there is evidence, at the $\alpha = .10$ level of significance, to indicate that at least one of the five predictor variables contributes information for the prediction of worker absenteeism when the variables are employed in a first-order model. Examining the t tests for each of the five individual parameters, $\beta_1, \beta_2, \ldots, \beta_5$, you will observe (Table 12.23) that two of the parameters, age of the worker in the plant A model and car ownership in the plant B model, are statistically significant for $\alpha = .05$.

One interesting aspect of the analysis concerns the relationship between absenteeism and worker age, x_3. If, as Constas and Vichas note, the relationship between absenteeism and worker age is "an envelope-shaped curve" as shown in Figure 12.18, then a straight line (equivalent to entering x_3 into the model as a first-order term) should possess a slope near 0 and should provide a very poor fit to data. Why, then, did the t test for the age variable indicate statistical significance for plant A? The answer is that the workers included in the plant A regression analysis were relatively young (the

TABLE 12.23   Parameter Estimates for the Case Study Data

Plant A	β_0	Sex	Marital Status	Age of Employee	Number of Dependents	Automobile Ownership
				Variable		
Parameter	β_0	β_1	β_2	β_3	β_4	β_5
Parameter estimate	12.388	5.113	4.756	−.315	.675	1.906
Estimated standard deviation of estimate		3.139	2.856	.152	.729	2.209
Computed value of t		1.63	1.67	−2.07*	.93	.86

Plant B	β_0	Sex	Marital Status	Age of Employee	Number of Dependents	Automobile Ownership
				Variable		
Parameter	β_0	β_1	β_2	β_3	β_4	β_5
Parameter estimate	13.180	−13.101	3.043	−.064	−1.218	10.714
Estimated standard deviation of estimate		8.914	5.831	.178	.933	4.150
Computed value of t		−1.47	.52	−.36	−1.31	2.58*

*Stars attached to t values indicate that they are statistically significant for $\alpha = .05$.

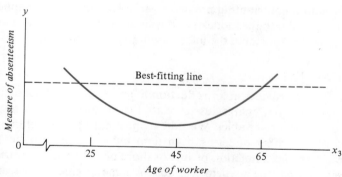

FIGURE 12.18   A Theoretical Relation Between Worker Absenteeism and Age of Worker

mean age for plant A was 32.54 years and the standard deviation was 7.65 years). Consequently, a first order (straight-line) model might be expected to provide an adequate fit to these data [see Figure 12.19(a)]. In contrast, the ages of the workers included in the regression analysis for plant B varied from those who were very young to some who were near retirement (the mean age was 34.80 years and the standard deviation was 19.01 years). A test of the significance of the slope (test of $H_0 : \beta_3 = 0$) for plant B produced a negligible t value (equal to −.36), a value that may be explained by "an envelope-shaped" curvilinear relation between absenteeism rate and age of worker [see Figure 12.19(b)].

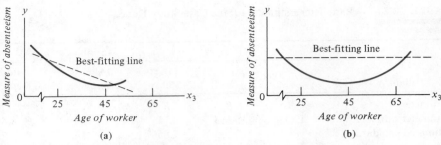

FIGURE 12.19   Hypothetical Relations Between Absenteeism and Age of Worker

So what can we conclude from the Constas-Vichas study? There is evidence to indicate that the first-order model provides some information for the prediction of the rate of worker absenteeism, but it is also clear that there is ample room for improvement in the model. The computed values of R^2 indicate that the prediction equations for plants A and B provide very poor fits to their respective sets of data. The prediction equation for plant A accounts for only 45.2% of the variability of the y values about the mean and the percentage corresponding to plant B is even lower, only 28.2%.

Prediction equations that provide poor fits to data sets are not uncommon, and they are prevalent when the response is some aspect of human behavior. Poor-fitting prediction equations occur because the model may not contain the appropriate information-contributing predictor variables, and/or the manner in which they have been entered into the model (i.e., the model formulation) may not permit the predictor variables to contribute the information that they contain.

SUMMARY

12.13

Chapter 12 provides an introduction to an extremely useful area of statistical methodology, one that enables us to relate the mean value of a response variable y to a set of predictor variables. We start by postulating a model that expresses $E(y)$ as the sum of a number of terms, each term involving the product of a single unknown parameter and a function of one or more of the predictor variables. Values of y are observed when the predictor variables assume specified values, and these data are used to estimate the unknown parameters in the model by using the method of least squares. The procedure for estimating the unknown parameters of the model, testing its utility, or testing hypotheses about sets of the model parameters is known as a multiple regression analysis.

Perhaps the most important result of a multiple regression analysis is the use of the fitted model—the prediction equation—to estimate the mean value of y or to predict a particular value of y for a given set of values of the predictor variables. Scientists, sociologists, engineers, and business managers all face the same problem: forecasting some quantitative response based on the values of a set of predictor variables that describe current or future conditions. When the appropriate assumptions are satisfied, a multiple regression analysis can be used to solve this important problem.

REFERENCES

Chou, Ya-lun. *Statistical Analysis with Business and Economic Applications*. 2nd ed. New York: Holt, Rinehart and Winston, 1975.

Constas, K., and Vichas, R. P. "An Interpretative Policy Making Model of Absenteeism with Reference to the Marginal Worker in Overseas Plants." *Journal of Management Studies*. Vol. 17, No. 2, 1980.

Dixon, W. J., Brown, M. B., Engelman, L., Frane, J. W., Hill, M. A., Jennrich, R. I., and Toporek, J. D. *BMDP Statistical Software*. Berkeley: University of California Press, 1985.

Draper, N. R., and Smith, H. *Applied Regression Analysis*. 2nd ed. New York: Wiley, 1981.

Hamburg, M. *Statistical Analysis for Decision Making*. 3rd ed. New York: Harcourt Brace Jovanovich, 1983.

Hill, MaryAnn, ed. *BMPD User's Digest*. 2nd ed. Los Angeles: BMPD Statistical Software, 1982.

Kleinbaum, D., and Kupper, L. *Applied Regression Analysis and Other Multivariable Methods*. 2nd ed. Boston: PWS-KENT, 1988.

Mendenhall, W., and Sincich, T. *A Second Course in Business Statistics: Regression Analysis*. 2nd ed. San Francisco: Dellen, 1986.

Miller, R. B., and Wichern, D. W. *Intermediate Business Statistics: Analysis of Variance, Regression and Time Series*. New York: Holt, Rinehart and Winston, 1977.

Neter, J., and Wasserman, W. *Applied Linear Statistical Models*. 2nd ed. Homewood, III.: Irwin, 1985.

Norman, H. N., Hull, C. H., Jenkins, J. G., Steinbrenner, K., and Bent, D. H. *SPSS Statistical Package for Social Sciences*. 2nd ed. New York: McGraw-Hill, 1975.

Ryan, T. A., Joiner, B. L., and Ryan, B. F. *Minitab Reference Manual*. University Park, Pa.: Minitab Project, 1985.

Ryan, T. A., Joiner, B. L., and Ryan, B. F. *Minitab Handbook*. 2nd ed. Boston: PWS-KENT, 1985.

SAS User's Guide: Basics. Version 5 ed. Cary, N. C.: SAS Institute, 1985.

SAS User's Guide: Statistics. Version 5 ed. Cary, N.C.: SAS Institute, 1985.

SPSS^x User's Guide. Chicago: SPSS, 1983.

Wonnacott, R. J., and Wonnacott, T. H. *Econometrics*. 2nd ed. New York: Wiley, 1979.

Younger, M. S. *A First Course in Linear Regression*. 2nd ed. Boston: PWS-KENT, 1985.

KEY TERMS

Multiple regression analysis (page 488)
General linear model (page 489)
Predictor variables (page 489)
Dummy variable (page 501)
Variable interaction (page 501)
Multiple coefficient of determination
  (page 503)
Mean square for regression (page 507)
Residuals (page 515)

Residual analysis (page 516)
Stepwise regression analysis (page 518)
Multicollinearity (page 520)
Quantitative independent variable
  (page 520)
Qualitative independent variable (page 520)
Interaction (page 521)
First-order model (page 521)
Second-order model (page 522)

SUPPLEMENTARY EXERCISES

Starred (*) exercises are optional.

12.31 Utility companies, which must plan the operation and expansion of electricity generation, are vitally interested in predicting customer demand over both short and long periods of time. A short-term study was conducted to investigate the effect of mean monthly daily temperature x_1 and cost per kilowatt x_2 on the mean daily consumption (kilowatt-hours, kWh) per household. The company expected the demand for electricity to rise in cold weather (due to heating), fall when the weather was moderate, and rise again when the temperature rose and there was a need for air-conditioning. They expected demand to decrease as the cost per kilowatt-hour increased, reflecting greater attention to conservation. Data were available for two years, a period in which the cost per kilowatt-hour, x_2, was increased owing to the increasing cost of fuel. The company fitted the model

$$E(y) = \beta_0 + \beta_1 x_1 + \beta_2 x_1^2 + \beta_3 x_2 + \beta_4 x_1 x_2 + \beta_5 x_1^2 x_2$$

to the data shown in Table 12.24. Before we analyze the data, let us examine the logic used in formulating the model.

(a) Examine the relationship between $E(y)$ and temperature x_1 for a fixed price per kilowatt-hour (kWh), x_2. Substitute a value for x_2, say 10¢, into the equation for $E(y)$. What type of curve will the model relating $E(y)$ to x_1 represent?

(b) If the company's theory regarding the relationship between mean daily consumption $E(y)$ and temperature x_1 is correct, what should be the sign (positive or negative) of the coefficient of x_1^2?

(c) Examine the relationship between $E(y)$ and price per kilowatt-hour, x_2, when temperature x_1 is held constant. Substitute a value for x_1 into the equation for $E(y)$, say $x_1 = 50°F$. What type of curve will the model relating $E(y)$ to x_2 represent?

(d) Refer to part (c). If the company's theory regarding the relationship between mean daily consumption $E(y)$ and price per kilowatt-hour x_2 is correct, what should be the sign of the coefficient of x_2?

(e) What effect do the terms $\beta_4 x_1 x_2$ and $\beta_5 x_1^2 x_2$ have on the curves relating $E(y)$ to x_1 for various values of price per kilowatt-hour?

TABLE 12.24   Electric Utility Company Data for Exercise 12.31

Price per kWh, x_2	Daily Temperature and Consumption	Mean Daily Consumption (kWh) per Household											
8¢	Mean daily temperature (°F), x_1	31	34	39	42	47	56	62	66	68	71	75	78
	Mean daily consumption, y	55	49	46	47	40	43	41	46	44	51	62	73
10¢	Mean daily temperature, x_1	32	36	39	42	48	56	62	66	68	72	75	79
	Mean daily consumption, y	50	44	42	42	38	40	39	44	40	44	50	55

12.32 The SAS multiple regression computer printout for the data of Exercise 12.31 is shown in Table 12.25.

(a) Find SSE and s^2 on the printout.

(b) How many degrees of freedom do SSE and s^2 possess? Show that $s^2 = $ SSE/(degrees of freedom).

(c) Do the data provide sufficient evidence to indicate that the model contributes information for the prediction of mean daily kilowatt-hour consumption per household? Test using $\alpha = .10$.

(d) Use Tables 7, 8, 9, 10, and 11 in the Appendix to find the approximate observed significance level for the test in part (c).

(e) Find the Total SS, SS_y, on the printout. Find the value of R^2 and interpret its value. Show that $R^2 = 1 - (SSE/SS_y)$.

(f) Use the prediction equation to predict mean daily consumption when the mean daily temperature is $60°F$ and the price per kilowatt-hour is 8¢.

(g) If you have access to a computer, use it to perform a multiple regression analysis for the data in Exercise 12.31. Compare your computer output with the SAS output shown in Table 12.25.

TABLE 12.25   SAS Output for Exercise 12.32

DEPENDENT VARIABLE: Y

SOURCE	DF	SUM OF SQUARES	MEAN SQUARE	F VALUE	PR > F	R-SQUARE	C.V.
MODEL	5	1346.44751546	269.28950309	31.85	0.0001	0.898455	6.2029
ERROR	18	152.17748454	8.45430470		ROOT MSE		Y MEAN
CORRECTED TOTAL	23	1498.62500000			2.90762871		46.87500000

SOURCE	DF	TYPE I SS	F VALUE	PR > F	DF	TYPE IV SS	F VALUE	PR > F
X1	1	140.71101071	16.64	0.0007	1	104.43456772	12.35	0.0025
X1*X1	1	892.77914933	105.60	0.0001	1	125.58263370	14.85	0.0012
X2	1	192.44266992	22.76	0.0002	1	46.78392523	5.53	0.0302
X1*X2	1	57.83521130	6.84	0.0175	1	50.03623552	5.92	0.0256
X1*X1*X2	1	62.67947420	7.41	0.0140	1	62.67947420	7.41	0.0140

PARAMETER ESTIMATES

VARIABLE	ESTIMATE	T FOR H0: PARAMETER=0	PR > |T|	STD ERROR
INTERCEPT	325.60644505	3.92	0.0010	83.06412820
X1	-11.38255606	-3.51	0.0025	3.23859476
X1*X1	0.11319735	3.85	0.0012	0.02944828
X2	-21.69920900	-2.35	0.0302	9.22432344
X1*X2	0.87302921	2.43	0.0256	0.35886030
X1*X1*X2	-0.00886945	-2.72	0.0140	0.00325742

 *12.33** Refer to Exercises 12.31 and 12.32.

(a) Graph the curve depicting $\hat{y}$ as a function of temperature x_1 when the cost per kilowatt-hour is $x_2 = 8¢$. Construct a similar graph for the case when $x_2 = 10¢$ per kilowatt-hour. Does it appear that the consumption curves differ?

(b) If cost per kilowatt-hour is unimportant in predicting use, then we do not need the terms involving x_2 in the model. Therefore, the null hypothesis H_0: "x_2 does not contribute information for the prediction of y" is equivalent to the hypothesis $H_0 : \beta_3 = \beta_4 = \beta_5 \geq 0$ (if $\beta_3 = \beta_4 = \beta_5 = 0$, the terms involving x_2 disappear from the model). This hypothesis is tested by using the procedure of Section 12.9. The SAS multiple regression computer printout, obtained by fitting the reduced model

$$E(y) = \beta_0 + \beta_1 x_1 + \beta_2 x_1^2$$

to the data, is shown in Table 12.26. The following steps enable you to conduct a test to determine whether the data provide sufficient evidence to indicate that price per kilowatt-hour x_2 contributes information for the prediction of y. Test using $\alpha = .05$.

(i) Find SSE_1 and SSE_2.
(ii) Give the values for v_1 and v_2.
(iii) Calculate the value of F.
(iv) Find the tabulated value of $F_{.05}$.
(v) State your conclusions.

TABLE 12.26   SAS Output for Exercise 12.33

```
DEPENDENT VARIABLE: Y

SOURCE              DF          SUM OF SQUARES        MEAN SQUARE   F VALUE    PR > F   R-SQUARE            C.V.

MODEL               2           1033.49016004         516.74908002   23.33    0.0001   0.689626          10.0401

ERROR               21          465.13483996          22.14927809             ROOT MSE                Y MEAN

CORRECTED TOTAL     23          1498.62500000                                 4.70630196            46.87500000


SOURCE              DF             TYPE I SS    F VALUE    PR > F    DF        TYPE IV SS    F VALUE    PR > F

X1                  1           140.71101071      6.35    0.0199     1      810.33211666      36.59    0.0001
X1*X1               1           892.77914933     40.31    0.0001     1      892.77914933      40.31    0.0001


                                PARAMETER ESTIMATE

                                T FOR H0:
VARIABLE            ESTIMATE    PARAMETER=0   PR > |T|    STD ERROR

INTERCEPT        130.00929147       8.74      0.0001    14.87580615
X1                -3.50171859      -6.05      0.0001     0.57893460
X1*X1              0.03337133       6.35      0.0001     0.00525631
```

 12.34 In Exercise 11.108 we gave the earnings per share (EPS) for Wendy's International (the fast-food company) for the years 1977 through 1985. The EPS over that period of time are reprinted in Table 12.27 along with the coded year x, where $x = $ year $- 1976$. A SAS multiple regression printout for fitting a second-order model to the data appears in Table 12.28.

TABLE 12.27   EPS Data for Exercise 12.34

| | Actual Year | | | | | | | | |
Variable	1977	1978	1979	1980	1981	1982	1983	1984	1985
Coded year, x	1	2	3	4	5	6	7	8	9
EPS ($), y	.27	.42	.39	.50	.57	.64	.76	.93	1.03

TABLE 12.28   SAS Output for Exercise 12.34

DEPENDENT VARIABLE: Y

ANALYSIS OF VARIANCE

SOURCE	DF	SUM OF SQUARES	MEAN SQUARE	F VALUE	PR > F	R-SQUARE	C.V.
MODEL	2	0.50747201	0.25373600	179.455	0.0001	0.9836	6.141919
ERROR	6	0.008483550	0.001413925		ROOT MSE	ADJ R-SQ	Y MEAN
CORRECTED TOTAL	8	0.51595556			0.03760219	0.9781	0.6122222

PARAMETER ESTIMATES

VARIABLE	DF	PARAMETER ESTIMATE	T FOR H0: PARAMETER=0	PR > |T|	STD ERROR
INTERCEP	1	0.27452381	5.738	0.0012	0.04784571
X	1	0.02730519	1.243	0.2603	0.02196889
XSQ	1	0.006352814	2.965	0.0251	0.002142584

OBSERVATION	ACTUAL	PREDICT VALUE	STD ERR PREDICT	LOWER 95% PREDICT	UPPER 95% PREDICT	RESIDUAL
1	0.2700	0.3082	0.0306	0.1396	0.4267	-0.0382
2	0.4200	0.3545	0.0199	0.2505	0.4586	0.0655
3	0.3900	0.4135	0.0169	0.3128	0.5144	-0.0236
4	0.5000	0.4854	0.0181	0.3833	0.5875	0.0146
5	0.5700	0.5699	0.0190	0.4668	0.6730	1.3E-04
6	0.6400	0.6671	0.0181	0.5649	0.7692	-0.0271
7	0.7600	0.7769	0.0169	0.6761	0.8778	-0.0169
8	0.9300	0.8995	0.0199	0.7955	1.0036	0.0305
9	1.0300	1.0348	0.0306	0.9163	1.1534	-.004848

SUM OF RESIDUALS   1.05471E-15
SUM OF SQUARED RESIDUALS   0.00848355

(a) Plot the data points on graph paper.

(b) Locate $\hat{\beta}_0$, $\hat{\beta}_1$, and $\hat{\beta}_2$ on the printout, and give the least-squares prediction equation.

(c) Graph the least-squares prediction equation on your data plot for part (a). Does the least-squares curve seem to provide a good fit to the data?

(d) Find SSE and s^2 on the printout.

(e) How many degrees of freedom do SSE and s^2 possess? Show that $s^2 = \text{SSE}/(\text{degrees of freedom})$.

(f) Do the data present sufficient evidence to indicate that the second-order term in the model contributes information for the prediction of y? (*Hint:* See the t-value shown on the printout for testing $H_0 : \beta_2 = 0$.)

(g) Find the observed significance level (p-value) for the test in part (f).

(h) Find R^2 on the printout and interpret its value.

(i) How does the number n of data points affect the significance that can be attached to a value of R^2?

12.35 Refer to the regression analysis of the annual earnings per share (EPS) of Wendy's International for Exercise 12.34. Suppose that the EPS for a company increased exactly 10% per year and that the EPS last year was $4.00. Then the EPS for this year is ($4.00)(1.10); for next year the EPS is ($4.00)(1.10)^2; and the following year the EPS will be ($4.00)(1.10)^3. This type of growth suggests that the model

$$\text{EPS} = ab^x$$

where

$$a = \text{earnings per share at end of last year (when } x = 0)$$

$$b = \text{annual multiplying factor}$$

(for our example, $a = \$4.00$ and $b = 1.10$) might provide a better fit to the data than the second-order polynomial model of Exercise 12.34. Although the model EPS $= ab^x$ is not linear, it can be changed into a linear model by taking the logarithm of each side of the equation,

$$\ln(\text{EPS}) = \ln a + x \ln b$$

and fitting the model

$$E(y) = \beta_0 + \beta_1 x$$

to the data, where

$$y = \ln(\text{EPS}) \qquad \beta_0 = \ln a \qquad \beta_1 = \ln b$$

Table 12.29 gives the values of $\ln(\text{EPS})$ for the years 1977 to 1985. The SAS computer printout for a multiple regression analysis relating $y = \ln(\text{EPS})$ to the coded year x is shown in Table 12.30.

TABLE 12.29   EPS Data (Logarithmic) for Exercise 12.35

	Actual Year								
Variable	1977	1978	1979	1980	1981	1982	1983	1984	1985
Coded year $= x$	1	2	3	4	5	6	7	8	9
$\ln(\text{EPS}) = y$	-1.309	$-.868$	$-.942$	$-.693$	$-.562$	$-.446$	$-.274$	$-.073$	0.030

(a) Plot the data points on graph paper.

(b) Locate $\hat{\beta}_0$ and $\hat{\beta}_1$ on the computer printout, and give the least-squares prediction equation.

(c) Graph the least-squares prediction equation on your data plot for part (a). Does your least-squares line provide a good fit to the data points?

(d) Find r^2 on the printout and interpret its value.

(e) Compare the value of r^2 obtained for this model with the value of R^2 obtained for the second-order polynomial model in Exercise 12.34. Which model seems to better fit the data?

(f) Estimate the annual multiplying factor b for Wendy's International. (*Hint:* Since $\beta_1 = \ln b$, $b = e^{\beta_1}$.)

*12.36 Danielson and Smith report on the use of stepwise regression analysis (SRA) to correct salary inequities for women and racial minorities (J. L. Danielson and R. Smith, "The Application of Regression Analysis to Equality and Merit in Personnel Decisions," *Public Personnel Management Journal*, January–April, 1981). Data are collected on a number of variables that an investigator believes are related to an employee's salary, grade in position, years of experience, sex, race, and so on. The data are then fed into a computer, and a stepwise regression analysis fits a first-order model

$$E(y) = \beta_0 + \beta_1 x_1 + \beta_2 x_2 + \beta_3 x_3 + \cdots$$

as described in Section 12.6. The stepwise regression prediction equation is then used to make

TABLE 12.30   SAS Output for Exercise 12.35

DEPENDENT VARIABLE: Y

ANALYSIS OF VARIANCE

SOURCE	DF	SUM OF SQUARES	MEAN SQUARE	F VALUE	PR > F	R-SQUARE	
MODEL	1	1.44894960	1.44894960	204.704	0.0001	0.9669	
ERROR	7	0.04954796	0.007078279		ROOT MSE	ADJ R-SQ	Y
CORRECTED TOTAL	8	1.49849756			0.08413251	0.9622	-0.5707

PARAMETER ESTIMATES

VARIABLE	DF	PARAMETER ESTIMATE	T FOR H0: PARAMETER=0	PR > |T|	STD ERROR
INTERCEP	1	-1.34777778	-22.051	0.0001	0.06112085
X	1	0.15540000	14.307	0.0001	0.01086146

OBSERVATION	ACTUAL	PREDICT VALUE	STD ERR PREDICT	LOWER 95% PREDICT	UPPER 95% PREDICT	RESIDUAL
1	-1.3090	-1.1924	0.0517	-1.4259	-0.9589	-0.1166
2	-0.8680	-1.0370	0.0430	-1.2604	-0.8136	0.1690
3	-0.9420	-0.8816	0.0355	-1.0975	-0.6657	-0.0604
4	-0.6930	-0.7262	0.0301	-0.9374	-0.5149	0.0332
5	-0.5620	-0.5708	0.0280	-0.7805	-0.3611	.0087778
6	-0.4460	-0.4154	0.0301	-0.6266	-0.2041	-0.0306
7	-0.2740	-0.2600	0.0355	-0.4759	-0.0441	-0.0140
8	-0.0730	-0.1046	0.0430	-0.3280	0.1188	0.0316
9	0.0300	0.0508	0.0517	-0.1827	0.2843	-0.0208

SUM OF RESIDUALS   -1.71998E-15
SUM OF SQUARED RESIDUALS   0.04954796

salary adjustments. They give the following hypothetical example. If

$$y = \text{an employee's salary}$$

$$x_1 = \begin{cases} 0, & \text{if female} \\ 1, & \text{if male} \end{cases}$$

$$x_2 = 1, 2, 3, \text{ or } 4, \text{ depending upon the employee's grade in position}$$

and $$\hat{y} = \hat{\beta}_0 + \hat{\beta}_1 x_1 + \hat{\beta}_2 x_2 = 1278.00 + 55.37 x_1 + 255.54 x_2$$

then it follows that the "hidden rules of the game are that women, on the average, receive over fifty-five dollars less than equivalent males." For the correction of this inequity the implication is that all women employed in this system receive a $55.37 increase in pay. Do you agree with Danielson and Smith's interpretation of the practical significance of the regression coefficients in a stepwise regression analysis? Explain.

MKTG *12.37 A department store conducted an experiment to investigate the effects of advertising expenditures on the weekly sales for its men's wear, children's wear, and women's wear departments. Five weeks for observation were randomly selected from each department, and an advertising budget x_1 (hundreds of dollars) was assigned for each. The weekly sales (thousands of dollars) are shown in Table 12.31 for each of the 15 one-week sales periods. If we expect weekly sales $E(y)$ to be linearly related to advertising expenditure x_1 and if we expect the slopes of the

549

.penditure Data (Hundreds of Dollars) for Exercise 12.37

Department	Week				
	1	2	3	4	5
Men's wear, A	5.2	5.9	7.7	7.9	9.4
Children's wear, B	8.2	9.0	9.1	10.5	10.5
Women's wear, C	10.0	10.3	12.1	12.7	13.6

lines corresponding to the three departments to differ, then an appropriate model for $E(y)$ is

$$E(y) = \beta_0 + \underbrace{\beta_1 x_1} + \underbrace{\beta_2 x_2 + \beta_3 x_3} + \underbrace{\beta_4 x_1 x_2 + \beta_5 x_1 x_3}$$

quantitative variable "advertising expenditure"	dummy variables used to introduce the qualitative variable "department" into the model	interaction terms that introduce differences in slopes

where $x_1 = $ advertising expenditure

$$x_2 = \begin{cases} 1, & \text{if children's wear department B} \\ 0, & \text{if not} \end{cases}$$

$$x_3 = \begin{cases} 1, & \text{if women's wear department C} \\ 0, & \text{if not} \end{cases}$$

(a) Find the equation of the line relating $E(y)$ to advertising expenditure x_1 for the men's wear department A. [Hint: According to the coding used for the dummy variables, the model represents mean sales $E(y)$ for the men's wear department A when $x_2 = x_3 = 0$. Substitute $x_2 = x_3 = 0$ into the equation for $E(y)$ to find the equation of this line.]

(b) Find the equation of the line relating $E(y)$ to x_1 for the children's wear department B. [Hint: According to the coding, the model represents $E(y)$ for the children's wear department when $x_2 = 1$ and $x_3 = 0$.]

(c) Find the equation of the line relating $E(y)$ to x_1 for the women's wear department C.

(d) Find the difference between the intercepts of the $E(y)$ lines corresponding to the children's wear B and men's wear A departments.

(e) Find the difference in slopes between $E(y)$ lines corresponding to the women's wear C and men's wear A departments.

(f) Refer to part (e). Suppose that you want to test the null hypothesis that the slopes of the lines corresponding to the three departments are equal. Express this as a test of an hypothesis about one or more of the model parameters.

*12.38 If you have access to a computer and a multiple regression computer program package, perform a multiple regression analysis for the data of Exercise 12.37.

(a) Verify that SSE $= 1.2190$, that $s^2 = .1354$, and that $s = .368$.

(b) How many degrees of freedom will SSE and s^2 possess?

(c) Verify that Total SS $= SS_y = 76.0493$.

(d) Calculate R^2 and interpret its value.

(e) Verify that the parameter estimates (values rounded) are approximately equal to

$$\hat{\beta}_0 \approx 4.10 \qquad \hat{\beta}_1 \approx 1.04 \qquad \hat{\beta}_2 \approx 3.53 \qquad \hat{\beta}_3 \approx 4.76$$
$$\hat{\beta}_4 \approx -.43 \qquad \hat{\beta}_5 \approx -.08$$

(f) Find the prediction equation, and graph the three department sales lines.

(g) Examine the graphs in part (f). Do the slopes of the lines corresponding to the children's wear B and the men's wear A departments appear to differ? Test the null hypothesis that the slopes do not differ (i.e., $H_0 : \beta_4 = 0$) against the alternative hypothesis that the slopes do differ (i.e., $H_a : \beta_4 \neq 0$). Test using $\alpha = .05$. (*Note:* Verify on your computer printout that the estimated standard deviation of $\hat{\beta}_4$ is $s_{\hat{\beta}_4} \approx .165$.)

(h) Find a 95% confidence interval for the difference between the slopes of lines for B and A.

(i) Do the data provide sufficient evidence to indicate a difference in the slopes between lines C and A? Test using $\alpha = .05$. (*Hint:* $s_{\hat{\beta}_5} \approx .165$.)

*12.39 Write a first-order linear model as a function of two quantitative variables x_1 and x_2. Describe the response surface.

*12.40 Suppose that y is a function of a single quantitative independent variable x and that $E(y)$ decreases, reaches a minimum, and then increases as x increases. Write a second-order model relating $E(y)$ to x.

*12.41 Write a first-order linear model as a function of three quantitative independent variables. Does this model imply that x_1, x_2, and x_3 affect $E(y)$ in an independent or a dependent manner? Explain.

*12.42 Suppose that $E(y)$ is related to a single qualitative variable at three levels. Write the model for $E(y)$.

*12.43 Write a complete second-order model for $E(y)$ as a function of two quantitative independent variables x_1 and x_2.

*12.44 Write a complete second-order model for $E(y)$ as a function of three quantitative independent variables x_1, x_2, and x_3.

*12.45 Suppose that $E(y)$ is related to two qualitative independent variables, one at three levels and the other at two levels. Write a linear model for $E(y)$. Assume that the two qualitative variables do not interact.

*12.46 Refer to Exercise 12.45, and assume that the two qualitative variables interact. Write a model for $E(y)$.

*12.47 In Example 9.3 we performed an analysis of variance for three replications of a 2×3 factorial experiment. Then in Example 12.9 we used multiple regression analyses to calculate the sum of squares for interaction when two of the observations in the complete factorial experiment were missing. The data for the complete factorial experiment (no missing data) are shown in Table 12.32. To further emphasize the relationship between analysis of variance and multiple regression analysis, use the procedure described in Example 12.9 to find the sum of squares for interaction, SS(AB).

(a) Commence by writing the complete and reduced models needed to find SS(AB). Explain how the models are to be used.

(b) The SAS multiple regression printouts for fitting the complete and reduced models in part (a) are shown in Table 12.33. Find SS(AB).

(c) Compare your answer with the value for SS(AB) given in the analysis of variance in Example 9.3.

(d) Do the data present sufficient evidence of factor interaction? Test using $\alpha = .05$.

TABLE 12.32 Output per Shift for the 2 × 3 Factorial Experiment of Example 9.3 (Exercise 12.47)

| Foreman (Factor A) | Shift (Factor B) | | | Total |
	B_1 (8 A.M.–4 P.M.)	B_2 (4 P.M.–12 P.M.)	B_3 (12 P.M.–8 A.M.)	
A_1	570 610 625	480 475 540	470 430 450	4650
A_2	480 515 465	625 600 580	630 680 660	5235
Total	3265	3300	3320	9885

TABLE 12.33 SAS Output for Exercise 12.47

```
                        COMPLETE MODEL FOR 2X3 FACTORIAL: BALANCED DATA

   MODEL: MODEL2
   DEP VARIABLE: Y

                                 ANALYSIS OF VARIANCE

   SOURCE              DF          SUM OF SQUARES     MEAN SQUARE  F VALUE   PR > F   R-SQUARE        C.V.

   MODEL                5           100179.16667      20035.83333   27.849   0.0001   0.9207      4.88421

   ERROR               12             8633.33333        719.44444            ROOT MSE  ADJ R-SQ    Y MEAN

   CORRECTED TOTAL     17           108812.50000                             26.82246   0.8876   549.16667


                           PARAMETER ESTIMATES

                           PARAMETER    T FOR H0:
   VARIABLE     DF          ESTIMATE    PARAMETER=0   PR > |T|    STD ERROR

   INTERCEP      1         601.666667      38.852      0.0001    15.48595541
   X1            1        -115.000000      -5.251      0.0002    21.90044816
   X2            1        -103.333333      -4.718      0.0005    21.90044816
   X3            1        -151.666667      -6.925      0.0001    21.90044816
   X1X2          1         218.333333       7.049      0.0001    30.97191081
   X1X3          1         321.666667      10.386      0.0001    30.97191081


                        REDUCED MODEL FOR 2X3 FACTORIAL: BALANCED DATA

   MODEL: MODEL1
   DEP VARIABLE: Y

                                 ANALYSIS OF VARIANCE

   SOURCE              DF          SUM OF SQUARES     MEAN SQUARE  F VALUE   PR > F   R-SQUARE        C.V.

   MODEL                3            19270.83333       6423.61111    1.004   0.4199   0.1771     14.56278

   ERROR               14            89541.66667       6395.83333            ROOT MSE  ADJ R-SQ    Y MEAN

   CORRECTED TOTAL     17           108812.50000                             79.97395   0.0008   549.16667


                           PARAMETER ESTIMATES

                           PARAMETER    T FOR H0:
   VARIABLE     DF          ESTIMATE    PARAMETER=0   PR > |T|    STD ERROR

   INTERCEP      1         511.666667      13.572      0.0001    37.70008351
   X1            1          65.000000       1.724      0.1067    37.70008351
   X2            1           5.833333       0.126      0.9013    46.17298392
   X3            1           9.166667       0.199      0.8455    46.17298392
```

The objectives of this chapter are to introduce index numbers and other variables that are used to monitor, over time, the health of a specific business and/or of the U.S. economy; to explain how sequences of data collected over time can be analyzed; and to identify the problems associated with the use of such data in business and economic forecasting.

13

TIME SERIES AND INDEX NUMBERS

Measuring the Cost of Living

A graph (Figure 13.1) of the Consumer Price Index for the period 1972 through 1984 shows that this measure of inflation has risen steadily over this period of time. So have the prices that you and I pay at the grocery store, the prices that we pay for housing, entertainment, and transportation. To what extent does the Consumer Price Index measure our cost of living? What is the Consumer Price Index? How is it computed, and what does it mean? How can we interpret the graph of Figure 13.1, and can we use the graph, or a statistical model, to forecast values

of the Consumer Price Index at some point in the future?

As you will subsequently learn, the Consumer Price Index, like many other economic indices, provides a measure of the change in consumer prices relative to the *level of prices* in some base year, in this case, 1967. Because it is calculated and reported monthly by the Bureau of Labor Statistics, it is called a time series variable; a sequence of monthly values of the index is called a *time series*.

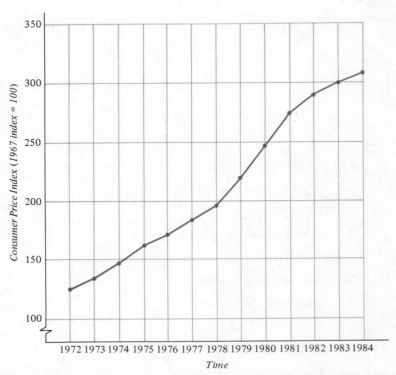

FIGURE 13.1   The Consumer Price Index, 1972 through 1984 [*Source: Business Statistics, 1984* (Washington, D.C.: U.S. Department of Commerce, Bureau of Economic Analysis).]

In this chapter we will introduce you to the difficult problem of business forecasting based on time series data. We will tell you what an economic index is and explain how some of the more common types are computed. Then in Section 13.9 we will attempt to unravel some of the mystery surrounding the Consumer Price Index.

WHAT IS A TIME SERIES?

13.1

Many types of business and economic data are observations on a variable at equidistant points in time. A data set of this type is called a **time series**, and the variable is called a **time series variable**.

The Dow-Jones Industrial Average is a time series variable that provides a measure of the level of stock prices; the set of its daily readings is a time series. The Index of Leading Economic Indicators is a time series variable that purports to measure the health of the U.S. economy. A set of its monthly values is a time series. Other time series variables of interest to economists and business managers are the monthly sales of a particular corporation, the weekly sales of automobiles, the weekly starts in new housing construction, and the like.

DEFINITION

A *time series variable* is one that is observed at specific (usually equidistant) points in time. A *time series* is a set of sequential measurements on a time series variable. ■

Most time series are graphed and analyzed so that economists and business managers can forecast the future state of the economy and of their respective businesses. Such forecasts, if moderately accurate, are useful in planning inventory size, production, and sales; they may also determine our thinking on investments. For example, Figure 13.2 is a graph of the value of the Dow-Jones Industrial Average (DJI) at the close of business at the end of each month, January 1985 to December 1986. Note that the graph is constructed so that the Dow-Jones Industrial Average y is plotted against time.

Figure 13.3 is a graph of another time series, the annual sales y of new American automobiles produced in the United States for the period 1972 to 1984. Note that the annual sales y drops sharply following the 1973 oil crisis, rises again, falls steadily through 1982, and then rises through 1983 and 1984 as import curbs on Japanese autos take effect. Where will the annual sales of domestic automobiles be in 1985, 1986, or 1987? The analysis of a time series, such as those shown in Figures 13.2 and 13.3, is done ultimately for the purpose of prediction. We think that past and present observations of a time series variable may be used to predict its future value.

Can we fit a multiple regression model to a time series variable y and use time and other time series variables as predictor variables to forecast future values of y? The answer is that forecasts, by their very nature, violate the assumptions of a regression analysis. You may recall that the regression model is appropriate for estimating $E(y)$ and predicting y within the range of values of the predictor variables that were used in fitting the model. Because a forecast at some future time is outside the time interval used to fit the regression model, time series forecasts based on regression analysis will always

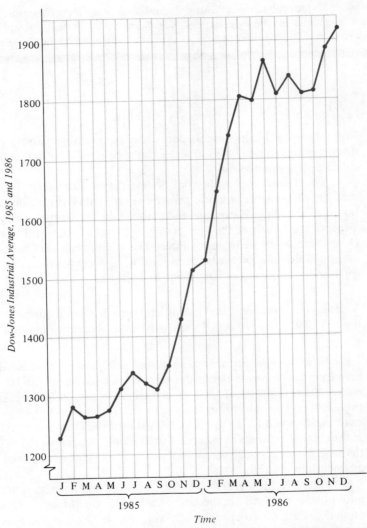

FIGURE 13.2   The Dow-Jones Industrial Average (End of Month), January 1985 to December 1986 [*Source: Survey of Current Business* (Washington, D.C.: U.S. Department of Commerce, Bureau of Economic Analysis, January 1986 and January 1987).]

be suspect. A second, but less obvious, difficulty is that observations over time often tend to be correlated and thus violate the assumption of independent errors.

The analysis of time series and the use of time series for forecasting is a difficult and complex topic. In this chapter we will introduce you to an important type of time series, index numbers; we will then describe some of the procedures used in a time series analysis. A more thorough discussion of this topic can be found in the references.

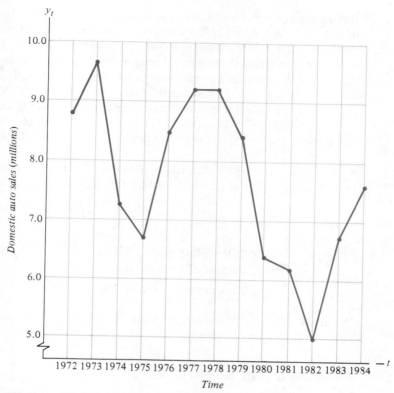

FIGURE 13.3   The Annual Sales of New American Automobiles, 1972 to 1984

INDEX NUMBERS

13.2

An **index number** is one that measures change in a time series variable in comparison to a **base year**. For example, the Consumer Price Index purports to measure the general level of consumer prices in comparison to the value of the index in the base year, 1967. (The base-year value is always set to 100.) Thus, a Consumer Price Index equal to 200 in a given year means that the general level of prices to the consumer, measured by the index, is double the level of prices in 1967.

Since an index number is reported at regular intervals of time, it is a time series variable. The Composite Index of Leading Economic Indicators is an index number that is constructed to provide a measure of the general level of the U.S. economy. The Dow-Jones Industrial Average is an index number that measures the general level of the prices of corporate common stock on the New York Stock Exchange. The Consumer Price Index measures the general level of prices to the consumer. These are just three examples of the many index numbers used to measure the general level of economic and business conditions.

Index numbers used to measure the changes in some business or economic phenomena range from those that are very simple to those that are very sophisticated.

For example, the ratio of the number of domestic automobiles sold annually to the number sold in 1967, in 1970, or in some other base year will provide a good measure of the relative levels of annual domestic automobile sales. In contrast, an index constructed to measure the general level of consumer prices cannot be constructed as the ratio of the prices of a single commodity, say new house prices; not everyone buys a new house every year. Consequently, this index will have to reflect the change in the prices of many different commodities, such as food, clothing, and transportation.

We will describe three types of indices and give examples of their construction in this section. The first index we will examine is the **simple index number**.

DEFINITION

A *simple index number* I_t is the ratio of the value of a single time series variable y_t at time t to its value y_0 at time t_0, multiplied by 100; that is,

$$I_t = \frac{y_t}{y_0}(100)$$

where

I_t = value of the simple index number at time t

y_t = value of the time series variable at time t

y_0 = value of the time series variable at base time t_0 ■

EXAMPLE 13.1

The sales of new U.S. automobiles for the years 1972 through 1984 are shown in Table 13.1. Construct a simple index of domestic sales, using 1974 as the base year.

TABLE 13.1   Annual New Domestic Automobile Sales

Year	Sales (Millions)	Year	Sales (Millions)
1972	8.8	1978	9.2
1973	9.7	1979	8.4
1974	7.3	1980	6.4
1975	6.7	1981	6.2
1976	8.5	1982	5.0
1977	9.2	1983	6.7
		1984	7.6

Source: Data from *Business Statistics, 1984* (Washington, D. C.: U.S. Department of Commerce, Bureau of Economic Analysis).

SOLUTION   Since 1974 was chosen as the base year, $y_0 = 7.3$ and

$$I_{1972} = \frac{y_{1972}}{y_0}(100) = \frac{8.3}{7.3}(100) = 121$$

$$I_{1973} = \frac{y_{1973}}{y_0}(100) = \frac{9.7}{7.3}(100) = 133$$

$$I_{1974} = \frac{y_{1974}}{y_0}(100) = \frac{7.3}{7.3}(100) = 100$$

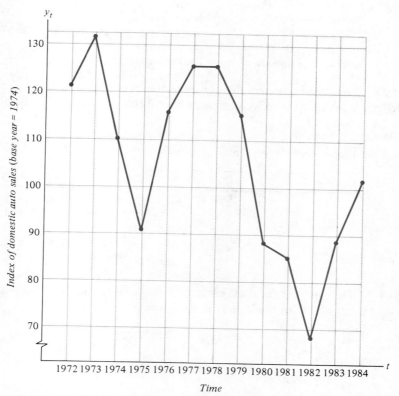

y_t

Index of domestic auto sales (base year = 1974)

1972 1973 1974 1975 1976 1977 1978 1979 1980 1981 1982 1983 1984   t

Time

FIGURE 13.4   A Graph of an Index of Domestic Car Sales for Example 13.1 [*Source:* Data from *Business Statistics, 1984* (Washington, D.C.: U.S. Department of Commerce, Bureau of Economic Analysis).]

You can verify that the values of I_t, 1975 to 1984, are

$I_{1975} = 92$ $I_{1976} = 116$ $I_{1977} = 126$ $I_{1978} = 126$ $I_{1979} = 115$

$I_{1980} = 88$ $I_{1981} = 85$ $I_{1982} = 68$ $I_{1983} = 92$ $I_{1984} = 104$

A graph of the new domestic car sales index for Example 13.1 is shown in Figure 13.4

A second type of index, one that incorporates the value of more than one time series variable, is called a **simple composite index number**. To compute a simple composite index number, you sum the values of the time series variables entering into the index and then compute the yearly value of the index in the same way that you compute a simple index number.

DEFINITION

A *simple composite index number* of k time series variables, call them $P_{1t}, P_{2t}, \ldots, P_{kt}$, is equal to

$$I_t = \frac{y_t}{y_0}(100)$$

where

$$y_t = P_{1t} + P_{2t} + \cdots + P_{kt}$$

and y_0 is the value of y_t for the base time period.

EXAMPLE 13.2

The year-end prices per pound of three commodities are shown in Table 13.2 for the years 1978 to 1987. Construct a simple composite index for the prices, using 1979 as the base year.

TABLE 13.2   Year-End Prices for Three Commodities

Commodity	1978	1979	1980	1981	1982	1983	1984	1985	1986	1987
1	2.20	2.35	2.64	2.77	3.01	3.10	3.42	3.50	3.62	3.81
2	1.33	1.46	1.65	1.87	1.99	2.23	2.44	2.61	2.86	2.77
3	.91	.99	1.08	1.17	1.19	1.47	1.62	1.74	1.93	1.99
y_t	4.44	4.80	5.37	5.81	6.19	6.80	7.48	7.85	8.41	8.57
I_t	93	100	112	121	129	142	156	164	175	179

SOLUTION

The sum y_t of the three commodity prices is shown in the fourth row of the table. Then $y_0 = 4.80$ for the base year 1979, and

$$I_{1978} = \frac{y_{1978}}{y_0}(100) = \frac{4.44}{4.80}(100) = 93$$

$$I_{1979} = 100$$

$$I_{1980} = \frac{y_{1980}}{y_0} = \frac{5.37}{4.80}(100) = 112$$

and so on. You can verify that the remaining values of I_t for 1981 through 1987 are as shown in the bottom row of Table 13.2. A graph of this time series is shown in Figure 13.5.

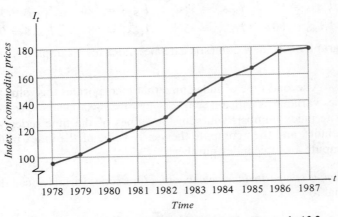

FIGURE 13.5   A Graph of the Index of Commodity Prices for Example 13.2

A third type of index number is a **weighted composite index**. Like the simple composite index, this index incorporates the values, $P_{1t}, P_{2t}, \ldots, P_{kt}$, of a number, say k, of time series variables. But rather than compute y_t as their sum, we multiply each of the values $P_{1t}, P_{2t}, \ldots, P_{kt}$ by a weight that reflects their importance in the index, and then we sum these weighted products. The reason for this procedure is clear if you consider the problem of constructing an index to reflect the general level of consumer meat prices. If you were to include the prices of beef, pork, chicken, fish, and alligator tail in the index, you might want to assign different weights to these prices because of the substantial differences in the consumption of these products. Not many people eat alligator tail, so it would seem unreasonable to give the price of this product the same weight in the index as the price of beef. Weights for a weighted composite index can be chosen in different ways, but those used in constructing price indices are usually the amounts of the commodities consumed. If the weights used to compute y_t are the respective commodity consumptions for the base year, the weighted composite index is said to be a **Laspeyres index**. If the weights are those for the time period t, the index is called a **Paasche index**.

DEFINITION   A *weighted composite index number* of k time series variables, call them $P_{1t}, P_{2t}, \ldots, P_{kt}$, is equal to

$$I_t = \frac{y_t}{y_0}(100)$$

where
$$y_t = w_1 P_{1t} + w_2 P_{2t} + \cdots + w_k P_{kt}$$
$$w_1, w_2, \ldots, w_k = \text{weights assigned to } P_{1t}, P_{2t}, \ldots, P_{kt},$$
$$y_0 = \text{value of } y_t \text{ for the base time period}$$

(*Note:* A simple composite index is the special case of a weighted composite index, where $w_1 = w_2 = \cdots = w_k = 1$.)   ∎

DEFINITION   A *Laspeyres index number* is a weighted composite index in which the weights are assigned the values that they assumed for the base year.   ∎

DEFINITION   A *Paasche index number* is a weighted composite index in which the weights used to compute the weighted sum for a given year are the values that the weights assumed for that year.   ∎

EXAMPLE 13.3   Suppose that the consumption, in millions of tons, for the commodities of Example 13.2 are 2.1, 2.7, and 4.8 million tons, respectively, for the base year 1979. Find the values of the Laspeyres index for the commodity price data for 1978 and 1979.

SOLUTION   Since a Laspeyres index uses the values of the weights for the base period, $w_1 = 2.1$, $w_2 = 2.7$, and $w_3 = 4.8$, then

$$y_{1978} = w_1 P_{1,1978} + w_2 P_{2,1978} + w_3 P_{3,1978}$$
$$= (2.1)(2.20) + (2.7)(1.33) + (4.8)(.91) = 12.579$$

$$y_{1979} = y_0 = w_1 P_{1,1979} + w_2 P_{2,1979} + w_3 P_{3,1979}$$
$$= (2.1)(2.35) + (2.7)(1.46) + (4.8)(.99) = 13.629$$

Then

$$I_{1978} = \frac{y_{1978}}{y_0}(100) = \frac{12.579}{13.629}(100) = 92$$

and

$$I_{1979} = \frac{y_{1979}}{y_0}(100) = \frac{y_0}{y_0}(100) = 100$$

The extent to which index numbers actually measure the level of the economic or business phenomenon that they are intended to measure is often a point of debate. For example, recent complaints about the Consumer Price Index stress that the price of new housing is too heavily weighted in the index, when you consider that most consumers do not buy a new house every month. Consequently, economic and business indices should be taken for what they are—man's attempt to achieve a simple measure for a very complicated phenomenon. Although economic indices may not be perfect, most perform the function for which they were intended: to provide a rough but general measure of change over time.

EXERCISES

APPLICATIONS

 13.1 The total monthly production (to the nearest million short ton) of raw steel for each month in 1984 is shown in the table:

Month	Jan.	Feb.	Mar.	Apr.	May	June	July	Aug.	Sept.	Oct.	Nov.	Dec.
Production	8.0	8.1	9.1	9.0	9.2	7.9	7.5	6.9	6.4	6.7	6.4	6.0

Source: Data from *Business Statistics, 1984* (Washington, D.C.: U.S. Department of Commerce, Bureau of Economic Analysis).

If January 1984 is taken as the base month, calculate the monthly simple index for this monthly time series.

 13.2 Table 13.3 gives the number of industrial and commercial business failures in the United States for the years 1972 through 1983. Calculate a simple index number I_t of business failures for the years 1972 through 1983, using 1975 as the base year.

 13.3 The average annual price (cents) per board foot and total annual production (millions of board feet) for three grades of plywood are shown in Table 13.4 for the years 1967, 1980, 1981, and 1982. Consider 1967 as the base year.

(a) Find the simple index number for the price of plywood grade 1 for 1980, 1981, and 1982.

(b) Compute the simple index numbers for plywood grade 2.

(c) Compute the simple index numbers for plywood grade 3.

TABLE 13.3   Business Failures Data for Exercise 13.2

Year	Number of Failures	Year	Number of Failures	Year	Number of Failures
1972	9566	1976	9628	1980	11742
1973	9345	1977	7919	1981	16794
1974	9915	1978	6619	1982	24908
1975	11432	1979	7564	1983	31334

Source: Data from *Business Statistics, 1984* (Washington, D.C.: U.S. Department of Commerce, Bureau of Economic Analysis).

TABLE 13.4   Price and Production Data for Exercise 13.3

| | Plywood grade | | | | | |
| | 1 | | 2 | | 3 | |
Year	Price	Production	Price	Production	Price	Production
1967	9.3	56.1	11.1	33.7	7.2	88.6
1980	18.1	112.7	22.4	69.5	18.8	204.1
1981	17.6	38.6	20.6	40.3	15.9	79.9
1982	17.4	30.9	19.3	37.2	15.7	65.0

13.4 Refer to Exercise 13.3, and compute the simple composite index numbers to measure price changes in the three grades of plywood for the years 1980, 1981, and 1982, relative to the base year 1967.

13.5 Refer to Exercise 13.3, and compute the Laspeyres index number for the data for years 1980, 1981, and 1982. Use 1967 as the base year and annual production as the weighting factor.

13.6 Refer to Exercise 13.3, and compute the Paasche index number for the data for years 1980, 1981, and 1982. Use 1967 as the base year and annual production as the weighting factor.

 13.7 The U.S. production (in millions of tons) of pig iron and raw steel are shown in Table 13.5 for the years 1967 and 1980 through 1984. Calculate a simple composite index for iron and steel production for 1980 through 1984, using 1967 as the base year.

TABLE 13.5   Production Data for Exercise 13.7

| | Year | | | | | |
Product	1967	1980	1981	1982	1983	1984
Pig iron	87.0	68.7	73.4	43.1	48.7	51.9
Steel	127.2	111.8	120.8	74.6	83.3	92.5

Source: Data from *Business Statistics, 1984* (Washington, D.C.: U.S. Department of Commerce, Bureau of Economic Analysis).

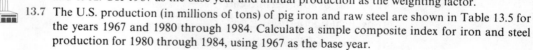

13.8 Suppose that you wanted to construct an index to measure the price level of the common stock of major chemical companies. Table 13.6 gives the approximate average price per share and the average number of shares outstanding (adjusted for stock splits) for the common stock of the Dow Chemical Company, Dupont, and Monsanto for the years 1980, 1985, and 1986.

TABLE 13.6   Stock Price Data for Exercise 13.8

Share and Price	Dow Chemical			Dupont			Monsanto		
	1980	1985	1986	1980	1985	1986	1980	1985	1986
Average number of shares (millions)	183	190	191	147	241	240	72	77	78
Average price per share (dollars)	33.6	33.9	53.4	41.0	57.0	78.7	27.1	46.1	66.1

Source: Data from *The Value Line Investment Survey, 1987.*

(a) Construct a simple composite price level index for the three chemical company common stocks for the years 1985 and 1986. Use 1980 as the base year.

(b) Calculate a Laspeyres index for the prices of the chemical stocks for the years 1985 and 1986, using the average number of shares outstanding as weights. Explain why the Laspeyres index might provide a better measure of the general level of the stock prices of large chemical companies. Use 1980 as the base year.

(c) Calculate a Paasche index for the data for the years 1985 and 1986, using 1980 as the base year. Explain the difference between the Laspeyres and Paasche indices.

The Components of a Time Series

13.3

Time series analysis is a complicated topic, and there is a diversity of opinion as to how analyses should be performed. One of the most accepted approaches is to view a time series as a composition of four components:

(1) secular or long-term trend

(2) cyclical fluctuation

(3) seasonal variation

(4) random, unpredictable variation

These components are then isolated and modeled by using one of several methods.

Secular or **long-term trend** is the tendency of a time series to gradually increase or decrease in a straight line or gradual curve, over time (see Figure 13.6). For example, a time series of the price of housing might vary upward and downward over short intervals of time; but because of long-term inflation, it would trend gradually upward.

Cyclical components of a time series tend to rise and fall in a cyclical pattern about the secular curve (or line). For example, a time series of the price of housing would cycle about a long-term trend curve due to the cycling of supply, interest rates, the state of the economy, and so on. Builders tend to overbuild in a housing market, thus driving down the price of housing. As time continues, the market recovers, prices rise, more

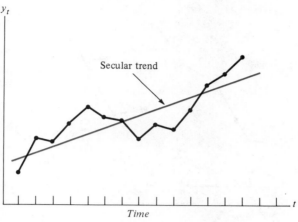

FIGURE 13.6   The Secular or Long-Term Trend in a Time Series

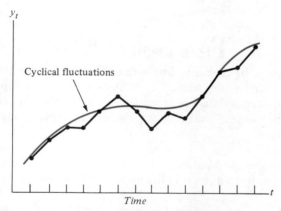

FIGURE 13.7   The Cyclical Component of a Time Series

people buy, housing tends to become scarce, prices peak, and the cycle repeats itself. The cyclical component of a time series is illustrated in Figure 13.7.

   Seasonal components represent the tendency for the time series to jump upward or downward during specific seasons of the year. For example, the prices of fresh vegetables tend to fall during harvesting seasons and rise during the winter or the growing season. A seasonal component might appear as shown in Figure 13.8.

   The fourth component of a time series is the unexplained **random variation** that exists in all economic and business time series. These random variations, which are added to the preceding three time series components, bob about in a haphazard manner and are sometimes correlated, owing to unexplained cyclical effects that have not been accounted for in the model.

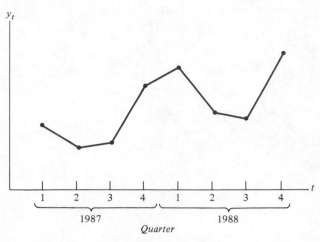

FIGURE 13.8   The Seasonal Component of a Time Series

SMOOTHING A TIME SERIES: MOVING AVERAGES

13.4

Before you attempt to model a time series, it is useful to graph the time series to determine the nature of any secular, cyclical, and seasonal components, if they exist. These components can often be revealed by *smoothing* the time series—that is, averaging out the effects of the random variation. This smoothing is called the method of **moving averages**.

DEFINITION

A *k-point moving average* M_t at time t is formed by averaging k sequential values of y_t. The time t is taken to be a point in the middle of these time intervals.   ■

For example, suppose that long-term trend in a time series is obscured by seasonal (say quarterly) components and random variation. This variation about the secular trend line (curve) can be reduced by computing a four-point moving average of the time series. We first compute the partial sums

$$S_1 = y_1 + y_2 + y_3 + y_4$$
$$S_2 = y_2 + y_3 + y_4 + y_5$$
$$S_3 = y_3 + y_4 + y_5 + y_6$$

where $y_1, y_2, y_3, \ldots$ are the values of y_t observed at the first, second, third, . . . time points, respectively. We then compute the corresponding moving averages, $M_1 = S_1/4$, $M_2 = S_2/4$, and so on, and plot them at the midpoints of their respective four-point intervals. The smoothing effect of a moving average can be seen in the following example.

TABLE 13.7   The Dow-Jones Industrial Average, 1985 and 1986

Year	Month											
	Jan.	Feb.	Mar.	Apr.	May	June	July	Aug.	Sept.	Oct.	Nov.	Dec.
1985	1238	1283	1269	1266	1279	1314	1343	1326	1318	1352	1433	1517
1986	1535	1653	1757	1807	1802	1868	1810	1843	1813	1817	1884	1924

Source: Data from *Survey of Current Business* (Washington, D.C.: U.S. Department of Commerce, Bureau of Economic Analysis, Vol. 66, January 1986, and Vol. 67, January 1987).

TABLE 13.8   Three-Point Moving Averages for the Data in Table 13.7

Year	Month											
	Jan.	Feb.	Mar.	Apr.	May	June	July	Aug.	Sept.	Oct.	Nov.	Dec.
1985	—	1263.3	1272.7	1271.3	1286.3	1312.0	1327.7	1329.0	1332.0	1367.7	1434.0	1495.0
1986	1568.3	1648.3	1739.0	1788.7	1825.7	1826.7	1840.3	1822.0	1824.3	1838.0	1875.0	—

EXAMPLE 13.4   The Dow-Jones Industrial Average is an average of the prices of the common stocks of 30 large, blue-chip, U.S. corporations divided by a constant that is modified from time to time to adjust for stock splits or, in some cases, the replacement of one corporation by another. The values of the Dow-Jones Industrial Average at the end of each month for the years 1985 and 1986 are shown in Table 13.7. Compute a three-point moving average for this time series, and graph the moving average along with the original time series.

SOLUTION   We compute

$$M_1 = \frac{y_1 + y_2 + y_3}{3} = \frac{1238 + 1283 + 1269}{3} = 1263.3$$

$$M_2 = \frac{y_2 + y_3 + y_4}{3} = \frac{1283 + 1269 + 1266}{3} = 1272.7$$

$$\vdots$$

$$M_{22} = \frac{y_{22} + y_{23} + y_{24}}{3} = \frac{1817 + 1884 + 1924}{3} = 1875.0$$

The moving averages for the data in Table 13.7 are shown in Table 13.8. Graphs of the moving average and of the original time series are shown in Figure 13.9. You can see in Figure 13.9 that much of the erratic variation in the original time series is removed by the three-point moving average. It shows the rapidly rising upward trend in the Dow-Jones Industrial Average that characterized the famous bull stock market that commenced in 1982 and that was still moving upward in early 1987. ∎

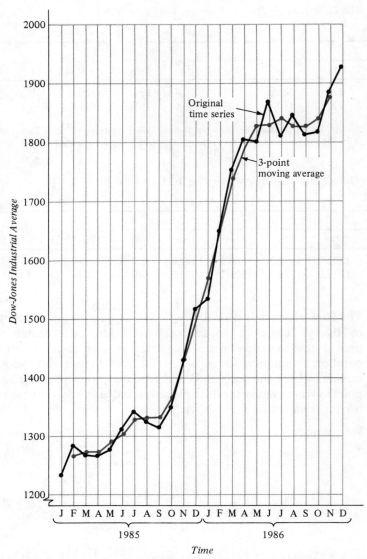

FIGURE 13.9   Graphs of the Three-Point Moving Average and of the Original Time Series for the Data of Table 13.7

EXPONENTIAL SMOOTHING

13.5

Another effective method for smoothing a time series is called **exponential smoothing**. Exponential smoothing is accomplished in the following way: Suppose that the values of the original time series are $y_1, y_2, \ldots, y_t$. Then the first, second, third, and last values of the exponentially smoothed series, denoted by the symbols $E_1, E_2, E_3,$

and E_t, are

$$E_1 = y_1$$
$$E_2 = \omega y_2 + (1 - \omega)E_1$$
$$E_3 = \omega y_3 + (1 - \omega)E_2$$
$$\vdots$$
$$E_t = \omega y_t + (1 - \omega)E_{t-1}$$

The symbol ω that appears in the formulas for $E_1, E_2, \ldots, E_t$ is a weighting factor, a number between 0 and 1, that you must choose. Small values of ω give less weight to the current value of y_t and tend to produce a smoother series. Large values of ω give more weight to the current value of y_t and produce values of E_t that are very close to those for y_t.

DEFINITION

An *exponentially smoothed value E_t* for a time series y_t is

$$E_t = \omega y_t + (1 - \omega)E_{t-1}$$

where

$$E_1 = y_1$$

and ω is a weight that can assume a value vetween 0 and 1.   ∎

EXAMPLE 13.5

Refer to the data on the Dow-Jones Industrial Average in Table 13.7. Calculate the exponentially smoothed time series for the original data, using a weight of $\omega = .4$. Then graph both on the same sheet of graph paper.

SOLUTION

The calculations for E_1, E_2, and E_3 follow, and all values of E_t, $t = 1, 2, \ldots, 24$, are shown in Table 13.9. The graphs of the exponentially smoothed time series and of the original time series are shown in Figure 13.10. Note the effect of the exponential smoothing on the time series. Like the moving average (Figure 13.9), it clearly shows the rapidly rising upward trend of the DJI stock during the 1982–1987 bull stock market.

$$E_1 = y_1 = 1238$$
$$E_2 = \omega y_2 + (1 - \omega)E_1 = (.4)(1283) + (.6)(1238) = 1256.0$$
$$E_3 = \omega y_3 + (1 - \omega)E_2 = (.4)(1269) + (.6)(1256) = 1261.2$$
$$\vdots$$
$$E_{24} = \omega y_{24} + (1 - \omega)E_{23} = (.4)(1924) + (.6)(1843.1) = 1875.5$$

TABLE 13.9   Exponentially Smoothed Values for the Time Series in Table 13.7 with $\omega = .4$

Year	Jan.	Feb.	Mar.	Apr.	May	June	July	Aug.	Sept.	Oct.	Nov.	Dec.
						Month						
1985	1238.0	1256.0	1261.2	1263.1	1269.5	1287.3	1309.6	1316.2	1316.9	1330.9	1371.7	1429.8
1986	1471.9	1544.3	1629.4	1700.4	1741.0	1791.8	1799.1	1816.7	1815.2	1815.9	1843.1	1875.5

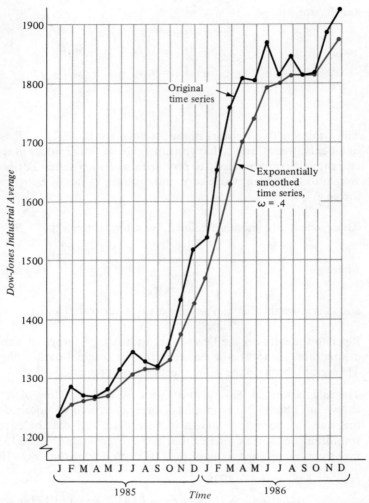

FIGURE 13.10   Graphs of the Exponentially Smoothed ($\omega = .4$) and of the Original Time Series for the Data of Table 13.7

EXERCISES

APPLICATIONS

13.9   Exercise 13.1 gave the total monthly production of raw steel (to the nearest million short ton) for each month in 1984. The data are reproduced below.

Month	Jan.	Feb.	Mar.	Apr.	May	June	July	Aug.	Sept.	Oct.	Nov.	Dec.
Production	8.0	8.1	9.1	9.0	9.2	7.9	7.5	6.9	6.4	6.7	6.4	6.0

Source: Data from *Business Statistics, 1984* (Washington, D.C.: U.S. Department of Commerce, Bureau of Economic Analysis).

(a) Plot the data points and connect them with line segments.

(b) Calculate a two-point moving average for the data.

(c) Calculate a three-point moving average for the data.

(d) Graph the original time series along with the two- and three-point moving averages on the same sheet of graph paper. Compare the smoothing effects of the two- and the three-point moving averages.

 13.10 Colin W. Clark's time series data on the Peruvian anchoveta fishing industry (Exercise 11.55) are reproduced in Table 13.10.

TABLE 13.10   Anchoveta Data for Exercises 13.10 and 13.11

Year	Number of Boats	Number of Fishing Days	Fishing Effort: Number of Boats × Number of Fishing Days (in Units of 10,000 Boat-days)	Catch (Million Tons)
1959	414	294	12.2	1.91
1960	667	279	18.6	
1961	756	298	22.5	4.58
1962	1069	294	31.4	6.27
1963	1655	269	44.5	6.42
1964	1744	297	51.8	8.86
1965	1623	265	43.0	7.23
1966	1650	190	31.4	8.53
1967	1569	170	26.7	9.82
1968	1490	167	24.9	10.26
1969	1455	162	23.6	8.96
1970	1499	180	27.0	12.27
1971	1473	89	13.1	10.28
1972	1399	89	12.5	4.45
1973	1256	27	3.39	1.78
1974				4.00
1975				3.30
1976				4.30
1977				.80
1978				.50

Source: C. W. Clark, "Bioeconomics of the Ocean," *BioScience.* Vol. 30, No. 3, March 1981, pp. 231–237. Copyright ©1981 by the American Institute of Biological Sciences.

(a) Graph the time series for the annual catch of anchoveta from 1961 to 1978.

(b) Compute and graph the two-point moving average for the data from 1961 to 1978. Note the smoothing effect of the averaging.

(c) Compute and graph the three-point moving average for the data from 1961 to 1978, and note the additional smoothing obtained.

13.11 Refer to Exercise 13.10.

(a) Graph the time series for the annual fishing effort.

(b) Compute and graph the two-point moving average for the data. Note the smoothing effect of the averaging.

(c) Compute and graph the three-point moving average for the data, and note the additional smoothing obtained.

 13.12 The mean wholesale prices of eggs, in cents per dozen, are shown in Table 13.11 for each month from January 1977 through January 1985.

TABLE 13.11   Price Data for Exercise 13.12

Year	Jan.	Feb.	Mar.	Apr.	May	June	July	Aug.	Sept.	Oct.	Nov.	Dec.	Average
1977	78.7	75.6	67.5	62.4	55.7	57.0	62.8	59.3	59.3	53.7	55.0	61.5	62
1978	55.2	62.8	62.0	57.0	52.0	49.3	61.2	61.8	63.2	60.8	67.2	71.6	60
1979	71.3	67.7	73.5	68.7	61.9	64.8	61.9	64.0	62.0	59.7	66.3	72.4	66
1980	59.9	56.3	60.6	56.8	50.8	54.6	63.2	65.9	68.8	64.3	75.7	77.3	62
1981	71.4	67.2	66.6	69.7	62.2	62.9	67.5	68.7	70.7	71.3	77.3	72.1	69
1982	76.2	74.2	75.2	68.3	60.4	60.8	61.7	61.6	65.9	66.8	66.2	64.1	66
1983	60.2	62.7	66.2	64.9	68.4	68.0	66.2	74.4	76.2	77.9	88.4	98.6	72
1984	112.3	102.6	88.3	101.8	74.3	68.1	69.0	66.5	67.2	60.7	70.4	62.2	78
1985	58.4												

Source: 1985 CRB Commodity Year Book (New York: Commodity Research Bureau, 1985).

(a) Plot the data points for the 36 months from January 1982 through December 1984.

(b) Construct a three-point moving average for the data in part (a).

(c) Construct a graph showing the original time series and the three-point moving averages. Does the smoothing begin to show any secular, cyclical, or seasonal components in the time series for egg prices?

13.13 Perform exponential smoothing for the time series in Exercise 13.9.

(a) Use $\omega = .2$.

(b) Use $\omega = .5$.

(c) Use $\omega = .8$.

(d) Graph the original time series along with the three smoothed series from parts (a), (b), and (c). Explain the effect of the value of ω on the smoothing.

13.14 Exponentially smooth the time series for the annual catch of anchoveta (Exercise 13.10), using a weighting factor of $\omega = .4$. Graph the original time series and the exponentially smoothed series to note the effect of the exponential smoothing on the original data.

13.15 Perform exponential smoothing for the egg price time series (Exercise 13.12), using a weight of $\omega = .3$. Construct a graph showing the original time series and the exponentially smoothed series. Does the smoothing begin to show any secular, cyclical, or seasonal components in the series?

 13.16 Table 13.12 gives the electric power production (in billions of kilowatt-hours) by electric utilities in the United States each month from January 1971 through October 1984.

(a) Plot the data for the months from January 1982 through October 1984.

(b) Smooth the data with a two-point moving average to reveal secular, cyclical, and (or) seasonal trends.

(c) Graph the original time series along with the two-point moving average. Explain what, if anything, is revealed by smoothing.

(d) Smooth the data, using a three-point moving average. Does it improve the smoothing?

TABLE 13.12   Electric Power Production Data* for Exercise 13.16

Year	Jan.	Feb.	Mar.	Apr.	May	June	July	Aug.	Sept.	Oct.	Nov.	Dec.	Total
1971	145.6	131.3	141.4	130.7	133.7	150.5	153.9	154.2	145.9	139.5	138.9	148.0	1,714
1972	153.0	145.5	148.9	140.5	146.5	154.4	166.7	171.8	155.8	152.5	152.4	163.1	1,851
1973*	159.3	143.1	147.8	139.3	147.0	161.0	173.5	177.0	156.3	153.8	147.8	153.3	1,861
1974	156.9	142.4	149.9	141.9	153.4	156.0	177.9	173.8	152.2	151.9	149.8	159.5	1,867
1975	164.3	147.1	155.5	146.2	153.2	162.4	176.8	179.7	155.2	154.9	152.8	169.4	1,918
1976	178.3	156.7	164.2	153.2	157.4	173.4	186.4	186.4	165.0	163.7	169.1	183.9	2,038
1977	196.4	162.7	169.1	156.9	169.3	180.8	198.9	196.1	176.2	166.4	167.1	184.2	2,124
1978	197.3	173.7	173.2	159.7	175.2	187.4	202.6	205.6	185.6	175.6	176.3	191.7	2,206
1979	209.7	186.3	182.8	170.0	178.1	186.7	202.3	204.9	180.8	179.7	177.5	188.7	2,247
1980	200.0	188.7	187.5	168.7	175.7	189.4	216.8	215.4	191.5	178.6	178.6	195.6	2,286
1981	206.5	179.6	185.6	172.5	177.8	202.7	220.4	210.4	186.8	181.4	175.6	195.6	2,295
1982†	209.4	180.3	187.7	172.6	177.1	186.1	210.6	205.7	180.7	173.0	173.4	184.7	2,241
1983†	195.7	172.5	182.5	170.4	174.4	191.0	220.2	230.0	195.6	182.9	182.9	212.3	2,310
1984†	216.5	189.5	199.4	180.9	191.9	209.4	220.7	229.1	194.9	190.4			

Source: Federal Power Commission data from *1985 CRB Commodity Year Book* (New York: Commodity Research Bureau, 1985).

*Data prior to 1973 are production by utilities and industrial establishments.

†Preliminary.

13.17   Use exponential smoothing on the time series for Exercise 13.16 with $\omega = .3$. Was exponential smoothing with $\omega = .3$ successful in smoothing the time series and revealing secular, cyclical, or seasonal trends?

TIME SERIES MODELING

13.6

There are a number of different ways to analyze a time series and to develop a **time series forecasting model**. One of the most common methods is to model the secular, cyclical, and seasonal components of a time series by using a regression model. This deterministic (nonrandom) portion of a time series model is fit to the time series data to obtain a prediction equation $\hat{y}_t$. The residuals—the deviations between the observed and the predicted values of y_t—are computed next. We then attempt to model these residuals by using a model that accounts for possible correlation between adjacent residual terms.

The secular or long-term trend in a time series is often modeled by using the first- or second-order polynomial regression models of Chapter 12. Straight-line, long-term trends in a time series, either up or down, are represented by the first-order model

$$E(y_t) = \beta_0 + \beta_1 t$$

A second-order model

$$E(y_t) = \beta_0 + \beta_1 t + \beta_2 t^2$$

is used when increases in $E(y_t)$ over time tend to decrease [see Figure 13.11(a)] or tend

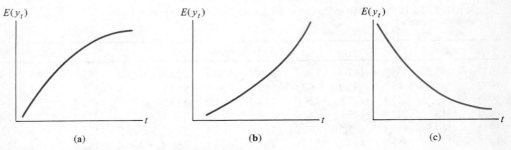

FIGURE 13.11   Second-Order Models to Remove Secular Trend

TABLE 13.13   Domestic Sales of U.S. Cars; Straight-Line Regression Model

DEPENDENT VARIABLE: Y

SOURCE	DF	SUM OF SQUARES	MEAN SQUARE	F VALUE	PR > F	R-SQUARE	C.V.
MODEL	1	7.89236264	7.89236264	5.31	0.0416	0.325758	15.8897
ERROR	11	16.33532967	1.48502997		ROOT MSE		Y MEAN
CORRECTED TOTAL	12	24.22769231			1.21861806		7.66923077

SOURCE	DF	TYPE I SS	F VALUE	PR > F	DF	TYPE III SS	F VALUE	PR > F
T	1	7.89236264	5.31	0.0416	1	7.89236264	5.31	0.0416

PARAMETER	ESTIMATE	T FOR HO: PARAMETER=0	PR > |T|	STD ERROR OF ESTIMATE
INTERCEPT	9.12692308	12.73	0.0001	0.71697199
T	-0.20824176	-2.31	0.0416	0.09032998

OBSERVATION	OBSERVED VALUE	PREDICTED VALUE	RESIDUAL	LOWER 95% CL INDIVIDUAL	UPPER 95% CL INDIVIDUAL
1	8.80000000	8.91868132	-0.11868132	5.89041072	11.94695192
2	9.70000000	8.71043956	0.98956044	5.75483162	11.66604750
3	7.30000000	8.50219780	-1.20219780	5.60739744	11.39699817
4	6.70000000	8.29395604	-1.59395604	5.44734835	11.14056374
5	8.50000000	8.08571429	0.41428571	5.27403562	10.89739295
6	9.20000000	7.87747253	1.32252747	5.08696113	10.66798393
7	9.20000000	7.66923077	1.53078923	4.88581089	10.45265064
8	8.40000000	7.46098901	0.93901099	4.67047761	10.25150041
9	6.40000000	7.25274725	-0.85274725	4.44106858	10.06442592
10	6.20000000	7.04450549	-0.84450549	4.19789780	9.89111319
11	5.00000000	6.83626374	-1.83626374	3.94146337	9.73106410
12	6.70000000	6.62802198	0.07197802	3.67241403	9.58362992
13	7.60000000	6.41978022	1.18021978	3.39150962	9.44805082

SUM OF RESIDUALS	0.00000000
SUM OF SQUARED RESIDUALS	16.33532967
SUM OF SQUARED RESIDUALS - ERROR SS	-0.00000000
PRESS STATISTIC	22.42067571
FIRST ORDER AUTOCORRELATION	0.32944116
DURBIN-WATSON D	1.25498510

to increase [see Figure 13.11(b)]. A second-order model would also be appropriate if $E(y_t)$ tended to decrease over time, as shown in Figure 13.11(c).

A straight line would seem to provide a good model for the long-term trend in U.S. automobile sales for 1972 through 1984. Using the SAS regression package to fit the model

$$E(y_t) = \beta_0 + \beta_1 t \qquad t = \text{year} - 1971$$

to the data of Table 13.1, we obtain the SAS printout shown in Table 13.13. A graph of this secular trend line,

$$\hat{y}_t = 9.1269 - .2082t$$

is shown in Figure 13.12. Note that the secular trend in new-car sales over the period 1972 to 1984 is downward. You will observe that the value of ROOT MSE shown in the SAS printout, $s = 1.21861806$, is quite large. It reflects the large amount of variation in new-car sales due to the rise and fall in the general level of economic activity as well as to other sources of variation.

Periodic movements of $E(y_t)$ about the secular trend line (curve) can be explained by the cyclical nature of the economy or (sometimes) by seasonal variations. Cyclical

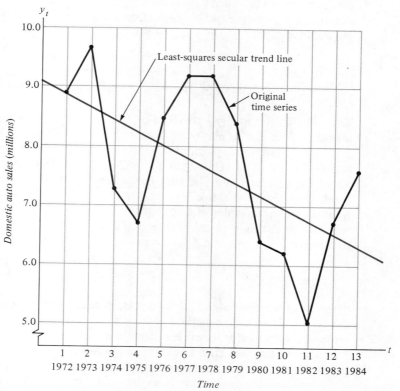

FIGURE 13.12   A Graph of the Secular Trend Regression Line for New Domestic Automobile Sales, $\hat{y}_t = 9.1269 - .2082t$

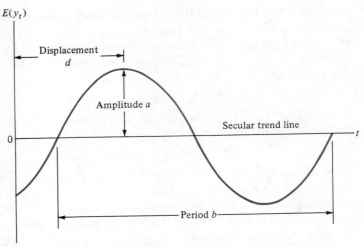

$E(y_t)$

Displacement
d

Amplitude a

Secular trend line

0

t

Period b

FIGURE 13.13   Contribution of Cyclical Terms, $\beta_2 \cos (2\pi t/b) + \beta_3 \sin (2\pi t/b)$

components can be added to the secular trend model by using trigonometric terms. For example, if we observe cyclical oscillation about a straight-line secular trend, we might use the model

$$\overbrace{E(y_t) = \beta_0 + \beta_1 t}^{\text{secular trend}} + \overbrace{\beta_2 \cos \frac{2\pi t}{b} + \beta_3 \sin \frac{2\pi t}{b}}^{\text{cyclical effect}}$$

The contribution to $E(y_t)$ provided by the trigonometric terms will produce a curve, measured from the secular trend line, as shown in Figure 13.13.

The time units, days, months, years (whatever), are measured along the horizontal axis of Figure 13.13. The terms $\beta_2 \cos (2\pi t/b) + \beta_3 \sin (2\pi t/b)$ trace a cyclical curve about the secular trend line that has an amplitude (maximum deviation from the secular trend line) equal to $a = \sqrt{\beta_2^2 + \beta_3^2}$. The standard position of the cyclical curve is for the maximum value of $E(y_t)$ (ignoring secular trend) to occur at $t = 0$. The curve will shift to the right of this position at a distance equal to $d = \tan^{-1}(\beta_3/\beta_2)$. The parameters $\beta_0, \beta_1, \beta_2$, and β_3 in the model

$$E(y_t) = \beta_0 + \beta_1 t + \beta_2 \cos\left(\frac{2\pi}{b} t\right) + \beta_3 \sin\left(\frac{2\pi}{b} t\right)$$

determine the amplitude a and the displacement d of the time series. These parameters can be estimated by the method of least squares. In contrast, the parameter b, which measures the period of the cycle, enters the model in a nonlinear manner and cannot be estimated by least squares. The value of b must be based on a visual observation of a graph of the time series and selected prior to estimating β_2 and β_3.

Seasonal effects that vary from the secular trend line (or curve) can be more easily inserted into a model. For example, new-housing starts are usually low in the first and fourth quarters of the year (during the winter) but tend upward from April through

September. If time is recorded in quarters, this type of seasonal effect is added to the long-term trend line by using the model

$$E(y_t) = \overbrace{\beta_0 + \beta_1 t}^{\text{secular trend}} + \beta_2 x_1 + \beta_3 x_2 + \beta_4 x_3$$

where

$$x_1 = \begin{cases} 1, & \text{if quarter 1} \\ 0, & \text{if not} \end{cases}$$

$$x_2 = \begin{cases} 1, & \text{if quarter 2} \\ 0, & \text{if not} \end{cases}$$

$$x_3 = \begin{cases} 1, & \text{if quarter 3} \\ 0, & \text{if not} \end{cases}$$

The independent variables x_1, x_2, and x_3 are dummy (indicator) variables that add β_2, β_3, or β_4 to the secular portion $E(y_t)$ depending on whether the quarter is, respectively, the first, second, or the third. When we want to model $E(y_t)$ for the fourth quarter, $x_1 = x_2 = x_3 = 0$ and $E(y_t) = \beta_0 + \beta_1 t$. Thus β_2, β_3, and β_4 are the positive or negative deviations of $E(y_t)$ from the secular trend line for quarters, 1, 2, and 3, respectively. A graph depicting this situation is shown in Figure 13.14. Exercise 13.18 provides an excellent illustration of the use of this model.

The independent variables x_1, x_2, and x_3 are dummy (indicator) variables that Almost all time series models will include terms to adjust for the secular trend, and they may include cyclical terms or terms to adjust for seasonal effects. We have described the nature of these terms and explained how they can be combined to form a model for the mean value of the time series variable y_t. The final step is to model the correlated residual of y_t, the unexplained deviation of y_t from $E(y_t)$, and to use it to place a bound on the error of prediction when $\hat{y}_t$ is used for forecasting. We will shed some light on the manner in which this is done in Section 13.7.

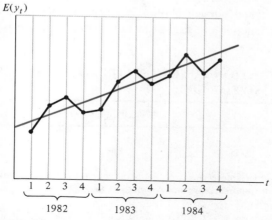

FIGURE 13.14   A Model That Adjusts for Seasonal Trends

13.7

TIME SERIES FORECASTING

The final step in forming a time series model is to add a term to account for random variation of the values of y_t from $E(y_t)$, where $E(y_t)$ is the deterministic portion of the model discussed in Section 13.6. In contrast to the regression model of Chapter 11, we will want to allow for a correlation between pairs of random errors. We would expect the errors associated with adjacent values of y_t to be more highly correlated than the errors corresponding to two values of y_t that are far apart in time. For example, if the index in U.S. economic activity in March is higher than the value explained by $E(y_t)$—that is, the deviation is positive—we think there is a good chance that the deviation in the following month will also be positive.

The random error term at time t for our time series model will be represented by the symbol z_t. One way to model the type of error correlation described above is to use an **autoregressive model** for z_t. A *first-order* autoregressive model is given by the equation in the following box.

FIRST-ORDER* AUTOREGRESSIVE MODEL

$$z_t = \phi z_{t-1} + \varepsilon_t$$

The symbol ϕ is an unknown constant that must be estimated, and ε_t, known as *white noise,* is assumed to possess a standard normal distribution—that is, one with mean equal to 0 and standard deviation equal to 1. A complete autoregressive time series model, one that contains both deterministic and random components, is of the form shown in the next box.

COMPLETE AUTOREGRESSIVE TIME SERIES MODEL

$$y_t = \text{(deterministic portion of the model)} + z_t \qquad \text{where} \qquad z_t = \phi z_{t-1} + \varepsilon_t$$

The correlation between pairs of values of z_t (and therefore y_t) separated by m units of time, called **autocorrelation**, is given by an autocorrelation function. The **autocorrelation function** for a first-order autoregressive model is given by the expression in the following box.

AUTOCORRELATION FUNCTION FOR A FIRST-ORDER AUTOREGRESSIVE MODEL

$$A(y_t, y_{t-m}) = \phi^m$$

---

*The first-order autoregressive model is the simplest in the family of autoregressive models. For example, a pth-order autoregressive model is given by the expression

$$z_t = \phi_1 z_{t-1} + \phi_2 z_{t-2} + \cdots + \phi_p z_{t-p} + \varepsilon_t$$

The parameters $\phi_1, \phi_2, \ldots, \phi_p$ are assumed to be unknown and must be estimated.

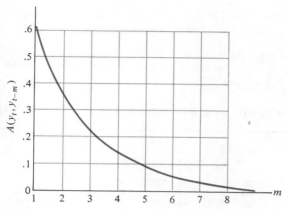

FIGURE 13.15   A Graph of the Autocorrelation Function for a First-Order Autoregressive Model, $\phi = .6$

For example, if $\phi = .6$, then the correlation between two adjacent ($m = 1$) values of y_t is

$$A(y_t, y_{t-1}) = (.6)^1 = .6$$

The autocorrelation between two values of y_t separated by $m = 2$ time units is

$$A(y_t, y_{t-2}) = (.6)^2 = .36$$

A graph of the autocorrelation function for the first-order autoregressive model, $\phi = .6$, is shown in Figure 13.15. Note that the autocorrelation decreases as the distance m between y_t and y_{t-m} increases. A test to detect autocorrelation in a time series is described in the references.

In order to forecast values of a time series to be observed in the future, we must fit the time series model to a set of data. We fit the model by using a modification of the least-squares method. This method fits the transformed variable y_t^* to x_t^*, where $y_t^* = y_t - \phi y_{t-1}$ and $x_t^* = x_t - \phi x_{t-1}$, for a given value of ϕ, using the method of least squares. The process is repeated for various values of ϕ until the sum of squares of the residuals is minimized. The resulting analysis will provide estimates of the parameters of $E(y_t)$—that is, $\beta_0, \beta_1, \ldots$—that differ slightly from those that would be obtained by using a standard regression analysis. It will also provide an estimate of the autocorrelation parameter ϕ as well as a printout of the residuals, the difference between the observed and predicted value of y_t, for each observation.

Because of the large amount of computation involved in fitting a time series model to a set of data, it is usually done on a computer by using a statistical program package. We will illustrate the output of the popular SAS AUTOREG procedure package in the following examples and will then show how the resulting prediction equation can be used for forecasting.

EXAMPLE 13.6   Fit the autoregressive time series model

$$y_t = \beta_0 + \beta_1 t + z_t$$

to the domestic automobile sales data of Table 13.1.

SOLUTION   The SAS printout for the SAS AUTOREG procedure package is shown in Table 13.14. The relevant parts of the printout are shaded and numbered.

(1) The ordinary least-squares estimates are shown in shaded area ①. Note that they agree with the values of the estimates shown in the SAS simple linear re-

TABLE 13.14   Domestic Sales of U.S. Cars; SAS Straight-Line Model with AR(1) Errors (Example 13.6)

LE = Y

ORDINARY LEAST SQUARES ESTIMATES

SSE	16.33533	DFE		11
MSE	1.48503	ROOT MSE	1.218618
SBC	44.99125	AIC	43.86135
REG RSQ	0.3258	TOTAL RSQ	0.3258
DURBIN-WATSON	1.2550		

VARIABLE	DF	B VALUE	STD ERROR	T RATIO	APPROX PROB
INTERCPT	1	9.12692308 ①	0.716971991	12.730	0.0001
T	1	-0.20824176	0.090329980	-2.305	0.0416

CORRELATION OF B-VALUES

	INTERCPT	T
INTERCPT	1.0000	-0.8819
T	-0.8819	1.0000

ESTIMATES OF AUTOCORRELATIONS

LAG	COVARIANCE	CORRELATION	-1 9 8 7 6 5 4 3 2 1 0 1 2 3 4 5 6 7 8 9 1
0	1.25656	1.000000	| |********************|
1	0.413964	0.329441	| |******* |

PRELIMINARY MSE=   1.120187

ESTIMATES OF THE AUTOREGRESSIVE PARAMETERS

LAG	COEFFICIENT	STD ERROR	T RATIO
1	-0.32944116 ②	0.29857470	-1.103379

YULE-WALKER ESTIMATES

SSE	14.35555 ⑤	DFE		10
MSE	1.435555	ROOT MSE	1.198146
SBC	45.99157	AIC	44.29672
REG RSQ	0.1987	TOTAL RSQ	0.4075

VARIABLE	DF	B VALUE	STD ERROR	T RATIO	APPROX PROB
INTERCPT	1	9.01626070 ③	0.959179593	9.400	0.0001
T	1	-0.18710452	0.118811968	-1.575	0.1464

CORRELATION OF B-VALUES

	INTERCPT	T
INTERCPT	1.0000	-0.8671
T	-0.8671	1.0000

TABLE 13.14   *(Continued)*

DOMESTIC SALES OF U.S. CARS
STRAIGHT-LINE MODEL WITH AR(1) ERRORS

④

OBS	T	Y	YHAT	RESID	LCL95	UCL95
1	1	8.8	8.82916	-0.0292	5.41578	12.2425
2	2	9.7	8.63245	1.0676	5.46818	11.7967
3	3	7.3	8.80348	-1.5035	5.74050	11.8665
4	4	6.7	7.88736	-1.1874	4.90554	10.8692
5	5	8.5	7.56423	0.9358	4.64175	10.4867
6	6	9.2	8.03176	1.1682	5.14548	10.9180
7	7	9.2	8.13690	1.0631	5.26279	11.0110
8	8	8.4	8.01144	0.3886	5.12516	10.8977
9	9	6.4	7.62242	-1.2224	4.69995	10.5449
10	10	6.2	6.83807	-0.6381	3.85625	9.8199
11	11	5.0	6.64672	-1.6467	3.58374	9.7097
12	12	6.7	6.12592	0.5741	2.96166	9.2902
13	13	7.6	6.56051	1.0395	3.27669	9.8443

gression printout in Table 13.13. These estimates are provided so that they can be compared with those obtained for the fitted autoregressive model.

(2) The estimated value(s) of the autoregressive parameters is (are) shown in shaded area ②. Because we are fitting a first-order model, we will estimate only one ϕ parameter. The SAS AUTOREG package uses a slightly different model for the autoregressive term, one that produces estimates of the autocorrelation parameters that are the negatives of the estimates of our parameters. Therefore, since the printout gives $-.32944116$ as the estimate of the autocorrelation parameter, the estimate of ϕ for our model is $+.32944116$.

(3) The AUTOREG estimates of the parameters of $E(y_t)$—in this case, β_0 and β_1— are shown in shaded area ③ as

$$\hat{\beta}_0 = 9.01626070 \quad \text{and} \quad \hat{\beta}_1 = -.18710452$$

Note that these estimates vary very little from the standard regression estimates in shaded area ①. If we round the estimates $\hat{\phi}$, $\hat{\beta}_0$, and $\hat{\beta}_1$, the fitted time series prediction equation is

$$\hat{y}_t = 9.0163 - .1871t + \hat{z}_t$$

where

$$\hat{z}_t = .3294\hat{z}_{t-1}$$

(4) The computer printout of the predicted values $\hat{y}_t$ and the residuals for the SAS AUTOREG fitted model are shown in shaded area ④. For example, the predicted value of y_t for 1972, that is, $t = 1$, is 8.82916; the observed value is 8.8; and the residual $y_t - \hat{y}_t$, is $-.0292$.

(5) The SSE for the fitted autoregressive model, SSE $= 14.35555$, is shown in shaded area ⑤. The value of the mean square error, MSE $= 1.435555$, is also shown. Note that this value is less than the value of MSE obtained for the regression model, MSE $= 1.48503$, shown in Table 13.13.   ■

FIGURE 13.16   A Graph of the Fitted First-Order Autoregressive Model for Car Sales, $\hat{y} = \hat{\beta}_0 + \hat{\beta}_1 t + \hat{z}_t$, Where $\hat{z}_t = \hat{\phi}\hat{z}_{t-1}$

A graph of the fitted first-order autoregressive prediction equation is shown in Figure 13.16. The autoregressive prediction equation is an improvement over the simple linear regression prediction equation. It adjusts for some of the cyclicality introduced by periodic rises and falls in economic activity but it is not sufficient to avoid some large residuals.

The introduction of trigonometric terms into $E(y_t)$ or the use of a second-order autoregressive model should provide a better fit to the data than obtained by using the autoregressive model (call it Model 1) of Example 13.6. Noting that the distance between adjacent pairs of "high-point" and between adjacent pairs of "low-point" years, we might choose a period $b = 6$ and fit the first-order autoregressive model

$$\text{Model 2:}\quad y_t = \beta_0 + \beta_1 t + \beta_2 \cos\left(\frac{2\pi}{6}t\right) + \beta_3 \sin\left(\frac{2\pi}{6}t\right) + z_t$$

where $z_t = \phi z_{t-1} + \varepsilon_t$

to the data. Another possibility may be to use the second-order autoregressive model

$$\text{Model 3:}\quad y_t = \beta_0 + \beta_1 t + z_t$$

where
$$z_t = \phi_1 z_{t-1} + \phi_2 z_{t-2}$$

The SAS AUTOREG printouts for fitting these models to the auto sales data are shown in Tables 13.15 and 13.16. Extracting the parameter estimates from the printouts and reversing the signs of the autocorrelation estimates, we see that the

TABLE 13.15   Domestic Sales of U.S. Cars; Sine-Cosine Model with AR(1) Errors

```
ABLE = Y
```

ORDINARY LEAST SQUARES ESTIMATES

SSE	6.067169	DFE	9
MSE	0.6741299	ROOT MSE	0.8210542
SBC	37.24546	AIC	34.98566
REG RSQ	0.7496	TOTAL RSQ	0.7496
DURBIN-WATSON	1.6803		

VARIABLE	DF	B VALUE	STD ERROR	T RATIO	APPROX PROB
INTERCPT	1	9.03957995	0.503834494	17.942	0.0001
T	1	-0.20914634	0.064113558	-3.262	0.0098
COST	1	-0.62260840	0.343305339	-1.814	0.1031
SINT	1	-1.04669997	0.322802253	-3.243	0.0101

CORRELATION OF B-VALUES

	INTERCPT	T	COST	SINT
INTERCPT	1.0000	-0.8908	-0.2279	0.1931
T	-0.8908	1.0000	0.2801	-0.1720
COST	-0.2279	0.2801	1.0000	-0.1067
SINT	0.1931	-0.1720	-0.1067	1.0000

ESTIMATES OF AUTOCORRELATIONS

LAG	COVARIANCE	CORRELATION	-1 9 8 7 6 5 4 3 2 1 0 1 2 3 4 5 6 7 8 9 1
0	0.466705	1.000000	| |******************|
1	0.0145432	0.031162	| |*

PRELIMINARY MSE=   0.4662521

ESTIMATES OF THE AUTOREGRESSIVE PARAMETERS

LAG	COEFFICIENT	STD ERROR	T RATIO
1	-0.03116150	0.35338169	-0.088181

YULE-WALKER ESTIMATES

SSE	6.058686	DFE	8
MSE	0.7573358	ROOT MSE	0.8702504
SBC	39.79319	AIC	36.96844
REG RSQ	0.7413	TOTAL RSQ	0.7499

VARIABLE	DF	B VALUE	STD ERROR	T RATIO	APPROX PROB
INTERCPT	1	9.02179578	0.546651181	16.504	0.0001
T	1	-0.20699820	0.069447173	-2.981	0.0176
COST	1	-0.61315900	0.368625938	-1.663	0.1348
SINT	1	-1.04968416	0.346759685	-3.027	0.0164

(*continues*)

TABLE 13.15   (*Continued*)

```
                        CORRELATION OF B-VALUES

                  INTERCPT           T          COST         SINT

        INTERCPT   1.0000        -0.8893      -0.2205       0.1911
        T         -0.8893         1.0000       0.2735      -0.1679
        COST      -0.2205         0.2735       1.0000      -0.1060
        SINT       0.1911        -0.1679      -0.1060       1.0000
```

```
                    DOMESTIC SALES OF U.S. CARS
                SINE-COSINE MODEL WITH AR(1) ERRORS

    OBS    T   COST    SINT       Y      YHAT     RESID     LCL95     UCL95

     1     1  -0.5   -0.86603    8.8   10.0304   -1.2304   7.62477   12.4361
     2     2   0.5   -0.86603    9.7    9.1719    0.5281   6.86925   11.4746
     3     3   1.0    0.00000    7.3    7.8029   -0.5029   5.51306   10.0927
     4     4   0.5    0.86603    6.7    6.9630   -0.2630   4.66391    9.2620
     5     5  -0.5    0.86603    8.5    7.3757    1.1243   5.05565    9.6957
     6     6  -1.0    0.00000    9.2    8.4277    0.7723   6.16198   10.6935
     7     7  -0.5   -0.86603    9.2    8.8136    0.3864   6.60904   11.0181
     8     8   0.5   -0.86603    8.4    7.9811    0.4189   5.71536   10.2469
     9     9   1.0    0.00000    6.4    6.5591   -0.1591   4.23910    8.8791
    10    10   0.5    0.86603    6.2    5.7316    0.4684   3.43258    8.0307
    11    11  -0.5    0.86603    5.0    6.1568   -1.1568   3.86694    8.4466
    12    12  -1.0    0.00000    6.7    7.1154   -0.4154   4.81270    9.4181
    13    13  -0.5   -0.86603    7.6    7.5324    0.0676   5.12755    9.9373
```

TABLE 13.16   Domestic Sales of U.S. Cars; Straight-Line Model with AR(2) Errors

```
    BLE = Y

                    ORDINARY LEAST SQUARES ESTIMATES

            SSE            16.33533    DFE                 11
            MSE             1.48503    ROOT MSE      1.218618
            SBC            44.99125    AIC           43.86135
            REG RSQ         0.3258     TOTAL RSQ       0.3258
            DURBIN-WATSON   1.2550


    VARIABLE DF      B VALUE      STD ERROR    T RATIO APPROX PROB

    INTERCPT  1    9.12692308   0.716971991    12.730     0.0001
    T         1   -0.20824176   0.090329980    -2.305     0.0416


                        CORRELATION OF B-VALUES

                              INTERCPT           T

                INTERCPT       1.0000        -0.8819
                T             -0.8819         1.0000

                    ESTIMATES OF AUTOCORRELATIONS

    LAG  COVARIANCE  CORRELATION  -1 9 8 7 6 5 4 3 2 1 0 1 2 3 4 5 6 7 8 9 1
      0    1.23656    1.000000    |                   |********************|
      1    0.413964   0.329441    |                   |*******             |
      2   -0.378859  -0.301504    |             ******|                    |

                    PRELIMINARY MSE=    0.8832017
```

TABLE 13.16   (*Continued*)

```
          ESTIMATES OF THE AUTOREGRESSIVE PARAMETERS
     LAG     COEFFICIENT       STD ERROR        T RATIO
      1      -0.48096934      0.29598071      -1.625002
      2       0.45995519      0.29598071       1.554004
```

```
                 YULE-WALKER ESTIMATES

        SSE          10.58051    DFE                    9
        MSE           1.175612   ROOT MSE        1.084257
        SBC          45.06532    AIC            42.80552
        REG RSQ       0.3296     TOTAL RSQ       0.5633
```

VARIABLE	DF	B VALUE	STD ERROR	T RATIO	APPROX PROB
INTERCPT	1	8.97367041	0.713776062	12.572	0.0001
T	1	-0.19196630	0.091264344	-2.103	0.0648

```
                CORRELATION OF B-VALUES

                            INTERCPT            T

            INTERCPT         1.0000        -0.8950
            T               -0.8950         1.0000
```

OBS	T	Y	YHAT	RESID	LCL95	UCL95
1	1	8.8	8.78170	0.0183	5.52405	12.0394
2	2	9.7	8.59577	1.1042	5.56023	11.6313
3	3	7.3	8.92336	-1.6234	6.23698	11.6097
4	4	6.7	7.16714	-0.4671	4.53688	9.7974
5	5	8.5	7.79452	0.7055	5.20509	10.3839
6	6	9.2	8.74830	0.4517	6.18368	11.3129
7	7	9.2	8.06913	1.1309	5.51283	10.6254
8	8	8.4	7.55923	0.8408	4.99461	10.1238
9	9	6.4	6.98652	-0.5865	4.39709	9.5760
10	10	6.2	6.20462	-0.0046	3.57436	8.8349
11	11	5.0	6.84040	-1.8404	4.15402	9.5268
12	12	6.7	6.16730	0.5327	3.41044	8.9241
13	13	7.6	7.34896	0.2510	4.50834	10.1896

prediction equations for the two models are

$$\text{Model 2:}\quad \hat{y}_t = 9.0218 - .2070t - .6132\cos\!\left(\frac{2\pi}{6}t\right) - 1.0497\sin\!\left(\frac{2\pi}{6}t\right) + \hat{z}_t$$

where
$$\hat{z}_t = .0312\hat{z}_{t-1}$$

$$\text{Model 3:}\quad \hat{y}_t = 8.9737 - .1920t + \hat{z}_t$$

where
$$\hat{z}_t = .4810\hat{z}_{t-1} - .4600\hat{z}_{t-2}$$

Plots of the original data and graphs of the predicted values for the prediction equations of Models 2 and 3 are shown in Figures 13.17 and 13.18, respectively. Note that both of these prediction equations fit the data better than the prediction equation for Model 1. The values of MSE for both are lower than for Model 1 and therefore

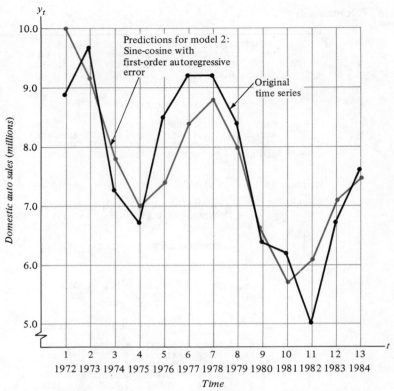

FIGURE 13.17   A Graph of the Fitted First-Order Autoregressive Model for Car Sales,
$\hat{y}_t = \hat{\beta}_0 + \hat{\beta}_1 t + \hat{\beta}_2 \cos{[(2\pi/6)t]} + \hat{\beta}_3 \sin{[(2\pi/6)t]} + \hat{z}_t$, Where $\hat{z}_t = \hat{\phi}\hat{z}_{t-1}$

confirm our visual comparisons:

$$\text{Model 2:}\quad \text{MSE} = .7573358 \qquad \text{Model 3:}\quad \text{MSE} = 1.175612$$

Once the time series prediction equation has been obtained, it can be used to forecast values of y_t to be observed in the future. The further into the future you attempt to forecast, the greater will be the possibility for error. An approximate prediction interval for the next observation in the time series, the one immediately beyond the last observed data point, is given in the following box.

APPROXIMATE PREDICTION INTERVAL FOR y_t

$$\hat{y}_t \pm 1.96\sqrt{\text{MSE}}$$

where MSE is the value of the mean square error shown in the **SAS AUTOREG** procedure printout.

We will illustrate the forecasting procedure with an example.

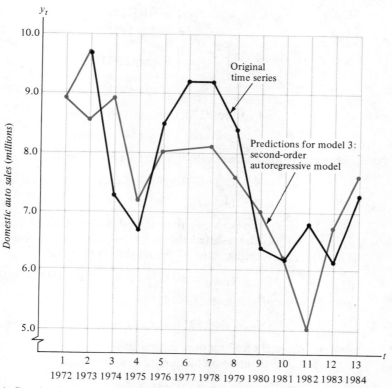

FIGURE 13.18 A Graph of the Fitted Second-Order Autoregressive Model for Car Sales, $\hat{y}t = \hat{\beta}_0 + \hat{\beta}_1 t + \hat{z}_t$, Where $\hat{z}_t = \hat{\phi}_1 \hat{z}_{t-1} + \hat{\phi}_2 \hat{z}_{t-2}$

EXAMPLE 13.7   Forecast the 1985 new domestic automobile sales, using Model 2 and the data in Table 13.1.

SOLUTION   The prediction equation for Model 2, obtained from the computer printout in Table 13.15, is

$$\hat{y}_t = 9.0218 - .2070t - .6132 \cos\left(\frac{2\pi}{6}t\right) - 1.0497 \sin\left(\frac{2\pi}{6}t\right) + \hat{z}_t$$

where

$$\hat{z}_t = \hat{\phi}\hat{z}_{t-1} = .0312\hat{z}_{t-1}$$

Substituting $t = 1985 - 1971 = 14$ into this equation yields

$$\hat{y}_{1985} = 9.0218 - .2070(14) - .6132 \cos\left[\frac{2\pi}{6}(14)\right] - 1.0497 \sin\left[\frac{2\pi}{6}(14)\right] + \hat{z}_t$$

where
$$\hat{z}_{1985} = 0.0312 \hat{z}_{1984}$$
$$\pi = 3.1415927$$
$$\left[\frac{2\pi}{6}(14) \right] = (2\pi)(2.3333)$$
$$= (2\pi)(.3333) \text{ radians, or } 120°$$

and
$$\cos(120°) = -\cos 60° = -.5$$
$$\sin(120°) = \sin 60° = .866$$

Substituting these values into the formula for $\hat{y}_t$ yields
$$\hat{y}_{1985} = 9.0218 - .2070(14) - .6132(-.500) - 1.0497(.866) + \hat{z}_{1985}$$
$$= 5.5214 + \hat{z}_{1985}$$

The next step is to calculate the estimated residual, $\hat{z}_{1985} = .0312\hat{z}_{1984}$, where $\hat{z}_{1984} = .0676$ is the residual shown in the printout in Table 13.15 for the year 1984. Therefore, the forecast value of the residual for 1985 is

$$\hat{z}_{1985} = .0312\hat{z}_{1984} = .0312(.0676) = .0021$$

and the value of y_t forecast for 1985 is

$$\hat{y}_{1985} = 5.5214 + \hat{z}_{1985} = 5.5214 + .0021 = 5.5235$$

or approximately 5.52 million automobiles.

The approximate prediction interval for $\hat{y}_{1985}$ is

$$\hat{y}_{1985} \pm 1.96\sqrt{\text{MSE}}$$
$$5.52 \pm 1.96\sqrt{.7573358}$$

or
$$5.52 \pm 1.71$$

Therefore, we forecast 1985 domestic new automobile sales to fall in the interval 3.81 to 7.23 million automobiles.   ∎

PROBLEMS IN BUSINESS FORECASTING

13.8

We are well aware that business forecasting can be a hazardous business—that is, subject to substantial error. The great disparity in the current economic forecasts by leading economists in the United States is a clear indication of this fact. Nevertheless, statistical forecasting methods are of great value when combined with experience, intuition, good judgment, and an awareness that any forecasting method will be subject to error.

One of the major problems with forecasting, unlike a regression analysis, is that we are forecasting *beyond* the range of values of the independent time variable. This subjects us to the risk that the underlying economic or political conditions, upon which the model was constructed, may change. A set of data collected during the pre-1980 inflationary economic policy period is of limited value for forecasting economic activity, interest rates, and so on, during the post-1980 deflationary policy period.

Consequently, the forecasts produced by a time series model depend on general economic and political stability.

As for the regression model, the quality of forecasts will depend on the model itself—that is, the selection of terms to be included in the model. For example, if a seasonal effect is present and you fail to account for it in the model, you will inflate the mean square error and increase your error of prediction.

Finally, note that Sections 13.6 and 13.7 present only an introduction to time series modeling. For example, we have presented only one of several models for the correlated errors z_t. A study of time series modeling and forecasting is an extensive subject. More information on this topic can be found in the references.

EXERCISES

APPLICATIONS

13.18 Table 13.17 gives data on quarterly U.S. investment (billions of dollars) on new plants and equipment for the years 1979 through 1981.

TABLE 13.17   Investment Data for Exercise 13.18

Quarter	1979	1980	1981
1	57.26	65.18	69.75
2	66.81	74.02	79.60
3	68.39	74.12	81.75
4	77.99	82.31	91.51

(a) Construct a graph of this time series. Note the upward secular trend and the distinct seasonal (quarterly) effect.

(b) Write a deterministic model for $E(y_t)$ that includes a straight-line secular component and three parameters, entered by dummy variables, to account for the four quarterly effects. (*Hint:* This model is discussed in Section 13.16.)

(c) Add the residual component to $E(y_t)$ in part (a) to form a complete first-order autoregressive model.

(d) A SAS AUTOREG computer printout for the fitted first-order autoregressive model is shown in Table 13.18. Find the prediction equation $\hat{y}_t$ for y_t.

(e) Graph the fitted time series on the graph of the original time series in part (a). Compare the fitted time series with the original.

13.19 Refer to Exercise 13.18.

(a) Use the prediction equation in Exercise 13.18 to forecast the quarterly U.S. investment for new plant and equipment for the first quarter of 1982.

(b) Find MSE on the computer printout in Table 13.18.

(c) Find an approximate 95% prediction interval for y_t in part (a).

13.20 Use the information in the computer printout of Table 13.16 for the fitted second-order autoregressive model to forecast the domestic new automobile sales for 1985.

13.21 Refer to Exercise 13.20. Find an approximate 95% prediction interval for the domestic new automobile sales for 1985.

TABLE 13.18   SAS PROC AUTOREG Printout for Exercises 13.18 and 13.19

```
DEPENDENT VARIABLE = DOLLARS


                    ORDINARY LEAST SQUARES ESTIMATES

           SSE        7.232867    DFE                 7
           MSE        1.033267    ROOT MSE    1.016497
           SBC        40.4038     AIC         37.97927
           REG RSQ    0.9923      TOTAL RSQ    0.9923
           DURBIN-WATSON  0.7182


       VARIABLE DF      B VALUE       STD ERROR    T RATIO APPROX PROB

       INTERCPT  1    70.8966667    0.927930792    76.403     0.0001
       T         1     1.6300000    0.089846513    18.142     0.0001
       X1        1   -14.9833333    0.872637386   -17.170     0.0001
       X2        1    -7.2000000    0.849196107    -8.479     0.0001
       X3        1    -7.5533333    0.834815453    -9.048     0.0001


                        CORRELATION OF B-VALUES

                INTERCPT          T          X1         X2         X3

    INTERCPT     1.0000     -0.7746     -0.6646    -0.6010    -0.5280
    T           -0.7746      1.0000      0.3089     0.2116     0.1076
    X1          -0.6646      0.3089      1.0000     0.5301     0.5060
    X2          -0.6010      0.2116      0.5301     1.0000     0.5086
    X3          -0.5280      0.1076      0.5060     0.5086     1.0000


                    ESTIMATES OF AUTOCORRELATION

   LAG   COVARIANCE   CORRELATION  -1 9 8 7 6 5 4 3 2 1 0 1 2 3 4 5 6 7 8 9 1
    0     0.602739     1.000000   |                   |*******************|
    1     0.336715     0.558641   |                   |***********        |


            PRELIMINARY MSE=     0.4146361

           ESTIMATES OF THE AUTOREGRESSIVE PARAMETERS
           LAG    COEFFICIENT     STD ERROR      T RATIO
            1    -0.55864126    0.33860497    -1.649832


                    YULE-WALKER ESTIMATES

           SSE        4.180967    DFE                 6
           MSE        0.6968278   ROOT MSE    0.8347621
           SBC        36.68568    AIC         33.77624
           REG RSQ    0.9948      TOTAL RSQ    0.9956


       VARIABLE DF      B VALUE       STD ERROR    T RATIO APPROX PROB

       INTERCPT  1    70.2999851    1.07522711    65.382     0.0001
       T         1     1.7044627    0.12446673    13.694     0.0001
       X1        1   -14.6078164    0.59763364   -24.443     0.0001
       X2        1    -6.9717083    0.62184782   -11.211     0.0001
       X3        1    -7.4449336    0.52711165   -14.124     0.0001
```

TABLE 13.18   (*Continued*)

	CORRELATION OF B-VALUES				
	INTERCPT	T	X1	X2	X3
INTERCPT	1.0000	-0.8310	-0.4906	-0.4214	-0.3106
T	-0.8310	1.0000	0.2827	0.1868	0.1001
X1	-0.4906	0.2827	1.0000	0.6270	0.3941
X2	-0.4214	0.1868	0.6270	1.0000	0.5841
X3	-0.3106	0.1001	0.3941	0.5841	1.0000

OBS	YHAT	RESID	LCL95	UCL95	T	QUARTER	DOLLARS	X1	X2	X3
1	57.3966	-0.1333	54.1775	60.6158	1	1	57.26	1	0	0
2	66.6609	0.1491	63.8167	69.5051	2	2	66.81	0	1	0
3	68.0091	0.3809	65.2296	70.7886	3	3	68.39	0	0	1
4	77.3533	0.6367	74.6605	80.0462	4	4	77.99	0	0	0
5	64.7017	0.4783	62.1765	67.2269	5	1	65.18	1	0	0
6	74.0944	-0.0744	71.5600	76.6289	6	2	74.02	0	1	0
7	75.0460	-0.9260	72.5116	77.5805	7	3	74.12	0	0	1
8	83.5635	-1.2535	81.0383	86.0887	8	4	82.31	0	0	0
9	70.1242	-0.3742	67.4313	72.8170	9	1	69.75	1	0	0
10	79.6565	-0.0565	76.8771	82.4360	10	2	79.60	0	1	0
11	81.1724	0.5776	78.3282	84.0166	11	3	81.75	0	0	1
12	90.8350	0.6750	87.9247	93.7454	12	4	91.51	0	0	0

13.22 Table 13.19 gives the prime interest rate charged by banks on short-term business loans each month for the years 1985 and 1986.

TABLE 13.19   Interest Rate Data for Exercise 13.22

Year	Jan.	Feb.	Mar.	Apr.	May	June	July	Aug.	Sept.	Oct.	Nov.	Dec.
1985	10.61	10.50	10.50	10.50	10.31	9.78	9.50	9.50	9.50	9.50	9.50	9.50
1986	9.50	9.50	9.10	8.83	8.50	8.50	8.16	7.90	7.50	7.50	7.50	7.50

Source: Data from *Survey of Current Business* (Washington, D.C.: U.S. Department of Commerce, Bureau of Economic Analysis, Vol. 66, January 1986, and Vol. 67, January 1987).

(a) Plot the data and connect the points to form a time series.

(b) Calculate a three-point moving average for the series. Plot the moving average, and compare it with the original time series.

(c) Table 13.20 gives the SAS AUTOREG procedure printout for fitting a first-order autoregressive model to the data. Write the equation of the fitted model, and explain the significance of each component of the model.

(d) Obtain the predicted values of the prime interest rate from the computer printout and plot them on the graph in part (a). Compare the fitted time series with the observed values of the prime interest rate.

13.23 Refer to Exercise 13.22.

(a) Use the fitted first-order autoregressive model of Exercise 13.22 to forecast the prime rate for banks for January 1987.

(b) Find MSE on the computer printout in Table 13.20.

(c) Find an approximate 95% prediction interval for y in part (a).

TABLE 13.20   SAS AUTOREG Printout for Exercises 13.22 and 13.23; Straight-Line Model with AR(1) Errors

```
                        ORDINARY LEAST SQUARES ESTIMATES

                SSE            1.53263     DFE                  22
                MSE         0.06966498     ROOT MSE      0.2639412
                SBC           8.439503     AIC            6.083396
                REG RSQ         0.9379     TOTAL RSQ        0.9379
                DURBIN-WATSON   0.4391


        VARIABLE DF        B VALUE        STD ERROR     T RATIO APPROX PROB

        INTERCPT  1     10.9069928      0.111211771      98.074     0.0001
        T         1     -0.1419261      0.007783203     -18.235     0.0001


                          CORRELATION OF B-VALUES

                                 INTERCPT              T

                   INTERCPT       1.0000          -0.8748
                   T             -0.8748           1.0000

                     ESTIMATES OF AUTOCORRELATIONS

    LAG  COVARIANCE  CORRELATION  -1 9 8 7 6 5 4 3 2 1 0 1 2 3 4 5 6 7 8 9 1
     0    0.0638596    1.000000   |                    |********************|
     1    0.0493376    0.772595   |                    |***************     |


               PRELIMINARY MSE=     0.0257416

           ESTIMATES OF THE AUTOREGRESSIVE PARAMETERS
              LAG   COEFFICIENT     STD ERROR      T RATIO
               1    -0.77259497    0.13854537     -5.576436


                       YULE-WALKER ESTIMATES

                SSE           0.601475     DFE                  21
                MSE         0.02864157     ROOT MSE      0.1692382
                SBC          -9.92247      AIC           -13.4566
                REG RSQ         0.7977     TOTAL RSQ        0.9756


        VARIABLE DF        B VALUE        STD ERROR     T RATIO APPROX PROB

        INTERCPT  1     10.8462543      0.232724204      46.606     0.0001
        T         1     -0.1384424      0.015215630      -9.099     0.0001


                          CORRELATION OF B-VALUES

                                 INTERCPT              T

                   INTERCPT       1.0000          -0.8173
                   T             -0.8173           1.0000
```

TABLE 13.20   *(Continued)*

DATA SET NO. 1
STRAIGHT-LINE MODEL WITH AR(1) ERRORS
95% PREDICTION INTERVALS

OBS	YEAR	MONTH	T	YHAT	RESID	LCL95	UCL95
1	1985	JAN	1	10.7078	-0.09781	9.98844	11.4272
2	1985	FEB	2	10.4938	0.00620	9.93519	11.0524
3	1985	MAR	3	10.3773	0.12267	9.83695	10.9177
4	1985	APR	4	10.3459	0.15415	9.82241	10.8693
5	1985	MAY	5	10.3144	-0.00467	9.80646	10.8223
6	1985	JUN	6	10.1361	-0.36609	9.64217	10.6300
7	1985	JUL	7	9.6951	-0.19513	9.21353	10.1767
8	1985	AUG	8	9.4473	0.05287	8.97623	9.9184
9	1985	SEP	9	9.4158	0.08416	8.95333	9.8784
10	1985	OCT	10	9.3844	0.11564	8.92839	9.8403
11	1985	NOV	11	9.3529	0.14712	8.90132	9.8044
12	1985	DEC	12	9.3214	0.17860	8.87206	9.7707
13	1986	JAN	13	9.2899	0.21009	8.84058	9.7392
14	1986	FEB	14	9.2584	0.24157	8.80687	9.7100
15	1986	MAR	15	9.2269	-0.12695	8.77098	9.6829
16	1986	APR	16	8.8864	-0.05643	8.42392	9.3489
17	1986	MAY	17	8.6463	-0.14634	8.17525	9.1174
18	1986	JUN	18	8.3599	0.14009	7.87830	8.8415
19	1986	JUL	19	8.3284	-0.16842	7.83450	8.8223
20	1986	AUG	20	8.0343	-0.13426	7.52635	8.5422
21	1986	SEP	21	7.8019	-0.30190	7.27846	8.3253
22	1986	OCT	22	7.4614	0.03862	6.92099	8.0018
23	1986	NOV	23	7.4299	0.07010	6.87129	7.9885
24	1986	DEC	24	7.3984	0.10158	6.82043	7.9764

THE CONSUMER PRICE INDEX

13.9

The Consumer Price Index (CPI), introduced in the Case Study, is an extremely complicated index number, but its general interpretation is like that of any other index. It provides a general measure of the level of consumer prices relative to the level of the index in the base year 1967. In describing the Consumer Price Index and its applications, we will present a definition and brief description provided by the U.S. Department of Labor and follow it with some data to show how it has changed over the period 1967 through 1980.

According to the bureau of Labor Statistics:*

The **Consumer Price Index** is a monthly statistical measure of the average change in prices in a fixed market basket of goods and services. Effective with the January 1978 index, the Bureau of Labor Statistics began publishing CPI's for two groups of the population. One index, a new CPI for All Urban Consumers, covers 80 percent of the total noninstitutional population; and the other index, a revised CPI for Urban Wage Earners and Clerical Workers, covers about half the new index population. The All Urban Consumers index includes, in addition to wage earners and clerical workers, professional,

* U.S. Department of Labor, Bureau of Statistics, *Monthly Labor Review,* Vol. 104, No. 7, July 1981.

managerial, and technical workers, the self-employed, short-term workers, the unemployed, retirees, and others not in the labor force.

The CPI is based on prices of food, clothing, shelter, fuel, drugs, transportation fares, doctor's and dentist's fees, and other goods and services that people buy for day-to-day living. The quantity and quality of these items is kept essentially unchanged between major revisions so that only price changes will be measured. Prices are collected from over 18,000 tenants, 24,000 retail establishments, and 18,000 housing units for property taxes in 85 urban areas across the country. All taxes directly associated with the purchase and use of items are included in the index. Because the CPIs are based on the expenditures of two population groups in 1972–1973, they may not accurately reflect the experience of individual families and single persons with different buying habits.

Though the CPI is often called the "Cost-of-Living Index," it measures only price change, which is just one of several important factors affecting living costs. Area indexes do not measure differences in the level of price among cities. They only measure the average change in prices for each area since the base period.

TABLE 13.21   Consumer Price Index Data: Commodity Prices—Consumer Prices

							Consumer Price Index							Food	
						Special Group Indexes (CPI-U)									
								Commodities							
									Nondurables						
Year	All Items, Wage Earners and Clerical Workers, Revised (CPI-W)	All Items, All Urban Consumers (CPI-U)	All Items Less Shelter	All Items Less Food	All Items Less Medical Care	Total	Total	Nondurables Less Food	Durables	Commod-ities Less Food	Services	Total	Food at Home
1967 = 100													
1961	89.6	89.6	89.9	89.7	90.3	92.0	90.2	91.2	96.6	93.4	85.2	89.1	90.4
1962	90.6	90.6	90.9	90.8	91.2	92.8	90.9	91.6	97.6	94.1	86.8	89.9	91.0
1963	91.7	91.7	92.1	92.0	92.3	93.6	92.0	92.7	97.9	94.8	88.5	91.2	92.2
1964	92.9	92.9	93.2	93.2	93.5	94.6	93.0	93.5	98.8	95.6	90.2	92.4	93.2
1965	94.5	94.5	94.6	94.5	94.9	95.7	94.0	94.8	98.4	96.2	92.2	94.4	95.5
1966	97.2	97.2	97.4	96.7	97.7	98.2	98.1	97.0	98.5	97.5	95.8	99.1	100.3
1967	100.0	100.0	100.0	100.0	100.0	100.0	100.0	100.0	100.0	100.0	100.0	100.0	100.0
1968	104.2	104.2	104.1	104.4	104.1	103.7	103.9	104.1	103.1	103.7	105.2	103.6	103.2
1969	109.8	109.8	109.0	110.1	109.7	108.4	108.9	108.8	107.0	108.1	112.5	108.9	108.2
1970	116.3	116.3	114.4	116.7	116.1	113.5	114.0	113.1	111.8	112.5	121.6	114.9	113.7
1971	121.3	121.3	119.3	122.1	120.9	117.4	117.7	117.0	116.5	116.8	128.4	118.4	116.4
1972	125.3	125.3	122.9	125.8	124.9	120.9	121.7	119.8	118.9	119.4	133.3	123.5	121.6
1973	133.1	133.1	131.1	130.7	132.9	129.9	132.8	124.8	121.9	123.5	139.1	141.4	141.4
1974	147.7	147.7	146.1	143.7	147.7	145.5	151.0	140.9	130.6	136.6	152.1	161.7	162.4
1975	161.2	161.2	159.1	157.1	160.9	158.4	163.2	151.7	145.5	149.1	166.6	175.4	175.8
1976	170.5	170.5	168.3	167.5	169.7	165.2	169.2	158.3	154.3	156.6	180.4	180.8	179.5
1977	181.5	181.5	179.1	178.4	180.3	174.7	178.9	166.5	163.2	165.1	194.3	192.2	190.2
1978	195.3	195.4	191.3	191.2	194.0	187.1	192.0	174.3	173.9	174.7	210.9	211.4	210.2
1979	217.7	217.4	210.8	213.0	216.1	208.4	215.9	198.7	191.1	195.1	234.2	234.5	232.9
1980	247.0	246.8	235.5	244.0	245.5	233.9	245.0	235.2	210.4	222.0	270.3	254.6	251.5
1981	272.3	272.4	258.5	270.6	270.9	253.6	266.3	257.5	227.1	241.2	305.7	274.6	269.9
1982	288.6	289.1	273.3	288.4	286.8	263.8	273.6	261.6	241.1	250.9	333.3	285.7	279.2
1983	297.4	298.4	283.5	298.3	295.1	271.5	279.0	266.3	253.0	259.0	344.9	291.7	282.2
1984	307.6	311.1	295.1	311.3	307.3	280.7	286.6	270.8	266.5	267.0	363.0	302.9	292.6

Source: Business Statistics, 1984 (Washington, D.C.: U.S. Department of Commerce, Bureau of Economic Analysis).

TABLE 13.21   (*Continued*)

	Consumer Price Index (CPI-U)														
	Housing								Apparel and Upkeep	Transportation					Medical Care
		Shelter			Fuel and Utilities			House-hold Furnish-ings and Operation			Private				
Year	Total	Total	Rent, Residential	Homeowners' Cost (December 1982 = 100)	Total	Fuel Oil, Coal, and Bottled Gas	Gas (Piped) and Electricity			Total	Total	New Cars	Used Cars	Public	
1967 = 100, except as noted															
1961		88.5	92.9		97.1	91.0	99.4	93.7	90.4	90.6	91.3	104.5	86.9	84.6	81.4
1962		89.6	94.0		97.3	91.5	99.4	93.8	90.9	92.5	93.0	104.1	94.8	87.4	83.5
1963		90.7	95.0		98.2	93.2	99.4	94.6	91.9	93.0	93.4	103.5	96.0	88.5	85.6
1964		92.2	95.9		98.4	92.7	99.4	95.0	92.7	94.3	94.7	103.2	100.1	90.1	87.3
1965		93.8	96.9		98.3	94.6	99.4	95.3	93.7	95.9	96.3	100.9	99.4	91.9	89.5
1966		96.8	98.2		98.8	97.0	99.6	97.0	96.1	97.2	97.5	99.1	97.0	95.2	93.4
1967	100.0	100.0	100.0		100.0	100.0	100.0	100.0	100.0	100.0	100.0	100.0	100.0	100.0	100.0
1968	104.0	104.8	102.4		101.3	103.1	100.9	103.8	105.4	103.2	103.0	102.8	103.6	104.6	106.1
1969	110.4	113.3	105.7		103.6	105.6	102.8	107.7	111.5	107.2	106.5	104.4	103.1	112.7	113.4
1970	118.2	123.6	110.1		107.6	110.1	107.3	111.5	116.1	112.7	111.1	107.6	104.3	128.5	120.6
1971	123.4	128.8	115.2		115.0	117.5	114.7	115.7	119.8	118.6	116.6	112.0	110.2	137.7	128.4
1972	128.1	134.5	119.2		120.1	118.5	120.5	118.3	122.3	119.9	117.5	111.0	110.5	143.4	132.5
1973	133.7	140.7	124.3		126.9	136.0	126.4	121.6	126.8	123.8	121.5	111.1	117.6	144.8	137.7
1974	148.8	154.4	130.6		150.2	214.6	145.8	135.3	136.2	137.7	136.6	117.5	122.6	148.0	150.5
1975	164.5	169.7	137.3		167.8	235.3	169.6	151.0	142.3	150.6	149.8	127.6	146.4	158.6	168.6
1976	174.6	179.0	144.7		182.7	250.8	189.0	160.1	147.6	165.5	164.6	135.7	167.9	174.2	184.7
1977	186.5	191.1	153.5		202.2	283.4	213.4	167.5	154.2	177.2	176.6	142.9	182.8	182.4	202.4
1978	202.8	210.4	164.0		216.0	298.3	232.6	177.7	159.6	185.5	185.0	153.8	186.5	187.8	219.4
1979	227.6	239.7	176.0		239.3	403.1	257.8	190.3	166.6	212.0	212.3	166.0	201.0	200.3	239.7
1980	263.3	281.7	191.6		278.6	556.0	301.8	205.4	178.4	249.7	249.2	179.3	208.1	251.6	265.9
1981	293.5	314.7	208.2		319.2	675.9	345.9	221.3	186.9	280.0	277.5	190.2	256.9	312.0	294.5
1982	314.7	337.0	224.0		350.8	667.9	393.8	233.2	191.8	291.5	287.5	197.6	296.4	346.0	328.7
1983	323.1	344.8	236.9	102.5	370.3	628.0	428.7	238.5	196.5	298.4	293.9	202.6	329.7	362.6	357.3
1984	336.5	361.7	249.3	107.3	387.3	641.8	445.2	242.5	200.2	311.7	306.6	208.5	375.7	385.2	379.5

The Consumer Price Index for the period 1961 to 1984, as well as the Consumer Price Index for specific groups and subgroups of selected items, is reproduced in Table 13.21. Note that the annual average value of the Consumer Price Index for 1967 is 100 and that it increased from 100 to 336.5 through 1984. Thus the general level of consumer prices in 1984, as measured by the CPI, is 3.365 times the general level in 1967.

A more extensive discussion of the statistical nature of the Consumer Price Index, provided by the Bureau of Labor Statistics (*1980 Supplement to Economic Indicators,* U.S. Government Printing Office), points out that the CPI prices for the market basket of goods and services are based on a probability sample of 24,000 retail stores and other outlets in 85 urban areas. Prices of medical, dental, and other health services are also acquired. Rental data on approximately 18,000 rental units and property tax data on 18,000 housing units are likewise included. The CPI is computed for each urban area and then combined to form a national index number by weighting the area CPI values by estimates of the 1970 population of urban consumers in each area.

The preceding descriptions of the Consumer Price Index should help you to understand how well the Consumer Price Index actually measures the increase in your cost of living. The answer is, "not very well," because the proportion of goods and services that we buy varies substantially from person to person and from one area of the country to another. However, that is not the intended purpose of the CPI. Rather, it is intended to provide an objective measure of the change in consumer prices that can be legally defined and used to make adjustments in salaries for labor contracts, Social Security benefits, and benefits from the many other federal entitlement programs. The CPI accomplishes this objective. It may not be perfect; it may overweight some expenditures (e.g., the cost of new housing); but it is clearly defined for legal purposes, and it does provide a satisfactory measure of the change in the cost of living.

13.10   SUMMARY

Time series, data sets collected sequentially over time, require particular treatment because the data are likely to be correlated and, thereby, violate the assumptions on which the preceding methodologies were based. Index numbers represent a particular type of time series variable, one that shows the general level of some economic or business phenomenon in relation to the level at some prechosen point in time.

A time series can be viewed as the sum of any or all of four components: a long-term or secular trend, a cyclical component, a seasonal component, and random unexplained error. Which (if any) of the first three components are present can sometimes be deduced by graphing the original time series or using moving averages or exponential smoothing to smooth the original time series and reveal long-term trends and cyclical or seasonal components.

The ultimate objective of most time series analyses is to construct a time series model, fit it to the data, and use the resulting prediction equation to forecast future values of y_t with a known bound on the error of prediction. One of the most common methods of modeling time series is to construct a regression model to represent secular, cyclical, and seasonal components of the time series. The residuals—the deviations between the observed and predicted values of y_t—are then modeled by using a model that accounts for autocorrelation between values of y_t separated in time. One of these, the autoregressive model, was described and its use was illustrated in Sections 13.6 and 13.7.

The problem of forecasting from time series is not one that is completely solved to the satisfaction of all economists, statisticians, and business managers. If you have any doubt on this point, we direct your attention to the wide variations in the economic and business forecasts provided by nationally recognized consulting firms.

REFERENCES

Bowerman, B. L., and O'Connell, R. T. *Time Series Forecasting: United Concepts and Computer Implementation.* 2nd ed. Boston: PWS-KENT, 1987.

Box, G. E. P., and Jenkins, G. M. *Time Series Analysis, Forecasting and Control.* 2nd ed. San Fransciso: Holden-Day, 1976.

Business Statistics, 1984. Washington, D.C.: U.S. Department of Commerce, Bureau of Economic Analysis.

Doody, F. S. *Introduction to the Use of Economic Indicators.* New York: Random House, 1965.

Fuller, W. A. *Introduction to Statistical Time Series.* New York: Wiley, 1976.

Granger, C. W. J., and Newbold, P. *Forecasting Economic Time Series.* New York: Academic Press, 1977.

Handbook of Labor Statistics. Washington, D.C.: Department of Labor, Bureau of Labor Statistics, 1985.

Mendenhall, W., Reinmuth, J., Beaver, R., and Duhan, D. *Statistics for Management and Economics.* 5th ed. Boston: PWS-KENT, 1986.

Nelson, C. R. *Applied Time Series Analysis for Managerial Forecasting.* San Francisco: Holden-Day, 1973.

1980 Supplement to Economic Indicators. Washington, D.C.: Government Printing Office, 1980.

1985 CRB Commodity Year Book. Jersey City, N.J.: Commodity Research Bureau, 1985.

Survey of Current Business. Vols. 66 and 67. Washington, D.C.: Department of Commerce, Bureau of Economic Analysis, 1986 and 1987.

KEY TERMS

Time series (page 555)

Time series variable (page 555)

Index number (page 557)

Base year (page 557)

Simple index number (page 558)

Simple composite index number (page 559)

Weighted composite index number (page 561)

Laspeyres index number (page 561)

Paasche index number (page 561)

Secular or long-term trend (page 564)

Cyclical component (page 564)

Seasonal component (page 565)

Random variation (page 565)

Moving average (page 566)

Exponential smoothing (page 568)

Time series forecasting model (page 573)

Autoregressive time series model (page 578)

Autocorrelation (page 578)

Autocorrelation function (page 578)

Consumer Price Index (CPI) (page 593)

SUPPLEMENTARY EXERCISES

 13.24 Tables 13.22 and 13.23 give data on the production, sales, and price for natural gas in the United States. Construct a simple composite consumer price index for gas based on two components: (1) price to residential customers and (2) industrial sales price for the years 1973 to 1984. Use 1975 as the base year. Prices are given in Table 13.23 in dollars per thousand cubic feet.

13.25 Refer to Exercise 13.24. Use the data to construct Laspeyres price index numbers for the years 1973 to 1984. Use 1975 as the base year and use the sales (in millions of therms) to (1) residential and (2) industrial customers as weights. Sales per year are given in Table 13.22 in columns 4 and 6, respectively. Plot the index numbers on graph paper, and connect the points to form a time series.

13.26 Refer to Exercises 13.24 and 13.25. Calculate Paasche index numbers for the gas price index. Plot the index numbers on graph paper, and connect the points to form a time series.

TABLE 13.22   Gas Utility Sales, by Types and Class of Service (Millions of Therms), for Exercise 13.24

Year	Total Utility Sales	No. of Customers (Million)	Class of Service				Revenue (Million $)				
			Residential	Commercial	Industrial	Other	Total	Residential	Commercial	Industrial	Other
1973	164,799	43.7	49,936	22,808	83,708	8347	12,987	6,247	2,172	4,197	371
1974	160,003	44.3	48,648	22,934	81,532	6890	15,242	6,899	2,539	5,391	413
1975	148,629	44.6	49,910	23,868	68,371	6480	19,074	8,445	3,303	6,718	608
1976	148,135	44.9	50,142	24,266	71,070	2696	23,701	9,941	4,075	9,374	311
1977	143,409	45.7	49,463	24,094	67,107	2746	28,303	11,541	4,980	11,385	397
1978	147,480	46.0	51,070	25,000	68,410	3010	32,150	12,939	5,696	13,065	451
1979	154,400	46.7	50,830	24,860	75,550	3160	38,947	14,833	6,624	17,045	446
1980	154,190	47.4	48,190	24,444	79,555	2020	48,312	17,408	8,159	22,213	532
1981	153,380	48.0	46,010	23,600	82,220	1990	56,340	19,218	9,231	27,246	645
1982	141,830	48.5	47,700	24,710	67,940	1470	63,200	23,700	11,666	27,200	634
1983*	128,590	48.9	44,500	22,980	59,700	1400	65,837	26,173	12,659	26,315	690
1984†	130,000	49.0	40,000	21,000	58,000	1300	65,000	27,000	12,000	25,000	600
1985											

Source: American Gas Association data from *1985 CRB Commodity Year Book* (New York: Commodity Research Bureau, 1985).

*Preliminary.

†Estimate.

TABLE 13.23   Salient Statistics of Natural Gas, for Exercise 13.23

Year	In Billions of Cubic Feet										Average Value Delivered to Consumers ($ Per Thousand Cubic Feet)				
	Supply				Disposition						Well-head Price	Imports	Residential	Industrial Sales	Electric Utilities
	Marketed Production	Storage Withdrawals	Import (Consumed)	Total Supply	Consumption	Exports	Stored	Extraction Loss	Adjustments	Total Disposition					
1973	22,648	1533	1033	25,213	22,049	77	1974	917	196	25,213	.22	N.A.	1.29	.98	.35
1974	21,601	1701	959	24,260	21,223	77	1784	887	289	24,260	.30	N.A.	1.43	1.12	.49
1975	20,109	1760	953	22,821	19,538	73	2104	872	235	22,821	.45	N.A.	1.71	1.40	.77
1976	19,952	1921	963	23,030	19,946	65	1756	854	216	22,837	.58	N.A.	1.98	1.69	1.06
1977	20,025	1750	1011	22,809	19,521	56	2307	863	41	22,786	.79	N.A.	2.35	2.10	1.33
1978	19,974	2158	966	23,126	19,627	53	2278	852	287	23,097	.91	2.21	2.56	1.54	1.48
1979	20,471	2047	1253	22,964	20,241	56	2295	808	372	23,772	1.18	2.60	2.98	2.01	1.80
1980	20,180	1972	985	22,515	19,877	49	1949	777	640	23,292	1.59	4.42	3.68	2.53	2.28
1981	19,956	1930	904	22,191	19,404	59	2228	775	501	22,967	1.98	4.84	4.29	3.11	2.91
1982	18,520	2165	933	21,001	18,001	52	2472	762	475	21,762	2.46	4.94	5.17	3.73	3.49
1983*	16,822	2270	920	19,354	16,835	55	1822	790	642	20,144	2.59	4.51	6.06	4.26	3.58
1984†	18,065	2038	861	20,254	17,489	55	2249	849	462	21,104	2.63	4.21	6.06	4.10	3.62
1985															

Source: U.S. Department of Energy data from *1985 CRB Commodity Year Book* (New York: Commodity Research Bureau, 1985).

*Preliminary.

†Estimate.

 13.27 Tables 13.24 and 13.25 give the average price of mercury and the U.S. consumption of mercury for the time period 1979 through 1984.

(a) Graph the time series depicting the average price of mercury for the years 1979 through 1984. Compare it with a similar graph for total U.S. consumption. Can you explain the relationship between price and consumption?

(b) Plot the quarterly price (March, June, September, December) for the years 1979 to 1984. Smooth the time series by using a three-point moving average.

(c) Smooth the series in part (b) by using exponential smoothing with $\omega = .3$.

TABLE 13.24   Average Price of Mercury in New York (Dollars Per Flask of 76 Pounds), for Exercise 13.27

Year	Jan.	Feb.	Mar.	Apr.	May	June	July	Aug.	Sept.	Oct.	Nov.	Dec.	Average
1979	190.80	202.63	224.32	255.00	300.55	343.90	322.34	300.33	313.16	324.13	328.63	362.08	288.99
1980	383.75	399.90	420.00	406.81	398.33	389.57	397.11	397.26	402.62	407.83	404.56	376.19	396.72
1981	366.00	386.79	411.18	423.41	418.50	423.07	433.75	441.14	436.55	425.91	421.84	413.07	416.77
1982	405.00	380.92	390.76	384.32	365.88	367.50	364.29	343.30	352.55	373.21	373.75	374.29	372.98
1983	366.67	346.18	338.91	327.62	316.31	300.23	282.25	279.02	299.05	339.29	344.50	331.69	322.64
1984	317.90	295.68	300.45	324.26	328.27	325.48	314.65	302.09	317.18	329.07	327.13	320.08	316.92
1985	317.30	315.03											

Source: American Metal Market data from *1985 CRB Commodity Year Book* (New York: Commodity Research Bureau, 1985).

TABLE 13.25   Mercury Consumed in the United States (Flasks), for Exercise 13.27

Year	Batteries	Chlorine & Caustic Soda	Catalysts	Dental Equip.	Electrical Lighting*	Electrolytic Prep.	General Lab Use	Industrial & Control Instrum.	Other Instruments + Relat.	Paints	Wiring Devices & Switches	Meas. & Control Devices	Other	Grand Total
1979	25,299	12,180	1257	1422	511	12,180	410	3603	192	9979	3213	3603	556	62,205
1980	27,829	9,470	765	1779	1036	9,470	363	3049	190	8621	3062	3049	790	58,983
1981	29,441	7,323	815	1613	1043	7,323	328	5671	253	7049	2641	5671	242	59,244
1982	24,880	6,243	499	1019	826	6,224	281	3064	194	6794	2004	3064	984	48,943
1983†	23,350	8,054	484	1597	1273		280	2465		6047	2316	2465	1356	49,138
1984‡	28,393	7,116		1053	1174		127	2453		4651	2402	2453		54,282

Source: Bureau of Mines data from *1985 CRB Commodity Year Book* (New York: Commodity Research Bureau, 1985).
*Data prior to 1980 are for electrical apparatus.
†Preliminary.
‡Estimate.

13.28 The price and farm production of three categories of products, (1) eggs, (2) beef and veal, and (3) cheese, are shown in Table 13.26 for the period January 1980 through November 1981. January 1980 is taken as the base month.

(a) Find the simple price index for eggs for June 1981.

(b) Find the simple price index for beef and veal for August 1981.

(c) Find the simple price index for cheese for December 1980.

13.29 Refer to Exercise 13.28. Using January 1980 as the base month, find the simple composite price index for the three categories of products.

(a) For January 1980.   (b) For July 1980.   (c) For December 1980.

(d) For July 1981.   (e) For November 1981.

13.30 Using January 1980 as the base month and farm production as the weighting factor, find the Laspeyres index for the prices of three categories of commodities in Exercise 13.28.

(a) For January 1980.   (b) For July 1980.   (c) For December 1980.

(d) For July 1981.   (e) For November 1981.

TABLE 13.26   Farm Production and Price Data for Exercise 13.28

Eggs

Year	Month	Farm Production (Million Cases)	Price ($ per Dozen)	Year	Month	Farm Production (Million Cases)	Price ($ per Dozen)
1980	January	201.6	.599	1981	January	199.2	.714
	February	198.0	.563		February	180.0	.672
	March	198.0	.606		March	199.2	.629
	April	189.6	.568		April	190.8	.697
	May	193.2	.508		May	194.4	.622
	June	186.0	.546		June	186.0	.629
	July	190.8	.632		July	190.8	.675
	August	192.0	.659		August	192.0	.687
	September	190.8	.688		September	187.2	.707
	October	198.0	.643		October	194.4	.713
	November	193.2	.757		November	194.4	.773
	December	201.6	.773				

Beef and Veal

Year	Month	Production (Million Pounds)	Price ($ per Pound)	Year	Month	Production (Million Pounds)	Price ($ per Pound)
1980	January	1917	1.023	1981	January	1971	.998
	February	1735	1.037		February	1751	.961
	March	1683	1.032		March	1931	.943
	April	1769	.994		April	1843	.977
	May	1813	1.020		May	1791	1.033
	June	1755	1.052		June	1888	1.065
	July	1815	1.101		July	1852	1.072
	August	1804	1.120		August	1858	1.039
	September	1860	1.080		September	1926	1.030
	October	2064	1.055		October	2006	.960
	November	1733	1.014		November	1837	.946
	December	1892	1.006				

Cheese

Year	Month	Factory Production (Million Pounds)	Price ($ per Pound)	Year	Month	Factory Production (Million Pounds)	Price ($ per Pound)
1980	January	310.5	1.467	1981	January	342.8	1.640
	February	297.9	1.472		February	316.5	1.640
	March	341.1	1.508		March	365.4	1.669
	April	332.8	1.535		April	371.2	1.670
	May	360.5	1.542		May	386.9	1.678
	June	359.9	1.548		June	385.9	1.679
	July	332.7	1.555		July	347.1	1.678
	August	317.6	1.570		August	333.7	1.678
	September	317.0	1.615		September	324.5	1.678
	October	332.1	1.653		October	338.8	1.685
	November	317.2	1.641		November	326.3	1.692
	December	354.4	1.641				

13.31 Using January 1980 as the base month and farm production as the weighting factor, find the Paasche index for the prices of the three categories of commodities in Exercise 13.28.

(a) For January 1980.   (b) For July 1980.   (c) For December 1980.

(d) For July 1981.   (e) For November 1981.

13.32 Refer to the time series for the beef and veal prices in Exercise 13.28.

(a) Graph the original time series.

(b) Compute and graph the two-point moving average for the time series.

(c) Compute and graph the four-point moving average for the time series.

13.33 Refer to the time series for the cheese prices in Exercise 13.28.

(a) Graph the original time series.

(b) Compute and graph the two-point moving average for the time series.

(c) Compute and graph the four-point moving average for the time series.

13.34 Graph the average annual Consumer Price index of Table 13.21 for the years 1967 to 1984. Then smooth the time series, using two- and three-point moving averages; and compare the graphs of the moving averages with the original time series.

13.35 Refer to the year-end prices of commodities in Table 13.2.

(a) Plot the time series for commodity 1 on graph paper. Note the apparent straight-line secular trend in the plotted points.

(b) Write a model for $E(y_t)$ to represent the straight-line secular trend in the commodity prices in part (a).

(c) Modify the model in part (b) to form a complete first-order autoregressive model for y_t.

(d) A SAS AUTOREG computer printout for the fitted first-order autoregressive model is shown in Table 13.27. Find the prediction equation for y_t.

13.36 Refer to Exercise 13.35.

(a) Forecast the year-end price for commodity 1 for 1988.

(b) Find an approximate 95% prediction interval for your forecast in part (a).

TABLE 13.27   SAS AUTOREG Printout for Exercises 13.35 and 13.36

DEPENDENT VARIABLE = PRICE

ORDINARY LEAST SQUARES ESTIMATES

SSE	0.02775879	DFE	8
MSE	0.003469848	ROOT MSE	0.05890542
SBC	-25.8839	AIC	-26.4891
REG RSQ	0.9897	TOTAL RSQ	0.9897
DURBIN-WATSON	2.1796		

VARIABLE	DF	B VALUE	STD ERROR	T RATIO	APPROX PROB
INTERCPT	1	-354.048303	12.8570677	-27.537	0.0001
YEAR	1	0.180121	0.006485273	27.774	0.0001

CORRELATION OF B-VALUES

	INTERCPT	YEAR
INTERCPT	1.0000	-1.0000
YEAR	-1.0000	1.0000

(continues)

TABLE 13.27   *(Continued)*

ESTIMATES OF AUTOCORRELATIONS

LAG	COVARIANCE	CORRELATION	-1 9 8 7 6 5 4 3 2 1 0 1 2 3 4 5 6 7 8 9 1
0	0.00277588	1.000000	||*******************|
1	-.00038922	-0.140217	| ***| |

PRELIMINARY MSE= 0.002721303

ESTIMATES OF THE AUTOREGRESSIVE PARAMETERS

LAG	COEFFICIENT	STD ERROR	T RATIO
1	0.14021658	0.37423051	0.374680

YULE-WALKER ESTIMATES

SSE	0.02714604	DFE	7
MSE	0.003878006	ROOT MSE	0.06227364
SBC	-23.7847	AIC	-24.6925
REG RSQ	0.9917	TOTAL RSQ	0.9900

VARIABLE	DF	B VALUE	STD ERROR	T RATIO	APPROX PROB
INTERCPT	1	-354.237301	12.3754499	-28.624	0.0001
YEAR	1	0.180217	0.006242339	28.870	0.0001

CORRELATION OF B-VALUES

	INTERCPT	YEAR
INTERCPT	1.0000	-1.0000
YEAR	-1.0000	1.0000

OBS	YHAT	RESID	LCL95	UCL95	YEAR	PRICE
1	2.23196	-0.031956	2.06391	2.40001	1978	2.20
2	2.41665	-0.066654	2.25522	2.57809	1979	2.35
3	2.60111	0.038892	2.44377	2.75845	1980	2.64
4	2.76593	0.004068	2.61139	2.92048	1981	2.77
5	2.95319	0.056810	2.80006	3.10632	1982	3.01
6	3.12502	-0.025024	2.97190	3.27815	1983	3.10
7	3.31789	0.102109	3.16335	3.47244	1984	3.42
8	3.47851	0.021491	3.32117	3.63585	1985	3.50
9	3.67278	-0.052778	3.51134	3.83422	1986	3.62
10	3.86144	-0.051438	3.69469	4.02819	1987	3.81

13.37 Exercise 13.22 gives data on the prime interest rate charged by banks on short-term business loans each month for the years 1985 and 1986. Shown in Table 13.28 is the SAS AUTOREG computer printout for fitting a second-order autoregressive model to the prime interest rate data.

(a) Write the equation of the fitted second-order autoregressive model.

(b) Plot the predicted values of the prime interest rate (given on the printout), and connect the points with line segments. Repeat this process for the observed values of *y* (given in Exercise 13.22). Compare the fitted time series with the observed time series.

(c) Does the second-order autoregressive model provide much of an improvement over the first-order autoregressive model of Exercise 13.22? Explain.

TABLE 13.28   SAS AUTOREG Printout for Exercise 13.37; Straight-Line Model with AR(2) Errors

```
                    ORDINARY LEAST SQUARES ESTIMATES

          SSE           1.53263     DFE                    22
          MSE           0.06966498  ROOT MSE         0.2639412
          SBC           8.439503    AIC              6.083396
          REG RSQ       0.9379      TOTAL RSQ        0.9379
          DURBIN-WATSON 0.4391
```

```
VARIABLE DF        B VALUE      STD ERROR    T RATIO APPROX PROB

INTERCPT  1      10.9069928     0.111211771   98.074    0.0001
T         1      -0.1419261     0.007783203  -18.235    0.0001
```

```
                   CORRELATION OF B-VALUES

                         INTERCPT            T

           INTERCPT       1.0000        -0.8748
           T             -0.8748         1.0000
```

```
                ESTIMATES OF AUTOCORRELATIONS

LAG  COVARIANCE  CORRELATION  -1 9 8 7 6 5 4 3 2 1 0 1 2 3 4 5 6 7 8 9 1
 0   0.0638596   1.000000     |                    |********************|
 1   0.0493376   0.772595     |                    |***************     |
 2   0.0260766   0.408343     |                    |********            |
```

```
            PRELIMINARY MSE=    0.0201089
```

```
        ESTIMATES OF THE AUTOREGRESSIVE PARAMETERS
        LAG     COEFFICIENT      STD ERROR       T RATIO
         1     -1.13399854      0.19763386     -5.737875
         2      0.46777882      0.19763388      2.366896
```

```
                   YULE-WALKER ESTIMATES

          SSE        0.4575571    DFE                    20
          MSE        0.02287786   ROOT MSE         0.1512543
          SBC        -12.814      AIC              -17.5263
          REG RSQ     0.8622      TOTAL RSQ        0.9815
```

```
VARIABLE DF        B VALUE      STD ERROR    T RATIO APPROX PROB

INTERCPT  1      10.8702959     0.179480819   60.565    0.0001
T         1      -0.1387950     0.812400275  -11.185    0.0001
```

```
                   CORRELATION OF B-VALUES

                         INTERCPT            T

           INTERCPT       1.0000        -0.8642
           T             -0.8642         1.0000
```

(continues)

TABLE 13.28   (*Continued*)

```
                          DATA SET NO. 1
                 STRAIGHT-LINE MODEL WITH AR(2) ERRORS
                      95% PREDICTION INTERVALS

  OBS   YEAR   MONTH   T    YHAT     RESID      LCL95    UCL95

    1   1985   JAN     1   10.7315  -0.12150   10.0680  11.3950
    2   1985   FEB     2   10.4988   0.00117   10.0122  10.9854
    3   1985   MAR     3   10.4056   0.09438    9.9635  10.8478
    4   1985   APR     4   10.4107   0.08925    9.9825  10.8390
    5   1985   MAY     5   10.3644  -0.06442    9.9488  10.7800
    6   1985   JUN     6   10.1026  -0.32263    9.6985  10.5068
    7   1985   JUL     7    9.5442  -0.04416    9.1501   9.9382
    8   1985   AUG     8    9.4282   0.07176    9.0428   9.8137
    9   1985   SEP     9    9.5129  -0.01289    9.1344   9.8913
   10   1985   OCT    10    9.4666   0.03344    9.0935   9.8397
   11   1985   NOV    11    9.4202   0.07976    9.0507   9.7897
   12   1985   DEC    12    9.3739   0.12609    9.0062   9.7416
   13   1986   JAN    13    9.3276   0.17242    8.9599   9.6953
   14   1986   FEB    14    9.2813   0.21874    8.9118   9.6508
   15   1986   MAR    15    9.2349  -0.13493    8.8618   9.6080
   16   1986   APR    16    8.7350   0.09500    8.3565   9.1135
   17   1986   MAY    17    8.5696  -0.06961    8.1841   8.9551
   18   1986   JUN    18    8.2754   0.22464    7.8813   8.6694
   19   1986   JUL    19    8.3834  -0.22340    7.9793   8.7875
   20   1986   AUG    20    7.9515  -0.05152    7.5359   8.3671
   21   1986   SEP    21    7.7694  -0.26939    7.3411   8.1977
   22   1986   OCT    22    7.3911   0.10891    6.9489   7.8332
   23   1986   NOV    23    7.5319  -0.03187    7.0748   7.9889
   24   1986   DEC    24    7.4855   0.01445    7.0126   7.9584
```

13.38 The data in Table 13.29 give the inventory-to-sales ratio for durable goods industries for the years 1972 to 1984. Time is coded as t = year − 1971.

TABLE 13.29   Durable Goods Data for Exercise 13.38

Statistic	Year												
	1972	1973	1974	1975	1976	1977	1978	1979	1980	1981	1982	1983	1984
Time t	1	2	3	4	5	6	7	8	9	10	11	12	13
Ratio of inventory to sales	1.67	1.58	1.65	1.84	1.69	1.61	1.57	1.57	1.66	1.64	1.73	1.52	1.45

Source: Data from *Business Statistics, 1984* (Washington, D.C.: U.S. Department of Commerce, Bureau of Economic Analysis).

(a) Plot the data points.

(b) The SAS AUTOREG computer printout for fitting a first-order autoregressive model to the data is shown in Table 13.30. Give the first-order autoregressive prediction equation.

TABLE 13.30 SAS AUTOREG Printout for Exercise 13.38; Straight-Line Model with AR(1) Errors

```
                    ORDINARY LEAST SQUARES ESTIMATES

          SSE           0.09331429    DFE                    11
          MSE           0.008483117   ROOT MSE      0.09210384
          SBC           -22.1552      AIC            -23.2851
          REG RSQ        0.1906       TOTAL RSQ       0.1906
          DURBIN-WATSON  1.5197


      VARIABLE DF        B VALUE       STD ERROR    T RATIO APPROX PROB

      INTERCPT  1        1.70615385    0.054159146   31.485    0.0001
      T         1       -0.01098901    0.006827191   -1.610    0.1358


                      CORRELATION OF B-VALUES

                            INTERCPT              T

          INTERCPT          1.0000          -0.8819
          T                -0.8819           1.0000


                  ESTIMATES OF AUTOCORRELATIONS

  LAG  COVARIANCE   CORRELATION  -1 9 8 7 6 5 4 3 2 1 0 1 2 3 4 5 6 7 8 9 1
   0   0.00717802   1.000000    |                    |********************|
   1   0.00120559   0.167955    |                    |***                 |


                  PRELIMINARY MSE=  0.006975538

          ESTIMATES OF THE AUTOREGRESSIVE PARAMETERS
          LAG    COEFFICIENT      STD ERROR        T RATIO
           1     -0.16795512      0.31173564      -0.538774


                     YULE-WALKER ESTIMATES

          SSE           0.09020471    DFE                    10
          MSE           0.009020471   ROOT MSE      0.09487616
          SBC           -20.0022      AIC            -21.6971
          REG RSQ        0.1716       TOTAL RSQ       0.2176


      VARIABLE DF        B VALUE       STD ERROR    T RATIO APPROX PROB

      INTERCPT  1        1.70856538    0.064600829   26.448    0.0001
      T         1       -0.01163140    0.008082695   -1.439    0.1807


                      CORRELATION OF B-VALUES

                            INTERCPT              T

          INTERCPT          1.0000          -0.8758
          T                -0.8758           1.0000
```

(*continues*)

TABLE 13.30   *(Continued)*

			DATA SET NO. 2 STRAIGHT-LINE MODEL WITH AR(1) ERRORS 95% PREDICTION INTERVALS			
OBS	YEAR	T	YHAT	RESID	LCL95	UCL95
1	1972	1	1.69693	−0.02693	1.44676	1.94710
2	1973	2	1.68078	−0.10078	1.44063	1.92102
3	1974	3	1.65599	−0.06599	1.42189	1.89008
4	1975	4	1.65806	0.18194	1.42887	1.88725
5	1976	5	1.68030	0.00970	1.45467	1.90592
6	1977	6	1.64543	−0.08543	1.42197	1.86888
7	1978	7	1.62231	−0.05231	1.39958	1.84504
8	1979	8	1.60592	−0.03592	1.38246	1.82937
9	1980	9	1.59624	0.06376	1.37061	1.82186
10	1981	10	1.60168	0.08632	1.37249	1.83087
11	1982	11	1.58864	0.14136	1.35455	1.82273
12	1983	12	1.59408	−0.07408	1.35383	1.83432
13	1984	13	1.54913	−0.09918	1.30157	1.79669

(c) Graph the fitted time series on your data plot for part (a) to see how well the fitted time series agrees with the data.

(d) Find MSE.

(e) Find an approximate 95% prediction interval for the inventory-to-sales ratio for 1985.

 13.39 Exercise 13.38 gave data on the inventory-to-sales ratio for durable goods industries from 1972 to 1984. The data shown in Table 13.31 give the corresponding ratio of inventory to sales for nondurable goods. Time is coded as $t = $ year $- 1971$.

TABLE 13.31   Nondurable Goods Data for Exercise 13.39

Statistic	Year

Statistic	1972	1973	1974	1975	1976	1977	1978	1979	1980	1981	1982	1983	1984
Time t	1	2	3	4	5	6	7	8	9	10	11	12	13
Ratio of inventory to sales	1.28	1.22	1.22	1.29	1.25	1.21	1.18	1.12	1.13	1.12	1.13	1.03	1.03

Source: Data from *Business Statistics, 1984* (Washington, D.C.: U.S. Department of Commerce, Bureau of Economic Analysis).

(a) Plot the data points.

(b) The SAS AUTOREG computer printout for fitting a first-order autoregressive model to the data is shown in Table 13.32. Time is coded as $t = $ year $- 1971$. Give the first-order autoregressive prediction equation.

(c) Graph the fitted time series on your data plot for part (a) to see how well the fitted model agrees with the data.

(d) Find an approximate 95% prediction interval for the inventory-to-sales ratio for 1985.

TABLE 13.32 SAS AUTOREG Printout for Exercise 13.39; Straight-Line Model with AR(1) Errors

```
                        ORDINARY LEAST SQUARES ESTIMATES

                SSE        0.01379945   DFE                     11
                MSE        0.001254496  ROOT MSE        0.03541886
                SBC        -47.0027     AIC             -48.1326
                REG RSQ      0.8414      TOTAL RSQ       0.8414
                DURBIN-WATSON  1.5435
```

VARIABLE	DF	B VALUE	STD ERROR	T RATIO	APPROX PROB
INTERCPT	1	1.31038462	0.020838629	62.882	0.0001
T	1	-0.02005495	0.002826420	-7.639	0.0001

```
                        CORRELATION OF B-VALUES

                              INTERCPT              T

                INTERCPT       1.0000          -0.8819
                T             -0.8819           1.0000
```

```
                      ESTIMATES OF AUTOCORRELATIONS

LAG  COVARIANCE  CORRELATION  -1 9 8 7 6 5 4 3 2 1 0 1 2 3 4 5 6 7 8 9 1
 0   0.0010615   1.000000     |                    |*******************|
 1   .000223321  0.210388     |                    |****               |
```

```
                      PRELIMINARY MSE=  0.001014513

                 ESTIMATES OF THE AUTOREGRESSIVE PARAMETERS
                 LAG    COEFFICIENT     STD ERROR     T RATIO
                  1     -0.21036301    0.30915029    -0.680520
```

```
                        YULE-WALKER ESTIMATES

                SSE        0.01316289   DFE                     10
                MSE        0.001316289  ROOT MSE        0.03628069
                SBC        -45.0064     AIC             -46.7013
                REG RSQ      0.7978      TOTAL RSQ       0.8487
```

VARIANCE	DF	B VALUE	STD ERROR	T RATIO	APPROX PROB
INTERCPT	1	1.31041077	0.025591337	51.008	0.0001
T	1	-0.02014306	0.003207273	-6.230	0.0001

```
                        CORRELATION OF B-VALUES

                              INTERCPT              T

                INTERCEPT      1.0000          -0.8739
                T             -0.8739           1.0000
```

(continues)

TABLE 13.32   (*Continued*)

DATA SET NO. 3
STRAIGHT-LINE MODEL WITH AR(1) ERRORS
95% PREDICTION INTERVALS

OBS	YEAR	T	YHAT	RESID	LCL95	UCL95
1	1972	1	1.29027	−0.010288	1.19305	1.38748
2	1973	2	1.26796	−0.047965	1.17530	1.36063
3	1974	3	1.23944	−0.019436	1.14929	1.32958
4	1975	4	1.22353	0.066469	1.13539	1.31167
5	1976	5	1.22235	0.027648	1.13567	1.30903
6	1977	6	1.19803	0.011968	1.11224	1.28382
7	1978	7	1.17371	0.006289	1.08822	1.25921
8	1979	8	1.15149	−0.031494	1.06570	1.23729
9	1980	9	1.12297	0.007034	1.03629	1.20965
10	1981	10	1.10916	0.010835	1.02102	1.19731
11	1982	11	1.09116	0.038844	1.00101	1.18130
12	1983	12	1.07735	−0.047354	0.98469	1.17002
13	1984	13	1.04041	−0.010410	0.94477	1.13605

The estimation procedures and tests of hypotheses described in the preceding chapters were based on the assumption that the sample was randomly selected from the population. In this chapter we note that selecting a simple random sample from a population may not be easy to accomplish. We will emphasize the importance of the sampling procedure in evaluating the goodness of an inference, and we will introduce you to some sampling procedures that will reduce the difficulties and the costs associated with sampling.

14 SAMPLING METHODS

CASE STUDY

Sampling 58 Million Beer Cans

This case study is derived from a statistical sampling that formed a small part of the defense in a multi-million-dollar lawsuit. The decision of the jury is currently under appeal. Although court records are public information, to avoid the possibilities of additional damage, we will leave the litigants unnamed, and we will refrain from revealing some of the more sensitive details of the case.

The plaintiff in the case, a brewer, claimed that the defendant had, through negligence, damaged 58 million empty beer cans stored in the brewer's canning plant. Whether or not the damage occurred, who was responsible, and the extent of the damage are some of the uncertain aspects of the case, upon which a just settlement must be based. Naturally, the defendants claimed that it had never happened, and if it did, only a small portion of the cans were damaged and unusable. At that juncture they sought a statistician to instruct them how to select a random sample of cans from among the 58 million empty cans. The objective of the defense was to use the sample to estimate the proportion of the 58 million cans that had been damaged.

So how would you select a random sample of, say, 500* cans from among 58 million beer cans? Simple, you say! Remembering our definition of a random sample given in Section 5.1, we would select the sample of 500 cans in such a way that each distinctly different set of 500 cans would have an equal probability of being selected. But remember, a collection of 58 million beer cans is not a deck of cards or a bag full of beans. You cannot thoroughly mix them, select 500, and expect to acquire a random sample. Can you imagine the immense pile produced by 58 million beer cans?

This chapter presents some of the difficult problems encountered in selecting samples. We will explain how (in principle) to select a random sample and then explain, in Section 14.7, how we selected the 500 cans from among the 58 million cans in the warehouse. Then we will survey some other sampling procedures and explain how they can reduce the cost of purchasing sample information. Finally, we will explain the relevance of the sampling procedure to statistical inference.

THE IMPORTANCE OF THE SAMPLING PROCEDURE TO STATISTICAL INFERENCE

14.1

We explained in Chapter 3 that probability is the vehicle that enables us to use sample data to make inferences about the population from which the sample was drawn. Because the sampling method is a key element of this process, we will review the logic involved.

Suppose that a soap manufacturer wants to estimate the proportion p of consumers in a given locale who favor soap brand A. A random sample of 10 persons is selected from among the consumers, and it is observed that only one out of ten favors soap brand A. How does probability play a role in making an inference about p?

---

*This sample size may seem small, but it was large enough to achieve the desired estimate. Incidentally, the cost of the testing was approximately $600 per can.

TABLE 14.1   The Probability of Observing $x = 1$ in a Sample of $n = 10$

p	$p(1)$
1.0	0
.9	.000
.8	.000
.7	.000
.6	.002
.5	.010
.4	.040
.3	.121
.2	.268
.1	.387
.05	.315
0	0

Since the number x in a sample of $n = 10$ from among the large number of consumers is a binomial random variable, we could calculate the probability of observing only $x = 1$ consumer in the sample for different values of p. These binomial probabilities, $p(1) = C_1^{10} p q^9$, for different values of p are shown in Table 14.1.

You can see from Table 14.1 that if the population proportion p of consumers favoring brand A is .4 or larger, the probability of observing a value of x as small as 1 is very small. Since the probability of observing $x = 1$ is a maximum (from among the values of p included in Table 14.1) when the population proportion p is .1, we would be inclined to select .1 as our estimate of p. This principle—selecting, as the best estimate, the value of p that gives the highest probability for the observed sample—is the theoretical basis for many methods of statistical estimation. It is known as the **principle of maximum likelihood**.

How and why does the sampling procedure play a role in statistical inference? The answer is that we need to know how the sample is selected in order to be able to calculate the probability of observing specific sample outcomes. For example, we were able to calculate the probability of observing $x = 1$ consumer favoring soap brand A because the sample of $n = 10$ consumers was randomly selected from among a large population of consumers. If we had selected our sample of ten by choosing the first ten consumers to emerge from a supermarket, the probability of selecting consumers favoring brand A would be unknown. Numerous reasons could be given to explain why the sample of ten would not represent a random sample.

Simple random sampling —that is, choosing a sample in such a way that every sample of fixed size has an equal chance of being selected—is known as **probability sampling**. There are many other methods for choosing probability samples; most of them were devised to reduce the cost of sampling or to overcome some physical obstacle to acquiring the sample observations. Although most of the methods of inference based upon these sampling methods are beyond the scope of an introductory course, we will summarize some of the most common. This will make you aware of their availability in case you need them in the future.

How to Draw a Simple Random Sample

14.2

We defined a simple random sample in Section 5.1, but drawing one from a population is a lot easier said than done. Selecting 5 cards from a standard 52-card bridge deck in such a way that every set of 5 cards in the deck has an equal probability of inclusion in the sample is not too difficult. By thorough shuffling of the cards in the deck, we can ensure (to a reasonable degree of approximation) that the 5 cards selected from the deck represent a random sample. But if we want to select a random sample of n consumers from among all consumers in a specified region, it is a difficult task. We need to know who the consumers are, and because they cannot be shuffled, we must devise a system for drawing the sample so that every different sample of n consumers in the population will have equal probability of being selected.

The first step in selecting a sample from a population is to list the objects from which the sample is to be selected. These objects are called **sampling units**, and the list is called a **frame**. Most of the time the sampling unit is a single **element**,* but as we will note in Section 14.5, a sampling unit could be clusters of elements.

For example, suppose that we want to sample the choices of all adult household members in a community regarding the amount of a proposed sales tax. One way to do this is to treat each adult household member in the community as a sampling unit. Then the frame for the sample is a complete list of adult household members in the community. Each sampling unit is a single individual and therefore contains one element of the population.

A second and less expensive way to construct the frame and select the sample is to let each household represent a sampling unit. This will reduce the cost of sampling because you can obtain the opinions of all members in a household on a single visit. For this type of sampling the frame is a list of all households in the city. The number of elements in a sampling unit will vary from one (for single member households) to several, depending upon the number of adults in the household.

In order to be consistent with standard terminology, we will subsequently refer to the objects selected from the population as sampling units. However, you will understand that all of the methodology contained in the preceding chapters assumes that a sampling unit and element of the population are synonymous; that is, that each sampling unit contains only one element.

DEFINITION   The objects to be selected from a population are called *sampling units*.   ∎

DEFINITION   A *frame* is a complete list of all sampling units contained in a population.   ∎

The simplest and most reliable way to select a random sample of n sampling units from a large population is to employ a table of **random numbers** such as that shown in Table 15 of the Appendix. **Random number tables** are constructed so that integers occur randomly and with equal frequency. For example, suppose that the frame for a

---

*In Chapter 1 we noted that the object upon which a measurement is made is called an **experimental unit** or, alternatively, an **element of the population**.

TABLE 14.2   Portion of a Table of Random Numbers, Table 15 in the Appendix

Line	Columns													
	1	2	3	4	5	6	7	8	9	10	11	12	13	14
1	10480	15011	01536	02011	81647	91646	69179	14194	62590	36207	20969	99570	91291	90700
2	22368	46573	25595	85393	30995	89198	27982	53402	93965	34095	52666	19174	39615	99505
3	24130	48360	22527	97265	76393	64809	15179	24830	49340	32081	30680	19655	63348	58629
4	42167	93093	06243	61680	07856	16376	39440	53537	71341	57004	00849	74917	97758	16379
5	37570	39975	81837	16656	06121	91782	60468	81305	49684	60672	14110	06927	01263	54613
6	77921	06907	11008	42751	27756	53498	18602	70659	90655	15053	21916	81825	44394	42880
7	99562	72905	56420	69994	98872	31016	71194	18738	44013	48840	63213	21069	10634	12952
8	96301	91977	05463	07972	18876	20922	94595	56869	69014	60045	18425	84903	42508	32307
9	89579	14342	63661	10281	17453	18103	57740	84378	25331	12566	58678	44947	05585	56941
10	85475	36857	53342	53988	53060	59533	38867	62300	08158	17983	16439	11458	18593	64952
11	28918	69578	88231	33276	70997	79936	56865	05859	90106	31595	01547	85590	91610	78188
12	63553	40961	48235	03427	49626	69445	18663	72695	52180	20847	12234	90511	33703	90322
13	09429	93969	52636	92737	88974	33488	36320	17617	30015	08272	84115	27156	30613	74952
14	10365	61129	87529	85689	48237	52267	67689	93394	01511	26358	85104	20285	29975	89868
15	07119	97336	71048	08178	77233	13916	47564	81056	97735	85977	29372	74461	28551	90707
16	51085	12765	51821	51259	77452	16308	60756	92144	49442	53900	70960	63990	75601	40719
17	02368	21382	52404	60268	89368	19885	55322	44819	01188	65255	64835	44919	05944	55157

population contains $N = 1000$ sampling units, numbered in sequence from 0 to 999. Then turn to a table of random numbers such as the excerpt shown in Table 14.2.

Select n of the random numbers in order. The numbers of the sampling units to be included in the random sample will be given by the first three digits of the random numbers. Thus if $n = 5$, we randomly select a starting point, say the random number in line 11, column 5 of Table 14.2. Using this random number and the four that follow in column 5, we will include sampling units numbered 709, 496, 889, 482, and 772. So as not to use the same sequence of random numbers over and over again, the experimenter should select different starting points in Table 15 to begin the selection of random numbers for different samples.

EXAMPLE 14.1

A county home builders association wanted to determine the proportion of homeowners in the county who planned major renovations, repairs, or additions during the coming year. The estimate of the proportion is to be based on a random sample of $n = 600$ homes to be selected from among the 712,524 homes in the county. Explain how the 600 homeowners should be selected in order to acquire a random sample.

SOLUTION

The frame for the population is a complete numbered list of the 712,524 homes in the county. We are hoping this list will be available at the county tax office. To select the sample of 600, we will select six-digit numbers from the random number table. Six-digit numbers that exceed 712,524 will be discarded, as well as any numbers that repeat themselves.

Consulting Table 14.2, we note that the random numbers in each line and column of the random number table contain five digits. We can obtain six-digit numbers by combining pairs of these five numbers and selecting the first six digits. For example, if we were to start our sample in line 5, columns 2 and 3, we would be using the ten-digit random numbers, 3997581837, 0690711008, 7290556420, 9197705463, and so on. Since we plan to use the first six digits of these numbers and include only numbers equal to 712524 or less, we will discard two of the four numbers shown above (because they exceed 712524) and will retain only 399758 and 069071. Therefore, homes numbered 399758 and 69071 in the frame will be included in the sample. We will continue selecting ten-digit random numbers, retaining numbers equal to 712524 or less, until we have acquired the numbers of the remaining 598 homes needed for the sample. ■

EXERCISES

BASIC TECHNIQUES

14.1 Explain how you can use a 52-card deck of bridge cards to draw a random of $n = 5$ from a population containing $N = 50$ sampling units.

14.2 Use the random number table, Table 15 in the Appendix, to draw a random sample of $n = 3$ sampling units from a population containing $N = 22$ sampling units. Explain precisely how you arrived at the sampling units to be included in your sample.

14.3 Use the random number table, Table 15 in the Appendix, to draw a random sample of $n = 12$ sampling units from a population containing $N = 12,500$ sampling units. Explain precisely how you arrived at the sampling units to be included in your sample.

14.4 Use the random number table, Table 15 in the Appendix, to draw a random sample of $n = 7$ sampling units from a population containing $N = 825$ sampling units. Explain precisely how you arrived at the sampling units to be included in your sample.

APPLICATIONS

 14.5 Suppose that a telephone company wishes to select a random sample of $n = 20$ (we select this small number to simplify this exercise) out of 7000 customers for a survey of customer attitudes concerning service. If the customers are numbered for identification purposes, indicate the customers you will include in your sample. Use the random number table, and explain how you selected your sample.

 14.6 A small city contains 20,000 voters. Use the random number table to identify the voters to be included in a random sample of $n = 15$.

 14.7 If a survey of a newspaper's readership is obtained by requesting readers to respond to a questionnaire published in the newspaper, are the resulting responses likely to give a random sample of readership opinion? Explain.

 14.8 A random sample of consumer preference for a new product was obtained by selecting and questioning every tenth person to pass by the busiest corner in a large city. Will this sample have the characteristics of a random sample selected from the consumers in the city? Explain.

14.9 Suppose that you decide to conduct a telephone public opinion survey, randomly sampling numbers from the telephone directory. The survey is conducted from 9 A.M. to 5 P.M. Will the resulting responses represent a random sample of adult public opinion in the community? Explain.

 14.10 "Do workers in restaurants run by the House of Representatives in Washington want to join a union?" An article in the *New York Times* (July 6, 1987) describes a survey conducted by George M. White, the architect of the Capitol, which purports to answer this question.

Questionnaires were sent to 235 eligible employees. Among several questions asked was the question "Do you believe your best interests would be served by becoming a member of a union?" Only 125 returned the questionnaire. "On the union question . . . there were 31 yeses, 68 noes, and 13 don't knows. Thirteen left the answer blank." William Raines, Mr. White's administrative assistant, noted that a majority had voted no on joining a union and stated that "the issue was 'closed'." Representative William L. Clay, Democrat of Missouri, said the poll was "a total farce." Do you think that the results of Mr. White's survey imply that the majority of the 235 eligible employees of the House of Representatives restaurant are opposed to joining a union? Explain.

14.3   ESTIMATION BASED ON SIMPLE RANDOM SAMPLING

Most sample surveys have one of three objectives, estimate a population mean μ, a population proportion p, or a population total τ. The total τ is defined to be the total of all x values in the population. If the population contains N values of x, x_1, x_2, $x_3, \ldots, x_N$, then

$$\tau = \sum_{i=1}^{N} x_i = N\mu$$

For example, a survey conducted to investigate the nature of household expenditures on food in a one-county area will be interested in the mean weekly expenditure μ on food by a single household in the county. It also may be interested in the total τ of the money spent on food by all households in the county during the given week.

In Chapter 6 we presented confidence intervals for a population mean μ and proportion p based on independent random sampling. These confidence intervals assumed that the sample size n is large and that the number N of elements in the population is large relative to n.

This latter assumption is often violated in survey sampling. For example, a survey of the opinions of the chief executives of *Fortune* 500 companies will involve sampling the opinions of 500 chief executives. If you sampled $n = 100$ of the $N = 500$, your sample will contain 20% of all elements in the population.

When the sample size n is large relative to the number N of elements in the population, the standard error of an estimator must be modified by a **finite population correction factor**,

$$\sqrt{\frac{N - n}{N}}$$

For example, if you use the sample mean $\bar{x}$ to estimate μ, the standard error of $\bar{x}$, $\sigma_{\bar{x}} = \sigma/\sqrt{n}$, should be multiplied by the finite population correction factor to obtain

$$\sigma_{\bar{x}} = \frac{\sigma}{\sqrt{n}} \sqrt{\frac{N - n}{N}}$$

When the sample size n is small relative to n, say less than .05, the finite population correction factor will be close to 1 and can be ignored. For example, if $n/N = .05$,

$$\sigma_{\bar{x}} = \frac{\sigma}{\sqrt{n}} \sqrt{\frac{N-n}{N}} = \frac{\sigma}{\sqrt{n}} \sqrt{1 - \frac{n}{N}} = \frac{\sigma}{\sqrt{n}} \sqrt{1 - .05}$$

$$= \frac{\sigma}{\sqrt{n}} \sqrt{.95} = \frac{\sigma}{\sqrt{n}} (.97)$$

Since .97 is close to 1, the standard error of $\bar{x}$ reduces to

$$\sigma_{\bar{x}} \approx \frac{\sigma}{\sqrt{n}}$$

the standard error for $\bar{x}$ given in Chapter 6.

The boxes that follow give approximate confidence intervals for a population mean μ, total τ, and proportion p for sampling from finite populations—that is, populations containing a finite number of elements.

APPROXIMATE 95% CONFIDENCE INTERVAL FOR A POPULATION MEAN μ: INDEPENDENT RANDOM SAMPLING FROM A FINITE POPULATION

$$\bar{x} \pm 1.96 \frac{s}{\sqrt{n}} \sqrt{\frac{N-n}{N}}$$

where
$$\bar{x} = \frac{\sum\limits_{i=1}^{n} x_i}{n} \qquad s = \sqrt{\frac{\sum\limits_{i=1}^{n} (x_i - \bar{x})^2}{n-1}}$$

N = number of sampling units in the population

n = number of sampling units in the sample

Note: For simple random sampling a sampling unit contains only one element.

APPROXIMATE 95% CONFIDENCE INTERVAL FOR A POPULATION TOTAL τ: INDEPENDENT RANDOM SAMPLING FROM A FINITE POPULATION

$$\hat{\tau} \pm 1.96 \frac{Ns}{\sqrt{n}} \sqrt{\frac{N-n}{N}}$$

where
$$\hat{\tau} = N\bar{x} \qquad s = \sqrt{\frac{\sum\limits_{i=1}^{n} (x_i - \bar{x})^2}{n-1}}$$

N = number of sampling units in the population

n = number of sampling units in the sample

Note: For simple random sampling a sampling unit contains only one element

**APPROXIMATE 95% CONFIDENCE INTERVAL FOR
A POPULATION PROPORTION p: INDEPENDENT
RANDOM SAMPLING FROM A FINITE POPULATION**

$$\hat{p} \pm 1.96 \sqrt{\frac{\hat{p}\hat{q}}{n-1}} \sqrt{\frac{N-n}{N}}$$

where $\hat{p} = \dfrac{x}{n}$ $\hat{q} = 1 - \hat{p}$

N = number of sampling units in the population

n = number of sampling units in the sample

Note: For simple random sampling a sampling unit contains one element.

EXAMPLE 14.2

The manager of an auto rental company wants to estimate the total number of miles put on its cars per month. A random sample of $n = 30$ cars was selected from the company's fleet of 280 cars, and the mileage was recorded for each car at the beginning and end of a particular month. The mean and standard deviation for the sample were $\bar{x} = 1342$ and $s = 227$. Find an approximate 95% confidence interval for the total mileage registered for the fleet during the month.

SOLUTION

For this example $N = 280$, $n = 30$, $\bar{x} = 1342$, and $s = 227$. Then

$$\hat{\tau} = N\bar{x} = (280)(1342) = 375{,}760$$

and the approximate 95% confidence interval for τ is

$$\hat{\tau} \pm 1.96 \frac{Ns}{\sqrt{n}} \sqrt{\frac{N-n}{N}}$$

$$375{,}760 \pm (1.96) \frac{(280)(227)}{\sqrt{30}} \sqrt{\frac{280-30}{280}}$$

or $375{,}760 \pm 21{,}491.7$

Therefore, we estimate the fleet mileage to be as low as 352,268.3 miles or as high as 397,251.7 miles per month. If the manager wants a smaller confidence interval for the estimate, a larger sample size must be used. ■

EXERCISES

BASIC TECHNIQUES

14.11 A random sample of $n = 50$ was selected from a population, and the sample mean and variance were $\bar{x} = 84.1$ and $s^2 = 122.44$.

(a) Calculate a 95% confidence interval for μ, assuming the number N of elements in the population to be very large.

(b) Calculate a 95% confidence interval for μ, assuming the number N of elements in the population to be equal to 100.

(c) Compare the two confidence intervals in parts (a) and (b), and note the effect of the finite population correction factor on the width of the interval in part (b).

14.12   Use the data in Exercise 14.1 to calculate an approximate 95% confidence interval for the population total τ if $N = 100$.

14.13   A random sample of $n = 100$ observations, each observation a success or failure, was selected from a population containing $N = 400$ elements. Find an approximate 95% confidence interval for the proportion p of successes in the population if the number of successes in the sample is 34.

14.14   Calculate the finite population correction factor for n/N equal to .001, .1, .3, .5, .7. Then graph the finite population correction factor as a function of n/N. Note how the correction factor decreases in value as n/N increases. What are the practical implications of this result?

APPLICATIONS

14.15   A dealer in floor coverings has the opportunity to buy the inventory of another dealer who is going out of business. The dealer randomly sampled 50 of 421 different whole or partial rolls of carpet offered for sale and estimated the value of each. The mean and standard deviation of the 50 estimates were $\bar{x} = \$1248$ and $s = \$175$. Find an approximate 95% confidence interval for the mean estimated value per roll for the 421 rolls.

14.16   Refer to Exercise 14.15. Find an approximate 95% confidence interval for the total estimated value of the 421 rolls.

14.17   An auto dealership in a small town wanted to acquire information on the market for new cars during the coming year. The dealer obtained a list of the 8746 persons in the town who were 18 or older and randomly sampled 500. The number of persons in the sample who planned to buy a new car during the coming year was 29. Find an approximate 95% confidence interval for the proportion of all persons, 18 or older, in the town who plan to buy a new car during the coming year.

14.18   A bank conducted a survey to investigate the potential market for home renovation loans among its customers. The bank randomly sampled 1000 from among its 9706 customers and asked each whether or not he or she planned home renovation (or addition) in the near future, whether the customer would seek a bank loan for the renovation, and what the approximate amount of money that they might want to borrow would be. Of the 1000 customers sampled, 46 indicated that they planned to borrow money for home renovation. The mean and standard deviation for the projected borrowings were $\bar{x} = \$6751$ and $s = \$1463$. Find an approximate 95% confidence interval for the mean value of a home loan for the bank's customers who wish to borrow money.

14.19   Refer to Exercise 14.18. Find an approximate 95% confidence interval for the proportion of the bank's 9706 customers who will seek a home renovation loan.

14.4   STRATIFIED RANDOM SAMPLING

Simple random sampling is not the only way to acquire a probability sample. Difficulties in constructing the frame and in contacting the elements of the population (particularly when the elements are people, households, etc.) suggest other methods of sampling that are easier to conduct and are less costly. Methods for selecting a sample are called **sampling designs**, and the sample obtained is often called a **sample survey**.

One method for reducing the cost of public opinion or consumer polls is to split the geographic region in which the elements (people) of the population reside into segments called **strata**. Samples are selected from within each stratum, and then this information is combined to make an inference about the entire population.

For example, suppose that you want to sample the opinions of homeowners in a state. Rather than selecting a simple random sample from among all homeowners in the state, it would be easier to sample each individual county separately and then combine the information in the county samples to make inferences about the state. Thus we can split the state into strata, one stratum corresponding to each county in the state. Frames for each county can easily be obtained from the county courthouses, and the costs of contacting people within the smaller county areas will be less than the costs encountered in nonstratified sampling.

Stratified random sampling has another advantage. You not only can combine the information in the strata samples to make inferences about the complete population, but you can also use the sample information about the characteristics of each stratum. For example, this would enable you to compare homeowners' opinions in one county with those of another.

The formulas for approximate 95% confidence intervals for a population mean μ, a population total τ, and a population proportion p, based on stratified random sampling, are given in the boxes. We will illustrate the estimation procedures with examples.

AN APPROXIMATE 95% CONFIDENCE INTERVAL FOR μ: STRATIFIED RANDOM SAMPLING

Notation

μ = mean of the population

N_i = number of elements in stratum i, $i = 1, 2, 3, \ldots, L$

N = total number of elements in the population
  = $N_1 + N_2 + N_3 + \cdots + N_L$

n_i = number of elements in the sample selected from stratum i, $i = 1, 2, 3, \ldots, L$

$\bar{x}_i$ = mean of the sample selected from stratum i, $i = 1, 2, 3, \ldots, L$

s_i^2 = variance of the sample measurements from stratum i, $i = 1, 2, 3, \ldots, L$

Approximate 95% Confidence Interval for μ

$$\bar{x}_{st} \pm 1.96 \sqrt{\frac{1}{N^2} \sum_{i=1}^{L} N_i^2 \left(\frac{N_i - n_i}{N_i}\right) \frac{s_i^2}{n_i}}$$

where

$$\bar{x}_{st} = \frac{1}{N}(N_1 \bar{x}_1 + N_2 \bar{x}_2 + \cdots + N_L \bar{x}_L) = \frac{1}{N} \sum_{i=1}^{L} N_i \bar{x}_i$$

is the estimate of the population mean μ based on the stratified random sample. When the sample size n_i is small relative to the stratum size N_i, $i = 1, 2, \ldots, L$, this formula reduces to approximately

$$\bar{x}_{st} \pm 1.96 \sqrt{\frac{1}{N^2} \sum_{i=1}^{L} N_i^2 \frac{s_i^2}{n_i}}$$

AN APPROXIMATE 95% CONFIDENCE INTERVAL FOR THE POPULATION TOTAL τ: STRATIFIED RANDOM SAMPLING

Notation

μ = mean of the population

N_i = number of elements in stratum i, $i = 1, 2, 3, \ldots, L$

N = total number of elements in the population
   = $N_1 + N_2 + N_3 + \cdots + N_L$

n_i = number of elements in the sample selected from stratum i, $i = 1, 2, 3, \ldots, L$

$\bar{x}_i$ = mean of the sample selected from stratum i, $i = 1, 2, 3, \ldots, L$

s_i^2 = variance of the sample measurements from stratum i, $i = 1, 2, 3, \ldots, L$

Approximate 95% Confidence Interval for τ

$$\hat{\tau} \pm 1.96 \sqrt{\sum_{i=1}^{L} N_i^2 \left(\frac{N_i - n_i}{N_i}\right) \frac{s_i^2}{n_i}}$$

where $\hat{\tau} = N\bar{x}_{st}$

$$\bar{x}_{st} = \frac{1}{N}[N_1\bar{x}_1 + N_2\bar{x}_2 + \cdots + N_L\bar{x}_L] = \frac{1}{N} \sum_{i=1}^{L} N_i\bar{x}_i$$

When the sample size n_i is small relative to the stratum size N_i, $i = 1, 2, \ldots, L$, this formula reduces to

$$\hat{\tau} \pm 1.96 \sqrt{\frac{1}{N^2} \sum_{i=1}^{L} N_i^2 \frac{s_i^2}{n_i}}$$

APPROXIMATE 95% CONFIDENCE INTERVAL FOR A POPULATION PROPORTION p: STRATIFIED RANDOM SAMPLING

$$\hat{p}_{st} \pm 1.96 \sqrt{\frac{1}{N^2} \sum_{i=1}^{L} N_i^2 \left(\frac{N_i - n_i}{N_i}\right) \frac{\hat{p}_i\hat{q}_i}{n_i - 1}}$$

where $\hat{p}_{st} = \frac{1}{N}[N_1\hat{p}_1 + N_2\hat{p}_2 + \cdots + N_L\hat{p}_L] = \frac{1}{N} \sum_{i=1}^{L} N_i\hat{p}_i$

is the estimate of p based on the stratified random sample and $\hat{p}_i$ is the sample proportion from stratum i, $i = 1, 2, 3, \ldots, L$.

When the sample size n_i is small relative to the stratum size N_i, $i = 1, 2, \ldots, L$, this formula reduces to approximately

$$\hat{p}_{st} \pm 1.96 \sqrt{\frac{1}{N^2} \sum_{i=1}^{L} N_i^2 \frac{\hat{p}_i\hat{q}_i}{n_i - 1}}$$

EXAMPLE 14.3   A television station serving a three-county area wished to estimate the mean number of hours per day of viewing time per household in its viewing area. The station decided to randomly select a 1% sample—that is, 1% of the total number of households in each county. A summary of the data is shown in Table 14.3. Find an approximate 95% confidence interval for the mean viewing time per household within the three-county viewing area.

TABLE 14.3   TV Viewing Data for Example 14.3

County	Number of Households in Stratum i, N_i	Stratum Sample Size, n_i	Stratum Sample Mean, $\bar{x}_i$	Stratum Sample Variance, s_i^2
1	12,473	125	2.92	1.96
2	35,241	352	2.14	1.21
3	23,178	232	3.63	3.24
	$N = 70{,}892$			

SOLUTION   The stratified mean is

$$\bar{x}_{st} = \frac{1}{N}(N_1\bar{x}_1 + N_2\bar{x}_2 + N_3\bar{x}_3)$$

$$= \frac{1}{70{,}892}[(12{,}473)(2.92) + (35{,}241)(2.14) + (23{,}178)(3.63)]$$

$$= 2.76 \text{ hours per day}$$

Then the confidence interval for μ is

$$\bar{x}_{st} \pm 1.96\sqrt{\frac{1}{N^2}\sum_{i=1}^{L} N_i^2 \left(\frac{N_i - n_i}{N_i}\right)\frac{s_i^2}{n_i}}$$

For our example, the quantity $(N_i - n_i)/N_i$ is approximately equal to 1 for each stratum because the sample size is so small (1%) in relation to the number of elements in the stratum. Therefore, the formula for our confidence interval reduces to

$$\bar{x}_{st} \pm 1.96\sqrt{\frac{1}{N^2}\sum_{i=1}^{L} N_i^2 \frac{s_i^2}{n_i}}$$

$$2.76 \pm 1.96\sqrt{\frac{1}{(70{,}892)^2}\left[(12{,}473)^2\left(\frac{1.96}{125}\right) + (35{,}241)^2\left(\frac{1.21}{352}\right) + (23{,}178)^2\left(\frac{3.24}{232}\right)\right]}$$

$$2.76 \pm 1.96\sqrt{.0028}$$

or

$$2.76 \pm .10$$

Thus we estimate the mean number of viewing hours per household to be in the interval 2.66 to 2.86 hours.

EXAMPLE 14.4

A large retailer serving two small towns conducted a survey to determine the total amount of money that households in the area planned to spend on "big-ticket" electric appliances during the coming year. Random samples of 200 households were selected from each town. The number of households in each town along with the sample mean and variance of the planned household expenditures are shown in Table 14.4. Find an approximate 95% confidence interval for the total planned expenditures for the two towns.

TABLE 14.4   Expenditures Data for Example 14.4

Town	Number of Households per Town N_i	Sample Size, n_i	Sample Mean (in Dollars), $\bar{x}_i$	Sample Variance, s_i^2
1	2149	200	134	40,122
2	1872	200	168	37,104
	$N = 4021$			

SOLUTION

The confidence interval for τ is

$$\hat{\tau} \pm 1.96 \sqrt{\sum N_i^2 \left(\frac{N_i - n_i}{N_i} \right) \frac{s_i^2}{n_i}}$$

where

$$\hat{\tau} = N\bar{x}_{st} = N\left[\frac{1}{N}(N_1\bar{x}_1 + N_2\bar{x}_2) \right]$$

$$= N_1\bar{x}_1 + N_2\bar{x}_2 = (2149)(134) + (1872)(168) = \$602,462$$

Substituting into the formula for the confidence interval yields

$$(602,462) \pm 1.96 \sqrt{(2149)^2 \left(\frac{2149 - 200}{2149} \right)\left(\frac{40,122}{200} \right) + (1872)^2 \left(\frac{1872 - 200}{1872} \right)\left(\frac{37,104}{200} \right)}$$

or

$$602,462 \pm 73,882$$

Therefore, we estimate the total expenditures on big-ticket electric appliances during the next year to be somewhere between \$528,580 and \$676,344. ∎

EXAMPLE 14.5

Refer to Example 14.3. Estimate the proportion of all households in the three-county area who prefer the television station's programs if the sample proportions preferring the station's programs are as shown in Table 14.5.

SOLUTION

$$\hat{p}_{st} = \frac{1}{70,892} [(12,473)(.21) + (35,241)(.17) + (23,178)(.34)]$$

$$= .23$$

Because the sample sizes are small relative to the strata sample sizes, $(N_i - n_i)/N_i \approx 1$

TABLE 14.5   TV Viewing Data for Example 14.5

County	Number of Households in Stratum i, N_i	Stratum Sample Size, n_i	Stratum Sample Proportion, $\hat{p}_i$
1	12,473	125	.21
2	35,241	352	.17
3	23,178	232	.34
	$N = 70{,}892$		

for $i = 1, 2, \ldots, L$, and the approximate 95% confidence interval for p is

$$\hat{p}_{\text{st}} \pm 1.96 \sqrt{\frac{1}{N^2} \sum_{i=1}^{L} N_i^2 \frac{\hat{p}_i \hat{q}_i}{n_i - 1}}$$

Substituting into this formula, we obtain

$$.23 \pm 1.96 \sqrt{\frac{1}{(70{,}892)^2} \left[(12{,}473)^2 \frac{(.21)(.79)}{124} + (35{,}241)^2 \frac{(.17)(.83)}{351} + (23{,}178)^2 \frac{(.34)(.66)}{231} \right]}$$

$$.23 \pm 1.96 \sqrt{.0002446}$$

or

$$.23 \pm .03$$

Therefore, we estimate the proportion of households who prefer the television station's programs to be in the interval .20 to .26.   ■

EXAMPLE 14.6   Refer to Example 14.4. Find a 95% confidence interval for the difference in the mean planned expenditures per household on big-ticket electric appliances between households in towns 1 and 2.

SOLUTION   The point estimator of the difference is $(\bar{x}_1 - \bar{x}_2)$, the difference in the sample means from strata 1 and 2. From Section 5.6 we know that the variance of this estimator is

$$\sigma^2_{(\bar{x}_1 - \bar{x}_2)} = \sigma^2_{\bar{x}_1} + \sigma^2_{\bar{x}_2}$$

which, for finite populations, is equal to

$$\sigma^2_{(\bar{x}_1 - \bar{x}_2)} = \frac{\sigma_1^2}{n_1} \left(\frac{N_1 - n_1}{N_1} \right) + \frac{\sigma_2^2}{n_2} \left(\frac{N_2 - n_2}{N_2} \right)$$

Then the 95% confidence interval for the difference $(\mu_1 - \mu_2)$ in strata means is

$$(\bar{x}_1 - \bar{x}_2) \pm 1.96 \sigma_{(\bar{x}_1 - \bar{x}_2)}$$

or approximately

$$(\bar{x}_1 - \bar{x}_2) \pm 1.96 \sqrt{\frac{s_1^2}{n_1} \left(\frac{N_1 - n_1}{N_1} \right) + \frac{s_2^2}{n_2} \left(\frac{N_2 - n_2}{N_2} \right)}$$

$$(134 - 168) \pm 1.96 \sqrt{\frac{40{,}122}{200} \left(\frac{2149 - 200}{2149} \right) + \frac{37{,}104}{200} \left(\frac{1872 - 200}{1872} \right)}$$

or $-\$34 \pm \$36.54$

Therefore, we estimate the difference in mean planned expenditures per household on big-ticket electric appliances between towns 1 and 2 to be between $-\$70.54$ and $\$2.54$. The expenditures per household for town 2 could exceed those for town 1 by as much as $\$70.54$ or could be less than town 1 by as much as $\$2.54$. ∎

EXERCISES

BASIC TECHNIQUES

14.20 A stratified random sample was selected from among four strata. Use the data in Table 14.6 to demonstrate the procedure for finding an approximate 95% confidence interval for the population mean μ. (*Note:* This exercise is presented for you to practice the mechanics of finding a confidence interval for μ. Because of the small sample sizes, it is unlikely that the confidence coefficient will be close to .95.)

TABLE 14.6   Stratified Random Sample Data for Exercise 14.20

	Stratum			
	1	2	3	4
Stratum size	40	30	30	50
Sample size	4	4	4	4
Sample observations	6, 8, 5, 6	7, 10, 8, 9	7, 8, 6, 6	5, 7, 6, 5

14.21 Use the data in Exercise 14.20 to find an approximate 95% confidence interval for the population total τ.

14.22 A stratified random sample was selected from among four strata. The pertinent data are shown in Table 14.7. Find an approximate 95% confidence interval for the population mean μ.

TABLE 14.7   Stratified Random Sample Data for Exercise 14.22

Stratum	Number of Sampling Units per Stratum, N_i	Stratum Sample Size, n_i	Stratum Sample Mean, $\bar{x}_i$	Stratum Sample Variance, s_i^2
1	1000	200	421	2410
2	3000	200	502	2938
3	2000	200	325	2047
4	1000	200	280	2214

14.23 Use the data in Exercise 14.22 to find an approximate 95% confidence interval for the population total τ.

14.24 A stratified random sample was selected from among four strata. Use the data shown in Table 14.8 to find an approximate 95% confidence interval for the population proportion p.

TABLE 14.8   Stratified Random Sample Data for Exercise 14.24

	Stratum			
	1	2	3	4
Stratum size	1000	1200	800	1500
Sample size	100	100	100	100
Sample proportion	.3	.25	.29	.34

14.25 A stratified random sample was selected from among three strata. Use the data shown in Table 14.9 to find an approximate 95% confidence interval for the population proportion p.

TABLE 14.9   Stratified Random Sample Data for Exercise 14.25

	Stratum		
	1	2	3
Stratum size	400	200	300
Sample size	100	100	100
Sample proportion	.62	.74	.55

APPLICATIONS

14.26 A zoning commission is formed to estimate the mean appraised value of houses in a residential suburb of a city. It is convenient to use the two voting districts in the suburb as strata because separate lists of dwellings are available for each district. From the data given in Table 14.10, find an approximate 95% confidence interval for the mean appraised value for all houses in the suburb.

TABLE 14.10   Appraised Value Sample Data for Exercise 14.26

Stratum I	Stratum II
$N_1 = 110$	$N_2 = 168$
$n_1 = 20$	$n_2 = 30$
$\sum_{i=1}^{n_1} x_i = 240,000$	$\sum_{i=1}^{n_2} x_1 = 420,000$
$\sum_{i=1}^{n_1} x_i^2 = 2,980,000,000$	$\sum_{i=1}^{n_2} x_i^2 = 6,010,000,000$

14.27 Refer to Exercise 14.26, and find an approximate 95% confidence interval for the total appraised value for all houses in the suburb.

14.28 A state energy office wished to estimate the proportion of public buildings that, based on energy analyses, were judged to be operating in an energy-efficient manner. The state was divided into three regions, two large urban areas and one rural area. The results of the survey are shown in Table 14.11. Find an approximate 95% confidence interval for the proportion p of all public buildings in the state that would be judged to be energy-efficient.

TABLE 14.11   Energy Efficiency Sample Data for Exercise 14.28

	Region		
	1	2	3
Number of state government buildings in region	249	432	316
Sample size	50	80	60
Number of energy-efficient buildings in sample	14	34	29

 14.29 An antique dealer planned to purchase the complete inventories of three English dealers and export the entire stock to the United States. To obtain an approximate value of the stock, the dealer randomly selected 50 items from each of the three inventories and had each appraised. The numbers of items in the three inventories, the sample means, and the sample variances are shown in Table 14.12. Find an approximate 95% confidence interval for the mean value per item of the dealer's purchases.

TABLE 14.12   Appraisal Sample Data for Exercise 14.29

	Inventory		
	1	2	3
N_i	425	316	559
$\bar{x}_i$	\$287	\$389	\$316
s_i^2	41,116	35,488	59,106

14.30 Refer to Exercise 14.29, and find an approximate 95% confidence interval for the total value of all three inventories.

14.31 Refer to Exercises 14.29 and 14.30. The estimate of the total value of inventory i is

$$\hat{\tau}_i = N_i \bar{x}_i$$

and the variance of the estimate (from Section 5.4) is

$$\sigma_{\hat{\tau}_i}^2 = N_i^2 \sigma_{\bar{x}_i}^2$$

where for a finite population

$$\sigma_{\bar{x}_i}^2 = \frac{\sigma_i^2}{n_i} \left(\frac{N_i - n_i}{N_i} \right)$$

Using this result and substituting s_i^2 for σ_i^2, we obtain an approximate 95% confidence interval for the difference in the total value of inventories i and j:

$$(\hat{\tau}_i - \hat{\tau}_j) \pm 1.96 \sqrt{N_i^2 \frac{s_i^2}{n_i} \left(\frac{N_i - n_i}{N_i} \right) + N_j^2 \frac{s_j^2}{n_j} \left(\frac{N_j - n_j}{N_j} \right)}$$

Use this formula to find an approximate 95% confidence interval on the difference in the total values of inventories 1 and 2.

14.5

CLUSTER SAMPLING

A **cluster** is a collection of elements. Sometimes, it is less costly to construct a frame and to sample clusters rather than the individual elements of a population. For example, suppose that you wanted to estimate the mean dollar amount that adults in a large suburban residential area planned to spend per month on key items. One easy way to do this estimation is to randomly sample residential blocks and then survey the buying intentions of all adults within each of the sampled blocks. Thus each block will contain a cluster of elements, the number of elements varying from one cluster to another. A frame can easily be constructed by using a map of the residential area and designating each block as a cluster. The travel costs involved in contacting the adults within a block will be minimal. Consequently, you will be able to contact many more people at lower cost than you could by using a simple random sample of all adults in the area.

Cluster sampling can reduce the cost of sampling, but selecting large numbers of elements in clusters is not a substitute for selecting a reasonable number of clusters. The observations from elements within a cluster may tend to give similar responses. For example, if the block (cluster) in the residential community happens to contain very expensive homes, many of the adults in the block may have plans to buy big-ticket items. If the block is in a lower-economic area, very few of the adults in the block may have buying intentions. Consequently, you need to sample enough clusters to obtain a measure of the variation in the responses from one cluster to another.

The formulas for approximate 95% confidence intervals for a population mean μ, a population total τ, and a population proportion p, based on cluster sampling, are given in the boxes. We will illustrate the estimation procedures with examples.

AN APPROXIMATE 95% CONFIDENCE INTERVAL FOR μ: CLUSTER SAMPLING

Notation

N = number of clusters in the population

n = number of clusters in the sample

m_i = number of elements in cluster i, $i = 1, 2, \ldots, n$

$$\overline{m} = \frac{\sum\limits_{i=1}^{n} m_i}{n} = \text{average cluster size in sample}$$

$$M = \sum\limits_{i=1}^{N} m_i = \text{number of elements in the population}$$

$$\overline{M} = \frac{M}{N} = \text{average cluster size for the population}$$

x_i = total of all observations in the ith cluster, $i = 1, 2, \ldots, n$

$$\bar{x} = \frac{\displaystyle\sum_{i=1}^{n} x_i}{\displaystyle\sum_{i=1}^{n} m_i}$$

Approximate 95% Confidence Interval for μ

$$\bar{x} \pm 1.96 \sqrt{\left(\frac{N-n}{Nn\overline{M}^2}\right) \frac{\displaystyle\sum_{i=1}^{n}(x_i - \bar{x}m_i)^2}{n-1}}$$

where

$$\sum_{i=1}^{n}(x_i - \bar{x}m_i)^2 = \sum_{i=1}^{n} x_i^2 - 2\bar{x}\sum_{i=1}^{n} x_i m_i + \bar{x}^2 \sum_{i=1}^{n} m_i^2$$

Note: $\overline{m}$ is used to approximate $\overline{M}$ when the number M of elements in the population is unknown.

AN APPROXIMATE 95% CONFIDENCE INTERVAL FOR τ: CLUSTER SAMPLING

Notation

N = number of clusters in the population

n = number of clusters in the sample

m_i = number of elements in cluster i, $i = 1, 2, \ldots, n$

$$\overline{m} = \frac{\displaystyle\sum_{i=1}^{n} m_i}{n} = \text{average cluster size in sample}$$

$$M = \sum_{i=1}^{N} m_i = \text{number of elements in the population}$$

$$\overline{M} = \frac{M}{N} = \text{average cluster size for the population}$$

x_i = total of all observations in the ith cluster, $i = 1, 2, \ldots, n$

$$\bar{x} = \frac{\displaystyle\sum_{i=1}^{n} x_i}{\displaystyle\sum_{i=1}^{n} m_i}$$

Approximate 95% Confidence Interval for τ

$$\hat{\tau} \pm 1.96 \sqrt{N^2\left(\frac{N-n}{Nn}\right)\frac{\sum\limits_{i=1}^{n}(x_i - \bar{x}m_i)^2}{n-1}}$$

where
$$\hat{\tau} = M\bar{x}$$

$$\sum_{i=1}^{n}(x_i - \bar{x}m_i)^2 = \sum_{i=1}^{n}x_i^2 - 2\bar{x}\sum_{i=1}^{n}x_i m_i + \bar{x}^2 \sum_{i=1}^{n}m_i^2$$

Note: $\overline{m}$ is used to approximate $\overline{M}$ when the number M of elements in the population is unknown.

AN APPROXIMATE 95% CONFIDENCE INTERVAL FOR p: CLUSTER SAMPLING

Notation

N = number of clusters in the population

n = number of clusters in the sample

m_i = number of elements in cluster i, $i = 1, 2, \ldots, n$

$$\overline{m} = \frac{\sum\limits_{i=1}^{n}m_i}{n} = \text{average cluster size in sample}$$

$$M = \sum_{i=1}^{N}m_i = \text{number of elements in the population}$$

$$\overline{M} = \frac{M}{N} = \text{average cluster size for the population}$$

a_i = number of "successes" in cluster i, $i = 1, 2, \ldots, n$

$$\hat{p} = \frac{\sum\limits_{i=1}^{n}a_i}{\sum\limits_{i=1}^{n}m_i}$$

Approximate 95% Confidence Interval for p

$$\hat{p} \pm 1.96 \sqrt{\left(\frac{N-n}{Nn\overline{M}^2}\right)\frac{\sum\limits_{i=1}^{n}(a_i - \hat{p}m_i)^2}{n-1}}$$

where
$$\sum_{i=1}^{n}(a_i - \hat{p}m_i)^2 = \sum_{i=1}^{n}a_i^2 - 2\hat{p}\sum_{i=1}^{n}a_i m_i + \hat{p}^2\sum_{i=1}^{n}m_i^2$$

Note: $\overline{m}$ is used to approximate $\overline{M}$ when the number M of elements in the population is unknown.

EXAMPLE 14.7   Twenty households were randomly selected from within a town in order to estimate the mean income per person. The town listed 12,205 households containing a total of 19,200 wage earners. The data are shown in Table 14.13. Find an approximate 95% confidence interval for the mean annual wage per person in the town.

TABLE 14.13   Wage Data for Example 14.7

Household i	Number of Wage Earners per Household, m_i	Annual Income ($)	Total Income per Household, x_i
1	2	12,100; 27,000	39,100
2	1	23,000	23,000
3	2	18,200; 12,800	31,000
4	2	20,900; 14,400	35,300
5	1	29,000	29,000
6	1	26,200	26,200
7	2	14,500; 18,300	32,800
8	2	16,900; 19,400	36,300
9	1	48,000	48,000
10	3	19,100; 12,000; 7,500	38,600
11	1	26,300	26,300
12	1	35,100	35,100
13	3	17,400; 18,900; 12,200	48,500
14	2	16,200; 19,900	36,100
15	1	13,200	13,200
16	1	18,400	18,400
17	2	13,100; 14,700	27,800
18	1	21,500	21,500
19	2	22,000; 8,000	30,000
20	2	14,000; 7,500	21,500

$$\sum_{i=1}^{20} m_i = 33 \qquad\qquad \sum_{i=1}^{20} x_i = 617,700$$

SOLUTION   We are given the information that the number of households (clusters) is $N = 12,205$ and that the total number of wage earners in the town is $M = \sum_{i=1}^{N} m_i = 19,200$.

From Table 14.13

$$\sum_{i=1}^{n} m_i = 33 \qquad \text{and} \qquad \sum_{i=1}^{n} x_i = 617,700$$

Therefore,

$$\overline{m} = \frac{\sum_{i=1}^{n} m_i}{n} = \frac{33}{20} = 1.6500 \qquad \text{and} \qquad \overline{M} = \frac{M}{N} = \frac{19,200}{12,205} = 1.5731258$$

The first step in finding the confidence interval for μ is to calculate

$$\bar{x} = \frac{\sum\limits_{i=1}^{n} x_i}{\sum\limits_{i=1}^{n} m_i} = \frac{617,700}{33} = 18,718.18$$

$$\sum_{i=1}^{n} x_i^2 = 20,669,130,000 \qquad \sum_{i=1}^{n} x_i m_i = 1,081,800 \qquad \sum_{i=1}^{n} m_i^2 = 63$$

$$\sum_{i=1}^{n} (x_i - \bar{x}m_i)^2 = \sum_{i=1}^{n} x_i^2 - 2\bar{x}\sum_{i=1}^{n} x_i m_i + \bar{x}^2 \sum_{i=1}^{n} m_i^2 = 2,243,802,645$$

Then substituting into the formula for the confidence interval, we have

$$\bar{x} \pm 1.96 \sqrt{\left(\frac{N-n}{Nn\overline{M}^2}\right) \frac{\sum\limits_{i=1}^{n} (x_i - \bar{x}m_i)^2}{n-1}}$$

$$18,718.18 \pm 1.96 \sqrt{\frac{(12,205-20)}{(12,205)(20)(1.5731258)^2} \left(\frac{2,243,802,645}{19}\right)}$$

$$18,718.18 \pm 3025.08$$

Therefore, we estimate the mean salary per wage earner in the town to be in the interval $15,693.10 to $21,743.26.

∎

EXAMPLE 14.8

Refer to Example 14.7, and find an approximate 95% confidence interval for the total annual wages earned by the town's 19,200 wage earners.

SOLUTION

The formula for the confidence interval is

$$\hat{\tau} \pm 1.96 \sqrt{N^2 \left(\frac{N-n}{Nn}\right) \frac{\sum\limits_{i=1}^{n} (x_i - \bar{x}m_i)^2}{n-1}}$$

where

$$\hat{\tau} = M\bar{x} = (19,200)(18,718.18) = \$359,389,056$$

Substituting into the formula for the confidence interval yields

$$\$359,389,056 \pm 1.96 \sqrt{(12,205)^2 \left[\frac{12,205-20}{(12,205)(20)}\right] \left(\frac{2,243,802,645}{19}\right)}$$

$$\$359,389,056 \pm \$58,081,558$$

Therefore, we estimate the total annual wages for all wage earners in the town to be in the interval $301,307,498 to $417,470,614.

∎

EXAMPLE 14.9

A large chain of retail stores purchases men's shirts in lots, each of which contains one dozen shirts. After receiving a shipment of 1000 lots, the retailer randomly selected 21 and counted the number of defective shirts per lot. Find an approximate 95%

TABLE 14.14   Shipment Data for Example 14.9

Lot i	Number Defective, a_i	Lot i	Number Defective, a_i	Lot i	Number Defective, a_i
1	0	8	1	15	1
2	1	9	6	16	1
3	0	10	0	17	0
4	1	11	0	18	2
5	2	12	2	19	8
6	0	13	1	20	0
7	0	14	0	21	0

confidence interval for the proportion p of defective shirts in the 1000-lot shipment based on the data shown in Table 14.14.

SOLUTION   We are given the information that $N = 1000$ and $n = 21$; and since a cluster is a single lot and each lot contains 12 shirts, it follows that $m_i = 12$, $i = 1, 2, \ldots, 21$, and $\overline{M} = 12$. Then

$$\hat{p} = \frac{\sum_{i=1}^{n} a_i}{\sum_{i=1}^{n} m_i} = \frac{26}{(21)(12)}$$

$$= .1031746$$

$$\sum_{i=1}^{n}(a_i - \hat{p}m_i)^2 = \sum_{i=1}^{n} a_i^2 - 2\hat{p}\sum_{i=1}^{n} a_i m_i + \hat{p}^2 \sum_{i=1}^{n} m_i^2$$

$$= 118 - 2(.1031746)(312) + (.1031746)^2(3024)$$

$$= 85.809524$$

Then the approximate 95% confidence interval for p is

$$\hat{p} \pm 1.96 \sqrt{\left(\frac{N - n}{Nn\overline{M}^2}\right)\frac{\sum_{i=1}^{n}(a_i - \hat{p}m_i)^2}{n - 1}}$$

$$.103 \pm 1.96 \sqrt{\frac{1000 - 21}{(1000)(21)(12)^2}\left(\frac{85.809524}{21 - 1}\right)}$$

or

$$.103 \pm .073$$

Therefore, we estimate the proportion p of defective shirts in the 1000-lot shipment to lie in the interval .030 to .176.   ∎

EXERCISES

BASIC TECHNIQUES

14.32 Find an approximate 95% confidence interval for the mean of a population based on cluster sampling and upon the following information:

$$N = 20,000 \qquad n = 200$$

$$m_1 = m_2 = \cdots = m_{200} = 10 \qquad M = 200,000$$

$$\sum_{i=1}^{n} x_i = 4944 \qquad \sum_{i=1}^{n} (x_i - \bar{x}m_i)^2 = 483$$

14.33 Refer to Exercise 14.32, and find an approximate 95% confidence interval for the population total τ.

14.34 Find an approximate 95% confidence interval for a population mean μ based on the cluster sample data in Table 14.15. Assume that the total number of clusters in the population is $N = 2000$ and that the average cluster size in the population is $\overline{M} = 3.2$.

TABLE 14.15   Cluster Sample Data for Exercise 14.34

Cluster i	m_i	x_i	Cluster i	m_i	x_i
1	3	15	6	4	20
2	5	34	7	3	18
3	3	18	8	6	41
4	2	11	9	1	5
5	2	15	10	2	13

14.35 Refer to Exercise 14.34, and find an approximate 95% confidence interval for the population total τ.

14.36 Find an approximate 95% confidence interval for a population proportion p based on the cluster sample data in Table 14.16. Assume that the number of clusters in the population is 2000 and that the average cluster size in the population is $\overline{M} = 10.7$.

TABLE 14.16   Cluster Sample Data for Exercise 14.36

Cluster i	m_i	a_i	Cluster i	m_i	a_i
1	15	7	6	8	3
2	9	4	7	16	9
3	10	3	8	12	7
4	6	4	9	10	5
5	12	7	10	7	4

APPLICATIONS

14.37 A survey was conducted to estimate the mean income of employed adult females in a small city. Because no list of adult females was available, the pollster divided the city into 415 blocks (clusters) and randomly selected $n = 25$ blocks from among the total of 415. The incomes of the employed adult females in the sample blocks are shown in Table 14.17. Find an approximate 95% confidence interval for the mean income of employed adult females in the city. (*Hint:* Since $\overline{M}$ is unknown, use $\overline{m}$ to approximate $\overline{M}$.)

TABLE 14.17   Income Data for Exercise 14.37

Cluster i	Number of Adult Females, m_i	Total Income per Cluster, x_i	Cluster i	Number of Adult Females, m_i	Total Income per Cluster, x_i
1	8	$192,000	14	10	$ 98,000
2	12	242,000	15	9	106,000
3	4	84,000	16	3	100,000
4	5	130,000	17	6	64,000
5	6	104,000	18	5	44,000
6	6	80,000	19	5	90,000
7	7	150,000	20	4	74,000
8	5	130,000	21	6	102,000
9	8	90,000	22	8	60,000
10	3	100,000	23	7	78,000
11	2	170,000	24	3	94,000
12	6	86,000	25	8	82,000
13	5	108,000			

$$\sum_{i=1}^{25} m_i = 151 \qquad \sum_{i=1}^{25} x_i = \$2,658,000$$

14.38 A subsequent census of the city (Exercise 14.37) showed that 2562 adult females were employed. Find an approximate 95% confidence interval for the total income of all employed adult females in the city.

TABLE 14.18   Opinion Data for Exercise 14.39

Plant	Number of Employees	Number Favoring New Policy	Plant	Number of Employees	Number Favoring New Policy
1	51	42	9	73	54
2	62	53	10	61	45
3	49	40	11	58	51
4	73	45	12	52	29
5	101	63	13	65	46
6	48	31	14	49	37
7	65	38	15	55	42
8	49	30			

14.39 An industry is considering revision of its retirement policy and wants to estimate the proportion of employees who favor the new policy. The industry consists of 87 separate plants located throughout the United States. Since results must be obtained quickly and with little cost, the industry decides to use cluster sampling with each plant as a cluster. A simple random sample of 15 plants is selected, and the opinions of the employees in these plants are obtained by questionnaire. The results are as shown in Table 14.18. Estimate the proportion of employees in the industry who favor the new retirement policy using a 95% confidence interval.

14.6   SAMPLING: SOME PROBLEMS

After constructing a frame and selecting the elements to be included in the sample, you will be faced with the problem of reaching the elements and making the observations. If an element is a human, as in the case of a consumer preference poll, you can send an interviewer to obtain a response or you can attempt to obtain the response by telephone or mail. Personal contact by an interviewer is the most reliable method, but it is often very costly. Telephone surveys are much less costly than personal interviews, but you must be certain that all of the elements in the population can be reached by telephone. Otherwise, you might fall into the trap that led to the demise of the *Literary Digest*.

In 1936 the *Literary Digest* conducted a telephone poll to determine the outcome of the Landon-Roosevelt presidential election. Unfortunately, most of the telephones in 1936 were owned by Republicans. Therefore, rather than surveying the voting intentions of all eligible voters, the population of interest to the readers of the *Literary Digest*, the researchers selected the random sample from among voting telephone owners. Needless to say, the sample provided ample evidence upon which to forecast a Landon victory (you know who won!).

An equally poor example of a telephone poll was one conducted by ABC Television immediately prior to the 1980 Carter-Reagan election. ABC invited its viewers to call in (long distance) their presidential preferences. Rather than achieving a random sample of voter sentiment, ABC obtained a sample that consisted of the preferences of those voters who were sufficiently interested in swaying the outcome of the poll that they were willing to invest in long-distance telephone calls. Clearly, ABC did not randomly sample the population of prospective voters. More Democrats made the long-distance calls, and ABC forecast a Carter victory.

Mail surveys are even more susceptible to error. Because mailing a questionnaire is relatively inexpensive, some pollsters send questionnaires to all persons in the population. Most of these questionnaires are relegated to the circular file and are never returned. The respondents to these surveys are often those who have an ax to grind—that is, they wish to influence the outcome of the poll. Thoughtful persons who may be in the majority may not have the time or the inclination to respond.

Even if the sample elements in a mail survey have been randomly selected, nonresponse is a problem. One way to cope with this problem is to contact the missing elements of the sample by other means, telephone or direct interview, in order to obtain a response. It is also possible to resample the nonrespondents. Then based on the subsample, we can modify an estimate to adjust for the nonrespondents.

A problem more serious than nonresponse occurs when the questions in a survey induce the respondent to lie. For example, suppose that a merchandiser wanted to estimate the proportion of its clientele who were shoplifters. If asked whether you had ever shoplifted in the store, guilty or not, most people would say no. Questions about personal hygiene, thoughts, and habits often tend to be sensitive. Rather than risk being viewed unfavorably by the interviewer, the respondent may give a false response. Thus in addition to the problem of constructing the frame and actually reaching the elements in the sample, we have the added problem of obtaining a correct response when an element is observed.

The method for coping with this problem is based on what is known as a **randomized response model**. Each person in the sample is presented two questions by the interviewer, one the sensitive question of interest to the pollster and the other a trivial nonsensitive question. For example, the second question might be, "Did you have cereal for breakfast?" The respondent is then given a mechanism for randomly selecting which of the two questions to answer. For example, the respondent might be asked to select a card from a deck of 52 cards. Without revealing the outcome to the interviewer, the respondent would be instructed to answer the sensitive question if the draw was a face card. Otherwise, the respondent answers the nonsensitive question. Thus the interviewer knows the *probability* that the respondent will select the sensitive question but does not know the outcome for any specific respondent. This allows the respondent to freely answer the question without risk of embarrassment. It also enables the statistician to use the sample data to estimate the value of the desired population parameter.

A study of survey sampling—the various procedures (designs) for collecting sample data and for estimating the values of population parameters—is a subject in itself. Almost all of the statistical methods for making inferences that are discussed in this text are based on simple random samples. To learn more about other sampling designs and the methods of inference associated with them, refer to a text on survey sampling.

Sampling 58 Million Beer Cans: How to Do It

14.7

Using a random number table to select a random sample from a frame is an easy task. Constructing the frame and obtaining the actual sample observations may be difficult or, in the case of the beer cans (see the Case Study), almost impossible.

Fifty-eight million is a large number of beer cans. Located in one spot, stacked side by side, they occupy the best part of a city block and tower almost to the ceiling of a two-story building. The cans were stacked in a warehouse in layers on wooden pallets, 21 cans wide, 20 cans deep, and 19 cans high (see Figure 14.2). The pallets were then stacked by forklift trucks, one pallet on top of another, in stacks containing either two or three pallets. The stacks were arranged in long rows, from one end of the warehouse to the other. Space was allowed every four or five rows for a passageway, large enough

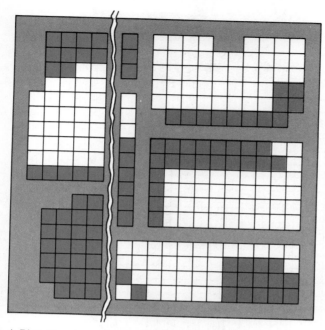

FIGURE 14.1   A Plan Showing a Portion of the Warehouse Floor

to accommodate a lift truck and permit removal of pallets. Passages in the opposite direction also occurred at irregular intervals.

Two problems arise in the sampling procedure. For the construction of a frame the cans (the elements of the population) need to be numbered so that the cans selected for the sample can be identified and located. Since the beer cans were not numbered, the alternative was to remove the 58 million cans from the warehouse and number them or to number the cans on a master drawing according to their location in the warehouse. The second problem involves the removal of the 500 sample cans from the midst of the 58 million. Fortunately, this difficulty was eliminated because the brewer planned to sell the cans for scrap aluminum. Therefore, cans in specific locations could be obtained as their respective pallets were trucked out of the warehouse.

Numbering each of the 58 million cans by location on a drawing seemed an impossible task. Instead, we decided to number *stacks* according to their location and then to record for each stack whether it contained two or three pallets. A plan of the warehouse showing the numbered stacks would be similar to the drawing in Figure 14.1. Each small square represents a stack. White squares represent two-pallet stacks; shaded squares represent three-pallet stacks.

The final step in drawing a random sample is to devise a procedure for selecting a can so that every group of 500 cans has an equal probability of selection. To illustrate our procedure for doing this, let us assume that the warehouse contains 3200 stacks, 2300 containing 2 pallets and 900 containing 3 pallets (a total of 7300 pallets). Intuitively, it would seem reasonable to randomly select one of the 3200 stacks, randomly select one of the pallets in the stack, and then randomly select a can within

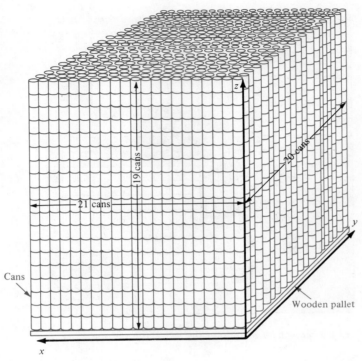

FIGURE 14.2   Locating a Can in a Pallet

the pallet. This procedure will not produce a simple random sample because cans in the two-pallet stacks will possess a higher probability of selection than cans in the three-pallet stacks.

One solution to this difficulty is to select a can according to the following multistep sampling procedure:

(1) Decide whether to select a can from either a two- or from a three-pallet stack.

(2) Choose the stack from among the stacks listed for the stack *type* chosen in step 1. Thus we must have a frame for each stack type. So all of the two-pallet stacks must be numbered and, separately, all of the three-pallet stacks must be numbered.

(3) Once the stack has been chosen (steps 1 and 2), choose the pallet within the stack.

(4) Once the pallet has been chosen (steps 1, 2, and 3), choose the can within the pallet. Since the cans are stacked in layers on the rectangular pallet (see Figure 14.2), the location of a can can be determined by its distance, x, y, z, from one of the corners of the pallet.

The probabilities of the various outcomes of each of the steps are as follows:

Step 1 (a) The probability that we select a type 2 stack (two-pallet stack) is p.
(b) The probability that we select a type 3 stack (three-pallet stack) is $1 - p$.

Step 2 (a) Given that a type 2 stack was selected in step 1, the probability of selecting a particular one of the $n_2 = 2300$ stacks of type 2 is $1/2300$.

Given that a type 3 stack was selected in step 1, the probability of selecting a particular one of the $n_3 = 900$ stacks of type 3 is $1/900$.

Step 3 (a) Given the selection of a particular type 2 stack (steps 1 and 2), the probability of selecting a particular pallet from among the two in the stack is $1/2$.

(b) Given the selection of a particular type 3 stack (steps 1 and 2), the probability of selecting a particular pallet from among the three in the stack is $1/3$

Step 4 Given the selection of a particular pallet (steps 1, 2, and 3), the probability of selecting a particular can by randomly choosing values for x, y, and z (see Figure 14.2) will equal $1/N$, where N is the number of cans in a pallet. For example, each pallet contains $(21)(20)(19) = 7980$ cans (see Figure 14.2); therefore, the probability of selecting a particular can in the pallet is $1/7980$.

Of the probabilities listed above, only one is unknown—the probability p of selecting a two-pallet stack. Since we want the probability of selecting a can in a two-pallet stack to equal the probability of selecting one in a three-pallet stack, we can equate these probabilities and solve for p.

The probability of selecting a particular can that is located in a two-pallet stack is equal to the probability of the intersection of four events corresponding to the four steps in the selection process:

$$P_2 = (p)\left(\frac{1}{2300}\right)\left(\frac{1}{2}\right)\left(\frac{1}{7980}\right)$$

$$\underset{\substack{\text{step}\\1}}{\downarrow} \quad \underset{\substack{\text{step}\\2}}{\downarrow} \quad \underset{\substack{\text{step}\\3}}{\downarrow} \quad \underset{\substack{\text{step}\\4}}{\downarrow}$$

Similarly, the probability of selecting a particular can in a three-pallet stack is

$$P_3 = (1 - p)\left(\frac{1}{900}\right)\left(\frac{1}{3}\right)\left(\frac{1}{7980}\right)$$

$$\underset{\substack{\text{step}\\1}}{\downarrow} \quad \underset{\substack{\text{step}\\2}}{\downarrow} \quad \underset{\substack{\text{step}\\3}}{\downarrow} \quad \underset{\substack{\text{step}\\4}}{\downarrow}$$

Since we want P_2 to equal P_3, we obtain

$$p\left(\frac{1}{2300}\right)\left(\frac{1}{2}\right)\left(\frac{1}{7980}\right) = (1 - p)\left(\frac{1}{900}\right)\left(\frac{1}{3}\right)\left(\frac{1}{7980}\right)$$

Since $(2300)(2)$ represents the total number N_2 of pallets in two-pallet stacks and $(900)(3) = N_3$ equals the corresponding number of pallets in three-pallet stacks, it follows that

$$p\left(\frac{1}{N_2}\right) = (1 - p)\left(\frac{1}{N_3}\right)$$

or

$$p = \frac{N_2}{N_2 + N_3} = \frac{\text{total number of pallets in two-pallet stacks}}{\text{total number of pallets in the warehouse}}$$

For our example,

$$p = \frac{(2300)(2)}{(2300)(2) + (900)(3)} = .63$$

Therefore, if we want to choose a random sample from among the 58 million cans, we will choose a can so that the probability of selecting a two-pallet stack is .63 and of selecting a three-pallet stack is .37. Then we will choose the stack so that every stack in the stack type has an equal probability of being selected. Each pallet within a two-pallet stack will have a probability of $1/2$ of being selected; each within a three-pallet stack will have a probability equal to $1/3$. Finally, since a pallet contains 7980 cans, we will select the appropriate can so that each of the 7980 cans will have an equal chance of selection. If each of the 500 cans is selected in this manner from among the 58 million cans in the warehouse, the result will be a simple random sample.

How can we use the random number table to perform one of the steps in the can selection? For example, how can we choose the stack type so that we give a probability of .63 to choosing a two-pallet stack and .37 to choosing a three-pallet stack? We will select three-digit random numbers from the table, retaining only those from 1 to and including 100. If the random number is less than or equal to 63, we decide to choose a two-pallet stack. If the number is equal to 64 or larger—that is, up to 100—we choose a three-pallet stack. The random number table is used in a similar manner to perform the other steps in the selection process.

This case study stresses an important aspect of sampling. Constructing a frame for a population is often difficult and costly. The unusual aspect of this case study is that we circumvented this difficult and costly procedure by developing a multistep sampling procedure that satisfies the definition of simple random sampling.

SUMMARY

14.8

This chapter stresses the role of the sampling procedure in making statistical inferences. Most statistical samples are probability samples, those selected in such a way that the probabilities of various sample outcomes are known in advance. By using these probabilities, we are able to infer the nature of the sampled population.

The most elementary type of probability sample, the one upon which almost all of the basic statistical methods are based, is the simple random sample. A simple random sample is one chosen so that every different sample of fixed size in the population has an equal probability of selection. The sampling units to be selected in a simple random sample can be identified by constructing a frame, a list of all elements in the population. Then the elements to be included in the sample are chosen by using a random number table.

Constructing a frame and making observations on elements in the sample may be difficult and costly. It also may be difficult to obtain true readings of the responses. Sampling designs, such as the stratified random sampling and cluster sampling designs, will, in certain situations, reduce the labor and the cost of sampling. Sampling by using the randomized response model can often be employed to elicit correct responses to sensitive questions.

The sample survey designs discussed in this chapter provide a glimpse into a broad subject—survey sampling. Survey sampling encompasses the designs and associated estimation procedures required to cope with the many difficulties that arise in sampling. Further information on this topic can be found by consulting the References.

REFERENCES

Cochran, W. G. *Sampling Techniques*. 3rd ed. New York: Wiley, 1977.

Greenberg, B. G., Kuebler, R. T., Abernathy, J. R., and Horvitz, D. G. "Application of Randomized Response Technique in Obtaining Quantitative Data." *Journal of the American Statistical Association,* Vol. 66, 1971.

Hansen, M. H., Hurwitz, W. N., and Madow, W. G. *Sample Survey Methods and Theory*. Vol. 1. New York: Wiley, 1953.

Kish, L. *Survey Sampling*. New York: Wiley, 1965.

Scheaffer, R. L., Mendenhall, W., and Ott, L. *Elementary Survey Sampling*. 3rd ed. Boston: PWS-KENT, 1986.

KEY TERMS

Principle of maximum likelihood (page 611)
Probability sampling (page 611)
Simple random sampling (page 611)
Sampling unit (page 612)
Frame (page 612)
Element (page 612)
Random number (page 612)
Random number table (page 612)

Finite population correction factor (page 615)
Sampling designs (page 618)
Sample survey (page 618)
Strata (page 618)
Stratified random sampling (page 619)
Cluster (page 627)
Cluster sampling (page 627)
Randomized response model (page 636)

SUPPLEMENTARY EXERCISES

14.40 Suppose that a population contains 49 elements. Use a random number table to identify the $n = 5$ elements to be included in a random sample from among the population. Explain how you arrived at your selection.

14.41 A city contains 474,159 homeowners listed on its tax rolls. Explain how you would use a random number table to draw a random sample of $n = 1000$ homeowners from among those listed on the tax rolls.

14.42 A stratified random sample was selected from among three strata. Find an approximate 95% confidence interval for the population mean μ, based on the data in Table 14.19.

TABLE 14.19   Stratified Sample Data for Exercise 14.42

	Stratum		
	1	2	3
Stratum size	2400	3000	900
Sample size	100	120	50
Sample mean	12.1	13.4	9.7
Sample variance	3.22	2.45	1.07

14.43 Use the data in Exercise 14.42 to find an approximate 95% confidence interval for the population total τ.

14.44 A stratified random sample was selected from among three strata. Use the data in Table 14.20 to find an approximate 95% confidence interval for a population proportion p.

TABLE 14.20   Stratified Sample Data for Exercise 14.44

	Stratum		
	1	2	3
Stratum size	900	1200	600
Sample size	100	100	100
Sample proportion	.43	.52	.38

 14.45 A survey was conducted to estimate the mean monthly expenditure for college room, board, books, supplies, and recreation for students at a university. Random samples of 100 male and 100 female students were randomly selected from among the 8435 male and 6453 females enrolled at the university. A summary of the information acquired in the survey is shown in Table 14.21.

TABLE 14.21   Expenditure Data for Exercise 14.45

Sex	Sample Size	Sample Mean ($)	Sample Variance
Female	100	717	22,000
Male	100	864	31,000

(a) Find an approximate 95% confidence interval for the mean monthly expenditure per student.
(b) Find an approximate 95% confidence interval for the mean monthly expenditure for female students. (*Hint:* Use the method of Section 6.5.)

14.46 How much money, in addition to tuition, does the university described in Exercise 14.45 bring into the community in which it is located? Find an approximate 95% confidence interval for the total amount of money expended per month on room, board, and so on, by all students at the university.

14.47 Suppose that the persons in the survey of Exercise 14.45 were asked whether they would approve the budgeting of additional student funds for the school's athletic programs.

(a) Given the data shown in the accompanying table, find an approximate 95% confidence interval for the proportion of students favoring the proposed budgeting change.

Sex	Sample Size	Number in Favor
Female	100	38
Male	100	61

(b) Find an approximate 95% confidence interval for the proportion of male students who favor the proposed budgeting change. (*Hint:* Use the method of Section 6.7.)

14.48 Find an approximate 95% confidence interval for a population mean μ, based on the cluster sample data in Table 14.22. Assume that the total number of clusters in the population is 5000 and that the average cluster size in the population is $\overline{M} = 4.9$.

TABLE 14.22   Cluster Sample Data for Exercise 14.48

Cluster i	m_i	x_i	Cluster i	m_i	x_i
1	3	6	7	5	10
2	5	12	8	4	9
3	6	11	9	5	9
4	4	10	10	8	20
5	7	14	11	4	6
6	4	5	12	5	9

14.49 Use the data in Exercise 14.48 to find an approximate 95% confidence interval for the population total τ.

14.50 Find an approximate 95% confidence interval for a population proportion p, based on the cluster sample data in Table 14.23. Assume that the total number of clusters in the population is 5000 and that the average cluster size in the population is $\overline{M} = 15.2$.

TABLE 14.23   Cluster Sample Data for Exercise 15.40

Cluster i	m_i	a_i	Cluster i	m_i	a_i
1	16	4	7	19	5
2	21	6	8	18	3
3	10	4	9	13	5
4	15	3	10	15	6
5	18	8	11	11	3
6	14	4	12	18	6

 14.51 An inspector wants to estimate the mean weight of fill for cereal boxes packaged in a certain factory. The cereal is available to him in cartons containing 12 boxes each. The inspector randomly selects five cartons and measures the weight of fill for every box in the sampled cartons, with the results (in ounces) as shown in Table 14.24. Find an approximate 95% confidence interval for the mean weight of fill per box packaged by the factory. Assume that the total number N of cartons packaged by the factory is large enough so that the quantity $(N - n)/N$ is close to 1 and can be ignored.

TABLE 14.24   Fill Data for Exercise 14.51

Carton	Ounces of Fill										
1	16.1	15.9	16.1	16.2	15.9	15.8	16.1	16.2	16.0	15.9	15.8	16.0
2	15.9	16.2	15.8	16.0	16.3	16.1	15.8	15.9	16.0	16.1	16.1	15.9
3	16.2	16.0	15.7	16.3	15.8	16.0	15.9	16.0	16.1	16.0	15.9	16.1
4	15.9	16.1	16.2	16.1	16.1	16.3	15.9	16.1	15.9	15.9	16.0	16.0
5	16.0	15.8	16.3	15.7	16.1	15.9	16.0	16.1	15.8	16.0	16.1	15.9

14.52 To emphasize safety, a taxicab company wants to estimate the proportion of unsafe tires on its 175 cabs. (Ignore spare tires.) It is impractical to select a simple random sample of tires, so cluster sampling is used, with each cab as a cluster. A random sample of 25 cabs gives the following number of unsafe tires per cab:

$$2, \ 4, \ 0, \ 1, \ 2, \ 0, \ 4, \ 1, \ 3, \ 1, \ 2, \ 0, \ 1,$$
$$1, \ 2, \ 2, \ 4, \ 1, \ 0, \ 0, \ 3, \ 1, \ 2, \ 2, \ 1$$

Estimate the proportion of unsafe tires being used on the company's cabs with an approximate 95% confidence interval.

Chapters 6, 7, 8, and 9 presented statistical techniques for comparing two or more populations by comparing their respective population parameters. The techniques are applicable to data measured on a continuum and to data possessing normal population relative frequency distributions. The purpose of this chapter is to present a set of statistical test procedures to compare populations for the many types of data that do not satisfy these assumptions.

15

NONPARAMETRIC STATISTICS

Does It Pay to Save? A Second Look

You may recall the Case Study of Chapter 11 that discussed Dr. Srully Blotnick's theory concerning the relationship between the percentage of total national income saved y and the approximate percentage of investment income x that must be paid in taxes. We calculated the simple coefficient of correlation r between y and x for $n = 8$ countries and found that there was sufficient evidence (p-value $= .00875$) to indicate that y and x were negatively correlated—in other words, that y tends to decrease as x increases. Then we issued a warning: that it was quite conceivable that the data did not satisfy the assumptions required for the regression analysis test for correlation (Chapter 11). So let us ask the question again. Does the national rate of savings tend to decrease as the investment tax income increases? Or to put it another way, are y and x negatively correlated?

The Case Study in Chapter 11 emphasizes an important aspect of statistical inference. Most statistical methods are based on assumptions concerning the nature of the sampled population(s) and the manner in which the sample(s) was (were) selected. Since the nature of the sampled population(s) is usually unknown, some doubt always exists concerning the validity of any statistical inferences based on unverified assumptions.

As discussed earlier in this text, studies have been conducted to determine the effect that moderate departures from the assumptions have on the measures of reliability associated with a method of inference. For example, we will want to know whether moderate departures from the assumption of normality will produce a substantial change in the confidence coefficient for a particular confidence interval or whether it will produce a substantial change in α and β, the probabilities of type I and type II errors for a particular test. Estimation and test procedures whose properties remain fairly stable when the assumptions are relaxed are said to be **robust**.

In addition to studying the robustness of statistical estimation and test procedures, efforts have been made to develop a methodology of statistical inference, estimation, and tests of hypotheses that require very few inferences concerning the sampled populations. Some of these methods, called **nonparametric statistical procedures**, are presented in this chapter. Particularly, we will reexamine the relationship between the rate of savings y and the investment tax rate x in Section 15.8.

INTRODUCTION

15.1

Some experiments yield response measurements that defy quantification. That is, they generate response measurements that can be ordered (ranked), but the location of the responses on a scale of measurement is arbitrary. For example, the data may admit only pairwise directional comparisons (whether one observation is larger than another or vice versa). Or we may be able to rank all observations in a data set but may not know the exact values of the measurements. To illustrate, suppose that a judge is employed to evaluate and rank the sales abilities of four salespeople, the edibility and taste characteristics of five brands of cornflakes, or the relative appeal of five new automobile designs. Clearly, it is impossible to give an exact measure of sales competence, palatability of food, or design appeal, but it is usually possible to rank the salespeople, brands, or design appeal according to which we think is best, second best, and so on. Thus the response measurements here differ markedly from those presented in preceding chapters. Experiments that produce this type of data occur in almost all fields of study, but they are particularly evident in social science research and in studies of consumer preference. The data that they produce can be analyzed by using *nonparametric statistical methods.*

Nonparametric statistical procedures are also useful in making inferences in situations where serious doubt exists about the assumptions that underlie standard methodology. For example, the t test for comparing a pair of means in Section 8.4 is based on the assumption that both populations are normally distributed with equal variances. The experimenter will never know whether these assumptions hold in a practical situation but will often be reasonably certain that departures from the assumptions will be small enough so that the properties of the statistical procedure will be undisturbed. That is, α and β will be approximately what the experimenter thinks they are. On the other hand, it is not uncommon for the experimenter seriously to question the assumptions and wonder whether he or she is using a valid statistical procedure. This difficulty may be circumvented by using a nonparametric statistical test and thereby avoiding reliance on a very uncertain set of assumptions.

Research has shown that nonparametric statistical tests are almost as capable of detecting differences among populations as the parametric methods of preceding chapters when normality and other assumptions are satisfied. They may be, and often are, more powerful in detecting population differences when the assumptions are not satisfied. For this reason, many statisticians advocate the use of nonparametric statistical procedures in preference to their parametric counterparts.

In this chapter we will discuss only the most common situations in which nonparametric methods are used. For a more complete treatment of the subject, see the texts by Gibbons (1971), Hollander and Wolfe (1973), or Conover (1980) listed in the References.

THE SIGN TEST FOR COMPARING TWO POPULATIONS

15.2

Without emphasizing the point, we used a nonparametric statistical test as an alternative procedure for determining whether evidence existed to indicate a difference in the mean wear for the two types of tires in the **paired-difference experiment** in Section 8.5. Each pair of responses was compared and x (the number of times A exceeded B) was used as the test statistic. This nonparametric test is known as the **sign test** because x is the number of positive (or negative) signs associated with the differences. The implied null hypothesis is that the two population distributions are identical, and the resulting technique is completely independent of the form of the distribution of differences. Thus regardless of the distribution of differences, the probability that A exceeds B for a given pair will be $p = .5$ when the null hypothesis is true (that is, when the distributions for A and B are identical). Then x will possess a binomial probability distribution, and a rejection region for x can be obtained using the binomial probability distribution of Chapter 4.

The sign test is summarized in the box and is illustrated by an example. The summary and example will help you to recall how the sign test was constructed and how it is used in a practical situation.

THE SIGN TEST FOR COMPARING TWO POPULATIONS

(1) *Null Hypothesis:* $H_0 : P(x_A > x_B) = 1/2$.

(2) *Alternative Hypothesis:*

One-Tailed	**Two-Tailed**
$H_a : P(x_A > x_B) > 1/2$; the A distribution is shifted to the right of the B distribution. [Or $H_a : P(x_A > x_B) < 1/2$; that is, the A distribution is shifted to the left of the B distribution.]	$H_a : P(x_A > x_B) \neq 1/2$.

(3) *Test Statistic:* x = number of pairs of observations for which x_A exceeds x_B.

(4) *Rejection Region:*

One-Tailed	**Two-Tailed**
For $H_a : P(x_A > x_B) > 1/2$, reject H_0 for very large values of x. For $H_a : P(x_A > x_B) < 1/2$, reject H_0 for very small values of x.	Reject H_0 for very large or very small values of x.

Assumptions: The observations x_A and x_B are randomly and independently selected in matched pairs. Tied observations (i.e., when $x_A = x_B$) are eliminated from the data, and the number of pairs n is reduced accordingly.

EXAMPLE 15.1   Table 15.1 gives the numbers of employee health insurance claims per month for ten randomly selected months at each of two physically identical automobile assembly plants. Do the data provide sufficient evidence to indicate a difference in the numbers of health insurance claims per month at the two assembly plants? Test using α near .10.

SOLUTION   Since we want to detect either a shift in the A distribution to the right or to the left of the B distribution—that is, $P(x_A > x_B) > 1/2$ or $P(x_A > x_B) < 1/2$—we will conduct a two-tailed test and reject $H_0 : P(x_A > x_B) = 1/2$ when x, the number of months for which the number of claims at plant A exceeded the number at plant B, is very small or very large. We will choose the values of x to be included in the rejection region so that half of the x values fall in each tail of the binomial probability distribution and so that α

TABLE 15.1   Numbers of Health Insurance Claims per Month at Two Assembly Plants (Example 15.1)

Month	Plant A	Plant B	Month	Plant A	Plant B
1	170	201	6	142	170
2	164	179	7	191	183
3	140	159	8	169	179
4	184	195	9	161	170
5	174	177	10	200	212

is approximately equal to .10. Consulting Table 1 in the Appendix for $n = 10$, you will find that for $x = 0, 1, 9,$ and 10,

$$\alpha = P(x \text{ is in the rejection region if in fact } H_0 \text{ is true})$$

$$= p(0) + p(1) + p(9) + p(10) = .022$$

Since this value of α is too small, the rejection region is expanded by including the next pair of x values that are most contradictory to the null hypothesis, namely, $x = 2$ and $x = 8$. The value of α for this rejection region ($x = 0, 1, 2, 8, 9, 10$) is obtained from Table 1 in the Appendix:

$$\alpha = p(0) + p(1) + p(2) + p(8) + p(9) + p(10) = .11$$

Since this value of α is close to .10, we will employ $x = 0, 1, 2, 8, 9, 10$ as the rejection region for the test. (See Figure 15.1.)

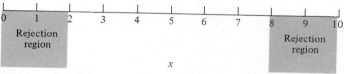

FIGURE 15.1   Rejection Region for Example 15.1

From the data we observe that $x = 1$, and therefore, we reject the null hypothesis. Thus we conclude that sufficient evidence exists to indicate that the population distributions differ in their relative locations. In fact, the data suggest that the number of health insurance claims in any one month at plant B tends to exceed the corresponding number at plant A. ∎

When the number of pairs in a paired-difference experiment is large, the probability distribution for x, the number of times x_A is larger than x_B, can be approximated by a normal distribution. Therefore, with $p = P(x_A > x_B)$ we can test

$$H_0 : p = .5$$

using the test for a binomial proportion described in Section 7.6. When H_0 is true—

that is, $p = .5$—then

$$\sigma_{\hat{p}} = \sqrt{\frac{pq}{n}} = \sqrt{\frac{(.5)(.5)}{n}} = \sqrt{\frac{.25}{n}}$$

and

$$z = \frac{\hat{p} - p}{\sqrt{\frac{pq}{n}}} = \frac{\dfrac{x}{n} - .5}{\sqrt{\frac{.25}{n}}} = \frac{x - .5n}{\sqrt{.25n}}$$

The test is summarized in the following box.

SIGN TEST FOR LARGE SAMPLES, $n \geq 25$

(1) *Null Hypothesis:* $H_0 : p = .5$ (i.e., neither treatment A nor B is preferred over the other).

(2) *Alternative Hypothesis:*

Two-Tailed Test	**Upper One-Tailed Test**
$H_a : p \neq .5$	$H_a : p > .5$

(3) *Test Statistic:*

$$z = \frac{x - .5n}{\sqrt{.25n}}.$$

(4) *Rejection Region:*

Two-Tailed Test	**Upper One-Tailed Test**
Reject H_0 if $z > z_{\alpha/2}$ or if $z < -z_{\alpha/2}$	Reject H_0 if $z > z_\alpha$

Assumptions: The observations x_A and x_B are randomly and independently selected in matched pairs. Tied observations (i.e., when $x_A = x_B$) are eliminated from the data and the number of pairs n is reduced accordingly.

Note: To find a z value, use the same procedure used in Chapter 7. The z values are given in Table 4 of the Appendix.

EXERCISES

BASIC TECHNIQUES

15.1 Suppose that you wish to use the sign test to test $H_0 : p = .5$ against $H_a : p > .5$ for a paired-difference experiment with $n = 25$ pairs.

(a) State the practical situation that would dictate the alternative hypothesis given.

(b) Use Table 1 in the Appendix to find values of α ($\alpha < .15$) available for the test.

15.2 Repeat the instructions of Exercise 15.1 for $H_a : p \neq .5$.

15.3 Suppose that you wish to use the sign test to test $H_0 : p = .5$ against $H_a : p > .5$ for a paired-difference experiment with $n = 15$ pairs.

   (a) State the practical situation that would dictate the alternative hypothesis given.
   (b) Use Table 1 in the Appendix to find values of α ($\alpha < .15$) available for the test.

15.4 Repeat the instructions of Exercise 15.3 for $H_a : p \neq .5$.

15.5 Give the values of x in the rejection region for the sign test in Exercise 15.2 for $\alpha = .05$. Then find the values of x in the rejection region for the sign test for large samples based on the z statistic. Compare the two rejection regions. Do they agree?

15.6 Refer to Exercise 15.1. Suppose that you were to conduct the test for $\alpha = .05$ and observed $x = 17$.

   (a) Do the data provide sufficient evidence to indicate that the distribution of x_A is shifted to the right of the distribution of x_B? Explain.
   (b) Find the p-value for the test and interpret its value.

15.7 The following data were collected in a paired-difference experiment:

x_A	x_B	x_A	x_B
3.4	3.2	4.3	4.0
4.1	4.1	4.3	4.2
3.9	3.8	2.9	2.5
3.5	3.6	4.0	3.8
3.8	3.4	3.5	3.4

Do the data provide sufficient evidence to indicate that $P(x_A > x_B)$ is larger than .5?
   (a) State H_0.   (b) State H_a.
   (c) Test H_0 for $\alpha = .05$, using a sign test.   (d) Find the p-value for the test.

15.8 Repeat the instructions of Exercise 15.7 if you wish to detect whether $P(x_A > x_B)$ is either less than .5 or greater than .5.

15.9 A paired-difference experiment was conducted, using $n = 30$ pairs. The number x of times that x_A exceeded x_B was $x = 10$. Do the data provide sufficient evidence to indicate that $p = P(x_A > x_B)$ differs from .5? Test using $\alpha = .05$.

   (a) State the null and alternative hypotheses.
   (b) Give the test statistic and rejection region for the large-sample z test.
   (c) Conduct the test and state the practical conclusions to be derived from the test results. Use $\alpha = .05$.

15.10 A paired-difference experiment was conducted, using $n = 35$ pairs. The number of times that x_A exceeded x_B was $x = 18$. Do the data provide sufficient evidence to indicate that the distribution for x_A is shifted to the right of the distribution for x_B?

   (a) State the null and alternative hypotheses.
   (b) Give the test statistic and rejection region for the test.
   (c) Conduct the test and state the practical conclusions to be derived from the test results. Use $\alpha = .05$.
   (d) Give the p-value for the test in part (c), and interpret its value.

APPLICATIONS

15.11 In Exercise 8.46 we compared property evaluations of two tax assessors, *A* and *B*. Their assessments for eight properties are shown in Table 15.2.

TABLE 15.2   Assessment Data for Exercise 15.11

| | Assessor | |
Property	A	B
1	36.3	35.1
2	48.4	46.8
3	40.2	37.3
4	54.7	50.6
5	28.7	29.1
6	42.8	41.0
7	36.1	35.3
8	39.0	39.1

(a) Use the sign test to determine whether the data present sufficient evidence to indicate that one of the assessors tends to be consistently more conservative than the other—that is, $P(x_A > x_B) \neq 1/2$. Test by using a value of α near .05. Find the *p*-value for the test and interpret its value.

(b) Exercise 8.46 uses the *t* statistic to test the null hypothesis that there is no difference in the mean level of property assessments between assessors *A* and *B*. Check the answer (in the answer section) for Exercise 8.46 and compare it with your answer to part (a). Do the test results agree? Explain why the answers are (or are not) consistent.

15.12 Two gourmets rated 20 meals on a scale of 1 to 10. The data are shown in Table 15.3. Do the data provide sufficient evidence to indicate that one of the gourmets tends to give higher ratings than the other? Test using the sign test with a value of α near .05.

TABLE 15.3   Meal-Ratings Data for Exercise 15.12

Meal	A	B	Meal	A	B
1	6	8	11	6	9
2	4	5	12	8	5
3	7	4	13	4	2
4	8	7	14	3	3
5	2	3	15	6	8
6	7	4	16	9	10
7	9	9	17	9	8
8	7	8	18	4	6
9	2	5	19	4	3
10	4	3	20	5	5

15.13 In preparing to add new inventory, the owner of a women's clothing store needs to know whether women have a preference for one or the other of two different dress styles. Twenty women customers were randomly selected and asked to choose the style they preferred. Six chose style A and 14 chose style B.

(a) Do these data provide sufficient evidence to indicate a difference in preference for the two dress styles? Test using α near .05.

(b) If the store owner wants to estimate the proportion of all customers who prefer dress style A correct to within .10 with probability equal to .95, approximately how many customers would the store owner have to sample?

15.14 The number of defective fuses proceeding from each of two production lines, A and B, was recorded daily for a period of 10 days, with the results shown in Table 15.4. Assume that both production lines produced the same daily output. Compare the number of defectives produced by A and B each day, and let x equal the number of days when B exceeded A. Do the data present sufficient evidence to indicate that production line B tends to produce more defectives than A? State the null and alternative hypotheses. Use x as a test statistic.

TABLE 15.4 Production Line Data for Exercise 15.14

Day	Line A	Line B	Day	Line A	Line B
1	172	201	6	142	170
2	165	179	7	190	182
3	206	159	8	169	179
4	184	192	9	161	169
5	174	177	10	200	210

15.15 In 1975 the General Accounting Office (GAO) examined 15 school districts in 14 states and concluded that it was debatable whether the multibillion dollar Title I program, aimed primarily at improving the reading ability of poor children, was effective. In particular, the GAO noted that the gap between the reading abilities of educationally deprived and of average children increased while the students were in the program (*Orlando Sentinel Star*, December 28, 1975). If the Title I program were completely ineffective, the change in the level of reading ability scores (before and after Title I) would depend on the random variation of individual student scores, so that it would be reasonable to assume that $P(\text{increase in level}) = P(\text{decrease in level}) = p = .5$. Test the hypothesis that $p = .5$, using x, the number of school districts showing an increase in the reading ability gap, as a test statistic.

(a) State the null and the alternative hypotheses.

(b) Locate a rejection region for a value of α near .05 (assume that $n = 15$).

(c) From the GAO report, it appears that $x = 15$. What do you conclude concerning the effectiveness of the Title I program?

15.16 Establishing the value of an art object is subjective in nature and difficult at best. To determine whether two art appraisers tend to give different levels of appraisals, two appraisers, A and B, were asked to appraise each of seven art objects. If appraiser A tends to give smaller appraisals (or give larger appraisals) than appraiser B, the probability p that the appraisal of A will exceed the appraisal for B will be less than $1/2$ (or greater than $1/2$). Under the assumption that there is no difference in the appraisal techniques of the two appraisers, $p = 1/2$. Let x, the number of art objects for which A's appraisal exceeds B's appraisal, be a test statistic.

(a) Find an appropriate rejection region to test the null hypothesis $p = 1/2$ for $\alpha \approx .10$.

(b) If A tends to give conservative evaluations, so that p actually is equal to .9, calculate β for the test.

(c) If A appraises five of the seven art objects to be worth more than β appraises them for, what do you conclude?

15.17 A manufacturer of a liquid cleaner has developed a new spray intended to reduce the accumulation of dirt on windows. Two adjacent windows in each of 50 houses were employed in the experiment, and one window in each pair was randomly selected and treated with the dirt retardant. After the windows were exposed to the elements for two months, each homeowner was asked to identify the cleaner window panel. (Ties were permitted.) Two homeowners found no difference in the appearance of the panels. Thirty-eight of the remaining 48 selected the treated panels as the cleaner of the two. Do these data provide sufficient evidence to indicate that the treated glass panels were preferred over the untreated panels? Test using $\alpha = .01$.

THE MANN-WHITNEY U TEST: INDEPENDENT RANDOM SAMPLES

15.3

A statistical test for comparing the relative locations of two populations A and B (a test for shift) based on independent random samples was proposed by Wilcoxon (1945) and in slightly different form by Mann and Whitney (1947). The test procedure involves **ranking** the n_1 and n_2 observations, randomly and independently selected from populations A and B, from the smallest (rank $= 1$) to the largest (rank $= n_1 + n_2$). Rankings for tied observations are averaged, and the average rank is assigned to each of the tied observations. Then the sum T_A of the ranks for sample A and the sum T_B of the ranks for sample B are calculated. The **rank sums** are used in constructing the test statistic.

The logic is that if distribution A is shifted to the right of distribution B, then the rank sum T_A should exceed T_B. The **Mann-Whitney U test statistic** will use one of the two quantities U_A or U_B shown in the following box.

FORMULAS FOR THE MANN-WHITNEY U STATISTIC

$$U_A = n_1 n_2 + \frac{n_1(n_1 + 1)}{2} - T_A$$

$$U_B = n_1 n_2 + \frac{n_2(n_2 + 1)}{2} - T_B$$

where
n_1 = number of observations in sample A

n_2 = number of observations in sample B

$U_A + U_B = n_1 n_2$

T_A and T_B = rank sums for samples A and B, respectively

As you can see from the formulas for U_A and U_B, U_A will be small when T_A is large, a situation that likely will occur when the population distribution of the A measurements is shifted to the right of the population distribution for the B measurements. Consequently, to conduct a one-tailed test to detect a shift in the A distribution to the right of the B distribution, you will reject the null hypothesis of "no difference in the population distributions" if U_A is less than some specified value U_0. That is, you will reject H_0 for small values of U_A. Similarly, to conduct a one-tailed test to detect a shift of the B distribution to the right of the A distribution, you will reject H_0 if U_B is less than some specified value, say U_0. Consequently, the rejection region for the Mann-Whitney U test will appear as shown in Figure 15.2.

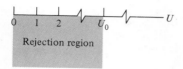

FIGURE 15.2   Rejection Region for a Mann-Whitney U Test

Table 12 in the Appendix gives the probability that an observed value of U will be less than some specified value, say U_0. This is the value of α for a one-tailed test. To conduct a two-tailed test—that is, to detect a shift in the population distributions for the A and B measurements in either direction—we will agree to always use U, the smaller of U_A or U_B, as the test statistic and reject H_0 for $U < U_0$ (see Figure 15.2). The value of α for the two-tailed test will be double the tabulated value given in Table 12 in the Appendix.

To see how to locate the rejection region for the Mann-Whitney U test, suppose that $n_1 = 4$ and $n_2 = 5$. Then you consult the third table in Table 12 in the Appendix, the one corresponding to $n_2 = 5$. The first few lines of Table 12, $n_2 = 5$, are shown here in Table 15.5. Note that the table is constructed on the assumption that $n_1 \leq n_2$.

Across the top of Table 15.5 you see values of n_1. Values of U_0 are shown down the left side of the table. The entries give the probability that U will assume a small value, namely, the probability that $U \leq U_0$. Since for our example $n_1 = 4$, we will move across the top of the table to $n_1 = 4$. Move to the third row of the table corresponding to $U_0 = 2$ for $n_1 = 4$. Then you see that the probability that U will be less than or equal to 2 is .0317. Similarly, moving across the row for $U_0 = 3$, you see that the probability that U is less than or equal to 3 is .0556. (This value is shaded in Table 15.5.) So, if you want to conduct a one-tailed Mann-Whitney U test with $n_1 = 4$ and $n_2 = 5$ and would like α to be near .05, you would reject the null hypothesis of equality of population

TABLE 15.5   An Abbreviated Version of Table 12 in the Appendix; $P(U \leq U_0)$ for $n_2 = 5$

	n_1	1	2	3	4	5
	0	.1667	.0376	.0179	.0079	.0040
	1	.3333	.0952	.0357	.0159	.0079
	2	.5000	.1905	.0714	.0317	.0159
U_0	3		.2857	.1250	.0556	.0278
	4		.4286	.1964	.0952	.0476
	5		.5714	.2857	.1429	.0754
	⋮		⋮	⋮	⋮	⋮

relative frequency distributions when $U \leq 3$. The probability of a type I error for the test would be $\alpha = .0556$. If you use this same rejection region for a two-tailed test, that is, $U \leq 3$, α will be double the tabulated value, or $\alpha = 2(.0556) = .1112$.

Table 12 in the Appendix can also be used to find the observed significance level for a test. For example, if $n_1 = 5$, $n_2 = 5$, and $U = 4$, then from Table 15.5 the p-value for a one-tailed test is

$$P(U \leq 4) = .0476$$

If the test is two-tailed, the p-value is

$$2(.0476) \quad \text{or} \quad .0952$$

The details of the test are summarized in the box on page 657.

EXAMPLE 15.2

An experiment was conducted to compare the strength of two types of kraft papers, one a standard kraft paper of a specified weight and the other the same standard kraft paper treated with a chemical substance. Ten pieces of each type of paper, randomly selected from production, produced the strength measurements shown in Table 15.6. Test the hypothesis of "no difference in the distributions of strengths for the two types of paper" against the alternative hypothesis that the treated paper tends to be of greater strength (i.e., its distribution of strength measurements is shifted to the right of the corresponding distribution for the untreated paper).

TABLE 15.6   Paper Strength Measurements for Example 15.2

	Standard, A	Treated, B
	1.21 (2)	1.49 (15)
	1.43 (12)	1.37 (7.5)
	1.35 (6)	1.67 (20)
	1.51 (17)	1.50 (16)
	1.39 (9)	1.31 (5)
	1.17 (1)	1.29 (3.5)
	1.48 (14)	1.52 (18)
	1.42 (11)	1.37 (7.5)
	1.29 (3.5)	1.44 (13)
	1.40 (10)	1.53 (19)
Rank sums	$T_A = 85.5$	$T_B = 124.5$

SOLUTION

The ranks are shown in parentheses alongside the $n_1 + n_2 = 10 + 10 = 20$ strength measurements; and the rank sums, T_A and T_B, are shown below the columns. Since we want to detect a shift in the distribution of the B measurements to the right of the distribution for the A measurements, we will reject the null hypothesis of "no difference in population strength distributions" when T_B is excessively large. Because this

THE MANN-WHITNEY U TEST

(1) *Null Hypothesis: H_0:* the population relative frequency distributions for A and B are identical.

(2) *Alternative Hypothesis: H_a:* the two population relative frequency distributions are shifted with respect to their relative locations (a two-tailed test). Or H_a: the population relative frequency distribution for A is shifted to the right of the relative frequency distribution for population B (a one-tailed test).*

(3) *Test Statistic:* For a two-tailed test, use U, the smaller of

$$U_A = n_1 n_2 + \frac{n_1(n_1 + 1)}{2} - T_A$$

and

$$U_B = n_1 n_2 + \frac{n_2(n_2 + 1)}{2} - T_B$$

where T_A and T_B are the rank sums for samples A and B, respectively. For a one-tailed test, use U_A.

(4) *Rejection Region:*

Two-Tailed Test

For a given value of α, reject H_0 if $U \leq U_0$, where $P(U \leq U_0) = \alpha/2$. [*Note:* Observe that U_0 is the value such that $P(U \leq U_0)$ is equal to half of α.]

One-Tailed Test

For a given value of α, reject H_0 if $U_A \leq U_0$, where $P(U_A \leq U_0) = \alpha$.

Assumptions: Samples have been randomly and independently selected from their respective populations. Ties in the observations can be handled by averaging the ranks that would have been assigned to the tied observations and assigning this average to each. Thus if three observations are tied and are due to receive ranks 3, 4, 5, we assign the rank of 4 to all three.

---

*For the sake of convenience, we will describe the one-tailed test as one designed to detect a shift in the distribution of the A measurements to the right of the distribution of the B measurements. To detect a shift in the B distribution to the right of the A distribution, just interchange the letters A and B in the discussion.

situation will occur when U_B is small, we will conduct a one-tailed statistical test and reject the null hypothesis when $U_B \leq U_0$.

Suppose that we choose a value of α near .05. Then we can find U_0 by consulting the portion of Table 12 in the Appendix corresponding to $n_2 = 10$. The probability $P(U \leq U_0)$ nearest .05 is .0526 and corresponds to $U_0 = 28$. Hence, we will reject H_0 if $U_B \leq 28$.

Calculating U_B, we have

$$U_B = n_1 n_2 + \frac{n_2(n_2 + 1)}{2} - T_B$$

$$= (10)(10) + \frac{(10)(11)}{2} - 124.5$$

$$= 30.5$$

As you can see, U_B is not less than $U_0 = 28$. Therefore, we cannot reject the null hypothesis. At the $\alpha = .05$ level of significance, there is not sufficient evidence to indicate that the treated kraft paper is stronger than the standard. ■

A simplified large-sample test ($n_1 \geq 10$ and $n_2 \geq 10$) can be obtained by using the familiar z statistic of Chapter 7. When the population distributions are identical, it can be shown that the U statistic has expected value and variance

$$E(U) = \frac{n_1 n_2}{2} \quad \text{and} \quad V(U) = \frac{n_1 n_2(n_1 + n_2 + 1)}{12}$$

and the distribution of

$$z = \frac{U - E(U)}{\sigma_U}$$

tends to normality with mean zero and variance equal to 1 as n_1 and n_2 become large. This approximation will be adequate when n_1 and n_2 are both greater than or equal to 10. Thus for a two-tailed test with $\alpha = .05$, we will reject the null hypothesis if $|z| > 1.96$.

The next box gives the details of the Mann-Whitney test for large samples.

THE MANN-WHITNEY U TEST FOR LARGE SAMPLES, $n_1 > 10$ AND $n_2 > 10$

(1) *Null Hypothesis: H_0*: the population relative frequency distributions for A and B are identical.

(2) *Alternative Hypothesis: H_a*: the two population relative frequency distributions are not identical (a two-tailed test). Or H_a: the population relative frequency distribution for A is shifted to the right (or left) of the relative frequency distribution for population B (a one-tailed test).

(3) *Test Statistic: $z = \dfrac{U - (n_1 n_2/2)}{\sqrt{n_1 n_2(n_1 + n_2 + 1)/12}}$*. Let $U = U_A$

(4) *Rejection Region:* Reject H_0 if $z > z_{\alpha/2}$ or $z < -z_{\alpha/2}$ for a two-tailed test. For a one-tailed test, place all of α in one tail of the z distribution. To detect a shift in the distribution of the A observations to the right of the distribution of the B observations, let $U = U_A$ and reject H_0 when $z < -z_\alpha$. To detect a shift in the opposite direction, let $U = U_A$ and reject H_0 when $z > z_\alpha$. Tabulated values of z are given in Table 4 in the Appendix.

Observe that the z statistic will reach the same conclusion as the exact U test for Example 15.2. Thus

$$z = \frac{30.5 - [(10)(10)/2]}{\sqrt{[(10)(10)(10 + 10 + 1)]/12}} = \frac{30.5 - 50}{\sqrt{2100/12}} = -\frac{19.5}{\sqrt{175}}$$

$$= -\frac{19.5}{13.23} = -1.47$$

For a one-tailed test with $\alpha = .05$ located in the lower tail of the z distribution, we will reject the null hypothesis if $z < -1.645$. You can see that $z = -1.47$ does not fall in the rejection region and that this test reaches the same conclusion as the exact U test of Example 15.2.

EXERCISES

BASIC TECHNIQUES

15.18 Suppose that you wish to detect a shift in distribution A to the right of distribution B based on sample sizes $n_1 = 6$ and $n_2 = 8$.
(a) Should you use U_A or U_B for your test statistic?
(b) Give the rejection region for the test if you wish α to be close to but less than .10.
(c) Give the value of α for the test.

15.19 Suppose that the alternative hypothesis for Exercise 15.18 is that distribution A is shifted either to the left or to the right of distribution B.
(a) Should you use U_A or U_B for your test statistic?
(b) Give the rejection region for the test if you wish α to be close to but less than .10.
(c) Give the value of α for the test.

15.20 Suppose that you wish to detect a shift in distribution A to the left of distribution B based on sample sizes $n_1 = 4$ and $n_2 = 5$.
(a) Should you use U_A or U_B for your test statistic?
(b) Give the rejection region for the test if you wish α to be close to but less than .10.
(c) Give the value of α for the test.

15.21 Suppose that the alternative hypothesis for Exercise 15.20 is that distribution A is shifted either to the left or to the right of distribution B.
(a) Should you use U_A or U_B for your test statistic?
(b) Give the rejection region for the test if you wish α to be close to but less than .10.
(c) Give the value of α for the test.

15.22 Suppose that you wish to detect a shift in distribution A to the right of distribution B based on sample sizes $n_1 = 12$ and $n_2 = 14$. If $T_A = 193$, what do you conclude? Use $\alpha = .05$.

15.23 Suppose that you wish to detect a difference in the location of two population distributions based on samples of $n_1 = 15$ and $n_2 = 15$ observations, respectively, selected from the populations. If $T_B = 251$, what do you conclude? Use $\alpha = .10$.

APPLICATIONS

 15.24 Is consumer reaction to a product marketing display different from one market to another? A company that manufactures kitchen appliances constructed the same product display in large department stores in each of two different markets, *A* and *B*. Ten persons viewing the display were randomly selected at each location and asked to rate the display on a scale of 1 to 20. The twenty ratings are shown below.

Market A	15	11	20	14	9	12	5	17	13	18
Market B	17	6	15	10	6	8	10	16	8	7

Do the data present sufficient evidence to indicate that the levels of ratings differ between the two markets?

15.25 The life, in months of service, before a failure of the color television picture tube in 8 television sets manufactured by firm *A* and 10 sets manufactured by firm *B* are as follows:

Firm	Life of Picture Tube (Months)									
A	32	25	40	31	35	29	37	39		
B	41	39	36	47	45	34	48	44	43	33

Use the *U* test to analyze the data, and test to see whether the life, in months of service, before failure of the picture tube is the same for the picture tubes manufactured by each firm. (Use $\alpha = .10$.)

15.26 In Exercise 8.36 we presented data on the sales of health and beauty aids per linear foot of floor space for 15 supermarket firms, 5 of which used rack jobbers (service merchandisers) to supply their stores and 10 of which did their own direct buying and warehousing. The sales (in dollars) per linear foot of floor space for the 15 firms are reproduced in Table 15.7.

TABLE 15.7   Method of Supply Data for Exercise 15.26

Service Merchandisers; $n = 5$	Direct Buying (In-House Warehousing); $n = 10$	
6100	4100	2000
2950	3500	1800
3800	3500	900
2200	2700	1800
2400	2400	1900

Source: R. C. Curhan, W. J. Salmon, and R. D. Buzzell, "Sales and Profitability of Health and Beauty Aids and General Merchandise in Supermarkets," *Journal of Retailing,* Vol. 59, No. 1, 1983.

(a) Do the data present sufficient evidence to indicate a difference in the level of sales per linear foot of floor space between firms supplied by rack jobbers and those that buy directly and warehouse? Test using the Mann-Whitney *U* test with $\alpha = .10$.

(b) Compare the results of the Mann-Whitney *U* test with those of the *t* test in Exercise 8.36.

15.27 A manufacturer of lawn mowers buys a particular bolt in boxes of 10,000 bolts each from two different suppliers. In order to compare the percentage of defectives shipped by the suppliers, the manufacturer sampled 100 bolts from each of ten cartons for each supplier. The number x of defective bolts in each sample of 1000 is shown in the table.

Supplier A	7	12	29	8	15	11	17	15	22	20
Supplier B	19	24	14	17	25	21	13	23	18	18

Do the data provide sufficient evidence to indicate that the proportions of defectives shipped by the two suppliers differ?

(a) Explain why the data violate the assumptions required for a Student's t test.

(b) Test for a difference, using the Mann-Whitney U test with $\alpha = .05$.

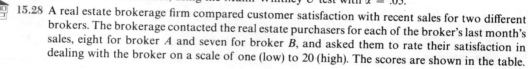 15.28 A real estate brokerage firm compared customer satisfaction with recent sales for two different brokers. The brokerage contacted the real estate purchasers for each of the broker's last month's sales, eight for broker A and seven for broker B, and asked them to rate their satisfaction in dealing with the broker on a scale of one (low) to 20 (high). The scores are shown in the table.

Broker A	13	18	17	20	16	20	14	15
Broker B	16	10	12	15	19	17	11	

Do the data provide sufficient evidence to indicate that the level-of-satisfaction scores differ from one broker to another? Test using $\alpha = .10$.

THE WILCOXON SIGNED RANK TEST FOR A PAIRED EXPERIMENT

15.4

Wilcoxon proposed a nonparametric test, similar to the test of Section 15.3, to analyze the paired-difference experiment of Section 8.5. The test uses the paired differences of the two treatments A and B to test the null hypothesis that $P(x_A > x_B) = 1/2$ versus either a one- or a two-sided alternative hypothesis.

To carry out the **Wilcoxon signed rank test**, calculate the differences $(x_A - x_B)$ for each of the n pairs. Differences equal to zero are eliminated and the number of pairs n is reduced accordingly. Rank the *absolute values* of the differences, assigning a 1 to the smallest, a 2 to the second smallest, and so on. Then calculate the rank sum for the negative differences, and also calculate the rank sum for the positive differences. For a two-tailed test we use the smaller of these two quantities, T, as a test statistic to test the null hypothesis that the two population relative frequency histograms are identical. The smaller the value of T, the greater will be the weight of evidence favoring rejection of the null hypothesis. Therefore, we will reject the null hypothesis if T is less than or equal to some value, say T_0.

To detect the one-sided alternative—that the distribution of the A observations is shifted to the right of the B observations—use the rank sum T^- of the negative differences and reject the null hypothesis for small values of T^-, say $T^- \leq T_0$. If you want to detect a shift of the distribution of B observations to the right of the distribution of A observations, use the rank sum T^+ of the positive differences as a test statistic and reject for small values of T^+, say $T^+ \leq T_0$.

The probability that T is less than or equal to some value T_0 has been calculated for a combination of sample sizes and values of T_0. These probabilities, given in Table 13 of the Appendix, can be used to find the rejection region for the T test.

An abbreviated version of Table 13 of the Appendix is shown here in Table 15.8. Across the top of the table you see the number of differences (the number of pairs), n. Values of α (denoted by the symbol P in Wilcoxon's table) for a one-tailed test appear in the first column of the table. The second column gives values of α (P in Wilcoxon's notation) for a two-tailed test. Table entries are the critical values of T. You will recall that the critical value of a test statistic is the value that locates the boundary of the rejection region.

TABLE 15.8   An Abbreviated Version of Table 13 in the Appendix; Critical Values of T

One-Sided	Two-Sided	$n = 5$	$n = 6$	$n = 7$	$n = 8$	$n = 9$	$n = 10$
$P = .05$	$P = .10$	1	2	4	6	8	11
$P = .025$	$P = .05$		1	2	4	6	8
$P = .01$	$P = .02$			0	2	3	5
$P = .005$	$P = .01$				0	2	3

One-Sided	Two-Sided	$n = 11$	$n = 12$	$n = 13$	$n = 14$	$n = 15$	$n = 16$
$P = .05$	$P = .10$	14	17	21	26	30	36
$P = .025$	$P = .05$	11	14	17	21	25	30
$P = .01$	$P = .02$	7	10	13	16	20	24
$P = .005$	$P = .01$	5	7	10	13	16	19

For example, suppose you have $n = 7$ pairs and you are conducting a two-tailed test of the null hypothesis that the two population relative frequency distributions are identical. Checking the $n = 7$ column of Table 13 and using the second row (corresponding to $P = \alpha = .05$ for a two-tailed test), you see the entry 2 (shaded in Table 15.8). This is T_0, the critical value of T. As noted earlier, the smaller the value of T, the greater will be the evidence to reject the null hypothesis. Therefore, you will reject the null hypothesis for all values of T less than or equal to 2. The rejection region for the Wilcoxon signed rank test for a paired experiment is always of this form: Reject H_0 if $T \leq T_0$, where T_0 is the critical value of T. The rejection region is shown symbolically in Figure 15.3.

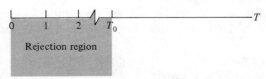

FIGURE 15.3   Rejection Region for the Wilcoxon Signed Rank Test for a Paired Experiment (Reject H_0 If $T \leq T_0$)

The details of the Wilcoxon test are summarized in the following box.

WILCOXON SIGNED RANK TEST FOR A PAIRED EXPERIMENT

(1) *Null Hypothesis:* H_0: the two population relative frequency distributions are identical.

(2) *Alternative Hypothesis:* H_a: the two population relative frequency distributions differ in location (a two-tailed test). Or H_a: the population relative frequency distribution for A is shifted to the right* of the relative frequency distribution for population B (a one-tailed test).

(3) *Test Statistic:*

Two-Tailed Test

Use T, the smaller of the rank sum for positive and the rank sum for negative differences.

One-Tailed Test

Use the rank sum T^- of the negative differences to detect the alternative hypothesis described above.

(4) *Rejection Region:*

Two-Tailed Test

Reject H_0 if $T \leq T_0$, where T_0 is the critical value given in Table 13 of the Appendix.

One-Tailed Test

Use the rank sum T^- of the negative differences. Reject H_0 if $T^- \leq T_0$ to detect the alternative hypothesis described above.

*To detect a shift of the distribution of B observations to the right of the distribution of A observations, use the rank sum T^+ of the positive differences as the test statistic and reject H_0 if $T^+ \leq T_0$.

EXAMPLE 15.3

The manager of a money fund compared the percentage monthly returns for two different types, A and B, of short-term loans. The data, collected over a six-month period, are shown in Table 15.9. Do the data provide sufficient evidence to indicate that the distributions of monthly returns for the two types of loans differ in location?

TABLE 15.9   Percentage Monthly Returns for Example 15.3

| Statistic | Month | | | | | |
	1	2	3	4	5	6
x_A	10.5	7.2	6.8	11.1	10.1	11.4
x_B	9.9	9.0	8.2	12.2	10.5	13.3
Difference $(x_A - x_B)$	.6	−1.8	−1.4	−1.1	−.4	−1.9
Rank	2	5	4	3	1	6

SOLUTION   The percentage monthly returns, x_A and x_B, their differences, and the ranks of their absolute differences for the two types of short-term loans are shown in Table 15.9.

As with our other nonparametric tests, the null hypothesis to be tested is that the two population frequency distributions of percentage monthly returns are identical. The alternative hypothesis, which implies a two-tailed test, is that one of the distributions is shifted to the right of the other.

Because the amount of data is small, we will conduct our test using $\alpha = .10$. From Table 13 the critical value of T for a two-tailed test, $\alpha = .10$, is $T_0 = 2$. Thus we will reject H_0 if $T \leq 2$ (see Figure 15.4).

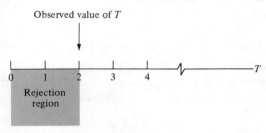

FIGURE 15.4   Rejection Region for Example 15.3, $\alpha = .10$

Now let us find the observed value of the test statistic T. Checking the ranks of the absolute differences, you can see that there is only one positive difference, and it has a rank of 2. Since we have agreed to always use the smaller rank sum as the test statistic, the observed value of the test statistic is $T = 2$. Since $T = 2$ falls in the rejection region, we reject H_0 and conclude that the two population frequency distributions of percentage monthly returns differ in respect to location.   ▪

Although Table 13 in the Appendix is applicable for values of n (number of data pairs) as large as $n = 50$, it is worth noting that T^+, like the Mann-Whitney U, will be approximately normally distributed when the null hypothesis is true and n is large (say 25 or more). This enables us to construct a large-sample z test, where

$$E(T^+) = \frac{n(n + 1)}{4}$$

$$V(T^+) = \frac{n(n + 1)(2n + 1)}{24}$$

Then the z statistic,

$$z = \frac{T^+ - E(T^+)}{\sigma_{T^+}} = \frac{T^+ - [n(n + 1)/4]}{\sqrt{[n(n + 1)(2n + 1)]/24}}$$

can be used as a test statistic. Thus for a two-tailed test and $\alpha = .05$, we will reject the hypothesis of "identical population distributions" when $|z| > 1.96$. The details of the large-sample test are given in the box on page 665.

A LARGE-SAMPLE WILCOXON SIGNED RANK TEST FOR A PAIRED EXPERIMENT, $n \geq 25$

(1) *Null Hypothesis: H_0:* the population relative frequency distributions for A and B are identical.

(2) *Alternative Hypothesis: H_a:* the two population relative frequency distributions differ in location (a two-tailed test). Or H_a: the population relative frequency distribution for A is shifted to the right (or left) of the relative frequency distribution for population B (a one-tailed test).

(3) *Test Statistic:* $z = \dfrac{T^+ - [n(n + 1)/4]}{\sqrt{[n(n + 1)(2n + 1)]/24}}$.

(4) *Rejection Region:* Reject H_0 if $z > z_{\alpha/2}$ or $z < -z_{\alpha/2}$ for a two-tailed test. For a one-tailed test, place all of α in one tail of the z distribution. To detect a shift in the distribution of the A observations to the right of the distribution of the B observations, reject H_0 when $z > z_\alpha$. To detect a shift in the opposite direction, reject H_0 if $z < -z_\alpha$. Tabulated values of z are given in Table 4 of the Appendix.

EXERCISES

BASIC TECHNIQUES

15.29 Suppose that you wish to detect a difference in location between two population distributions based on a paired-difference experiment consisting of $n = 30$ pairs.

(a) Give the null and alternative hypotheses for the Wilcoxon signed rank test.

(b) Give the test statistic.

(c) Give the rejection region for the test for $\alpha = .05$.

(d) If $T^+ = 249$, what are your conclusions? [*Note: $T^+ + T^- = n(n + 1)/2$.*]

15.30 Refer to Exercise 15.29. Suppose that you wish to detect only a shift in distribution A to the right of distribution B.

(a) Give the null and alternative hypotheses for the Wilcoxon signed rank text.

(b) Give the test statistic.

(c) Give the rejection region for the test for $\alpha = .05$.

(d) If $T^+ = 249$, what are your conclusions? [*Note: $T^+ + T^- = n(n + 1)/2$.*]

15.31 Refer to Exercise 15.29. Conduct the test using the large-sample z test. Compare your results with the nonparametric test results in Exercise 15.29(d).

15.32 Refer to Exercise 15.30. Conduct the test using the large-sample z test. Compare your results with the nonparametric test results in Exercise 15.30(d).

APPLICATIONS

15.33 In Exercise 15.11 we used the sign test to determine whether the data provided sufficient evidence to indicate a shift in the distributions of property assessments for assessors A and B.

(a) Use the Wilcoxon signed rank test for a paired experiment to test the null hypothesis that there is no difference in the distributions of property assessments between assessors A and B. Test using a value of α near .05.

(b) Compare the conclusion of the test in part (a) with the conclusions derived from the t test in Exercise 8.46 and the sign test in Exercise 15.11. Explain why these test conclusions are (or are not) consistent.

 15.34 The number of machine breakdowns per month was recorded for nine months on two identical machines used to make wire rope. The data are shown in Table 15.10.

TABLE 15.10   Breakdown Data for Exercise 15.34

	Machine	
Month	A	B
1	3	7
2	14	12
3	7	9
4	10	15
5	9	12
6	6	6
7	13	12
8	6	5
9	7	13

(a) Do the data provide sufficient evidence to indicate a difference in the monthly breakdown rates for the two machines? Test using a value of α near .05.

(b) Can you think of a reason why the breakdown rates for the two machines might vary from month to month?

 15.35 Two investment counselors were asked to rate each of ten investments on a scale of 1 to 100 based on the counselor's evaluation of the projected annual return and the intended risks of the investment. Do the data, shown in Table 15.11, provide sufficient evidence to indicate that one of the counselors tends to rate investments higher than the other? Test using $\alpha = .10$.

TABLE 15.11   Investment Data for Exercise 15.35

Investment	Counselor 1, x_1	Counselor 2, x_2
1	83	75
2	40	48
3	86	100
4	70	67
5	30	20
6	84	80
7	67	61
8	50	44
9	84	86
10	56	50

 15.36 The personnel director at a manufacturing plant compared the number of accidents per month for two different production lines over a 12-month period. The data are shown in Table 15.12.

TABLE 15.12   Accident Data for Exercise 15.36

Production Line	Month											
	Jan.	Feb.	Mar.	Apr.	May	June	July	Aug.	Sept.	Oct.	Nov.	Dec.
1	2	1	0	2	2	3	1	2	0	1	3	2
2	0	2	1	1	0	2	1	0	0	1	0	2

(a) Do the data provide sufficient evidence to indicate differences in the monthly rates of accidents between the two production lines? Use the Wilcoxon signed rank test with $\alpha = .05$.

(b) Which assumption required for the Student's t test do you think these data might violate? (*Note:* See optional Section 3.8 to learn why the data violate the assumptions required for a Student's t test.)

15.37 A CPA firm compared the auditing ability of two auditors by having each audit the same eight financial statements. The number of errors per audit found by each of the two auditors for each of the eight statements is shown in Table 15.13.

TABLE 15.13   Auditing Data for Exercise 15.37

Statement	Auditor	
	A	B
1	6	5
2	8	7
3	6	9
4	12	14
5	4	5
6	10	15
7	8	12
8	14	14

(a) Do the data provide sufficient evidence to indicate that the level of error detection differs for the two auditors? Test using the Wilcoxon signed rank test with $\alpha = .05$, and state the practical conclusions to be derived from the test results.

(b) Give the approximate p-value for the test and interpret it.

15.38 Exercise 8.48 gives the shipments (in dollars) for the current year and the last year for six different exporters. The data are reproduced in Table 15.14.

TABLE 15.14   Shipment Data for Exercise 15.38

Exporter	Year	
	Current	Last
1	4.81	4.27
2	5.03	5.97
3	2.38	2.61
4	4.26	3.96
5	5.14	4.86
6	3.93	3.17

(a) Do the data provide sufficient evidence to indicate a higher level of exports this year over the preceding year? Test using the Wilcoxon signed rank test with $\alpha = .05$.

(b) Find the approximate p-value for the test, and compare it with the results of the t test in Exercise 8.48. Do the test conclusions agree?

THE KRUSKAL-WALLIS H TEST FOR COMPLETELY RANDOMIZED DESIGNS

15.5

Just as the Mann-Whitney U test is the nonparametric alternative to the Student's t test for a comparison of population means, the **Kruskal-Wallis H test** is the nonparametric alternative to the analysis of variance F test for a completely randomized design. It is used to detect differences in location among more than two population distributions based on independent random sampling.

The procedure for conducting the Kruskal-Wallis H test is similar to that used for the Mann-Whitney U test. Suppose that we are comparing k populations based on independent random samples, n_1 from population 1, n_2 from population 2, . . . , and n_k from population k, where

$$n_1 + n_2 + \cdots + n_k = n$$

The first step is to rank all n observations from the smallest (rank 1) to the largest (rank n). Tied observations are assigned a rank equal to the average of the ranks they would have received if they had been nearly equal but not tied. We then calculate the rank sums $T_1, T_2, \ldots, T_k$ for the k samples and calculate the test statistic

$$H = \frac{12}{n(n + 1)} \sum_{i=1}^{k} \frac{T_i^2}{n_i} - 3(n + 1)$$

The greater the differences in location among the k population distributions, the larger will be the value of the H statistic. Thus we reject the null hypothesis that the k population distributions are identical for large values of H.

How large is large? It can be shown (proof omitted) that when the sample sizes are moderate to large—say, each sample size equal to 5 or larger—and when H_0 is true, the H statistic will possess approximately a chi-square distribution with $(k - 1)$ degrees of freedom. Therefore, for a given value of α we reject H_0 when the H statistic exceeds χ_α^2 (see Figure 15.5).

EXAMPLE 15.4

The data shown in Table 15.15 represent the achievement test scores for four different groups of sales trainees, each group taught by a different teaching technique. The objective of the experiment is to test the hypothesis of "no difference in the population distributions of achievement test scores" against the alternative that they differ in location, that is, that at least one of the distributions is shifted above the others. Conduct the test by using the Kruskal-Wallis H test with $\alpha = .05$.

SOLUTION

The first step is to rank the $n = 23$ observations from the smallest (rank 1) to the largest (rank 23). These ranks are shown in parentheses in the table. Note how the ties are

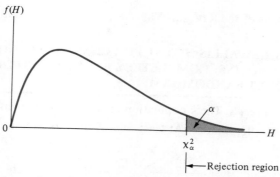

$f(H)$

α

0

χ_α^2

H

Rejection region

FIGURE 15.5   Approximate Distribution of the H Statistic When H_0 Is True

TABLE 15.15   Achievement Test Scores for Example 15.4 (Ranks in Parentheses)

	Group 1	Group 2	Group 3	Group 4
	65 (3)	75 (9)	59 (1)	94 (23)
	87 (19)	69 (5.5)	78 (11)	89 (21)
	73 (8)	83 (17.5)	67 (4)	80 (14)
	79 (12.5)	81 (15.5)	62 (2)	88 (20)
	81 (15.5)	72 (7)	83 (17.5)	
	69 (5.5)	79 (12.5)	76 (10)	
		90 (22)		
Rank sum	$T_1 = 63.5$	$T_2 = 89$	$T_3 = 45.5$	$T_4 = 78$

handled. For example, two observations at 69 were tied for rank 5. Therefore, they were assigned the average 5.5 of the two ranks (5 and 6) that they would have occupied if they had been slightly different. The rank sums T_1, T_2, T_3, and T_4 for the four samples are shown in the bottom row of the table.

Substituting rank sums and sample sizes into the formula for the H statistic, we obtain

$$H = \frac{12}{n(n+1)} \sum_{i=1}^{k} \frac{T_i^2}{n_i} - 3(n+1)$$

$$= \frac{12}{23(24)} \left[\frac{(63.5)^2}{6} + \frac{(89)^2}{7} + \frac{(45.5)^2}{6} + \frac{(78)^2}{4} \right] - 3(24)$$

$$= 79.775103 - 72 = 7.775103$$

The rejection region for the H statistic for $\alpha = .05$ includes values of H satisfying $H \geq \chi_{.05}^2$, where $\chi_{.05}^2$ is based on $(k-1) = (4-1) = 3$ degrees of freedom. This value of χ^2, given in Table 6 of the Appendix, is $\chi_{.05}^2 = 7.81473$.

Since we reject H_0 for large value of H, those larger than $\chi_{.05}^2$ (see Figure 15.5), the observed value of the H statistic, $H = 7.775103$, does not fall in the rejection region for the test. Therefore, there is insufficient evidence to indicate differences in the distributions of achievement test scores for the four teaching techniques.   ∎

The details of the Kruskal-Wallis test are summarized in the next box.

**THE KRUSKAL-WALLIS H TEST FOR COMPARING MORE THAN
TWO POPULATIONS: COMPLETELY RANDOMIZED DESIGN
(INDEPENDENT RANDOM SAMPLES)**

(1) *Null Hypothesis:* The k population distributions are identical.

(2) *Alternative Hypothesis:* At least two of the k population distributions differ in location.

(3) *Test Statistic:* $H = \dfrac{12}{n(n+1)} \sum\limits_{i=1}^{k} \dfrac{T_i^2}{n_i} - 3(n+1)$, where

$$n_i = \text{sample size for population } i$$
$$T_i = \text{rank sum for population } i$$
$$n = \text{total number of observations}$$
$$= n_1 + n_2 + \cdots + n_k$$

(4) *Rejection Region:* For a given α; reject H_0 when $H > \chi_\alpha^2$, where χ_α^2 has $(k-1)$ degrees of freedom.

Assumptions:

(1) All sample sizes are greater than or equal to 5.

(2) Ties assume the average of the ranks that they would have occupied if they had not been tied.

EXERCISES

BASIC TECHNIQUES

15.39 Three treatments were compared by using a completely randomized design. The data are shown in Table 15.16. Do the data provide sufficient evidence to indicate a difference in location for at least two of the population distributions? Test using $\alpha = .05$.

TABLE 15.16   Treatment Data for Exercise 15.39.

Treatment 1	Treatment 2	Treatment 3
26	27	25
29	31	24
23	30	27
24	28	22
28	29	24
26	32	20
	30	21
	33	

15.40 Four treatments were compared by using a completely randomized design. The data are shown in Table 15.17. Do the data provide sufficient evidence to indicate a difference in location for at least two of the population distributions? Test using $\alpha = .05$.

TABLE 15.17   Treatment Data for Exercise 15.40.

Treatment 1	Treatment 2	Treatment 3	Treatment 4
124	147	141	117
167	121	144	128
135	136	139	102
160	114	162	119
159	129	155	128
144	117	150	123
133	109		

APPLICATIONS

15.41 In Exercise 9.14 we compared the mean price of a loaf of bread (a particular brand) at four city locations using an analysis of variance. The data are reproduced in Table 15.18.

TABLE 15.18   Bread Price Data for Exercise 15.41

Location	Prices (Cents)			
1	59	63	65	61
2	58	61	64	63
3	54	59	55	58
4	69	70		

(a) Use the Kruskal-Wallis H test to determine whether the data present sufficient evidence to indicate a difference in the level of bread prices among the four city locations. Test using $\alpha = .05$.
(b) Find the approximate p-value for the test.
(c) Consult the SAS printout for the analysis of variance given in Exercise 9.14, and find the p-value for the analysis of variance F test used to detect differences in mean price levels among the four city locations.
(d) Compare the Kruskal-Wallis test results in part (a) with those of the analysis of variance F test in Exercise 9.14.

15.42 In Exercise 9.15 we used an analysis of variance F test to detect differences in the mean time to assemble a device among assemblers exposed to one of three different training programs. The data are reproduced in Table 15.19.

TABLE 15.19   Assembly Time Data for Exercise 15.42

Training Program	Average Assembly Time (Minutes)				
A	59	64	57	62	
B	52	58	54		
C	58	65	71	63	64

(a) Use the Kruskal-Wallis H test to determine whether the data present sufficient evidence to indicate differences in the length of time to assemble the device among assemblers trained by the three programs. Test using $\alpha = .05$.

(b) Find the approximate p-value for the test.

(c) Use the SAS printout in Exercise 9.15 to find the p-value for the analysis of variance F test.

(d) Compare the results of the Kruskal-Wallis H test in part (a) with the results of the analysis of variance F test in Exercise 9.15.

MKTG 15.43 A supermarket chain conducted an experiment to investigate customer response to the use of background music. Fifteen stores were selected for the experiment, and five each were assigned to three different types of background music: type 1, soft and slow contemporary; type 2, medium-volume, slow contemporary; and type 3, medium-volume, medium tempo. After the background music was used for one week, 100 customers were randomly selected and questioned to determine whether they liked the background music. The percentages that liked the music and favored its continued use are shown in Table 15.20. Do the data provide sufficient evidence to indicate differences in levels of acceptance of the three types of background music? Test using the Kruskal-Wallis H test with $\alpha = .10$.

TABLE 15.20   Music Type Data for Exercise 15.43

Type 1	Type 2	Type 3
94	84	81
87	89	76
90	82	73
86	90	79
91	78	84

THE FRIEDMAN F_r TEST FOR RANDOMIZED BLOCK DESIGNS

15.6

The **Friedman F_r test**, proposed by Nobel prize-winning economist Milton Friedman, is a nonparametric test for comparing the distributions of measurements for k treatments laid out in b blocks, using a randomized block design. The procedure for conducting the test is very similar to that used for the Kruskal-Wallis H test. The first step in the procedure is to rank the k treatment observations within each block. Ties are treated in the usual way—that is, they receive an average of the ranks occupied by the tied observations. The rank sums $T_1, T_2, \ldots, T_k$ are then obtained, and the test statistic

$$F_r = \frac{12}{bk(k+1)} \sum_{i=1}^{k} T_i^2 - 3b(k+1)$$

is calculated.

The value of the F_r statistic will be at a minimum when the rank sums are equal—that is, $T_1 = T_2 = \cdots = T_k$—and will increase in value as the differences among the rank sums increase. When either the number k of treatments or the number b of blocks is larger than 5, the sampling distribution of F_r can be approximated by a chi-square distribution with $(k - 1)$ degrees of freedom. Therefore, like the Kruskal-Wallis H test, the rejection region for the F_r test is

$$F_r > \chi_\alpha^2$$

We will illustrate the use of the test with an example.

EXAMPLE 15.5   Suppose that you want to compare consumer ratings of six different television advertisements. Each of four consumers rated each advertisement on a scale of 1 (poor) to 10 (excellent). The objective of the experiment is to determine whether differences exist in the rating levels for the six advertisements. The data are reproduced in Table 15.21 (ranks of the observations within each block are shown in parentheses). Use the Friedman F_r test to determine whether the data present sufficient evidence to indicate differences in the ratings of the six television advertisements. Test using $\alpha = .05$.

TABLE 15.21   Consumer Ratings Data for Example 15.15

Subject	Advertisement					
	A	B	C	D	E	F
1	5 (2.5)	8 (6)	7 (5)	6 (4)	4 (1)	5 (2.5)
2	6 (3.5)	10 (6)	6 (3.5)	7 (5)	4 (1.5)	4 (1.5)
3	8 (3)	10 (6)	9 (4.5)	9 (4.5)	6 (1)	7 (2)
4	4 (2)	6 (5)	7 (6)	5 (3.5)	3 (1)	5 (3.5)
Rank sum	$T_1 = 11$	$T_2 = 23$	$T_3 = 19$	$T_4 = 17$	$T_5 = 4.5$	$T_6 = 9.5$

SOLUTION   We wish to test

H_0:   the distributions of ratings for the six television advertisements are identical

against the alternative hypothesis

H_a: at least two of the distributions of ratings for the six television advertisements differ in location

The table shows the ranks (in parentheses) of the observations within each block and the rank sums for each of the six advertisements (the treatments). The value of the F_r statistic for these data is

$$F_r = \frac{12}{bk(k + 1)} \sum_{i=1}^{k} T_i^2 - 3b(k + 1)$$

$$= \frac{12}{(4)(6)(7)} [(11)^2 + (23)^2 + (19)^2 + \cdots + (9.5)^2] - 3(4)(7)$$

$$= 100.75 - 84 = 16.75$$

Since the number $k = 6$ of treatments exceeds 5, the sampling distribution of F_r can be approximated by a chi-square distribution with $(k - 1) = (6 - 1) = 5$ degrees of freedom. Therefore, for $\alpha = .05$ we reject H_0 if

$$F_r > \chi^2_{.05} \quad \text{where} \quad \chi^2_{.05} = 11.0705$$

This rejection region is shown in Figure 15.6.

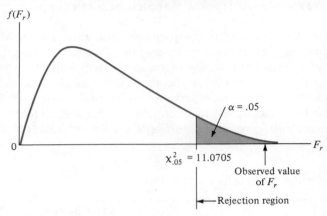

FIGURE 15.6   Rejection Region for Example 15.5

Since the observed value of F_r, $F_r = 16.75$, exceeds $\chi^2_{.05} = 11.0705$, it falls in the rejection region. We therefore reject H_0 and conclude that the distributions of ratings, for at least two of the advertisements, differ in location.   ■

The details of the Friedman F_r test are summarized in the next box and illustrated by Example 15.6.

THE FRIEDMAN F_r TEST FOR A RANDOMIZED BLOCK DESIGN

(1) *Null Hypothesis:* The k population distributions are identical.

(2) *Alternative Hypothesis:* At least two of the k population distributions differ in location.

(3) *Test Statistic:* $F_r = \dfrac{12}{bk(k+1)} \sum\limits_{i=1}^{k} T_i^2 - 3b(k+1)$

where $b =$ number of blocks

$k =$ number of treatments

$T_i =$ rank sum for treatment $i, i = 1, 2, \ldots, k$

(4) *Rejection Region:* Reject H_0 when $F_r > \chi^2_\alpha$, where χ^2_α is based on $(p - 1)$ degrees of freedom.

Assumption: Either the number k of treatments or the number b of blocks is larger than 5.

EXAMPLE 15.6   Find the approximate p-value for the test in Example 15.5.

SOLUTION   The values of χ^2 for $\alpha = .05, .025, .010,$ and $.005$ for 5 degrees of freedom are $\chi^2_{.05} = 11.0705, \chi^2_{.025} = 12.8325, \chi^2_{.010} = 15.0863,$ and $\chi^2_{.005} = 16.7496$. The observed value of F_r, $F_r = 16.75$, is very close to $\chi^2_{.005} = 16.7496$. Therefore, the p-value for the test is approximately equal to .005.   ■

EXERCISES

BASIC TECHNIQUES

15.44 A randomized block design is employed to compare three treatments in six blocks. The data are shown in Table 15.22.

TABLE 15.22   Treatment and Block Data for Exercise 15.44

Block	Treatment		
	1	2	3
1	3.2	3.1	2.4
2	2.8	3.0	1.7
3	4.5	5.0	3.9
4	2.5	2.7	2.6
5	3.7	4.1	3.5
6	2.4	2.4	2.0

(a) Use the Friedman F_r test to detect differences in location among the three treatment distributions. Test using $\alpha = .05$.
(b) Find the approximate p-value for the test.
(c) Perform an analysis of variance, and give the ANOVA table for the analysis.
(d) Give the value of the F statistic for testing the equality of the three treatment means.
(e) Give the approximate p-value for the F statistic in part (d).
(f) Compare the p-values for the tests in parts (a) and (d), and explain the practical implications of the comparison.

15.45 A randomized block design is employed to compare four treatments in eight blocks. The data are shown in Table 15.23.

TABLE 15.23   Treatment and Block Data for Exercise 15.45

Block	Treatment			
	1	2	3	4
1	89	81	84	85
2	93	86	86	88
3	91	85	87	86
4	85	79	80	82
5	90	84	85	85
6	86	78	83	84
7	87	80	83	82
8	93	86	88	90

(a) Use the Friedman F_r test to detect differences in location among the three treatment distributions. Test using $\alpha = .05$.

(b) Find the approximate p-value for the test.

(c) Perform an analysis of variance, and give the ANOVA table for the analysis.

(d) Give the value of the F statistic for testing the equality of the three treatment means.

(e) Give the approximate p-value for the F statistic in part (d).

(f) Compare the p-values for the tests in parts (a) and (d), and explain the practical implications of the comparison.

APPLICATIONS

15.46 In Exercise 9.37 we compared the prices of items at five supermarkets. Six items were randomly selected for the comparison, and the price of each was recorded for each of the five supermarkets. The objective of the study was to see whether the data indicated differences in the level of prices among the five supermarkets. The data are shown in Table 15.24.

TABLE 15.24   Supermarket Data for Exercise 15.46

Item	Supermarket				
	Kash n' Karry	Publix	Winn-Dixie	Albertsons	Food 4 Less
Celery	.33	.34	.69	.59	.58
Colgate toothpaste	1.28	1.49	1.44	1.37	1.28
Campbell's beef soup	1.05	1.19	1.23	1.19	1.10
Crushed pineapple	.83	.95	.95	.87	.84
Mueller's spaghetti	.68	.79	.83	.69	.69
Heinz catsup	1.41	1.69	1.79	1.65	1.49

(a) Do the distributions of the prices of items differ in location from one supermarket to another? Test using the F_r test with $\alpha = .05$.

(b) Find the approximate p-value for the test and interpret it.

(c) Compare your conclusion in part (a) with the conclusion reached by using the analysis of variance in Exercise 9.37. Do they agree? Explain.

15.47 A management consulting firm conducted a survey to compare estimates by senior-level management, middle-level management, and a company's chief financial officer of the

TABLE 15.25   Earnings Growth Estimate Data for Exercise 15.47

Company	Senior Management	Middle Management	Financial Officer
1	10	7	9
2	16	10	11
3	13	20	10
4	22	15	6
5	14	12	12
6	19	8	6
7	25	10	8
8	14	12	12
9	16	12	13
10	21	15	12

company's prospective percentage annual growth in earnings. Random samples of ten companies were selected for the experiment, and representatives of senior- and middle-level management were randomly selected from each company. The estimates of percentage increase (or decrease) in annual earnings are shown in Table 15.25. Do the data provide sufficient evidence to indicate differences in the levels of forecast earnings increases for the three types of forecasters? Test using the Friedman F_r test with $\alpha = .10$.

 15.48 The price-earnings ratio (P/E) of a company's common stock is the ratio of the current price of the stock to the company's previous 12 months' earnings. For example, if a company's stock sells for $20 a share and the annual earnings are $2.00 a share, then the P/E for the stock is $20/2 = 10$. Do the common stocks of similar companies tend to sell at a common level (i.e., with nearly equal P/E's), or do some sell at a premium compared with others? Shown in Table 15.26 are the average annual P/E's for three high-quality food company stocks each year from 1981 through 1986. Note the general rise in P/E's over time, due, in large part, to the lowering of interest rates over the time period.

TABLE 15.26   P/E Ratio Data for Exercise 15.48

Company	1981	1982	1983	1984	1985	1986
Campbell Soup	7.6	6.8	8.7	9.9	11.2	14.5
General Mills	7.4	8.2	9.8	10.3	15.2	15.5
Pillsbury	6.5	6.9	8.0	9.4	10.5	13.9

(a) Explain why this design is or is not a randomized block design.

(b) Do the data provide sufficient evidence to indicate differences in P/E levels for the three food companies' common stock? Test using $\alpha = .05$.

15.7 RANK CORRELATION COEFFICIENT

In the preceding sections we have used ranks to indicate the relative magnitude of observations in nonparametric tests for comparison of treatments. We will now use the same technique in testing for a relation between two ranked variables. Two common **rank correlation coefficients** are the **Spearman** r_s and the Kendall τ. We will present the Spearman r_s because its computation is identical to that for the sample correlation coefficient r of Chapter 11. Kendall's rank correlation coefficient is discussed in detail in Kendall and Stuart (1961). The formula for r_s is given in the box on page 678.

Suppose that eight middle-level managers have been ranked by senior management on their managerial skills, and all have taken a psychological test for which the score is purported to be correlated with the potential for management. The data for the eight managers is shown in Table 15.27. Do the data suggest an agreement between the senior management's ranking of managerial skills and the examination score? Or one might express this question by asking whether a correlation exists between ranks and test scores.

SPEARMAN'S RANK CORRELATION COEFFICIENT

$$r_s = \frac{SS_{xy}}{\sqrt{SS_x SS_y}}$$

where x_i and y_i represent the ranks of the ith pair of observations and

$$SS_{xy} = \sum_{i=1}^{n}(x_i - \bar{x})(y_i - \bar{y}) = \sum_{i=1}^{n} x_i y_i - \frac{\left(\sum\limits_{i=1}^{n} x_i\right)\left(\sum\limits_{i=1}^{n} y_i\right)}{n}$$

$$SS_x = \sum_{i=1}^{n}(x_i - \bar{x})^2 = \sum_{i=1}^{n} x_i^2 - \frac{\left(\sum\limits_{i=1}^{n} x_i\right)^2}{n}$$

$$SS_y = \sum_{i=1}^{n}(y_i - \bar{y})^2 = \sum_{i=1}^{n} y_i^2 - \frac{\left(\sum\limits_{i=1}^{n} y_i\right)^2}{n}$$

When there are no ties in either the x observations or the y observations, the expression for r_s algebraically reduces to the simpler expression

$$r_s = 1 - \frac{6 \sum\limits_{i=1}^{n} d_i^2}{n(n^2 - 1)} \qquad \text{where} \qquad d_i = x_i - y_i$$

If the number of ties is small in comparison with the number of data pairs, little error will result in using this shortcut formula.

TABLE 15.27   Management Test Score Data

Manager	Rank for Managerial Skills	Test Scores
1	7	44
2	4	72
3	2	69
4	6	70
5	1 •	93
6	3	82
7	8	67
8	5	80

The two variables of interest are rank and test score. The former is already in rank form, and the test scores may be ranked similarly, as shown in Table 15.28. The ranks for tied observations are obtained by averaging the ranks that the tied observations would occupy, as we did for the Mann-Whitney U statistic. The Spearman rank correlation coefficient r_s is calculated by using the ranks as the paired measurements on

TABLE 15.28   Ranking of Test Scores

Manager	Rank for Managerial Skills, x_i	Ranked Test Score, y_i
1	7	1
2	4	5
3	2	3
4	6	4
5	1	8
6	3	7
7	8	2
8	5	6

the two variables x and y in the formula for r in Chapter 11. The next example illustrates the calculation.

EXAMPLE 15.7   Calculate r_s for the management-ranking test score data.

SOLUTION   The differences and squares of differences between the two rankings are as shown in Table 15.29. Substituting into the formula for r_s yields

$$r_s = 1 - \frac{6 \sum_{i=1}^{n} d_i^2}{n(n^2 - 1)}$$

$$= 1 - \frac{6(144)}{8(64 - 1)}$$

$$= -.714$$

TABLE 15.29   Data Calculations for Example 15.7

Manager	x_i	y_i	d_i	d_i^2
1	7	1	6	36
2	4	5	−1	1
3	2	3	−1	1
4	6	4	2	4
5	1	8	−7	49
6	3	7	−4	16
7	8	2	6	36
8	5	6	−1	1
Total				144

The Spearman rank correlation coefficient can be used as a test statistic to test an hypothesis of *no association* between two populations. We assume that the n pairs of

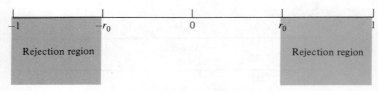

r_s: Spearman's rank correlation coefficient

FIGURE 15.7   Rejection Region for a Two-Tailed Test of the Null Hypothesis of No Association, Using Spearman's Rank Correlation Test

TABLE 15.30   An Abbreviated Version of Table 14 in the Appendix for Spearman's Rank Correlation Coefficient

n	$\alpha = 0.05$	$\alpha = 0.025$	$\alpha = 0.01$	$\alpha = 0.005$
5	0.900	—	—	—
6	0.829	0.886	0.943	—
7	0.714	0.786	0.893	—
8	0.643	0.738	0.833	0.881
9	0.600	0.683	0.783	0.833
10	0.564	0.648	0.745	0.794
11	0.523	0.623	0.736	0.818
12	0.497	0.591	0.703	0.780
13	0.475	0.566	0.673	0.745
14	0.457	0.545		
15	0.441	0.525		
16	0.425			
17	0.412			
18	0.399	$\vdots$	$\vdots$	$\vdots$
19	0.388			
20	0.377			
$\vdots$	$\vdots$			

observations (x_i, y_i) have been randomly selected, and therefore, *no association between the populations* will imply a random assignment of the n ranks within each sample. Each random assignment (for the two samples) will represent a simple event associated with the experiment, and a value of r_s can be calculated for each. Thus it is possible to calculate the probability that r_s assumes a large absolute value due solely to chance and thereby suggests an association between populations when none exists.

The rejection region for a two-tailed test is shown in Figure 15.7. If the alternative hypothesis is that the correlation between the ranks of x and y is negative, you will reject H_0 for negative values of r_s that are close to -1 (in the lower tail of Figure 15.7). Similarly, if the alternative hypothesis is that the correlation between the ranks of x and y is positive, you will reject H_0 for large positive values of r_s (in the upper tail of Figure 15.7).

The critical values of r_s are given in Table 14 of the Appendix. An abbreviated version of Table 14 is shown here in Table 15.30.

Across the top of Table 15.30 (and Table 14 in the Appendix) are recorded values of α that you may want to use for a one-tailed test of the null hypothesis of *no association* between x and y. The number of rank pairs, n, appears at the left side of the table. The table entries give the critical value r_0 for a one-tailed test. Thus $P(r_s \geq r_0) = \alpha$. For example, suppose you have $n = 8$ rank pairs and the alternative hypothesis is that the correlation between the ranks is positive. Then you will want to reject the null hypothesis of "no association" only for large positive values of r_s and will use a one-tailed test. Referring to Table 15.30 and using the row corresponding to $n = 8$ and the column for $\alpha = .05$, you read $r_0 = .643$. Therefore, you will reject H_0 for all values of r_s greater than or equal to .643.

The test is conducted in exactly the same manner if you want to test only the alternative hypothesis that the ranks are negatively correlated. The only difference is that you will reject the null hypothesis if $r_s \leq -.643$. That is, you just place a minus sign in front of the tabulated value of r_0 to get the lower-tail critical value.

To conduct a two-tailed test, reject the null hypothesis if $r_s \geq r_0$ or $r_s \leq -r_0$. The value of α for the test will be double the value shown at the top of the table. For example, if $n = 8$ and you choose the .025 column, you will reject H_0 if $r_s \geq .738$ or $r_s \leq -.738$. The α value for the test will be $2(.025) = .05$.

EXAMPLE 15.8   Test an hypothesis of "no association" between the populations for Example 15.7.

SOLUTION   The critical value of r_s for a one-tailed test with $\alpha = .05$ and $n = 8$ is .643. Let us assume that a correlation between rank assigned by senior management and the middle-level managers' test scores could not possibly be positive. Lower ranks are assigned to the managers with the best skills. Therefore, a low rank should be associated with a high test score if the senior-management rankings and the tests agree in identifying managers with managerial skill. The alternative hypothesis is that the population rank coefficient ρ_s is less than zero, and we will be concerned with a one-tailed statistical test. Thus α for the test will be the tabulated value .05, and we will reject the null hypothesis if $r_s \leq -.643$.

The calculated value of the test statistic, $r_s = -.714$, is less than the critical value for $\alpha = .05$. Thus the null hypothesis will be rejected at the $\alpha = .05$ level of significance. It appears that some agreement does exist between senior-management's rankings and the test scores. However, note that this agreement can exist when *neither* provides an adequate yardstick for measuring managerial ability. For example, the association can exist if both the senior management and those who constructed the psychological examination possessed a completely erroneous, but identical, concept of the characteristics of good managerial skills.   ∎

The details of Spearman's rank correlation test are given in the following box.

SPEARMAN'S RANK CORRELATION TEST

(1) *Null Hypothesis: H_0*: there is no association between the rank pairs.

(2) *Alternative Hypothesis: H_a*: there is an association between the rank pairs (a two-tailed test). Or H_a: the correlation between the rank pairs is positive (or negative) (a one-tailed test).

(3) *Test Statistic:* $r_s = \dfrac{SS_{xy}}{\sqrt{SS_x SS_y}}$

where x_i and y_i represent the ranks of the *i*th pair of observations.

(4) *Rejection Region:* For a two-tailed test, reject H_0 if $r_s \geq r_0$ or $r_s \leq -r_0$, where r_0 is given in Table 14 of the Appendix. Double the tabulated probability to obtain the value of α for the two-tailed test. For a one-tailed test, reject H_0 if $r_s \geq r_0$ (for an upper-tailed test) or $r_s \leq -r_0$ (for a lower-tailed test). The α value for a one-tailed test is the value shown in Table 14 of the Appendix.

EXERCISES

BASIC TECHNIQUES

15.49 Give the rejection region for a test to detect positive rank correlation if the number of pairs of ranks is 16 and α is as follows: (a) $\alpha = .05$ (b) $\alpha = .01$

15.50 Give the rejection region for a test to detect negative rank correlation if the number of pairs of ranks is 12 and α is as follows: (a) $\alpha = .05$ (b) $\alpha = .01$

15.51 Give the rejection region for a test to detect rank correlation if the number of pairs of ranks is 25 and α is as follows: (a) $\alpha = .05$ (b) $\alpha = .01$

15.52 The following paired observations were obtained on two variables x and y.

x	1.2	.8	2.1	3.5	2.7	1.5
y	1.0	1.3	.1	−.8	−.2	.6

(a) Calculate the Spearman's rank correlation coefficient r_s.

(b) Do the data present sufficient evidence to indicate a correlation between x and y? Test using $\alpha = .05$.

APPLICATIONS

 15.53 Do personal savings increase in proportion to disposable personal income? Annual data for the United States from 1975 through 1982 are shown in Table 15.31.

TABLE 15.31   Savings and Income Data for Exercise 15.53

Savings and Income	Year							
	1975	1976	1977	1978	1979	1980	1981	1982
Annual savings, y	94.3	82.5	78.0	89.4	96.7	106.2	130.2	142.7
Disposable personal income, x	1096.1	1194.4	1314.0	1474.0	1650.2	1824.1	2029.1	2173.4

Source: Data from *National Food Review* (Washington, D.C.: U.S. Department of Agriculture, Spring 1983).

(a) Calculate Spearman's rank correlation coefficient for the data. Compare it with the simple linear coefficient of correlation calculated in Exercise 11.105.

(b) Use the Spearman's rank correlation coefficient calculated in part (a) to test for rank correlation between annual savings and disposable personal income. Test using $\alpha = .05$, and compare your results with those of the parametric test in Exercise 11.105.

 15.54 Two art buyers each ranked 12 paintings by contemporary (but anonymous) artists in accordance with their estimate of the investment potential of a painting. The ratings are shown in Table 15.32. Do the critics seem to agree on their rating of contemporary art? That is, do the data provide sufficient evidence to indicate a positive correlation between critics A and B? Test using a value of α near .05.

TABLE 15.32   Art-Rankings Data for Exercise 15.54

Painting	Critic A	Critic B	Painting	Critic A	Critic B
1	6	5	6	7	8
2	4	6	7	3	1
3	9	10	8	8	7
4	1	2	9	5	4
5	2	3	10	10	9

 15.55 In a study of the grocery shopping attitudes of males and females, H. F. Ezell and W. H. Motes of the University of Alabama surveyed the attitudes of 376 shoppers, 165 males and 211 females. One portion of the questionnaire presented to the participants contained 22 supermarket selection criteria. Each person interviewed was asked to rate the importance of each criterion on a 5-point Likert Scale, 1 indicating the criterion as very important and 5 indicating that the criterion was very unimportant. Table 15.33 gives the mean scores for the 165 males and for the 211 females for each criterion. The criterion with the lowest mean score was judged most important and ranked 1. In a similar manner, the ranks of the other criteria were determined by the relative size of their mean scores. The ranks of the 22 criteria are shown for both male and female shoppers. Do the rankings provide sufficient information to indicate agreement in the relative importance of the 22 store selection criteria?

(a) Calculate Spearman's rank order correlation coefficient. Does it agree with the value obtained by Ezell and Motes, $r_s = .96$?

(b) Do the data provide sufficient evidence of rank correlation? Test using $\alpha = .05$.

(c) Give the approximate p-value for the test in part (b).

MKTG 15.56 Exercise 11.15 gives data on the sales per linear foot for home beauty aids (HBA) versus HBA linear feet of shelf space per store for ten supermarket firms (R. C. Curhan, W. J. Salmon, and R. D. Buzzell, "Sales and Profitability of Health and Beauty Aids and General Merchandise in Supermarkets," *Journal of Retailing*, Vol. 59, No. 1, 1983).

(a) Calculate Spearman's rank correlation coefficient for the data.

(b) Do the data provide sufficient evidence to indicate an association between HBA sales per linear foot to HBA linear feet of shelf space per store? Test using $\alpha = .05$. Compare your results with those of the parametric test in Exercise 11.34.

TABLE 15.33   Store Selection Criteria Data for Exercise 15.55

Store Selection Criteria	Male Shoppers		Female Shoppers	
	Rankings	Mean*	Rankings	Mean*
Quality of meats	1	1.433	2	1.210
Quality of produce	2	1.494	1	1.195
Fast checkout	3	1.549	4	1.495
Easy to find the items you want	4	1.738	6	1.652
Cleanliness of the store	5	1.756	3	1.410
Convenient location	6	1.840	9	1.729
Easy to move through the store	7	1.866	11	1.740
General price level	8	1.970	7	1.681
Convenient parking	9	1.982	8	1.700
Friendly and helpful personnel	10	2.024	5	1.633
Services offered	11	2.079	12	1.752
Neat, well-organized display of merchandise on shelves	12	2.134	10	1.738
Extensive selection of products and brands	13	2.135	13	1.793
Offers many price specials	14	2.276	14	1.795
Nearness to other stores where you shop	15	2.622	15	2.229
Attractive store appearance and decor	16	2.624	16	2.267
Provides informative, helpful advertising	17	2.724	17	2.343
Availability and quality of store's own brand	18	2.829	18	2.448
Recommendations of friends and family members	19	3.213	19	2.986
Availability of generics	20	3.274	20	3.090
Gives trading stamps	21	3.476	21	3.233
Redeems food stamps	22	3.628	22	3.452

Source: H. F. Ezell and W. H. Motes, "Differentiating Between the Sexes: A Focus on Male-Female Grocery Shopping Attitudes and Behavior," *Journal of Consumer Marketing*, Vol. 2, No. 2, 1985.

Note: The Spearman's rank order correlation coefficient between the two groups' rankings is .96, suggesting little difference between the relative importance ratings of the 22 store selection criteria by the two groups.

*Mean importance scores ranged from 1 (very important) to 5 (very unimportant).

Does It Pay to Save? A Rank Correlation Analysis

15.8

Is the national savings rate y (the percentage of national income saved) negatively correlated with the investment income tax rate? The data of Table 11.1 are reproduced in Table 15.34. Because we suspect that these percentages may not satisfy the assumptions required for the test of correlation given in Chapter 11, the ranks of the y values and x values are shown in parentheses to the right of their respective values.

The Spearman rank correlation analysis of the savings rate y and investment tax rate x data of Table 15.34 was performed by using the SAS statistical program package. The computer printout is shown in Table 15.35.

The SAS program assigns ranks to the raw scores and computes the quantities

SECTION 15.8   Does It Pay to Save? A Rank Correlation Analysis

685

TABLE 15.34   A Comparison of Personal Savings Rates and Taxation Rates on Investment Income

Country	y, Personal Savings Rate (%)	Rank of y	x, Investment Income Tax Liability (%)	Rank of x
Italy	23.1	(8)	6.4	(1)
Japan	21.5	(7)	14.4	(4)
France	17.2	(6)	7.3	(2)
W. Germany	14.5	(5)	11.8	(3)
United Kingdom	12.2	(4)	32.5	(6)
Canada	10.3	(3)	30.0	(5)
Sweden	9.1	(2)	52.7	(8)
United States	6.3	(1)	33.5	(7)

Source: New York Stock Exchange, with assistance of Price Waterhouse.

TABLE 15.35   Computer Printout for a Spearman Rank Correlation Analysis of the Savings Rate/Investment Tax Rate Data

```
                    SPEARMAN'S RANK CORRELATION COEFFICIENT
              Y = SAVINGS RATE,     X = INVESTMENT INCOME


VARIABLE   N       MEAN         STD DEV        MEDIAN        MINIMUM        MAXIMUM

Y          8    14.27500000    5.96627426    13.34999847    6.30000000    23.10000000

X          8    23.57500000   16.25860212    22.19999695    6.40000000    52.70000000

         SPEARMAN CORRELATION COEFFICIENTS/PROB > |R| UNDER HO:RHO=0/N = 8

                               Y             X
                 Y          1.00000       -0.88095
                            0.0000         0.0039

                 X         -0.88095        1.00000
                            0.0039         0.0000
```

shown on the printout. The top two rows of the printout give the means, standard deviations, medians, minimum values, and maximum values for the two sets of data. The Spearman rank correlation coefficient and the associated observed significance level are shown at the bottom of the printout:

$$r_s = -.88095$$

$$p\text{-value} = .0039$$

Since the program computes the p-value for a two-tailed test, the p-value for our one-tailed test (corresponding to $H_a: \rho_s < 0$) is one-half of the p-value shown on the printout, or .00195.

The small observed significance level, .00195, leaves little doubt that there is a negative correlation between the national savings rate y and the investment income rate x of a country.

SUMMARY

15.9

The nonparametric statistical tests presented in the preceding pages represent only a few of the many nonparametric statistical methods of inference available. A much larger collection of nonparametric test procedures, along with worked examples, are given by Gibbons (1971), Hollander and Wolfe (1973), and Conover (1980) (see the References).

We have indicated that nonparametric statistical procedures are particularly useful when the experimental observations are susceptible to ordering but cannot be measured on a quantitative scale. Parametric statistical procedures usually cannot be applied to this type of data; hence all inferential procedures must be based on nonparametric methods. A second application of nonparametric statistical methods is in testing hypotheses associated with populations of quantitative data when uncertainty exists concerning the satisfaction of assumptions about the form of the population distributions.

In this chapter we presented a number of useful nonparametric methods along with illustrations of their applications. The Mann-Whitney U test can be used to compare the locations of two population frequency distributions when the observations can be ranked according to their relative magnitudes and when the samples have been randomly and independently selected from the two populations. The Kruskal-Wallis H test provides similar methodology for comparing the locations of three or more population frequency distributions. The simplest nonparametric test, the sign test, provides a rapid procedure for comparing the locations of two population distributions when the observations have been independently selected in matched pairs. If the differences between pairs can be ranked according to their relative magnitudes, you can use the Wilcoxon signed rank test for comparing the two populations. This latter test utilizes more sample information than the sign test and consequently is more likely to detect a difference in location if a difference exists. The Friedman F_r test enables us to extend this comparison to more than two population distributions when the data have been collected in matched sets—that is, according to a randomized block design. Finally, we presented a nonparametric method, Spearman's rank correlation test, for testing the correlation between two variables when the observations associated with each variable can be ranked according to their relative magnitudes.

REFERENCES

Conover, W. J. *Practical Nonparametric Statistics*. 2nd ed. New York: Wiley, 1980.

Friedman, M. "The Use of Ranks to Avoid the Assumption of Normality Implicit in the Analysis of Variance." *Journal of the American Statistical Association*, Vol. 32, 1937.

Gibbons, J. D. *Nonparametric Statistical Inference*. New York: McGraw-Hill, 1971.

Hollander, M., and Wolfe, D. A. *Nonparametric Statistical Methods*. New York: Wiley, 1973.

Kendall, M. G., and Stuart, A. *The Advanced Theory of Statistics.* Vol. 2. New York: Hafner Press, 1974.

Kruskal, W. H. "A Nonparametric Test for the Several Sample Problem." *Annuals of Mathematical Statistics,* Vol. 23, 1952.

Mann, H. B., and Whitney, D. R. "On a Test of Whether One of Two Random Variables Is Stochastically Larger Than the Other," *Annals of Mathematical Statistics,* Vol. 18, 1947, pp. 50–60.

Noether, G. E. *Elements of Nonparametric Statistics.* New York: Wiley, 1967.

Siegel, S. *Nonparametric Statistics for the Behavioral Sciences.* New York: McGraw-Hill, 1956.

Wilcoxon, F. "Individual Comparisons by Ranking Methods," *Biometrics,* Vol. 1, 1945, pp. 80–83.

KEY TERMS

Robust statistical methods (page 646)
Nonparametric statistical methods (page 646)
Paired-difference experiment (page 647)
Sign test (page 647)
Ranking (page 654)
Rank sum (page 654)

Mann-Whitney U test (page 654)
Wilcoxon signed rank test (page 661)
Kruskal-Wallis H test (page 668)
Friedman F_r test (page 672)
Spearman's rank correlation coefficient
  (page 677)

SUPPLEMENTARY EXERCISES

15.57 A time study was conducted to compare the length of time (in seconds) to assemble a device using two different assembly methods, A and B. The data are shown in Table 15.36. So that natural person-to-person variability in the responses was removed, both assembly methods were used by each of nine workers, thus permitting an analysis of the difference between assembly times *within* each worker.

TABLE 15.36   Assembly Time Data for Exercise 15.57

Worker	Method A	Method B
1	9.4	10.3
2	7.8	8.9
3	5.6	4.1
4	12.1	14.7
5	6.9	8.7
6	4.2	7.1
7	8.8	11.3
8	7.7	5.2
9	6.4	7.8

(a) Use the sign test to determine whether sufficient evidence exists to indicate a difference in the distribution of assembly times for the two methods. Use a rejection region for which $\alpha \leq .05$.

(b) Test the hypothesis of no difference in mean response using Student's t test.

15.58 Refer to Exercise 15.57. Test the hypothesis that no difference exists in the distributions of responses for the two methods, using the Wilcoxon signed rank test. Use a rejection region for which α is as near as possible to the α achieved in Exercise 15.57(a).

15.59 The coded values for a measure of brightness in paper (light reflectivity), prepared by two different processes, are given in the accompanying table for samples of size nine drawn randomly from each of the two processes.

Process	Brightness								
A	6.1	9.2	8.7	8.9	7.6	7.1	9.5	8.3	9.0
B	9.1	8.2	8.6	6.9	7.5	7.9	8.3	7.8	8.9

Do the data present sufficient evidence ($\alpha = .10$) to indicate a difference in the populations of brightness measurements for the two processes?

(a) Use the Mann-Whitney U test.

(b) Use Student's t test.

15.60 If (as in the case of measurements produced by two well-calibrated measuring instruments) the means of two populations are equal, it is possible to use the Mann-Whitney U statistic for testing hypotheses concerning the population variances as follows:

(1) Rank the combined sample.

(2) Number the ranked observations "from the outside in"; that is, number the smallest observation 1; the largest, 2; the next-to-smallest, 3; the next-to-largest, 4; and so on. This final sequence of numbers induces an ordering on the symbols A (population A items) and B (population B items). If $\sigma_A^2 > \sigma_B^2$, one would expect to find a preponderance of A's near the first of the sequences and, thus, a relatively small "sum of ranks" for the A observations.

(a) Given the following measurements produced by well-calibrated precision instruments A and B, test at or near the $\alpha = .05$ level to determine whether the more expensive instrument, B, is more precise than A. (Note that this would imply a one-tailed test.) Use the Mann-Whitney U test.

Instrument A	Instrument B
1060.21	1060.24
1060.34	1060.28
1060.27	1060.32
1060.36	1060.30
1060.40	

(b) Test using the F statistic of Section 8.7.

15.61 Two certified public accountants (CPAs) were asked to estimate the tax liability associated with each of six long-term investments. The data are given in Table 15.37. Suppose we suspect that CPA 1 tends to give higher estimates of tax liability than CPA 2. Do the data support this theory? Test with $\alpha = .01$.

(a) Use the sign test.

(b) Use the Wilcoxon signed rank test.

15.62 Does the IRS audit income tax returns in the same percentages from four different regions of the country? The percentage of income tax returns audited, from five western, southern, and

TABLE 15.37   CPA Estimate Data for Exercise 15.61

Investment	CPA 1	CPA 2
1	89,600	86,500
2	105,000	110,000
3	75,000	72,000
4	91,000	86,000
5	63,000	60,000
6	71,000	70,000

northeastern states (see Exercise 2.6), are given in Table 15.38. Do the data provide sufficient evidence of differences in the rates of auditing for the three different regions of the United States? Test using $\alpha = .10$.

TABLE 15.38   IRS Audit Data for Exercise 15.62

South		West		Northeast	
Alabama	1.11	California	1.49	Maine	.85
Florida	1.37	Arizona	1.45	Connecticut	1.22
Georgia	1.21	Utah	1.97	Massachusetts	.82
Mississippi	1.28	Nevada	2.51	Rhode Island	1.16
Louisiana	1.31	Washington	1.42	New Hampshire	.80

15.63 Three investment advisory firms were asked to rate each of six investments on a scale of 1 (low) to 10 (high) in terms of potential appreciation for the coming year. All investments were considered to be of moderate risk. The ratings are shown in Table 15.39. Do the data provide sufficient evidence to indicate that one or more of the advisory firms tend to rate investments higher than the other firm(s)? Test using the Friedman F_r test with $\alpha = .05$.

TABLE 15.39   Investment-Rating Data for Exercise 15.63

Investment	Firm 1	2	3
1	7	5	9
2	7	4	7
3	5	3	3
4	8	9	10
5	6	7	8
6	7	6	9

15.64 An experiment was conducted to study the relationship between the ratings of a tobacco leaf grader and the moisture content of the corresponding tobacco leaves. Twelve leaves were rated by the grader on a scale of 1 to 10, and corresponding readings of moisture content were made. The data are as shown in Table 15.40. Calculate r_s. Do the data provide sufficient evidence to indicate an association between the grader's ratings and the moisture content of the leaves?

TABLE 15.40   Tobacco Leaf Data for Exercise 15.64

Leaf	Grader's Rating	Moisture Content
1	9	.22
2	6	.16
3	7	.17
4	7	.14
5	5	.12
6	8	.19
7	2	.10
8	6	.12
9	1	.05
10	10	.20
11	9	.16
12	3	.09

15.65 A large corporation selects college graduates for employment, using both interviews and a psychological achievement test. Interviews conducted at the home office of the company were far more expensive than the tests, which could be conducted on campus. Consequently, the personnel office was interested in determining whether the test scores were correlated with interview ratings and whether tests could be substituted for interviews. The idea was not to eliminate interviews but to reduce their number. For a determination of whether correlation was present, ten prospects were ranked during interviews and tested. The paired scores are as shown in Table 15.41. Calculate the Spearman rank correlation coefficient r_s. Rank 1 is assigned to the candidate judged to be the best.

TABLE 15.41   Interview/Test Data for Exercise 15.65

Subject	Interview Rank	Test Score
1	8	74
2	5	81
3	10	66
4	3	83
5	6	66
6	1	94
7	4	96
8	7	70
9	9	61
10	2	86

15.66 Refer to Exercise 15.65. Do the data present sufficient evidence to indicate that the correlation between interview rankings and ranked test scores is less than zero? If this evidence does exist, can we say that tests could be used to reduce the number of interviews?

The objective of this chapter is to present some very useful techniques used by industry to monitor and to improve the quality of manufactured products. Example 16.4 will show how some of these techniques can be used to improve the quality of business systems.

16 QUALITY CONTROL

The Case of the Missing Oil Stocks

Consider a management problem. You are the manager of a motor oil can filling operation. The one-quart cans, the type that you purchase at your local filling station, are filled on a filling machine that contains 28 spindles (or nozzles). Each spindle releases oil into a single can, and the machine fills 28 cans, one can at each spindle.

The problem arises when your company accountants detect an unusual discrepancy. Although the oil stocks received for the filling operation amount to 10,000,000 quarts per month, the number of filled one-quart cans is always considerably less. If the number of cans filled in a given month is 9,700,000 cans, what has happened to the missing 300,000 quarts of oil?

The problem that we have just described is similar to one encountered by V. Filimon and colleagues, who at the time were employed by the Standard Oil Company, Cleveland, Ohio (V. Filimon, R. Maggass, D. Frazier, and A. Klingel, "Some Applications of Quality Control Techniques in Motor Oil Can Filling," *Industrial Quality Control*, Vol. 12, No. 2, 1955). Their operation consisted of three filling machines, a one-quart machine containing 6 spindles, another one-quart machine containing 28 spindles, and a 16-spindle, one-gallon machine.

The search for the missing oil stocks quickly focused on the filling machine. Can you set a machine so that an individual spindle will discharge exactly one quart of oil into each can? The answer to this question is no, because the amount of oil discharged from a single spindle

differs slightly from one discharge to another due to variation in the flow of oil through the spindle. Thus the amount x of oil discharged into a can, measured in either volume or weight, varies from can to can and possesses a relative frequency distribution similar to those described in Chapter 2. This variation in fill weight led Filimon and colleagues to suspect that the missing oil stocks left the plant in overfilled cans.

The can-filling operation, and its associated problems, is typical of most ongoing business operations. Each operation yields a product that is judged to be acceptable or unacceptable depending upon one or more variables that measure the quality of the product. The product of an oil can filling operation is a can of oil, and one measure of its "quality" is the amount of oil in the can. The product of a machine producing electric light bulbs is a single bulb, and one measure of its quality is the amount of light that it emits. The product of a hospital is treatment and care for a single patient. The quality of patient care would undoubtedly be measured by a number of different quality variables.

In this chapter we will present some management and statistical techniques used to monitor, improve, and control the quality of the product of an ongoing business operation. Then in Section 16.11 we will learn how Filimon and colleagues applied some of these techniques to reduce the loss of oil stocks in their can-filling operation.

16.1 QUALITY CONTROL

As the title suggests, **quality control** methodology was developed to control and improve the product of a manufacturing process. Steel bars must possess a specified tensile strength, soap must be produced with a low level of impurities, a box of cereal must contain a specified weight, and the financial entries into a business computer must, with high probability, be accurate. Thus the objective of a quality control program is to ensure that the variables that measure a product's quality fall into ranges that are acceptable to prospective customers.

Quality control methods fall into one of three categories: (1) **monitoring techniques**, designed to track the level of quality variables and to detect undesirable shifts in product quality; (2) **troubleshooting techniques**, used to help locate the cause of undesirable changes in product quality; and (3) **screening techniques**, designed to remove defective or poor-quality products entering the process as raw materials and to perform the same job for finished products before shipment to a customer.

It is often said that quality control is 10% statistics and 90% engineering and common sense. As you will learn, most quality control methods are based on elementary statistical concepts presented in the preceding sections: the sampling distributions of Chapter 5 and the Empirical Rule of Chapter 2. The real problem arises when trouble is detected, either in the monitoring or screening processes. Thus quality control methods can tell you *when* but not *why* trouble occurs. Finding the cause of poor product quality and correcting the situation requires knowledge of the process and problem-solving ability.

This chapter will be concerned with two of the three types of quality control methods, methods for monitoring an ongoing production process and methods used to screen out unsatisfactory raw materials entering a process and/or defective product leaving a process. The third category of methodology, statistical methods for locating the cause of a downward shift in product quality, consists of all of the methods described in the preceding chapters. Two of the most useful of these methods are regression analysis and contingency table analysis, methods that may establish a correlation between one or more raw materials, or process or environmental variables, and product quality.

MONITORING PRODUCT QUALITY USING CONTROL CHARTS

16.2 Measurements on a quality variable change from one point in time to another. For example, measurements on the inside diameter of a one-inch diameter bearing will vary slightly from one bearing to another. The bearing diameter may tend to become smaller over time due to wear in the cutting edge in the machining process. Variation of this type is said to be due to an *assignable cause*. Other variation—small haphazard changes due to the many unknown variables that affect the diameter, changes in raw materials, environmental conditions, and so on—is regarded as *random variation.*

If the variation of a quality variable is solely random, the process is said to be *in control*. Being in control does not mean that a process is producing 100% good product. The values of the quality variable may or may not fall in a random pattern within the limits specified by the manufacturer's customers.

Figure 16.1(a) shows a plot of bearing diameters, one measured each hour, for a process that is in control and that is producing bearings that fall within customer specifications, say .980 to 1.020 inches. Figure 16.1(b) shows a similar plot for a process that is in control but is producing many bearings with diameters that exceed the customer's specification and would be judged defective. Figure 16.1(c) shows how a plot might look if an assignable cause of variation were present. Note that the plotted

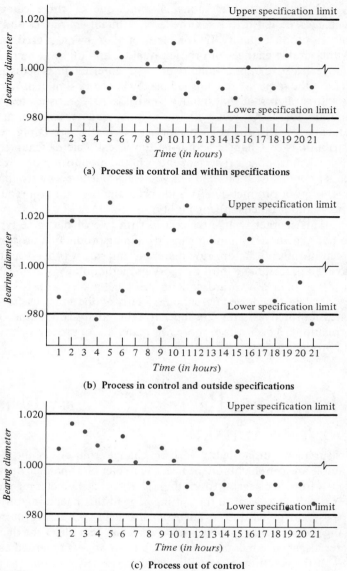

(a) Process in control and within specifications

(b) Process in control and outside specifications

(c) Process out of control

FIGURE 16.1   Plots of Bearing Diameters over Time

diameters no longer appear to vary in a random manner but trend downward over time.

The first objective of a manufacturer is to eliminate assignable causes of variation in a quality variable and to get the process in control. The next step is to reduce process variation and to get the distribution of quality measurements within specifications. The mean value of the distribution should fall at or near the center of the specifications

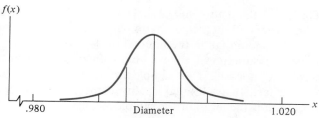

FIGURE 16.2   A Desirable Distribution

interval, and the variance of the distributions should be as small as possible. A desirable distribution for the inside bearing diameters is one that falls entirely within specifications, as shown in Figure 16.2.

Once a process is in control and producing satisfactory product, the process mean and variance are monitored by using **control charts**. Samples of n items are drawn from the process at specified intervals of time, say every half hour or hour, and the sample mean $\bar{x}$ and range R are computed. These statistics are plotted on $\bar{x}$ and R charts similar to the charts shown in Figure 16.1. A control chart for the sample mean $\bar{x}$ is used to detect possible shifts in the distribution mean for a quality variable. Similarly, a control chart for the sample range R is used to detect changes in the distribution variance. Control charts for the mean $\bar{x}$ and the range R are discussed in Sections 16.3 and 16.4, respectively. Two other useful control charts are presented in Sections 16.5 and 16.6.

A CONTROL CHART FOR THE PROCESS MEAN: THE $\bar{x}$ CHART

16.3

Assume that n items are selected from the production process at equal intervals (of time or number of items produced) and that the measurements on a quality variable are recorded. For example, Figure 16.3 shows a plot of the mean $\bar{x}$ of the diameters of $n = 5$ bearings selected hourly from a machining process.

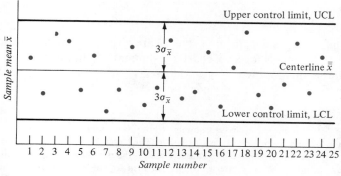

FIGURE 16.3   An $\bar{x}$ Control Chart

The logic behind an $\bar{x}$ **control chart** is that if the process is in control, the sample means should vary about the population mean μ in a random manner and that almost all values of $\bar{x}$ should fall in the interval $(\mu \pm 3\sigma_{\bar{x}})$. Although the exact value of the process mean μ is unknown, we can obtain an accurate estimate of it by averaging a large number k (at least 25)* of sample means. This estimate locates the centerline of the control chart. In traditional quality control notation it is represented by the symbol $\bar{\bar{x}}$ (i.e., it is the mean of the sample means).

The upper and lower control limits are located

$$3\sigma_{\bar{x}} = \frac{3\sigma}{\sqrt{n}}$$

above and below the centerline. The value of σ can be estimated by calculating the sample standard deviation s, using the combined set of data from the k samples. If the data collected each time period are entered into a computer, the estimate s can be obtained by a computer command. If a computer is unavailable (which was the case when these methods were developed), the calculation of s is time-consuming and, in some cases, beyond the arithmetic abilities of some production workers. For that reason, it has been traditional to calculate a range estimate of σ. To obtain this estimate, we calculate the range R for each sample, the difference between the largest and smallest measurements in the sample; then we calculate the average $\bar{R}$ for the 25 (or more) sample R values. Then

$$\hat{\sigma} = \frac{\bar{R}}{d_2} = \frac{\sum_{i=1}^{k} \dfrac{R_i}{k}}{d_2}$$

where d_2 is the constant that will make $\hat{\sigma}$ an unbiased estimator of σ when sampling from a normally distributed population.† Substituting this estimate of σ into the formula for $3\sigma_{\bar{x}}$, we obtain

$$3\hat{\sigma}_{\bar{x}} = 3\frac{\hat{\sigma}}{\sqrt{n}} = 3\frac{\bar{R}}{d_2\sqrt{n}} = A_2\bar{R}$$

where

$$A_2 = \frac{3}{d_2\sqrt{n}}$$

Values of A_2 and d_2 for $n = 2$ to 25 are given in Table 19 of the Appendix.

The details for an $\bar{x}$ chart are summarized in the next box and illustrated in the example that follows.

---

*The number $k \geq 25$ is recommended by Grant and Leavenworth (1979). This number is not critical; that is, k could be smaller, say as small as 20. The larger the value of k, the better will be the chart.

†This range estimate of σ can be biased if the population of quality measurements is not approximately normal. The large interval $6\sigma_{\bar{x}}$ (rather than $4\sigma_{\bar{x}}$) between the control limits probably compensates for error in estimating σ. Nevertheless, in this computer age it would be better to estimate σ^2 by using the sample variance s^2 based on the kn measurements from the k samples of n measurements each.

A CONTROL CHART FOR THE PROCESS MEAN: THE $\bar{x}$ CHART

Centerline: $\hat{\mu} = \bar{\bar{x}} = \dfrac{\displaystyle\sum_{i=1}^{k} \bar{x}_i}{k}$

Upper Control Limit: $UCL = \bar{\bar{x}} + A_2 \bar{R}$

Lower Control Limit: $LCL = \bar{\bar{x}} - A_2 \bar{R}$

where $\bar{R} = \dfrac{\displaystyle\sum_{i=1}^{k} R_i}{k}$

and the values of A_2 are given in Table 19 of the Appendix.

Assumption: $k \geq 25$.

EXAMPLE 16.1

A quality control monitoring system samples the inside diameter of $n = 3$ bearings each hour. Table 16.1 provides data for 25 samples. Construct an $\bar{x}$ chart for the sample means.

SOLUTION

The sample mean $\bar{x}$ and the sample range R were calculated for each of the $k = 25$ samples. For example, the sample mean $\bar{x}$ and range R for sample 1 are

$$\bar{x} = \frac{.992 + 1.007 + 1.016}{3} = 1.0050$$

and

$$R = 1.016 - .992 = .024$$

The sample means and ranges are shown in columns 5 and 6, respectively, of Table 16.1. The mean $\bar{\bar{x}}$ of the $k = 25$ values of $\bar{x}$ and the mean $\bar{R}$ of the $k = 25$ sample R values are shown at the bottom of their respective columns.

Figure 16.4 shows the $\bar{x}$ chart constructed from the data. The centerline is located at $\bar{\bar{x}} = .999856$, or $\bar{\bar{x}} \approx .9999$. The estimate of $3\sigma_{\bar{x}}$ is

$$3\hat{\sigma}_{\bar{x}} = A_2 \bar{R}$$

where $\bar{R} = .02348$, or $\approx .0235$, and the value of A_2 for $n = 3$ (given in Table 19 of the Appendix) is 1.023. Therefore,

$$3\hat{\sigma}_{\bar{x}} = A_2 \bar{R} = (1.023)(.0235) = .0240$$
$$UCL = \bar{\bar{x}} + A_2 \bar{R} = .9999 + .0240 = 1.0239$$

and

$$LCL = \bar{\bar{x}} - A_2 \bar{R} = .9999 - .0240 = .9759$$

Therefore, lines locating the upper and lower control limits are located at 1.0239 and .9759, respectively.

TABLE 16.1   25 Hourly Samples of Bearing Diameters, $n = 3$ Bearings per Sample, for Example 16.1

Sample	Sample Measurements			Sample Mean, $\bar{x}$	Sample Range, R
1	.992	1.007	1.016	1.0050	.024
2	1.015	.984	.976	.9917	.039
3	.988	.993	1.011	.9973	.023
4	.996	1.020	1.004	1.0067	.024
5	1.015	1.006	1.002	1.0077	.013
6	1.000	.982	1.005	.9957	.023
7	.989	1.009	1.019	1.0057	.030
8	.994	1.010	1.009	1.0043	.016
9	1.018	1.016	.990	1.0080	.028
10	.997	1.005	.989	.9970	.016
11	1.020	.986	1.002	1.0027	.034
12	1.007	.986	.981	.9913	.026
13	1.016	1.002	1.010	1.0093	.014
14	.982	.995	1.011	.9960	.029
15	1.001	1.000	.983	.9947	.018
16	.992	1.008	1.001	1.0003	.016
17	1.020	.988	1.015	1.0077	.032
18	.993	.987	1.006	.9953	.019
19	.978	1.006	1.002	.9953	.028
20	.984	1.009	.983	.9920	.026
21	.990	1.012	1.010	1.0040	.022
22	1.015	.983	1.003	1.0003	.032
23	.986	.990	.994	.9900	.014
24	1.011	1.012	.991	1.0047	.021
25	.987	.987	1.007	.9937	.020

$$\bar{\bar{x}} = .999856 \qquad \bar{R} = .02348$$

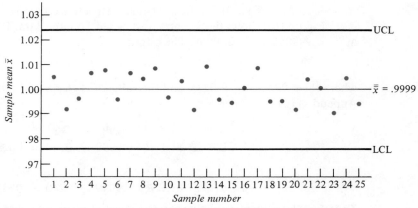

FIGURE 16.4   An $\bar{x}$ Chart for the Bearing Diameters of Table 16.1 (Example 16.1)

Assuming that the samples used to construct the $\bar{x}$ chart in Figure 16.4 were collected when the process was in control, the chart can now be used to detect changes in the process mean. Sample means can be plotted on the chart periodically. If a sample mean falls outside the control limits, it conveys a warning of a possible shift in the process mean. The process will be monitored closely, and efforts will be made to locate the cause of the errant mean. Do the sample means for Figure 16.4 vary about the centerline in a random manner, or do they suggest trends and the possibility of assignable causes in variation? A test for nonrandomness is presented in Section 16.7.

16.4   A CONTROL CHART FOR PROCESS VARIATION: THE R CHART

Just as it is important to keep the mean value of a quality variable near the center of the specification interval, it is desirable to control the process variation. The smaller the variance of the quality measurements, the greater will be the probability that the measurements fall within the customer's specification limits (assuming the process mean is within specifications).

The variation in a process quality variable is monitored by plotting the sample range R on an **R chart**. The R chart is constructed in essentially the same manner as the $\bar{x}$ chart. A centerline is located at the estimated value of μ_R, and control limits are located $3\sigma_R$ above and below μ_R.

The estimate of μ_R is $\bar{R}$, the mean of the ranges of the k samples used to construct the $\bar{x}$ chart. Calculation of the control limits,

$$\text{UCL} = \hat{\mu}_R + 3\hat{\sigma}_R \quad \text{and} \quad \text{LCL} = \hat{\mu}_R - 3\hat{\sigma}_R$$

has been reduced to a single calculation,

$$\text{UCL} = D_4\bar{R} \quad \text{and} \quad \text{LCL} = D_3\bar{R}$$

The values of D_4 and D_3, based on sampling from a normally distributed population of quality measurements, are given in Appendix Table 19 for different values of n. The details for the R chart are summarized in the next box and illustrated in Example 16.2.

A CONTROL CHART FOR PROCESS VARIATION: THE R CHART

Centerline:	$\hat{\mu}_R = \bar{R} = \dfrac{\sum\limits_{i=1}^{k} R_i}{k}$
Upper Control Limit:	$\text{UCL} = D_4\bar{R}$
Lower Control Limit:	$\text{LCL} = D_3\bar{R}$

The values of D_3 and D_4 for sample size n are given in Table 19 of the Appendix.

Assumption: $k \geq 25$.

EXAMPLE 16.2   Construct an R chart based on the data in Table 16.1.

SOLUTION   In Example 16.1 we found $\bar{R} = .0235$. For sample size $n = 3$, Table 19 in the Appendix gives $D_3 = 0$ and $D_4 = 2.575.$* Therefore, the centerline for the control chart is located at $\bar{R} = .0235$, and the upper and lower control limits are

$$\text{UCL} = D_4\bar{R} = (2.575)(.0235) = .0605$$

and

$$\text{LCL} = D_3\bar{R} = (0)(\bar{R}) = 0$$

The R chart is shown in Figure 16.5.

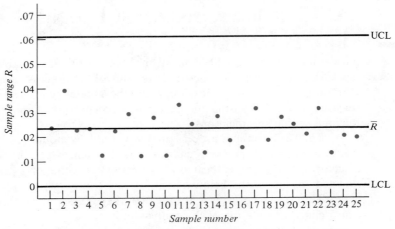

FIGURE 16.5   An R Chart for the Bearing Diameters of Table 16.1 (Example 16.2)

The R chart in Figure 16.5 is evaluated in the same manner as the $\bar{x}$ chart. The sample range R, calculated for samples taken periodically, should vary about the centerline $\bar{R}$ in a random manner and fall within the control limits when the process is in control. A sample range that falls outside the control limits will be taken as a warning of a possible change in process variation. The process will then be examined to determine whether the unusually large (or small) R value was caused by changes in the raw materials, environment, or one of the many other variables that affect the process.

EXERCISES

BASIC TECHNIQUES

16.1 The sample means and ranges were calculated for 30 samples of size $n = 10$ for a process that was judged to be in control. The means of the 30 $\bar{x}$ values and of the 30 R values were $\bar{\bar{x}} = 20.74$ and $\bar{R} = 3.49$.

---

*The lower control limit, $\mu_R - 3\sigma_R$, is negative for sample size $n = 3$. Since a range R cannot be negative, the value for D_3 is given as 0.

(a) Calculate a range estimate for the process standard deviation σ.

(b) Explain why a sample standard deviation, calculated from the 300 observations in 30 samples, might provide a better estimate of σ than the range estimate.

(c) Use the data to determine the upper and lower control limits for an $\bar{x}$ chart.

(d) What is the purpose of an $\bar{x}$ chart?

(e) Construct an $\bar{x}$ chart for the process, and explain how it can be used.

16.2 The sample means and ranges were calculated for 40 samples of size $n = 5$ for a process that was judged to be in control. The means of the 40 $\bar{x}$ values and of the 40 R values were $\bar{\bar{x}} = 155.9$ and $\bar{R} = 17.2$.

(a) Calculate a range estimate for the process standard deviation σ.

(b) Use the data to determine the upper and lower control limits for an $\bar{x}$ chart.

(c) Construct an $\bar{x}$ chart for the process, and explain how it can be used.

16.3 Use the information in Exercise 16.1 to construct an R chart. What is the purpose of an R chart?

16.4 Use the information in Exercise 16.2 to construct an R chart. What is the purpose of an R chart?

APPLICATIONS

16.5 A gambling casino records and plots the mean and range of the daily gain or loss from five blackjack tables on $\bar{x}$ and R charts. The means of the sample means and ranges for over 40 weeks were $\bar{\bar{x}} = \$10,752$ and $\bar{R} = \$6425$.

(a) Construct an $\bar{x}$ chart for the mean daily gain per blackjack table.

(b) How might this $\bar{x}$ chart be of value to the manager of the casino?

16.6 Construct an R chart for the range of the daily gain per blackjack table. How might this chart be of value to the manager of the casino?

16.7 The manager of the gambling casino in Exercise 16.5 also plots the daily gain or losses for each blackjack table on a chart. This is, essentially, an $\bar{x}$ chart for the special case where $n = 1$. The mean gain for table 1, calculated over 40 days, was $\bar{x} = \$10,940$, and the sample standard deviation was $\$5,130$.

(a) If the gain x for the dealer at table 1 has a distribution with mean μ and standard deviation σ, within what limits would you expect x to fall on almost all days?

(b) Since you have estimates of μ and σ, construct an $\bar{x}$ chart ($n = 1$) for the daily gains from table 1.

(c) Of what value might the chart in part (b) be to the manager of the casino?

16.8 The data given in Table 16.2 (page 702) measure the radiation in air particulates at a nuclear power plant. Four measurements were recorded at weekly intervals over a 26-week period. Use the data to construct an $\bar{x}$ chart, and plot the 26 values of $\bar{x}$. Explain how the chart will be used.

16.9 Construct an R chart for the data in Exercise 16.8, and explain how the chart will be used.

16.10 A coal-burning power plant tests and measures three specimens of coal each day to monitor the percentage of ash in the coal. The means of 30 daily sample means and ranges were $\bar{\bar{x}} = 7.24$ and $\bar{R} = .27$.

(a) Construct an $\bar{x}$ chart for the process, and explain how it can be of value to the manager of the power plant.

(b) Construct an R chart for the process. Explain how it can be of value to the manager.

TABLE 16.2   Radiation Measurement in Air Particulates

Week	Radiation				Week	Radiation			
1	.031	.032	.030	.031	14	.029	.028	.029	.029
2	.025	.026	.025	.025	15	.031	.029	.030	.031
3	.029	.029	.031	.030	16	.014	.016	.016	.017
4	.035	.037	.034	.035	17	.019	.019	.021	.020
5	.022	.024	.022	.023	18	.024	.024	.024	.025
6	.030	.029	.030	.030	19	.029	.027	.028	.028
7	.019	.019	.018	.019	20	.032	.030	.031	.030
8	.027	.028	.028	.028	21	.041	.042	.038	.039
9	.034	.032	.033	.033	22	.034	.036	.036	.035
10	.017	.016	.018	.018	23	.021	.022	.024	.022
11	.022	.020	.020	.021	24	.029	.029	.030	.029
12	.016	.018	.017	.017	25	.016	.017	.017	.016
13	.015	.017	.018	.017	26	.020	.021	.020	.022

A CONTROL CHART FOR THE PROPORTION DEFECTIVE: THE p CHART

16.5

Sometimes, the observation made on manufactured items is simply whether an item meets the manufacturer's (or customer's) specifications. Thus each item is judged either defective or nondefective. If the proportion* of defectives produced by the process is p, then the number x of defectives in a random sample of n items possesses the binomial probability distribution of Section 3.5.

For the monitoring of items that are either defective or nondefective, samples of size n are selected at periodic intervals, and the sample proportion $\hat{p}$ is calculated. If the process is in control, the sample proportion $\hat{p}$ should fall in the interval, $p \pm 3\sigma_{\hat{p}}$, where p is the process mean proportion of defectives, and

$$\sigma_{\hat{p}} = \sqrt{\frac{p(1-p)}{n}}$$

The process mean proportion p of defectives is estimated by using the average of k sample proportions:

$$\bar{\hat{p}} = \frac{\sum_{i=1}^{k} \hat{p}_i}{k}$$

and $\sigma_{\hat{p}}$ is estimated by

$$\hat{\sigma}_{\hat{p}} = \sqrt{\frac{\bar{\hat{p}}(1-\bar{\hat{p}})}{k}}$$

*Quality control texts usually speak of "fraction defective" rather than "proportion defective."

The centerline for the **p chart** is located at $\bar{\bar{p}}$, and the upper and lower control limits are

$$UCL = \bar{\bar{p}} + 3\hat{\sigma}_{\hat{p}}$$

$$= \bar{\bar{p}} + 3\sqrt{\frac{\bar{\bar{p}}(1 - \bar{\bar{p}})}{n}}$$

and

$$LCL = \bar{\bar{p}} - 3\hat{\sigma}_{\hat{p}}$$

$$= \bar{\bar{p}} - 3\sqrt{\frac{\bar{\bar{p}}(1 - \bar{\bar{p}})}{n}}$$

The details for a *p* chart are summarized in the box and are illustrated in the example that follows.

A CONTROL CHART FOR PROPORTION DEFECTIVE: A *p* CHART

Centerline: $\qquad\qquad \bar{\bar{p}} = \dfrac{\sum\limits_{i=1}^{k} \hat{p}_i}{k}$

Upper Control Limit: $\qquad UCL = \bar{\bar{p}} + 3\sqrt{\dfrac{\bar{\bar{p}}(1 - \bar{\bar{p}})}{n}}$

Lower Control Limit: $\qquad UCL = \bar{\bar{p}} - 3\sqrt{\dfrac{\bar{\bar{p}}(1 - \bar{\bar{p}})}{n}}$

Assumption: $k \geq 25$.

EXAMPLE 16.3

A manufacturer of ballpoint pens randomly samples 400 pens per day and tests each to see whether the ink flow is acceptable. The proportions of pens judged defective each day over a 40-day period are shown in Table 16.3. Construct a control chart for the proportion $\hat{p}$ defective in samples of $n = 400$ pens selected from the process.

SOLUTION

The estimate of the process proportion defective is the average of the $k = 40$ sample proportions of Table 16.3. Therefore, the centerline of the control chart is located at

$$\bar{\bar{p}} = \frac{\sum\limits_{i=1}^{k} p_i}{k} = \frac{.0200 + .0125 + \cdots + .0225}{40} = \frac{.7600}{40} = .019$$

An estimate of σ_p, the standard deviation of the sample proportions, is

$$\hat{\sigma}_{\hat{p}} = \sqrt{\frac{\bar{\bar{p}}(1 - \bar{\bar{p}})}{n}} = \sqrt{\frac{(.019)(.981)}{400}} = .00683$$

and $3\hat{\sigma}_{\hat{p}} = (3)(.00683) = .0205$. Therefore, the upper and lower control limits for the *p* chart are located at

TABLE 16.3   Proportions of Defectives in Samples of $n = 400$ Pens for Example 16.3

Day	Proportion	Day	Proportion	Day	Proportion	Day	Proportion
1	.0200	11	.0100	21	.0300	31	.0225
2	.0125	12	.0175	22	.0200	32	.0175
3	.0225	13	.0250	23	.0125	33	.0225
4	.0100	14	.0175	24	.0175	34	.0100
5	.0150	15	.0275	25	.0225	35	.0125
6	.0200	16	.0200	26	.0150	36	.0300
7	.0275	17	.0225	27	.0200	37	.0200
8	.0175	18	.0100	28	.0250	38	.0150
9	.0200	19	.0175	29	.0150	39	.0150
10	.0250	20	.0200	30	.0175	40	.0225

$$\text{UCL} = \bar{\bar{p}} + 3\hat{\sigma}_{\bar{p}} = .0190 + .0205 = .0395$$

and

$$\text{LCL} = \bar{\bar{p}} - 3\hat{\sigma}_{\bar{p}} = .0190 - .0205 = -.0015$$

Or since p cannot be negative, LCL = 0.

The $\hat{p}$ control chart is shown in Figure 16.6. Note that all 40 sample proportions fall within the control limits. If a sample proportion collected at some time in the future falls outside the control limits, the manufacturer will be warned of a possible increase in the value of the process proportion defective. Efforts will be initiated to seek possible causes for an increase in the process proportion defective.

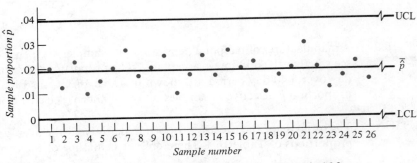

FIGURE 16.6   A Proportion Defective Chart for Ballpoint Pens for Example 16.3

Although it is convenient to choose samples of the same size n at each sampling, there may be occasions when the number of items in a sample differs from the numbers collected at previous samplings. Since $\hat{\sigma}_{\bar{p}}$, UCL, and LCL depend upon the sample size n, you will not be able to calculate the limits for a single sample size. When the sample size varies for each sampling, the estimate of the mean process proportion p of defectives is equal to the sample proportion based on the number of defectives in the k samples. Then you compare each $\hat{p}_i$ with values for UCL and LCL calculated for that particular sample's sample size. This process will cause the control limits to change from sample to sample, and the graphs of the control limits will be a sequence of connected line segments.

A CONTROL CHART FOR THE NUMBER OF DEFECTS PER ITEM: THE c CHART

16.6

An important measure of quality for some products is the number of defects per manufactured item. A textile manufacturer often classifies irregularities in a woven product as defects. Since the eventual selling price of the material will depend upon its quality, the manufacturer wishes to reduce the number of defects per square yard of material to a minimum. Then the manufacturer will want to get the number of defects per square yard in control.

The number of defects per unit area, volume, or weight or on a single manufactured item is an important measure of quality for many products. Typical examples are the number of defects in the paint job on a new automobile, the number of defects on the varnish coating for a piece of furniture, the number of air holes in a cubic inch of cheese, and the number of incorrect billing entries per computer printout page for a plumbing company.

The number of defects per unit area, volume, weight, or single item, usually denoted by the symbol c, is monitored at equal intervals of time by using a c chart. For most applications the probability distribution of c can be approximated by a Poisson probability distribution,* a distribution that possesses a very unique property. Its variance σ^2 is equal to its mean μ; that is,

$$\sigma_c^2 = \mu_c \quad \text{and} \quad \sigma_c = \sqrt{\mu_c}$$

Therefore, the number c of defects per item should fall in the interval

$$\mu_c \pm 3\sigma_c \quad \text{or} \quad \mu_c \pm 3\sqrt{\mu_c}$$

To construct a c chart, we sample the process while it is in control and record the value of c for at least $k = 25$ points in time. The process mean μ_c is estimated by the sample mean:

$$\hat{\mu}_c = \bar{c} = \frac{\sum_{i=1}^{k} c_i}{k}$$

and the process standard deviation σ_c is estimated by

$$\hat{\sigma}_c = \sqrt{\bar{c}}$$

The centerline of the c chart is located at $\bar{c}$, and the upper and lower control limits are

$$\text{UCL} = \hat{\mu}_c + 3\hat{\sigma}_c = \bar{c} + 3\sqrt{\bar{c}}$$

---

*The Poisson probability distribution is discussed in greater detail in optional Section 3.8. The information in Section 3.8 is not a prerequisite for this section.

and

$$LCL = \hat{\mu}_c - 3\hat{\sigma}_c = \bar{c} - 3\sqrt{\bar{c}}$$

The features of a c chart are summarized in the box, and their use is illustrated by the example that follows.

A CONTROL CHART FOR NUMBER OF DEFECTS PER ITEM: THE c CHART

Centerline:	$\hat{\mu}_c = \bar{c} = \dfrac{\sum\limits_{i=1}^{k} c_i}{k}$
Upper Control Limit:	$UCL = \bar{c} + 3\sqrt{\bar{c}}$
Lower Control Limit:	$LCL = \bar{c} - 3\sqrt{\bar{c}}$
Assumption: $k \geq 25$.	

EXAMPLE 16.4   An auditor monitors a company's billing system each week. This monitoring is accomplished by comparing actual bills with computer entries on all entries that appear on ten computer printout pages. The number c of incorrect entries on ten pages of printout was recorded each week for 40 weeks. The data are shown in Table 16.4. Use the data to construct a c chart for the auditing process.

TABLE 16.4   Number c of Incorrect Entries per Ten Pages of Computer Printout for Example 16.4

Week	1	2	3	4	5	6	7	8	9	10
c	1	3	2	0	0	1	4	2	1	1
Week	11	12	13	14	15	16	17	18	19	20
c	1	0	1	1	3	2	1	1	0	3
Week	21	22	23	24	25	26	27	28	29	30
c	0	2	1	0	1	1	2	2	1	0
Week	31	32	33	34	35	36	37	38	39	40
c	1	2	0	3	1	1	2	0	1	0

SOLUTION   The value of $\bar{c}$, calculated for data collected over $k = 40$ weeks, is

$$\bar{c} = \frac{\sum\limits_{i=1}^{k} c_i}{k} = \frac{49}{40} = 1.225$$

Then the centerline for the c chart is located at $\bar{c} = 1.225$, and the upper and lower control limits are located at

$$\text{UCL} = \bar{c} + 3\sqrt{\bar{c}} = 1.225 + 3\sqrt{1.225}$$
$$= 4.55$$

and

$$\text{LCL} = \bar{c} - 3\sqrt{\bar{c}} = 1.225 - 3\sqrt{1.225}$$
$$= -2.10$$

or since c cannot be negative, LCL = 0.

The c chart for the data, along with the plotted values of c, is shown in Figure 16.7. Note that all $k = 40$ of the c values fall within the upper and lower control limits, something that we would expect if the process is in control.

In the use of the c chart, values of c will be recorded each week in the future and plotted on the c chart. A value of c falling outside the control limits will be a warning of possible problems with the data entry operation.

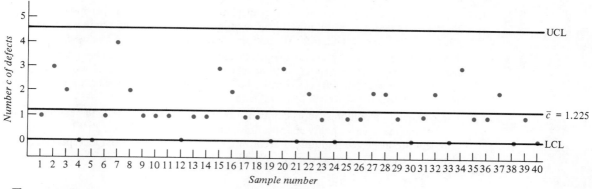

FIGURE 16.7 A c Chart for the Number of Incorrect Billings for Example 16.4

EXERCISES

BASIC TECHNIQUES

16.11 Explain the difference between a p chart and a c chart.

16.12 Samples of $n = 100$ items were selected hourly over a 100-hour period, and the sample proportion of defectives was calculated each hour. The mean of the 100 sample proportions was .035.

(a) Use the data to find the upper and lower control limits for a p chart.

(b) Construct a p chart for the process, and explain how it will be used.

16.13 Samples of $n = 200$ items were selected hourly over a 100-hour period, and the sample proportion of defectives was calculated each hour. The mean of the 100 sample proportions was .041.

(a) Use the data to find the upper and lower control limits for a p chart.

(b) Construct a p chart for the process, and explain how it will be used.

16.14 The number c of defects per item was recorded every hour over a period of 100 hours, and the mean number of defects per item was found to equal .7.

(a) Use the data to find the upper and lower control limits for a c chart.

(b) Construct a c chart, and explain how it will be used.

16.15 The number c of defects per item was recorded every hour over a period of 200 hours, and the mean number of defects per item was found to equal 1.3.

(a) Use the data to find the upper and lower control limits for a c chart.

(b) Construct a c chart, and explain how it will be used.

APPLICATIONS

 16.16 A producer of brass rivets randomly samples 400 rivets each hour and calculates the proportion of defectives in the sample. The mean sample proportion, calculated from 200 samples, was equal to .021. Construct a control chart for the proportion of defectives in samples of 400 rivets. Explain how the control chart can be of value to a manager.

16.17 A personnel manager plots the number of plant personnel accidents per month on a control chart. Over a period of 30 months the mean number of accidents per month was found to equal 3.7. Construct a control chart for the manager, and explain how it will be used.

16.18 A company records and plots on a control chart the number of customer complaints received each week. The mean number of customer complaints, collected over a 52-week period, was 4.9 complaints per week. Construct a control chart for the number of customer complaints per week, and explain how the chart can be of value to a manager.

16.19 The manager of a building supply company randomly samples incoming lumber to see whether it meets the manager's quality specifications. One hundred pieces of 2 × 4 lumber from each shipment are inspected and judged according to whether they are first (acceptable) or second (defective) grade. The proportions of second-grade 2 × 4s recorded for 30 shipments were

.14, .21, .19, .18, .23, .20, .25, .19, .22, .17, .21, .15, .23, .12, .19,
.22, .15, .26, .22, .21, .14, .20, .18, .22, .21, .13, .20, .23, .19, .26

Construct a control chart for the proportion of second-grade 2 × 4s in samples of 100 from shipments. Explain how the control chart can be of use to the manager of the building supply company.

A TEST FOR NONRANDOMNESS

16.7

We stated in earlier sections that a process is in control when all assignable causes of variation in a quality variable have been removed and all that remains is random variation. Therefore, if a process is in control, variables that measure a product's quality should vary in a random manner about their process means. Similarly, plotted sample means, ranges, proportions, and counts of defects on $\bar{x}$, R, p, and c control charts should vary in a random manner above and below their respective centerlines.

One way to detect nonrandomness in the behavior of a plotted quality variable is to record, for each point on a control chart, whether the point lies above (A) or below (B) the centerline. For example, the sequence of A's and B's for the $\bar{x}$ chart

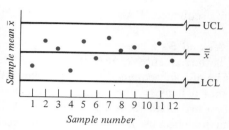

FIGURE 16.8   An $\bar{x}$ Chart

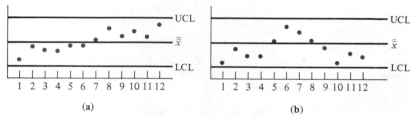

(a)   (b)

FIGURE 16.9 $\bar{x}$ Charts That Suggest Possible Assignable Causes of Variation

in Figure 16.8 is

B, A, A, B, A, B, A, A, A, B, A, B

The sequence of A's and B's associated with a control chart often suggests nonrandomness and the possible presence of assignable causes of variation. For example, Figure 16.9(a) shows an $\bar{x}$ chart in which the mean appears to be trending upward. Figure 16.9(b) is an $\bar{x}$ chart in which the mean appears to be cycling above and below the process mean.

The $\bar{x}$ charts shown in Figures 16.9(a) and 16.9(b) both suggest assignable causes of variation, both indicate trends in the values of $\bar{x}$, and both exhibit a sequence of deviations above and below the centerline that possess a unique pattern. For the $\bar{x}$ chart in Figure 16.9(a) the sequence of A's and B's is

B, B, B, B, B, B, A, A, A, A, A, A

The sequence for the $\bar{x}$ chart in Figure 16.9(b) is

B, B, B, B, A, A, A, A, B, B, B, B

Notice the difference between these two sequences of A's and B's and the sequence associated with the apparent random behavior of $\bar{x}$ in Figure 16.8. Both consist of large runs of A's and B's. The sequence in Figure 16.9(a) contains two runs, a run of six B's followed by a run of six A's. The sequence in Figure 16.9(b) contains three runs, four B's, then four A's, then four B's. In contrast, the sequence of A's and B's for the seemingly random behavior of $\bar{x}$ in Figure 16.8 contains nine runs. This discussion suggests that the number r of runs in a sequence of A's and B's can be used to detect nonrandom behavior in a process.

In a sequence of A's and B's a **run** is defined as a maximal subsequence of like elements. For example, in the sequence A, A, A, B, A, B, B, A, the subsequence A, A, A is a run because it consists of a subsequence of like elements (all of them A's), and it is maximal in the sense that it includes the maximal number of like elements before encountering a B. The first two elements in the sequence, A, A, is a subsequence of like elements, but it is not maximal because it is followed by another A. With this definition of a run the sequence

$$\underset{\text{A, A, A,}}{\underline{1}} \quad \underset{\text{B,}}{\underline{2}} \quad \underset{\text{A,}}{\underline{3}} \quad \underset{\text{B, B,}}{\underline{4}} \quad \underset{\text{A}}{\underline{5}}$$

contains five runs.

DEFINITION   In a sequence of elements A and B, a *run* is a maximal subsequence of like elements. ∎

The number r of runs in a sequence of n_1 A's and n_2 B's can be used as a test statistic to test for nonrandomness. The null and alternative hypotheses for the test are

H_0:   the sequence of A's and B's have been generated by a random process

H_a: the sequence of A's and B's have been generated by a nonrandom process

Either a very large or a very small number of runs can be indicators of a nonrandom sequence of A's and B's, although trends in a process mean are usually indicated by a small number of runs. Therefore, the rejection region can be either one-tailed or two-tailed (see Figure 16.10).

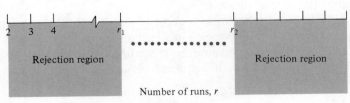

FIGURE 16.10   The Rejection Region for a Runs Test

The values of $P(r \leq r_0)$, given H_0 is true, are given in Table 20 in the Appendix for all combinations of n_1 and n_2, $n_1 \leq 10$ and $n_2 \leq 10$. A large-sample standard normal z test can be used when both n_1 and n_2 are larger than 10. The details of the test are summarized in the box, and the example that follows illustrates the use of Table 20 in the Appendix for small samples.

A RUNS TEST FOR NONRANDOMNESS

(1) *Null Hypothesis:* H_0: the sequence of A's and B's has been generated by a random process.

(2) *Alternative Hypothesis:* H_a: the sequence of A's and B's has been generated by a nonrandom process.

(3) *Test Statistic:* r = number of runs in the sequence of A's and B's.

(4) *Rejection Region:*

One-Tailed Test	**Two-Tailed Test**
$r \leq r_1$	$r \leq r_1$ and $r \geq r_2$ (see Figure 16.10)

Values of $P(r \leq r_0)$ are given in Table 20 of the Appendix for $n_1 \leq 10$ and $n_2 \leq 10$.

EXAMPLE 16.5   Use the first 15 sample means in Table 16.1 to test for nonrandomness in the sequence of sample means used to construct the $\bar{x}$ chart in Figure 16.4. Use a two-tailed test with $\alpha \approx .10$.

SOLUTION   The mean for the $k = 20$ samples used to locate the centerline of the $\bar{x}$ chart in Figure 16.4 was $\bar{\bar{x}} = .9999$. The $\bar{x}$ values for the first 15 samples are reproduced in Table 16.5. Each is identified by an A or B, depending upon whether the sample mean lies above or below the centerline $\bar{\bar{x}} = .9999$.

The sequence of the 15 A's and B's, extracted from Table 16.5,

$$A, B, B, A, A, B, A, A, A, B, A, B, A, B, B$$

contains $n_1 = 8$ A's and $n_2 = 7$ B's; and $r = 10$.

The two-tailed rejection region for the test will appear as shown in Figure 16.10, with r_1 and r_2 determined from Table 20 in the Appendix. Since we want α to be approximately .10, we will choose r_1 so that $\alpha/2 \approx .05$ falls in the lower tail of the distribution of r—that is, so that $P(r \leq r_1) \approx .05$.

Table 20 in the Appendix gives values of $P(r \leq r_0)$ for combinations of n_1 and n_2 and for values of r_0. Values of r_0, from 2 to 20, are shown in the top row of the table. Combinations of (n_1, n_2) are given in the left column of the table. The value of $P(r \leq r_0)$ for $n_1 = 8, n_2 = 7$ is the same as for $n_1 = 7, n_2 = 8$. Therefore, we proceed

TABLE 16.5   Sample Means for Samples 1–15 of Table 16.1 (Example 16.5)

Sample	$\bar{x}$	Deviation	Sample	$\bar{x}$	Deviation	Sample	$\bar{x}$	Deviation
1	1.0050	A	6	.9957	B	11	1.0027	A
2	.9917	B	7	1.0057	A	12	.9913	B
3	.9973	B	8	1.0043	A	13	1.0093	A
4	1.0067	A	9	1.0080	A	14	.9960	B
5	1.0077	A	10	.9970	B	15	.9947	B

down the (n_1, n_2) column to the row corresponding to $(7, 8)$. Moving across the $(7, 8)$ row in the table, we find the $P(r \leq r_0)$ for $r_0 = 4$ to be .015, for $r_0 = 5$ to be .051, and for $r_0 = 6$ to be .149. Since we want $\alpha/2$ to be approximately .05, we will reject H_0 if $r \leq 5$ (i.e., $r_1 = 5$). The upper-tail rejection value r_2 is a value such that $P(r < r_2) \approx .95$. Proceeding across the $(7, 8)$ row, we find $P(r \leq 10) = .867$ and $P(r \leq 11) = .949$. Therefore, we will reject H_0 when $r \geq 12$ (i.e., $r_2 = 12$). This places .051 in the lower tail and $1 - .949 = .051$ in the upper tail of the r distribution. Therefore, $\alpha = .051 + .051 = .102$. The rejection region for the test is shown in Figure 16.11. Since the observed number of runs in our sequence of $n_1 = 8$ A's and $n_2 = 7$ B's, $r = 10$, does not fall in the rejection region, there is insufficient evidence to indicate nonrandomness in the process.

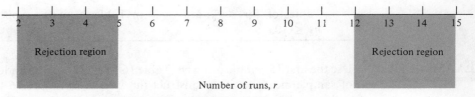

FIGURE 16.11   Rejection Region for the Runs Test of Example 16.5

When n_1 and n_2 are both large, $n_1 > 10, n_2 > 10$, we can conduct the runs test by using the familiar standard normal z test statistic of Chapter 7, where

$$z = \frac{r - \mu_r}{\sigma_r} \qquad \mu_r = \frac{2n_1 n_2}{n_1 + n_2} + 1$$

and

$$\sigma_r = \sqrt{\frac{2n_1 n_2 (2n_1 n_2 - n_1 - n_2)}{(n_1 + n_2)^2 (n_1 + n_2 - 1)}}$$

We summarize the test in the next box and illustrate it in Example 16.6.

EXAMPLE 16.6   Use the large-sample runs test to test for nonrandomness in the sequence of $k = 40$ observations on the number of incorrect billing entries per ten pages of computer printout in Table 16.4. Employ a lower one-tailed test with $\alpha = .05$.

SOLUTION   The mean number of incorrect billing entries per ten pages of computer printout for the $k = 40$ observations, calculated in Example 16.4, is $\bar{c} = 1.225$. The sequence of A's (larger than $\bar{c} = 1.225$) and B's (smaller than $\bar{c} = 1.225$) for the $k = 40$ weekly entries in Table 16.4 is

B, A, A, B, B, B, A, A, B, B, B, B, B, B, A, A, B, B, B, A, B, A, B, B, B, B, A, A,

B, B, B, A, B, A, B, B, A, B, B, B

The numbers of A's and B's in this sequence of $k = 40$ letters are, respectively, $n_1 = 13$ and $n_2 = 27$. The number of runs is $r = 19$. The mean and standard deviation for r,

LARGE-SAMPLE RUNS TEST

(1) *Null Hypothesis: H_0:* the sequence of A's and B's have been generated by a random process.

(2) *Alternative Hypothesis: H_a:* the sequence of A's and B's have been generated by a nonrandom process.

(3) *Test Statistic:* $z = \dfrac{r - \mu_r}{\sigma_r}$

where
$$\mu_r = \frac{2n_1 n_2}{n_1 + n_2} + 1$$

and
$$\sigma_r = \sqrt{\frac{2n_1 n_2 (2n_1 n_2 - n_1 - n_2)}{(n_1 + n_2)^2 (n_1 + n_2 - 1)}}$$

(4) *Rejection Region:*

Lower One-Tailed Test

$z < -z_\alpha$

Two-Tailed Test

$z < -z_{\alpha/2}$ or $z > z_{\alpha/2}$

Assumptions: $n_1 > 10$ and $n_2 > 10$.

assuming H_0 true, are

$$\mu_r = \frac{2n_1 n_2}{n_1 + n_2} + 1 = \frac{2(13)(27)}{40} + 1 = 18.55$$

and $\sigma_r = \sqrt{\dfrac{2n_1 n_2 (2n_1 n_2 - n_1 - n_2)}{(n_1 + n_2)^2 (n_1 + n_2 - 1)}} = \sqrt{\dfrac{2(13)(27)[2(13)(27) - 13 - 27]}{(13 + 27)^2 (13 + 27 - 1)}}$

$$= \sqrt{7.4475} = 2.73$$

Then
$$z = \frac{r - \mu_r}{\sigma_r} = \frac{19 - 18.55}{2.73} = .16$$

The rejection region for a lower one-tailed test with $\alpha = .05$ is $z < -z_{.05}$, or $z < -1.645$. Since the observed value of z is positive, there is insufficient evidence to indicate an unusually small number of runs, assuming randomness in the process.   ∎

EXERCISES

BASIC TECHNIQUES

16.20 For a random sequence of n_1 A's and n_2 B's, find the probability that the number r of runs is less than or equal to r_0 for the following.

(a) $n_1 = 5, n_2 = 7, r_0 = 4$

(b) $n_1 = 6, n_2 = 7, r_0 = 4$

(c) $n_1 = 8, n_2 = 10, r_0 = 7$

(d) $n_1 = 10, n_2 = 10, r_0 = 5$

16.21 For a random sequence of n_1 A's and n_2 B's, find the number of runs r_0 such that $P(r \le r_0) \approx .05$ for the following.

(a) $n_1 = 4, n_2 = 10$

(b) $n_1 = 6, n_2 = 10$

(c) $n_1 = 7, n_2 = 8$

(d) $n_1 = 3, n_2 = 4$

16.22 For a random sequence of n_1 A's and n_2 B's, find the number of runs r_0 such that $P(r \le r_0) \approx .10$ for the following.

(a) $n_1 = 5, n_2 = 10$

(b) $n_1 = 4, n_2 = 5$

(c) $n_1 = 8, n_2 = 8$

(d) $n_1 = 10, n_2 = 10$

16.23 Calculate μ_r and σ_r when $n_1 = 20$ and $n_2 = 15$.

16.24 Calculate μ_r and σ_r when $n_1 = 25$ and $n_2 = 30$.

16.25 Use the large-sample normal approximation to the distribution of the number of runs r in a random sequence of $n_1 = 10$ A's and $n_2 = 10$ B's to calculate $P(r \le 8)$. Compare the approximation with the exact value given in Table 20 of the Appendix.

APPLICATIONS

16.26 Use the runs test to test for nonrandomness in the deviations about the centerline for the 26 values of $\bar{x}$ in Exercise 16.8.

16.27 Use the runs test to test for nonrandomness in the deviations about the centerline for the 30 values of $\hat{p}$ in Exercise 16.19.

 16.28 The home office of a corporation selects its executives from the staff personnel of its two subsidiary companies, Company A and Company B. During the past three years, nine executives have been selected by the parent company from the subsidiaries, the first selected from B, the second from A, and so on. The following sequence shows the order in which the executives have been selected and the subsidiary firms from which they came:

B, A, A, A, B, A, A, A, B

Does this selection sequence provide sufficient evidence to imply nonrandomness in the selection of executives by the parent company from its subsidiaries?

 16.29 A quality control chart has been maintained for a certain measurable characteristic of items taken from a conveyor belt at a certain point in a production line. The measurements obtained today in order of time are

68.2, 71.6, 69.3, 71.6, 70.4, 65.0, 63.6, 64.7,
65.3, 64.2, 67.6, 68.6, 66.8, 68.9, 66.8, 70.1

(a) Classify the measurements in this time series as above or below the sample mean, and determine (use the runs test) whether consecutive observations suggest lack of stability in the production process.

(b) Divide the time period into two equal parts and compare the means, using Student's t test. Do the data provide evidence of a shift in the mean level of the quality characteristic?

LOT ACCEPTANCE SAMPLING FOR DEFECTIVES

16.8

Manufactured product emerging from a production process is usually divided into groups of items called lots. Thus every 1000 items leaving the production process might be identified as a lot and packaged in boxes, each marked with an identifying lot number. A lot might be a day's production, or it might be a fixed number of items, say one gross, packed into a shipping carton.

The reason for partitioning production into lots is to make it easy to locate faulty products in case a customer encounters a number of defective items. It also enables the manufacturer to identify the time period in which the lot was produced, information that helps in identifying the cause of defective products. The most noticeable use of lot numbers is by the Food and Drug Administration (FDA). If a can of food is found to contain botulism bacteria, the FDA releases the lot numbers to the news media and also issues orders to retailers to remove all items in those lot numbers from their shelves.

Suppose that each item in a lot must satisfy certain specifications and can, therefore, be classified as either **defective** or nondefective. Customers want to receive lots containing a very low lot fraction p of defectives. To reduce the risk of shipping lots containing a high lot fraction defective, a manufacturer employs a lot acceptance sampling plan for defectives.

A **lot acceptance sampling plan for defectives** is analogous to the screen on a door. The object of a screen door is to let air pass through the screen and keep the insects out. Similarly, a lot acceptance sampling plan for defectives is designed to allow lots containing a low fraction defective to pass through the screen and to reject lots containing a high fraction defective. Rejected lots can then be reinspected and the defectives removed prior to shipment. The result is an improvement in the quality of product emerging from the screening process.

Manufacturers use lot acceptance sampling plans to screen both incoming raw materials and outgoing product. A graphical depiction of a screen for incoming raw materials is shown in Figure 16.12.

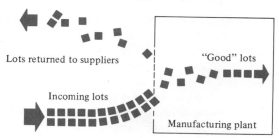

Lots returned to suppliers

"Good" lots

Incoming lots

Manufacturing plant

FIGURE 16.12   Screening for Defectives

In a lot acceptance sampling plan a random sample of n items is selected from each lot. Each of the n items in the sample is inspected, and the number x of defectives in the sample is recorded. If x is less than or equal to a predetermined **acceptance number** a, the lot is accepted. If x is larger than a, the lot is rejected. **Thus every sampling plan is specified by two numbers, the sample size n and the acceptance number a.**

EXAMPLE 16.7   A lot acceptance sampling plan employs a random sample of size $n = 25$ with acceptance number $a = 1$. Find the probability of accepting a lot that contains $p = .05$ fraction defective. Then calculate the probability of lot acceptance for $p = .1, .2, .5, .7, 0$ and 1.0.

SOLUTION   Assuming that the number N of items in the lot is large relative to the sample size n, the number x of defectives in a random sample of $n = 25$ items possesses the binomial probability distribution of Section 3.5:

$$p(x) = C_x^n p^x q^{n-x} \qquad \text{where} \qquad q = 1 - p$$

Since the acceptance number for the sampling plan is $a = 1$, a lot will be accepted if $x = 0$ or 1 and rejected if $x = 2, 3, \ldots, 25$. Therefore, the probability of accepting a lot containing a fraction defective p is

$$P(\text{accept lot}) = P(x = 0 \text{ or } 1) = p(0) + p(1)$$
$$= C_0^{25} p^0 q^{25} + C_1^{25} p q^{24}$$

We could calculate these probabilities by using a hand calculator, but we can avoid the tedium of these calculations by using Table 1 in the Appendix. Recall that Table 1 gives

$$\sum_{x=0}^{a} p(x) = p(0) + p(1) + \cdots + p(a)$$

for $n = 5, 10, 15, 20,$ and 25. Using the table for $n = 25$, we find

$$P(\text{accept lot}) = p(0) + p(1)$$
$$P(\text{accept when } p = .05) = .642$$

Similarly, Table 1 gives the probabilities of lot acceptance when the fraction defective p is .1, .2, .5, and .7 as

$$P(\text{accept when } p = .1) = .271 \qquad P(\text{accept when } p = .5) = .000$$
$$P(\text{accept when } p = .2) = .027 \qquad P(\text{accept when } p = .7) = .000$$

When a lot contains no defectives—that is, $p = 0$—the probability of lot acceptance is always $P(\text{accept when } p = 0) = 1$. In contrast, if all of the items in a lot are defective, the probability of lot acceptance is always $P(\text{accept when } p = 1.0) = 0$.   ■

A graph of the probability of lot acceptance versus lot fraction defective p is called the **operating characteristic curve** for a sampling plan. The operating characteristic curve for the lot acceptance sampling plan in Example 16.7 is shown in Figure 16.13.

The operating characteristic curve for a sampling plan completely defines the characteristics of the screen because it shows the probability of accepting lots with any specified probability, p, of fraction defective. For example, the operating characteristic curve in Figure 16.13 shows that the probability of accepting a lot with only 5% defectives is high, .642. As the fraction p of defectives in a lot increases, the probability of accepting lots containing 20% defectives is only .027, and the probability of accepting lots containing 50% or more defectives is .000.

If you are the producer, you will want the probability of accepting lots with a low fraction defective p to be high. Usually, the producer specifies that the lot fraction defective must be less than some value p_0. This fraction defective is called the **acceptable quality level (AQL)** for the plan.

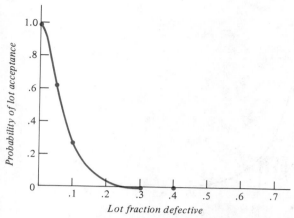

FIGURE 16.13   Operating Characteristic Curve ($n = 25$, $a = 1$) for Example 16.7

DEFINITION   The *acceptable quality level* (AQL) is an upper limit p_0 on the fraction defective that the producer (or consumer) is willing to accept.   ∎

The probability of *rejecting good lots*—that is, lots for which $p = p_0$—is called the **producer's risk**:

$$\text{producer's risk} = 1 - P(\text{accept when } p = p_0)$$

DEFINITION   The *producer's risk* is the probability of rejecting a lot when the lot fraction defective is equal to p_0, the AQL.   ∎

In contrast, the purchaser of the product (the consumer) will want the probability of accepting bad lots (lots with high fraction defective) to be small. The consumer will have in mind some value p_1, usually larger than p_0, and will want to accept lots only if the fraction defective p is less than p_1. The probability of accepting lots, given that $p = p_1$, is called the **consumer's risk**. The producer's risk for AQL $= p_0 = .05$ and the consumer's risk for $p_1 = .10$ are shown on the operating characteristic curve in Figure 16.14.

DEFINITION   The *consumer's risk* is the probability of accepting lots when the fraction defective p is equal to p_1.   ∎

Both the producer's risk and the consumer's risk are quite large for sample sizes as small as $n = 25$. Both risks can be reduced by choosing a sampling plan based on a larger sample size n.

In theory, a manufacturer specifies the AQL, p_0, and a customer specifies p_1. Then the manufacturer selects a sampling plan (a combination of sample size n and acceptance number a) that yields producer and consumer risks satisfactory to both the manufacturer and the customer. In practice, the manufacturer and the customer agree

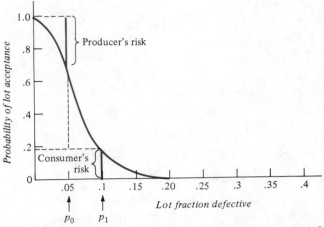

FIGURE 16.14   Operating Characteristic Curve Showing the Producer's Risk for AQL $= p_0 = .05$ and the Consumer's Risk for $p_1 = .1$

on one of the many collections of sampling plans that have been developed over the years.

One of the most widely used set of sampling plans, known as Military Standard 105D, or **MIL–STD–105D sampling plans**, was developed during World War II to control the quality of manufactured war material. These plans employ a sample size n that varies depending upon the *lot size*—that is, the number N of items in a lot. The sampling plans are also categorized according to levels of consumer risk: Level I is reduced (moderate consumer risk), Level II is normal, and Level III is tightened (low level of consumer risk). Two of the MIL–STD–105D tables are reproduced in Tables 21 and 22 in the Appendix. Another widely used set of sampling plans was developed by Dodge and Romig. Sources for both the MIL–STD–105D and the Dodge-Romig plans are listed in the References.

EXAMPLE 16.8   Find the MIL–STD–105D lot acceptance sampling plan for lot size $N = 1000$, a normal level of consumer risk, and an AQL $= .04$.

SOLUTION   The first step is to locate the code letter corresponding to lot size $N = 1000$ and the normal level (II) of consumer risk. This code is given in Table 21 in the Appendix under column II, in the row corresponding to lot size 501 to 1200, as J.

The sample size n and acceptance number a for the sampling plan can be found in Table 22 in the Appendix. The lot size code letters are shown in the first column of Table 22, and the AQL is shown, in percentages, across the top of the table. Since we want the sampling plan corresponding to a lot size with code letter J and an AQL of $p_0 = .04$, or 4%, we move down the left-hand column to row J and find the required sample size to be $n = 80$. We then move across row J to the column corresponding to an AQL of 4.0% and read, under Ac (i.e., accept), the number 7. This is the acceptance number. Therefore, the MIL–STD–105D lot acceptance sampling plan for defectives, with AQL $= 4\%$ and a normal level of consumer risk, requires that you randomly select 80 items from each lot of $N = 1000$. If the number x of defectives is equal to 7 or less, you accept the lot. If $x = 8$ or more, you reject the lot. ∎

EXERCISES

BASIC TECHNIQUES

16.30 A buyer and a seller agree to use a sampling plan with sample size $n = 5$ and acceptance number $a = 0$. What is the probability that the buyer will accept a lot having the following fractions defective?

(a) $p = .1$ (b) $p = .3$ (c) $p = .5$

(d) $p = 0$ (e) $p = 1$

Construct the operating characteristic curve for this plan.

16.31 Repeat Exercise 16.30 for $n = 5$, $a = 1$.

16.32 Repeat Exercise 16.30 for $n = 10$, $a = 0$.

16.33 Repeat Exercise 16.30 for $n = 10$, $a = 1$.

16.34 Graph the operating characteristic curves for the four plans given in Exercises 16.30, 16.31, 16.32, and 16.33 on the same sheet of graph paper. What is the effect of increasing the acceptance number a when n is held constant? What is the effect of increasing the sample size n when a is held constant?

APPLICATIONS

16.35 Find the producer's risk for a sampling plan with $n = 25$, $a = 0$, and an AQL $= .05$.

16.36 Refer to the sampling plan in Exercise 16.35. Find the consumer's risk of accepting lots containing $p_1 = .20$ fraction defective.

16.37 Suppose that you want the MIL–STD–105D lot acceptance sampling plan for lot size $N = 2000$ and a normal inspection level. Find the appropriate sample size n and acceptance number a for AQL $= .015$.

16.38 Suppose that you want the MIL–STD–105D lot acceptance sampling plan for lot size $N = 400$ and the tightened inspection level, Level III. Find the appropriate sample size n and acceptance number a for AQL $= .025$.

16.39 Suppose that you want the MIL–STD–105D lot acceptance sampling plan for lot size $N = 5000$ and a normal inspection level. Find the appropriate sample size n and acceptance number a for AQL $= .01$.

DOUBLE AND SEQUENTIAL LOT ACCEPTANCE SAMPLING PLANS

16.9

The lot acceptance sampling plan for defectives that we have just described is called a *single sampling plan*—that is, the decision to accept or reject a lot is based on the number of defectives in a *single* sample of n observations selected from the lot. Other sampling plans can sometimes provide the same protection as a single sampling plan at lower cost. One of them is a **double sampling plan**.

A single sampling plan reaches one of two decisions based on the number of defectives in a random sample of n items from each lot, either accept the lot or reject it. A double sampling plan reaches one of *three* decisions, accept the lot, reject the lot, or defer the decision and draw a second sample. Thus for a double sampling plan you select n_1 items from each lot. If the number x_1 in the sample of n_1 is less than or equal to an acceptance number a_1, you accept the lot. If it is equal to or larger than a rejection number r_1, you reject the lot. If x_1 falls between a_1 and r_1, you withhold judgment and draw a second sample of n_2, items from the lot and record the number x_2 of defectives in this second sample. If the total number of defectives $x = (x_1 + x_2)$ in the sample of $n = (n_1 + n_2)$ is less than or equal to an acceptance number a_2, the lot is accepted. Otherwise, it is rejected. The values of x_1 that imply accept the lot, reject the lot, or draw a second sample for the first stage of the double sampling plan are shown in Figure 16.15.

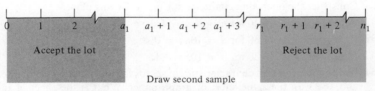

FIGURE 16.15   The Location of the Acceptance Number a_1 and Rejection Number r_1 for a Double Sampling Plan

Multiple sampling plans are similar to double sampling plans except that they involve three or more stages of sampling, each stage resulting in a decision to accept the lot, reject the lot, or continue sampling. The ultimate multiple sampling plan is called a **sequential sampling plan**. A sequential sampling plan is an extension of the concept embodied in a multiple sampling plan. A sequential sampling plan selects items from a lot, one by one, and the decision to accept the lot, reject the lot, or draw again is made after each draw. Thus the plan gives an acceptance number a_1 and a rejection number r_1 for the first draw. If the first item is less than or equal to a_1, the lot is accepted; if it is equal to or larger than r_1, the lot is rejected; otherwise, a second item is drawn from the lot. At this second stage the decision to accept the lot, reject the lot, or draw another item is based on the combined sample of $n = 2$ items and on a new pair of acceptance and rejection numbers, a_2 and r_2. If the second-stage decision is to draw again, the third-stage decision is based on the number x_3 of defectives in the combined sample of $n = 3$ items and a new pair of acceptance and rejection numbers, a_3 and r_3. This procedure is continued, stage by stage, until the number of defectives implies either acceptance or rejection of the lot.

Suppose that we were to compare a single sampling plan with a multiple sampling plan, say a sequential sampling plan. In order to make a fair comparison, we will assume that the acceptance and rejection numbers for the sequential plan are such that the operating characteristic curves for the two plans are identical so that both plans possess the same screening properties. Which plan is better?

The number n of sampled items required to reach a final decision (to accept or reject the lot) is a random variable for a sequential sampling plan. Sometimes, n will be smaller than the sample size required for the comparable single sampling plan; sometimes, larger; but the mean sample size required for the sequential plan will always be (proof omitted) less than the sample size for the comparable single sampling plan. This is a very important advantage for sequential sampling plans. If the inspection of each item is costly or if inspection is destructive,* the sequential sampling plan will test, on the average, fewer items per lot and will be less expensive. Single sampling plans may be preferred if the cost of inspecting an item is relatively low, because it usually is easier to draw all n items from a lot at one time, and the single sampling plan is easier to use.

Double, multiple, and sequential sampling plans based on various values of AQL and with differing producer and consumer risks are available and can be found in the References.

16.10   ACCEPTANCE SAMPLING BY VARIABLES

Most lot acceptance sampling plans involve sampling for defectives, but sometimes, it is more appropriate to make a decision to reject or accept a lot based on the measured values of some quality variable. For example, a company that purchases large rolls of steel cable will want the cable to meet specifications on its tensile strength. Therefore, the decision to accept a roll will be based on the mean $\bar{x}$ of a sample of n tensile strength measurements made on the cable. Similarly, a purchaser of gasoline will specify certain octane ratings for the gasoline. Therefore, a shipment of gasoline will be accepted based on the mean octane rating of a sample of n octane readings made on the shipment. Both of these acceptance sampling plans are said to be **acceptance sampling by variables**.

The decision to accept or reject a lot based on a continuous variable x is essentially a test of an hypothesis about the process mean, using the sample mean $\bar{x}$ as a test statistic (see Section 7.4).

Suppose that good quality is associated with small values of μ_x. Then the producer will want a high probability of accepting a lot when μ_x is less than some value μ_0. This value μ_0 is the **acceptable quality level** (AQL) for the sampling plan.

Assuming that n is large, the rejection region for a test of

$$H_0 : \mu = \mu_0$$

against the alternative hypothesis

$$H_a : \mu > \mu_0$$

is, for $\alpha = .05$,

$$\bar{x} > \mu_0 + z_{.05}\sigma_{\bar{x}}$$

or

$$\bar{x} > \mu_0 + 1.645\frac{\sigma}{\sqrt{n}}$$

If $\bar{x}$ is less than or equal to $\mu_0 + 1.645\sigma/\sqrt{n}$, the lot is accepted. Otherwise, it is rejected.

*In the decision of whether some products are defective, the item must be destroyed. For example, in the decision of whether a photographic film is defective or nondefective, it must be exposed. Similarly, a test of an explosive charge will destroy the charge.

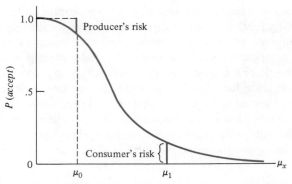

FIGURE 16.16   An Operating Characteristic Curve for Sampling by Variables

A graph of the probability β of accepting a lot versus μ_x is the operating characteristic curve for the sampling plan. It shows the probability of accepting a lot for given values of μ_x. These β probabilities are calculated by using the procedure employed in Example 7.2 in Section 7.4. A typical operating characteristic curve for a sampling plan will appear as shown in Figure 16.16.

The consumer will want to accept lots with a small value of μ_x, say $\mu_x = \mu_1$. Therefore, the consumer's risk is defined to be the probability of accepting lots with $\mu_x = \mu_1$ (see Figure 16.16). The producer's risk is the probability of rejecting lots when $\mu = \mu_0$—that is, when μ_x equals the acceptable quality level (AQL) (see Figure 16.16).

You can see that lot acceptance by variables is very similar to lot acceptance sampling for defectives. The only difference is that lot acceptance sampling plans for defectives use the number x of defectives in a sample of n items to decide whether to accept or reject a lot. In contrast, lot acceptance sampling plans for variables use the sample mean $\bar{x}$ to make the decision. Acceptance sampling plans for variables have been developed for different levels of producer and consumer risks. These plans can be found in Bowker and Goode (1952).

A Solution to the Missing Oil Stocks

16.11

The Case Study described at the beginning of this chapter involves a motor oil can–filling operation and a problem brought to light by a monthly shortage of oil stocks. The number of filled cans was always less than the number of quarts of oil assigned to the filling operation.

Suspecting that the cause of the missing oil stocks was due to overfilling of the cans, the group assigned to solve the problem focused their attention on the filling machines. The first step that they took to solve the problem was to convince both management and plant personnel that the amount of fill, measured in pounds, varied from can to can. To show this variance, they randomly selected 200 to 300 cans of oil from each filling machine, measured the weight of oil in each can, and constructed a

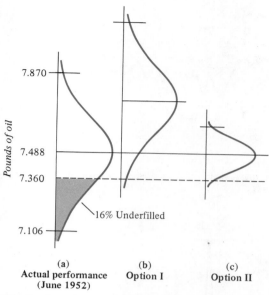

FIGURE 16.17   Distribution of Individual Can Weights on the One-Gallon Filling Machine (*Source:*
V. Filimon, R. Maggass, D. Frazier, and A. Klingel, "Some Applications of Quality
Control Techniques in Motor Oil Can Filling," *Industrial Quality Control*, Vol. 12,
No. 2, 1955. © 1955 American Society for Quality Control. Reprinted by permission.)

relative frequency histogram for the oil weights. They found the resulting distributions
to be approximately normal and to vary from one filling machine to another.

Figure 16.17(a) shows a graph (turned sideways) of the relative frequency
distribution of the fill weights for the one-gallon filling machine. You can see that there
is substantial variation in the fill weights and that 16% of the cans are underfilled. One
way to correct the problem of the underfilled cans is to reset the filling machine to shift
the mean can fill weight upward [see Figure 16.17(b)] by .25 pound per gallon. This
method will cause additional loss of oil stocks due to even greater overfill, a move
estimated to cost an additional $25,000 per year. (This was no small sum in 1952.) The
second and better option is to eliminate the underfill by reducing the variation in the
distribution of fill weights, as shown in Figure 16.17(c). This option was done by
constructing $\bar{x}$ and R control charts for the machine and, over the one-year period to
May 1953, eliminating a number of assignable causes of variation.

The control charts were based on samples of five cans randomly selected at five-
minute intervals. Figures 16.18(a) and 16.18(b) show portions of the $\bar{x}$ and R charts,
respectively, for the one-gallon filling machine in June 1952. Figures 16.18(c) and
16.18(d) show portions of the $\bar{x}$ and R charts for May 1953. Note the reduction in
variation of the fill weights from June 1952 to May 1953, as indicated by the smaller
distance between the control limits for the charts in 1953. This reduction in the variance
of the distribution allows the manufacturer to reduce the percentage of underfilled
cans and, at the same time, reduce the amount of overfill.

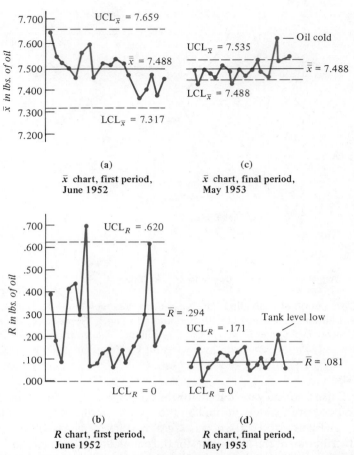

FIGURE 16.18 $\bar{x}$ and R Charts for a One-Gallon Filling Machine (*Source:* V. Filimon, R. Maggass, D. Frazier, and A. Klingel, "Some Applications of Quality Control Techniques in Motor Oil Can Filling," *Industrial Quality Control,* Vol. 12, No. 2, 1955. © 1955 American Society for Quality Control. Reprinted by permission.)

The portions of the 1953 charts [Figures 16.18(c) and 16.18(d)] were chosen during a period of time when the process experienced a run of small values of $\bar{x}$. In fact, 12 of the 14 sample means are below the centerline. The authors concluded that the mean fill had drifted lower, and they adjusted the machine fill setting to increase the mean fill per can.

Figures 16.18(c) and 16.18(d) also show values of $\bar{x}$ and R that lie above the upper control limits of the charts. An investigation of the circumstances surrounding the filling operation when the errant $\bar{x}$ was observed revealed lower-than-desirable temperature in the oil stocks. A similar investigation of the R value that lies above the upper control limit found that it occurred when the oil tank level was low. Presumably, these indications of possible causes of variation in fill weight prompted management to maintain more careful control of the oil stock temperatures and storage tank levels.

TABLE 16.6   Analysis of Variance for the 28-Spindle, One-Quart Filling Machine

Source of Variation	Sum of Squares	Degrees of Freedom	Mean Square	F Ratio
Spindles	26,971	27	999	1.73*
Days	1,854	2	927	1.6†
Spindles × days	31,228	54	578	6.4‡
Error	30,285	336	90.1	
Total	90,338	419		

Source: V. Filimon, R. Maggass, D. Frazier, and A. Klingel, "Some Applications of Quality Control Techniques in Motor Oil Can Filling," *Industrial Quality Control,* Vol. 12, No. 2, 1955. © 1955 American Society for Quality Control. Reprinted by permission.
*Significant at the .05 probability level.
†Not significant.
‡Significant at the .001 probability level.

In addition to using control charts to detect assignable causes of variation, Filimon and colleagues also conducted some experiments. Particularly, they suspected that the mean fill weight varied from spindle to spindle and from day to day. To test this theory, they selected five cans on each of three days from each of the 28 spindles of the one-quart filling machine. Although this design appears to represent a matched pairing of cans for the 28 spindles (matched by selection within the same day), the authors analyzed their data as if they had come from a two-factor factorial experiment with spindles as one factor and days as the other. Their analysis of variance table is shown in Table 16.6. (For a review of the analysis of variance for a two-factor factorial experiment, see Section 9.9.)

Examine their ANOVA table. Spindles and days are the two factors. Since there were 28 spindles and 3 days, the degrees of freedom for these sources of variation are 27 and 2, respectively; and the number of degrees of freedom for spindle-by-day interaction is $27 \times 2 = 54$. The remaining degrees of freedom, 336, is the pooled variation of the sum of squares of deviations in weights of the 5 cans for each of the $(28)(3) = 84$ factor level combinations. Since there will be $(5 - 1) = 4$ degrees of freedom to estimate within-sample variation for each factor level combination, the total number of degrees of freedom for error is $(4)(84) = 336$.

Whether you view their design as a modified randomized block design or as a factorial experiment, it is clear from the F tests that the mean fill weight appears to differ from spindle to spindle and that the differences between pairs of spindles vary from one day to another. Thus efforts should be made to reduce the spindle-to-spindle variation in fill weights. The results also suggest that other unidentified variables that vary from one day to another are having a decided effect on the variation in spindle fill weights.

Filimon and colleagues do not identify the specific assignable causes of variation that they discovered, but Figures 16.17 and 16.18 show that they achieved some success in reducing the variation in can fill weights over the period June 1952 to May 1953. This reduction in variation produced a decrease in the amount of overfill per can and resulted in smaller monthly losses of oil stocks in the filling operation.

SUMMARY

16.12

Traditional quality control methods fall into two categories, control charts, which are designed to detect changes in product quality, and lot acceptance sampling plans, which screen out bad lots (lots containing product of poor quality) and allow good lots to pass through. A third and important quality control problem is locating the cause of poor product quality when it is detected. The statistical methodology presented in earlier chapters may sometimes help in this task.

We presented four types of control charts. An $\bar{x}$ chart is used to detect shifts in the mean for a process quality variable; the R chart is used to detect changes in process variation. The p chart is used to monitor the process percentage defective when the quality measurement is simply whether or not an item meets specifications. The c chart is used to monitor the number c of defects per item.

Each of these charts is constructed when the process is judged to be in control—that is, when assignable causes in the variation of the quality variable have been removed. After chart construction, sample values of the plotted variables should fall within the chart control limits. If an observation falls outside the control limits, it indicates a possible shift in the mean of the plotted statistic and is a warning of a possible change in the product quality.

Lot acceptance sampling procedures can be of two types, sampling for defectives or sampling by variables. The most commonly used plans are those that sample for defectives. They can be either single, double, multiple, or sequential sampling plans.

The single lot acceptance sampling plan for defectives involves the selection of a single sample of n items from each lot. If the number x of defectives in the lot is less than or equal to an acceptance number a, the lot is accepted. Otherwise, it is rejected. Double, multiple, and sequential sampling plans involve two or more stages of sampling, where the decision is made at every (all but the last) stage to accept the lot, reject the lot, or continue sampling.

The properties of every sampling plan can be acquired from its operating characteristic curve, a graph of the probability of lot acceptance versus the lot fraction defective p. From the operating characteristic curve the producer can determine the probability of rejecting good lots (i.e., lots containing a low fraction defective, say $p \le p_0$), and the consumer can determine the probability of accepting bad lots (say $p \ge p_1$). These probabilities are called the producer's and consumer's risk, respectively, for the sampling plan.

Tables of sampling plans that give the sample sizes and acceptance number for values of p_0 [the acceptable quality level (AQL)] and for various levels of producer and consumer risks are listed in the References.

REFERENCES

Bowker, A. H., and Goode, H. P. *Sampling Inspection by Variables*. New York: McGraw-Hill, 1952.

Deming, W. E. "Some Principles of the Shewhart Methods of Quality Control." *Mechanical Engineering*, Vol. 66, 1944.

Deming, W. E. *Some Theory of Sampling.* New York: Dover, 1984.

Dodge, H. F., and Romig, H. G. *Sampling Inspection Tables.* 2nd ed. New York: Wiley, 1959.

Feller, W. *An Introduction to Probability Theory and Its Applications.* Vol. 1. 3rd ed. New York: Wiley, 1968.

Grant, E. L., and Leavenworth, R. S. *Statistical Quality Control.* 5th ed. New York: McGraw-Hill, 1979.

National Bureau of Standards. *Tables of the Binomial Probability Distribution.* Washington, D.C.: Government Printing Office, 1949.

Romig, H. G. *50–100 Binomial Tables.* New York: Wiley, 1953.

Sampling Procedures and Tables for Inspection by Attributes. MIL–STD–105D. Washington, D. C.: Government Printing Office, 1963.

KEY TERMS

Quality control (page 692)
Monitoring techniques (page 693)
Troubleshooting techniques (page 693)
Screening techniques (page 693)
Control chart (page 695)
$\bar{x}$ control chart (page 696)
R chart (page 699)
p chart (page 703)
c chart (page 705)
Run (page 710)
Lots (page 714)
Defective (page 715)

Lot acceptance sampling plan for defectives (page 715)
Acceptance number a (page 715)
Operating characteristic curve (page 716)
Acceptance quality level (AQL) (page 716)
Producer's risk (page 717)
Consumer's risk (page 717)
MIL–STD–105D sampling plans (page 718)
Double sampling plans (page 719)
Multiple sampling plans (page 720)
Sequential sampling plans (page 720)
Acceptance sampling by variables (page 721)

SUPPLEMENTARY EXERCISES

16.40 Explain the concept behind a control chart.

16.41 List the elements of a control chart, and explain how a control chart is used.

16.42 What will be the intent of a study and what statistics will be measured by using each of the following types of quality control charts? Give an example of a business problem where each chart will be useful in a quality control study.

(a) An $\bar{x}$ chart.

(b) An R chart.

(c) A p chart

(d) A c chart

16.43 A bottle manufacturer has observed that over a period of time when his manufacturing process was assumed to be in control, the average weight of the finished bottles was 5.2 ounces with a standard deviation of .3 ounce. The observed data was gathered in samples of six bottles selected from the production process at 50 different points in time. The average range of all the samples was found to be .6 ounce, and the standard deviation of ranges was .2. During each of the next five days samples of size $n = 6$ were selected from the manufacturing process, showing the following results:

Day	$\bar{x}$	R
1	5.70	.43
2	5.32	.51
3	6.21	1.25
4	6.09	.98
5	5.63	.60

(a) Construct the $\bar{x}$ chart and the R chart from the data obtained during which the process was assumed to be in control, and plot data for the last five days.

(b) Use the control charts constructed in part (a) to monitor the process for the sample data from the next five days.

(c) Does the production of bottles appear to be out of control during any of these five days? Interpret your results.

 16.44 Refer to Exercise 16.43. Suppose a soft-drink bottler specifies that the bottles she purchases from the manufacturer must weigh at least 4.8 ounces but not more than 5.5 ounces each. If the manufacturing process is in control, find the following.

(a) The probability that the manufacturing process is capable of meeting the stated specifications.

(b) The number of bottles in a shipment of 10,000 bottles from the manufacturer that can be expected not to meet the bottler's stated specifications.

 16.45 The following table lists the number of defective 60-watt light bulbs found in samples of 100 light bulbs selected over 25 days from a manufacturing process. Assume that during these 25 days the manufacturing process was not producing an excessively large fraction of defectives.

Day	1	2	3	4	5	6	7	8	9	10	11	12	13	14	15
Defectives	4	2	5	8	3	4	4	5	6	1	2	4	3	4	0

Day	16	17	18	19	20	21	22	23	24	25
Defectives	2	3	1	4	0	2	2	3	5	3

(a) Construct a p chart to monitor the manufacturing process, and plot the data.

(b) How large must the fraction of defective items be in a sample selected from the manufacturing process before the process is assumed to be out of control?

(c) During a given day, suppose a sample of 100 items is selected from the manufacturing process and that 15 defective bulbs are found. If a decision is made to shut down the manufacturing process in an attempt to locate the source of the implied controllable variation, explain how this decision might lead to erronous conclusions.

 16.46 A hardware store chain purchases large shipments of light bulbs from the manufacturer described in Exercise 16.45 and specifies that each shipment must contain no more than 4% defectives. When the manufacturing process is in control, what is the probability that the hardware store's specifications are met?

 16.47 Refer to Exercise 16.45. During a given week the number of defective bulbs in each of 5 samples of 100 were found to be 2, 4, 9, 7, and 11. Is there reason to believe that the production process has been producing an excess proportion of defectives at any time during the week?

16.48 A production process yields a long-run fraction defective of .03 when within control. Once each hour, 100 items are selected from the production process, their measurements are recorded, and the fraction of defectives is noted.

(a) Construct the control limits for the p chart to monitor the production process.

(b) Suppose the true fraction of defectives within the production process suddenly shifts to .06. What is the probability that the shift will be detected in the first sample selected from the production process?

 16.49 The following data represent the number of imperfections (scratches, chips, cracks, blisters) noted in 25 finished (4×8) walnut wall panels:

$$7, \ 5, \ 4, \ 10, \ 9, \ 5, \ 6, \ 3, \ 8, \ 8, \ 3, \ 5, \ 4, \ 9, \ 3, \ 3, \ 2, \ 4, \ 1, \ 5, \ 7, \ 3, \ 2, \ 6, \ 3$$

The total number of defects on 75 finished panels previously inspected was 375.

(a) Assuming the manufacturing process was in statistical control during the period when the data was gathered, construct a c chart to monitor the process (use the total number of defects for the 100 panels to construct the chart). Plot the number of defects listed for the 25 panels.

(b) If one wall panel is found to have more imperfections than the upper control limit allows, should the quality control engineer assume the manufacturing process is out of control, or should he wait until he finds repeated panels with an excessive number of imperfections before assuming the process is out of control? Explain.

 16.50 A quality control engineer wishes to study the alternative sampling plans $n = 5, a = 1$ and $n = 25, a = 5$. On the same sheet of graph paper, construct the operating characteristic curve for both plans, making use of acceptance probabilities at $p = .05$, $p = .10$, $p = .20$, $p = .30$, and $p = .40$ in each case.

(a) If you were a seller producing lots with fraction defective ranging from $p = 0$ to $p = .10$, which of the two sampling plans would you prefer?

(b) If you were a buyer wishing to be protected against accepting lots with fraction defective exceeding $p = .30$, which of the two sampling plans would you prefer?

16.51 A radio and television manufacturer who buys large lots of transistors from an electronics supplier wishes to accept all lots for which the fraction defective is less than 6%. The manufacturer's sampling inspector selects $n = 25$ transistors from each lot shipped by the supplier and notes the number of defectives.

(a) On the same sheet of graph paper, construct the operating characteristic curves for the sampling plans $n = 25, a = 1, 2$, and 3.

(b) Which sampling plan best protects the supplier from having acceptable lots rejected and returned by the manufacturer?

(c) Which sampling plan best protects the manufacturer from accepting lots for which the fraction of defectives exceeds 6%?

(d) How might the sampling inspector arrive at an acceptance level that compromises between the risk to the producer and the risk to the consumer?

 16.52 Refer to Exercise 16.51 and assume that the manufacturer wishes the probability to be at least .90 of his accepting lots containing 1% defective and the probability to be about .90 of rejecting any lot with 10% or more defective. If the manufacturer's sampling inspector samples $n = 25$ items from the supplier's incoming shipments, what is the acceptance level (a) that meets the requirements?

16.53 Find the MIL–STD–105D lot acceptance sampling plan for a lot size of $N = 800$, a normal inspection level, and AQL $= .01$.

16.54 Find the MIL–STD–105D lot acceptance sampling plan for a lot size of $N = 3000$, the tightened inspection level, level III, and AQL $= 0.065$.

When faced with a business decision, business managers are usually confronted with an array of possible actions, a variety of economic environments, and corporate gains (or losses) that depend on the manager's chosen action and the state of nature that occurs. This chapter presents an introduction to business decision theory, a systematic procedure for analyzing a decision problem and arriving at an appropriate action.

17

DECISION ANALYSIS

The Traveling Salesman Problem

In contrast to the other case studies presented in this text, this case study does not address a specific business problem. Rather, it deals with a type of problem encountered by many different businesses, which has been called the traveling salesman problem. We will illustrate the problem with an example.

Suppose that a salesman wants to travel from his present location to ten different cities and then to return home. Since the distances between different pairs of cities will almost certainly differ, how should the salesman schedule the cities so that he will minimize the distance that he must travel? Should he travel first to city A, then to B, and then to C, and so on, or would it require less distance if he went first to C, then to A, and then to B, and so on? The traveling salesman problem can also have as its objective the minimization of the length of time required for the trip. Thus we specify the lengths of times required to travel between all possible pairs of cities and select the travel schedule that minimizes the length of time required for the trip.

As described, the traveling salesman problem is an oversimplification of one of the many different types of decision problems that business managers must face on a daily basis. Most business decision problems are very complex. They usually offer the manager a number of different decision choices, a variety of different and uncertain economic environments, and a variety of economic decision outcomes that depend on the manager's choice of action and the economic environment that eventually prevails. This chapter deals with business decision analysis, a systematic procedure for diagnosing and solving business decision problems.

How does business decision analysis relate to statistics? The answer is that statistical methods attempt to assess, via sampling, the nature of some unknown phenomenon that is characterized by a conceptual or existing population of measurements. Statistical methods enable us to estimate the values of the population parameters, to make decisions about them, and to predict the outcome of uncertain events. As such, statistical sampling and inferential methods shed light on some of the uncertain environments facing decision makers and, in this way, play a role in business decision making. We will demonstrate, in an elementary way, how this is done in Section 17.5.

17.1 DECISION PROBLEMS

Business managers are faced daily with the need to make decisions. Should they expand their inventory? Should they increase or reduce their sales staff? Should they invest $200,000 in a new production line? These and many other decisions are made by using the manager's experience and intuition. Others are made by using experience, intuition, and methodology of business management known as decision analysis.

Decision analysis is a methodology that attempts to diagnose the anatomy of a decision problem and, thereby, to arrive at a better decision. To illustrate, suppose that you are the manager of a small manufacturing company and you are trying to decide whether you should add one or two new production lines to your ongoing operation.

You want to choose between the following three **actions**:

a_1: add two new production lines

a_2: add one new production line

a_3: do not add the new production lines

Which action will lead to the best decision? You decide that it depends on which one of four mutually exclusive and collectively exhaustive economic environments, called **states of nature**, you will face next year. Mutually exclusive (from Chapter 3) means that you can be in only one state at any one time. Collectively exhaustive means that the list of states is complete. You will always be in one and only one state. These states of nature—which, in this case, characterize the economy—are

s_1: a state of recession

s_2: a state of low business activity

s_3: a state of moderate business activity

s_4: a state of high business activity

The best action for one state of nature may not be the best action for another. If business activity next year is moderate to high, it may benefit you to add one or perhaps two production lines. If the state of business is low or is in a state of recession, making the capital investment in one or more production lines may be a poor decision.

In order to decide which action is best, we must define an **objective variable**, a variable that measures the relative merits of one outcome with respect to another when a certain action is taken and when a particular state of nature exists. For our problem we would probably select profit as the objective variable, but the objective variable need not be so simplistic. It could be a variable that is a weighted composite of profit, numbers of persons employed, or other social or business variables that possess tangible and/or intangible value.

If the state of nature that will exist next year were known, we could calculate the value of the objective variable, profit, for each action and then choose the action that produced the maximum profit. This type of problem, called **decision making under certainty**, is easy to solve if the number of possible actions is not too large. If the number of possible actions is very large, it may be necessary to use a computer to calculate the values of the objective variable corresponding to each of the many actions.

If the state of nature that exists next year is uncertain, then we must assign probabilities, $P(s_1), P(s_2), \ldots, P(s_4)$, to the mutually exclusive states of nature; and we must decide which action is best, in the face of uncertainty about the state of nature that will develop. For example, a consensus of economists might assign the probabilities $P(s_1) = .1, P(s_2) = .5, P(s_3) = .3$, and $P(s_4) = .1$ to the four economic conditions that define the four states of nature for our production line decision problem. Note that the sum of the probabilities over all states of nature will always equal 1 because the list of states must be mutually exclusive and collectively exhaustive. For our example

$$P(s_1) + P(s_2) + P(s_3) + P(s_4) = 1$$

When the state of nature that will exist next year is uncertain, we can no longer select the action that maximizes or minimizes the value of the objective variable because the objective variable is now a random variable, varying, for any given action, from one state to another. Finding the best action when the states of nature are uncertain is called **decision making under uncertainty**.

As we have noted, solving the decision problem under certainty is a straightforward problem; it really represents a special case of decision making under uncertainty, the case where the probability of one of the states is equal to 1 and the probabilities for all other states are equal to 0. Consequently, in this chapter we will examine the problem of making decisions under uncertainty (see the box).

SUMMARY OF THE ELEMENTS OF A DECISION ANALYSIS

(1) *Actions:* List all actions that you might take in solving your decision problem. From this list, you plan to select one. If the list contains r possible actions, they will be denoted as $a_1, a_2, \ldots, a_r$.

(2) *States of Nature:* List all of the states of nature that might exist after your decision is made. The list must be mutually exclusive and collectively exhaustive. If your list contains t states, they will be denoted as $s_1, s_2, \ldots, s_t$. The probabilities that the states of nature $s_1, s_2, \ldots, s_t$ occur are denoted, respectively, as

$$P(s_1), P(s_2), \ldots, P(s_t) \quad \text{where} \quad P(s_1) + P(s_2) + \cdots + P(s_t) = 1$$

(3) *Objective Variable:* The objective variable measures an outcome when a specific action is taken and a particular state of nature occurs.

PAYOFF AND OPPORTUNITY LOSS TABLES

17.2

The first step in solving a decision problem under uncertainty is determining the **payoffs** and constructing a **payoff table**.

DEFINITION

The *payoff* for any action and state of nature is the value assumed by the objective variable for that action–state of nature combination. ■

DEFINITION

A *payoff table* is one that shows the payoffs for every action–state of nature combination. ■

The payoff table for the production line problem of Section 17.1 is shown in Table 17.1. The probabilities of the respective states of nature are shown in parentheses. Payoffs are anticipated increases in profit (in thousands of dollars) over current operating profit. (A decrease in profit would be shown as a "negative increase.") For example, suppose that the company is currently making $100,000 a year. If under action a_1 (add two production lines) and state of nature s_1 (recession), it is estimated that the profit will be $20,000 per year, then the payoff for action a_1 and state of nature

TABLE 17.1   Payoff Table for Deciding Whether to Add New Production Lines

	State of Nature (Business Activity Level)			
Action	Recession (s_1) (.1)	Low (s_2) (.5)	Moderate (s_3) (.3)	High (s_4) (.1)
Add two production lines (a_1)	−80	−28	47	99
Add one production line (a_2)	−35	2	20	41
Add no production lines (a_3)	0	0	0	0

s_1 is ($20,000 − $100,000) = − $80,000, or − 80. We will assume that the company has calculated the payoffs for the different action–state of nature combinations and that they appear as shown in Table 17.1.

Examining Table 17.1, you can see that if state s_1 (a recession) occurs, the optimal strategy a_3 is to add no production lines. Adding either one or two production lines will result in a loss. If state s_2 occurs, the optimal strategy a_2 is to add one production line. Note that $P(s_1) = .1$ and $P(s_2) = .5$. However, if state s_3 occurs [with probability $P(s_3) = .3$], the optimal action a_1 (add two lines) produces an increase in profit of $47,000. Similarly, if state s_4 occurs [with probability $P(s_4) = .1$], the optimal action a_1 produces an increase in profit equal to $99,000. Thus the optimal action depends on the state of nature—that is, the state of the economy next year, a chance event.

Another way to characterize a decision problem is in terms of **opportunity loss**.

DEFINITION   The *opportunity loss* for a particular action a_i and state of nature s_j is the difference between the maximum payoff attainable when the state of nature s_j occurs and the payoff when action a_i and the state of nature s_j occurs.   ∎

For example, examining the payoff table, Table 17.1, you can see that the maximum payoff when s_1 occurs (the maximum payoff in column 1 of Table 17.1) is 0. Then the opportunity loss for action a_1 is [0 − (−80)], or 80. The opportunity losses corresponding to a_2 and a_3 are [0 − (−35)] = 35 and [0 − 0] = 0, respectively. Similarly, the opportunity losses when s_2 occurs are the differences between the maximum payoff when s_2 occurs (the maximum payoff in column 2 of Table 17.1) and the payoffs for the specific actions when s_2 occurs. The maximum payoff in column 2 of Table 17.1 is 2. Therefore, the opportunity losses corresponding to actions a_1, a_2, and a_3 are, respectively, 30, 0, and 2. The other opportunity losses can be calculated by using the rule in the following box. All the opportunity losses are then shown in an **opportunity loss table**.

DEFINITION   An *opportunity loss table* is one that shows the opportunity loss for every action–state of nature combination.   ∎

RULE FOR CALCULATING OPPORTUNITY LOSSES

> The opportunity losses corresponding to the possible actions when state of nature s_j occurs are found by using the following steps:
>
> (1) Locate the maximum payoff in the column of the payoff table corresponding to the state of nature s_j.
>
> (2) Find the opportunity loss for an action by subtracting its payoff (shown in the same column, i.e., column j) from the maximum payoff (found in step 1).
>
> Note that the opportunity loss for the maximum payoff in column j will always equal 0.

EXAMPLE 17.1   Refer to Table 17.1, and find the opportunity loss corresponding to action a_2 and state s_3.

SOLUTION   The opportunity loss for this action–state of nature combination is equal to the difference between the maximum payoff for state of nature s_3 (47) and the payoff corresponding to action a_2 and state s_3, namely 20. Therefore, the opportunity loss corresponding to action a_2 and state s_3 is $(47 - 20) = 27$. The opportunity loss table corresponding to the payoff table in Table 17.1 is shown in Table 17.2.

TABLE 17.2   Opportunity Loss Table for Deciding Whether to Add Production Lines

	State of Nature (Business Activity Level)			
Action	Recession (s_1) (.1)	Low (s_2) (.5)	Moderate (s_3) (.3)	High (s_4) (.1)
Add two production lines (a_1)	80	30	0	0
Add one production line (a_2)	35	0	27	58
Add no production lines (a_3)	0	2	47	99

The payoff table (and the corresponding opportunity loss table) provides a good characterization of a decision problem. At a glance you can see all of the actions, states of nature, and the payoffs for various combinations. In the next section we will learn how to use this table (or the opportunity loss table) to make a *good* decision.

17.3 CHOOSING THE BEST ACTION

It is unlikely that any one action will produce the largest payoff for all possible states of nature (see Table 17.1). Therefore, we need to define some criteria for selecting the best action. We will present two.

If we are very cautious and want to guard against losses, we may choose as the best action the one that minimizes the largest (maximum) loss. This decision is known as the **minimax criterion**.

DEFINITION

The *minimax criterion* chooses the action that produces the smallest (minimum) maximum opportunity loss.   ■

EXAMPLE 17.2

Find the minimax solution for the decision problem, using Table 17.2.

SOLUTION

If you examine Table 17.2, you will see that if you select action a_1, the maximum opportunity loss is 80 (or $80,000). If you select action a_2, the maximum opportunity loss is 58 (or $58,000). If you select action a_3, the maximum opportunity loss is 99. The maximum opportunity loss for each action is shown in Table 17.3.

TABLE 17.3

Maximum Losses for Actions a_1, a_2, and a_3

Action	Maximum Opportunity Loss
Add two production lines, a_1	80
Add one production line, a_2	58
Add no production lines, a_3	99

Examining Table 17.3 you can see that the smallest (minimum) maximum opportunity loss occurs if you choose action a_2. Thus you minimize the maximum opportunity loss if you add one production line.   ■

If you are not so conservative, you may want to choose the best action as the one that, on the average, will produce the largest payoff, by using the **maximum expected payoff criterion**.

DEFINITION

The *maximum expected payoff criterion* chooses the action that has the largest expected payoff.   ■

EXAMPLE 17.3

Use the maximum expected payoff criterion to find the optimal action for the decision problem of Table 17.1.

SOLUTION

You will recall (Section 3.4) that the expected value of a random variable y is

$$E(y) = \sum_y yp(y)$$

For this particular problem the random variable y is the payoff for a particular action and state of nature. We will denote the payoff for action a_1 and state s_1 as y_{11}; for action a_1 and state s_2 as $y_{12}, \ldots$; and in general, for action a_i and state of nature s_j as y_{ij}, $i = 1, 2, 3$ and $j = 1, 2, 3, 4$. For a given action a_i the probabilities associated with the four payoffs y_{i1}, y_{i2}, y_{i3}, and y_{i4} are, respectively, $P(s_1)$, $P(s_2)$, $P(s_3)$, and $P(s_4)$.

Therefore, the expected (or mean) payoff for action a_1 is the following:

Expected Payoff for Action a_1

$$E_1(y) = \sum_{i=1}^{4} y_{1i}P(s_i)$$

$$= y_{11}P(s_1) + y_{12}P(s_2) + y_{13}P(s_3) + y_{14}P(s_4)$$

$$= (-80)(.1) + (-28)(.5) + (47)(.3) + 99(.1) = 2.0$$

Similarly, the expected payoffs for actions a_2 and a_3 are the following:

Expected Payoff for Action a_2

$$E_2(y) = \sum_{i=1}^{4} y_{2i}P(s_i)$$

$$= y_{21}P(s_1) + y_{22}P(s_2) + \cdots + y_{24}P(s_4)$$

$$= (-35)(.1) + (2)(.5) + (20)(.3) + (41)(.1) = 7.6$$

Expected Payoff for Action a_3

$$E_3(y) = \sum_{i=1}^{4} y_{3i}P(s_i)$$

$$= y_{31}P(s_1) + y_{32}P(s_2) + \cdots + y_{34}P(s_4)$$

$$= (0)(.1) + (0)(.5) + (0)(.3) + (0)(.1) = 0$$

The expected payoffs for actions a_1, a_2, and a_3 are shown in Table 17.4. You can see that the expected payoff is largest (7.6, or $7600) for action a_2—that is, install one production line. Consequently, our decision, according to the maximum expected payoff criterion, will be to choose action a_2.

What is the practical implication in stating that the expected payoff for action a_2 is 7.6 (or $7600)? It means that if we were to repeat this decision process over and over again, sometimes state s_1 would occur and we would lose 35 ($35,000), sometimes s_2 would occur and we would make 2 ($2000), . . . , and sometimes s_4 would occur and we would make 41 ($41,000). Over the long run, our losses and profits would average to 7.6, or $7600. Unfortunately, we will not be repeating this decision making many times. We plan to make the decision now and only once. This fact does not lessen the usefulness of

TABLE 17.4 Expected Payoff for Actions a_1, a_2, and a_3

Action	Expected Payoff
Add two production lines, a_1	2.0
Add one production line, a_2	7.6
Add no production lines, a_3	0

the maximum expected payoff criterion in making a decision. Since this business decision (like most) is a gamble, we think you will choose the action that produces the greatest gain in the "long run." ∎

Before concluding this section, we state (without proof) that the solution (the action) that produces the maximum expected payoff is also the solution that corresponds to the minimum expected opportunity loss. If we were to calculate the expected opportunity loss (using Table 17.2) for each action, the smallest expected opportunity loss would correspond to action a_2. We will ask you to show this in Exercise 17.8.

EXERCISES

BASIC TECHNIQUES

17.1 Given the payoff table shown in Table 17.5, find these actions:
(a) That will satisfy the minimax criterion for selecting an optimal action.
(b) That maximizes the expected payoff.
The probabilities for the states of nature are shown in parentheses in the table.

TABLE 17.5   Payoff Table for Exercise 17.1

	State of Nature			
Action	s_1 (.2)	s_2 (.4)	s_3 (.3)	s_4 (.1)
a_1	−50	30	40	80
a_2	−90	40	50	70
a_3	0	30	20	10

17.2 Given the payoff table shown in Table 17.6, find these actions:
(a) That will satisfy the minimax criterion for selecting an optimal action.
(b) That maximizes the expected payoff.
The probabilities for the states of nature are shown in parentheses in the table.

TABLE 17.6   Payoff Table for Exercise 17.2

	State of Nature		
Action	s_1 (.1)	s_2 (.5)	s_3 (.4)
a_1	5	10	40
a_2	3	30	10
a_3	16	16	10
a_4	80	10	0

17.3 Given the payoff table shown in Table 17.7, find these actions:
(a) That will satisfy the minimax criterion for selecting an optimal action.

(b) That maximizes the expected payoff.

The probabilities for the states of nature are shown in parentheses in the table.

TABLE 17.7   Payoff Table for Exercise 17.3

	State of Nature		
Action	s_1 (.3)	s_2 (.5)	s_3 (.2)
a_1	5	4	7
a_2	2	6	3
a_3	−5	10	2

17.4 Given the payoff table shown in Table 17.8, find these actions:

(a) That will satisfy the minimax criterion for selecting an optimal action.

(b) That maximizes the expected payoff.

The probabilities for the states of nature are shown in parentheses in the table.

TABLE 17.8   Payoff Table for Exercise 17.4

	State of Nature			
Action	s_1 (.1)	s_2 (.3)	s_3 (.1)	s_4 (.5)
a_1	10	15	0	8
a_2	25	10	20	9
a_3	15	15	5	10

17.5 Construct an opportunity loss table for Exercise 17.1. Find the action that minimizes the expected opportunity loss and confirm that this action is also the one that maximizes the expected payoff.

APPLICATIONS

17.6 A pharmaceutical company has developed two new drugs and must decide whether to invest the money and time necessary to acquire Federal Drug Administration (FDA) approval to market one or both of the new products. The actions being considered, the states of nature and their probabilities, and the payoffs (in millions of dollars) are shown in Table 17.9.

(a) Find the action that will satisfy the minimax criterion for selecting an optimal action.

(b) Find the action that maximizes the expected payoff.

17.7 Suppose that you have $10,000 that you want to invest and you are considering the possibility of an oil-drilling operation. One option is to invest the $10,000 in the oil-drilling operation, with the prospects and payoffs over a two-year period as shown in Table 17.10. As a second option, you can limit your investment to $5000 (receiving half of the payoffs shown in the table) and invest the remaining $5000 at 14% interest, compounded annually, for two years. Or you can invest the entire $10,000 at 14% interest, compounded annually, for two years.

(a) Construct the payoff table for this decision problem.

(b) Use the maximum expected payoff criterion to acquire the optimal action for this decision problem.

TABLE 17.9   Pharmaceutical Payoff Data for Exercise 17.6

	State of Nature (Number of Years Required for FDA Approval)			
Action	s_1, less than 4 years (.1)	s_2, 4 to 6 years (.5)	s_3, 6 to 8 years (.3)	s_4, 8 to 10 years (.1)
Continue developing drug 1 only, a_1	90	65	10	-40
Continue developing drug 2 only, a_2	60	50	40	-30
Develop both drugs, a_3	160	120	5	-90
Develop none of the drugs, a_4	40	40	40	40

TABLE 17.10   Oil-Drilling Data for Exercise 17.7

Action	Probability	Payoff
Hit a high-producing oil and gas well	.04	$200,000
Hit a modest-producing oil and gas well	.08	$90,000
Hit only gas	.10	$25,000
Hit no economically recoverable amounts of oil and/or gas	.78	$ $-10,000$

17.8 Find the action that produces the minimum expected opportunity loss for Table 17.2. Confirm that this action is also the one that maximizes the expected payoff.

MODIFYING STATE-OF-NATURE PROBABILITIES USING BAYES' RULE

17.4

Armed with the methodology of Sections 17.1, 17.2, and 17.3, we might think that our decision-making problems are over. That is not the case. In addition to the possibility that we may have oversimplified our problem, we rarely know the correct values of the probabilities of the states of nature. Modest changes in these probabilities, which are usually chosen on the basis of experience and intuition, can often lead to sizable differences in the expected payoffs and in the action that produces a maximum expected payoff. For instance, if we choose $P(s_1) = .2$, $P(s_2) = .3$, $P(s_3) = .3$, and $P(s_4) = .2$ for our production line decision problem of Table 17.1, we arrive at a different optimal action. Action a_1 produces the largest expected payoff. This presents a problem. If we cannot be certain that our state-of-nature probabilities are correct, how can we be confident that our solution for the optimal action is correct?

There are two ways of coping with this problem. One way is to determine the optimal action for different sets of state-of-nature probabilities. For example, suppose that a decision problem involves four actions and three states of nature. Our initial choice for the state-of-nature probabilities, $P(s_1) = .1$, $P(s_2) = .6$, and $P(s_3) = .3$, leads to the selection of a_2 as the optimal action. Suppose that we reanalyze the problem for other values of $P(s_1)$, $P(s_2)$, and $P(s_3)$ that are *near* the initial selection, say $P(s_1) = .05$, $P(s_2) = .55$, and $P(s_3) = .4$, and still obtain a_2 as the optimal action. If we repeat this process for a spread of values near $P(s_1) = .1$, $P(s_2) = .6$, and $P(s_3) = .3$ and always obtain action a_2 as the optimal solution, we may feel reasonably confident (assuming that our initial selections were not too greatly in error) that we have arrived at the optimal solution.

A second method for coping with this uncertainty is to select sample data and to use this information to adjust the initial state-of-nature probabilities. The adjusted probabilities are the *conditional probabilities* of the states, given the additional sample information. The initial probabilities are usually called **prior probabilities** because they are the probabilities used prior to the acquisition of the sample information. The adjusted state-of-nature probabilities are called **posterior probabilities**.

The procedure for finding the posterior probabilities is known as **Bayes' Rule**. Suppose, for example, that the state of nature can assume one and only one of three possibilities, s_1, s_2 and s_3, with prior probabilities $P(s_1)$, $P(s_2)$, and $P(s_3)$; and let I represent some sample outcome (the sample measurements or the values of some sample statistics). As noted, the objective of Bayes' Rule is to modify the prior probabilities based on the fact that we know that event I has occurred. These posterior probabilities are the conditional probabilities of observing s_1, s_2, and s_3, respectively, given that event I has occurred—that is, $P(s_1 \mid I)$, $P(s_2 \mid I)$, and $P(s_3 \mid I)$.

A posterior probability can be calculated by using the formula given in the definition for a conditional probability in Section 3.3. Thus

$$P(s_1 \mid I) = \frac{P(s_1, I)}{P(I)}$$

where $P(s_1, I)$ is the probability that *both* s_1 and I occur and $P(I)$ is the unconditional probability that I will occur.

The probability $P(s_1, I)$ that both events s_1 and I occur, given in Section 3.3, is

$$P(s_1, I) = P(s_1)P(I \mid s_1)$$

where $P(s_1)$, the prior probability, is known and the probability of the sample, given state of nature s_1—that is, $P(I \mid s_1)$—can usually be calculated. The unconditional probability of event I, $P(I)$, is the union of three mutually exclusive events:

(1) State of nature s_1 exists and I occurs.

(2) State of nature s_2 exists and I occurs.

(3) State of nature s_3 exists and I occurs.

that is, $P(I) = P(s_1, I) + P(s_2, I) + P(s_3, I)$

Therefore, the posterior probability for state of nature s_1 is

$$P(s_1|I) = \frac{P(s_1, I)}{P(I)} = \frac{P(s_1, I)}{P(s_1, I) + P(s_2, I) + P(s_3, I)}$$

$$= \frac{P(s_1)P(I|s_1)}{P(s_1)P(I|s_1) + P(s_2)P(I|s_2) + P(s_3)P(I|s_3)}$$

The posterior probabilities for states of nature s_2 and s_3 can be calculated in a similar manner:

$$P(s_2|I) = \frac{P(s_2, I)}{P(I)} \quad \text{and} \quad P(s_3|I) = \frac{P(s_3, I)}{P(I)}$$

where $P(s_2, I) = P(s_2)P(I|s_2)$, $P(s_3, I) = P(s_3)P(I|s_3)$, and $P(I)$ appear in the calculations for $P(s_1|I)$.

  The following box gives Bayes' Rule for any number, say k, states of nature, and the example that follows illustrates its use.

BAYES' RULE

Suppose that one and only one state of nature, $s_1, s_2, \ldots, s_k$, can exist with unconditional (prior) probabilities $P(s_1)$, $P(s_2), \ldots, P(s_k)$, and let I represent the occurrence of a specific sample outcome. Then the probability that state of nature s_i exists, given the sample information I, is

$$P(s_i|I) = \frac{P(s_i)P(I|s_i)}{P(s_1)P(I|s_1) + P(s_2)P(I|s_2) + \cdots + P(s_k)P(I|s_k)}$$

EXAMPLE 17.4   Suppose that you wish to infer which of two mutually exclusive economic conditions, H_1 or H_2, will exist next year. You have observed some economic evidence A, which could have occurred with probability .2, given that H_1 will exist next year, and with probability .4, given that H_2 will exist next year. That is,

$$P(A|H_1) = .2 \quad \text{and} \quad P(A|H_2) = .4.$$

Suppose that prior information suggests that the probability that economic condition H_1 will exist next year is .7—that is, $P(H_1) = .7$. If you know that event A has occurred, would you revise your probability that H_1 will exist next year upward or downward?

SOLUTION   The two "states of nature" in this problem are represented by the symbols H_1 and H_2. The information I is represented by the symbol A, and we want to find the posterior probabilities for H_1 and H_2, the probabilities that H_1 and H_2, respectively, will occur, given that A has been observed. One of these posterior probabilities is

$$P(H_1|A) = \frac{P(H_1, A)}{P(A)} = \frac{P(H_1)P(A|H_1)}{P(H_1)P(A|H_1) + P(H_2)P(A|H_2)}$$

Since only one state of nature can exist and we are given $P(H_1) = .7$, it follows that $P(H_2) = 1 - P(H_1) = 1 - .7 = .3$. We are also given $P(A|H_1) = .2$ and $P(A|H_2) = .4$. Substituting these values into the formula for $P(H_1|A)$ yields

$$P(H_1|A) = \frac{(.7)(.2)}{(.7)(.2) + (.3)(.4)} = \frac{.14}{.26} = .54$$

Similarly,

$$P(H_2|A) = \frac{P(H_2)P(A|H_2)}{P(H_1)P(A|H_1) + P(H_2)P(A|H_2)} = \frac{(.3)(.4)}{.26} = .46$$

What do these values tell us? Without the additional sample information we would use the prior probabilities $P(H_1) = .7$ and $P(H_2) = .3$ to measure the likelihood that states of nature H_1 and H_2 will occur next year. But given the sample information, we would modify the probabilities of the states of nature and employ the posterior probabilities,

$$P(H_1|A) = .54 \quad \text{and} \quad P(H_2|A) = .46$$

Thus, initially, we would have given 7–3 odds that state of nature H_1 will occur. Having observed event A, we modify our odds to 54–46. ∎

EXERCISES

BASIC TECHNIQUES

17.9 Suppose that three mutually exclusive states of nature, s_1, s_2, s_3, can exist with probabilities

$$P(s_1) = .4 \qquad P(s_2) = .5 \qquad P(s_3) = .1$$

and that given these states of nature, an event I can occur with probabilities

$$P(I|s_1) = .1 \qquad P(I|s_2) = .3 \qquad P(I|s_3) = .2$$

Suppose that event I is observed. Find $P(s_1|I)$, $P(s_2|I)$, and $P(s_3|I)$.

17.10 Suppose that two mutually exclusive states of nature, s_1, s_2, can exist with probabilities

$$P(s_1) = .4 \qquad P(s_2) = .6$$

and that given these states of nature, an event I can occur with probabilities

$$P(I|s_1) = .2 \qquad P(I|s_2) = .3$$

Suppose that event I is observed. Find $P(s_1|I)$ and $P(s_2|I)$.

17.11 Suppose that four mutually exclusive states of nature, s_1, s_2, s_3, and s_4, can exist with probabilities

$$P(s_1) = .1 \qquad P(s_2) = .4 \qquad P(s_3) = .3 \qquad P(s_4) = .2$$

and that given these states of nature, an event I can occur with probabilities

$$P(I|s_1) = .6 \qquad P(I|s_2) = .2 \qquad P(I|s_3) = .2 \qquad P(I|s_4) = .5$$

Suppose that event I is observed. Find $P(s_1|I)$, $P(s_2|I)$, $P(s_3|I)$, and $P(s_4|I)$.

APPLICATIONS

 17.12 A study of Georgia residents suggests that those who worked in shipyards during World War II were subjected to a significantly higher risk of lung cancer (*Wall Street Journal*, September 21, 1978). It was found that approximately 22% of those persons who had lung cancer worked at some prior time in a shipyard. In contrast, only 14% of those who had no lung cancer worked at some prior time in a shipyard. Suppose that the proportion of all Georgians living during World War II who have or will have contracted lung cancer is .04%. Find the percentage of Georgians living during the same period who will contract (or have contracted) lung cancer, given that they have at some prior time worked in a shipyard.

 17.13 As items come to the end of a production line, an inspector chooses which items are to go through a complete inspection. Ten percent of all items produced are defective. Sixty percent of all defective items go through a complete inspection, and 20% of all good items go through a complete inspection. Given that an item is completely inspected, what is the probability it is defective?

 17.14 Suppose that 5% of all people filing the long income tax form seek deductions that they know to be illegal and an additional 2% will incorrectly list deductions because of lack of knowledge of the income tax regulations. Of the 5% guilty of cheating, 80% will deny knowledge of the error if confronted by an investigator. If a filer of the long form is confronted with an unwarranted deduction and he denies knowledge of the error, what is the probability that he is guilty?

MODIFICATION OF THE DECISION PROBLEM WHEN SAMPLE INFORMATION IS AVAILABLE

17.5

As explained in Section 17.4, sometimes we have only sketchy information on the probabilities of the states of nature. When this situation occurs, it may pay to draw sample information and use it to more accurately establish their values. Thus we use Bayes' Rule to modify the prior probabilities to obtain posterior probabilities for the states of nature.

The process of solving a decision problem when sample information is available is exactly the same as described in Sections 17.1, 17.2, and 17.3, except for one difference: We use the posterior rather than the prior probability to measure the likelihood that a particular state of nature will occur. The following example illustrates the procedure.

EXAMPLE 17.5   A real estate investor wants to make a choice from among three $400,000 investment options:

> a_1: investing $400,000 in a 50-unit apartment complex

> a_2: investing $200,000 in a 20-unit apartment complex and placing the remaining $200,000 in a money fund that will average a 14% return

> a_3: placing the entire $400,000 in a money fund that will average a 14% return

In the investor's opinion, success in the apartment investment rests on the condition of the rental market, measured by the number per 1000 high-income renters who would want to rent an apartment in one of the two complexes. The investor characterized these states of nature as follows:

$$s_1: 1 \text{ per } 1000$$
$$s_2: 2 \text{ per } 1000$$
$$s_3: 3 \text{ per } 1000$$

The payoff table, constructed by the investor, is shown in Table 17.11. Payoffs (in thousands of dollars) were based on the return over a five-year period, adjusted for taxes.

TABLE 17.11   Payoff Table for the Real Estate Investor of Example 17.5

Action	State of Nature (Number per 1000 Renters Who Will Rent New Apartment Unit)		
	$s_1 : P(s_1) = .4$	$s_2 : P(s_2) = .4$	$s_3 : P(s_3) = .2$
Invest in 50 units, a_1	−170	50	480
Invest in 20 units, a_2	−50	110	210
Invest in money fund, a_3	105	105	105

From an analysis of the market, the investor assigned probabilities $P(s_1) = .4$, $P(s_2) = .4$, and $P(s_3) = .2$ to the three states of nature. The expected payoffs, based on these probabilities,

$$E_1(y) = (-170)(.4) + (50)(.4) + (480)(.2) = 48$$
$$E_2(y) = (-50)(.4) + (110)(.4) + (210)(.2) = 66$$
$$E_3(y) = (105)(.4) + (105)(.4) + (105)(.2) = 105$$

indicate that the best investment is a_3, place the money in a money fund.

Dissatisfied with this conclusion, the investor commissioned a random sampling of 3000 high-income renters in the area and found that 6 in the sample stated that they would rent one of the new apartments if they were built. Use this information to adjust the prior state-of-nature probabilities and obtain the optimal action based on the revised probabilities.

SOLUTION   Since we are using the symbol y to represent the payoffs, we will use the symbol x to represent the number in the sample of 3000 renters who indicate that they will rent one of the new apartments. The observed value of this random variable is $x = 6$. The posterior probabilities (the adjusted state-of-nature probabilities) are the conditional probabilities of s_1, s_2, and s_3, given the sample information $x = 6$. These conditional probabilities are acquired by using Bayes' Rule (Section 17.4). For example, the posterior probability for state s_1 is the conditional probability

$$P(s_1 \mid x = 6) = \frac{P(x = 6, s_1)}{P(x = 6)}$$

$$= \frac{P(x = 6, s_1)}{P(x = 6, s_1) + P(x = 6, s_2) + P(x = 6, s_3)}$$

$$= \frac{P(s_1)P(x = 6 \mid s_1)}{P(s_1)P(x = 6 \mid s_1) + P(s_2)P(x = 6 \mid s_2) + P(s_3)P(x = 6 \mid s_3)}$$

Examine this expression and note that we know the values of the prior probabilities, $P(s_1) = .4$, $P(s_2) = .4$, and $P(s_3) = .2$. Therefore, the only additional quantities that we need to find are the conditional probabilities, $P(x = 6 \mid s_1)$, $P(x = 6 \mid s_2)$, and $P(x = 6 \mid s_3)$.

The probability $P(x = 6 \mid s_1)$ is the probability of observing $x = 6$ renters in the sample of 3000 when s_1 is the state of nature—that is, *on the average,* one per thousand renters will want to rent one of the new apartments. Thus x is a binomial random variable with $n = 3000$ and $p = .001$.

A binomial probability $p(x)$ when $n = 3000$ and $p = .001$ is difficult to calculate directly, but it can be approximated by using the Poisson probability*

$$p(x) = \frac{\mu^x e^{-\mu}}{x!} \qquad \text{where} \qquad \mu = np$$

To approximate the binomial probability for $p(6)$ when $\mu = np = (3000)(.001) = 3$, we use

$$P(x = 6 \mid s_1) = \frac{\mu^x e^{-\mu}}{x!} = \frac{(3)^6 e^{-3}}{6!} = .05$$

Similarly, when state s_2 exists, $p = .002$, $\mu = np = (3000)(.002) = 6$, and

$$P(x = 6 \mid s_2) = \frac{\mu^x e^{-\mu}}{x!} = \frac{(6)^6 e^{-6}}{6!} = .16$$

Finally, when state s_3 exists, $p = .003$, $\mu = np = (3000)(.003) = 9$, and

$$P(x = 6 \mid s_3) = \frac{\mu^x e^{-\mu}}{x!} = \frac{(9)^6 e^{-9}}{6!} = .09$$

Substituting the values of the prior probabilities and these conditional probabilities into Bayes' Rule, we find the posterior probability for state s_1 to be

$$P(s_1 \mid x = 6) = \frac{P(s_1)P(x = 6 \mid s_1)}{P(s_1)P(x = 6 \mid s_1) + P(s_2)P(x = 6 \mid s_2) + P(s_3)P(x = 6 \mid s_3)}$$

$$= \frac{(.4)(.05)}{(.4)(.05) + (.4)(.16) + (.2)(.09)} = \frac{.02}{.102} = .196$$

---

*The Poisson probability distribution provides a good approximation to the binomial probability distribution when n is large, p is small, and $np \leq 7$. This approximation is discussed in optional Section 3.8.

Similarly, the posterior probability for s_2 is

$$P(s_2 \mid x = 6) = \frac{P(s_2)P(x = 6 \mid s_2)}{P(x = 6)} = \frac{(.4)(.16)}{.102} = .627$$

Finally, the posterior probability for s_3 is

$$P(s_3 \mid x = 6) = 1 - P(s_1 \mid x = 6) - P(s_2 \mid x = 6)$$
$$= 1 - .196 - .627 = .177$$

At this point, let us summarize what we have done. We have used our renter sample survey information to modify our prior state-of-nature probabilities. We will now use the new posterior state probabilities to calculate the expected payoff for each action. These expected payoffs are

$$E_1(y) = (-170)(.196) + (50)(.627) + (480)(.177) = 82.99$$
$$E_2(y) = (-50)(.196) + (110)(.627) + (210)(.177) = 96.34$$
$$E_3(y) = (105)(.196) + (105)(.627) + (105)(.177) = 105$$

Comparing these expected payoffs, you can see, based on the additional sample information, that investing in the money fund (our initial solution) is still the best action! Action a_3, invest in the money fund, has the largest expected payoff based on the posterior probabilities.

EXERCISES

BASIC TECHNIQUES

17.15 Refer to Exercise 17.1. A sample was collected and produced information that we will denote by the symbol I. Calculation of the probabilities of the sample information I, given each of the states of nature, produced the following results:

$$P(I \mid s_1) = .02 \qquad P(I \mid s_2) = .10 \qquad P(I \mid s_3) = .18 \qquad P(I \mid s_4) = .11$$

Find the posterior state-of-nature probabilities, and use them to find the action that maximizes the expected payoff.

17.16 Refer to Exercise 17.2. A sample was collected and produced information that we will denote by the symbol I. Calculation of the probabilities of the sample information I, given each of the states of nature, produced the following results:

$$P(I \mid s_1) = .4 \qquad P(I \mid s_2) = .2 \qquad P(I \mid s_3) = .3$$

Find the posterior state-of-nature probabilities, and use them to find the action that maximizes the expected payoff.

APPLICATIONS

17.17 Refer to Exercise 17.6. A sample was collected and produced information that we will denote by the symbol I. Calculation of the probabilities of the sample information I, given each of the states of nature, produced the following results:

$$P(I \mid s_1) = .3 \qquad P(I \mid s_2) = .2 \qquad P(I \mid s_3) = .2 \qquad P(I \mid s_4) = .4$$

Find the posterior state-of-nature probabilities, and use them to find the action that maximizes the expected payoff.

17.18 Refer to Exercise 17.7. Before making a decision, you, as an investor, sought the aid of a geologist. Samples selected by the geologist from the drilling site could have occurred with the following probabilities:

(i)   With probability .1, given that the well is a high-producing prospect.

(ii) With probability .2, given that the well is a moderate producer.

(iii) with probability .8, given that the well contains only gas.

(iv) With probability .1, given that the well contains no economically recoverable amounts of oil and gas.

Use this information to calculate the posterior probabilities for the states of nature, and find the action that maximizes the expected payoff.

The Traveling Salesman Problem: A Postview

17.6

Now that you have had an introduction to the basic concepts of decision analysis, we will reexamine the traveling salesman problem described in the Case Study and see how it can be solved by using our decision methodology. We will discuss the problem with minimization of the total distance traveled as our objective but will understand that we could have chosen to minimize total travel time.

Our Case Study characterization of the traveling salesman problem is an example of decision making under certainty. As described in the Case Study, we have assumed that it is possible to travel between all pairs of cities. Although it complicates the solution of the problem, we can delete the possibility of traveling between one or more pairs of cities or we can omit the possibility of traveling in one direction between a pair of cities. Thus it may be possible to travel from city A to city B but, for some reason, impossible to travel from B to A. If we list the distances between all pairs of cities where travel is possible and if we assume that, once the distance is listed, it is always possible to make the trip, then each different routing corresponds to an action and no uncertainty is present. The solution of the decision problem then involves selection of the action that minimizes the total travel distance. A number of papers have been written on the solution of the traveling salesman problem, some of which are listed in the References. If many cities are involved, the solution is a job for a computer.

Solving the traveling salesman problem becomes decision making under uncertainty when the ability to travel between one or more pairs of cities becomes uncertain. For example, a flight from city A to city B may be canceled because of bad weather; or a rental car, reserved in advance and required to travel from city C to city D, may, with a certain probability, be unavailable. Thus in addition to having the actions (routes) presented when making decisions under certainty, we now possess a set of states of nature that will occur with specified (but usually unknown) probabilities. Under these conditions the traveling salesman problem fits the model for decision making under uncertainty.

SUMMARY

17.7

The preceding sections present an introduction, a glimpse into a fascinating subject, business decision analysis. We learned how to dissect a business decision problem into a set of actions and states of nature and to summarize the results of the actions in a payoff (or opportunity loss) table. Various criteria can be specified (and justified, depending on the business objective) for selecting the best action. We presented two of them, the minimax criterion and the maximum expected payoff criterion. Procedures for coping with the uncertainty surrounding the initial selection of the state of nature probabilities were presented in Section 17.4. Particularly, we learned how to adjust the prior probabilities based on additional sample information. These topics represent only an introduction to business decision analysis.

Because decision analysis often oversimplifies a decision problem—that is, perhaps many more actions and states of nature should be included in the study—and because the state of nature probabilities are rarely precisely known, of what value is decision analysis? The answer is that a decision analysis forces us to examine our decision problem in detail. This in itself helps us to better understand the problem and to arrive at a better decision. It also leads us, in a rational way, to a so-called "optimal" decision. This decision, moderated by experience and intuition, should be better than a decision based on experience and intuition alone.

REFERENCES

Baird, B. F. *Introduction to Decision Analysis*. Boston: Duxbury Press, 1978.

Brown, R. V., Kahr, A. S., and Peterson, C. *Decision Analysis for the Manager*. New York: Holt, Rinehart and Winston, 1974.

Flood, Merrill M. "Application of Transportation Theory to Scheduling a Military Tanker Fleet." *Journal of the Operations Research Society of America*, Vol. 2, 1954, pp. 150–162.

Flood, Merrill M. "The Traveling Salesman Problem." *Operations Research*, Vol. 4, No. 1, 1956.

Hadley, G. *Introduction to Probability and Statistical Decision Theory*. San Francisco: Holden-Day, 1967.

Heller, Isidor. "The Traveling-Salesman's Problem, Part I: Basic Facts." The George Washington University Logistics Research Project, June 1954.

Keeney, R. L., and Raiffa, H. *Decisions with Multiple Objectives: Preferences and Value Tradeoffs*. New York: Wiley, 1976.

Kuhn, H. W. "The Traveling-Salesman Problem." *Proceedings of the Sixth Symposium in Applied Mathematics* (American Mathematical Society). New York: McGraw-Hill, 1956.

Raiffa, H. *Decision Analysis. Introductory Lectures on Choices Under Uncertainty*. Reading, Mass.: Addison-Wesley, 1968.

Raiffa, H., and Schlaifer, R. *Applied Statistical Decision Theory*. Cambridge, Mass.: MIT Press, 1961.

Winkler, R. L. *An Introduction to Bayesian Inference and Decision*. New York: Holt, Rinehart and Winston, 1972.

KEY TERMS

Decision analysis (page 731)

Actions (page 732)

States of nature (page 732)

Objective variable (page 732)

Decision making under certainty (page 732)

Decision making under uncertainty (page 733)

Payoff (page 733)

Payoff table (page 733)

Opportunity loss (page 734)

Opportunity loss table (page 734)

Minimax criterion (page 736)

Maximum expected payoff criterion (page 736)

Conditional probabilities (page 741)

Prior probabilities (page 741)

Posterior probabilities (page 741)

Bayes' Rule (page 741)

SUPPLEMENTARY EXERCISES

17.19 One way to reduce the size of a decision problem is to remove *dominated* actions from consideration (and, consequently, from the payoff table). Action a_1 is said to be dominated by action a_2 if, for every state of nature, the payoff for action a_2 is greater than or equal to the payoff for action a_1. That is, a_1 is never the best decision, regardless of which state of nature occurs. Examine Table 17.12 and identify both the dominated actions and the actions that dominate them.

TABLE 17.12   Payoff Table for Exercise 17.19

Action	s_1 (.3)	s_2 (.2)	s_3 (.2)	s_4 (.1)	s_5 (.2)
a_1	-30	70	70	90	10
a_2	12	60	50	40	8
a_3	13	70	52	31	5
a_4	17	65	51	51	9
a_5	-23	80	91	95	12

(States of Nature span columns s_1–s_5.)

17.20 Find the maximum expected payoff in Exercise 17.19.

17.21 Refer to Exercise 17.19. Additional sample information I was acquired and the following probabilities were calculated: $P(I|s_1) = .07$, $P(I|s_2) = .09$, $P(I|s_3) = .14$, $P(I|s_4) = .15$, $P(I|s_5) = .02$. Find the posterior state-of-nature probabilities, and use them to find the action that maximizes the expected payoff.

17.22 Share of the market readership is the major factor involved in deciding whether to publish a new novel. Examining a manuscript, a publisher calculates that if only 1 in 100 habitual readers buy the book, the costs of production and advertising will outweigh sales income and she will lose $400,000. If 1 in 50 habitual readers buys the book, she will make $300,000; if 1 in 20 readers buys the book, she will make $1,000,000. If she foregoes the pleasure of publishing the novel, she will make $80,000 in interest on her uninvested money. She estimates the probabilities associated with the three market shares as

$$P(1 \text{ in } 100) = .4 \qquad P(1 \text{ in } 50) = .5 \qquad P(1 \text{ in } 20) = .1$$

(a) Construct a payoff table for the publisher's decision problem.

(b) Should the publisher publish the new novel?

17.23 Refer to Exercise 17.22. The publisher decided to buy some additional information before making a decision. Two hundred habitual readers were randomly selected and were presented the advertising material prepared for the new novel. Based on this material, 3 stated that they would buy the book when it was published.

(a) Use this sample information to calculate the posterior state-of-nature probabilities. (Use the Poisson probability distribution with $\mu = np$ to approximate the binomial probability distribution.)

(b) Use the sample information to help you decide whether the publisher should publish the novel.

APPENDIX TABLES

Tabulated values are $P(x \leq a) = \sum_{x=0}^{a} p(x)$. (Computations are rounded at the third decimal place.)

(a) $n = 5$

							p							
a	0.01	0.05	0.10	0.20	0.30	0.40	0.50	0.60	0.70	0.80	0.90	0.95	0.99	a
0	.951	.774	.590	.328	.168	.078	.031	.010	.002	.000	.000	.000	.000	0
1	.999	.977	.919	.737	.528	.337	.188	.087	.031	.007	.000	.000	.000	1
2	1.000	.999	.991	.942	.837	.683	.500	.317	.163	.058	.009	.001	.000	2
3	1.000	1.000	1.000	.993	.969	.913	.812	.663	.472	.263	.081	.023	.001	3
4	1.000	1.000	1.000	1.000	.998	.990	.969	.922	.832	.672	.410	.226	.049	4

(continues)

TABLE 1   (*Continued*)

(b) *n* = 10

							p							
a	0.01	0.05	0.10	0.20	0.30	0.40	0.50	0.60	0.70	0.80	0.90	0.95	0.99	*a*
0	.904	.599	.349	.107	.028	.006	.001	.000	.000	.000	.000	.000	.000	0
1	.996	.914	.736	.376	.149	.046	.011	.002	.000	.000	.000	.000	.000	1
2	1.000	.988	.930	.678	.383	.167	.055	.012	.002	.000	.000	.000	.000	2
3	1.000	.999	.987	.879	.650	.382	.172	.055	.011	.001	.000	.000	.000	3
4	1.000	1.000	.998	.967	.850	.633	.377	.166	.047	.006	.000	.000	.000	4
5	1.000	1.000	1.000	.994	.953	.834	.623	.367	.150	.033	.002	.000	.000	5
6	1.000	1.000	1.000	.999	.989	.945	.828	.618	.350	.121	.013	.001	.000	6
7	1.000	1.000	1.000	1.000	.998	.988	.945	.833	.617	.322	.070	.012	.000	7
8	1.000	1.000	1.000	1.000	1.000	.998	.989	.954	.851	.624	.264	.086	.004	8
9	1.000	1.000	1.000	1.000	1.000	1.000	.999	.994	.972	.893	.651	.401	.096	9

(c) *n* = 15

							p							
a	0.01	0.05	0.10	0.20	0.30	0.40	0.50	0.60	0.70	0.80	0.90	0.95	0.99	*a*
0	.860	.463	.206	.035	.005	.000	.000	.000	.000	.000	.000	.000	.000	0
1	.990	.829	.549	.167	.035	.005	.000	.000	.000	.000	.000	.000	.000	1
2	1.000	.964	.816	.398	.127	.027	.004	.000	.000	.000	.000	.000	.000	2
3	1.000	.995	.944	.648	.297	.091	.018	.002	.000	.000	.000	.000	.000	3
4	1.000	.999	.987	.836	.515	.217	.059	.009	.001	.000	.000	.000	.000	4
5	1.000	1.000	.998	.939	.722	.403	.151	.034	.004	.000	.000	.000	.000	5
6	1.000	1.000	1.000	.982	.869	.610	.304	.095	.015	.001	.000	.000	.000	6
7	1.000	1.000	1.000	.996	.950	.787	.500	.213	.050	.004	.000	.000	.000	7
8	1.000	1.000	1.000	.999	.985	.905	.696	.390	.131	.018	.000	.000	.000	8
9	1.000	1.000	1.000	1.000	.996	.966	.849	.597	.278	.061	.002	.000	.000	9
10	1.000	1.000	1.000	1.000	.999	.991	.941	.783	.485	.164	.013	.001	.000	10
11	1.000	1.000	1.000	1.000	1.000	.998	.982	.909	.703	.352	.056	.005	.000	11
12	1.000	1.000	1.000	1.000	1.000	1.000	.996	.973	.873	.602	.184	.036	.000	12
13	1.000	1.000	1.000	1.000	1.000	1.000	1.000	.995	.965	.833	.451	.171	.010	13
14	1.000	1.000	1.000	1.000	1.000	1.000	1.000	1.000	.995	.965	.794	.537	.140	14

TABLE 1   (*Continued*)

(d) *n* = 20

a	0.01	0.05	0.10	0.20	0.30	0.40	0.50	0.60	0.70	0.80	0.90	0.95	0.99	*a*
0	.818	.358	.122	.012	.001	.000	.000	.000	.000	.000	.000	.000	.000	0
1	.983	.736	.392	.069	.008	.001	.000	.000	.000	.000	.000	.000	.000	1
2	.999	.925	.677	.206	.035	.004	.000	.000	.000	.000	.000	.000	.000	2
3	1.000	.984	.867	.411	.107	.016	.001	.000	.000	.000	.000	.000	.000	3
4	1.000	.997	.957	.630	.238	.051	.006	.000	.000	.000	.000	.000	.000	4
5	1.000	1.000	.989	.804	.416	.126	.021	.002	.000	.000	.000	.000	.000	5
6	1.000	1.000	.998	.913	.608	.250	.058	.006	.000	.000	.000	.000	.000	6
7	1.000	1.000	1.000	.968	.772	.416	.132	.021	.001	.000	.000	.000	.000	7
8	1.000	1.000	1.000	.990	.887	.596	.252	.057	.005	.000	.000	.000	.000	8
9	1.000	1.000	1.000	.997	.952	.755	.412	.128	.017	.001	.000	.000	.000	9
10	1.000	1.000	1.000	.999	.983	.872	.588	.245	.048	.003	.000	.000	.000	10
11	1.000	1.000	1.000	1.000	.995	.943	.748	.404	.113	.010	.000	.000	.000	11
12	1.000	1.000	1.000	1.000	.999	.979	.868	.584	.228	.032	.000	.000	.000	12
13	1.000	1.000	1.000	1.000	1.000	.994	.942	.750	.392	.087	.002	.000	.000	13
14	1.000	1.000	1.000	1.000	1.000	.998	.979	.874	.584	.196	.011	.000	.000	14
15	1.000	1.000	1.000	1.000	1.000	1.000	.994	.949	.762	.370	.043	.003	.000	15
16	1.000	1.000	1.000	1.000	1.000	1.000	.999	.984	.893	.589	.133	.016	.000	16
17	1.000	1.000	1.000	1.000	1.000	1.000	1.000	.996	.965	.794	.323	.075	.001	17
18	1.000	1.000	1.000	1.000	1.000	1.000	1.000	.999	.992	.931	.608	.264	.017	18
19	1.000	1.000	1.000	1.000	1.000	1.000	1.000	1.000	.999	.988	.878	.642	.182	19

(*continues*)

TABLE 1　　*(Concluded)*

(e) *n* = 25

							p							
a	*0.01*	*0.05*	*0.10*	*0.20*	*0.30*	*0.40*	*0.50*	*0.60*	*0.70*	*0.80*	*0.90*	*0.95*	*0.99*	*a*
0	.778	.277	.072	.004	.000	.000	.000	.000	.000	.000	.000	.000	.000	0
1	.974	.642	.271	.027	.002	.000	.000	.000	.000	.000	.000	.000	.000	1
2	.998	.873	.537	.098	.009	.000	.000	.000	.000	.000	.000	.000	.000	2
3	1.000	.966	.764	.234	.033	.002	.000	.000	.000	.000	.000	.000	.000	3
4	1.000	.993	.902	.421	.090	.009	.000	.000	.000	.000	.000	.000	.000	4
5	1.000	.999	.967	.617	.193	.029	.002	.000	.000	.000	.000	.000	.000	5
6	1.000	1.000	.991	.780	.341	.074	.007	.000	.000	.000	.000	.000	.000	6
7	1.000	1.000	.998	.891	.512	.154	.022	.001	.000	.000	.000	.000	.000	7
8	1.000	1.000	1.000	.953	.677	.274	.054	.004	.000	.000	.000	.000	.000	8
9	1.000	1.000	1.000	.983	.811	.425	.115	.013	.000	.000	.000	.000	.000	9
10	1.000	1.000	1.000	.994	.902	.586	.212	.034	.002	.000	.000	.000	.000	10
11	1.000	1.000	1.000	.998	.956	.732	.345	.078	.006	.000	.000	.000	.000	11
12	1.000	1.000	1.000	1.000	.983	.846	.500	.154	.017	.000	.000	.000	.000	12
13	1.000	1.000	1.000	1.000	.994	.922	.655	.268	.044	.002	.000	.000	.000	13
14	1.000	1.000	1.000	1.000	.998	.966	.788	.414	.098	.006	.000	.000	.000	14
15	1.000	1.000	1.000	1.000	1.000	.987	.885	.575	.189	.017	.000	.000	.000	15
16	1.000	1.000	1.000	1.000	1.000	.996	.946	.726	.323	.047	.000	.000	.000	16
17	1.000	1.000	1.000	1.000	1.000	.999	.978	.846	.488	.109	.002	.000	.000	17
18	1.000	1.000	1.000	1.000	1.000	1.000	.993	.926	.659	.220	.009	.000	.000	18
19	1.000	1.000	1.000	1.000	1.000	1.000	.998	.971	.807	.383	.033	.001	.000	19
20	1.000	1.000	1.000	1.000	1.000	1.000	1.000	.991	.910	.579	.098	.007	.000	20
21	1.000	1.000	1.000	1.000	1.000	1.000	1.000	.998	.967	.766	.236	.034	.000	21
22	1.000	1.000	1.000	1.000	1.000	1.000	1.000	1.000	.991	.902	.463	.127	.002	22
23	1.000	1.000	1.000	1.000	1.000	1.000	1.000	1.000	.998	.973	.729	.358	.026	23
24	1.000	1.000	1.000	1.000	1.000	1.000	1.000	1.000	1.000	.996	.928	.723	.222	24

Handwritten annotations in left margin: cumulative; P(x≥10) ← ; To find P(X=10); P(10-9)

TABLE 2   Values of $e^{-\mu}$

μ	$e^{-\mu}$	μ	$e^{-\mu}$	μ	$e^{-\mu}$	μ	$e^{-\mu}$
0.00	1.000000	**0.40**	0.670320	**0.80**	0.449329	**1.20**	0.301194
0.01	0.990050	0.41	.663650	0.81	.444858	1.21	.298197
0.02	.980199	0.42	.657047	0.82	.440432	1.22	.295230
0.03	.970446	0.43	.650509	0.83	.436049	1.23	.292293
0.04	.960789	0.44	.644036	0.84	.431711	1.24	.289384
0.05	0.951229	**0.45**	0.637628	**0.85**	0.427415	**1.25**	0.286505
0.06	.941765	0.46	.631284	0.86	.423162	1.26	.283654
0.07	.932394	0.47	.625002	0.87	.418952	1.27	.280832
0.08	.923116	0.48	.618783	0.88	.414783	1.28	.278037
0.09	.913931	0.49	.612626	0.89	.410656	1.29	.275271
0.10	0.904837	**0.50**	0.606531	**0.90**	0.406570	**1.30**	0.272532
0.11	.895834	0.51	.600496	0.91	.402524	1.31	.269820
0.12	.886920	0.52	.594521	0.92	.398519	1.32	.267135
0.13	.878095	0.53	.588605	0.93	.394554	1.33	.264477
0.14	.869358	0.54	.582748	0.94	.390628	1.34	.261846
0.15	0.860708	**0.55**	0.576950	**0.95**	0.386741	**1.35**	0.259240
0.16	.852144	0.56	.571209	0.96	.382893	1.36	.256661
0.17	.843665	0.57	.565525	0.97	.379083	1.37	.254107
0.18	.835270	0.58	.559898	0.98	.375311	1.38	.251579
0.19	.826959	0.59	.554327	0.99	.371577	1.39	.249075
0.20	0.818731	**0.60**	0.548812	**1.00**	0.367879	**1.40**	0.246597
0.21	.810584	0.61	.543351	1.01	.364219	1.41	.244143
0.22	.802519	0.62	.537944	1.02	.360595	1.42	.241714
0.23	.794534	0.63	.532592	1.03	.357007	1.43	.239309
0.24	.786628	0.64	.527292	1.04	.353455	1.44	.236928
0.25	0.778801	**0.65**	0.522046	**1.05**	0.349938	**1.45**	0.234570
0.26	.771052	0.66	.516851	1.06	.346456	1.46	.232236
0.27	.763379	0.67	.511709	1.07	.343009	1.47	.229925
0.28	.755784	0.68	.506617	1.08	.339596	1.48	.227638
0.29	.748264	0.69	.501576	1.09	.336216	1.49	.225373
0.30	0.740818	**0.70**	0.496585	**1.10**	0.332871	**1.50**	0.223130
0.31	.733447	0.71	.491644	1.11	.329559	1.51	.220910
0.32	.726149	0.72	.486752	1.12	.326280	1.52	.218712
0.33	.718924	0.73	.481909	1.13	.323033	1.53	.216536
0.34	.711770	0.74	.477114	1.14	.319819	1.54	.214381
0.35	0.704688	**0.75**	0.472367	**1.15**	0.316637	**1.55**	0.212248
0.36	.697676	0.76	.467666	1.16	.313486	1.56	.210136
0.37	.690734	0.77	.463013	1.17	.310367	1.57	.208045
0.38	.683861	0.78	.458406	1.18	.307279	1.58	.205975
0.39	.677057	0.79	.453845	1.19	.304221	1.59	.203926
0.40	0.670320	**0.80**	0.449329	**1.20**	0.301194	**1.60**	0.201897

(continues)

TABLE 2   (*Continued*)

μ	$e^{-\mu}$	μ	$e^{-\mu}$	μ	$e^{-\mu}$	μ	$e^{-\mu}$
1.60	0.201897	**2.00**	0.135335	**2.40**	0.090718	**2.80**	0.060810
1.61	.199888	2.01	.133989	2.41	.089815	2.81	.060205
1.62	.197899	2.02	.132655	2.42	.088922	2.82	.059606
1.63	.195930	2.03	.131336	2.43	.088037	2.83	.059013
1.64	.193980	2.04	.130029	2.44	.087161	2.84	.058426
1.65	0.192050	**2.05**	0.128735	**2.45**	0.086294	**2.85**	0.057844
1.66	.190139	2.06	.127454	2.46	.085435	2.86	.057269
1.67	.188247	2.07	.126186	2.47	.084585	2.87	.056699
1.68	.186374	2.08	.124930	2.48	.083743	2.88	.056135
1.69	.184520	2.09	.123687	2.49	.082910	2.89	.055576
1.70	0.182684	**2.10**	0.122456	**2.50**	0.082085	**2.90**	0.055023
1.71	.180866	2.11	.121238	2.51	.081268	2.91	.054476
1.72	.179066	2.12	.120032	2.52	.080460	2.92	.053934
1.73	.177284	2.13	.118837	2.53	.079659	2.93	.053397
1.74	.175520	2.14	.117655	2.54	.078866	2.94	.052866
1.75	0.173774	**2.15**	0.116484	**2.55**	0.078082	**2.95**	0.052340
1.76	.172045	2.16	.115325	2.56	.077305	2.96	.051819
1.77	.170333	2.17	.114178	2.57	.076536	2.97	.051303
1.78	.168638	2.18	.113042	2.58	.075774	2.98	.050793
1.79	.166960	2.19	.111917	2.59	.075020	2.99	.050287
1.80	0.165299	**2.20**	0.110803	**2.60**	0.074274	**3.00**	0.049787
1.81	.163654	2.21	.109701	2.61	.073535	3.01	.049292
1.82	.162026	2.22	.108609	2.62	.072803	3.02	.048801
1.83	.160414	2.23	.107528	2.63	.072078	3.03	.048316
1.84	.158817	2.24	.106459	2.64	.071361	3.04	.047835
1.85	0.157237	**2.25**	0.105399	**2.65**	0.070651	**3.05**	0.047359
1.86	.155673	2.26	.104350	2.66	.069948	3.06	.046888
1.87	.154124	2.27	.103312	2.67	.069252	3.07	.046421
1.88	.152590	2.28	.102284	2.68	.068563	3.08	.045959
1.89	.151072	2.29	.101266	2.69	.067881	3.09	.045502
1.90	0.149569	**2.30**	0.100259	**2.70**	0.067206	**3.10**	0.045049
1.91	.148080	2.31	.099261	2.71	.066537	3.11	.044601
1.92	.146607	2.32	.098274	2.72	.065875	3.12	.044157
1.93	.145148	2.33	.097296	2.73	.065219	3.13	.043718
1.94	.143704	2.34	.096328	2.74	.064570	3.14	.043283
1.95	0.142274	**2.35**	0.095369	**2.75**	0.063928	**3.15**	0.042852
1.96	.140858	2.36	.094420	2.76	.063292	3.16	.042426
1.97	.139457	2.37	.093481	2.77	.062662	3.17	.042004
1.98	.138069	2.38	.092551	2.78	.062039	3.18	.041586
1.99	.136695	2.39	.091630	2.79	.061421	3.19	.041172
2.00	0.135335	**2.40**	0.090718	**2.80**	0.060810	**3.20**	0.040762

TABLE 2   (*Continued*)

μ	$e^{-\mu}$	μ	$e^{-\mu}$	μ	$e^{-\mu}$	μ	$e^{-\mu}$
3.20	0.040762	**3.60**	0.027324	**4.00**	0.018316	**4.40**	0.012277
3.21	.040357	3.61	.027052	4.01	.018133	4.41	.012155
3.22	.039955	3.62	.026783	4.02	.017953	4.42	.012034
3.23	.039557	3.63	.026516	4.03	.017774	4.43	.011914
3.24	.039164	3.64	.026252	4.04	.017597	4.44	.011796
3.25	0.038774	**3.65**	0.025991	**4.05**	0.017422	**4.45**	0.011679
3.26	.038388	3.66	.025733	4.06	.017249	4.46	.011562
3.27	.038006	3.67	.025476	4.07	.017077	4.47	.011447
3.28	.037628	3.68	.025223	4.08	.016907	4.48	.011333
3.29	.037254	3.69	.024972	4.09	.016739	4.49	.011221
3.30	0.036883	**3.70**	0.024724	**4.10**	0.016573	**4.50**	0.011109
3.31	.036516	3.71	.024478	4.11	.016408	4.51	.010998
3.32	.036153	3.72	.024234	4.12	.016245	4.52	.010889
3.33	.035793	3.73	.023993	4.13	.016083	4.53	.010781
3.34	.035437	3.74	.023754	4.14	.015923	4.54	.010673
3.35	0.035084	**3.75**	0.023518	**4.15**	0.015764	**4.55**	0.010567
3.36	.034735	3.76	.023284	4.16	.015608	4.56	.010462
3.37	.034390	3.77	.023052	4.17	.015452	4.57	.010358
3.38	.034047	3.78	.022823	4.18	.015299	4.58	.010255
3.39	.033709	3.79	.022596	4.19	.015146	4.59	.010153
3.40	0.033373	**3.80**	0.022371	**4.20**	0.014996	**4.60**	0.010052
3.41	.033041	3.81	.022148	4.21	.014846	4.61	.009952
3.42	.032712	3.82	.021928	4.22	.014699	4.62	.009853
3.43	.032387	3.83	.021710	4.23	.014552	4.63	.009755
3.44	.032065	3.84	.021494	4.24	.014408	4.64	.009658
3.45	0.031746	**3.85**	0.021280	**4.25**	0.014264	**4.65**	0.009562
3.46	.031430	3.86	.021068	4.26	.014122	4.66	.009466
3.47	.031117	3.87	.020858	4.27	.013982	4.67	.009372
3.48	.030807	3.88	.020651	4.28	.013843	4.68	.009279
3.49	.030501	3.89	.020445	4.29	.013705	4.69	.009187
3.50	0.030197	**3.90**	0.020242	**4.30**	0.013569	**4.70**	0.009095
3.51	.029897	3.91	.020041	4.31	.013434	4.71	.009005
3.52	.029599	3.92	.019841	4.32	.013300	4.72	.008915
3.53	.029305	3.93	.019644	4.33	.013168	4.73	.008826
3.54	.029013	3.94	.019448	4.34	.013037	4.74	.008739
3.55	0.028725	**3.95**	0.019255	**4.35**	0.012907	**4.75**	0.008652
3.56	.028439	3.96	.019063	4.36	.012778	4.76	.008566
3.57	.028156	3.97	.018873	4.37	.012651	4.77	.008480
3.58	.027876	3.98	.018686	4.38	.012525	4.78	.008396
3.59	.027598	3.99	.018500	4.39	.012401	4.79	.008312
3.60	0.027324	**4.00**	0.018316	**4.40**	0.012277	**4.80**	0.008230

(*continues*)

TABLE 2   *(Concluded)*

μ	$e^{-\mu}$	μ	$e^{-\mu}$	μ	$e^{-\mu}$	μ	$e^{-\mu}$
4.80	0.008230	**5.20**	0.005517	**6.00**	0.0024788	**8.00**	0.0003355
4.81	.008148	5.21	.005462	6.05	.0023579	8.05	.0003191
4.82	.008067	5.22	.005407	6.10	.0022429	8.10	.0003035
4.83	.007987	5.23	.005354	6.15	.0021335	8.15	.0002887
4.84	.007907	5.24	.005300	6.20	.0020294	8.20	.0002747
4.85	0.007828	**5.25**	0.005248	**6.25**	0.0019305	**8.25**	0.0002613
4.86	.007750	5.26	.005195	6.30	.0018363	8.30	.0002485
4.87	.007673	5.27	.005144	6.35	.0017467	8.35	.0002364
4.88	.007597	5.28	.005092	6.40	.0016616	8.40	.0002249
4.89	.007521	5.29	.005042	6.45	.0015805	8.45	.0002139
4.90	0.007447	**5.30**	0.004992	**6.50**	0.0015034	**8.50**	0.0002035
4.91	.007372	5.31	.004942	6.55	.0014301	8.55	.0001935
4.92	.007299	5.32	.004893	6.60	.0013604	8.60	.0001841
4.93	.007227	5.33	.004844	6.65	.0012940	8.65	.0001751
4.94	.007155	5.34	.004796	6.70	.0012309	8.70	.0001666
4.95	0.007083	**5.35**	0.004748	**6.75**	0.0011709	**8.75**	0.0001585
4.96	.007013	5.36	.004701	6.80	.0011138	8.80	.0001507
4.97	.006943	5.37	.004654	6.85	.0010595	8.85	.0001434
4.98	.006874	5.38	.004608	6.90	.0010078	8.90	.0001364
4.99	.006806	5.39	.004562	6.95	.0009586	8.95	.0001297
5.00	0.006738	**5.40**	0.004517	**7.00**	0.0009119	**9.00**	0.0001234
5.01	.006671	5.41	.004472	7.05	.0008674	9.05	.0001174
5.02	.006605	5.42	.004427	7.10	.0008251	9.10	.0001117
5.03	.006539	5.43	.004383	7.15	.0007849	9.15	.0001062
5.04	.006474	5.44	.004339	7.20	.0007466	9.20	.0001010
5.05	0.006409	**5.45**	0.004296	**7.25**	0.0007102	**9.25**	0.0000961
5.06	.006346	5.46	.004254	7.30	.0006755	9.30	.0000914
5.07	.006282	5.47	.004211	7.35	.0006426	9.35	.0000870
5.08	.006220	5.48	.004169	7.40	.0006113	9.40	.0000827
5.09	.006158	5.49	.004128	7.45	.0005814	9.45	.0000787
5.10	0.006097	**5.50**	0.0040868	**7.50**	0.0005531	**9.50**	0.0000749
5.11	.006036	5.55	.0038875	7.55	.0005261	9.55	.0000712
5.12	.005976	5.60	.0036979	7.60	.0005005	9.60	.0000677
5.13	.005917	5.65	.0035175	7.65	.0004760	9.65	.0000644
5.14	.005858	5.70	.0033460	7.70	.0004528	9.70	.0000613
5.15	0.005799	**5.75**	0.0031828	**7.75**	0.0004307	**9.75**	0.0000583
5.16	.005742	5.80	.0030276	7.80	.0004097	9.80	.0000555
5.17	.005685	5.85	.0028799	7.85	.0003898	9.85	.0000527
5.18	.005628	5.90	.0027394	7.90	.0003707	9.90	.0000502
5.19	.005572	5.95	.0026058	7.95	.0003527	9.95	0.0000477
5.20	0.005517	**6.00**	0.0024788	**8.00**	0.0003355	**10.00**	0.0000454

Source: Reproduced from *Handbook of Tables for Probability and Statistics*, 2nd ed. Edited by William H. Beyer (Cleveland: The Chemical Rubber Company, 1968). © Copyright The Chemical Rubber Co., CRC Press, Inc.

TABLE 3   Cumulative Probabilities of the Poisson Distribution

	Mean									
a	0.250	0.500	0.750	1.000	1.250	1.500	1.750	2.000	2.250	2.500
0	0.779	0.607	0.472	0.368	0.287	0.223	0.174	0.135	0.105	0.082
1	0.974	0.910	0.827	0.736	0.645	0.558	0.478	0.406	0.343	0.287
2	0.998	0.986	0.959	0.920	0.868	0.809	0.744	0.677	0.609	0.544
3	1.000	0.998	0.993	0.981	0.962	0.934	0.899	0.857	0.809	0.758
4	1.000	1.000	0.999	0.996	0.991	0.981	0.967	0.947	0.922	0.891
5	1.000	1.000	1.000	0.999	0.998	0.996	0.991	0.983	0.973	0.958
6	1.000	1.000	1.000	1.000	1.000	0.999	0.998	0.995	0.992	0.986
7	1.000	1.000	1.000	1.000	1.000	1.000	1.000	0.999	0.998	0.996
8	1.000	1.000	1.000	1.000	1.000	1.000	1.000	1.000	0.999	0.999
9	1.000	1.000	1.000	1.000	1.000	1.000	1.000	1.000	1.000	1.000
10	1.000	1.000	1.000	1.000	1.000	1.000	1.000	1.000	1.000	1.000
11	1.000	1.000	1.000	1.000	1.000	1.000	1.000	1.000	1.000	1.000
12	1.000	1.000	1.000	1.000	1.000	1.000	1.000	1.000	1.000	1.000
13	1.000	1.000	1.000	1.000	1.000	1.000	1.000	1.000	1.000	1.000
14	1.000	1.000	1.000	1.000	1.000	1.000	1.000	1.000	1.000	1.000

	Mean									
a	2.750	3.000	3.250	3.500	3.750	4.000	4.250	4.500	4.750	5.000
0	0.064	0.050	0.039	0.030	0.024	0.018	0.014	0.011	0.009	0.007
1	0.240	0.199	0.165	0.136	0.112	0.092	0.075	0.061	0.050	0.040
2	0.481	0.423	0.370	0.321	0.277	0.238	0.204	0.174	0.147	0.125
3	0.703	0.647	0.591	0.537	0.484	0.433	0.386	0.342	0.302	0.265
4	0.855	0.815	0.772	0.725	0.678	0.629	0.580	0.532	0.485	0.440
5	0.939	0.916	0.889	0.858	0.823	0.785	0.745	0.703	0.660	0.616
6	0.978	0.966	0.952	0.935	0.914	0.889	0.862	0.831	0.798	0.762
7	0.993	0.988	0.982	0.973	0.962	0.949	0.933	0.913	0.891	0.867
8	0.998	0.996	0.994	0.990	0.985	0.979	0.970	0.960	0.947	0.932
9	0.999	0.999	0.998	0.997	0.995	0.992	0.988	0.983	0.976	0.968
10	1.000	1.000	0.999	0.999	0.998	0.997	0.996	0.993	0.990	0.986
11	1.000	1.000	1.000	1.000	0.999	0.999	0.998	0.998	0.996	0.995
12	1.000	1.000	1.000	1.000	1.000	1.000	1.000	0.999	0.999	0.998
13	1.000	1.000	1.000	1.000	1.000	1.000	1.000	1.000	1.000	0.999
14	1.000	1.000	1.000	1.000	1.000	1.000	1.000	1.000	1.000	1.000

TABLE 4 Normal Curve Areas

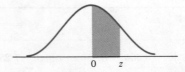

z	.00	.01	.02	.03	.04	.05	.06	.07	.08	.09
0.0	.0000	.0040	.0080	.0120	.0160	.0199	.0239	.0279	.0319	.0359
0.1	.0398	.0438	.0478	.0517	.0557	.0596	.0636	.0675	.0714	.0753
0.2	.0793	.0832	.0871	.0910	.0948	.0987	.1026	.1064	.1103	.1141
0.3	.1179	.1217	.1255	.1293	.1331	.1368	.1406	.1443	.1480	.1517
0.4	.1554	.1591	.1628	.1664	.1700	.1736	.1772	.1808	.1844	.1879
0.5	.1915	.1950	.1985	.2019	.2054	.2088	.2123	.2157	.2190	.2224
0.6	.2257	.2291	.2324	.2357	.2389	.2422	.2454	.2486	.2517	.2549
0.7	.2580	.2611	.2642	.2673	.2704	.2734	.2764	.2794	.2823	.2852
0.8	.2881	.2910	.2939	.2967	.2995	.3023	.3051	.3078	.3106	.3133
0.9	.3159	.3186	.3212	.3238	.3264	.3289	.3315	.3340	.3365	.3389
1.0	.3413	.3438	.3461	.3485	.3508	.3531	.3554	.3577	.3599	.3621
1.1	.3643	.3665	.3686	.3708	.3729	.3749	.3770	.3790	.3810	.3830
1.2	.3849	.3869	.3888	.3907	.3925	.3944	.3962	.3980	.3997	.4015
1.3	.4032	.4049	.4066	.4082	.4099	.4115	.4131	.4147	.4162	.4177
1.4	.4192	.4207	.4222	.4236	.4251	.4265	.4279	.4292	.4306	.4319
1.5	.4332	.4345	.4357	.4370	.4382	.4394	.4406	.4418	.4429	.4441
1.6	.4452	.4463	.4474	.4484	.4495	.4505	.4515	.4525	.4535	.4545
1.7	.4554	.4564	.4573	.4582	.4591	.4599	.4608	.4616	.4625	.4633
1.8	.4641	.4649	.4656	.4664	.4671	.4678	.4686	.4693	.4699	.4706
1.9	.4713	.4719	.4726	.4732	.4738	.4744	.4750	.4756	.4761	.4767
2.0	.4772	.4778	.4783	.4788	.4793	.4798	.4803	.4808	.4812	.4817
2.1	.4821	.4826	.4830	.4834	.4838	.4842	.4846	.4850	.4854	.4857
2.2	.4861	.4864	.4868	.4871	.4875	.4878	.4881	.4884	.4887	.4890
2.3	.4893	.4896	.4898	.4901	.4904	.4906	.4909	.4911	.4913	.4916
2.4	.4918	.4920	.4922	.4925	.4927	.4929	.4931	.4932	.4934	.4936
2.5	.4938	.4940	.4941	.4943	.4945	.4946	.4948	.4949	.4951	.4952
2.6	.4953	.4955	.4956	.4957	.4959	.4960	.4961	.4962	.4963	.4964
2.7	.4965	.4966	.4967	.4968	.4969	.4970	.4971	.4972	.4973	.4974
2.8	.4974	.4975	.4976	.4977	.4977	.4978	.4979	.4979	.4980	.4981
2.9	.4981	.4982	.4982	.4983	.4984	.4984	.4985	.4985	.4986	.4986
3.0	.4987	.4987	.4987	.4988	.4988	.4989	.4989	.4989	.4990	.4990

Source: This table is abridged from Table 1 of *Statistical Tables and Formulas,* by A. Hald (New York: John Wiley & Sons, Inc., 1952). Reproduced by permission of A. Hald and the publishers, John Wiley & Sons, Inc.

TABLE 5   Critical Values of t

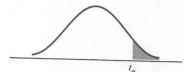

t_α

d.f.	$t_{.100}$	$t_{.050}$	$t_{.025}$	$t_{.010}$	$t_{.005}$	d.f.
1	3.078	6.314	12.706	31.821	63.657	1
2	1.886	2.920	4.303	6.965	9.925	2
3	1.638	2.353	3.182	4.541	5.841	3
4	1.533	2.132	2.776	3.747	4.604	4
5	1.476	2.015	2.571	3.365	4.032	5
6	1.440	1.943	2.447	3.143	3.707	6
7	1.415	1.895	2.365	2.998	3.499	7
8	1.397	1.860	2.306	2.896	3.355	8
9	1.383	1.833	2.262	2.821	3.250	9
10	1.372	1.812	2.228	2.764	3.169	10
11	1.363	1.796	2.201	2.718	3.106	11
12	1.356	1.782	2.179	2.681	3.055	12
13	1.350	1.771	2.160	2.650	3.012	13
14	1.345	1.761	2.145	2.624	2.977	14
15	1.341	1.753	2.131	2.602	2.947	15
16	1.337	1.746	2.120	2.583	2.921	16
17	1.333	1.740	2.110	2.567	2.898	17
18	1.330	1.734	2.101	2.552	2.878	18
19	1.328	1.729	2.093	2.539	2.861	19
20	1.325	1.725	2.086	2.528	2.845	20
21	1.323	1.721	2.080	2.518	2.831	21
22	1.321	1.717	2.074	2.508	2.819	22
23	1.319	1.714	2.069	2.500	2.807	23
24	1.318	1.711	2.064	2.492	2.797	24
25	1.316	1.708	2.060	2.485	2.787	25
26	1.315	1.706	2.056	2.479	2.779	26
27	1.314	1.703	2.052	2.473	2.771	27
28	1.313	1.701	2.048	2.467	2.763	28
29	1.311	1.699	2.045	2.462	2.756	29
inf.	1.282	1.645	1.960	2.326	2.576	inf.

TABLE 6   Critical Values of Chi-square

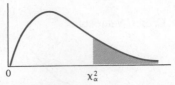

d.f.	$\chi^2_{0.995}$	$\chi^2_{0.990}$	$\chi^2_{0.975}$	$\chi^2_{0.950}$	$\chi^2_{0.900}$
1	0.0000393	0.0001571	0.0009821	0.0039321	0.0157908
2	0.0100251	0.0201007	0.0506356	0.102587	0.210720
3	0.0717212	0.114832	0.215795	0.351846	0.584375
4	0.206990	0.297110	0.484419	0.710721	1.063623
5	0.411740	0.554300	0.831211	1.145476	1.61031
6	0.675727	0.872085	1.237347	1.63539	2.20413
7	0.989265	1.239043	1.68987	2.16735	2.83311
8	1.344419	1.646482	2.17973	2.73264	3.48954
9	1.734926	2.087912	2.70039	3.32511	4.16816
10	2.15585	2.55821	3.24697	3.94030	4.86518
11	2.60321	3.05347	3.81575	4.57481	5.57779
12	3.07382	3.57056	4.40379	5.22603	6.30380
13	3.56503	4.10691	5.00874	5.89186	7.04150
14	4.07468	4.66043	5.62872	6.57063	7.78953
15	4.60094	5.22935	6.26214	7.26094	8.54675
16	5.14224	5.81221	6.90766	7.96164	9.31223
17	5.69724	6.40776	7.56418	8.67176	10.0852
18	6.26481	7.01491	8.23075	9.39046	10.8649
19	6.84398	7.63273	8.90655	10.1170	11.6509
20	7.43386	8.26040	9.59083	10.8508	12.4426
21	8.03366	8.89720	10.28293	11.5913	13.2396
22	8.64272	9.54249	10.9823	12.3380	14.0415
23	9.26042	10.19567	11.6885	13.0905	14.8479
24	9.88623	10.8564	12.4011	13.8484	15.6587
25	10.5197	11.5240	13.1197	14.6114	16.4734
26	11.1603	12.1981	13.8439	15.3791	17.2919
27	11.8076	12.8786	14.5733	16.1513	18.1138
28	12.4613	13.5648	15.3079	16.9279	18.9392
29	13.1211	14.2565	16.0471	17.7083	19.7677
30	13.7867	14.9535	16.7908	18.4926	20.5992
40	20.7065	22.1643	24.4331	26.5093	29.0505
50	27.9907	29.7067	32.3574	34.7642	37.6886
60	35.5346	37.4848	40.4817	43.1879	46.4589
70	43.2752	45.4418	48.7576	51.7393	55.3290
80	51.1720	53.5400	57.1532	60.3915	64.2778
90	59.1963	61.7541	65.6466	69.1260	73.2912
100	67.3276	70.0648	74.2219	77.9295	82.3581

$\chi^2_{0.100}$	$\chi^2_{0.050}$	$\chi^2_{0.025}$	$\chi^2_{0.010}$	$\chi^2_{0.005}$	d.f.
2.70554	3.84146	5.02389	6.63490	7.87944	1
4.60517	5.99147	7.37776	9.21034	10.5966	2
6.25139	7.81473	9.34840	11.3449	12.8381	3
7.77944	9.48773	11.1433	13.2767	14.8602	4
9.23635	11.0705	12.8325	15.0863	16.7496	5
10.6446	12.5916	14.4494	16.8119	18.5476	6
12.0170	14.0671	16.0128	18.4753	20.2777	7
13.3616	15.5073	17.5346	20.0902	21.9550	8
14.6837	16.9190	19.0228	21.6660	23.5893	9
15.9871	18.3070	20.4831	23.2093	25.1882	10
17.2750	19.6751	21.9200	24.7250	26.7569	11
18.5494	21.0261	23.3367	26.2170	28.2995	12
19.8119	22.3621	24.7356	27.6883	29.8194	13
21.0642	23.6848	26.1190	29.1413	31.3193	14
22.3072	24.9958	27.4884	30.5779	32.8013	15
23.5418	26.2962	28.8454	31.9999	34.2672	16
24.7690	27.5871	30.1910	33.4087	35.7185	17
25.9894	28.8693	31.5264	34.8053	37.1564	18
27.2036	30.1435	32.8523	36.1908	38.5822	19
28.4120	31.4104	34.1696	37.5662	39.9968	20
29.6151	32.6705	35.4789	38.9321	41.4010	21
30.8133	33.9244	36.7807	40.2894	42.7956	22
32.0069	35.1725	38.0757	41.6384	44.1813	23
33.1963	36.4151	39.3641	42.9798	45.5585	24
34.3816	37.6525	40.6465	44.3141	46.9278	25
35.5631	38.8852	41.9232	45.6417	48.2899	26
36.7412	40.1133	43.1944	46.9630	49.6449	27
37.9159	41.3372	44.4607	48.2782	50.9933	28
39.0875	42.5569	45.7222	49.5879	52.3356	29
40.2560	43.7729	46.9792	50.8922	53.6720	30
51.8050	55.7585	59.3417	63.6907	66.7659	40
63.1671	67.5048	71.4202	76.1539	79.4900	50
74.3970	79.0819	83.2976	88.3794	91.9517	60
85.5271	90.5312	95.0231	100.425	104.215	70
96.5782	101.879	106.629	112.329	116.321	80
107.565	113.145	118.136	124.116	128.299	90
118.498	124.342	129.561	135.807	140.169	100

Source: From "Tables of the Percentage Points of the χ^2-Distribution." *Biometrika Tables for Statisticians*, Vol. 1, 3rd ed. (1966). Reproduced by permission of the Biometrika Trustees.

TABLE 7   Percentage Points of the F Distribution: $\alpha = .10$

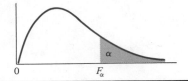

| | | | | | v_1 (d.f.) | | | | |
v_2 (d.f.)	1	2	3	4	5	6	7	8	9
1	39.86	49.50	53.59	55.83	57.24	58.20	58.91	59.44	59.86
2	8.53	9.00	9.16	9.24	9.29	9.33	9.35	9.37	9.38
3	5.54	5.46	5.39	5.34	5.31	5.28	5.27	5.25	5.24
4	4.54	4.32	4.19	4.11	4.05	4.01	3.98	3.95	3.94
5	4.06	3.78	3.62	3.52	3.45	3.40	3.37	3.34	3.32
6	3.78	3.46	3.29	3.18	3.11	3.05	3.01	2.98	2.96
7	3.59	3.26	3.07	2.96	2.88	2.83	2.78	2.75	2.72
8	3.46	3.11	2.92	2.81	2.73	2.67	2.62	2.59	2.56
9	3.36	3.01	2.81	2.69	2.61	2.55	2.51	2.47	2.44
10	3.29	2.92	2.73	2.61	2.52	2.46	2.41	2.38	2.35
11	3.23	2.86	2.66	2.54	2.45	2.39	2.34	2.30	2.27
12	3.18	2.81	2.61	2.48	2.39	2.33	2.28	2.24	2.21
13	3.14	2.76	2.56	2.43	2.35	2.28	2.23	2.20	2.16
14	3.10	2.73	2.52	2.39	2.31	2.24	2.19	2.15	2.12
15	3.07	2.70	2.49	2.36	2.27	2.21	2.16	2.12	2.09
16	3.05	2.67	2.46	2.33	2.24	2.18	2.13	2.09	2.06
17	3.03	2.64	2.44	2.31	2.22	2.15	2.10	2.06	2.03
18	3.01	2.62	2.42	2.29	2.20	2.13	2.08	2.04	2.00
19	2.99	2.61	2.40	2.27	2.18	2.11	2.06	2.02	1.98
20	2.97	2.59	2.38	2.25	2.16	2.09	2.04	2.00	1.96
21	2.96	2.57	2.36	2.23	2.14	2.08	2.02	1.98	1.95
22	2.95	2.56	2.35	2.22	2.13	2.06	2.01	1.97	1.93
23	2.94	2.55	2.34	2.21	2.11	2.05	1.99	1.95	1.92
24	2.93	2.54	2.33	2.19	2.10	2.04	1.98	1.94	1.91
25	2.92	2.53	2.32	2.18	2.09	2.02	1.97	1.93	1.89
26	2.91	2.52	2.31	2.17	2.08	2.01	1.96	1.92	1.88
27	2.90	2.51	2.30	2.17	2.07	2.00	1.95	1.91	1.87
28	2.89	2.50	2.29	2.16	2.06	2.00	1.94	1.90	1.87
29	2.89	2.50	2.28	2.15	2.06	1.99	1.93	1.89	1.86
30	2.88	2.49	2.28	2.14	2.05	1.98	1.93	1.88	1.85
40	2.84	2.44	2.23	2.09	2.00	1.93	1.87	1.83	1.79
60	2.79	2.39	2.18	2.04	1.95	1.87	1.82	1.77	1.74
120	2.75	2.35	2.13	1.99	1.90	1.82	1.77	1.72	1.68
∞	2.71	2.30	2.08	1.94	1.85	1.77	1.72	1.67	1.63

				v_1 (d.f.)						
10	12	15	20	24	30	40	60	120	∞	v_2 (d.f.)
60.19	60.71	61.22	61.74	62.00	62.26	62.53	62.79	63.06	63.33	1
9.39	9.41	9.42	9.44	9.45	9.46	9.47	9.47	9.48	9.49	2
5.23	5.22	5.20	5.18	5.18	5.17	5.16	5.15	5.14	5.13	3
3.92	3.90	3.87	3.84	3.83	3.82	3.80	3.79	3.78	3.76	4
3.30	3.27	3.24	3.21	3.19	3.17	3.16	3.14	3.12	3.10	5
2.94	2.90	2.87	2.84	2.82	2.80	2.78	2.76	2.74	2.72	6
2.70	2.67	2.63	2.59	2.58	2.56	2.54	2.51	2.49	2.47	7
2.54	2.50	2.46	2.42	2.40	2.38	2.36	2.34	2.32	2.29	8
2.42	2.38	2.34	2.30	2.28	2.25	2.23	2.21	2.18	2.16	9
2.32	2.28	2.24	2.20	2.18	2.16	2.13	2.11	2.08	2.06	10
2.25	2.21	2.17	2.12	2.10	2.08	2.05	2.03	2.00	1.97	11
2.19	2.15	2.10	2.06	2.04	2.01	1.99	1.96	1.93	1.90	12
2.14	2.10	2.05	2.01	1.98	1.96	1.93	1.90	1.88	1.85	13
2.10	2.05	2.01	1.96	1.94	1.91	1.89	1.86	1.83	1.80	14
2.06	2.02	1.97	1.92	1.90	1.87	1.85	1.82	1.79	1.76	15
2.03	1.99	1.94	1.89	1.87	1.84	1.81	1.78	1.75	1.72	16
2.00	1.96	1.91	1.86	1.84	1.81	1.78	1.75	1.72	1.69	17
1.98	1.93	1.89	1.84	1.81	1.78	1.75	1.72	1.69	1.66	18
1.96	1.91	1.86	1.81	1.79	1.76	1.73	1.70	1.67	1.63	19
1.94	1.89	1.84	1.79	1.77	1.74	1.71	1.68	1.64	1.61	20
1.92	1.87	1.83	1.78	1.75	1.72	1.69	1.66	1.62	1.59	21
1.90	1.86	1.81	1.76	1.73	1.70	1.67	1.64	1.60	1.57	22
1.89	1.84	1.80	1.74	1.72	1.69	1.66	1.62	1.59	1.55	23
1.88	1.83	1.78	1.73	1.70	1.67	1.64	1.61	1.57	1.53	24
1.87	1.82	1.77	1.72	1.69	1.66	1.63	1.59	1.56	1.52	25
1.86	1.81	1.76	1.71	1.68	1.65	1.61	1.58	1.54	1.50	26
1.85	1.80	1.75	1.70	1.67	1.64	1.60	1.57	1.53	1.49	27
1.84	1.79	1.74	1.69	1.66	1.63	1.59	1.56	1.52	1.48	28
1.83	1.78	1.73	1.68	1.65	1.62	1.58	1.55	1.51	1.47	29
1.82	1.77	1.72	1.67	1.64	1.61	1.57	1.54	1.50	1.46	30
1.76	1.71	1.66	1.61	1.57	1.54	1.51	1.47	1.42	1.38	40
1.71	1.66	1.60	1.54	1.51	1.48	1.44	1.40	1.35	1.29	60
1.65	1.60	1.55	1.48	1.45	1.41	1.37	1.32	1.26	1.19	120
1.60	1.55	1.49	1.42	1.38	1.34	1.30	1.24	1.17	1.00	∞

Source: From "Tables of Percentage Points of the Inverted Beta (*F*)-Distribution," *Biometrika,* Vol. 33 (1943), pp. 73–88, by Maxine Merrington and Catherine M. Thompson. Reproduced by permission of the Biometrika Trustees.

TABLE 8 Percentage Points of the F Distribution: $\alpha = .05$

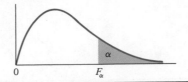

| | v_1 (d.f.) | | | | | | | | |
v_2 (d.f.)	1	2	3	4	5	6	7	8	9
1	161.4	199.5	215.7	224.6	230.2	234.0	236.8	238.9	240.5
2	18.51	19.00	19.16	19.25	19.30	19.33	19.35	19.37	19.38
3	10.13	9.55	9.28	9.12	9.01	8.94	8.89	8.85	8.81
4	7.71	6.94	6.59	6.39	6.26	6.16	6.09	6.04	6.00
5	6.61	5.79	5.41	5.19	5.05	4.95	4.88	4.82	4.77
6	5.99	5.14	4.76	4.53	4.39	4.28	4.21	4.15	4.10
7	5.59	4.74	4.35	4.12	3.97	3.87	3.79	3.73	3.68
8	5.32	4.46	4.07	3.84	3.69	3.58	3.50	3.44	3.39
9	5.12	4.26	3.86	3.63	3.48	3.37	3.29	3.23	3.18
10	4.96	4.10	3.71	3.48	3.33	3.22	3.14	3.07	3.02
11	4.84	3.98	3.59	3.36	3.20	3.09	3.01	2.95	2.90
12	4.75	3.89	3.49	3.26	3.11	3.00	2.91	2.85	2.80
13	4.67	3.81	3.41	3.18	3.03	2.92	2.83	2.77	2.71
14	4.60	3.74	3.34	3.11	2.96	2.85	2.76	2.70	2.65
15	4.54	3.68	3.29	3.06	2.90	2.79	2.71	2.64	2.59
16	4.49	3.63	3.24	3.01	2.85	2.74	2.66	2.59	2.54
17	4.45	3.59	3.20	2.96	2.81	2.70	2.61	2.55	2.49
18	4.41	3.55	3.16	2.93	2.77	2.66	2.58	2.51	2.46
19	4.38	3.52	3.13	2.90	2.74	2.63	2.54	2.48	2.42
20	4.35	3.49	3.10	2.87	2.71	2.60	2.51	2.45	2.39
21	4.32	3.47	3.07	2.84	2.68	2.57	2.49	2.42	2.37
22	4.30	3.44	3.05	2.82	2.66	2.55	2.46	2.40	2.34
23	4.28	3.42	3.03	2.80	2.64	2.53	2.44	2.37	2.32
24	4.26	3.40	3.01	2.78	2.62	2.51	2.42	2.36	2.30
25	4.24	3.39	2.99	2.76	2.60	2.49	2.40	2.34	2.28
26	4.23	3.37	2.98	2.74	2.59	2.47	2.39	2.32	2.27
27	4.21	3.35	2.96	2.73	2.57	2.46	2.37	2.31	2.25
28	4.20	3.34	2.95	2.71	2.56	2.45	2.36	2.29	2.24
29	4.18	3.33	2.93	2.70	2.55	2.43	2.35	2.28	2.22
30	4.17	3.32	2.92	2.69	2.53	2.42	2.33	2.27	2.21
40	4.08	3.23	2.84	2.61	2.45	2.34	2.25	2.18	2.12
60	4.00	3.15	2.76	2.53	2.37	2.25	2.17	2.10	2.04
120	3.92	3.07	2.68	2.45	2.29	2.17	2.09	2.02	1.96
∞	3.84	3.00	2.60	2.37	2.21	2.10	2.01	1.94	1.88

				v_1 (d.f.)						
10	12	15	20	24	30	40	60	120	∞	v_2 (d.f.)
241.9	243.9	245.9	248.0	249.1	250.1	251.1	252.2	253.3	254.3	1
19.40	19.41	19.43	19.45	19.45	19.46	19.47	19.48	19.49	19.50	2
8.79	8.74	8.70	8.66	8.64	8.62	8.59	8.57	8.55	8.53	3
5.96	5.91	5.86	5.80	5.77	5.75	5.72	5.69	5.66	5.63	4
4.74	4.68	4.62	4.56	4.53	4.50	4.46	4.43	4.40	4.36	5
4.06	4.00	3.94	3.87	3.84	3.81	3.77	3.74	3.70	3.67	6
3.64	3.57	3.51	3.44	3.41	3.38	3.34	3.30	3.27	3.23	7
3.35	3.28	3.22	3.15	3.12	3.08	3.04	3.01	2.97	2.93	8
3.14	3.07	3.01	2.94	2.90	2.86	2.83	2.79	2.75	2.71	9
2.98	2.91	2.85	2.77	2.74	2.70	2.66	2.62	2.58	2.54	10
2.85	2.79	2.72	2.65	2.61	2.57	2.53	2.49	2.45	2.40	11
2.75	2.69	2.62	2.54	2.51	2.47	2.43	2.38	2.34	2.30	12
2.67	2.60	2.53	2.46	2.42	2.38	2.34	2.30	2.25	2.21	13
2.60	2.53	2.46	2.39	2.35	2.31	2.27	2.22	2.18	2.13	14
2.54	2.48	2.40	2.33	2.29	2.25	2.20	2.16	2.11	2.07	15
2.49	2.42	2.35	2.28	2.24	2.19	2.15	2.11	2.06	2.01	16
2.45	2.38	2.31	2.23	2.19	2.15	2.10	2.06	2.01	1.96	17
2.41	2.34	2.27	2.19	2.15	2.11	2.06	2.02	1.97	1.92	18
2.38	2.31	2.23	2.16	2.11	2.07	2.03	1.98	1.93	1.88	19
2.35	2.28	2.20	2.12	2.08	2.04	1.99	1.95	1.90	1.84	20
2.32	2.25	2.18	2.10	2.05	2.01	1.96	1.92	1.87	1.81	21
2.30	2.23	2.15	2.07	2.03	1.98	1.94	1.89	1.84	1.78	22
2.27	2.20	2.13	2.05	2.01	1.96	1.91	1.86	1.81	1.76	23
2.25	2.18	2.11	2.03	1.98	1.94	1.89	1.84	1.79	1.73	24
2.24	2.16	2.09	2.01	1.96	1.92	1.87	1.82	1.77	1.71	25
2.22	2.15	2.07	1.99	1.95	1.90	1.85	1.80	1.75	1.69	26
2.20	2.13	2.06	1.97	1.93	1.88	1.84	1.79	1.73	1.67	27
2.19	2.12	2.04	1.96	1.91	1.87	1.82	1.77	1.71	1.65	28
2.18	2.10	2.03	1.94	1.90	1.85	1.81	1.75	1.70	1.64	29
2.16	2.09	2.01	1.93	1.89	1.84	1.79	1.74	1.68	1.62	30
2.08	2.00	1.92	1.84	1.79	1.74	1.69	1.64	1.58	1.51	40
1.99	1.92	1.84	1.75	1.70	1.65	1.59	1.53	1.47	1.39	60
1.91	1.83	1.75	1.66	1.61	1.55	1.50	1.43	1.35	1.25	120
1.83	1.75	1.67	1.57	1.52	1.46	1.39	1.32	1.22	1.00	∞

Source: From "Tables of Percentage Points of the Inverted Beta (*F*)-Distribution," *Biometrika,* Vol. 33 (1943), pp. 73–88, by Maxine Merrington and Catherine M. Thompson. Reproduced by permission of the Biometrika Trustees.

TABLE 9   Percentage Points of the F Distribution: α = .025

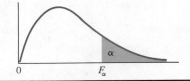

| | v_1 (d.f.) | | | | | | | | |
v_2 (d.f.)	1	2	3	4	5	6	7	8	9
1	647.8	799.5	864.2	899.6	921.8	937.1	948.2	956.7	963.3
2	38.51	39.00	39.17	39.25	39.30	39.33	39.36	39.37	39.39
3	17.44	16.04	15.44	15.10	14.88	14.73	14.62	14.54	14.47
4	12.22	10.65	9.98	9.60	9.36	9.20	9.07	8.98	8.90
5	10.01	8.43	7.76	7.39	7.15	6.98	6.85	6.76	6.68
6	8.81	7.26	6.60	6.23	5.99	5.82	5.70	5.60	5.52
7	8.07	6.54	5.89	5.52	5.29	5.12	4.99	4.90	4.82
8	7.57	6.06	5.42	5.05	4.82	4.65	4.53	4.43	4.36
9	7.21	5.71	5.08	4.72	4.48	4.32	4.20	4.10	4.03
10	6.94	5.46	4.83	4.47	4.24	4.07	3.95	3.85	3.78
11	6.72	5.26	4.63	4.28	4.04	3.88	3.76	3.66	3.59
12	6.55	5.10	4.47	4.12	3.89	3.73	3.61	3.51	3.44
13	6.41	4.97	4.35	4.00	3.77	3.60	3.48	3.39	3.31
14	6.30	4.86	4.24	3.89	3.66	3.50	3.38	3.29	3.21
15	6.20	4.77	4.15	3.80	3.58	3.41	3.29	3.20	3.12
16	6.12	4.69	4.08	3.73	3.50	3.34	3.22	3.12	3.05
17	6.04	4.62	4.01	3.66	3.44	3.28	3.16	3.06	2.98
18	5.98	4.56	3.95	3.61	3.38	3.22	3.10	3.01	2.93
19	5.92	4.51	3.90	3.56	3.33	3.17	3.05	2.96	2.88
20	5.87	4.46	3.86	3.51	3.29	3.13	3.01	2.91	2.84
21	5.83	4.42	3.82	3.48	3.25	3.09	2.97	2.87	2.80
22	5.79	4.38	3.78	3.44	3.22	3.05	2.93	2.84	2.76
23	5.75	4.35	3.75	3.41	3.18	3.02	2.90	2.81	2.73
24	5.72	4.32	3.72	3.38	3.15	2.99	2.87	2.78	2.70
25	5.69	4.29	3.69	3.35	3.13	2.97	2.85	2.75	2.68
26	5.66	4.27	3.67	3.33	3.10	2.94	2.82	2.73	2.65
27	5.63	4.24	3.65	3.31	3.08	2.92	2.80	2.71	2.63
28	5.61	4.22	3.63	3.29	3.06	2.90	2.78	2.69	2.61
29	5.59	4.20	3.61	3.27	3.04	2.88	2.76	2.67	2.59
30	5.57	4.18	3.59	3.25	3.03	2.87	2.75	2.65	2.57
40	5.42	4.05	3.46	3.13	2.90	2.74	2.62	2.53	2.45
60	5.29	3.93	3.34	3.01	2.79	2.63	2.51	2.41	2.33
120	5.15	3.80	3.23	2.89	2.67	2.52	2.39	2.30	2.22
∞	5.02	3.69	3.12	2.79	2.57	2.41	2.29	2.19	2.11

				v_1 (d.f.)						
10	*12*	*15*	*20*	*24*	*30*	*40*	*60*	*120*	∞	v_2 (d.f.)
968.6	976.7	984.9	993.1	997.2	1001	1006	1010	1014	1018	1
39.40	39.41	39.43	39.45	39.46	39.46	39.47	39.48	39.49	39.50	2
14.42	14.34	14.25	14.17	14.12	14.08	14.04	13.99	13.95	13.90	3
8.84	8.75	8.66	8.56	8.51	8.46	8.41	8.36	8.31	8.26	4
6.62	6.52	6.43	6.33	6.28	6.23	6.18	6.12	6.07	6.02	5
5.46	5.37	5.27	5.17	5.12	5.07	5.01	4.96	4.90	4.85	6
4.76	4.67	4.57	4.47	4.42	4.36	4.31	4.25	4.20	4.14	7
4.30	4.20	4.10	4.00	3.95	3.89	3.84	3.78	3.73	3.67	8
3.96	3.87	3.77	3.67	3.61	3.56	3.51	3.45	3.39	3.33	9
3.72	3.62	3.52	3.42	3.37	3.31	3.26	3.20	3.14	3.08	10
3.53	3.43	3.33	3.23	3.17	3.12	3.06	3.00	2.94	2.88	11
3.37	3.28	3.18	3.07	3.02	2.96	2.91	2.85	2.79	2.72	12
3.25	3.15	3.05	2.95	2.89	2.84	2.78	2.72	2.66	2.60	13
3.15	3.05	2.95	2.84	2.79	2.73	2.67	2.61	2.55	2.49	14
3.06	2.96	2.86	2.76	2.70	2.64	2.59	2.52	2.46	2.40	15
2.99	2.89	2.79	2.68	2.63	2.57	2.51	2.45	2.38	2.32	16
2.92	2.82	2.72	2.62	2.56	2.50	2.44	2.38	2.32	2.25	17
2.87	2.77	2.67	2.56	2.50	2.44	2.38	2.32	2.26	2.19	18
2.82	2.72	2.62	2.51	2.45	2.39	2.33	2.27	2.20	2.13	19
2.77	2.68	2.57	2.46	2.41	2.35	2.29	2.22	2.16	2.09	20
2.73	2.64	2.53	2.42	2.37	2.31	2.25	2.18	2.11	2.04	21
2.70	2.60	2.50	2.39	2.33	2.27	2.21	2.14	2.08	2.00	22
2.67	2.57	2.47	2.36	2.30	2.24	2.18	2.11	2.04	1.97	23
2.64	2.54	2.44	2.33	2.27	2.21	2.15	2.08	2.01	1.94	24
2.61	2.51	2.41	2.30	2.24	2.18	2.12	2.05	1.98	1.91	25
2.59	2.49	2.39	2.28	2.22	2.16	2.09	2.03	1.95	1.88	26
2.57	2.47	2.36	2.25	2.19	2.13	2.07	2.00	1.93	1.85	27
2.55	2.45	2.34	2.23	2.17	2.11	2.05	1.98	1.91	1.83	28
2.53	2.43	2.32	2.21	2.15	2.09	2.03	1.96	1.89	1.81	29
2.51	2.41	2.31	2.20	2.14	2.07	2.01	1.94	1.87	1.79	30
2.39	2.29	2.18	2.07	2.01	1.94	1.88	1.80	1.72	1.64	40
2.27	2.17	2.06	1.94	1.88	1.82	1.74	1.67	1.58	1.48	60
2.16	2.05	1.94	1.82	1.76	1.69	1.61	1.53	1.43	1.31	120
2.05	1.94	1.83	1.71	1.64	1.57	1.48	1.39	1.27	1.00	∞

TABLE 10   Percentage Points of the F Distribution: $\alpha = .01$

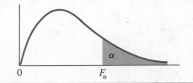

| v_2 (d.f.) | \multicolumn{9}{c}{v_1 (d.f.)} |
	1	2	3	4	5	6	7	8	9
1	4052	4999.5	5403	5625	5764	5859	5928	5982	6022
2	98.50	99.00	99.17	99.25	99.30	99.33	99.36	99.37	99.39
3	34.12	30.82	29.46	28.71	28.24	27.91	27.67	27.49	27.35
4	21.20	18.00	16.69	15.98	15.52	15.21	14.98	14.80	14.66
5	16.26	13.27	12.06	11.39	10.97	10.67	10.46	10.29	10.16
6	13.75	10.92	9.78	9.15	8.75	8.47	8.26	8.10	7.98
7	12.25	9.55	8.45	7.85	7.46	7.19	6.99	6.84	6.72
8	11.26	8.65	7.59	7.01	6.63	6.37	6.18	6.03	5.91
9	10.56	8.02	6.99	6.42	6.06	5.80	5.61	5.47	5.35
10	10.04	7.56	6.55	5.99	5.64	5.39	5.20	5.06	4.94
11	9.65	7.21	6.22	5.67	5.32	5.07	4.89	4.74	4.63
12	9.33	6.93	5.95	5.41	5.06	4.82	4.64	4.50	4.39
13	9.07	6.70	5.74	5.21	4.86	4.62	4.44	4.30	4.19
14	8.86	6.51	5.56	5.04	4.69	4.46	4.28	4.14	4.03
15	8.68	6.36	5.42	4.89	4.56	4.32	4.14	4.00	3.89
16	8.53	6.23	5.29	4.77	4.44	4.20	4.03	3.89	3.78
17	8.40	6.11	5.18	4.67	4.34	4.10	3.93	3.79	3.68
18	8.29	6.01	5.09	4.58	4.25	4.01	3.84	3.71	3.60
19	8.18	5.93	5.01	4.50	4.17	3.94	3.77	3.63	3.52
20	8.10	5.85	4.94	4.43	4.10	3.87	3.70	3.56	3.46
21	8.02	5.78	4.87	4.37	4.04	3.81	3.64	3.51	3.40
22	7.95	5.72	4.82	4.31	3.99	3.76	3.59	3.45	3.35
23	7.88	5.66	4.76	4.26	3.94	3.71	3.54	3.41	3.30
24	7.82	5.61	4.72	4.22	3.90	3.67	3.50	3.36	3.26
25	7.77	5.57	4.68	4.18	3.85	3.63	3.46	3.32	3.22
26	7.72	5.53	4.64	4.14	3.82	3.59	3.42	3.29	3.18
27	7.68	5.49	4.60	4.11	3.78	3.56	3.39	3.26	3.15
28	7.64	5.45	4.57	4.07	3.75	3.53	3.36	3.23	3.12
29	7.60	5.42	4.54	4.04	3.73	3.50	3.33	3.20	3.09
30	7.56	5.39	4.51	4.02	3.70	3.47	3.30	3.17	3.07
40	7.31	5.18	4.31	3.83	3.51	3.29	3.12	2.99	2.89
60	7.08	4.98	4.13	3.65	3.34	3.12	2.95	2.82	2.72
120	6.85	4.79	3.95	3.48	3.17	2.96	2.79	2.66	2.56
∞	6.63	4.61	3.78	3.32	3.02	2.80	2.64	2.51	2.41

				v_1 (d.f.)						
10	12	15	20	24	30	40	60	120	∞	v_2 (d.f.)
6056	6106	6157	6209	6235	6261	6287	6313	6339	6366	1
99.40	99.42	99.43	99.45	99:46	99.47	99.47	99.48	99.49	99.50	2
27.23	27.05	26.87	26.69	26.60	26.50	26.41	26.32	26.22	26.13	3
14.55	14.37	14.20	14.02	13.93	13.84	13.75	13.65	13.56	13.46	4
10.05	9.89	9.72	9.55	9.47	9.38	9.29	9.20	9.11	9.02	5
7.87	7.72	7.56	7.40	7.31	7.23	7.14	7.06	6.97	6.88	6
6.62	6.47	6.31	6.16	6.07	5.99	5.91	5.82	5.74	5.65	7
5.81	5.67	5.52	5.36	5.28	5.20	5.12	5.03	4.95	4.86	8
5.26	5.11	4.96	4.81	4.73	4.65	4.57	4.48	4.40	4.31	9
4.85	4.71	4.56	4.41	4.33	4.25	4.17	4.08	4.00	3.91	10
4.54	4.40	4.25	4.10	4.02	3.94	3.86	3.78	3.69	3.60	11
4.30	4.16	4.01	3.86	3.78	3.70	3.62	3.54	3.45	3.36	12
4.10	3.96	3.82	3.66	3.59	3.51	3.43	3.34	3.25	3.17	13
3.94	3.80	3.66	3.51	3.43	3.35	3.27	3.18	3.09	3.00	14
3.80	3.67	3.52	3.37	3.29	3.21	3.13	3.05	2.96	2.87	15
3.69	3.55	3.41	3.26	3.18	3.10	3.02	2.93	2.84	2.75	16
3.59	3.46	3.31	3.16	3.08	3.00	2.92	2.83	2.75	2.65	17
3.51	3.37	3.23	3.08	3.00	2.92	2.84	2.75	2.66	2.57	18
3.43	3.30	3.15	3.00	2.92	2.84	2.76	2.67	2.58	2.49	19
3.37	3.23	3.09	2.94	2.86	2.78	2.69	2.61	2.52	2.42	20
3.31	3.17	3.03	2.88	2.80	2.72	2.64	2.55	2.46	2.36	21
3.26	3.12	2.98	2.83	2.75	2.67	2.58	2.50	2.40	2.31	22
3.21	3.07	2.93	2.78	2.70	2.62	2.54	2.45	2.35	2.26	23
3.17	3.03	2.89	2.74	2.66	2.58	2.49	2.40	2.31	2.21	24
3.13	2.99	2.85	2.70	2.62	2.54	2.45	2.36	2.27	2.17	25
3.09	2.96	2.81	2.66	2.58	2.50	2.42	2.33	2.23	2.13	26
3.06	2.93	2.78	2.63	2.55	2.47	2.38	2.29	2.20	2.10	27
3.03	2.90	2.75	2.60	2.52	2.44	2.35	2.26	2.17	2.06	28
3.00	2.87	2.73	2.57	2.49	2.41	2.33	2.23	2.14	2.03	29
2.98	2.84	2.70	2.55	2.47	2.39	2.30	2.21	2.11	2.01	30
2.80	2.66	2.52	2.37	2.29	2.20	2.11	2.02	1.92	1.80	40
2.63	2.50	2.35	2.20	2.12	2.03	1.94	1.84	1.73	1.60	60
2.47	2.34	2.19	2.03	1.95	1.86	1.76	1.66	1.53	1.38	120
2.32	2.18	2.04	1.88	1.79	1.70	1.59	1.47	1.32	1.00	∞

Source: From "Tables of Percentage Points of the Inverted Beta (F)-Distribution," Biometrika, Vol. 33 (1943), pp. 73–88, by Maxine Merrington and Catherine M. Thompson. Reproduced by permission of the Biometrika Trustees.

TABLE 11   Percentage Points of the F Distribution: $\alpha = .005$

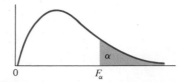

v_2 (d.f.)					v_1 (d.f.)				
	1	*2*	*3*	*4*	*5*	*6*	*7*	*8*	*9*
1	16211	20000	21615	22500	23056	23437	23715	23925	24091
2	198.5	199.0	199.2	199.2	199.3	199.3	199.4	199.4	199.4
3	55.55	49.80	47.47	46.19	45.39	44.84	44.43	44.13	43.88
4	31.33	26.28	24.26	23.15	22.46	21.97	21.62	21.35	21.14
5	22.78	18.31	16.53	15.56	14.94	14.51	14.20	13.96	13.77
6	18.63	14.54	12.92	12.03	11.46	11.07	10.79	10.57	10.39
7	16.24	12.40	10.88	10.05	9.52	9.16	8.89	8.68	8.51
8	14.69	11.04	9.60	8.81	8.30	7.95	7.69	7.50	7.34
9	13.61	10.11	8.72	7.96	7.47	7.13	6.88	6.69	6.54
10	12.83	9.43	8.08	7.34	6.87	6.54	6.30	6.12	5.97
11	12.23	8.91	7.60	6.88	6.42	6.10	5.86	5.68	5.54
12	11.75	8.51	7.23	6.52	6.07	5.76	5.52	5.35	5.20
13	11.37	8.19	6.93	6.23	5.79	5.48	5.25	5.08	4.94
14	11.06	7.92	6.68	6.00	5.56	5.26	5.03	4.86	4.72
15	10.80	7.70	6.48	5.80	5.37	5.07	4.85	4.67	4.54
16	10.58	7.51	6.30	5.64	5.21	4.91	4.69	4.52	4.38
17	10.38	7.35	6.16	5.50	5.07	4.78	4.56	4.39	4.25
18	10.22	7.21	6.03	5.37	4.96	4.66	4.44	4.28	4.14
19	10.07	7.09	5.92	5.27	4.85	4.56	4.34	4.18	4.04
20	9.94	6.99	5.82	5.17	4.76	4.47	4.26	4.09	3.96
21	9.83	6.89	5.73	5.09	4.68	4.39	4.18	4.01	3.88
22	9.73	6.81	5.65	5.02	4.61	4.32	4.11	3.94	3.81
23	9.63	6.73	5.58	4.95	4.54	4.26	4.05	3.88	3.75
24	9.55	6.66	5.52	4.89	4.49	4.20	3.99	3.83	3.69
25	9.48	6.60	5.46	4.84	4.43	4.15	3.94	3.78	3.64
26	9.41	6.54	5.41	4.79	4.38	4.10	3.89	3.73	3.60
27	9.34	6.49	5.36	4.74	4.34	4.06	3.85	3.69	3.56
28	9.28	6.44	5.32	4.70	4.30	4.02	3.81	3.65	3.52
29	9.23	6.40	5.28	4.66	4.26	3.98	3.77	3.61	3.48
30	9.18	6.35	5.24	4.62	4.23	3.95	3.74	3.58	3.45
40	8.83	6.07	4.98	4.37	3.99	3.71	3.51	3.35	3.22
60	8.49	5.79	4.73	4.14	3.76	3.49	3.29	3.13	3.01
120	8.18	5.54	4.50	3.92	3.55	3.28	3.09	2.93	2.81
∞	7.88	5.30	4.28	3.72	3.35	3.09	2.90	2.74	2.62

				v_1 (d.f.)						
10	12	15	20	24	30	40	60	120	∞	v_2 (d.f.)
24224	24426	24630	24836	24940	25044	25148	25253	25359	25465	1
199.4	199.4	199.4	199.4	199.5	199.5	199.5	199.5	199.5	199.5	2
43.69	43.39	43.08	42.78	42.62	42.47	42.31	42.15	41.99	41.83	3
20.97	20.70	20.44	20.17	20.03	19.89	19.75	19.61	19.47	19.32	4
13.62	13.38	13.15	12.90	12.78	12.66	12.53	12.40	12.27	12.14	5
10.25	10.03	9.81	9.59	9.47	9.36	9.24	9.12	9.00	8.88	6
8.38	8.18	7.97	7.75	7.65	7.53	7.42	7.31	7.19	7.08	7
7.21	7.01	6.81	6.61	6.50	6.40	6.29	6.18	6.06	5.95	8
6.42	6.23	6.03	5.83	5.73	5.62	5.52	5.41	5.30	5.19	9
5.85	5.66	5.47	5.27	5.17	5.07	4.97	4.86	4.75	4.64	10
5.42	5.24	5.05	4.86	4.76	4.65	4.55	4.44	4.34	4.23	11
5.09	4.91	4.72	4.53	4.43	4.33	4.23	4.12	4.01	3.90	12
4.82	4.64	4.46	4.27	4.17	4.07	3.97	3.87	3.76	3.65	13
4.60	4.43	4.25	4.06	3.96	3.86	3.76	3.66	3.55	3.44	14
4.42	4.25	4.07	3.88	3.79	3.69	3.58	3.48	3.37	3.26	15
4.27	4.10	3.92	3.73	3.64	3.54	3.44	3.33	3.22	3.11	16
4.14	3.97	3.79	3.61	3.51	3.41	3.31	3.21	3.10	2.98	17
4.03	3.86	3.68	3.50	3.40	3.30	3.20	3.10	2.99	2.87	18
3.93	3.76	3.59	3.40	3.31	3.21	3.11	3.00	2.89	2.78	19
3.85	3.68	3.50	3.32	3.22	3.12	3.02	2.92	2.81	2.69	20
3.77	3.60	3.43	3.24	3.15	3.05	2.95	2.84	2.73	2.61	21
3.70	3.54	3.36	3.18	3.08	2.98	2.88	2.77	2.66	2.55	22
3.64	3.47	3.30	3.12	3.02	2.92	2.82	2.71	2.60	2.48	23
3.59	3.42	3.25	3.06	2.97	2.87	2.77	2.66	2.55	2.43	24
3.54	3.37	3.20	3.01	2.92	2.82	2.72	2.61	2.50	2.38	25
3.49	3.33	3.15	2.97	2.87	2.77	2.67	2.56	2.45	2.33	26
3.45	3.28	3.11	2.93	2.83	2.73	2.63	2.52	2.41	2.29	27
3.41	3.25	3.07	2.89	2.79	2.69	2.59	2.48	2.37	2.25	28
3.38	3.21	3.04	2.86	2.76	2.66	2.56	2.45	2.33	2.21	29
3.34	3.18	3.01	2.82	2.73	2.63	2.52	2.42	2.30	2.18	30
3.12	2.95	2.78	2.60	2.50	2.40	2.30	2.18	2.06	1.93	40
2.90	2.74	2.57	2.39	2.29	2.19	2.08	1.96	1.83	1.69	60
2.71	2.54	2.37	2.19	2.09	1.98	1.87	1.75	1.61	1.43	120
2.52	2.36	2.19	2.00	1.90	1.79	1.67	1.53	1.36	1.00	∞

TABLE 12 Distribution Function of U

$P(U \leq U_0)$; U_0 is the argument; $n_1 \leq n_2$; $3 \leq n_2 \leq 10$.

$n_2 = 3$

U_0	n_1		
	1	*2*	*3*
0	.25	.10	.05
1	.50	.20	.10
2		.40	.20
3		.60	.35
4			.50

$n_2 = 4$

U_0	n_1			
	1	*2*	*3*	*4*
0	.2000	.0667	.0286	.0143
1	.4000	.1333	.0571	.0286
2	.6000	.2667	.1143	.0571
3		.4000	.2000	.1000
4		.6000	.3143	.1714
5			.4286	.2429
6			.5714	.3429
7				.4429
8				.5571

TABLE 12   (*Continued*)

$n_2 = 5$

U_0	n_1				
	1	*2*	*3*	*4*	*5*
0	.1667	.0476	.0179	.0079	.0040
1	.3333	.0952	.0357	.0159	.0079
2	.5000	.1905	.0714	.0317	.0159
3		.2857	.1250	.0556	.0278
4		.4286	.1964	.0952	.0476
5		.5714	.2857	.1429	.0754
6			.3929	.2063	.1111
7			.5000	.2778	.1548
8				.3651	.2103
9				.4524	.2738
10				.5476	.3452
11					.4206
12					.5000

$n_2 = 6$

U_0	n_1					
	1	*2*	*3*	*4*	*5*	*6*
0	.1429	.0357	.0119	.0048	.0022	.0011
1	.2857	.0714	.0238	.0095	.0043	.0022
2	.4286	.1429	.0476	.0190	.0087	.0043
3	.5714	.2143	.0833	.0333	.0152	.0076
4		.3214	.1310	.0571	.0260	.0130
5		.4286	.1905	.0857	.0411	.0206
6		.5714	.2738	.1286	.0628	.0325
7			.3571	.1762	.0887	.0465
8			.4524	.2381	.1234	.0660
9			.5476	.3048	.1645	.0898
10				.3810	.2143	.1201
11				.4571	.2684	.1548
12				.5429	.3312	.1970
13					.3961	.2424
14					.4654	.2944
15					.5346	.3496
16						.4091
17						.4686
18						.5314

(*continues*)

TABLE 12   (*Continued*)

$n_2 = 7$

U_0				n_1			
	1	2	3	4	5	6	7
0	.1250	.0278	.0083	.0030	.0013	.0006	.0003
1	.2500	.0556	.0167	.0061	.0025	.0012	.0006
2	.3750	.1111	.0333	.0121	.0051	.0023	.0012
3	.5000	.1667	.0583	.0212	.0088	.0041	.0020
4		.2500	.0917	.0364	.0152	.0070	.0035
5		.3333	.1333	.0545	.0240	.0111	.0055
6		.4444	.1917	.0818	.0366	.0175	.0087
7		.5556	.2583	.1152	.0530	.0256	.0131
8			.3333	.1576	.0745	.0367	.0189
9			.4167	.2061	.1010	.0507	.0265
10			.5000	.2636	.1338	.0688	.0364
11				.3242	.1717	.0903	.0487
12				.3939	.2159	.1171	.0641
13				.4636	.2652	.1474	.0825
14				.5364	.3194	.1830	.1043
15					.3775	.2226	.1297
16					.4381	.2669	.1588
17					.5000	.3141	.1914
18						.3654	.2279
19						.4178	.2675
20						.4726	.3100
21						.5274	.3552
22							.4024
23							.4508
24							.5000

TABLE 12   (*Continued*)

$n_2 = 8$

U_0	|			n_1				
	1	2	3	4	5	6	7	8
0	.1111	.0222	.0061	.0020	.0008	.0003	.0002	.0001
1	.2222	.0444	.0121	.0040	.0016	.0007	.0003	.0002
2	.3333	.0889	.0242	.0081	.0031	.0013	.0006	.0003
3	.4444	.1333	.0424	.0141	.0054	.0023	.0011	.0005
4	.5556	.2000	.0667	.0242	.0093	.0040	.0019	.0009
5		.2667	.0970	.0364	.0148	.0063	.0030	.0015
6		.3556	.1394	.0545	.0225	.0100	.0047	.0023
7		.4444	.1879	.0768	.0326	.0147	.0070	.0035
8		.5556	.2485	.1071	.0466	.0213	.0103	.0052
9			.3152	.1414	.0637	.0296	.0145	.0074
10			.3879	.1838	.0855	.0406	.0200	.0103
11			.4606	.2303	.1111	.0539	.0270	.0141
12			.5394	.2848	.1422	.0709	.0361	.0190
13				.3414	.1772	.0906	.0469	.0249
14				.4040	.2176	.1142	.0603	.0325
15				.4667	.2618	.1412	.0760	.0415
16				.5333	.3108	.1725	.0946	.0524
17					.3621	.2068	.1159	.0652
18					.4165	.2454	.1405	.0803
19					.4716	.2864	.1678	.0974
20					.5284	.3310	.1984	.1172
21						.3773	.2317	.1393
22						.4259	.2679	.1641
23						.4749	.3063	.1911
24						.5251	.3472	.2209
25							.3894	.2527
26							.4333	.2869
27							.4775	.3227
28							.5225	.3605
29								.3992
30								.4392
31								.4796
32								.5204

(*continues*)

TABLE 12 (*Continued*)

$n_2 = 9$

U_0	n_1								
	1	*2*	*3*	*4*	*5*	*6*	*7*	*8*	*9*
0	.1000	.0182	.0045	.0014	.0005	.0002	.0001	.0000	.0000
1	.2000	.0364	.0091	.0028	.0010	.0004	.0002	.0001	.0000
2	.3000	.0727	.0182	.0056	.0020	.0008	.0003	.0002	.0001
3	.4000	.1091	.0318	.0098	.0035	.0014	.0006	.0003	.0001
4	.5000	.1636	.0500	.0168	.0060	.0024	.0010	.0005	.0002
5		.2182	.0727	.0252	.0095	.0038	.0017	.0008	.0004
6		.2909	.1045	.0378	.0145	.0060	.0026	.0012	.0006
7		.3636	.1409	.0531	.0210	.0088	.0039	.0019	.0009
8		.4545	.1864	.0741	.0300	.0128	.0058	.0028	.0014
9		.5455	.2409	.0993	.0415	.0180	.0082	.0039	.0020
10			.3000	.1301	.0559	.0248	.0115	.0056	.0028
11			.3636	.1650	.0734	.0332	.0156	.0076	.0039
12			.4318	.2070	.0949	.0440	.0209	.0103	.0053
13			.5000	.2517	.1199	.0567	.0274	.0137	.0071
14				.3021	.1489	.0723	.0356	.0180	.0094
15				.3552	.1818	.0905	.0454	.0232	.0122
16				.4126	.2188	.1119	.0571	.0296	.0157
17				.4699	.2592	.1361	.0708	.0372	.0200
18				.5301	.3032	.1638	.0869	.0464	.0252
19					.3497	.1942	.1052	.0570	.0313
20					.3986	.2280	.1261	.0694	.0385
21					.4491	.2643	.1496	.0836	.0470
22					.5000	.3035	.1755	.0998	.0567
23						.3445	.2039	.1179	.0680
24						.3878	.2349	.1383	.0807
25						.4320	.2680	.1606	.0951
26						.4773	.3032	.1852	.1112
27						.5227	.3403	.2117	.1290
28							.3788	.2404	.1487
29							.4185	.2707	.1701
30							.4591	.3029	.1933
31							.5000	.3365	.2181
32								.3715	.2447
33								.4074	.2729
34								.4442	.3024
35								.4813	.3332
36								.5187	.3652
37									.3981
38									.4317
39									.4657
40									.5000

TABLE 12   (*Continued*)

$n_2 = 10$

U_0	1	2	3	4	5	6	7	8	9	10
0	.0909	.0152	.0035	.0010	.0003	.0001	.0001	.0000	.0000	.0000
1	.1818	.0303	.0070	.0020	.0007	.0002	.0001	.0000	.0000	.0000
2	.2727	.0606	.0140	.0040	.0013	.0005	.0002	.0001	.0000	.0000
3	.3636	.0909	.0245	.0070	.0023	.0009	.0004	.0002	.0001	.0000
4	.4545	.1364	.0385	.0120	.0040	.0015	.0006	.0003	.0001	.0001
5	.5455	.1818	.0559	.0180	.0063	.0024	.0010	.0004	.0002	.0001
6		.2424	.0804	.0270	.0097	.0037	.0015	.0007	.0003	.0002
7		.3030	.1084	.0380	.0140	.0055	.0023	.0010	.0005	.0002
8		.3788	.1434	.0529	.0200	.0080	.0034	.0015	.0007	.0004
9		.4545	.1853	.0709	.0276	.0112	.0048	.0022	.0011	.0005
10		.5455	.2343	.0939	.0376	.0156	.0068	.0031	.0015	.0008
11			.2867	.1199	.0496	.0210	.0093	.0043	.0021	.0010
12			.3462	.1518	.0646	.0280	.0125	.0058	.0028	.0014
13			.4056	.1868	.0823	.0363	.0165	.0078	.0038	.0019
14			.4685	.2268	.1032	.0467	.0215	.0103	.0051	.0026
15			.5315	.2697	.1272	.0589	.0277	.0133	.0066	.0034
16				.3177	.1548	.0736	.0351	.0171	.0086	.0045
17				.3666	.1855	.0903	.0439	.0217	.0110	.0057
18				.4196	.2198	.1099	.0544	.0273	.0140	.0073
19				.4725	.2567	.1317	.0665	.0338	.0175	.0093
20				.5275	.2970	.1566	.0806	.0416	.0217	.0116
21					.3393	.1838	.0966	.0506	.0267	.0144
22					.3839	.2139	.1148	.0610	.0326	.0177
23					.4296	.2461	.1349	.0729	.0394	.0216
24					.4765	.2811	.1574	.0864	.0474	.0262
25					.5235	.3177	.1819	.1015	.0564	.0315
26						.3564	.2087	.1185	.0667	.0376
27						.3962	.2374	.1371	.0782	.0446
28						.4374	.2681	.1577	.0912	.0526
29						.4789	.3004	.1800	.1055	.0615
30						.5211	.3345	.2041	.1214	.0716
31							.3698	.2299	.1388	.0827
32							.4063	.2574	.1577	.0952
33							.4434	.2863	.1781	.1088
34							.4811	.3167	.2001	.1237
35							.5189	.3482	.2235	.1399
36								.3809	.2483	.1575
37								.4143	.2745	.1763
38								.4484	.3019	.1965
39								.4827	.3304	.2179

(*continues*)

TABLE 12   (*Concluded*)

$n_2 = 10$

					n_1					
U_0	*1*	*2*	*3*	*4*	*5*	*6*	*7*	*8*	*9*	*10*
40								.5173	.3598	.2406
41									.3901	.2644
42									.4211	.2894
43									.4524	.3153
44									.4841	.3421
45									.5159	.3697
46										.3980
47										.4267
48										.4559
49										.4853
50										.5147

Computed by M. Pagano, Department of Statistics, University of Florida.

TABLE 13   Critical Values of T in the Wilcoxon Signed Rank Test: $n = 5(1)50$

One-sided	*Two-sided*	$n = 5$	$n = 6$	$n = 7$	$n = 8$	$n = 9$	$n = 10$
$P = .05$	$P = .10$	1	2	4	6	8	11
$P = .025$	$P = .05$		1	2	4	6	8
$P = .01$	$P = .02$			0	2	3	5
$P = .005$	$P = .01$				0	2	3

One-sided	*Two-sided*	$n = 11$	$n = 12$	$n = 13$	$n = 14$	$n = 15$	$n = 16$
$P = .05$	$P = .10$	14	17	21	26	30	36
$P = .025$	$P = .05$	11	14	17	21	25	30
$P = .01$	$P = .02$	7	10	13	16	20	24
$P = .005$	$P = .01$	5	7	10	13	16	19

One-sided	*Two-sided*	$n = 17$	$n = 18$	$n = 19$	$n = 20$	$n = 21$	$n = 22$
$P = .05$	$P = .10$	41	47	54	60	68	75
$P = .025$	$P = .05$	35	40	46	52	59	66
$P = .01$	$P = .02$	28	33	38	43	49	56
$P = .005$	$P = .01$	23	28	32	37	43	49

TABLE 13   *(Concluded)*

One-sided	Two-sided	n = 23	n = 24	n = 25	n = 26	n = 27	n = 28
P = .05	P = .10	83	92	101	110	120	130
P = .025	P = .05	73	81	90	98	107	117
P = .01	P = .02	62	69	77	85	93	102
P = .005	P = .01	55	68	68	76	84	92

One-sided	Two-sided	n = 29	n = 30	n = 31	n = 32	n = 33	n = 34
P = .05	P = .10	141	152	163	175	188	201
P = .025	P = .05	127	137	148	159	171	183
P = .01	P = .02	111	120	130	141	151	162
P = .005	P = .01	100	109	118	128	138	149

One-sided	Two-sided	n = 35	n = 36	n = 37	n = 38	n = 39
P = .05	P = .10	214	228	242	256	271
P = .025	P = .05	195	208	222	235	250
P = .01	P = .02	174	186	198	211	224
P = .005	P = .01	160	171	183	195	208

One-sided	Two-sided	n = 40	n = 41	n = 42	n = 43	n = 44	n = 45
P = .05	P = .10	287	303	319	336	353	371
P = .025	P = .05	264	279	295	311	327	344
P = .01	P = .02	238	252	267	281	297	313
P = .005	P = .01	221	234	248	262	277	292

One-sided	Two-sided	n = 46	n = 47	n = 48	n = 49	n = 50
P = .05	P = .10	389	408	427	446	466
P = .025	P = .05	361	379	397	415	434
P = .01	P = .02	329	345	362	380	398
P = .005	P = .01	307	323	339	356	373

Source: From "Some Rapid Approximate Statistical Procedures" (1964), 28, F. Wilcoxon and R. A. Wilcox. Reproduced with the kind permission of the American Cyanamid Company.

TABLE 14   Critical Values of Spearman's Rank Correlation Coefficient

n	$\alpha = .05$	$\alpha = .025$	$\alpha = .01$	$\alpha = .005$
5	0.900	—	—	—
6	0.829	0.886	0.943	—
7	0.714	0.786	0.893	—
8	0.643	0.738	0.833	0.881
9	0.600	0.683	0.783	0.833
10	0.564	0.648	0.745	0.794
11	0.523	0.623	0.736	0.818
12	0.497	0.591	0.703	0.780
13	0.475	0.566	0.673	0.745
14	0.457	0.545	0.646	0.716
15	0.441	0.525	0.623	0.689
16	0.425	0.507	0.601	0.666
17	0.412	0.490	0.582	0.645
18	0.399	0.476	0.564	0.625
19	0.388	0.462	0.549	0.608
20	0.377	0.450	0.534	0.591
21	0.368	0.438	0.521	0.576
22	0.359	0.428	0.508	0.562
23	0.351	0.418	0.496	0.549
24	0.343	0.409	0.485	0.537
25	0.336	0.400	0.475	0.526
26	0.329	0.392	0.465	0.515
27	0.323	0.385	0.456	0.505
28	0.317	0.377	0.448	0.496
29	0.311	0.370	0.440	0.487
30	0.305	0.364	0.432	0.478

Source: From "Distribution of Sums of Squares of Rank Differences for Small Samples," E. G. Olds, *Annals of Mathematical Statistics.* Volume 9 (1938). Reproduced with the kind permission of the Institute of Mathematical Statistics.

TABLE 15 Random Numbers

Line	1	2	3	4	5	6	7	8	9	10	11	12	13	14
										Column				
1	10480	15011	01536	02011	81647	91646	69179	14194	62590	36207	20969	99570	91291	90700
2	22368	46573	25595	85393	30995	89198	27982	53402	93965	34095	52666	19174	39615	99505
3	24130	48360	22527	97265	76393	64809	15179	24830	49340	32081	30680	19655	63348	58629
4	42167	93093	06243	61680	07856	16376	39440	53537	71341	57004	00849	74917	97758	16379
5	37570	39975	81837	16656	06121	91782	60468	81305	49684	60672	14110	06927	01263	54613
6	77921	06907	11008	42751	27756	53498	18602	70659	90655	15053	21916	81825	44394	42880
7	99562	72905	56420	69994	98872	31016	71194	18738	44013	48840	63213	21069	10634	12952
8	96301	91977	05463	07972	18876	20922	94595	56869	69014	60045	18425	84903	42508	32307
9	89579	14342	63661	10281	17453	18103	57740	84378	25331	12566	58678	44947	05585	56941
10	85475	36857	53342	53988	53060	59533	38867	62300	08158	17983	16439	11458	18593	64952
11	28918	69578	88231	33276	70997	79936	56865	05859	90106	31595	01547	85590	91610	78188
12	63553	40961	48235	03427	49626	69445	18663	72695	52180	20847	12234	90511	33703	90322
13	09429	93969	52636	92737	88974	33488	36320	17617	30015	08272	84115	27156	30613	74952
14	10365	61129	87529	85689	48237	52267	67689	93394	01511	26358	85104	20285	29975	89868
15	07119	97336	71048	08178	77233	13916	47564	81056	97735	85977	29372	74461	28551	90707
16	51085	12765	51821	51259	77452	16308	60756	92144	49442	53900	70960	63990	75601	40719
17	02368	21382	52404	60268	89368	19885	55322	44819	01188	65255	64835	44919	05944	55157
18	01011	54092	33362	94904	31273	04146	18594	29852	71585	85030	51132	01915	92747	64951
19	52162	53916	46369	58586	23216	14513	83149	98736	23495	64350	94738	17752	35156	35749
20	07056	97628	33787	09998	42698	06691	76988	13602	51851	46104	88916	19509	25625	58104
21	48663	91245	85828	14346	09172	30168	90229	04734	59193	22178	30421	61666	99904	32812
22	54164	58492	22421	74103	47070	25306	76468	26384	58151	06646	21524	15227	96909	44592
23	32639	32363	05597	24200	13363	38005	94342	28728	35806	06912	17012	64161	18296	22851
24	29334	27001	87637	87308	58731	00256	45834	15398	46557	41135	10367	07684	36188	18510
25	02488	33062	28834	07351	19731	92420	60952	61280	50001	67658	32586	86679	50720	94953
26	81525	72295	04839	96423	24878	82651	66566	14778	76797	14780	13300	87074	79666	95725
27	29676	20591	68086	26432	46901	20849	89768	81536	86645	12659	92259	57102	80428	25280
28	00742	57392	39064	66432	84673	40027	32832	61362	98947	96067	64760	64584	96096	98253
29	05366	04213	25669	26422	44407	44048	37937	63904	45766	66134	75470	66520	34693	90449
30	91921	26418	64117	94305	26766	25940	39972	22209	71500	64568	91402	42416	07844	69618
31	00582	04711	87917	77341	42206	35126	74087	99547	81817	42607	43808	76655	62028	76630
32	00725	69884	62797	56170	86324	88072	76222	36086	84637	93161	76038	65855	77919	88006
34	69011	65795	95876	55293	18988	27354	26575	08625	40801	59920	29841	80150	12777	48501
34	25976	57948	29888	88604	67917	48708	18912	82271	65424	69774	33611	54262	85963	03547
35	09763	83473	73577	12908	30883	18317	28290	35797	05998	41688	34952	37888	38917	88050
36	91567	42595	27958	30134	04024	86385	29880	99730	55536	84855	29080	09250	79656	73211
37	17955	56349	90999	49127	20044	59931	06115	20542	18059	02008	73708	83517	36103	42791
38	46503	18584	18845	49618	02304	51038	20655	58727	28168	15475	56942	53389	20562	87338
39	92157	89634	94822	78171	84610	82834	09922	25417	44137	48413	25555	21246	35509	20468
40	14577	62765	35605	81263	39667	47358	56873	56307	61607	49518	89656	20103	77490	18062
41	98427	07523	33362	64270	01638	92477	66969	98420	04880	45585	46565	04102	46880	45709
42	34914	63976	88720	82765	34476	17032	87589	40836	32427	70002	70663	88863	77775	69348
43	70060	28277	39475	46473	23219	53416	94970	25832	69975	94884	19661	72828	00102	66794
44	53976	54914	06990	67245	68350	82948	11398	42878	80287	88267	47363	46634	06541	97809
45	76072	29515	40980	07391	58745	25774	22987	80059	39911	96189	41151	14222	60697	59583
46	90725	52210	83974	29992	65831	38857	50490	83765	55657	14361	31720	57375	56228	41546
47	64364	67412	33339	31926	14883	24413	59744	92351	97473	89286	35931	04110	23726	51900
48	08962	00358	31662	25388	61642	34072	81249	35648	56891	69352	48373	45578	78547	81788
49	95012	68379	93526	70765	10592	04542	76463	54328	02349	17247	28865	14777	62730	92277
50	15664	10493	20492	38391	91132	21999	59516	81652	27195	48223	46751	22923	32261	85653
51	16408	81899	04153	53381	79401	21438	83035	92350	36693	31238	59649	91754	72772	02338

TABLE 15   *(Concluded)*

Line	Column													
	1	2	3	4	5	6	7	8	9	10	11	12	13	14
52	18629	81953	05520	91962	04739	13092	97662	24822	94730	06496	35090	04822	86774	98289
53	73115	35101	47498	87637	99016	71060	88824	71013	18735	20286	23153	72924	35165	43040
54	57491	16703	23167	49323	45021	33132	12544	41035	80780	45393	44812	12515	98931	91202
55	30405	83946	23792	14422	15059	45799	22716	19792	09983	74353	68668	30429	70735	25499
56	16631	35006	85900	98275	32388	52390	16815	69298	82732	38480	73817	32523	41961	44437
57	96773	20206	42559	78985	05300	22164	24369	54224	35083	19687	11052	91491	60383	19746
58	38935	64202	14349	82674	66523	44133	00697	35552	35970	19124	63318	29686	03387	59846
59	31624	76384	17403	53363	44167	64486	64758	75366	76554	31601	12614	33072	60332	92325
60	78919	19474	23632	27889	47914	02584	37680	20801	72152	39339	34806	08930	85001	87820
61	03931	33309	57047	74211	63445	17361	62825	39908	05607	91284	68833	25570	38818	46920
62	74426	33278	43972	10119	89917	15665	52872	73823	73144	88662	88970	74492	51805	99378
63	09066	00903	20795	95452	92648	45454	09552	88815	16553	51125	79375	97596	16296	66092
64	42238	12426	87025	14267	20979	04508	64535	31355	86064	29472	47689	05974	52468	16834
65	16153	08002	26504	41744	81959	65642	74240	56302	00033	67107	77510	70625	28725	34191
66	21457	40742	29820	96783	29400	21840	15035	34537	33310	06116	95240	15957	16572	06004
67	21581	57802	02050	89728	17937	37621	47075	42080	97403	48626	68995	43805	33386	21597
68	55612	78095	83197	33732	05810	24813	86902	60397	16489	03264	88525	42786	05269	92532
69	44657	66999	99324	51281	84463	60563	79312	93454	68876	25471	93911	25650	12682	73572
70	91340	84979	46949	81973	37949	61023	43997	15263	80644	43942	89203	71795	99533	50501
71	91227	21199	31935	27022	84067	05462	35216	14486	29891	68607	41867	14951	91696	85065
72	50001	38140	66321	19924	72163	09538	12151	06878	91903	18749	34405	56087	82790	70925
73	65390	05224	72958	28609	81406	39147	25549	48542	42627	45233	57202	94617	23772	07896
74	27504	96131	83944	41575	10573	08619	64482	73923	36152	05184	94142	25299	84387	34925
75	37169	94851	39117	89632	00959	16487	65536	49071	39782	17095	02330	74301	00275	48280
76	11508	70225	51111	38351	19444	66499	71945	05422	13442	78675	84081	66938	93654	59894
77	37449	30362	06694	54690	04052	53115	62757	95348	78662	11163	81651	50245	34971	52924
78	46515	70331	85922	38329	57015	15765	97161	17869	45349	61796	66345	81073	49106	79860
79	30986	81223	42416	58353	21532	30502	32305	86482	05174	07901	54339	58861	74818	46942
80	63798	64995	46583	09785	44160	78128	83991	42865	92520	83531	80377	35909	81250	54238
81	82486	84846	99254	67632	43218	50076	21361	64816	51202	88124	41870	52689	51275	83556
82	21885	32906	92431	09060	64297	51674	64126	62570	26123	05155	59194	52799	28225	85762
83	60336	98782	07408	53458	13564	59089	26445	29789	85205	41001	12535	12133	14645	23541
84	43937	46891	24010	25560	86355	33941	25786	54990	71899	15475	95434	98227	21824	19585
85	97656	63175	89303	16275	07100	92063	21942	18611	47348	20203	18534	03862	78095	50136
86	03299	01221	05418	38982	55758	92237	26759	86367	21216	98442	08303	56613	91511	75928
87	79626	06486	03574	17668	07785	76020	79924	25651	83325	88428	85076	72811	22717	50585
88	85636	68335	47539	03129	65651	11977	02510	26113	99447	68645	34327	15152	55230	93448
89	18039	14367	61337	06177	12143	46609	32989	74014	64708	00533	35398	58408	13261	47908
90	08362	15656	60627	36478	65648	16764	53412	09013	07832	41574	17639	82163	60859	75567
91	79556	29068	04142	16268	15387	12856	66227	38358	22478	73373	88732	09443	82558	05250
92	92608	82674	27072	32534	17075	27698	98204	63863	11951	34648	88022	56148	34925	57031
93	23982	25835	40055	67006	12293	02753	14827	23235	35071	99704	37543	11601	35503	85171
94	09915	96306	05908	97901	28395	14186	00821	80703	70426	75647	76310	88717	37890	40129
95	59037	33300	26695	62247	69927	76123	50842	43834	86654	70959	79725	93872	28117	19233
96	42488	78077	69882	61657	34136	79180	97526	43092	04098	73571	80799	76536	71255	64239
97	46764	86273	63003	93017	31204	36692	40202	35275	57306	55543	53203	18098	47625	88684
98	03237	45430	55417	63282	90816	17349	88298	90183	36600	78406	06216	95787	42579	90730
99	86591	81482	52667	61582	14972	90053	89534	76036	49199	43716	97548	04379	46370	28672
100	38534	01715	94964	87288	65680	43772	39560	12918	86537	62738	19636	51132	25739	56947

Source: Abridged from *Handbook of Tables for Probability and Statistics*, 2nd ed. Edited by William H. Beyer (Cleveland: The Chemical Rubber Company, 1968). © Copyright The Chemical Rubber Co., CRC Press, Inc.

TABLE 16   Percentage Points of the Studentized Range, $q(k, v)$; Upper 5% Points

					k					
v	2	3	4	5	6	7	8	9	10	11
1	17.97	26.98	32.82	37.08	40.41	43.12	45.40	47.36	49.07	50.59
2	6.08	8.33	9.80	10.88	11.74	12.44	13.03	13.54	13.99	14.39
3	4.50	5.91	6.82	7.50	8.04	8.48	8.85	9.18	9.46	9.72
4	3.93	5.04	5.76	6.29	6.71	7.05	7.35	7.60	7.83	8.03
5	3.64	4.60	5.22	5.67	6.03	6.33	6.58	6.80	6.99	7.17
6	3.46	4.34	4.90	5.30	5.63	5.90	6.12	6.32	6.49	6.65
7	3.34	4.16	4.68	5.06	5.36	5.61	5.82	6.00	6.16	6.30
8	3.26	4.04	4.53	4.89	5.17	5.40	5.60	5.77	5.92	6.05
9	3.20	3.95	4.41	4.76	5.02	5.24	5.43	5.59	5.74	5.87
10	3.15	3.88	4.33	4.65	4.91	5.12	5.30	5.46	5.60	5.72
11	3.11	3.82	4.26	4.57	4.82	5.03	5.20	5.35	5.49	5.61
12	3.08	3.77	4.20	4.51	4.75	4.95	5.12	5.27	5.39	5.51
13	3.06	3.73	4.15	4.45	4.69	4.88	5.05	5.19	5.32	5.43
14	3.03	3.70	4.11	4.41	4.64	4.83	4.99	5.13	5.25	5.36
15	3.01	3.67	4.08	4.37	4.60	4.78	4.94	5.08	5.20	5.31
16	3.00	3.65	4.05	4.33	4.56	4.74	4.90	5.03	5.15	5.26
17	2.98	3.63	4.02	4.30	4.52	4.70	4.86	4.99	5.11	5.21
18	2.97	3.61	4.00	4.28	4.49	4.67	4.82	4.96	5.07	5.17
19	2.96	3.59	3.98	4.25	4.47	4.65	4.79	4.92	5.04	5.14
20	2.95	3.58	3.96	4.23	4.45	4.62	4.77	4.90	5.01	5.11
24	2.92	3.53	3.90	4.17	4.37	4.54	4.68	4.81	4.92	5.01
30	2.89	3.49	3.85	4.10	4.30	4.46	4.60	4.72	4.82	4.92
40	2.86	3.44	3.79	4.04	4.23	4.39	4.52	4.63	4.73	4.82
60	2.83	3.40	3.74	3.98	4.16	4.31	4.44	4.55	4.65	4.73
120	2.80	3.36	3.68	3.92	4.10	4.24	4.36	4.47	4.56	4.64
∞	2.77	3.31	3.63	3.86	4.03	4.17	4.29	4.39	4.47	4.55

(*continues*)

TABLE 16   (*Concluded*)

				k					
12	13	14	15	16	17	18	19	20	v
51.96	53.20	54.33	55.36	56.32	57.22	58.04	58.83	59.56	1
14.75	15.08	15.38	15.65	15.91	16.14	16.37	16.57	16.77	2
9.95	10.15	10.35	10.52	10.69	10.84	10.98	11.11	11.24	3
8.21	8.37	8.52	8.66	8.79	8.91	9.03	9.13	9.23	4
7.32	7.47	7.60	7.72	7.83	7.93	8.03	8.12	8.21	5
6.79	6.92	7.03	7.14	7.24	7.34	7.43	7.51	7.59	6
6.43	6.55	6.66	6.76	6.85	6.94	7.02	7.10	7.17	7
6.18	6.29	6.39	6.48	6.57	6.65	6.73	6.80	6.87	8
5.98	6.09	6.19	6.28	6.36	6.44	6.51	6.58	6.64	9
5.83	5.93	6.03	6.11	6.19	6.27	6.34	6.40	6.47	10
5.71	5.81	5.90	5.98	6.06	6.13	6.20	6.27	6.33	11
5.61	5.71	5.80	5.88	5.95	6.02	6.09	6.15	6.21	12
5.53	5.63	5.71	5.79	5.86	5.93	5.99	6.05	6.11	13
5.46	5.55	5.64	5.71	5.79	5.85	5.91	5.97	6.03	14
5.40	5.49	5.57	5.65	5.72	5.78	5.85	5.90	5.96	15
5.35	5.44	5.52	5.59	5.66	5.73	5.79	5.84	5.90	16
5.31	5.39	5.47	5.54	5.61	5.67	5.73	5.79	5.84	17
5.27	5.35	5.43	5.50	5.57	5.63	5.69	5.74	5.79	18
5.23	5.31	5.39	5.46	5.53	5.59	5.65	5.70	5.75	19
5.20	5.28	5.36	5.43	5.49	5.55	5.61	5.66	5.71	20
5.10	5.18	5.25	5.32	5.38	5.44	5.49	5.55	5.59	24
5.00	5.08	5.15	5.21	5.27	5.33	5.38	5.43	5.47	30
4.90	4.98	5.04	5.11	5.16	5.22	5.27	5.31	5.36	40
4.81	4.88	4.94	5.00	5.06	5.11	5.15	5.20	5.24	60
4.71	4.78	4.84	4.90	4.95	5.00	5.04	5.09	5.13	120
4.62	4.68	4.74	4.80	4.85	4.89	4.93	4.97	5.01	∞

TABLE 17   Percentage Points of the Studentized Range, $q(k, v)$; Upper 1% Points

v					k					
	2	3	4	5	6	7	8	9	10	11
1	90.03	135.0	164.3	185.6	202.2	215.8	227.2	237.0	245.6	253.2
2	14.04	19.02	22.29	24.72	26.63	28.20	29.53	30.68	31.69	32.59
3	8.26	10.62	12.17	13.33	14.24	15.00	15.64	16.20	16.69	17.13
4	6.51	8.12	9.17	9.96	10.58	11.10	11.55	11.93	12.27	12.57
5	5.70	6.98	7.80	8.42	8.91	9.32	9.67	9.97	10.24	10.48
6	5.24	6.33	7.03	7.56	7.97	8.32	8.61	8.87	9.10	9.30
7	4.95	5.92	6.54	7.01	7.37	7.68	7.94	8.17	8.37	8.55
8	4.75	5.64	6.20	6.62	6.96	7.24	7.47	7.68	7.86	8.03
9	4.60	5.43	5.96	6.35	6.66	6.91	7.13	7.33	7.49	7.65
10	4.48	5.27	5.77	6.14	6.43	6.67	6.87	7.05	7.21	7.36
11	4.39	5.15	5.62	5.97	6.25	6.48	6.67	6.84	6.99	7.13
12	4.32	5.05	5.50	5.84	6.10	6.32	6.51	6.67	6.81	6.94
13	4.26	4.96	5.40	5.73	5.98	6.19	6.37	6.53	6.67	6.79
14	4.21	4.89	5.32	5.63	5.88	6.08	6.26	6.41	6.54	6.66
15	4.17	4.84	5.25	5.56	5.80	5.99	6.16	6.31	6.44	6.55
16	4.13	4.79	5.19	5.49	5.72	5.92	6.08	6.22	6.35	6.46
17	4.10	4.74	5.14	5.43	5.66	5.85	6.01	6.15	6.27	6.38
18	4.07	4.70	5.09	5.38	5.60	5.79	5.94	6.08	6.20	6.31
19	4.05	4.67	5.05	5.33	5.55	5.73	5.89	6.02	6.14	6.25
20	4.02	4.64	5.02	5.29	5.51	5.69	5.84	5.97	6.09	6.19
24	3.96	4.55	4.91	5.17	5.37	5.54	5.69	5.81	5.92	6.02
30	3.89	4.45	4.80	5.05	5.24	5.40	5.54	5.65	5.76	5.85
40	3.82	4.37	4.70	4.93	5.11	5.26	5.39	5.50	5.60	5.69
60	3.76	4.28	4.59	4.82	4.99	5.13	5.25	5.36	5.45	5.53
120	3.70	4.20	4.50	4.71	4.87	5.01	5.12	5.21	5.30	5.37
∞	3.64	4.12	4.40	4.60	4.76	4.88	4.99	5.08	5.16	5.23

(continues)

TABLE 17 (*Concluded*)

12	13	14	15	16	17	18	19	20	v
260.0	266.2	271.8	277.0	281.8	286.3	290.0	294.3	298.0	1
33.40	34.13	34.81	35.43	36.00	36.53	37.03	37.50	37.95	2
17.53	17.89	18.22	18.52	18.81	19.07	19.32	19.55	19.77	3
12.84	13.09	13.32	13.53	13.73	13.91	14.08	14.24	14.40	4
10.70	10.89	11.08	11.24	11.40	11.55	11.68	11.81	11.93	5
9.48	9.65	9.81	9.95	10.08	10.21	10.32	10.43	10.54	6
8.71	8.86	9.00	9.12	9.24	9.35	9.46	9.55	9.65	7
8.18	8.31	8.44	8.55	8.66	8.76	8.85	8.94	9.03	8
7.78	7.91	8.03	8.13	8.23	8.33	8.41	8.49	8.57	9
7.49	7.60	7.71	7.81	7.91	7.99	8.08	8.15	8.23	10
7.25	7.36	7.46	7.56	7.65	7.73	7.81	7.88	7.95	11
7.06	7.17	7.26	7.36	7.44	7.52	7.59	7.66	7.73	12
6.90	7.01	7.10	7.19	7.27	7.35	7.42	7.48	7.55	13
6.77	6.87	6.96	7.05	7.13	7.20	7.27	7.33	7.39	14
6.66	6.76	6.84	6.93	7.00	7.07	7.14	7.20	7.26	15
6.56	6.66	6.74	6.82	6.90	6.97	7.03	7.09	7.15	16
6.48	6.57	6.66	6.73	6.81	6.87	6.94	7.00	7.05	17
6.41	6.50	6.58	6.65	6.72	6.79	6.85	6.91	6.97	18
6.34	6.43	6.51	6.58	6.65	6.72	6.78	6.84	6.89	19
6.28	6.37	6.45	6.52	6.59	6.65	6.71	6.77	6.82	20
6.11	6.19	6.26	6.33	6.39	6.45	6.51	6.56	6.61	24
5.93	6.01	6.08	6.14	6.20	6.26	6.31	6.36	6.41	30
5.76	5.83	5.90	5.96	6.02	6.07	6.12	6.16	6.21	40
5.60	5.67	5.73	5.78	5.84	5.89	5.93	5.97	6.01	60
5.44	5.50	5.56	5.61	5.66	5.71	5.75	5.79	5.83	120
5.29	5.35	5.40	5.45	5.49	5.54	5.57	5.61	5.65	∞

Source: From *Biometrika Tables for Statisticians,* Vol. I, 3rd ed., edited by E. S. Pearson and H. O. Hartley (Cambridge University Press, 1966.) Reproduced by permission of the Biometrika Trustees.

TABLE 18   Values of $\sin \sqrt{x}$

y (Rad.)	$\sin \sqrt{x}$	y (Rad.)	$\sin \sqrt{x}$	y (Rad.)	$\sin \sqrt{x}$	y (Rad.)	$\sin \sqrt{x}$
.00	.00000	**.40**	.38942	**.80**	.71736	**1.20**	.93204
.01	.01000	.41	.39861	.81	.72429	1.21	.93562
.02	.02000	.42	.40776	.82	.73115	1.22	.93910
.03	.03000	.43	.41687	.83	.73793	1.23	.94249
.04	.03999	.44	.42594	.84	.74464	1.24	.94578
.05	.04998	.45	.43497	.85	.75128	1.25	.94898
.06	.05996	.46	.44395	.86	.75784	1.26	.95209
.07	.06994	.47	.45289	.87	.76433	1.27	.95510
.08	.07991	.48	.46178	.88	.77074	1.28	.95802
.09	.08988	.49	.47063	.89	.77707	1.29	.96084
.10	.09983	**.50**	.47943	**.90**	.78333	**1.30**	.96356
.11	.10978	.51	.48818	.91	.78950	1.31	.96618
.12	.11971	.52	.49688	.92	.79560	1.32	.96872
.13	.12963	.53	.50553	.93	.80162	1.33	.97115
.14	.13954	.54	.51414	.94	.80756	1.34	.97348
.15	.14944	.55	.52269	.95	.81342	1.35	.97572
.16	.15932	.56	.53119	.96	.81919	1.36	.97786
.17	.16918	.57	.53963	.97	.82489	1.37	.97991
.18	.17903	.58	.54802	.98	.83050	1.38	.98185
.19	.18886	.59	.55636	.99	.83603	1.39	.98370
.20	.19867	**.60**	.56464	**1.00**	.84147	**1.40**	.98545
.21	.20846	.61	.57287	1.01	.84683	1.41	.98710
.22	.21823	.62	.58104	1.02	.85211	1.42	.98865
.23	.22798	.63	.58914	1.03	.85730	1.43	.99010
.24	.23770	.64	.59720	1.04	.86240	1.44	.99146
.25	.24740	.65	.60519	1.05	.86742	1.45	.99271
.26	.25708	.66	.61312	1.06	.87236	1.46	.99387
.27	.26673	.67	.62099	1.07	.87720	1.47	.99492
.28	.27636	.68	.62879	1.08	.88196	1.48	.99588
.29	.28595	.69	.63654	1.09	.88663	1.49	.99674
.30	.29552	**.70**	.64422	**1.10**	.89121	**1.50**	.99749
.31	.30506	.71	.65183	1.11	.89570	1.51	.99815
.32	.31457	.72	.65938	1.12	.90010	1.52	.99871
.33	.32404	.73	.66687	1.13	.90441	1.53	.99917
.34	.33349	.74	.67429	1.14	.90863	1.54	.99953
.35	.34290	.75	.68164	1.15	.91276	1.55	.99978
.36	.35227	.76	.68892	1.16	.91680	1.56	.99994
.37	.36162	.77	.69614	1.17	.92075	1.57	1.00000
.38	.37092	.78	.70328	1.18	.92461		
.39	.38019	.79	.71035	1.19	.92837		
.40	.38942	**.80**	.71736	**1.20**	.93204		

Source: Reproduced from Table XIII.4 in *Handbook of Tables for Probability and Statistics,* 2nd ed. Edited by William H. Beyer (Cleveland: The Chemical Rubber Company, 1968). © Copyright The Chemical Rubber Co., CRC Press, Inc.

TABLE 19   Factors Used When Constructing Control Charts

| Number of Observations in Sample, n | Chart for Averages | | | Chart for Standard Deviations | | | | | | Chart for Ranges | | | | | | |
| | Factors for Control Limits | | | Factors for Central Line | | Factors for Control Limits | | | | Factors for Central Line | | | Factors for Control Limits | | | |
	A	A₁	A₂	c₂	1/c₂	B₁	B₂	B₃	B₄	d₂	1/d₂	d₃	D₁	D₂	D₃	D₄
2	2.121	3.760	1.880	0.5642	1.7725	0	1.843	0	3.267	1.128	0.8865	0.853	0	3.686	0	3.276
3	1.732	2.394	1.023	0.7236	1.3820	0	1.858	0	2.568	1.693	0.5907	0.888	0	4.358	0	2.575
4	1.501	1.880	0.729	0.7979	1.2533	0	1.808	0	2.266	2.059	0.4857	0.880	0	4.698	0	2.282
5	1.342	1.596	0.577	0.8407	1.1894	0	1.756	0	2.089	2.326	0.4299	0.864	0	4.918	0	2.115
6	1.225	1.410	0.483	0.8686	1.1512	0.026	1.711	0.030	1.970	2.534	0.3946	0.848	0	5.078	0	2.004
7	1.134	1.277	0.419	0.8882	1.1259	0.105	1.672	0.118	1.882	2.704	0.3698	0.833	0.205	5.203	0.076	1.924
8	1.061	1.175	0.373	0.9027	1.1078	0.167	1.638	0.185	1.815	2.847	0.3512	0.820	0.387	5.307	0.136	1.864
9	1.000	1.094	0.337	0.9139	1.0942	0.219	1.609	0.239	1.761	2.970	0.3367	0.808	0.546	5.394	0.184	1.816
10	0.949	1.028	0.308	0.9227	1.0837	0.262	1.584	0.284	1.716	3.078	0.3249	0.797	0.687	5.469	0.223	1.777
11	0.905	0.973	0.285	0.9300	1.0753	0.299	1.561	0.321	1.679	3.173	0.3152	0.787	0.812	5.534	0.256	1.744
12	0.866	0.925	0.266	0.9359	1.0684	0.331	1.541	0.354	1.646	3.258	0.3069	0.778	0.924	5.592	0.284	1.719
13	0.832	0.884	0.249	0.9410	1.0627	0.359	1.523	0.382	1.618	3.336	0.2998	0.770	1.026	5.646	0.308	1.692
14	0.802	0.848	0.235	0.9453	1.0579	0.384	1.507	0.406	1.594	3.407	0.2935	0.762	1.121	5.693	0.329	1.671
15	0.775	0.816	0.223	0.9490	1.0537	0.406	1.492	0.428	1.572	3.472	0.2880	0.755	1.207	5.737	0.348	1.652
16	0.750	0.788	0.212	0.9523	1.0501	0.427	1.478	0.448	1.552	3.532	0.2831	0.749	1.285	5.779	0.364	1.636
17	0.728	0.762	0.203	0.9551	1.0470	0.445	1.465	0.466	1.534	3.588	0.2787	0.743	1.359	5.817	0.379	1.621
18	0.707	0.738	0.194	0.9576	1.0442	0.461	1.454	0.482	1.518	3.640	0.2747	0.738	1.426	5.854	0.392	1.608
19	0.688	0.717	0.187	0.9599	1.0418	0.477	1.443	0.497	1.503	3.689	0.2711	0.733	1.490	5.888	0.404	1.596
20	0.671	0.697	0.180	0.9619	1.0396	0.491	1.433	0.510	1.490	3.735	0.2677	0.729	1.548	5.922	0.414	1.586
21	0.655	0.679	0.173	0.9638	1.0376	0.504	1.424	0.523	1.477	3.778	0.2647	0.724	1.606	5.950	0.425	1.575
22	0.640	0.662	0.167	0.9655	1.0358	0.516	1.415	0.534	1.466	3.819	0.2618	0.720	1.659	5.979	0.434	1.566
23	0.626	0.647	0.162	0.9670	1.0342	0.527	1.407	0.545	1.455	3.858	0.2592	0.716	1.710	6.006	0.443	1.557
24	0.612	0.632	0.157	0.9684	1.0327	0.538	1.399	0.555	1.445	3.895	0.2567	0.712	1.759	6.031	0.452	1.548
25	0.600	0.619	0.153	0.9696	1.0313	0.548	1.392	0.565	1.435	3.931	0.2544	0.709	1.804	6.058	0.459	1.541
Over 25	$\dfrac{3}{\sqrt{n}}$	$\dfrac{3}{\sqrt{n}}$	—	—	—	*	†	*	†	—	—	—	—	—	—	—

Source: Reproduced by permission from *ASTM Manual on Quality Control of Materials*, American Society for Testing Materials, Philadelphia, Pa., 1951.

*1 − 3/$\sqrt{2n}$.
†1 + 3/$\sqrt{2n}$.

TABLE 20   Distribution of the Total Number of Runs r in Samples of Size (n_1, n_2); $P(r \leq r_0)$

(n_1, n_2)	2	3	4	5	6	7	8	9	10
(2,3)	.200	.500	.900	1.000					
(2,4)	.133	.400	.800	1.000					
(2,5)	.095	.333	.714	1.000					
(2,6)	.071	.286	.643	1.000					
(2,7)	.056	.250	.583	1.000					
(2,8)	.044	.222	.533	1.000					
(2,9)	.036	.200	.491	1.000					
(2,10)	.030	.182	.455	1.000					
(3,3)	.100	.300	.700	.900	1.000				
(3,4)	.057	.200	.543	.800	.971	1.000			
(3,5)	.036	.143	.429	.714	.929	1.000			
(3,6)	.024	.107	.345	.643	.881	1.000			
(3,7)	.017	.083	.283	.583	.833	1.000			
(3,8)	.012	.067	.236	.533	.788	1.000			
(3,9)	.009	.055	.200	.491	.745	1.000			
(3,10)	.007	.045	.171	.455	.706	1.000			
(4,4)	.029	.114	.371	.629	.886	.971	1.000		
(4,5)	.016	.071	.262	.500	.786	.929	.992	1.000	
(4,6)	.010	.048	.190	.405	.690	.881	.976	1.000	
(4,7)	.006	.033	.142	.333	.606	.833	.954	1.000	
(4,8)	.004	.024	.109	.279	.533	.788	.929	1.000	
(4,9)	.003	.018	.085	.236	.471	.745	.902	1.000	
(4,10)	.002	.014	.068	.203	.419	.706	.874	1.000	
(5,5)	.008	.040	.167	.357	.643	.833	.960	.992	1.000
(5,6)	.004	.024	.110	.262	.522	.738	.911	.976	.998
(5,7)	.003	°015	.076	.197	.424	.652	.854	.955	.992
(5,8)	.002	.010	.054	.152	.347	.576	.793	.929	.984
(5,9)	.001	.007	.039	.119	.287	.510	.734	.902	.972
(5,10)	.001	.005	.029	.095	.239	.455	.678	.874	.958
(6,6)	.002	.013	.067	.175	.392	.608	.825	.933	.987
(6,7)	.001	.008	.043	.121	.296	.500	.733	.879	.966
(6,8)	.001	.005	.028	.086	.226	.413	.646	.821	.937
(6,9)	.000	.003	.019	.063	.175	.343	.566	.762	.902
(6,10)	.000	.002	.013	.047	.137	.288	.497	.706	.864
(7,7)	.001	.004	.025	.078	.209	.383	.617	.791	.922
(7,8)	.000	.002	.015	.051	.149	.296	.514	.704	.867
(7,9)	.000	.001	.010	.035	.108	.231	.427	.622	.806
(7,10)	.000	.001	.006	.024	.080	.182	.355	.549	.743
(8,8)	.000	.001	.009	.032	.100	.214	.405	.595	.786
(8,9)	.000	.001	.005	.020	.069	.157	.319	.500	.702
(8,10)	.000	.000	.003	.013	.048	.117	.251	.419	.621
(9,9)	.000	.000	.003	.012	.044	.109	.238	.399	.601
(9,10)	.000	.000	.002	.008	.029	.077	.179	.319	.510
(10,10)	.000	.000	.001	.004	.019	.051	.128	.242	.414

(*continues*)

TABLE 20   (*Concluded*)

					a					
(n_1, n_2)	11	12	13	14	15	16	17	18	19	20
(2,3)										
(2,4)										
(2,5)										
(2,6)										
(2,7)										
(2,8)										
(2,9)										
(2,10)										
(3,3)										
(3,4)										
(3,5)										
(3,6)										
(3,7)										
(3,8)										
(3,9)										
(3,10)										
(4,4)										
(4,5)										
(4,6)										
(4,7)										
(4,8)										
(4,9)										
(4,10)										
(5,5)										
(5,6)	1.000									
(5,7)	1.000									
(5,8)	1.000									
(5,9)	1.000									
(5,10)	1.000									
(6,6)	.998	1.000								
(6,7)	.992	.999	1.000							
(6,8)	.984	.998	1.000							
(6,9)	.972	.994	1.000							
(6,10)	.958	.990	1.000							
(7,7)	.975	.996	.999	1.000						
(7,8)	.949	.988	.998	1.000	1.000					
(7,9)	.916	.975	.994	.999	1.000					
(7,10)	.879	.957	.990	.998	1.000					
(8,8)	.900	.968	.991	.999	1.000	1.000				
(8,9)	.843	.939	.980	.996	.999	1.000	1.000			
(8,10)	.782	.903	.964	.990	.998	1.000	1.000			
(9,9)	.762	.891	.956	.988	.997	1.000	1.000	1.000		
(9,10)	.681	.834	.923	.974	.992	.999	1.000	1.000	1.000	
(10,10)	.586	.758	.872	.949	.981	.996	.999	1.000	1.000	1.000

Source: From "Tables for Testing Randomness of Grouping in a Sequence of Alternatives," C. Eisenhart and F. Swed, *Annals of Mathematical Statistics,* Volume 14 (1943). Reproduced with the kind permission of the Editor, *Annals of Mathematical Statistics.*

TABLE 21 — Sample Size Code Letters: MIL–STD–105D

Lot or Batch Size	Special Inspection Levels				General Inspection Levels		
	S–1	S–2	S–3	S–4	I	II	III
2–8	A	A	A	A	A	A	B
9–15	A	A	A	A	A	B	C
16–25	A	A	B	B	B	C	D
26–50	A	B	B	C	C	D	E
51–90	B	B	C	C	C	D	E
91–150	B	B	C	D	D	F	G
151–280	B	C	D	E	E	G	H
281–500	B	C	D	E	F	H	J
501–1,200	C	C	E	F	G	J	K
1,201–3,200	C	D	E	G	H	K	L
3,201–10,000	C	D	F	G	J	L	M
10,001–35,000	C	D	F	H	K	M	N
35,001–150,000	D	E	G	J	L	N	P
150,001–500,000	D	E	G	J	M	P	Q
500,001 and over	D	E	H	K	N	Q	R

TABLE 22 — A Portion of the Master Table for Normal Inspection (Single Sampling): MIL–STD–105D

Acceptable Quality Levels (Normal Inspection) (Percent). Each entry is given as "Ac Re".

Sample Size Code Letter	Sample Size	0.010	0.015	0.025	0.040	0.065	0.10	0.15	0.25	0.40	0.65	1.0	1.5	2.5	4.0	6.5	10	15	25	40	65
A	2	↓	↓	↓	↓	↓	↓	↓	↓	↓	↓	↓	↓	↓	↓	↓	↓	0 1	1 2	2 3	3 4
B	3	↓	↓	↓	↓	↓	↓	↓	↓	↓	↓	↓	↓	↓	↓	↓	0 1	1 2	2 3	3 4	5 6
C	5	↓	↓	↓	↓	↓	↓	↓	↓	↓	↓	↓	↓	↓	↓	0 1	1 2	2 3	3 4	5 6	7 8
D	8	↓	↓	↓	↓	↓	↓	↓	↓	↓	↓	↓	↓	↓	0 1	1 2	2 3	3 4	5 6	7 8	10 11
E	13	↓	↓	↓	↓	↓	↓	↓	↓	↓	↓	↓	↓	0 1	1 2	2 3	3 4	5 6	7 8	10 11	14 15
F	20	↓	↓	↓	↓	↓	↓	↓	↓	↓	↓	↓	0 1	1 2	2 3	3 4	5 6	7 8	10 11	14 15	21 22
G	32	↓	↓	↓	↓	↓	↓	↓	↓	↓	↓	0 1	1 2	2 3	3 4	5 6	7 8	10 11	14 15	21 22	↑
H	50	↓	↓	↓	↓	↓	↓	↓	↓	↓	0 1	1 2	2 3	3 4	5 6	7 8	10 11	14 15	21 22	↑	↑
J	80	↓	↓	↓	↓	↓	↓	↓	↓	0 1	1 2	2 3	3 4	5 6	7 8	10 11	14 15	21 22	↑	↑	↑
K	125	↓	↓	↓	↓	↓	↓	↓	0 1	1 2	2 3	3 4	5 6	7 8	10 11	14 15	21 22	↑	↑	↑	↑
L	200	↓	↓	↓	↓	↓	↓	0 1	1 2	2 3	3 4	5 6	7 8	10 11	14 15	21 22	↑	↑	↑	↑	↑
M	315	↓	↓	↓	↓	↓	0 1	1 2	2 3	3 4	5 6	7 8	10 11	14 15	21 22	↑	↑	↑	↑	↑	↑
N	500	↓	↓	↓	↓	0 1	1 2	2 3	3 4	5 6	7 8	10 11	14 15	21 22	↑	↑	↑	↑	↑	↑	↑
P	800	↓	↓	↓	0 1	1 2	2 3	3 4	5 6	7 8	10 11	14 15	21 22	↑	↑	↑	↑	↑	↑	↑	↑
Q	1,250	↓	↓	0 1	1 2	2 3	3 4	5 6	7 8	10 11	14 15	21 22	↑	↑	↑	↑	↑	↑	↑	↑	↑
R	2,000	↓	0 1	1 2	2 3	3 4	5 6	7 8	10 11	14 15	21 22	↑	↑	↑	↑	↑	↑	↑	↑	↑	↑

Note: ↓ = Use first sampling plan below arrow. If sample size equals or exceeds lot or batch size, do 100% inspection.

↑ = Use first sampling plan above arrow.

Ac = acceptance number; Re = rejection number.

ANSWERS TO SELECTED EXERCISES

CHAPTER 2

2.2 (a) 8–10 classes   (c) 43/50   (d) 33/50
2.4 (b) 25/60
2.16 (b) 3.1
2.22 (a) 2   (b) 1   (c) 2
2.24 (a) 5.8   (b) 5.5   (c) 2.573
2.26 (a) 2   (b) 2   (c) 1.581
2.28 0 to 27.7
2.30 (a) .68   (b) .95   (c) ≈ 0.00
2.32 (a) Skewed right   (b) Larger
2.34 (a) Skewed   (b) Median
2.36 (a) 1/2   (b) At least 3/4
2.38 (b) $54/58 = .93$ of the measurements lie in the interval 0 to 7.9; yes
2.40 (a) 2.4   (b) $s^2 = 2.8, s = 1.673$
(c) $s \approx 1$
2.42 (a) .625   (b) $s^2 = 4.268, s = 2.066$
2.44 (a) $s \approx 3.5$ (b) $\bar{x} = 6.22, s = 3.497$
(c) 96%
2.46 (a) 32   (b) 8   (c) 7.562

2.48 (a) $R = 5.0, s \approx 1.25$
(b) $\bar{x} = 1.367, s = 1.003$

(c), (d)

k	$\bar{x} \pm ks$	Fraction in Interval
1	.36 to 2.37	.88
2	−.64 to 3.37	.95
3	−1.64 to 4.37	.97

2.50 (a) 1.4, 19.6   (b) 1.4, 19.6
2.52 $\bar{x} = 2.855, s = .329$

k	$\bar{x} \pm ks$	Actual	Empirical Rule
1	2.526 to 3.184	76%	$\approx 68\%$
2	2.197 to 3.513	96%	$\approx 95\%$
3	1.868 to 3.842	100%	$\approx 100\%$

2.54 $m = 6, Q_L = 4, Q_U = 7$
2.56 $m = 5.5, Q_L = 3, Q_U = 7$
2.58 (a) $m = 1.195, Q_L = .96, Q_U = 1.38$

2.60 (a) $m = 197, Q_L = 63, Q_U = 723$ (b) 16.4
(c) Between Q_L and Q_U

2.62 (a) $m = 6.51, Q_L = 6.27, Q_U = 6.71$
(b) 5.98 (c) Between m and Q_U

2.64 (a) 22 is an outlier; $z = 2.92$
(b) Inner fences: -1 and 15; outer fences: -7 and 21; 22 is an outlier.

2.66 (a) $IQR = .42$
(b) Inner fences: .33 and 2.01; outer fences: $-.30$ and 2.64
(c) 2.48 and 2.51 are suspect outliers.

2.72 $\bar{x} = 3, s^2 = 6.8, s = 2.608$

2.74 (a) 7.75 (b) 59.2, 10.369 vs. 7.75

2.76 (a) $\bar{x} = 8.632, s = 1.747$

(b), (c)

k	$\bar{x} \pm ks$	Fraction in Interval
1	6.885 to 10.379	$19/25 = .76$
2	5.138 to 12.126	$24/25 = .96$
3	3.391 to 13.873	$25/25 = 1.00$

2.78 (a) $s \approx 1.6$ (b) $s = 1.483$

2.80 (a) $\bar{x} = 22.557, s = 12.153$ (b) $s \approx 15.425$
(c) 38, 42, 43

2.82 (a) .025 (b) .84

2.84 (a) At least 75% (b) Approximately .16

2.86 (a)

k	$\mu \pm k\sigma$	Approx. Fraction in Interval
1	(420, 570)	.68
2	(345, 645)	.95
3	(270, 720)	1.00

(b) .16

2.88

Price	Percentile
$ 20,000	1st
30,000	4th
70,000	61st
120,000	88th
200,000	97th

CHAPTER 3

3.2 Assignment is valid.

3.4 $P(E_4) = .2, P(E_5) = .1$

3.6 (b) $P(E_i) = 1/38$ (c) $P(A) = 1/19$
(d) 9/19

3.8 No

3.10 No; yes; yes

3.12 (a) .09 (b) .19

3.14 (a) 9 simple events (d) $P(A) = 5/9$
(e) $P(B) = 1/3$

3.16 (a) Assign four men, one to each of the four jobs.
(c) 1/6

3.18 (a) 1 (b) 2/3 (c) 0 (d) 0 (e) No

3.20 (a) .55 (b) .39 (c) .545

3.22 (a) .0004 (b) .9996 (c) .0004

3.24 .0713

3.26 .108

3.28 (a) D (b) C (c) C (d) C (e) D

3.30 (a) $p(4) = .05$

3.32 (a) $(B_1 B_2), (B_1 W_1), (B_1 W_2), (B_2 W_1), (B_2 W_2),$
$(W_1 W_2); P(E_i) = 1/6, i = 1, 2, \ldots, 6$
(c) $p(0) = 1/6, p(1) = 2/3, p(2) = 1/6$

3.34 (a) 3.45, 2.0475, 1.4309 (c) (.59, 6.31); .95
(d) Yes

3.36 (a) 2.15 (b) 1.5275 (d) .95

3.38 (a) 7.9 (b) 2.1749 (c) .96

3.40 2960

3.42 Not binomial; nonindependent trials, p varies from trial to trial.

3.44 (a) 6 (b) 120 (c) 15 (d) 56
(e) 45 (f) 1 (g) 1 (h) 9 (i) 1

3.46

$p = .1$		$p = .5$		$p = .9$	
x	$p(x)$	x	$p(x)$	x	$p(x)$
0	.5314	0	.0156	0	.000001
1	.3543	1	.0938	1	.0001
2	.0984	2	.2344	2	.0012
3	.0146	3	.3125	3	.0146
4	.0012	4	.2344	4	.0984
5	.0001	5	.0938	5	.3543
6	.000001	6	.0156	6	.5314

3.48

a	$\sum_{x=0}^{a} p(x)$
0	.03125
1	.18750
2	.50000
3	.81250
4	.96875

3.50 .469

3.52 (a) .925 (b) .131 (c) .651

3.54 (a) $\mu = 300, \sigma = 14.49$ (b) $\mu = 4, \sigma = 1.99$
(c) $\mu = 250, \sigma = 11.18$
(d) $\mu = 1280, \sigma = 16$

3.58 (a) .834 (b) .317 (c) .965 (d) .035
(e) .403

3.60 (a) .377 (b) .172 (c) .623 (d) .205

3.62 Not binomial; experiment does not result in one of two outcomes.

3.64 (a) 1/2401 (b) 1105/2401 (c) 864/2401

3.66 .884; .572

3.68

x	$p(x)$
0	.2401
1	.4116
2	.2646
3	.0756
4	.0081

3.70 (a) .349 (b) .264 (c) .194

3.72 (a) 3,333,333.33 (b) 1490.71
(c) No; $x = 3,300,000$ lies more than 22 standard deviations below the mean.

3.74 $\mu = 1875; \sigma^2 = 468.75; \sigma = 21.651$

k	$\mu \pm k\sigma$	Tchebysheff's Theorem
2	1832 to 1918	$\geq 3/4$
3	1810 to 1940	$\geq 8/9$

3.76 (a) 200, 11.5470
(b) No; $x = 270$ lies more than 6 standard deviations above the mean.

3.78 (a) $p(0) = .5965, p(1) = .3579, p(2) = .0447,$ $p(3) = .0009$

3.80 .0163

3.82 .0238

3.84 (a) $p(1) = .8, p(2) = .16, p(3) = .032,$ $p(4) = .0064, p(5) = .00128, p(6) = .000256$

3.86 (a) .1; .09; .081
(b) $p(x) = (.9)^{x-1}(.1); x = 1, 2, 3, \ldots$

3.88 (a) $p(x) = (.7)^{x-1}(.3); x = 1, 2, 3, \ldots$
(b) $\mu = 3.33, \sigma = 2.7889$
(c) No; $x = 10$ lies more than 2 standard deviations above the mean.

3.90 (a) .301194 (b) .3614 (c) .8132
(d) .3374

3.94 (a) .423 (b) .632 (c) .271

3.96 .3679; .3679; .1839; .6321

3.98 (a) .073; .092
(b) No; $x = 9$ lies 2.5 standard deviations above μ.

3.100 (a) .085; .125 (b) No; $P(x > 10) = .014.$

3.102 (a) $p(0) = .125, p(1) = .375, p(2) = .375,$ $p(3) = .125$
(c) 1.5; .866

3.104 .03125; .18750

(d) k	$\mu \pm k\sigma$	Probability
1	.63 to 2.37	.75
2	−.23 to 3.23	1.00

3.106 (a) .251 (b) .092 (c) .205

3.108 .608

3.110 (a) .012 (b) .630
(c) Trials may not be independent.

3.112 (a) 805 (b) 22.875
(c) 759.251 to 850.749
(d) No; 249 lies more than 24 standard deviations below the mean.

3.114 (a) .983 (b) .736 (c) .392 (d) .069

3.116 .021

3.118 (a) 6.25 (b) 2.165
(c) Yes; $x = 10$ lies only 1.7 standard deviations above the mean.

3.120 No; $x = 4$ lies more than 2 standard deviations above the mean.

3.124 (a) .009 (b) .01

CHAPTER 4

4.2 (a) .3159 (b) .3159

4.4 (a) .8384 (b) .9544 (c) .9974

4.6 (a) .6626 (b) .5319 (c) .2417

4.8 1.44

4.10 −.52

4.12 .36

4.14 .63

4.16 −1.30

4.18 −1.645

4.20 2.575

4.22 (a) .1596 (b) .1151 (c) .1359

4.24 13.464

4.26 (a) .0618 (b) .7794

4.28 .0505

4.30 (a) .0174 (b) .1112

4.32 (a) $\sigma = 10.53$ (b) .3192

4.34 .0401

4.36 63,550

4.38 .3745

4.40 .2676

4.42 (a) .546 (b) .5468

4.44 .3531

4.46 (a) .9504 (b) .0708
(c) No; 30 lies 1.37 standard deviations above the mean.

4.48 ≈ 0

4.50 (a) .0582 (b) .2514

4.52 (a) .3849 (b) .3159

4.54 (a) .4279 (b) .1628

4.56 (a) .3227 (b) .1586

4.58 (a) .0730 (b) .8623

4.60 .9115

4.62 1.10

4.64 .1596

4.66 .8612

4.68 (a) .1056 (b) .8944 (c) .1056

4.70 .16

4.72 .0344

4.74 (a) .421 (b) .4013

4.76 .8980

4.78 .9929

4.80 (a) No (b) .0179

4.82 Every 383.5 hours

CHAPTER 5

5.4 (b) .5468

5.8 3.5; .442

5.10 (a) 106; 2.4 (b) .0475 (c) .9050

5.12 (b) $\sigma_{\bar{x}} = .1297$ (c) $\sigma_{\bar{x}} = .0917$
(d) $\sigma_{\bar{x}} = .058$

5.14 (b) $\mu = 6.66; \sigma_{\bar{x}} = .265$

5.16

n	1	2	4	9	16	25	100
$\sigma_{\bar{x}}$	1	.707	.500	.333	.250	.200	.100

5.20 Approximately normal; 1500; 35.355

5.22 (a) ≈ 0 (b) .0764 (c) .9236

5.24 $\mu_{3x} = 18; \sigma_{3x} = 15$

5.26 y is normally distributed with $\mu_y = 2.3167$, $\sigma_y^2 = .01$.

5.30 (a) .0174 (b) .5 (c) .9652

5.32 $\sigma_{\hat{p}}$ decreases; yes

5.34 (b) .9556

5.36 (a) $-10; .8062$ (b) $-2; .2$

5.42 (a) .1; .0574 (b) $-.5; .0287$

5.44 (b) .7016

5.48 Within $2\sqrt{\dfrac{p_1 q_1}{400} + \dfrac{p_2 q_2}{400}}$ of $p_1 - p_2$

5.50 (a) .1142
(b) Question the randomness of the samples.

5.52 No; normal

5.54 Approximately normal with $\mu_\ell = 380$, $\sigma_\ell^2 = 1060$

5.58 (a) 64; 12.49 (b) 16; 12.49

5.60 (a) 40 (b) .4 (c) .0062

CHAPTER 6

6.2 (a) .620 (b) .186 (c) .960

6.4 (a) $13.1 \pm .604$ (b) $2.73 \pm .079$
(c) $28.6 \pm .320$

6.6 (a) 34 ± 1.450 (b) 1049 ± 1.457
(c) $66.3 \pm .327$

6.8 (a) 148.702 (b) 13.175 (c) 1474.390

6.10 (a) Decreases by $1/\sqrt{2}$
(b) Decreases by $1/2$

6.12 $7.2\% \pm .776\%$

6.14 (a) $s \approx 1500$ (b) 166.445

6.16 (a) $s \approx 8415$ (b) 933.755

6.18 $11.7 \pm .611$

6.20 5636.987

6.22 .690

6.24 -1.947

6.26 -11 ± 1.051

6.28 $-.7 \pm .332$

6.30 $-1.1 \pm .777$

6.32 -4600 ± 1987.732

6.34 $.877 \pm .031$

6.36 $.054 \pm .020$

6.38 May: .077; December: .073

6.40 All estimates should fall within .04 of the corresponding population percentages.

6.42 $.67 \pm .045$

6.44 (a) $.4 \pm .016$ (b) $.55 \pm .017$
(c) $.2 \pm .018$

6.46 (a) $-.16 \pm .043$ (b) Random samples

6.48 (a) $-.149 \pm .086$ (b) Random samples

6.50 $.022 \pm .025$

6.52 $.167 \pm .091$

6.54 505

6.56 1086

6.58 $n_1 = n_2 = 347$

6.60 with $n = 43$, the bound on error, .15, is quite large

6.62 56

6.64 384

6.66 $29.1 \pm .9555$

6.68 234

6.70 $n_1 = n_2 = 224$

6.72 1083

6.74 $n_1 = n_2 = 376$

6.76 $.1 \pm .025$

6.78   44

6.80   **(a)** $.0625 \pm .0237$ **(b)** 563

6.82   65

6.84 $34 \pm .588$

6.86 $.1 \pm .041$

6.88 39.1 ± 2.846

6.90 $n_1 = n_2 = 92$

CHAPTER 7

7.2 $H_0 : \mu = 2.9;\ H_a : \mu < 2.9$; one-tailed

7.4   **(a)** $H_a : \mu < 84$ **(b)** $H_0 : \mu = 84$ **(c)** .05
     (d) Yes; $z = -5.34$

7.6   **(a)** $H_a : \mu > 4.8$ **(c)** $H_0 : \mu = 4.8$
     (e) Reject H_0 if $z > 2.33$.
     (f) Do not reject H_0; $z = .16$.

7.8   No; $z = -.992$

7.10   **(a)** Poisson

7.12   **(a)** $H_0 : \mu_1 - \mu_2 = 0;\ H_a : \mu_1 - \mu_2 > 0$
     (b) One-tailed   **(c)** $z > 1.28$
     (e) Reject H_0; $z = 2.087$.

7.14   **(b)** $H_0 : \mu_1 - \mu_2 = 0;\ H_a : \mu_1 - \mu_2 \neq 0$
     (c) Reject H_0; $z = 2.087$.

7.16 $\alpha = .20$

7.18   **(a)** Yes; reject H_0, $z = -3.807$.
     (b) Conclusion is the same.

7.20   **(a)** $H_a : \mu_1 - \mu_2 > 0$
     (b) One-tailed; $z > 1.645$ with $\alpha = .05$
     (c) Reject H_0; $z = 4.899$.

7.22   **(a)** $H_0 : p = .3;\ H_a : p < .3$ **(b)** One-tailed
     (c) Do not reject H_0; $z = -1.449$.

7.24   **(a)** $H_0 : p = .4;\ H_a : p \neq .4$ **(b)** Two-tailed
     (c) Reject H_0; $z = -1.680$.

7.26   **(a)** $H_0 : p = .55;\ H_a : p > .55$

     (b) $z = \dfrac{.70 - .55}{\sqrt{\dfrac{.55(.45)}{80}}}$ **(c)** $z > 1.645$

7.28   **(a)** $H_0 : p = .05;\ H_a : p < .05$
     (b) One-tailed
     (d) Do not reject H_0; $z = -1.538$.

7.30   **(a)** $H_0 : p = .6;\ H_a : p < .6$
     (b) Reject H_0; $z = -1.732$ **(c)** $.54 \pm .069$
     (d) 9220

7.32   **(a)** $H_0 : p_1 - p_2 = 0;\ H_a : p_1 - p_2 < 0$
     (b) One-tailed
     (c) Do not reject H_0; $z = -.84$.

7.34   **(a)** $H_0 : p_1 - p_2 = 0;\ H_a : p_1 - p_2 > 0$

     (b) One-tailed   **(c)** Reject H_0; $z = 2.086$.

7.36   **(a)** $H_a : p_1 - p_2 > 0$ **(b)** $H_0 : p_1 - p_2 = 0$
     (c) Reject H_0; $z = 3.509$.   **(d)** .243

7.38   No; $z = .555$

7.40   **(a)** Yes; $z = -2.38$

7.42   **(a)** .0268   **(b)** Reject H_0.

7.44   **(a)** .0718   **(b)** Do not reject H_0.

7.46   Reject H_0 if p-value $< .05$.

7.48   .0035

7.50   **(a)** Reject H_0; $z = 13.097$.
     (b) p-value $< .001$

7.54   **(a)** .0025   **(b)** Reject H_0; $z = -2.811$.

7.56   **(a)** p-value $< .001$ **(b)** Reject H_0; $z = 4.47$.

7.58   No; $z = -1.0$

7.60   Reject H_0; $z = 3.122$.

7.62   **(a)** .0062   **(b)** Reject H_0; $z = -2.5$.

7.64   **(a)** $H_0 : \mu = 1100;\ H_a : \mu < 1100$
     (b) $z < -1.645$ **(c)** Yes; $z = -1.897$

7.66   Reject $H_0 : p_1 - p_2 = 0$; $z = 2.385$. Since we know that $p_1 = p_2$, something must be wrong with the survey method or data analysis.

7.68

μ	β
870	.0793
873	.3446
875	.6103
877	.8274

CHAPTER 8

8.2   **(a)** 1.356   **(b)** 2.485   **(c)** 1.746

8.4 10.975 ± 1.432

8.6 6.15 ± 1.636

8.8   Reject H_0; $t = -2.076$.

8.10   46.529

8.12 36.1 ± 3.239

8.14   **(a)** $H_a : \mu > 19$ **(b)** $H_0 : \mu = 19$
     (c) $t > 2.920$ **(d)** Reject H_0; $t = -2.750$
     (e) p-value $> .10$

8.16   **(a)** $H_a : \mu < 9.8$ **(b)** $H_0 : \mu = 9.8$
     (c) $t < -1.383$ **(d)** Reject H_0; $t = -2.811$.
     (e) $.01 < p$-value $< .025$

8.18   **(a)** $H_a : \mu > 8500$ **(b)** $H_0 : \mu = 8500$
     (c) $t < -2.132$
     (d) Do not reject H_0; $t = .235$.
     (e) p-value $> .10$

8.20   No; $t = -.647$

8.22 32.333 ± 30.220

8.24   **(a)** 22   **(b)** 20   **(c)** 16

8.26 $s^2 = 12.4571$

8.28 -1.6 ± 4.487

8.30 2.4 ± 1.462

8.32   (a) Yes; $t = -3.354$; Reject H_0.
(b) p-value $< .01$

8.34   Approximately 136

8.36   No; do not reject H_0; $z = 1.564$.

8.38   (a) No; $t = -1.033$ (b) p-value $> .20$
(c) $-.24 \pm .432$

8.40 $.3 \pm .286$

8.42   (a) $H_0 : \mu_d = 0$; $H_a : \mu_d > 0$
(b) Do not reject H_0; $t = 1.511$

8.44   (a) No; $t = 1.177$ (b) p-value $> .20$
(c) $.06 \pm .142$

8.46   (a) Yes; $t = 2.821$; reject H_0.
(b) 1.4875 ± 1.247 (a 95% confidence interval)
(d) Yes

8.48   (a) No; $t = .471$ (b) p-value $> .10$
(c) $.118 \pm .645$

8.50   (a) 72   (b) Week 7   (c) Yes

8.52   No; $\chi^2 = 34.24$

8.54   No; $\chi^2 = 11.8776$

8.56 $.00703 < \sigma^2 < .03264$

8.58 $(.227, 2.194)$

8.60 $(1.408, 31.264)$

8.62   (a) No; $F = 1.774$ (b) p-value $> .20$

8.64   (a) No; $F = 2.74$ (b) $.10 < p$-value $< .20$

8.66   (a) No; $F = 2.316$ (b) $.05 < p$-value $< .10$

8.68 $(1.544, 4.003)$

8.70   (a) No; $F = 2.904$ (b) $.050 < \sigma_2^2 < .254$

8.72 $16.486 < \sigma^2 < 52.331$

8.74   Yes; $t = 2.108$; $.025 < p$-value $< .05$

8.76 $7.1 \pm .070$

8.78 -4.9 ± 4.541

8.80   Yes; $F = 3.268$

8.82   No; paired analysis is not appropriate.

8.84   (a) $.02 < p$-value $< .05$
(b) Reject H_0; $t = 2.497$

8.86   (a) $H_a : \mu > 48,000$ (b) $H_0 : \mu = 48,000$
(c) Small   (d) $t > 1.796$
(e) Reject H_0; $t = 2.096$.

8.88 $\chi^2 = 12.6$; do not reject H_0.

8.92   No; $\chi^2 = 7.008$

8.94   No; $t = -1.8$

8.96   (a) $t = -2.657$; $.02 < p$-value $< .05$
(b) -4.542 ± 3.046

8.98   No; population distribution is not normal.

8.100   (a) Do not reject H_0; $F = 2.605$.
(b) $.10 < p$-value $< .20$

8.102   No; $t = -1.950$; do not reject H_0.

8.104   Approximately 20

8.106   Yes; $t = 3.038$; reject H_0.

8.108 $(24.582, 73.243)$

8.110 $n_1 = n_2 = 32$

CHAPTER 9

9.2   (a)

Source	d.f.	SS	MS	F
Treatments	5	5.2	1.04	3.467
Error	54	16.2	.30	
Total	59	21.4		

(b) $v_1 = 5$, $v_2 = 54$ (c) $F > 2.37$
(d) Yes; $F = 3.467$

9.4

Source	d.f.
Treatments	3
Error	20
Total	23

9.6   (a) 88.0 ± 1.819 (b) 4.1 ± 2.572

9.8   (a) $CM = 103.142857$; Total SS $= 26.8571$
(b) $SST = 14.5071$; $MST = 7.2536$
(c) $SSE = 12.3500$; $MSE = 1.1227$
(f) $F > 3.98$
(g) $F = 6.46$; reject H_0.

9.10   (a) $2.8 \pm .85$ (b) 1.55 ± 1.28

9.12   No; $t = -1.66$

9.14   (a) Yes; $F = 13.03$ (b) -7.5 ± 4.67

9.16   (b) Yes; $F = 8.11$ (c) Yes; $t = 3.025$

9.20

Source	d.f.	SS	MS	F
Treatments	2	11.4	5.70	4.01
Blocks	5	17.1	3.42	2.41
Error	10	14.2	1.42	
Total	17	42.7		

9.22 -2.3 ± 1.533

9.24

Source	d.f.
Treatments	5
Blocks	3
Error	15
Total	23

9.26   Yes; $F = 4.69$

9.28 $.05 < p$-value $< .10$; reject H_0 at $\alpha = .10$ but not $\alpha = .05$

9.30   (a) $CM = 1064.0833$; Total SS $= 148.9167$
(b) $SST = 25.5833$; $MST = 8.5278$

(c) $SSB = 120.6667$; $MSB = 60.3333$

(d) $SSE = 2.6667$; $MSE = .4444$

(f) Yes; $F = 19.19$

(g) Yes; $F = 135.75$

(h) Yes

9.32 **(a)** $CM = 159.414$; Total $SS = 6.496$

(b) $SST = 4.476$; $MST = 2.238$

(c) $SSB = 1.796$; $MSB = .449$

(d) $SSE = .224$; $MSE = .028$

(f) Yes; $F = 79.93$

(g) Yes; $F = 16.04$

(h) Yes

9.34 **(b)** Yes; $F = 22.03$ **(c)** Yes; $F = 6.551$

9.36 **(b)** No   **(c)** $15.1375 \pm .903$

9.42 **(a)** 15   **(b)** 45

(c)

Source	d.f.
A	2
B	4
AB	8
Error	30
Total	44

9.44 **(a)**

Source	d.f.	SS	MS	F
A	2	5.3	2.6500	1.30
B	3	9.1	3.0333	1.49
AB	6	4.8	.8000	.39
Error	12	24.5	2.0417	
Total	23	43.7		

(b) No; $F = .39$

(c) No; $F_A = 1.30$; $F_B = 1.49$

9.46 **(a)** No; $F = 1.4$ **(b)** Yes; $F = 6.51$

(c) Yes; $F = 7.37$

9.48 **(a)**

Source	d.f.	SS	MS
A	2	3.1111	1.5556
B	2	81.4444	40.7222
AB	4	62.2222	15.5556
Error	9	21.0000	2.3333
Total	17	167.7778	

(c) Yes; $F = 6.67$ **(d)** $.005 < p$-value $< .01$

(e) 12.5 ± 2.443 **(f)** 7.5 ± 3.455

9.50 **(b)** Yes; $F = 8.48$ **(c)** $.0001$

(d) 1.533 ± 1.971

9.52 **(b)** Yes

(c) Since the interaction is significant, attention should be focused on means for the individual factor level combinations.

9.56 **(a)** 5.06   **(b)** 3.88   **(c)** 6.20   **(d)** 9.32

9.58 **(a)** $\omega = 6.78$ **(b)** $\bar{x}_4 \; \bar{x}_2 \; \bar{x}_1 \; \bar{x}_5 \; \bar{x}_3 \; \bar{x}_6$

9.60 $\omega = .631$; $\bar{x}_{11} \; \bar{x}_{22} \; \bar{x}_{12} \; \bar{x}_{21}$

9.62 $A_1 B_2 \; A_3 B_2 \; A_2 B_2 \; A_4 B_2$ $(\omega = 2.63)$

9.64 $A_3 B_1 \; A_3 B_2 \; A_2 B_1 \; A_2 B_2 \; A_1 B_1 \; A_1 B_2$ $(\omega = 23.61)$

9.66 **(a)** Yes; $F = 5.20$ **(b)** No; $t = .88$

(c) $-.348 \pm .231$

9.68 **(b)** No; $F = 1.53$ **(c)** 23.6 ± 2.144

(d) $-.425 \pm 3.389$

9.70 **(a)** Yes; $F = 19.44$ $(F_{.05} = 4.76)$

(b) Yes; $F = 40.21$ $(F_{.05} = 5.14)$

(c) $-1.4 \pm .697$

9.72 **(a)** Randomized block

(c)

Source	d.f.	SS	MS	F
Treatments	2	11.610	5.805	5.92
Blocks	5	26.665	5.333	5.44
Error	10	9.810	.981	
Total	17	48.085		

(d) Yes; $F = 5.92$ $(F_{.05} = 4.10)$

9.74 **(a)** Yes; $F = 6.46$ $(F_{.05} = 5.14)$

(b) No; $F = 3.75$ $(F_{.05} = 4.76)$

(c) $-1.2 \pm .65$

9.76 **(a)**

Source	d.f.	SS	MS	F
Treatments	2	.01084	.00542	1.86
Error	12	.03496	.00291	
Total	14	.04580		

(b) No; $F = 1.86$ $(F_{.05} = 3.89)$ **(c)** No

CHAPTER 10

10.2 **(a)** 10.6446   **(b)** 21.6660   **(c)** 22.3621

(d) 5.99147

10.4 **(a)** 4   **(b)** $X^2 > 9.4877$

(c) $H_a : p_i \neq p_j$ for some pair i, j $(i \neq j)$

(d) $X^2 = 8.00$; do not reject H_0.

(e) $.05 < p$-value $< .10$

10.6 Yes; $X^2 = 24.48$ $(\chi^2_{.05} = 7.81)$

10.8 Yes; $X^2 = 173.64$ $(\chi^2_{.05} = 12.59)$

10.10 **(a)** $X^2 = 211.71$; d.f. $= 6$

(b) $X^2 = 8.93$; d.f. $= 2$

10.12 **(a)** 2   **(b)** $X^2 = 3.059$ **(c)** $X^2 > 4.605$

(d) do not reject H_0.   **(e)** p-value $> .10$

10.14 **(a)** Yes; $X^2 = 14.496$; reject H_0

(b) p-value $< .005$

10.16 Yes; $X^2 = 3472.03$

10.18 Do not reject H_0; $z = -1.003$.

10.20 (a) $H_0 : p_1 = p_2$, where p_1 and p_2 are the switching proportions with an without a qualified opinion, respectively.
(b) $H_a : p_1 > p_2$
(c) $\hat{p}_1 < \hat{p}_2$; do not reject H_0.

10.22 (a) $X^2 = 10.597$ (b) $X^2 > 7.779$
(c) reject H_0. (d) $.025 < p$-value $< .05$

10.24 No; $X^2 = 5.491$ ($\chi^2_{.05} = 5.99$)

10.26 (a) Yes; $X^2 = 932.592$ ($\chi^2_{.05} = 15.5073$)
(b) p-value $< .005$

10.28 Yes; $X^2 = 7.193$ ($\chi^2_{.05} = 5.99$)

10.30 (a) Reject H_0; $z = -2.300$

10.32 No; $X^2 = 1.885$ ($\chi^2_{.05} = 5.99$)

10.34 Yes; $X^2 = 12.5$ ($\chi^2_{.10} = 4.61$)

10.36 (a) $X^2 = 10.12$ (b) reject H_0; $\chi^2_{.05} = 9.49$
(c) $.025 < p$-value $< .05$

10.38 Letter 2: $X^2 = .31$; do not reject $H_0 : p_1 = p_2$.
Letter 4: $X^2 = 15.29$; reject $H_0 : p_1 = p_2$.
Letter 5: $X^2 = .47$; do not reject $H_0 : p_1 = p_2$.

10.40 (a) Yes; $X^2 = 10.27$ ($\chi^2_{.05} = 3.84$)
(b) Yes; $z = 3.205$ ($z_{.05} = 1.645$)

CHAPTER 11

11.2 y intercept $= 1$; slope $= -2$

11.4 same line, but with negative slope; lines are perpendicular.

11.6 $y = x - 3$

11.8 (a) $\hat{y} = 3.0 + 1.2x$

11.10 (a) $\hat{y} = 6 - .557x$

11.12 (b) $\hat{y} = -2.00 + 3.15x$ (d) 16.91

11.16 $SSE = 1.6$; $s^2 = .5333$

11.18 $SSE = .1429$; $s^2 = .0357$

11.20 $SSE = 48.61$; $s^2 = 8.10$

11.22 $SSE = 545.10$; $s^2 = 68.14$

11.24 $1.2 \pm .543$

11.26 $.5 \pm .192$

11.28 $-.557 \pm .096$

11.30 $-1.5 \pm .266$

11.32 3.15 ± 1.631

11.34 No; $t = -2.21$

11.36 (a) $\hat{y} = 41.3 + .69x$ (c) $s^2 = 9.445$

11.38 (b) $z = 3.44$; reject $H_0 : p_1 = p_2$.

11.40 $4.2 \pm .941$

11.42 $4.886 \pm .219$

11.44 20.065 ± 2.825

11.46 (a) 27.406 ± 3.313

(b) $76,017.87 \pm 1341.879$ (c) 39.24

11.48 4.2 ± 1.882

11.50 $4.886 \pm .459$

11.52 246.306 ± 132.440

11.54 54.0 ± 12.806

11.58 (a) $+1$ (b) -1

11.60 (a) $\hat{y} = 8.267 - 1.314x$ (c) $-.982$
(d) 96.5%

11.62 (a) $r = -.9864$ (b) $r^2 = .973$

11.64 $r^2 = .79$

11.66 (a) $\hat{y} = 198.925 + .0385x$ (c) $r = .3297$
(d) No, $t = .924$

11.68 (a) $r = .6578$ (b) Yes; $t = 3.025$
(c) $r^2 = .4328$

11.72 y intercept $= -5/3$; slope $= 2/3$

11.74 (a) $\hat{y} = 1 + .7x$

11.76 $s^2 = .3667$

11.78 Yes; $t = 3.656$

11.80 All points fall on a straight line.

11.82 $.7 \pm .451$

11.84 $1.7 \pm .780$

11.86 3.75 ± 1.850

11.88 $.851$

11.90 (a) $\hat{y} = -.333 + 1.4x$ (c) 1.2410

11.92 (a) $\hat{y} = .067 + .517x$ (b) $2.133 \pm .282$

11.94 (a) $\hat{y} = .9552 + .0462x$ (c) $.00274$
(d) Yes; $t = 10.55$ (e) $.0462 \pm .0079$
(f) $.0462$ pound

11.96 (a) $\hat{y} = .1067 + .00164x$ (c) $.0003239$
(d) No; $t = 1.092$ (e) $.00164 \pm .00273$
(f) $.00164$ pound

11.98 (a) $\hat{y} = 9.590 + .653x$ (b) 21.346 ± 2.291

11.100 No; $t = 1.584$

11.102 (a) $\hat{y} = 3 + .475x$ (c) 5.025

11.104 8.7 ± 1.615

11.106 Yes; $t = 4.91$

11.108 (a) $\hat{y} = .1581 + .0908x$ (c) $r^2 = .9595$
(d) Yes; $t = 12.872$ (e) $.0908 \pm .0167$

CHAPTER 12

12.2 (a) y intercept (b) y intercept

12.4 (b) Shifts the parabola to the right along the x axis.
(c) Shifts the parabola to the left along the x axis by the same amount.

12.8 (b) Parallel lines

12.10 (b) Changes the slopes
(c) Allows the interaction

12.12 All three independent variables contribute information; $t_1 = 3.07, t_2 = 4.185,$ $t_3 = 2.412.$

12.14 $1.29 \pm .754$

12.16 (a) $\hat{y} = 1.21 + 7.60x - .94x^2$

12.18 (a) $\beta_2 = 0$ (b) Yes; $t = -2.848$

12.20 (a) Negative
(b) SSE $= 1.05985748; s^2 = .35328583$ (c) 3
(d) Yes; $F = 332.53$ (e) p-value $= .0003$
(f) Yes; $t = -4.49$ (g) p-value $= .0206$
(h) $\hat{y} = -44.192 + 16.334x - .820x^2$
(i) $R^2 = .9955$ (j) $\hat{y} = 27.3424$

12.22 (a) 2.306 (b) 5.32

12.24 (a) SSE $= .05368; s^2 = .00596$
(b) $\hat{y} = .4381 + .0053x_1 - .0302x_2 +$
$0007x_1x_2 - .00038x_1^2 + .0004x_2^2$
(c) $R^2 = .9888$ (d) Yes; $F = 159.23$
(e) p-value $= .0001$ (f) No
(g) $\hat{y} = .9618$

12.26 x_2, x_7, x_9

12.28 (a) $\hat{y} = 220 + .06x_1 + .007x_2 -$
$3.98x_3 - 1.73x_4$
(b) Yes; $F = 6.345$ (c) p-value $< .01$
(d) x_1, x_3

12.30 (a) $\hat{y} = 466 + .02x_1 - .009x_2 -$
$1.90x_3 - 2.88x_4$
(b) Yes; $F = 5.389$ (c) p-value $< .01$
(d) x_3

12.32 SSE $= 152.17748; s^2 = 8.4543$ (b) 18
(c) Yes; $F = 31.85$ (d) p-value $< .005$
(e) SS$_y = 1498.625; R^2 = .898$
(f) $\hat{y} = 41.262$

12.34 (b) $\hat{y} = .2745 + .0273x + .00635x^2$
(d) SSE $= .00848; s^2 = .00141$ (e) 6
(f) Yes; $t = 2.965$ (g) p-value $= .0251$
(h) $R^2 = .9836$ (i) Increases v_2

12.38 (b) 9 (d) $R^2 = .98397$
(f) $\hat{y} = 4.10 + 1.04x_1 + 3.53x_2 +$
$4.76x_3 - .43x_1x_2 - .08x_1x_3$
(g) Yes; $t = -2.613$ (h) $-.43 \pm .372$
(i) No; $t = -.486$

12.40 $E(y) = \beta_0 + \beta_1x + \beta_2x^2$

12.42 $E(y) = \beta_0 + \beta_1x_1 + \beta_2x_2$, where
$$x_1 = \begin{cases} 1, & \text{if level 2} \\ 0, & \text{otherwise} \end{cases}$$
$$x_2 = \begin{cases} 1, & \text{if level 3} \\ 0, & \text{otherwise} \end{cases}$$

12.44 $E(y) = \beta_0 + \beta_1x_1 + \beta_2x_2 + \beta_3x_3 + \beta_4x_1^2 +$
$\beta_5x_2^2 + \beta_6x_3^2 + \beta_7x_1x_2 + \beta_8x_1x_3 + \beta_9x_2x_3$

12.46 $E(y) = \beta_0 + \beta_1x_1 + \beta_2x_2 + \beta_3x_3 +$
$\beta_4x_1x_3 + \beta_5x_2x_3$, where
$$x_1 = \begin{cases} 1, & \text{if level 2, factor } A \\ 0, & \text{otherwise} \end{cases}$$
$$x_2 = \begin{cases} 1, & \text{if level 3, factor } A \\ 0, & \text{otherwise} \end{cases}$$
$$x_3 = \begin{cases} 1, & \text{if level 2, factor } B \\ 0, & \text{otherwise} \end{cases}$$

CHAPTER 13

13.2 $I_{72} = 83.7, I_{73} = 81.7; I_{74} = 86.7; I_{75} = 100;$
$I_{76} = 84.2; I_{77} = 69.3; I_{78} = 57.9; I_{79} = 66.2;$
$I_{80} = 102.7; I_{81} = 146.9; I_{82} = 217.9; I_{83} = 274.1$

13.4 $I_{80} = 214.86; I_{81} = 196.01; I_{82} = 189.86$

13.6 $I_{80} = 226.01; I_{81} = 201.21; I_{82} = 194.82$

13.8 (a) $I_{85} = 134.7; I_{86} = 194.9$
(b) $I_{85} = 126.72; I_{86} = 184.75$
(c) $I_{85} = 129.29; I_{86} = 186.39$

13.18 (b) $E(y_t) = \beta_0 + \beta_1t + \beta_2x_1 + \beta_3x_2 + \beta_4x_3$,
with $x_i = 1$ if quarter i, 0 if not, for $i = 1, 2, 3$
(c) From (b), $y_t = E(y_t) + z_t$, where
$z_t = \phi z_{t-1} + \varepsilon_t$
(d) $\hat{y}_t = 70.3000 + 1.7045t - 14.6078x_1 -$
$6.9717x_2 - 7.4449x_3 + .5586\hat{z}_{t-1}$

13.20 $\hat{y}_{1985} = 7.4090$

13.22 (c) $\hat{y}_t = 10.846 - .1384t + .7726\hat{z}_{t-1}$

13.24 $I_{73} = 73.0; I_{74} = 82.0; I_{75} = 100.0; I_{76} = 118.0;$
$I_{77} = 143.1; I_{78} = 131.8; I_{79} = 160.5;$
$I_{80} = 199.7; I_{81} = 237.9; I_{82} = 286.2;$
$I_{83} = 331.8; I_{84} = 326.7$

13.26 $I_{73} = 72.3; I_{74} = 81.5; I_{75} = 100.0;$
$I_{76} = 118.4; I_{77} = 144.0; I_{78} = 128.9;$
$I_{79} = 157.4; I_{80} = 195.4; I_{81} = 233.8;$
$I_{82} = 283.0; I_{83} = 328.2; I_{84} = 321.0$

13.28 (a) 105.01 (b) 101.56 (c) 111.86

13.30 (a) 100.00 (b) 107.23 (c) 102.23
(d) 106.89 (e) 98.32

13.36 (a) $\hat{y}_{88} = 4.0413$ (b) $4.0413 \pm .1221$

13.38 (b) $\hat{y}_t = 1.7086 - .01163t + \hat{z}_t$, with $\hat{z}_t = .1680\hat{z}_{t-1}$
(d) MSE $= .00902$ (e) $1.529 \pm .186$

CHAPTER 14

14.12 8410 ± 216.879

14.16 $525,408 \pm 19,170.662$

14.18 6751 ± 400.415

14.20 $6.633 \pm .523$

14.22 408.143 ± 3.743

14.24 $.298 \pm .0443$

14.26 $13,208.633 \pm 549.2741$

14.28 $.4073 \pm .0627$

14.30 $421,543 \pm 44,997.546$

14.32 $2.472 \pm .02148$

14.34 $6.129 \pm .5472$

14.36 $.5048 \pm .0599$

14.38 $45,097,986.75 \pm 8,120,499.265$

14.42 $12.376 \pm .189$

14.44 $.4589 \pm .0554$

14.46 $11,914,614 \pm 344,056.0727$

14.48 $2.0167 \pm .2213$

14.50 $.303 \pm .0513$

14.52 $.4 \pm .1142$

CHAPTER 15

15.2 (b) $\alpha = .004, .014, .044, .108$

15.4 (b) $\alpha = .008, .036, .118$

15.6 (a) No (b) p-value $= .054$

15.8 (a) $H_0 : p = .5$ (b) $H_a : p \neq .5$
(c) Reject H_0; $x = 8$.
(d) p-value $= .0390625$

15.10 (a) $H_0 : p = .5$; $H_a : p > .5$
(b) $z = (x - .5n)/\sqrt{.25n} = .169$; reject H_0
if $z > 1.645$.
(c) Do not reject H_0. (d) p-value $= .4325$

15.12 No; do not reject H_0; $x = 8$.

15.14 Yes; reject H_0; $x = 8$.

15.16 (a) $x \leq 1$ or $x \geq 6$ with $\alpha = .125$
(b) $\beta = .149688$ (c) Do not reject H_0.

15.18 (a) U_A (b) $U \leq 13$ (c) $\alpha = .0906$

15.20 (a) U_B (b) $U \leq 4$ (c) $\alpha = .0952$

15.22 Do not reject H_0; $z = -1.59$

15.24 No; $U = 30$ (rejection region: $U \leq 24$
with $\alpha = .0524$).

15.26 (a) No; $U = 13.5$ (rejection region: $U \leq 11$
with $\alpha = .0992$).

15.28 No; $U = 16.5$ (rejection region: $U \leq 13$
with $\alpha = .0938$).

15.30 (a) H_0: the two population distributions are
identical; H_a: population distribution A is
shifted to the right of distribution B.
(b) T^- (c) $T \leq 152$
(d) $T^- = 216$; do not reject H_0.

15.32 $z = -.34$; do not reject H_0.

15.34 (a) No; $T^+ = 6.5$ (reject H_0 if $T \leq 4$
with $\alpha = .05$).

15.36 (a) No; $T^- = 5$ (reject H_0 if $T \leq 4$
with $\alpha = .05$).

15.38 (a) No; $T^- = 7$ (reject H_0 if $T \leq 2$
with $\alpha = .05$).
(b) p-value $> .05$

15.40 Yes; $H = 13.90$ ($\chi^2_{.05} = 7.81$).

15.42 (a) Reject H_0; $H = 6.101$.
(b) $.025 < p$-value $< .05$
(c) p-value $= .0251$

15.44 (a) Reject H_0; $F_r = 7.58$ ($\chi^2_{.05} = 5.99$).
(b) $.01 < p$-value $< .025$ (d) $F = 10.83$
(e) p-value $< .005$

15.46 (a) Yes; $F_r = 19.57$ ($\chi^2_{.05} = 9.49$).
(b) p-value $< .005$ (c) Yes

15.48 (a) Randomized block
(b) Yes; $F_r = 8.33$ ($\chi^2_{.05} = 5.99$).

15.50 (a) $r_s \leq -.497$ (b) $r_s \leq -.703$

15.52 (a) $r_s = -1$
(b) Yes; reject H_0 for $|r_s| \geq .886$.

15.54 Yes; $r_s = .903$ (reject H_0 if $r_s > .564$
with $\alpha = .05$)

15.56 (a) $r_s = -.841$
(b) Yes; reject H_0 if $|r_s| > .648$.

15.58 Do not reject H_0; $T = 10.5$; rejection region:
$\{T \leq 6\}$ for $\alpha = .05$.

15.60 (a) $U_B = 3$; reject H_0; rejection region:
$U \leq 3$ for $\alpha = .0556$.

15.62 Yes; $H = 11.18$ ($\chi^2_{10} = 4.605$).

15.64 Yes; $r_s = .9118$.

15.66 Yes; $r_s = -.845$; reject H_0 if $r_s < -.564$.

CHAPTER 16

16.2 (a) $\hat{\sigma} = 7.395$
(b) LCL $= 145.976$; UCL $= 165.824$

16.4 UCL $= 36.378$; LCL $= 0$

16.6 UCL $= 13,588.875$; LCL $= 0$

16.8 UCL $= .0270$; LCL $= .0242$; $\bar{x} = .0256$

16.10 (a) UCL $= 7.516$; LCL $= 6.964$
(b) UCL $= .69525$; LCL $= 0$

16.12 (a) LCL $= 0$; UCL $= .090$
(b) Centerline at $.035$; LCL and UCL as in (a).

16.14 (a) LCL $= 0$; UCL $= 3.210$
(b) Centerline at $\bar{c} = .7$.

16.16 Centerline at $\hat{p} = .021$; UCL $= .043$; LCL $= 0$.

16.18 Centerline at $\bar{c} = 4.9$; UCL $= 11.54$; LCL $= 0$.

16.20 (a) $.076$ (b) $.043$ (c) $.117$ (d) $.004$

16.22 (a) 5 (b) 3 (c) 6 (d) 8

16.24 $\mu_r = 28.27$; $\sigma_r = 3.643$

16.26 Do not reject H_0; $z = 0$; no evidence of nonrandomness.

16.28 Do not reject H_0; $r = 5$ with $\alpha = .143$.

16.30 **(a)** .590   **(b)** .168   **(c)** .031   **(d)** 1   **(e)** 0

16.32 **(a)** .349   **(b)** .028   **(c)** .001   **(d)** 1   **(e)** 0

16.34 For a given value of n and p, $P(\text{accept})$ increases as a increases; for a given value of a and p, $P(\text{accept})$ decreases as n increases.

16.36 .004

16.38 $n = 80$; $a = 0$

16.44 **(a)** .7495   **(b)** 2505

16.46 $\approx .78$, using the Poisson approximation

16.48 **(a)** LCL $= 0$; UCL $= .081$ **(b)** .1894

16.50 **(a)** $(25, 5)$ **(b)** $(25, 5)$

16.52 $a = 1$

16.54 $n = 200$; $a = 0$

CHAPTER 17

17.2 **(a)** Choose a_4.   **(b)** Choose a_1.

17.4 **(a)** Choose a_2.   **(b)** Choose a_2.

17.6 **(a)** Choose a_1.   **(b)** Choose a_3.

17.8 Choose a_2.

17.10 .3077; .6923

17.12 .00063

17.14 .6667

17.16 Choose a_1; $E_1(y) = 23.075$

17.18 Choose a_1; $E_1(y) = 19.444$

17.20 Choose a_5 with $E_5(y) = 39.2$

17.22 **(a)**

	s_1	s_2	s_3
a_1	-400	300	1000
a_2	80	80	80

(b) Yes

INDEX